(

M.

FRIEDEL-CRAFTS
AND RELATED REACTIONS

Volume I   General Aspects

Volume II   Alkylation and Related Reactions

Volume III   Acylation and Related Reactions

Volume IV   Miscellaneous Reactions

FRIEDEL-CRAFTS
AND
RELATED REACTIONS

Edited by

GEORGE A. OLAH

Research Scientist, Dow Chemical of Canada, Limited,
Sarnia, Ontario

II

Alkylation and Related Reactions

PART 1

1964

INTERSCIENCE PUBLISHERS
a division of John Wiley & Sons Inc.
New York - London - Sydney

First published 1964 by John Wiley & Sons, Ltd.

Library of Congress Catalog Card No. 63–18351

Made and printed in Great Britain by
William Clowes and Sons Limited, London and Beccles

Contributors

M. Baaz, Institute of Inorganic and General Chemistry, Technical University of Vienna, Austria

A. T. Balaban, Institute of Atomic Physics, Academy of Sciences, Bucharest, Romania

L. R. C. Barclay, Department of Chemistry, Mount Allison University, Sackville, New Brunswick, Canada

H. P. Braendlin, Department of Chemistry, University of Southern California, Los Angeles, California, U.S.A.

J. M. Canon, The Harshaw Chemical Company, Cleveland, Ohio, U.S.A.

D. Cook, Dow Chemical of Canada, Limited, Sarnia, Ontario, Canada

R. E. A. Dear, Dow Chemical of Canada, Limited, Sarnia, Ontario, Canada

F. A. Drahowzal, Institute of Organic Chemistry, Technical University of Vienna, Austria

G. J. Fonken, Department of Chemistry, University of Texas, Austin, Texas, U.S.A.

V. Franzen, Max Planck Institut für Medizinische Forschung, Heidelberg, Germany

B. S. Friedman, Sinclair Research, Inc., Harvey, Illinois, U.S.A.

A. Gerecs, Institute of Chemical Technology, Eötvös L. University, Budapest, Hungary

R. J. Gillespie, Department of Chemistry, McMaster University, Hamilton, Ontario, Canada

V. Gold, Department of Chemistry, King's College, University of London, Great Britain

G. Goldman, California Research Corporation, Richmond, California, U.S.A.

P. H. Gore, Department of Chemistry, Brunel College, London, Great Britain

N. N. Greenwood, Department of Chemistry, University of Durham, Newcastle upon Tyne, Great Britain

V. Gutmann, Institute of Inorganic and General Chemistry, Technical University of Vienna, Austria

K. Hafner, Institute of Organic Chemistry, University of Munich, Germany

H. Hart, Department of Chemistry, Michigan State University, East Lansing, Michigan, U.S.A.

N. E. Hoffman, Department of Chemistry, Marquette University, Milwaukee, Wisconsin, U.S.A.

J. E. Hofmann, Esso Research and Engineering Company, Linden, New Jersey, U.S.A.

C. E. Inman, Pennsalt Chemical Corporation, Philadelphia, Pennsylvania, U.S.A.

F. R. Jensen, Department of Chemistry, University of California, Berkeley, California, U.S.A.

v

F. JOHNSON, The Dow Chemical Company, Framingham, Massachusetts, U.S.A.

R. KONCOS, Sinclair Research, Inc., Harvey, Illinois, U.S.A.

G. M. KOSOLAPOFF, Department of Chemistry, Auburn University, Auburn, Alabama, U.S.A.

P. KOVACIC, Department of Chemistry, Case Institute of Technology, Cleveland, Ohio, U.S.A.

S. J. KUHN, Dow Chemical of Canada, Limited, Sarnia, Ontario, Canada

D. R. MARTIN, The Harshaw Chemical Company, Cleveland, Ohio, U.S.A.

E. T. McBEE, Department of Chemistry, Purdue University, Lafayette Indiana, U.S.A.

D. A. McCAULAY, American Oil Company, Whiting, Indiana, U.S.A.

M. W. MEYER, Dow Chemical of Canada, Limited, Sarnia, Ontario, Canada

K. L. MORITZ, Institute of Organic Chemistry, University of Munich, Germany

K. L. NELSON, Department of Chemistry, Brigham Young University, Provo, Utah, U.S.A.

C. D. NENITZESCU, Chemical Institute, Academy of Sciences, Bucharest, Romania

R. E. OESTERLING, U.S. Naval Ordnance Laboratory, White Oak, Maryland, U.S.A.

G. A. OLAH, Dow Chemical of Canada, Limited, Sarnia, Ontario, Canada

J. A. OLAH, Sarnia, Ontario, Canada

S. H. PATINKIN, Sinclair Research, Inc., Harvey, Illinois, U.S.A.

D. C. PEPPER, Department of Chemistry, University of Dublin, Ireland

A. G. PETO, Proprietary Perfumes Ltd. (Unilever Ltd.), Ashford, Kent, Great Britain

H. PINES, Department of Chemistry, Northwestern University, Evanston, Illinois, U.S.A.

H. W. QUINN, Dow Chemical of Canada, Limited, Sarnia, Ontario, Canada

C. W. ROBERTS, The Dow Chemical Company, Midland, Michigan, U.S.A.

R. M. ROBERTS, Department of Chemistry, University of Texas, Austin, Texas, U.S.A.

W. RUSKE, Berlin-Halensee, Germany

G. A. RUSSELL, Department of Chemistry, Iowa State University, Ames, Iowa, U.S.A.

L. SCHMERLING, Universal Oil Products Company, Des Plaines, Illinois, U.S.A.

A. SCHRIESHEIM, Esso Research and Engineering Company, Process Research Division, Linden, New Jersey, U.S.A.

F. L. SCOTT, Department of Chemistry, University College, Cork, Ireland

S. SETHNA, Department of Chemistry, M.S. University of Baroda, Baroda, India

D. R. STULL, The Dow Chemical Company, Midland, Michigan, U.S.A.

W. S. TOLGYESI, Dow Chemical of Canada, Limited, Sarnia, Ontario, Canada

K. WADE, Department of Chemistry, The University of Durham, Great Britain

A. WAGNER, Institute of Organic Chemistry, Technical University, Stuttgart, Germany

Editor's Preface to Volume I

It was eighty-six years ago that Friedel and Crafts published from their Sorbonne Laboratory the first observation on the action of aluminum chloride in organic reactions, a work which led to numerous synthetic methods bearing their names. Friedel-Crafts reactions, as we know them today, have grown with the Grignard methods to perhaps the most versatile and frequently used tools of organic chemistry, covering aromatic and aliphatic systems alike. This latter field has long failed to receive its deserved recognition and many of our textbooks still leave the unjustified impression that the Friedel-Crafts reactions are related only to aromatic systems.

The realization that Friedel-Crafts reactions are general acid-catalyzed processes and by no means limited to anhydrous aluminum chloride as the catalyst, extended substantially the scope and versatility of the reactions. It is indeed somewhat difficult today to define the limitations of what we understand by Friedel-Crafts type reactions and what should differentiate them from general acid-catalyzed electrophilic reactions. Authors contributing to *Friedel-Crafts and Related Reactions* considered this question before defining the scope of their treatment and agreed that the time-honored custom in organic chemistry to name basic reactions from their original investigators should be maintained by naming Friedel-Crafts type reactions those processes which proceed under the general conditions laid down by the pioneering investigators, and which can also be carried out by the later realization of the general acid-catalyzed nature of the reactions. Thus in the present treatise reactions catalyzed by all related acid catalyst systems are incorporated: Lewis acid type halide, Brønsted-Lowry type proton acid and other related acid-catalyzed reactions are treated alike if they are equally capable of effecting the reactions.

Over the years the number of investigators in the Friedel-Crafts field and the amount of material in both the scientific and patent literature have grown tremendously. It is obviously no longer possible for any individual to attempt to survey the field, even if limitations were introduced confining it to one specific catalyst, as was done in the time-honored and excellent books of Thomas and Kränzlein dealing with aluminum chloride catalyzed reactions.

The reason for a collective effort of collaboration by a rather large number of contributing authors is therefore indicated.

It was with considerable reluctance three years ago that I accepted the Publishers' invitation to act as editor of a comprehensive monograph on Friedel-Crafts reactions. My reluctance was due neither to a lack of enthusiasm for the topic nor the conviction that a comprehensive and critical coverage of the field would be untimely; it was entirely due to the realization that the field of Friedel-Crafts reactions had grown to such proportions that an attempt to try to survey it—even in a somewhat limited way—would inevitably put a very substantial and perhaps even prohibiting burden on all the authors participating in the project.

The deepest gratitude is extended to all those who generously agreed to participate in this project. The authors sacrificed time and effort in a way that can only be appreciated by those actually involved, and it was through their efforts that this book was born. The editor can only add that it was a unique pleasure to give his limited services in coordinating this project. His task was greatly facilitated by the splendid cooperation and unselfish help given by all contributors.

The extraordinary convergence of organic and inorganic reagents and catalysts in the Friedel-Crafts field provides an area of mutual interest shared by experimental and theoretical chemists of both fields alike—hence our effort to include a number of chapters emphasizing the inorganic and physical-chemical aspects of the field. It is hoped that discussion of the inorganic catalyst systems, the nature of acid catalysts, the complexes formed between catalysts and reagents or products, as well as the thermochemical, kinetic, and mechanistic aspects of the systems, will arouse interest in readers otherwise interested perhaps only in the organic chemical aspects and will add to a better understanding of the problems involved.

In all fields undergoing rapid expansion, and Friedel-Crafts type reactions are in a state of continuous growth of extreme proportions, the problem of merely reporting significant advances is difficult enough. To attempt a critical evaluation of data and results in a permanent reference text is next to impossible. On the other hand as the volume of published information in a field becomes larger, the greater is the need for the average chemist to be informed of new lines of progress having significance, and one hopes, major scientific merit. It is therefore highly desirable to provide not only a more or less complete summary of data—which could today perhaps be achieved much better by electronic rather than human brains—but also to attempt to achieve some evaluation of the data and to formulate a general picture of a specific field from both a theoretical and preparative chemical point of view. This latter consideration is emphasized throughout the book.

We cannot claim to have achieved a really complete coverage of such an immense field, but perhaps this would have been too much to expect. The individual authors have used their own judgment in limitation, critical evaluation, and discussion of their topics. Whenever comprehensive surveys on any field were available (like those available in monographs, chapters of *Organic Reactions*, articles of *Chemical Reviews*, etc.) no repetition was attempted—besides the essentials needed for the general discussion up to the time of the previous survey. In general the authors have provided comprehensive data, frequently in tabular form, to cover the literature to the end of 1960, and in most essential novel developments making use of additions during proofreading up to late 1962.

Limitation was impressed on the treatment of rearrangements (with the exceptions of typical Friedel-Crafts isomerizations) as an extensive monograph on "Molecular Rearrangements" (edited by de Mayo) is currently being published covering many of these.

Short indexes at the end of the individual volumes and a comprehensive author and subject index at the end of Volume IV are provided.

No attempt has been made to equate styles of presentation of different chapters besides a combined effort by the authors and editor to coordinate topics in order to achieve a suitable unity of the general project and to eliminate unnecessary overlapping. It is believed that each of the authors—who are actively engaged in research in their own specific field of interest—knows best how to present his own subject. Indeed it is hoped that each chapter will reflect to a certain degree the character and personality of its author.

It was realized from the beginning of this project that owing to the scope and volume of the material to be covered we would inevitably be dealing with a multi-volume publication. Lest the first volumes should be outdated when the last was published, it was decided from the beginning to plan the book as a whole and to proceed with all volumes simultaneously. As the first volume is published, Volumes II–III are being printed and it is hoped that publication of the whole project will be completed by the end of the year. Considering the inevitable delays in a technical publication of this size where, owing to the substantial number of contributing authors, we are dealing with a "chain process" determined by the

1*

slowest member of the series—frequently the editor himself—this is considered a fair, although by no means a spotless record.

It is not possible to thank all who contributed so greatly to the realization of this project. The editor personally would like to thank the Dow Chemical Company for its generous understanding and substantial help given to this project, without which he would have been unable to cope with his task. Particular gratitude is expressed to the staff of the Midland and Sarnia Technical Libraries of Dow Chemical in connection with their help in providing literature. My wife, Judith, gave most valuable assistance throughout the whole editing and preparation of the manuscript. Dr. R. E. A. Dear helped in the editorial work and prepared the indexes. Dr. C. G. Carlson shared in the task of proofreading. Mrs. Bernice Robb and Mrs. Fran Cadwallader are thanked for typing the manuscript. Nearly all of the contributing authors and many other colleagues and friends, too numerous to be thanked here individually, read parts or all of the different chapters and helped with their useful suggestions and criticism to improve the manuscript.

The publishers and the printer are thanked for their excellent job.

Sarnia, Ontario   GEORGE A. OLAH
January, 1963

Contents

Volume I. General Aspects

CH. 1. Historical *by G. A. Olah and R. E. A. Dear*

2. Definition and Scope *by G. A. Olah*

3. Proton Acids and Lewis Acids *by R. J. Gillespie*

4. Catalysts and Solvents *by G. A. Olah*

5. Lewis Acid Catalysts in Non-aqueous Solutions *by M. Baaz and V. Gutmann*

6. Coordination Compounds of the Boron Halides *by D. R. Martin and J. M. Canon*

7. Coordination Compounds of Aluminum and Gallium Halides *by N. N. Greenwood and K. Wade*

8. Intermediate Complexes *by G. A. Olah and M. W. Meyer*

9. Spectroscopic Investigations *by D. Cook*

10. Application of Isotopic Tracers to the Study of Reactions *by R. M. Roberts and G. J. Fonken*

11. Reactivity and Selectivity *by G. A. Olah*

12. Thermodynamic Aspects *by D. R. Stull*

13. Stereochemical Aspects *by H. Hart*

Volume II. Alkylation and Related Reactions

CH. 14. Alkylation of Aromatics with Alkenes and Alkanes *by S. H. Patinkin and B. S. Friedman*

15. Alkylation of Aromatics with Dienes and Substituted Alkenes *by R. Koncos and B. S. Friedman*

16. Alkylation of Aromatics with Alkynes *by V. Franzen*

17. Alkylation of Aromatics with Haloalkanes *by F. A. Drahowzal*

18. Alkylation of Aromatics with Alcohols and Ethers *by A. Schriesheim*

19. Alkylation of Aromatics with Aldehydes and Ketones *by J. E. Hofmann and A. Schriesheim*

20. Alkylation of Aromatics with Esters of Inorganic Acids and Alkyl Arenesulfonates *by F. A. Drahowzal*

21. Haloalkylations *by G. A. Olah and W. S. Tolgyesi*

22. Cyclialkylation of Aromatics *by L. R. C. Barclay*

23. Dehydrogenation Condensation of Aromatics (Scholl and Related Reactions) *by A. T. Balaban and C. D. Nenitzescu*

24. Isomerization of Aromatic Hydrocarbons *by D. A. McCaulay*

25. Alkylation of Saturated Hydrocarbons *by L. Schmerling*

26. Condensation of Haloalkanes with Alkenes and Haloalkenes *by L. Schmerling*

CH. 27. Alkylation of Alkenes with Carbonyl Compounds (Prins Reaction) *by C. W. Roberts*

28. Isomerization of Saturated Hydrocarbons *by H. Pines and N. E. Hoffman*

29. Hydrogen Exchange in Aromatic Compounds *by V. Gold*

30. Polymerization *by D. C. Pepper*

Volume III.   Acylation and Related Reactions

CH. 31. Aromatic Ketone Synthesis *by P. H. Gore*

32. Houben-Hoesch and Related Syntheses *by W. Ruske*

33. The Fries Reaction *by A. Gerecs*

34. Acylation with Di- and Polycarboxylic Acid Derivatives *by A. G. Peto*

35. Cycliacylation *by S. Sethna*

36. Mechanism of Acylations *by F. R. Jensen and G. Goldman*

37. Aliphatic Acylation *by C. D. Nenitzescu and A. T. Balaban*

38. Aldehyde Syntheses *by G. A. Olah and S. J. Kuhn*

39. Acid Syntheses *by G. A. Olah and J. A. Olah*

40. Sulfonylation *by F. R. Jensen and G. Goldman*

41. Fries Reaction of Aryl Arenesulfonates *by F. R. Jensen and G. Goldman*

42. Sulfonation *by K. L. Nelson*

43. Nitration *by G. A. Olah and S. J. Kuhn*

44. Amination *by P. Kovacic*

45. Perchlorylation *by C. E. Inman, R. E. Oesterling and F. L. Scott*

46. Halogenation *by H. P. Braendlin and E. T. McBee*

Volume IV.   Miscellaneous Reactions

CH. 47. Reactions of Ethers and Cyclic Ethers *by F. Johnson*

48. Reactions of Aromatics with Lewis Acid Metal Halides *by P. Kovacic*

49. Reactions of Non-benzenoid Aromatics *by K. Hafner and K. L. Moritz*

50. Reactions with Organometallic Compounds *by G. A. Russell*

51. Reactions in Organophosphorus Chemistry *by G. M. Kosolapoff*

52. Reactions in Carbohydrate Chemistry *by A. Wagner*

53. Reactions with Metathetic Cation-forming Salts *by G. A. Olah and H. W. Quinn*

54. Practical Applications and Future Outlook *by G. A. Olah*

Author Index—Volumes I–IV

Subject Index—Volumes I–IV

Contents—Volume II

PART 1

Editor's Preface to Volume I vii

XIV. **Alkylation of Aromatics with Alkenes and Alkanes** *by S. H. Patinkin and B. S. Friedman* 1

  I. Introduction 1
    1. Scope 1
    2. Reviews 2
    3. Commercial Aspects 2

  II. Alkylation of Aromatic Hydrocarbons 3
    1. Benzene and Its Homologs 3
      A. Mechanism 3
      B. Orientation 8
        a. Polar effects and the role of isomerization and transalkylation 9
        b. Steric factors 16
      C. Relative Reactivity of Benzene and its Homologs . 18
      D. Liquid-phase Alkylation with Ethylene, Propene, and Butenes 21
        a. Metal halide catalysts 21
        b. Protonic acid catalysts 24
        c. Boron fluoride complexes . . . 27
      E. Vapor-phase Alkylation 30
        a. The mechanism of alkylation catalyzed by silica–alumina and other cracking catalysts . 30
        b. Ethylbenzene production . . . 32
        c. Cumene production 35
        d. Alkylation with n-butenes . . . 37
      F. Alkylation with n-Pentenes and Higher n-Olefins . 37
      G. Alkylation with Isoolefins 40
        a. Steric factors 40
        b. Hydride transfer 41
        c. Selectivity, isomerization, and transalkylation . 43
        d. Skeletal isomerization in side chain . 44
        e. Side reactions involving cleavage and/or polymerization 48
        f. Migration of double bond . . . 49
      H. Alkylation with Polymers of Isoolefins . . 50
        a. Depolyalkylation 50
        b. Intact alkylation 51
      I. Alkylation with Polymers of n-Olefins . . 54
        a. Propene polymers 54
        b. n-Butene polymers 56
      J. Alkylation with Aryl-substituted Olefins . 57
        a. Styrene 57

               b.   α-Methylstyrenes 57
               c.   Unconjugated aryl-substituted olefins . . 58
               d.   Polyaryl-substituted olefins 59
         K.   Alkylation with Cycloolefins 60
               a.   Unbranched cycloolefins 60
               b.   Branched cycloolefins 61
         L.   Telomerization 64
     2.   Halogenated and Nitrated Benzenes . . 66
         A.   Halogenated Benzenes 66
         B.   Nitrated Benzenes 68
     3.   Polycyclic Aromatic Hydrocarbons . . 68
         A.   Naphthalenes 68
         B.   Tetralin and Indane 72
         C.   Tricyclics 74
         D.   Polyphenyl Derivatives 74

III.   Alkylation of Phenols and Derivatives . . . 75
     1.   Theory 75
     2.   Phenols, Cresols and Dimethylphenols. . . 77
         A.   Thermal Alkylation 77
         B.   Alkylation with n-Olefins 78
                a.   Ethylene 78
                b.   Propene 78
                c.   n-Butene and higher 79
         C.   Alkylation with Isoolefins 79
                a.   Phenol. 80
                b.   Cresols and dimethylphenols . . . 81
         D.   Alkylation with Olefin Polymers . . . 84
                a.   Diisobutylene 84
                b.   Triisobutylene and tetraisobutylene . . 85
                c.   Polypropenes 86
         E.   Alkylation with Cyclic Olefins . . . 86
     3.   Halogenated and Nitrated Phenols . . . 88
          A.   Halogenated Phenols 88
         B.   Nitrophenols 89
     4.   Higher Phenols. 89
     5.   Polyhydric Phenols and Bisphenols . . 90
     6.   Aromatic Ethers 91
     7.   Methoxyphenols 93
     8.   Halogenated and Nitrated Aromatic Ethers . 93
     9.   Phenoxide Catalysts 94

  IV.   Alkylation of Thiophenols and their Ethers . . 97

   V.   Alkylation of Aromatic Amines . . . 101

  VI.   Alkylation of Furans and Thiophenes . . . 104
     1.   Furans 104
     2.   Thiophenes 105

 VII.   Alkylation of Aromatic Acids 109

VIII.   Alkylation with Alkanes and Cycloalkanes. . . 110
     1.   Alkanes 110
     2.   Cycloalkanes 112

IX. Appendix 116
   Alkylation of:
      Benzene (Tables 1–8). 116
      Toluene (Tables 9–14) 147
      C$_8$ Aromatics (Tables 15–19) 159
      C$_9$ Aromatics and higher (Tables 20–23) . . . 170
      Indanes (Table 24) 180
      Naphthalene and derivatives (Tables 25–29) . . 181
      Tetralins and halogenated tetralins (Table 30) . . 187
      Polyphenyl hydrocarbons (Table 31) 188
      Tricyclic hydrocarbons (Table 32) 190
      Halogenated and nitrated benzenes and homologs (Tables 33, 34) 192
      Phenol (Tables 35–41) 196
      Cresols (Tables 42, 43) 211
      Higher phenol homologs (Table 44) 219
      Indanols and naphthols (Table 45) 222
      Halogenated phenols and nitrophenols (Tables 46, 47) . 223
      Anisole (Table 48) 226
      Higher ethers (Table 49) 228
      Halogenated anisoles (Table 50) 231
      Polyhydric phenols and bisphenols (Table 51) . . 232
      Methoxyphenols and dimethoxybenzenes (Table 52) . 235
      Thiophenol (Table 53) 236
      Thiophenol homologs and ethers (Table 53A) . . 237
      Aniline (Tables 54, 55) 238
      Aniline homologs and derivatives and phenylenediamine (Table 56) 240
      Heterocyclic amines (Table 57) 243
      Aromatic acids (Table 58) 245
      Thiophene (Tables 59–63) 247
      Thiophene derivatives (Table 64) 252
      Furans, pyrrole, and phenthiazine (Table 65) . . 253
      Aromatics with alkanes (Table 66) 254
      Aromatics with cycloalkanes (Table 67) . . . 257

XV. **Alkylation of Aromatics with Dienes and Substituted Alkenes** by *Robert Koncos and B. S. Friedman* 289

   I. Introduction 289

   II. Dienes 290
      1. Side-chain Structure 290
      2. The Effect of Catalysts and Conditions on the Alkenylation Reaction 298
      3. Summary. 300

   III. Unsaturated Halides 300
      1. Vinyl Halides 300
         A. Monohalides 300
         B. Polyhalides 303
         C. Side Reactions 305

2. Allyl Halides 307
   A. Monohalides 307
   B. Polyhalides 312
3. Miscellaneous Halides 313
4. Summary. 313

IV. Unsaturated Alcohols and Ethers 313
1. Unsaturated Alcohols 313
2. Unsaturated Ethers 316
3. Summary. 318

V. Unsaturated Acids 318
1. Addition 319
2. Rearrangement. 323
3. Replacement 324
4. Hydrogen Transfer 327
5. Summary. 327

VI. Unsaturated Esters. 328
1. Summary. 331

VII. Unsaturated Aldehydes 331

VIII. Unsaturated Ketones 332
1. Addition 332
2. Replacement 339
3. Hydrogen Transfer 340
4. Miscellaneous Reactions 341
5. Summary. 342

IX. Unsaturated Acid Chlorides 342

X. Unsaturated Nitriles 344

XI. Miscellaneous Unsaturated Alkylating Agents . . 345

XII. Appendix 347
Alkylation with dienes (Tables I–VIII) . . 347
Alkylation with unsaturated halides (Tables IX–XIV) . 358
Alkylation with unsaturated alcohols and ethers (Tables XV–XVII) 368
Alkylation with unsaturated acids (Tables XVIII–XXII) 373
Alkylation with unsaturated esters (Tables XXIII–XXVIII) 381
Alkylation with unsaturated ketones and aldehydes (Tables XXIX–XXXIV) 389
Alkylation with unsaturated nitriles (Table XXXV) . 400
Alkylation with miscellaneous unsaturated compounds (Tables XXXVI–XXXVIII) 401

XVI. Alkylation of Aromatics with Alkynes by V. Franzen . 413

I. Alkylation with Acetylene 413

II. Alkylation with Haloalkynes 415

XVII. **Alkylation of Aromatics with Haloalkanes** *by Franz A.*
    Drahowzal 417

   I. Introduction 417

  II. Catalysts and Solvents 417
       1. Aluminum Halides 417
       2. Gallium Halides 421
       3. Boron Trifluoride 422
       4. Titanium Tetrachloride 422
       5. Antimony Pentachloride 423
       6. Zinc Chloride 423
       7. Ferric Chloride 424
       8. Proton Acids 424
       9. Acidic Oxides: Alumina 425
      10. Aqueous Metal Halides 425
      11. Metal Catalysts (*in situ* formation of metal halides). . 425
           A. Aluminum 425
           B. Zinc 427
           C. Copper 427
           D. Other Metals 427

 III. Haloalkanes 428
       1. Fluorides, Chlorides, Bromides, and Iodides . . . 428
       2. Relative Reactivity 428
       3. Cyclialkylation with Haloaralkanes 428

  IV. Aromatic Substrates 431
       1. Mono- and Polynuclear Hydrocarbons 431
       2. Heterocyclic Compounds 433
       3. Effect of Substituents 433

   V. Mechanism 436
       1. General Considerations 436
       2. Carbonium-ion Mechanism or Nucleophilic Displacement
           of the Alkyl Halide–Catalyst Complex 438
       3. The Preferred *meta*-Position 440
       4. Complexes 443
       5. Rearrangements accompanying Alkylation . . 444

  VI. Alkylations with Substituted, Polyfunctional Haloalkanes . 448
       1. Di- and Polyhaloalkanes 449
       2. Haloalkenes 454
       3. Alkoxyhaloalkanes (Haloalkyl Ethers) . . . 460
       4. Haloalkyl Sulfides 465
       5. Haloalkyl Amines and Imines 465
       6. Haloalkyl Halosilanes 466
       7. Haloacyl Halides, Halocarboxylic Acids and Esters . 466
       8. Unsaturated Halocarboxylic Acids . . . 467

XVIII. **Alkylation of Aromatics with Alcohols and Ethers** *by*
    Alan Schriesheim 477

   I. Introduction 477

  II. Consideration of Reaction Mechanisms . . . 479

     1. Carbonium-ion Reactions 480
     2. Aromatic Substitution 481
       A. Alkylation, Isomerization, and Disproportionation 482
       B. Conclusions 485

III. Alkylation using Alcohols as Alkylating Agents . . . 486
     1. Friedel-Crafts Halides 486
       A. Alkylation by Alcohols, using Boron Fluoride . . 486
         a. Alkylation of benzene and phenol and their homologs 488
         b. Alkylation of naphthalene and other polycyclic aromatics. 494
         c. Alkylation of esters 495
         d. Miscellaneous 496
       B. Alkylation by Alcohols using $AlCl_3$ . . . 497
         a. Alkylation of benzene and phenol and their homologs 497
         b. Miscellaneous 506
       C. Other Halides as Alcohol Alkylation Catalysts . 508
         a. Zinc chloride 508
         b. Ferric chloride 513
         c. Stannic chloride and titanium tetrachloride . 513
     2. Proton-donating Acids 514
       A. Alkylation by Alcohols using Sulfuric Acid . 517
       B. Alkylation by Alcohols using Phosphoric Acid . 522
     3. Metal Oxides 524
       A. Alkylation of Benzene and Phenols by Alcohols 525
       B. Alkylation of Naphthalene by Alcohols . . 527
       C. Alkylation of Ammonia by Alcohols . . 528
       D. Alkylation of Amines by Alcohols . . . 531
       E. Alkylation of Heterocyclics by Alcohols . . 533
       F. Alkylation of Mercaptans and Hydrogen Sulfide by Alcohols 534

IV. Alkylation using Acyclic Ethers as Alkylating Agents . 534
     1. Friedel-Crafts Halides 536
       A. Alkylation of Benzene and its Homologs by Ethers using Boron Fluoride 536
       B. Alkylation of Naphthalene by Ethers using Boron Fluoride 538
       C. Alkylation of Phenols by Ethers using Boron Fluoride 539
       D. Alkylation of Active Methylene Groups by Ethers using Boron Fluoride 539
     2. Metal Oxides 541
       A. Alkylation of Benzene and its Homologs by Ethers using Metal Oxides 541
       B. Alkylation of Naphthalenes by Ethers using Metal Oxides. 542
       C. Alkylation of Phenols by Ethers using Metal Oxides 542

3. Miscellaneous 542
    A. Ether Rearrangement 542

V. Alkylation using Cyclic Ethers as Alkylating Agents . . 543

VI. Appendix 546
    Alkylation with alcohols (Tables 1–13) . . . 547
    Alkylation with ethers (Tables 14–25) . . . 579

XIX. Alkylation of Aromatics with Aldehydes and Ketones *by J. E. Hofmann and A. Schriesheim* 597

I. Introduction 597
    1. General Mechanism Consideration 598

II. Addition of Ketene to Aromatics 600

III. Addition of Aromatic Aldehydes and Ketones to Aromatics 602
    1. Reactions of Benzaldehyde 602
    2. Reactions of Aromatic Ketones 607

IV. Condensation of Aldehydes and Ketones with Aromatics . 610
    1. Reactions of Aldehydes and Ketones . . . 610
        A. Aldehydes 610
        B. Ketones 613
    2. Reactions of Chloral 616

V. Miscellaneous Additions involving Aldehydes and Ketones 621

VI. Appendix 625

XX. Alkylation of Aromatics with Esters of Inorganic Acids and Alkyl Arenesulfonates *by Franz A. Drahowzal* . . 641

I. Introduction 641

II. Alkyl Sulfates, Sulfites, Phosphates, Silicates, and Carbonates 642

III. Alkyl Borates 643

IV. Alkyl Chloroformates, Hypochlorites, Chlorosulfonates, and Chlorosulfites 644

V. Alkyl Benzenesulfonates 646

VI. Alkyl *p*-Toluenesulfonates 648

VII. Alkyl Perchlorates 653

VIII. Alkyl Nitrates 656

PART 2

XXI. Haloalkylations *by George A. Olah and William S. Tolgyesi* . 659

I. Introduction 659

II. Haloalkylation of Aromatic Compounds 659
    1. Scope 659
    2. Catalysts and Solvents 660
    3. Chloromethylation 661
        A. Hydrocarbons 662
            a. Benzene and alkylbenzenes . . . 662
            b. Biphenyl, terphenyl, and diphenylmethane . 667

c. Indan 667
d. Naphthalene and derivatives . . . 667
e. Anthracene and phenanthrene . . . 669
f. Miscellaneous hydrocarbons . . . 670
g. Polymeric hydrocarbons (polystyrenes) . 670
B. Heterocyclic Compounds 671
a. Furan derivatives 671
b. Thiophene and derivatives . . . 683
c. Selenophene derivatives 685
d. Pyrazoles and isoxazoles 685
e. Benzofurans and benzopyrans . . . 685
f. Benzothiophenes 686
g. Quinolines 686
h. Pyrimidines 686
i. Miscellaneous heterocyclic compounds . 686
C. Haloaromatic Compounds 687
a. Haloarenes 687
b. Haloaralkanes 699
D. Phenols and Phenol Ethers 701
E. Aldehydes and Ketones 712
F. Nitrogen Compounds 721
a. Nitroaromatics 721
b. Amines, amides, imines, and imides . . 724
c. Azo compounds 725
G. Acids and Esters 725
H. Sulfur Compounds 731
a. Thiophenol ethers (sulfides) . . . 731
b. Sultones and sultams 731
I. Silicon Compounds 734
4. Bromomethylation 734
5. Iodomethylation 735
6. Fluoromethylation 735
7. Haloethylations, Halopropylations, and Halobutylations 737
A. With Aldehydes and Haloalkyl Ethers . . 737
B. With Haloalkenes 741
C. With Di- and Polyhaloalkanes . . . 746
D. With Haloalcohols 752
E. With Di(chloroalkyl) Sulfates, Haloalkyl Chlorosulfonates, and Haloalkyl-p-tosylates . . 755
8. Mechanism 756
A. Aldehydes and Hydrogen Halides or Haloalkyl Ethers 756
a. Orientation 756
b. Rates 759
c. General aspects of mechanism . . . 762
B. Haloalkenes 765
C. Dihaloalkanes 766
D. Haloalcohols 766
E. Haloalkyl Esters 766

III. Haloalkylation of Aliphatic Compounds 767
    1. Alkanes 767
    2. Alkenes 767
    3. Ketones and Aldehydes 771

XXII. Cyclialkylation of Aromatics by L. Ross C. Barclay . . 785

  I. Introduction 785
  II. Intramolecular Ring Closure of Aryl-substituted Compounds 786
    1. Intramolecular Ring Closure of Aryl-substituted
      Halides 786
    2. Intramolecular Ring Closure of Arylalkenes . . 793
      A. Cyclialkylations producing Polynuclear Hydro-
        carbons and Derivatives. The Mechanism of the
        Ring Closure 793
      B. Cyclialkylations of Unsaturated Carbonyl Com-
        pounds 805
      C. Cyclialkylations of Unsaturated Compounds
        yielding Heterocyclic Systems 807
    3. Cyclialkylations through Arylaliphatic Alcohols . 813
      A. Cyclizations yielding Bicyclic Compounds
        (Tetralins and Indans) and Derivatives . . 816
      B. Cyclizations yielding Hydrophenanthrenes and
        Derivatives. The Mechanism of the Cyclization 826
      C. Related Cyclizations yielding Polycyclic Hydro-
        aromatic Systems 840
      D. Cyclizations of Di- and Triaryl Carbinols . . 843
        a. Cyclizations of di- and triaryl carbinols
          yielding substituted fluorenes . . . 843
        b. Intramolecular condensation of arylamides
          of benzilic acid and derivatives . . . 847
      E. Cyclizations with Rearrangements. Phenan-
        threnes from Fluorenyl Carbinols . . . 854
    4. Cyclodehydration of Aryl-substituted Carbonyl Com-
      pounds 859
      A. Cyclodehydrations producing Indenes and Poly-
        cyclic Hydroaromatics 859
        a. Indenes and related systems by the cyclo-
          dehydrations of β-aryl ketones . . . 859
        b. Cyclodehydration of γ-aryl ketones yielding
          polycyclic hydroaromatic compounds . 866
        c. Cyclodehydration of δ-aryl carbonyl com-
          pounds 872
        d. Cyclodehydration of aryl-substituted amides.
          The Bischler-Napieralski and related reac-
          tions 873

      B. Aromatic Cyclodehydration 888
         a. Cyclodehydrations yielding polycyclic aro-
            matic hydrocarbons: naphthalene, phenan-
            threne, anthracene, and derivatives . . 888
         b. Cyclodehydrations yielding heterocyclic
            systems 901
  III. Cyclialkylation by Di- and Polyfunctional Alkylating
      Agents 927
      1. Cyclialkylations with Dihalides . . . 927
      2. Cyclialkylations with Diols and Derivatives and with
         Tetrahydrofurans 933
      3. Cyclization involving Acylation–Alkylation . . 939
  IV. Cyclialkylation of Aromatic Hydrocarbons with Olefins . 944
      1. Cyclialkylation of Styrene Compounds with Olefins
         to yield Indans 944
      2. Cyclialkylations of Aromatic Hydrocarbons involving
         Hydride-ion Transfer Processes 952

XXIII. **Dehydrogenation Condensation of Aromatics (Scholl
      and Related Reactions)** *by A. T. Balaban and C. D. Nenitzescu* 979
  I. Introduction 979
  II. Inter- and Intramolecular Scholl Reaction . . 979
      1. Definition of the Scholl Reaction . . . 979
      2. Historical 980
      3. Scope and Limitations 982
      4. Reaction Mechanism 983
         A. The First Stage, Protolytic Reaction . . 987
         B. The Second Stage, Electrophilic Substitution . 989
         C. The Third Stage, Dehydrogenation . . 993
      5. Thermodynamic Aspects 997
      6. Technique of the Reaction 998
      7. Allied Reactions 1000
         A. General Considerations 1000
            Table I. General scheme of Friedel-Crafts
            reactions 1001
         B. Cyclialkylations 1001
         C. Alkaline Fusion 1002
         D. Oxidation 1003
      8. Classification and Review of Scholl Reactions . . 1004
            Table II.   Intermolecular: Hydrocarbons . 1006
            Table III. Intermolecular: Miscellaneous . 1008
            Table IV. Intramolecular: Fluorene . . 1010
            Table V.   Intramolecular: Carbazole . . 1011
            Table VI. Intramolecular: {1,5} . . 1012
            Table VII Intramolecular: {1,2,5} . . 1014
            Table VIII. Intramolecular: {1,3,5} . . 1020
            Table IX. Intramolecular: {1,2,4,5} . . 1020
            Table X.   Intramolecular: {1,2,3,5} . . 1022

Table XI.   Intramolecular: {1,2,3,4,5} .   . 1023
Table XII.   Rearrangements in the Scholl
reaction 1024

III. Related Reactions   1025
      1. Reactions yielding Anthracene   .   .   . 1025
      2. Reaction of Aromatics with Quinones   .   . 1032

XXIV. Isomerization of Aromatic Hydrocarbons *by* *D. A.*
       McCaulay   1049

   I. Introduction   1049

  II. Measurement of Relative Stability 1049
       1. Vapor-pressure Measurements   .   .   . 1049
       2. Competitive Extraction   1050

 III. Nature of Arene Complexes   1052
       1. Complex Formation   1053
       2. Structure of the Cation   1055
       3. Effect of Structure of the Alkyl Group on Basicity . 1058

  IV. Reactions of Arenes   1061
       1. Alkyl Migration 1061
           A. Isomerization   1062
           B. Disproportionation   1066
       2. Halogen Migration   1069

   V. Conclusion 1071

XXV. Alkylation of Saturated Hydrocarbons *by* *Louis Schmerling* 1075

   I. Introduction   1075

  II. Thermal Alkylation   1076

 III. Mechanism of Catalytic Alkylation of Isoparaffins   . 1079
       1. The Primary Reaction 1080
       2. Side Reactions   1083
           A. Hydrogen Transfer   1083
           B. Destructive Alkylation   .   .   . 1084
           C. Polymerization   1087
           D. Formation of Catalyst Complex   .   . 1088
           E. Formation of Esters   1088

  IV. Catalytic Alkylation of Isobutane with Olefins .   . 1089
       1. Aluminum Chloride   1089
           A. Ethylene   1090
           B. Propene   1091
           C. *n*-Butylenes 1091
       2. Aluminum Chloride Sludges 1093
       3. Aluminum Chloride Complexes   .   .   . 1095

4. Nitroalkane Solutions of Aluminum Chloride . . 1097
5. Aluminum Chloride Double Salts 1098
6. Aluminum Bromide 1098
7. Boron Fluoride 1099
8. Zirconium Chloride 1100
9. Hydrogen Fluoride 1100
   A. Propene 1101
   B. n-Butylenes 1102
   C. Isobutylene 1104
   D. Higher Olefins 1104
10. Sulfuric Acid 1104
   A. Propene 1105
   B. n-Butylenes 1105
   C. Isobutylene 1106
   D. Higher Olefins 1106
   E. Cyclohexene 1108

V. Catalytic Alkylation of Isopentane with Olefins . . 1109
1. Boron Fluoride 1109
2. Hydrogen Fluoride 1109
3. Sulfuric Acid 1110

VI. Catalytic Alkylation of Hexanes with Olefins . . . 1110

VII. Reaction of Isoalkanes with Alkyl Halides . . . 1111
1. With Alkyl Chlorides 1111
   A. Aluminum Chloride 1111
   B. Nitromethane Solutions of Aluminum Chloride . 1112
   C. Sulfuric Acid 1112
   D. Dichloroaluminum Acid Sulfate . . . 1113
2. With Alkyl Bromides 1114
3. With Alkyl Fluorides 1114
   A. Boron Fluoride 1114
   B. Hydrogen Fluoride 1118

VIII. Reaction of Isoalkanes with Alcohols 1119
1. Hydrogen Fluoride 1119
2. Sulfuric Acid 1120

IX. Condensation of Isobutane with Chloroolefins . . 1121

X. Catalytic Alkylation of Cycloparaffins . . . 1123
1. Aluminum Chloride 1123
   A. Methylcyclohexane 1123
   B. Cyclohexane 1124
   C. Methylcyclopentane with t-Butyl Chloride . 1125
2. Aluminum Bromide 1125
3. Hydrogen Fluoride 1127
4. Sulfuric Acid 1128
   A. Methylcyclopentane 1128
   B. Alkylcyclohexanes 1129

XXVI.   **Condensation of Haloalkanes with Alkenes and Halo-alkenes** *by Louis Schmerling* 1133

   I.   Condensation of Alkyl Halides with Unsaturated Hydro-carbons 1133
     1.   Ethylene 1133
       A.   Tertiary Alkyl Halides 1134
       B.   Secondary Alkyl Halides 1136
       C.   Primary Alkyl Halides 1137
     2.   Propene 1138
     3.   Butenes 1139
     4.   Cyclohexene 1140
     5.   Alkadienes 1141
     6.   Acetylenes 1144
     7.   Vinylacetylenes 1145

  II.   Condensation of Cycloalkyl Halides with Ethylene . . 1148

  III.   Condensation of Alkyl Halides with Haloolefins . . 1150
     1.   Vinyl Chloride 1151
     2.   2-Chloropropene 1153
     3.   Allyl Halides 1154
     4.   Vinylidene Chloride 1154
     5.   1,2-Dichloroethylene 1155
     6.   Chlorotrifluoroethylene 1157
     7.   Dichloropropenes 1157
     8.   Trichloroethylene 1158

  IV.   Condensation of Cycloalkyl Halides with Haloethylenes . 1158
     1.   Vinyl Halides 1158
     2.   Vinylidene Chloride 1159

  V.   Condensation of Dihaloalkanes with Ethylene . . . 1159

  VI.   Condensation of Dichloroalkanes with Chloroethylenes . 1161

  VII.   Condensation of Polychloroalkanes with Chloroolefins . 1162
     1.   Dichloroethylene 1164
       A.   Chloroform 1164
       B.   Carbon Tetrachloride 1166
       C.   Polychloroethanes 1168
       D.   Polychloropropanes 1169
     2.   Trichloroethylene 1169
       A.   Chloroform 1169
       B.   Carbon Tetrachloride 1170
       C.   Polychloroethanes 1171
     3.   Tetrachloroethylene 1171
     4.   Hexachlorocyclopentadiene 1172
     5.   1,1,2,3,4,5,5-Heptachloro-1-pentene . . . 1172

XXVII.   **Alkylation of Alkenes with Carbonyl Compounds (Prins Reaction)** *by Carleton W. Roberts* 1175

   I.   Introduction 1175

II. Reactions of Alkenes and Cycloalkenes with Carbonyl Compounds 1177
   1. With Formaldehyde 1177
   2. With Other Carbonyl Compounds 1180

III. Reactions of Simple Hydroxy-substituted Alkenes . . 1180
   1. Non-allylic Olefins with Aldehydes and Ketones . 1180
   2. Allylic Olefins with Aldehydes and Ketones . 1182

IV. Halogen-substituted Olefins with Aldehydes . . . 1185

V. Conjugated Olefins with Aldehydes and Ketones . 1187

VI. Aryl-substituted Olefins 1189
   1. Styrene and Ring-substituted Styrenes . . . 1189
   2. Substituted Vinylaromatics 1191
      A. Halovinylbenzenes 1191
      B. Miscellaneous Substituted Vinylaromatics. . 1192
   3. α-Methylstyrenes 1194

VII. Lewis Acid Catalyzed Reactions of Unsaturated Compounds with Carbonyl Compounds 1196

VIII. Thermal Reactions of Carbonyl Compounds with Unsaturated Compounds 1198

IX. Mechanisms of the Prins Reaction 1202

XXVIII. Isomerization of Saturated Hydrocarbons by *Herman Pines and Norman E. Hoffman* 1211

I. Introduction 1211

II. Generalized Mechanism 1212

III. Carbonium Ions 1213
   1. Formation of Carbonium Ions 1213
      A. Addition of Protons to Olefins. . . . 1213
      B. Dissociation of Halides 1213
      C. Oxidation of Saturated Hydrocarbons . . 1213
      D. Protonation of Alcohols 1214
      E. Other Methods 1214
   2. Reactions of Carbonium Ions 1214
      A. Hydride Shift 1214
      B. Alkide Shift 1214
      C. Abstraction of a Hydride from a Hydrocarbon Molecule 1215
      D. Loss of a Proton 1216
      E. Addition of a Carbonium Ion to an Olefin or Aromatic 1216
      F. Reduction 1216
      G. Beta-Scission 1217
      H. Exchange between Carbonium-ion Hydrogens and Acid Hydrogen 1217

IV.   Lewis Acids 1218
      1. Catalyst Activity 1218
      2. Rate Correlations 1219
      3. Alkanes 1219
          A. Propane 1219
          B. Butanes 1220
              a. Equilibrium 1220
              b. Mechanism 1221
          C. Pentanes 1222
              a. Equilibrium 1222
              b. Mechanism 1223
          D. Hexanes 1226
              a. Equilibrium 1226
              b. Mechanism 1226
          E. Heptanes 1228
              a. Equilibrium 1228
              b. Mechanism 1229
          F. Higher Paraffins 1229
      4. Cycloalkanes 1230
          A. Equilibrium 1230
          B. Mechanism 1230
              a. Cyclopentanes 1230
              b. Cyclohexanes 1233
              c. Cyclopropanes 1234
              d. Cyclobutanes 1234
              e. Bicycloalkanes 1234
V.   Sulfuric and Related Acids 1235
      1. Catalyst Activity 1236
      2. Mechanism 1236
          A. Hydrogen–Deuterium Exchange . . 1238
          B. Racemization and cis–trans Isomerization . 1239
VI.   Silica–Alumina 1240
      1. Chain Initiation 1241
      2. Rearrangement 1242
      3. Propagation 1242
VII. Hydroisomerization Catalysts 1243
      1. Nickel on Silica–Alumina 1243
          A. Experimental Results 1243
          B. Mechanism 1243
          C. Isotopic Labeling 1245
      2. Platinum on Alumina 1245
VIII. Conclusion 1248

XXIX. Hydrogen Exchange in Aromatic Compounds by V. Gold 1253
  I. Introduction 1253
      1. Historical Background 1253
      2. The General Design of Exchange Experiments . 1254
      3. Conditions for the Occurrence of Electrophilic
          Hydrogen Exchange in Aromatic Compounds . 1259

II. The Electrophilic Character of the Reaction . . . 1262
   1. The Position of Attack in the Aromatic Compound,
      and Exchange Reactivity 1262
      A. Substituents in the Benzene Nucleus . . 1262
      B. Condensed Polycyclic Aromatic Hydrocarbons . 1265
      C. Other Systems 1268
   2. The Interpretation of Quantitative Comparisons of
      Exchange Reactivity 1268
   3. The Medium and Catalyst System 1269

III. Reaction Mechanism 1270
   1. The Composition of the Transition State . . . 1270
   2. The Potential-energy Profile 1275
   3. Isotope Effects 1279

IV. The Application of Hydrogen Exchange to the Study of
    Complex Catalyst Systems 1284

XXX. **Polymerization** by D. C. Pepper 1293

I. Scope 1293

II. Introduction 1293

III. Initiating Agents and Systems 1294
   1. Protonic Acids 1295
   2. Friedel-Crafts Halides 1296
   3. Carbonium Salts 1298
   4. Cationogenic Substances 1299
   5. High-energy Radiations 1300

IV. Monomers 1300
   1. Alkenes 1301
   2. Vinyl Ethers 1302
   3. Styrene and Derivatives 1303
   4. Heterocyclic Monomers 1305
   5. Miscellaneous 1305

V. Solvents 1306

VI. Experimental Conditions 1307

VII. Polymer Structure 1308
   1. Head to Tail Addition: Chain Branching . . 1308
   2. Stereoregularity 1309

VIII. Mechanisms 1310
   1. Carbonium-ion Mechanism (Proton-initiated) . . 1310
   2. The Polarized Bond Mechanism 1311
   3. Water Co-catalyzed (Proton-initiated) Mechanism . 1312
   4. Carbonium-ion Initiated (Halide Co-catalyzed)
      Mechanism 1312
   5. Propagation Reactions 1315

6.   Transfer and Termination Reactions   .   .   . 1317

    A.   Spontaneous Transfer   1318

    B.   Transfer to Monomer   1318

    C.   Transfer to Solvent   1319

    D.   Termination Processes   1320

7.   Ions or Ion Pairs 1321

IX. Kinetics   1324

    1.   General Considerations 1324

    2.   Non-stationary Kinetic Schemes   .   . . 1328

    3.   Equilibrium Ionic Polymerization 1330

X. Energetics   1331

XI. Solvent Effects   1333

XII. Copolymerization 1335

    1.   Graft Copolymers.   1335

    A.   By Transfer Reactions   1335

    B.   By Co-catalysis using Halogenated Polymers . 1335

    2.   Reactivity Ratios   1336

Index 1349

CHAPTER XIV

Alkylation of Aromatics with Alkenes and Alkanes

S. H. Patinkin and B. S. Friedman

Sinclair Research, Inc., Harvey, Illinois

I. Introduction

1. Scope

This chapter covers the cationic nuclear alkylation of various aromatics such as monocyclic and polycyclic hydrocarbons, phenols, amines, thiophenes, furans, etc., with simple olefins including the aryl-substituted olefins, styrene, and allylbenzene, etc.

Alkylations with substituted olefins such as unsaturated halides, ethers, alcohols, acids, esters, ketones, etc., as well as dienes, are described in Chapter XV.

The range of catalysts which have been used for the aromatic alkylation reaction is a broad one. It includes Brønsted acids, e.g., sulfuric, phosphoric, and hydrofluoric acid as well as the usual Lewis acids such as the metallic halides. Solid oxide catalysts such as alumina and silica–alumina are also included since these contain acid sites of both Lewis and Brønsted types and are capable of promoting the aromatic alkylation reaction.

Because alkylation of aromatics with paraffins and cycloparaffins appears to take place via a carbonium-ion mechanism, this reaction is also discussed.

A fairly comprehensive survey of the scientific, technical, and patent literature was attempted. Patents were covered, however, only if they contained examples supplying a fair amount of experimental detail.

The essential information abstracted from each article or patent regarding reactants, catalysts, conditions, and products has been listed in the 68 Tables which will be found in the Appendix.

1

2. Reviews

In compiling the data for this chapter, the reviewers have utilized to good advantage the material provided by a number of earlier reviews in this field.

The most recent reviews in the last decade of some aspects of the aromatic–olefin reaction have been books by Dalin *et al.* (149) and Topchiev *et al.* (mainly boron fluoride catalysis (866a)). McAllister wrote a chaper reviewing some industrial applications of aromatic alkylation (462). In their chapter on "Aromatic Substitution" Nelson and Brown reviewed the theory and mechanism of the aromatic alkylation reaction (542). R. N. Shreve and co-authors have each year since 1948 published brief surveys of the literature in *Industrial and Engineering Chemistry.*

In 1948 Francis wrote a review article on the liquid-phase ethylation and isopropylation reactions (208). Two years earlier he and Reid (210) had thoroughly covered the ethylation of benzene.

Nightingale's article published in 1939 (559a) and Thomas' book published in 1941 (829a) provided reviews of aluminum chloride catalyzed aromatic–olefin reactions as well as aromatic–paraffin condensations.

Other catalysts as well as aluminum chloride were included in Price's review (649) which appeared in 1946. However, he did not cover the patent literature. Carleton Ellis reviewed patents as well as journal articles in his extensive summaries of the chemistry of petroleum derivatives (182a) published in 1934 and 1937.

Chemical Abstracts was searched through December, 1961, and thus most of the literature references appearing before June, 1961, have been reasonably well covered.

3. Commercial Aspects

Alkylation of aromatics with olefins may not have been the first of all the reactions studied by Friedel and Crafts, but it certainly has become a most important one commercially.

Thus, in the United States alone, in 1960 industry produced by aromatic olefin alkylation: 1,750,000,000 lbs. of ethylbenzene (200), 330,000,000 lbs.*,† of cumene, and 467,000,000 lbs. of dodecyl- and tridecylbenzene (116,200). Large tonnages of butyl-, octyl-, nonyl-, and dodecylphenols were also synthesized.

---

* Est. for 1962 (116).

† Five times this amount was produced for aviation gasoline during 1944 and 1945 (462).

The commercial exploitation of the aromatic–olefin alkylation reaction may be attributed to:

1. the ready availability of huge amounts of olefins resulting mainly from cracking of petroleum, and in some instances from polymerization;

2. the ready availability of pure aromatics from petroleum refining and petrochemical manufacturing as well as from coal tar;

3. the fairly simple processing required and the low catalyst costs.

II. Alkylation of Aromatic Hydrocarbons

1. Benzene and Its Homologs

A. Mechanism

To provide a basis for discussion of the more descriptive aspects of aromatic alkylation with olefins, some of the general mechanistic features of the reaction are presented in this section. No attempt at a thorough discussion of mechanism is made here, since there are other chapters in this treatise devoted to the mechanism and theory of Friedel-Crafts reactions. Mechanistic arguments are also examined, where appropriate, in other sections of this chapter.

The alkylation of aromatics with olefins is initiated by the interaction of a catalyst with an olefin to produce a carbonium ion, the corresponding ion pair, or a polarized complex. It is one of these intermediates which reacts with the aromatic ring.

The intermediate carbonium ion or polarized complex is formed by protonation of the double bond.

$$\begin{array}{c}\diagup\\C{=}C\\\diagup\quad\diagdown\end{array} + HA \rightarrow R^{\delta+}A^{\delta-}$$

The formation of the intermediate occurs in the presence of protonic acids and promoted Lewis acids.

In the absence of a co-catalyst such as water, hydrogen chloride, or other proton-donating compounds, metal halides do not promote so-called acid-catalyzed reactions of olefins. For example, boron fluoride will catalyze the low-temperature polymerization of isobutylene only if trace quantities of water or other co-catalysts such as t-butyl alcohol or acetic acid are added to the reaction medium (193a,193b,193c). Similarly it has been shown that in the absence of co-catalysts, aluminum chloride (364a), titanium tetrachloride (624b), and stannic chloride (563a) do not catalyze the polymerization of olefins. It was early recognized that the activity of aluminum chloride in olefin condensations with aromatic compounds is probably a result of the promotion by trace amounts of water (521). Further, Lebedev et al. (428,429) have shown that the rate of alkylation is directly proportional to the hydrogen chloride concentration when an aluminum chloride–hydrogen chloride catalyst couple is used.

The protonation of the olefin does not appear to be the rate-determining step in olefin alkylation of aromatics, at least as reported for two strong catalysts. The failure to observe an isotope effect in the alkylation of benzene with ethylene-C^{14} in the presence of aluminum bromide was interpreted by Hodnett and Feldman (282) as evidence that the olefin–catalyst interaction was not rate-determining. Lebedev (428) found that the rate of cyclohexylation of benzene with cyclohexene in the presence of aluminum chloride–hydrogen chloride was independent of cyclohexene concentration, directly proportional to hydrogen chloride concentration (when excess cyclohexene is present), and about one-half order in aluminum chloride concentration. Lebedev proposed that cyclohexyl chloride was formed at a very rapid rate and that the rate-determining step was not the reaction between benzene and cyclohexene, but the reaction of benzene with cyclohexyl chloride. The concentration of cyclohexyl chloride presumably remained constant and equal to the hydrogen chloride concentration.

The reviewers believe that Lebedev's data could be equally well interpreted in terms of rapid formation of a stable complex from cyclohexene, hydrogen chloride, and aluminum chloride. The concentration of the complex is determined by the hydrogen chloride concentration. The rate-determining step is the reaction of the complex with benzene.

The formation of the reactive intermediate in metal halide catalysis can be written as follows:

$$\overset{\diagdown}{\underset{\diagup}{C}}{=}\overset{\diagup}{\underset{\diagdown}{C}} + HX + MX_n \rightarrow R^{\delta+}MX_{n+1}^{\delta-}$$

The prior formation of the hypothetical acid, HMX_{n+1}, does not occur in most instances. Specifically, it has been shown that $HAlCl_4$, $HAlBr_4$, and HBF_4 do not exist as free acids, although stable salts of these compounds can be prepared (542).

As discussed in more detail in Section II-1-D-a, alkylation probably occurs in the catalyst layer. When aluminum chloride is used, the reaction proceeds rapidly only after an incubation period during which the so-called red oil forms.   Nelson and Brown (542) proposed that the red oil consists of σ-complexes which are organic salts with structures, $ArH_2^+ AlCl_4^-$ and $ArH_2^+ Al_2Cl_7^-$.   Aluminum chloride is very soluble in the oil and the general formula for the complexes in the catalyst layer is $ArH_2^+ (AlCl_4 \cdot nAlCl_3)^-$.

Elsewhere in this treatise and in Nelson and Brown's review (542) a more detailed discussion of the evidence for these complexes is presented with extensive references to the original literature.   More recently, Olah and Kuhn (579a) isolated $1:1:1$ complexes of aromatics (toluene, m-xylene, mesitylene, and isodurene) with hydrogen fluoride and boron fluoride, by mixing the three reagents and also by reaction of the aromatic with hydrogen bromide and silver fluoroborate.   The complex was formulated as a salt-like derivative of the hypothetical fluoroboric acid and could be represented by the protonated methylbenzene tetrafluoborate (A):

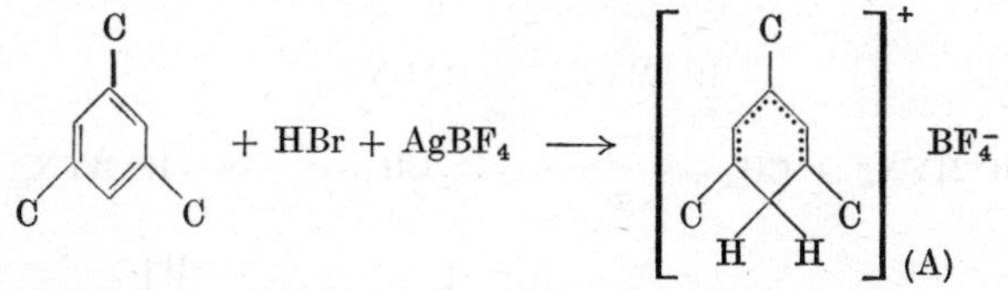

The σ-complex layer formed during the alkylation reaction is a highly polar medium.   It was suggested by Nelson and Brown that these complexes not only serve as excellent solvents for metal halides but also provide a highly polar medium in which the ionic or polar intermediates may form and react.

The interaction of the catalyst–olefin complex with the aromatic substrate is the second step in the alkylation sequence.   The catalyst–olefin complex is either completely polarized to an ion pair or to a solvated carbonium ion, or it is only partially polarized.   In either event it undergoes a displacement reaction with the aromatic ring.   The reaction rate is highly dependent on the ability of the alkyl group to accommodate a positive charge.   It would appear almost certain that isobutylene is converted to a solvated tertiary butyl cation or corresponding ion pair, but there is disagreement concerning primary and secondary cation formation.   Arguments concerning these alternatives are discussed in Section II-1-B-a and elsewhere in this treatise.

The contribution of ionic species to the alkylation reaction is probably best evaluated in terms of the products formed.   Carbonium ions are capable of undergoing a number of typical reactions including addition to olefins to form polymers, carbon skeleton rearrangement, β-cleavage, and hydride transfer. These reactions accompany alkylation of aromatics in varying degrees, depending on the structure of the aromatic, the structure of the alkylating agent, the strength of the catalyst, and the conditions of the reaction. The contribution of these reactions to product distributions for specific alkylations are discussed in appropriate sections.

It has been suggested by Nelson and Brown that in aromatic substitution the electrophilic reagent interacts with the π-electrons of the aromatic to form a π-complex which then rearranges to a σ-complex. Olah and Kuhn (579a) further suggest that the incoming group attacks at the center of highest electron density forming a localized π-complex. The overall reaction mechanism, for metal halide catalyzed alkylation can be written as follows:

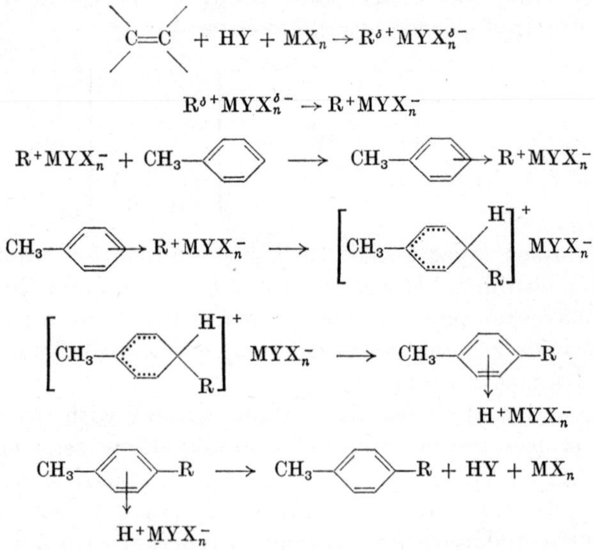

$$\text{C=C} + HY + MX_n \rightarrow R^{\delta+}MYX_n^{\delta-}$$

$$R^{\delta+}MYX_n^{\delta-} \rightarrow R^{+}MYX_n^{-}$$

$$R^{+}MYX_n^{-} + CH_3\!-\!\langle\ \rangle \longrightarrow CH_3\!-\!\langle\ \rangle \rightarrow R^{+}MYX_n^{-}$$

$$CH_3\!-\!\langle\ \rangle \rightarrow R^{+}MYX_n^{-} \longrightarrow \left[CH_3\!-\!\langle\ \rangle\!\!\overset{H}{\underset{R}{}}\right]^{+} MYX_n^{-}$$

$$\left[CH_3\!-\!\langle\ \rangle\!\!\overset{H}{\underset{R}{}}\right]^{+} MYX_n^{-} \longrightarrow CH_3\!-\!\langle\ \rangle\!-\!R \xrightarrow{} H^{+}MYX_n^{-}$$

$$CH_3\!-\!\langle\ \rangle\!-\!R \longrightarrow CH_3\!-\!\langle\ \rangle\!-\!R + HY + MX_n$$
$$\qquad\qquad H^{+}MYX_n^{-}$$

If ionization does not occur, the π-complex is formed as follows:

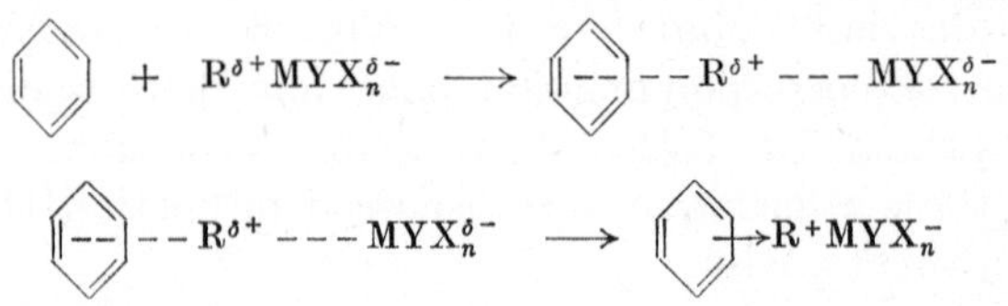

$$\langle\ \rangle + R^{\delta+}MYX_n^{\delta-} \longrightarrow \langle\!-\!\rangle\text{---}R^{\delta+}\text{----}MYX_n^{\delta-}$$

$$\langle\!-\!\rangle\text{---}R^{\delta+}\text{----}MYX_n^{\delta-} \longrightarrow \langle\ \rangle\!\!\rightarrow R^{+}MYX_n^{-}$$

The rate of electrophilic substitution reactions has been shown to be a function of the basicity of aromatic hydrocarbons as measured by the stability of the complex formed with the hydrogen fluoride–boron fluoride couple (80).   Therefore, the transition state must be closer in structure to the σ-complex than to the π-complex.

Olah and Kuhn (579b)* have presented strong evidence for the formation of the σ-complex as an important intermediate in aromatic alkylation.   They isolated a σ-complex by passing one mole of boron fluoride into a mixture of one mole of an aromatic, such as mesitylene, and one mole of ethyl fluoride:

$$
\text{mesitylene} + C_2H_5F + BF_3 \longrightarrow \left[\text{σ-complex}\right]^+ BF_4^-
$$

When the complex was heated, the ethylated aromatic was isolated in high yield.

$$
\left[\text{σ-complex}\right]^+ BF_4^- \longrightarrow \text{ethylmesitylene} + HF + BF_3
$$

As shown by McCaulay and Lien (465), the basicity of aromatic compounds or the stability of the σ-complexes of these aromatics, increases with the number of alkyl groups on the ring and is highest with *meta*-derivatives.   The stability of these complexes is also a function of the acid strength of the catalysts (466,467a).

As discussed in detail in Section II-1-B-a, the *para/meta* ratio, in the kinetically controlled alkylation of monoalkylbenzenes, may be a function of the reactivity of the alkylating species.   The most stable, hence the least reactive, carbonium ion, the *t*-butyl cation, is most selective and gives the highest *para/meta* ratio.

The product distribution is generally altered by concurrent isomerization and disproportionation.   Disproportionation of tertiary and secondary alkylbenzenes probably occurs *via* reversal of

* After the completion of this chapter, Olah *et al.* (579c) published a study of benzylation of benzene and alkylbenzenes which provides evidence that the rate-determining transition state for benzylation correlates better with π-complex stability than with σ-complex stability.   They suggest that for benzylations and probably other alkylations the first transition state has the nature of an *oriented* π-complex, followed by a second transition state of σ-complex nature, where the substituent stabilizes into individual positions (*ortho, meta, para*).

σ-complex formation to form the carbonium ion which then alkylates a second aromatic nucleus.

$$\left[\underset{H \quad R}{\bigotimes} \right]^{+} \quad Cat^{-} \longrightarrow \bigcirc\!\!\!-\!\!\!\!\rightarrow R^{+}Cat^{-}$$

$$\bigcirc\!\!\!-\!\!\!\!\rightarrow R^{+}Cat^{-} \longrightarrow \bigcirc \quad + \quad R^{+}Cat^{-}$$

$$R^{+}Cat^{-} \quad + \quad \underset{}{\bigcirc} \longrightarrow \underset{R}{\bigcirc}\!\!\!-\!\!\!\!\rightarrow R^{+}Cat^{-} \longrightarrow \underset{R}{\bigcirc}\!\!-\!\!R$$

According to Allen (7b) isomerization of di- or polyalkylated benzenes occurs primarily by the disproportionation mechanism when the migrating group is a secondary or tertiary alkyl group. On the other hand a primary substituent disproportionates by an S_N2 reaction involving attack of a second aromatic on the π-complex (84a). Isomerization of the primary substituent may occur by rearrangement of the π-complex to a new σ-complex.

When large amounts of very strong catalysts such as boron fluoride–hydrogen fluoride or aluminum chloride–hydrogen chloride are used, the product is mainly *meta* because of the much greater stability of the *meta*-isomer σ-complex. McCaulay and Lien (467a) found that when molar quantities of strongly acidic catalysts are used, alkylation stops at the trialkyl level and the product is almost completely the 1,3,5-derivative. The complex of the 1,3,5-derivative is very stable and because it is positively charged further alkylation does not occur. The formation of such strong σ-complexes accounts at least partially for the loss of activity of these catalysts as alkylation proceeds.

B. Orientation

The problem of orientation of alkyl groups in di- and polyalkylated benzene is a complex one. The ratio of position isomers isolated on quenching the alkylation reaction is the result not only of the selectivity of the initial attack, but also of the concomitant isomerization and transalkylation reactions. The initial distribution of the isomers is influenced by the substituents already on the nucleus, the reactivity of the alkylating species, and the steric requirements of both the entering group and the substituent already present. The role played by isomerization and transalkylation is determined by the severity of the reaction conditions, namely the strength and amount of the catalyst, the temperature, and the time of reaction.*

a. Polar effects and the role of isomerization and transalkylation

Kutz and co-workers (424) found that the isomer distributions of diethylbenzenes and ethyltoluenes obtained by the condensation of benzene, ethylbenzene, and toluene with ethylene were dependent on the nature of the catalyst. The ethylation of toluene in the presence of phosphoric acid or iron phosphate yielded monoethyltoluenes with an isomer distribution of 43% *o*-, 29% *m*-, and 28% *p*-. In the presence of aluminum chloride a distribution of 11% *o*-, 64% *m*-, and 25% *p*-ethyltoluene was obtained which was close to equilibrium distribution, reported to be 9.0% *o*-, 64.8% *m*-, and 26.2% *p*- (10b).

Condon (130) obtained 38% *o*-, 27% *m*-, and 35% *p*-cymene by isopropylating toluene under conditions in which dealkylation and isomerization were believed to be unimportant. This distribution was obtained when the reaction was catalyzed with aluminum chloride–nitromethane in benzene solvent, or with boron fluoride etherate at 65°. These results were considered good evidence that the *meta*-derivative was the product of direct alkylation. The application of infra-red techniques to the analysis of these isomer mixtures by Condon (130), Simons and Hart (761), and Schlatter and Clark (696) established that earlier reports of the synthesis of nearly pure *p*-cymene by toluene isopropylation were in error (649). However, the formation of very large amounts of *meta*-cymene in the presence of strong Friedel-Crafts catalysts was undoubtedly a result of isomerization and disproportionation.

Results of studies which have been carried out within the past fifteen years are in substantial agreement with those of Condon. Simons and Hart (761) reported that a hydrogen chloride catalyzed isopropylation yielded a distribution of 31% *o*-, 25% *m*-, and 44% *p*-cymene. Schlatter and Clark obtained 41% *o*-, 26% *m*-, and 33% *p*-cymene with hydrogen fluoride and phosphoric acid catalysts. Patinkin and Sanford (596) obtained similar results with hydrogen fluoride–boron fluoride, sulfuric acid–boron fluoride, ferric chloride, and aluminum chloride–nitromethane.

Melpolder *et al.* (509a) showed that the dialkylbenzene fraction obtained by the isopropylation of benzene with propylene in the

---

* E. P. Babin (29a) published a review in 1961 (103 references) in which he tabulated the isomeric composition of di- and polyalkylbenzene fractions prepared by alkylation.

presence of phosphoric acid supported on kieselguhr contained 6% *o*-, 36% *m*-, and 42% *p*-diisopropylbenzene.

Schlatter and Clark found toluene could be alkylated under mild alkylating conditions with isobutylene or other *t*-butylating agents in the presence of small amounts of hydrogen fluoride to yield a monoalkylate containing 93% *p*- and 7% *m*-*t*-butyltoluene. This distribution was obtained at temperatures of about 0°, with reaction times of about 1.5 hours. This high *para* to *meta* ratio was considered to be the initial distribution formed by direct alkylation. Patinkin and Sanford (597,598), however, found that alkylation at lower temperatures, *e.g.*, − 20°, with hydrogen fluoride or sulfuric acid, afforded a product containing 98% *p*-*t*-butyltoluene and 2% *m*-*t*-butyltoluene.

Topchiev *et al.* (866) obtained the following monoalkylates in condensing *o*-, *m*-, and *p*-xylenes with propene in the presence of boron fluoride–phosphoric acid:

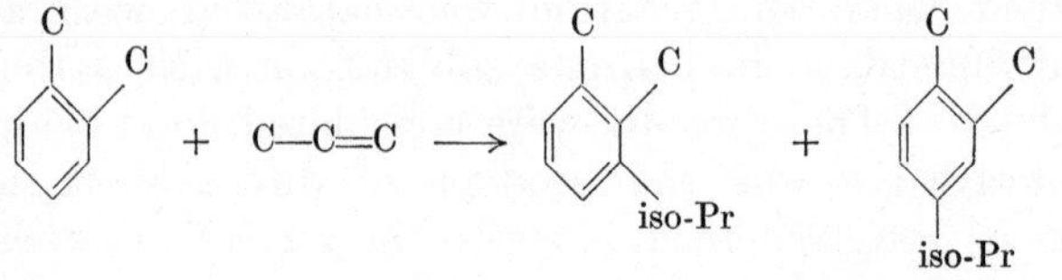

Temp.	(A)	(B)
20°	40%	60%
60°	20%	80%
80°	4%	96%

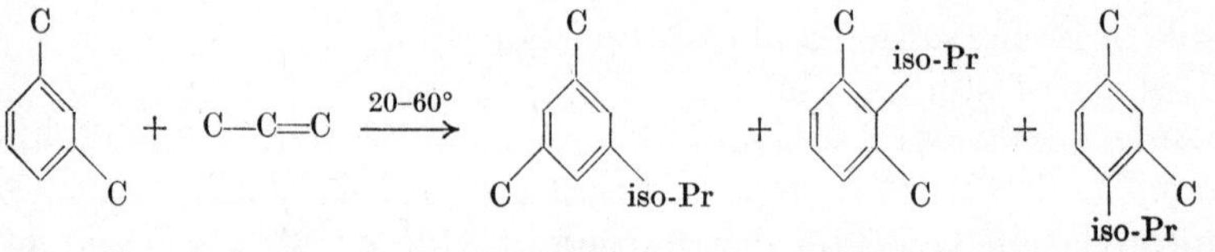

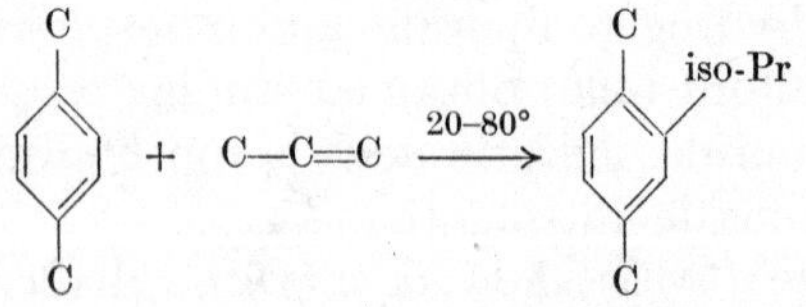

They suggested that (A) and (E) are the initial products and that these isomerize to give the other products. It was concluded that the isomerization occurred by intramolecular migration of isopropyl groups since very little disproportionation took place during isomerization experiments. Although their evidence appears convincing, it would have been more conclusive had a foreign aromatic such as toluene or benzene been included as an acceptor for the isopropyl groups in distinguishing between intramolecular or intermolecular mechanisms.

Kirkland and co-workers (383) found that when m-xylene was alkylated with propene, the ratio of 1,3,5 isomer (C) to the 1,2,4 isomer (E) decreased with decreasing strength of the alkylation catalyst. They found that at temperatures of less than 100° with an aluminum chloride/aromatic mole ratio of < 0.05, the monoalkylate contained 99% of the 1,3,5 product (C). On the other hand, with boron fluoride–phosphoric acid and boron fluoride–phosphoric anhydride, 65–75% and 80–90%, respectively, of the 1,2,4-isomer (E) was obtained. The alkylation of p-xylene with propene in the presence of aluminum chloride at 90–95° was accompanied by a considerable amount of isomerization, since 44% of the product was the 1,3,5-isomer. The same reaction in the presence of a solid catalyst, $BF_3 \cdot P_2O_5$, yielded 100% of 2-isopropyl-1,4-dimethyl-benzene. This product was clearly the result of initial alkylation. Similar results were obtained in ethylation with these catalyst systems except that somewhat larger yields of the 1,2,4-isomers were obtained.

Thus the results of Kirkland et al. are similar to those of Topchiev et al., but it is important to note that the latter isolated the 1,2,3-isomer (D) from the m-xylene alkylate.

Kirkland et al. also demonstrated the effect of catalyst strength on isomer distribution in the alkylation of xylenes by using aluminum chloride catalysts containing up to 2% water. The ratio of 1,2,4- to 1,3,5-isomers in m-xylene propylation was increased by adding increasing amounts of water to the aluminum chloride. The presence of adventitious water may have been responsible for many of the discrepancies in earlier publications on aluminum chloride catalyzed alkylations.

Allen and Yats (10) recently published the results of an extensive investigation of methylation, ethylation, and isopropylation of toluene with various catalysts and alkylating agents. In earlier isomerization rate studies by these authors (8,9,10b) equations were developed for each of the dialkylbenzenes which allowed the generation of a trajectory from any initial composition to the equilibrium composition on a triangular three-component composition diagram.

2*

From these graphs it could be determined whether any given experimental distribution was consistent with a selected initial isomer distribution. These authors showed that the isomer distributions obtained in their study and by others could have been obtained by alkylation to produce the isomer distributions in Table I followed

TABLE I.[a]   Alkylation of toluene

	% p-	% m-	% o-	$2p/m$	$\Delta S^{\ddagger b}$	Relative rates[b]
Methylation	26	14	60	3.7	− 20.0	1.0
Ethylation	34	18	48	3.8	− 21.5	13.7
Isopropylation	36.5	21.5	42	3.4	− 19.3	20,000
t-Butylation	93	7	0	26.6		

[a] Initial isomer distributions reported by Allen and Yats (10).
[b] Obtained for $GaBr_3$–alkyl bromide alkylations by Choi and Brown (120).

by isomerization. The catalyst affected the distribution only insofar as it influenced isomerization.

Only one initial isopropyltoluene isomer distribution was needed to explain the products of all toluene isopropylation experiments. On the other hand ethylene appeared to produce an initial distribution lower in p-ethyltoluene and higher in m-ethyltoluene than was formed by ethyl halides or ethanol. However, in a detailed study of the ethylation of toluene Gau (227) found that the isomer distribution was dependent on the rate of ethylene addition to the reaction mixture. Ethylene and ethyl chloride gave identical results if, during the alkylation with ethylene, the reaction media was kept saturated with ethylene. The results (50% o-, 20% m-, and 30% p-) were close to the initial composition chosen by Allen and Yats for the general case. Under conditions of partial saturation the isomer distribution approached the equilibrium composition: 9.0% o-/26.2% m-/64.8% p-.

Gau showed that disproportionation and isomerization occurred at significant rates concurrently with ethylation of toluene. In the course of a single experiment no change in isomer distribution or the disproportionation ratio $\dfrac{[\text{Toluene}]\,[\text{Diethyltoluene}]}{[\text{Monoethyltoluene}]}$ occurred with time. Accompanying these reactions was a build-up of higher alkylated toluenes which poisoned the catalyst. These data indicate that the isomer distribution obtained in his study was the result of a steady state condition.

The present knowledge of aromatic alkylation indicates that the distribution of position isomers obtained under non-isomerizing conditions is a function of both the aromatic compound and the alkylating agent. Brown and Nelson (82) have proposed that the *meta/para* ratio in the alkylation of alkylbenzenes is determined by the reactivity of the alkylating agent. The large amount of *meta*-isomer obtained in the isopropylation of toluene was attributed by these authors to the high reactivity and consequent low selectivity of the intermediate alkylating species. The high selectivity observed in *t*-butylations is consistent with the far greater stability of the *t*-butyl cation. A detailed discussion of the quantitative relationship between reactivity, as measured by the relative rates of electrophilic substitution of toluene and benzene, and selectivity, as measured by the p/m ratio of the partial rate factors, is given in earlier reviews and papers by Brown and Nelson (80,82,541,542).

It is generally accepted that the Friedel-Crafts alkylation involves the attack of a carbonium ion or a polarized complex on an aromatic nucleus to form a π-complex which rearranges to form a σ-complex. Brown and Smoot (84) originally considered the high rates of isopropylation and *t*-butylation relative to methylation and ethylation to be the consequence of a change in mechanism. Methylation and ethylation presumably took place *via* an S_N2 displacement mechanism, whereas isopropylation and *t*-butylation took place *via* an S_E carbonium-ion mechanism. However in a more recent paper Choi and Brown (120) reported that the entropies of activation were essentially constant for alkylation with methyl, ethyl, and isopropyl bromide in the presence of gallium bromide (Table I). These results indicate that the mechanism did not change in going from primary to secondary alkylation. The order of selectivity, *t*-butylation $\gg$ methylation > ethylation > isopropylation, suggested that the ability of the alkyl group to tolerate a positive charge must contribute in an important way to the stability of the transition state. Since the change in rate with alkyl group is far larger than the change in rate with variation of the aromatic, carbon–bromine bond breaking must be of greater importance in the transition state stabilization than bond making by the aromatic. Furthermore, bond making decreases in importance with increasing ability of the alkyl group to accommodate a positive charge (120), a conclusion which is applicable to olefin alkylation if it is assumed the intermediate alkylating species is the same as in alkyl halide alkylation.

In contrast, Allen and Yats (10) found that the ratio $2p/m$ (Table I) was the same for methylation, ethylation, and isopropylation for a variety of catalysts and alkylating agents including the alkyl bromide–gallium bromide system of Brown and co-workers. They concluded that there was no significant change either of selectivity or of reactivity of the alkylating species. The enormous change in relative rates with change of alkyl group was ascribed to relative quantities or rates of formation of the polarized alkyl species. If a displacement mechanism were involved one would expect the distribution of isomers to be significantly affected by the alkylating reagent and catalyst since the amount of polarization in the polarized complex should affect the selectivity of the reaction for the activated positions of the toluene ring. Since Allen and Yats found that this was not true, they concluded that polarization was complete or nearly complete.

Choi and Brown found in competitive tests that the relative rates of alkylation of toluene/benzene were 5.7, 2.5, and 1.82 with methyl bromide, ethyl bromide, and isopropyl bromide, respectively. The Brown selectivity relationship predicts increasing p/m ratios with increasing relative rates of alkylation of toluene/benzene. The constant p/m ratios reported by Allen and Yats and the toluene/benzene relative rates reported by Choi and Brown are inconsistent if the selectivity theory of Brown *et al.* is valid. It is interesting to note that the results of Allen and Yats lead to the conclusion that methyl, ethyl, and isopropyl cations or the ion pairs formed with the catalyst have equal reactivity or selectivity in the reaction with aromatic compounds.

It appears to the reviewers that the conflicting results and conclusions are caused by the difficulty of obtaining true initial isomer distributions unaffected by transalkylation. Allen and Yats (10) maintained that their analytical results are more accurate than Brown's because they were able to make use of gas-phase chromatography. The work of Gau (227) indicates that at least in the ethylation with ethylene a constant isomer distribution may not indicate non-occurrence of isomerization, but might instead be a result of the establishment of a pseudo-equilibrium involving isomerization and disproportionation as well as alkylation. It is interesting that Brown and Smoot (84) reported that the isomer distribution of ethyltoluenes did not vary with time during alkylation of toluene with ethyl bromide in the presence of gallium bromide. G. A. Olah has informed the reviewers by private communication that he has obtained higher selectivities than Allen and Yats (10) for the reaction of isopropyl bromide with toluene catalyzed by a number of Friedel-Crafts catalysts. It is unfortunate that neither

Allen and Yats (10) nor Brown and co-workers (84,120) gave complete distribution of products. To interpret these reactions more fully, it would be important to know the amount and identity of the poly- as well as monoalkyltoluenes and how they vary with time.

[*Note added in Proof:* In their recent publication on the benzylation of toluene and other alkylbenzenes, Olah *et al.* (579c) found much lower *meta*-substitution than was predicted from the alkylaromatic/benzene selectivity ratios. Isopropylations and *t*-butylations with alkyl halides were said to give somewhat similar results but the data have not yet been published. These authors suggested that reagent reactivity affects substrate selectivity in competitive reactions but not necessarily positional selectivity. They proposed that this is not an unreasonable outcome if the substrate rate-determining transition state has an oriented π-complex structure, followed by σ-complex type transition states determining the isomer distribution.

Olah *et al.* questioned the conclusion of previous authors who claimed they had isolated monoalkylation products in the absence of isomerization. They questioned Condon's conclusion (129) that the failure of *p*-cymene to undergo change when present during isopropylation of benzene proved the absence of isomerization and/or disproportionation in toluene isopropylation. They point out that the σ-complex which is the requisite intermediate for isomerization of *p*-cymene may not form during the alkylation of benzene, whereas it must form during the isopropylation of toluene.]

Since isomerization accompanies Friedel-Crafts alkylations in most if not all instances, a brief discussion of the mechanism of that reaction appears warranted. The isomerization of xylenes has been shown by several workers to be an intramolecular 1,2-shift (36,443, 466). On the other hand Allen (7b) concluded that the mechanism of isomerization of ethyl-, isopropyl-, and *t*-butyltoluene proceeds by an intermolecular mechanism to the extent of 15, 85, and 100% respectively. Any alkylation which is accompanied by isomerization will probably also be accompanied by disproportionation. The detailed mechanism of these reactions is discussed by McCaulay in detail in Chapter XXIV.

McCaulay and Lien (467a) stated that the product distribution under isomerization conditions is a function of the acid strength and the amount of the catalyst. They found, for example, that the ethylation of *m*-xylene in the presence of hydrogen fluoride containing molar quantities or more of boron fluoride yielded predominantly 1,3,5-ethylxylene and a small amount of polyethylxylenes. Similar results were obtained with ethyl chloride by Norris and Rubinstein

(563) using aluminum chloride–hydrogen chloride when the aluminum chloride (Al_2Cl_6) to aromatic ratio was greater than one. It has been known for over sixty years that the use of high ratios of aluminum chloride to benzene (1.0/1.4) in the condensation of ethylene and benzene would favor the formation of 1,3,5-triethylbenzene (226). However, hydrogen fluoride alone produced mainly polyethylxylenes, the ethylxylene fraction being predominantly 1,3,4-ethylxylene.

These results were explained by McCaulay and Lien by the hypothesis that the strong acid, HF/BF_3, isomerizes the first-formed 1,3,4-ethylxylene into the 1,3,5-isomer. Because of its greater basicity the 1,3,5-isomer preferentially forms a positively charged σ-complex (465) with the strong acid which does not further react with the positively charged ethyl group. High yields of the monoalkylate were therefore possible. The importance of the σ-complex in alkylation has been discussed in several publications of Brown *et al.* (80,82,541,542), and in Chapter VIII of this treatise.

b. *Steric factors*

The amount of *ortho*-substitution obtained in the alkylation of alkylbenzenes and in the dialkylation of benzene is to a large extent determined by the steric requirements of the first alkyl substituent on the benzene ring and of the incoming group. Brown *et al.* (542) concluded that because of crowding the σ-complex which leads to the *ortho*-disubstituted product is of low stability relative to the isomeric *meta*- and *para*-complexes. Under equilibrium conditions the isomer distribution is not determined by the relative stabilities of the σ-complex, but by the relative stabilities of the final products. The relative amount of *ortho*-substitution under equilibrium conditions will in fact generally be lower than under kinetically controlled conditions. The reason for this is that the rigid planar structure of an aromatic compound causes greater interference of adjacent groups than exists in the σ-complex where the new group is out of the plane of the ring.

In a study of the isopropylation of toluene, cumene, and *t*-butylbenzene, Condon (129) found that the ratio of *meta/para* partial rate factors was approximately the same for each aromatic. However, the partial rate factors for isopropylation in the *ortho*-position for toluene, cumene, and *t*-butylbenzene were 2.4, 0.37, and 0.0 respectively. The decreasing partial rate factors for *ortho*-substitution are thus responsible for the decreasing overall rate as the steric requirements of the alkyl substituents increase.

Steric requirements of entering isopropyl and ethyl groups in the alkylation of toluene are modest, especially when compared to a t-alkyl group. Bloch and Hervert (59) concluded from their work that, in general, primary olefins have low steric requirements in alkylation. In the alkylation of toluene with 1-dodecene catalyzed by hydrogen fluoride, these authors obtained 33% *ortho*-substitution, which is about the same as that obtained in the propylation of toluene. Further evidence of the moderate steric requirements of isopropyl groups are found in the results of Melpolder *et al.* (509a) who obtained 6 to 7% of *o*-diisopropylbenzene in the reaction of benzene with propene in the presence of the U.O.P. phosphoric acid catalyst.

Nevertheless, attempts to introduce three or four isopropyl groups adjacent to each other have not been successful. The 1,2,3-triisopropyl derivative of benzene has not been synthesized; trialkylation yields either the 1,3,4- or 1,3,5-structure (546); tetraalkylation, only the 1,2,4,5-structure (110,313,389,546,923). In no case has penta- or hexaisopropylbenzene been isolated. Only starting material was recovered when an attempt was made to further propylate tetraisopropylbenzene (389). Attempts at exhaustive cyclopentylation (536), cyclohexylation (141,216,535), and secondary butylation (216) of benzene also failed to yield products with more than four substituents.

Only three isopropyl (68,216,652) or cyclohexyl (634) groups have been introduced into the toluene nucleus.

Apparently only two isopropyl groups may be introduced into the xylene nucleus (383,866). Using boron fluoride–phosphoric acid as catalyst Topchiev *et al.* (866) obtained only 4,5-diisopropyl-*o*-xylene and 2,5-diisopropyl-*p*-xylene from *o*-xylene and *p*-xylene respectively. However, both 4,6- and 2,5- diisopropyl-*m*-xylene were obtained from *m*-xylene. A patent (174a) claimed the introduction of three isopropyl groups into the xylene, diethylbenzene, and chlorotoluene nuclei; however, no proof of structure was given to eliminate the possibility that the product contained hexyl substituents.

No more than two isopropyl (216), cyclopentyl, or cyclohexyl groups have been introduced into the mesitylene nucleus (634,636). Only one isopropyl or cyclohexyl group can be introduced into durene (216). One mole of propene has been added to pentamethylbenzene (216). It is therefore well established that an isopropyl group can be inserted between two methyl groups on the benzene nucleus. However, just as it has been impossible to introduce three

adjacent isopropyl groups in the benzene nucleus to form compound
(G) by Friedel-Crafts alkylation, it has also been impossible to
introduce two adjacent isopropyl groups next to a methyl group to
form (H).

(G)   (H)

Pokrovskaya (635) reported that isomerization accompanied the
alkylation of mesitylene with 0.6 moles of propene in the presence of
aluminum chloride at about 0°. He obtained an 85% yield of a
monoisopropyl derivative to which Galpern et al. (224a), on the basis
of ultraviolet absorption spectra, assigned the 1,2,4,5- structure.
Diisopropylation yielded 1,2,4-trimethyl-3,5-diisopropyl benzene.
Pokrovskaya and Shimanko observed similar isomerization reactions
in aluminum chloride catalyzed alkylations of mesitylene with
cyclopentene and cyclohexene, but sulfuric acid afforded the unrearranged mono- and dicycloalkyl derivatives of mesitylene (636).

Lysenko and Plyusnin (459) observed that no more than two
secondary butyl groups could be incorporated in isopropylbenzene.
This is in accord with the poor yield of tetra-s-butylbenzene obtained
by others (216) in alkylating benzene with four moles of 2-butene
in the presence of the same catalyst (hydrogen fluoride) used by
Lysenko and Plyusnin. However, since aluminum chloride afforded
30% of 1,2,4,5-tetra-s-butylbenzene (216) it should be possible, using
this catalyst, to prepare the tri-s-butyl derivative of cumene.

C. Relative Reactivity of Benzene and its Homologs

Benzene is quite reactive towards olefins in the presence of metal
halide and protonic acid catalysts. In fact, Condon and Matuszak
(134) estimated that benzene was 350 times more reactive than
isobutane in reaction with isopropyl cation in the presence of hydrogen fluoride.

In the early literature it was generally assumed that alkylation of
alkylbenzenes was faster than the alkylation of benzene itself (649).
These conclusions were based on the observation that large quantities
of polyalkylation accompanied the monoalkylation of benzene.
However, Francis and Reid (210) favored the view that the rates of

reaction of benzene with ethylene, and ethylbenzene with ethylene, were equal. As Condon (129) indicated, some of their calculations showed that under some conditions benzene appeared to be twice as readily alkylated as ethylbenzene.

This problem was studied by Condon who propylated toluene and benzene in a manner which avoided complicating reactions such as transalkylation and isomerization. He found that the relative rates of propylation of toluene versus benzene at 40° was about 2.1 in the presence of either boron fluoride etherate or aluminum chloride–nitromethane. Convincing evidence that transalkylation and isomerization did not occur was provided by the fact that no o- or m-cymene and no toluene was found when propylene was passed into a mixture of benzene and p-cymene, in the presence of aluminum chloride–nitromethane at 65°. (However, see Note regarding reference 579c on p. 15.) It is also significant that Condon's catalysts were miscible with the hydrocarbon reactants and products. No doubt heterogeneity and transalkylation caused the conflicting data that have appeared in the earlier literature.

Others have obtained results confirming Condon's observations. Lebedev et al. (429) reported that the relative rates of the ethylation of ethylbenzene and benzene was 2.09. The toluene/benzene rate ratios obtained by Brown and co-workers (120) in their study of selectivity of alkylation with alkyl halides were all greater than 1.8 (see Section II-1-B-a).

It is therefore surprising to note that in their study of the alkylation of binary mixtures of benzene and alkybenzenes with a number of olefins, Volkov and Zavgorodnii (903) found that with the exception of isobutylene all olefins tested were more reactive towards benzene than towards alkylbenzenes. The alkylations were carried out in the presence of boron fluoride–phosphoric acid at 60°.

TABLE II.   Alkylation of alkylbenzenes (903)

Aromatic hydrocarbon	Relative Alkylation Rate (Benzene = 1.0)				
	Propene	2-Butene	1-Butene	Isobutylene	Cyclohexene
Toluene	0.62	0.56	0.72	3.78	0.94
Ethylbenzene	0.35	0.29	0.28	3.04	0.61
Isopropylbenzene	0.19	0.17	0.20	2.15	0.34
s-Butylbenzene	0.17	0.16	0.17	—	—
t-Butylbenzene	0.14	0.12	—	0.89	0.23
o-Xylene	0.45	0.40	0.49	7.51	1.07
m-Xylene	0.38	0.31	0.39	0.68	0.58
p-Xylene	0.32	0.26	0.31	0.0	0.46

These authors suggested that alkyl groups on the benzene ring strongly activate the ring only when the attacking reagent has a significant positive charge. When such a positive charge is not developed, stereochemical and probability factors do not favor the alkylation of benzene homologs and therefore benzene can exhibit greater reactivity (903). Thus isobutylene, which is known to polarize readily, preferentially alkylated the benzene homologs. The rate of alkylbenzene alkylation relative to benzene alkylation decreases in the order isobutylene, cyclohexene, 1-butene, propene, and 2-butene.

These reactions were reported by Volkov and Zavgorodnii to be free of transalkylation which would interfere with the determination of valid rate ratios. There is some doubt, however, about the validity of the experiments these authors performed, which were designed to determine the rate of dealkylation. No indication was given that they were conducted in a manner which would expose the substrate to a true alkylation environment, e.g., one that would provide a continuous supply of carbonium ions by virtue of constantly supplied olefin feed. Such a precaution was taken by Condon in his studies, referred to above, of the role of isomerization and trans-alkylation during propylation.

Volkov and Zavgorodnii considered the difference in the relative reactivities of alkylbenzenes to benzene with respect to 1- and 2-butene as evidence that the rupture of a π-bond during alkylation proceeds simultaneously with the formation of the bond with the aromatic ring. If free carbonium ions were involved, there would have been no difference between 1-butene and 2-butene since both butenes yield identical ions (903). However, the reviewers feel that the differences noted in the results with 1- and 2-butenes may well be within experimental error.

In general, alkylbenzenes are alkylated more readily and under milder conditions than benzene. For example, high yields of pure t-octyltoluene were obtained by low-temperature alkylation of toluene with diisobutylene. On the other hand, a similar reaction between benzene and diisobutylene required a higher temperature and afforded a much larger amount of cleavage products and skeletally rearranged octyl side chain—a result that may be attributed to the greater resistance of benzene to alkylation (Section II-1-H-b).

When several alkyl groups are present on the benzene ring, steric interference becomes significant and the rate of alkylation may be slower than benzene alkylation or the reaction may fail to occur.   A more thorough discussion of this subject is presented in Sections II-1-B-b and II-1-G.

D.   Liquid-phase Alkylation with Ethylene, Propene, and Butenes

a.   Metal halide catalysts

Most of the early work on aromatic alkylation with olefins employed aluminum chloride and other metal halide catalysts.   Hydrogen chloride or small amounts of water have been used as promoters with metal halide catalysts.   The preferred temperature for the aluminum chloride catalyzed ethylation of benzene was reported to be in the range of 70–90° (521).

Grosse and Ipatieff (245) evaluated a number of metal halides for the reaction of ethylene and benzene.   Based on the temperature at which appreciable reaction occurred, the following order of reactivity was indicated: $AlCl_3$ > $ZrCl_4$ > $TaCl_5$ > BF_3 > $CbCl_5$ > $TiCl_4$.   Burk (93a) included these data along with data from other metal halide catalyzed reactions to arrive at a more generalized table of reactivity: $AlBr_3$ > $AlCl_3$ > $FeCl_3$ > $ZrCl_4$ > $TaCl_5$ > BF_3 > UCl_4 > $TiCl_3$ > WCl_6 > $CbCl_5$ > $ZnCl_2$ > $SnCl_4$ > $TiCl_4$ > $BeCl_2$ > $SbCl_5$ > $HgCl_2$ > $CuCl_2$ > $BiCl_3$ > AsF_3.

In the presence of solid aluminum chloride the absorption of ethylene in the ethylation of benzene is very slow for about twenty minutes (521).   It is during this period that the dense catalyst layer is formed.   This "incubation" period has been eliminated by the use of preformed catalyst complexes consisting of aluminum chloride, hydrogen chloride, and aromatic compounds (462a,429).   The addition of alkylbenzenes also reduces the incubation period (52).

The catalytic layer can be repeatedly used.   However, the activity of the catalyst declines with re-use unless fresh aluminum chloride is added.   Gau (227) showed that with a low concentration (4%) of aluminum chloride the alkylation stopped at low conversions because of complex formation with the polyethylbenzenes.   The formation of condensed aromatic systems such as anthracene (739b) and 9,10-dimethylanthracene (739a) probably accounts for permanent deactivation of the catalyst.

The transalkylation activity of the catalyst layer makes the recycling of diethylbenzenes feasible.   The use of a large excess of benzene coupled with recycling permits almost complete conversion of ethylene to monoethylbenzenes.   In one commercial process the diethylbenzenes are recycled to the reactor which is operated at 95°, and the higher homologs are condensed with benzene in a separate reactor at still higher temperatures where transalkylation is accelerated (462a).

The rate of ethylene absorption is greatly accelerated by the use of high-speed stirring (521) and superatmospheric pressure (210). Various optimum temperatures have been reported ranging from 50° to 100° (52,122,210,355,429,495,521). The discrepancies in reported optimum temperatures can probably be explained in terms of the balance between the chemical reaction velocity and diffusion of ethylene to the reactive phase (429). Lebedev et al. (429) predicted that operating conditions which accelerate the absorption of ethylene should displace the optimum temperatures to higher values. Therefore, one would expect higher optimum temperatures at high stirring rates, high pressures, and low catalyst concentrations.

The beneficial effect of hydrogen chloride as a co-catalyst was recognized early. The catalytic activity of unpromoted aluminum chloride is undoubtedly brought about by traces of water which reacts with aluminum chloride to produce hydrogen chloride (521). The reaction rate has been shown by several workers to be dependent on the quantity of hydrogen chloride introduced (429,538). A convenient method of addition of hydrogen chloride, and one which is used commercially, is to introduce ethyl chloride into the reaction mixture.

Reid and co-workers (52,122,210,495,521) established that large amounts of polyethylbenzenes, including hexaethylbenzene, were formed in the aluminum chloride catalyzed ethylations even with a large excess of benzene. The higher ethylated benzenes are more concentrated in the sludge layer than in the hydrocarbon layer; this suggests that the mono- and polyethylated benzenes are selectively dissolved in the catalyst layer. Increased yields of monoethylbenzene were obtained by Francis and Reid (210) when the reaction was conducted in a homogeneous reaction media produced by the use of a mutual solvent such as diethyl ether. At temperatures of about 100° the aluminum chloride is sufficiently soluble so that reaction apparently takes place in the hydrocarbon layer. If the ethylene is added from the vapor phase under pressure at a high temperature, improved yields of monoethylbenzene are obtained. It was concluded by these authors that under these conditions the partially alkylated benzenes are not exposed to high local concentrations of catalyst and alkylating agent in the catalyst phase (208,210).

It has been claimed by Dalin et al. (150) that the composition of the alkylation products in both ethylation and propylation depend chiefly upon the thermodynamic equilibrium of the various alkyl-benzenes. At 95° the distribution of benzene, mono-, and poly-alkylbenzenes was dependent only on the ratio of alkyl groups to benzene rings. The reaction of one mole of benzene with ethylene or propene gave about 45% yield of monoalkylbenzenes. The same concentration of monoalkylbenzenes was asymptotically approached when monoalkylbenzene or an equimolar mixture of dialkylbenzene and benzene was treated with aluminum chloride at 95°. Similar experiments with other ratios of alkyl group to benzene gave essentially equivalent results.

Lebedev *et al.* (429) confirmed the results of Dalin *et al.* and also obtained the relative rates of ethylation of ethylbenzene and benzene $(K/K_0 = 2.09)$. A maximum yield of 24% ethylbenzene was calculated from the relative rates. A large part of the experimental data of the Reid group lies between Lebedev's equilibrium and kinetic curves. Lebedev *et al.* suggested that the observed low yields of ethylbenzene resulted from the low rates of transalkylation relative to alkylation. It was therefore concluded by these authors that when ethylene is absorbed at very high rates, the products would be distributed according to the kinetic curve, whereas when the olefin is absorbed at low rates, the yields would come close to the equilibrium curve. Similar conclusions can be drawn from the work of Gau on the ethylation of toluene (227).

Lebedev *et al.* dismissed the selective solvency theory of Francis and Reid (210) on the basis of experiments in which mixtures of a monoalkylbenzene and an aluminum chloride–benzene complex were stirred at a temperature of 20° and at 60 r.p.m. The bottom and top layers were found to differ only slightly in composition. The reviewers regard these results as inconclusive since the complex, as described, is not likely to be equivalent to the complex formed under alkylation conditions. Furthermore, as mentioned above, the sludge layer formed during alkylation has been reported to contain substantially more polyethylated benzenes than the hydrocarbon layer (52).

The most extensively used commercial process for ethylbenzene production employs aluminum chloride as catalyst. McAllister (462) reported that the overall yield of ethylbenzene in the Dow aluminum chloride process is 95.5% based on benzene and 96.8% based on ethylene. Aluminum chloride is consumed at the rate of 1 to 3 pounds per 100 pounds of ethylbenzene. The process is operated at 95°, with a benzene/ethylene mole ratio of 1.7/1, and with recycle of diethylbenzenes. The reaction time is adjusted to give 95% conversion of ethylene. Under these conditions the

equilibrium distribution of benzene, ethylbenzene, and polyethylbenzenes is economically optimal.

The alkylation of benzene with propene and isobutylene in the
presence of aluminum chloride is much more rapid than ethylation.
The rate of absorption of propene was so much more rapid than
ethylene that Lebedev *et al.* were unable to study the reaction in the
same equipment at temperatures as low as 20°. High yields of di-
and trialkylbenzenes are obtained in the propene and isobutylene
alkylation reaction (52,429). The polymerization of isobutylene is
an important side reaction, particularly at low temperatures.

Schmerling (700) found that aluminum chloride dissolves readily
in excess nitroalkane to produce a catalytically active solution of the
addition compound, $AlCl_3 \cdot RNO_2$, which is miscible with benzene or
other aromatic compounds. In contrast, 1:1 complexes of aluminum
chloride with alcohols, ethers, and ketones are active for alkylations
but their solutions in excess quantities of these complexing agents
are non-catalytic. The advantages of conducting alkylations in
the homogeneous liquid phase *via* solubilization with nitroalkanes
are these: (a) it avoids excessive initial activity which leads to
undesirable side reactions; (b) it maintains a more uniform activity
and a longer catalyst life by avoiding selective complexing with
alkylation products; and (c) it avoids loss of activity caused by
coating of aluminum chloride particles with sludge. The activity
of the catalyst is lower than unmodified aluminum chloride, and
higher reaction temperatures are required for alkylation.

It is somewhat surprising to note the absence of references to the
successful use of ferric halides as catalysts for ethylation of benzene,
toluene, or xylenes. Gallay and Whitby (224) stated that "no
reaction" was observed when they attempted to ethylate benzene
at 75–85° in the presence of ferric chloride.

Potts and Carpenter (645) obtained high yields of cumene and
t-butylbenzene even at room temperature in the presence of ferric
chloride. Approximately 90% of the alkylate in either case was the
monoalkylated product. This catalyst gave much less polymer
than did aluminum chloride. Although of lower activity than
aluminum chloride, ferric chloride sometimes gives higher yields of
the desired products because of its lower polymerization, transalkylation, and isomerization activity.

b. Protonic acid catalysts

Strong protonic acids are also very active catalysts for the reaction
of olefins with aromatics. Sulfuric acid (313), phosphoric acid (334),

alkanesulfonic acids (653), and hydrogen fluoride (754) are effective catalysts for the condensation of benzene with propene. Sulfuric acid has had the most widespread use, both in the laboratory and commercially, because of its ease of handling and low price. However, sulfuric acid, in contrast to the other acids, has the disadvantage of being a strong oxidizing and sulfonating agent. In recent years hydrogen fluoride has been used commercially because of its high activity and ease of recovery by distillation. Phosphoric acid has not been used commercially, but phosphoric acid supported on a carrier (kieselguhr) has been extensively used in high temperature fixed-bed tubular reactors (343) (see Sections II-1-E-b-(2) and II-1-E-c).

The protonic acid catalysts are generally of lower activity in Friedel-Crafts reactions than aluminum chloride and other very active metal halides. Brochet (78) was unable to effect the ethylation of benzene in the presence of concentrated sulfuric acid at superatmospheric pressure. Higher acid strengths and temperatures are impractical because of loss by sulfonation of both the benzene feed and the ethylbenzene product. Since 85% phosphoric acid does not enter into such side reactions, it may be employed at high temperatures, and so one obtains good results in ethylation of benzene at 300° and 60 atmospheres of ethylene pressure (334). Hydrogen fluoride, the most active of the strong protonic acid catalysts, affords low yields of ethylbenzenes at temperatures as low as 5° and at 116 psi (21a), but substantial yields of ethylbenzenes were claimed at reaction temperatures above 100° (21a,212).

Hydrogen chloride is not usually considered a Friedel-Crafts catalyst, but Schmerling et al. (703) were able to alkylate benzene with propene using this catalyst at 300° under high pressure. Simons and Hart (760), taking precautions to avoid contact of hydrogen chloride with steel or iron, were able to condense a number of alkyl halides as well as cyclohexene with benzene and toluene at 75–235° and initial hydrogen chloride pressures of 100–400 pounds per square inch.

Olefins and aromatic compounds, under the influence of sulfuric acid, react to form products which vary with the concentration of the acid (313). When mixed with benzene and 70% sulfuric acid at 6–15°, isobutylene is converted to the t-butyl sulfate acid ester. In the presence of 80% sulfuric acid the principal reaction is polymerization of isobutylene, accompanied by some ester formation. t-Butylbenzene is formed almost exclusively when the reaction is carried out in 96% sulfuric acid. Propene is absorbed very slowly in 80% sulfuric acid at 6–15°, but at 60° it is absorbed at a rapid rate, about one-half forming the sulfuric acid ester and the balance forming isopropylbenzenes.

These results were explained in terms of carbonium ions by Hammett (253b) as follows: The carbonium ion formed will react with that nucleophilic species which is most active and present in the reaction mixture in highest concentration. In aqueous acid the predominant nucleophilic species is water and in 70% acid the bisulfate ion predominates. As acid concentration is increased to 80%, the bisulfate concentration decreases and the t-butyl cation attacks dissolved isobutylene. As the concentration of the acid is further increased, there is a decrease of olefin concentration because of more complete conversion to the carbonium ion. The rate of isobutylene polymerization therefore decreases and alkylation becomes the predominant reaction.

The stability of the carbonium ions formed from isobutylene, propene, and ethylene decreases in that order. This is, of course, the reason why the formation of sulfate esters requires 70% acid for isobutylene, 80% for propene, and 98% for ethylene (78a,313).

Propene has less of a tendency to polymerize during the alkylation of benzene than isobutylene. Apparently, as the bisulfate concentration decreases, the isopropyl cation attacks benzene rather than dissolved propene. This could be a consequence of lower propene solubility in the acid phase. On the other hand, benzene may be better able to compete with propene for the isopropyl cation in the propylation reaction than it is able to compete with isobutylene for the tertiary butyl cation in the t-butylation reaction.

In their study of the propylation of benzene Pushkin and Kurashev (599b) found that catalyst consumption was higher in the sulfuric acid catalyzed reaction than with aluminum chloride or boron fluoride complexes (see Section II-1-D-c). The deactivation of sulfuric acid is a consequence of dilution with water, sulfonic acids, sulfates, and olefin polymers. Commercially the catalytic activity of the sulfuric acid is maintained by the addition of make-up acid.

Sulfuric acid does not promote transalkylation under alkylation conditions (599b). For this reason recycling of polyalkylbenzenes does not improve the yield of cumene. High ratios of benzene to propene are therefore required if high yields of cumene are to be obtained.

McAllister et al. (462,462a), have described in some detail commercial processes for cumene manufacture using either sulfuric acid or phosphoric acid on kieselguhr as catalysts (see Section II-1-E-c for a discussion of the latter process). The conditions of the sulfuric acid process are quite critical (462a). The highest yield of cumene is obtained when 88% sulfuric acid is used at 40°. The optimum temperature is a function of acid strength and varies from 20° to 50° as the acid concentration varies from 90% to 86%. Typically, the contact time is 20 minutes, the hydrocarbon to acid phase is 1/1, and the benzene to propene mole ratio is 5/1. Sufficient pressure is maintained to keep the reactants liquid. Under optimum conditions propene, introduced as a propane–propene mixture, is 99% converted and 10–12 volumes of crude cumene is produced per volume of 90% acid. The crude product is 95% cumene.

Ester formation and polymerization of the olefin are side reactions which accompany to a greater or lesser degree the condensation of olefins with aromatics in the presence of any protonic acid catalyst (212,313,760). These reactions also occur with metal halide catalysts. It is important that inorganic esters be eliminated from the alkylation products; otherwise decomposition of the desired products takes place during distillation. The sulfuric acid esters may be removed by washing the reaction products with cold sulfuric acid (313). Similarly, alkyl fluorides can be extracted with hydrogen fluoride (499). Thompson (832) extracted the last traces of chlorides by using hot 84% sulfuric acid. In the laboratory an excellent procedure for the elimination of chlorides or fluorides is to reflux the washed and dried reaction product with metallic sodium before fractionation. It is also quite common to fractionate the products in the presence of a base such as potassium carbonate.

c. Boron fluoride complexes

Many complexes and solutions of boron fluoride qualify as Friedel-Crafts catalysts covering a wide range of catalytic activity. There have been a few reports (866b) of alkylation of aromatics with olefins in the presence of unpromoted boron fluoride. However, a number of authors have published convincing evidence that olefins cannot be activated in the presence of pure Lewis acids (see Section II-1-A).

The catalytic activity of boron fluoride complexes is attributed to their ability to donate protons to olefins.

$$HX{:}BF_3 \;+\; \underset{/}{\overset{\backslash}{C}}{=}\underset{\backslash}{\overset{/}{C}} \;\rightarrow\; R^+ \; BXF_3^-$$

$$X = F^-,\; HSO_4^-,\; H_2PO_4^-,\; CH_3CO_2^-,\; OH^-,\; C_6H_5O^-,\; etc.$$

The relative activity of the boron fluoride complexes is not strictly determined by the acid strength of the co-catalysts. Although the activity of the co-catalysts appears to decrease in the order hydrogen fluoride > sulfuric acid > phosphoric acid > phenol > water > carboxylic acids > methanol (769,853,866b), no systematic quantitative study of the relative effectiveness of co-catalysts has been reported.

Solutions of boron fluoride in strong protonic acids such as hydrogen fluoride, sulfuric acid, and phosphoric acid, are very active Friedel-Crafts catalysts. Unlike sulfuric acid, boron fluoride dissolved in sulfuric acid is a strong enough catalyst to promote the condensation of ethylene with benzene (923). Boron fluoride in excess hydrogen fluoride appears to be the strongest of the Friedel-Crafts catalysts. Patinkin and Sanford (596) obtained high yields in propylating toluene and cumene in the presence of boron fluoride–hydrogen fluoride at − 40°. Comparable results were obtained with boron fluoride in sulfuric acid and with aluminum chloride–hydrogen chloride at − 20°.

Boron fluoride complexed with phosphoric acid is a very active and useful catalyst which was first applied to the alkylation of aromatics with olefins by Axe (27) and has been very extensively investigated by Topchiev et al. (853,866b). The catalyst is prepared by passing boron fluoride into 70–100% phosphoric acid with cooling until boron fluoride fumes escape. According to Topchiev et al. the most active catalyst is prepared with 100% phosphoric acid.

It has been shown by Topchiev et al., by Paushkin and Kurashev (599b), and by Axe (27) that the yield of polyalkylbenzenes formed in the presence of the boron fluoride–phosphoric acid catalyst is substantially lower than with aluminum chloride or sulfuric acid. Axe obtained a 70% yield of an alkylate consisting of 85% ethylbenzene and 15% diethylbenzene when benzene was treated with 0.89 mole of ethylene at 29–38° in the presence of boron fluoride–(85%) phosphoric acid. Topchiev and Paushkin (853) propylated benzene at 50° using a 2/1 benzene to propene ratio in the presence of boron fluoride–phosphoric acid, sulfuric acid, boron fluoride–water, aluminum chloride, and the catalyst derived by heating aluminum chloride with sulfuric acid. They obtained 91%, 83%, 62%, 51%, and 49%, respectively, of cumene.

Topchiev and co-workers (37,853) compared the commercial potential of boron fluoride–phosphoric acid and aluminum chloride as catalysts for the production of cumene by the alkylation of benzene with a propene–propane mixture.   Among the many advantages found for the boron fluoride–phosphoric acid catalyst were these:

(1) increased plant output because of higher yields, per pass, of cumene, and less of the intermediate fractions and bottoms;

(2) savings in raw material since consumption of benzene and catalyst was lower per unit of product;

(3) because of reduced amounts of secondary products, the cumene product gave higher yields in the acetone–phenol process.

A major disadvantage of the boron fluoride–phosphoric acid catalyst is that transalkylation does not occur under alkylation conditions (599b).   Therefore, it is not possible to minimize the formation of polyalkylbenzenes by recycling the heavier products as is done in the process using aluminum chloride.

Boron fluoride complexed with phenol is comparable in activity to the boron fluoride–sulfuric acid catalyst system (769).   The activity of the phenol promoted system is particularly notable because it is much greater than the activity of boron fluoride promoted by the much stronger carboxylic acids, including trichloracetic acid. The boron trifluoride–phenol catalyst apparently does not lose its activity in use, and all propylation products through tetraisopropyl-benzene are formed during the alkylation.   In contrast, it was reported that essentially no products above diisopropylbenzene were formed in the presence of the boron fluoride–sulfuric acid catalyst at room temperature (uncontrolled) and that the catalyst loses activity (769).   This result may have been caused by sulfonation at the temperature used.

As indicated earlier, boron fluoride–carboxylic acid complexes are very poor catalysts for aromatic alkylation.   The reviewers believe that this low catalytic activity is related to the ease with which carboxylic acids are esterified with olefins in the presence of boron fluoride (169a).   This is supported by the results of Slanina et al. (769) who found that boron fluoride–ester complexes did not promote the alkylation of aromatics with olefins.

With the exception of boron fluoride etherates (129) the complexes of boron fluoride with compounds which are not potential proton sources are not Friedel-Crafts catalysts (853).   Condon (129,130) alkylated benzene and monoalkyl benzenes with propene in the presence of boron fluoride monoetherate.   It is possible that the catalytic system in this instance is actually the hydrate, since it appears that no special precautions were taken to ensure anhydrous reagents. An alternate explanation is that the reaction is initiated *via* dissociation of some of the etherate to produce an ethyl carbonium ion. This carbonium ion then reacts with an aromatic molecule producing a σ-complex, which in turn transfers a proton to a propene molecule.

$$\begin{matrix} Et \\ \diagdown \\ O-BF_3 \longrightarrow Et^+ EtOBF_3^- \\ \diagup \\ Et \end{matrix}$$

$$Et^+ EtOBF_3^- + \text{(benzene)} \longrightarrow \left[\text{(σ-complex)} \begin{matrix} H \\ Et \end{matrix}\right] EtOBF_3^-$$

$$\left[\text{(σ-complex)} \begin{matrix} H \\ Et \end{matrix}\right] EtOBF_3^- + C=C-C \rightarrow C-C^+EtOBF_3^- + \text{(ring)}-Et$$
$$\qquad\qquad\qquad\qquad\qquad\qquad\qquad\qquad |$$
$$\qquad\qquad\qquad\qquad\qquad\qquad\qquad\qquad C$$

The σ-complex could also be formed by a direct displacement reaction. Efforts to distinguish between the possible mechanisms of this reaction have not been reported in the literature.

E. Vapor-phase Alkylation

Vapor-phase alkylation processes using acidic solid state catalysts have been widely employed for alkylation of aromatics with olefins. These catalysts are attractive because of their applicability to fixed-bed vapor-phase processes.

Three classes of these catalysts may be defined: (1) combinations of two or more metal oxides, such as silica–alumina, silica–magnesia, or natural clays; (2) supported Lewis acids on metal oxides or natural clays, such as zinc chloride on alumina; and (3) supported protonic acids on metal oxides or natural clays, such as phosphoric acid on kieselguhr or hydrogen fluoride on alumina.

The most interesting, from a commercial standpoint, are the silica–alumina and phosphoric acid on kieselguhr catalysts. These have been used extensively in large-scale petroleum refining processes.

a. The mechanism of alkylation catalyzed by silica–alumina and other cracking catalysts

The ability of silica–alumina, silica–magnesia, and other cracking catalysts to catalyze the alkylation of aromatics with olefins is clearly a consequence of the acidic nature of the surface of the catalysts. At petroleum cracking temperatures of 450–550°, these catalysts perform many functions in addition to the cleavage of carbon–carbon bonds in paraffins and naphthenes. They cause the olefins formed by cracking to undergo double bond shifts, cyclization, skeletal isomerization, hydrogen transfer, and polymerization to coke-like material. At lower temperatures they promote other reactions such as polymerization of olefins (228), alkylation of aromatics (577), and dealkylation of alkylaromatics (360,460,624a). These are all reactions which have been catalyzed by a variety of Friedel-Crafts or acid catalysts such as aluminum chloride, boron fluoride, hydrogen fluoride, phosphoric acid, sulfuric acid, etc. This similarity of the functions of cracking catalysts and acidic catalysts is itself a strong indication that cracking catalyst surfaces are acidic.

Investigations of catalyst acidity with indicators in non-aqueous solvents show rather conclusively that cracking catalysts have centers of high acid strength (361,823,912,918). Benesi (50) estimated the relative acid strengths of various cracking catalysts by n-butylamine titration using a series of indicators of varying pK values. Oblad and co-workers (522,524) demonstrated acidic properties of silica–alumina catalysts by reaction with carbonate solutions, titrations with basic solutions, reaction with Zerewitinoff reagent and more significantly by adsorption of ammonia and quinoline from the vapor phase.

As discussed previously (see Section II-1-A), the activation of an olefin for alkylation of aromatics or polymerization requires protonation of the double bond to produce a carbonium ion or catalyst complex. Apparently protonic acids are formed on silica–alumina surfaces by coordination of water with Lewis acid sites in a manner similar to the activation of boron fluoride and aluminum chloride with water or protonic acids (257). Several authors have shown that the catalytic activity of silica–alumina is increased by small amounts of water (256,259,280,823) and the catalytic activity is lost if the catalyst is severely dehydrated. It has also been found that excessive amounts of water deactivate the catalyst (259,280). The latter observation probably means that excess water competes with the substrate for the proton.

Direct evidence for the protonation of a double bond by a clay catalyst was reported by Evans (192). This investigator found that 1,1-diphenylethylene in a suspension of activated floridin (in paraffin) had the same ultraviolet absorption maxima as that of 1,1-diphenylethylene dissolved in sulfuric acid or dissolved in a solution of boron fluoride in benzene. The observed ultraviolet spectra were different from the parent molecule and were attributed to the ion, $\overset{+}{\emptyset_2C}CH_3$, formed by protonation of the olefin.

The origin of these acid centers in silica–alumina and other acidic surfaces has been the subject of much discussion and has been reviewed extensively by Oblad, Millikin, and Mills (574) and Hansford (257). The theory most generally accepted is that both the Brønsted and the Lewis acid sites owe their existence to an isomorphous substitution of trivalent aluminum for tetravalent silicon in the silica lattice (257).

b. *Ethylbenzene production* (Table 1)

(1) *Silica–alumina and similar catalysts.* Schollkopf, in 1938, first reported the alkylation of an aromatic with an olefin over a silica–alumina catalyst (719). In this study naphthalene was condensed with ethylene at 230° and 20–40 atmospheres in the presence of Tonsil, an activated hydrosilicate catalyst. A few years later Schulze and Lyon (728) reported high yields of alkylate containing 68% monoethylbenzene from the reaction of ethylene and benzene over 2% alumina on silica gel at 270° and 1000 psi.

High pressures are very important in the silica–alumina catalyzed alkylation of benzene with ethylene. O'Kelly et al. (577) found that at 50–75 psig it was necessary to use temperatures of 425–500° to obtain ethylbenzene yields of 46–81%. Garner and Iverson (225a) reported that inlet conditions at the catalyst case in commercial installations averages 900 psig and 310°, or approximately the conditions disclosed in the patent of Schulze and Lyon (728).

O'Kelly et al. obtained complete conversion of ethylene only at benzene to ethylene ratios of approximately 10/1. A high circulation rate of benzene is required to maintain a high conversion and also to minimize polyethylbenzene formation. The percentage of polyethylbenzenes in the alkylate varies from 11 to 17% as the mole ratio of benzene to ethylene is varied from 10.5/1 to 6/1, respectively (225a).

O'Kelly et al. found that under the severe conditions of their alkylation experiments transalkylation occurred. This was in agreement with the transalkylation results obtained by Hansford et al. (258a) at about the same temperature range at atmospheric pressure. O'Kelly et al. suggested that the distillation residue did not represent a loss of monoethylbenzene production since on recycling the polyethylbenzenes were converted to monoethylbenzene. However, 3 to 7% of polycyclics were formed during transalkylation in the experiments of Hansford *et al.*; furthermore, Kutz *et al.* have reported that 5% of the diethylbenzene fraction is *s*-butyl benzene (424).

Under the high pressure conditions used commercially the temperature is too low for transalkylation to occur to an appreciable extent. The polyethylbenzenes are therefore dealkylated in a separate unit at a much higher temperature, 532°, and lower pressure, 4 psig (462). The conversion per pass under these conditions is only 25–30%; however, the overall efficiency for the formation of benzene, ethylbenzene, and ethylene is high.

O'Kelly *et al.* reported that coke make during alkylation was small and the catalyst was completely restored to initial activity after each of eight consecutive experiments by burning off the carbon with controlled amounts of air. A reduced activity was noted with a catalyst which had been used for 100 days under the relatively severe conditions of a cracking unit. With reduced space velocity the yield of ethylbenzene could be restored to the yields obtained with a fresh catalyst. However, a high conversion level is maintained in commercial plants by increasing the inlet temperature. Unfortunately, increased temperature is accompanied by increased polyethylbenzene formation.

(2) *Supported phosphoric acid catalysts.* The vapor-phase ethylation of benzene over phosphoric acid on kieselguhr is operated at essentially the same conditions as the silica–alumina process. Ipatieff and Schmerling (343) report 90% conversion of ethylene per pass at 280° and 900 psig with a benzene space velocity of 2. Because the yield is improved with increases in pressure, high operating pressures are preferred. This permits use of lower temperatures which in turn favor longer catalyst life.

Alkylates containing about 90% monoethylbenzene can be obtained at benzene to ethylene ratios of 4/1 (343). Mattox (497), however, reported that only 50% of the ethylene was converted in commercial operation, and that the product contained 78% ethylbenzene and 22% polyethylbenzene.

Coke deposition and dehydration of the catalyst causes a decline in activity (497). The addition of small amounts of water or ethyl alcohol prevents dehydration and the catalyst can be regenerated by controlled burning. Ethylbenzene yields of approximately 350 pounds/pound of catalyst have been obtained commercially without regeneration.

Phosphoric acid on copper oxide or on diatomaceous earth (881) was equal in activity to the kieselguhr supported catalyst. Catalysts prepared from polyphosphoric acid (891) are apparently equivalent to those prepared from orthophosphoric acid.

The importance of the nature of the support is indicated by the work of Pardee and Dodge (591). These investigators reported 13–15% conversion of ethylene to ethylbenzene in the presence of phosphoric acid on kieselguhr at 239°, 100 psig, and 27.2 L.H.S.V., but obtained no conversion at the same conditions when the catalyst consisted of phosphoric acid on charcoal.

(3) *Other catalysts.* Hammick and Roberts (254) obtained a yield of 8.2% ethylbenzene based on benzene using bauxite at temperatures of 450–500° at atmospheric pressure. Under the same conditions small to negligible yields were obtained over alumina silicate, silica gel, basic aluminum phosphate, activated alumina, and titanic gel.

Pfefferle *et al.* (611) employed boria–alumina at 200° in a batch reaction. An alkylate containing 81% ethylbenzene was obtained by passing ethylene and benzene over silica–alumina–zirconia at 270° and 800 psig (725). At high temperatures chromia–alumina exhibits dehydrogenation activity as well as alkylation activity. Egloff (182) claimed a 55% ultimate yield of styrene by passing ethylene and benzene over an 88% alumina–12% chromia catalyst at 550°.

Shuikin *et al.* (740) obtained a 16% yield of alkylate by using zinc chloride on alumina at 300° and 40 atm. The alumina base was itself non-catalytic. Zinc chloride on silica gel was found by O'Kelly and Work (578) to give about a 30% yield of alkylate at 325° and 100 atmospheres, and about a 60% yield when chloroform was used as a promoter. Under these conditions about 74% of the alkylate is ethylbenzene. Zirconium chloride on tungsta (457) and titanium chloride on alumina (908) have been claimed to give good yields of alkylate at 200°.

Pardee and Dodge (591,592) obtained a 90% conversion of ethylene to ethylbenzenes with an aluminum chloride–sodium chloride–pumice catalyst at 268°, and 200 psig and 39.3 S.V. The catalyst was prepared by pouring a fused 1/1 molal complex of aluminum chloride–sodium chloride over dry pumice. Unfortunately, the catalyst declined in activity very rapidly and the higher ethylated products were favored as the catalyst aged.

Mixtures of phosphoric acid and sulfuric acid supported on charcoal were ineffective ethylation catalysts. This was also true of the following catalysts supported on Alfrax (fused aluminum oxide): strontium chloride, zinc chloride, ferric chloride, and sulfuric acid (591).

(4) *Comparison of processes.* Kutz *et al.* (424) have shown that the diethylbenzene fraction produced by ethylation of benzene over fixed-bed catalysts contained considerable amounts of s-butylbenzene, whereas the aluminum chloride product was free from this by-product.

TABLE III.   Comparison of ethylation processes

Mole ratio benzene/ ethylene	Catalyst	s-Butylbenzene in the diethyl-benzene fraction	Product distribution mono/di/poly
10/1	Silica–alumina	5%	10/1/0.3
10/1	Phosphoric acid–kieselguhr	30%	38/1/0.3
10/1	Iron phosphate	41%	25/1/0.3
10/1	Aluminum chloride	< 1%	35/1/0.8

The s-butylbenzene was attributed to dimerization of the ethylene followed by alkylation of benzene with the dimer. The data obtained by these authors also indicated that silica–alumina catalyzes the formation of polyethylbenzenes to a much greater extent than the other three catalysts tested.

Vapor-phase processes for ethylbenzene production have had only limited commercial use because of s-butylbenzene formation and because the vapor-phase catalysts do not convert diethyl-benzene to monoethylbenzene during alkylation. Because equilibrium distributions are not obtained with the vapor-phase catalysts, higher benzene to ethylene feed ratios are required with these catalysts than with aluminum chloride, thus limiting the flexibility and increasing the cost of the plant. The necessity for high pressures is another disadvantage of the vapor-phase processes. However, the aluminum chloride process does have the disadvantages of corrosion, sensitivity to water, higher catalyst consumption, and emulsion problems during product work-up.

c. Cumene production (Table 2)

The alkylation of benzene with propene occurs over the same catalysts used for the ethylation reaction but at less severe conditions. For example, Shulze (725) obtained a 40% yield of cumene and a 13% yield of diisopropylbenzenes in the propylation of benzene over silica–alumina at 177° and 400 psig. The silica–alumina catalyzed

3+F.C. II

reaction has been reported to occur at temperatures as low as 20° (849).

Phosphoric acid on kieselghuhr is the most extensively used catalyst for commercial cumene manufacture. This catalyst is widely used also for propene polymerization to make polymer gasoline and these "poly" plants are easily converted for cumene manufacture.

In an extensive study of the operating variables Dalin et al. (149) found that the optimal conditions were 220–230°, 20–25 atm. pressure, 2.5 to 3.5 space velocity, and 3.5/1 benzene/propene ratio. McAllister (462,462a) reported that an industrial plant operating at 250–260°, 3.5 S.V., 3/1 feed ratio, 0.06% (on hydrocarbon) of water, converted 94% of the propene feed (30% in propane) to produce 1.7 liters of raw cumene per liter of propene consumed, or 1.54 liters per liter of benzene consumed. The catalyst life in this industrial plant was reported to be 92 gallons of cumene per pound of catalyst. For good catalyst life controlled amounts of water must be added to the feed.

Rustamov et al. (671) have emphasized that failure to maintain constant water vapor pressure results in irreversible conversion of orthophosphoric acid to metaphosphoric acid, which in turn causes a decline of activity. In a kinetic study of propylation of benzene they obtained fair second-order rate constants only if the water vapor pressure was kept constant both before and during the entire period of the experiment.

McAllister (462,462a), reported that temperatures over 300° cause a rapid decline in catalyst activity. The percentage of cumene in the product is not significantly changed by increasing the temperature from 200° to 250° but conversion is increased. However, Rustamov et al. found that the percentage of monoalkylbenzenes (mole ratio propene/benzene = 1/3) increases from an average of 74% at 150° to 83% at 210°. McAllister indicated that conversion increases somewhat as the pressure is increased from 200 to 500 psig, but the yield is not improved.

The major by-products of the propene–benzene condensation are polyisopropylbenzenes. High benzene to propene ratios are needed for high cumene yields. McAllister found little increase in the conversion of propene or in cumene yield at feed ratios greater than 5/1. At this feed ratio the alkylate contains about 90% cumene. Rustamov et al. confirmed the effect of feed ratio, but reported that the ultimate yield of cumene was independent of conversion in the range investigated (10–60%).

Schaad (685) converted propene and benzene to cumene in the presence of a copper pyrophosphate catalyst at 350°, 50 atm., and a residence time of four hours. Apparently this type of catalyst was used commercially by the M. W. Kellogg Company, but no process data have been published. It was claimed that 95–97% yields based on benzene were obtained, compared to other processes which yield 90–93%. It was also claimed that this catalyst does not catalyze ethylation and therefore ethylene removal from the olefin feed is unnecessary.

Other catalysts claimed for benzene propylation, but which have not been used for ethylation, include hydrogen chloride treated silica gel and hydrogen chloride treated alumina–zinc oxide (703), hydrogen fluoride treated silica–alumina (922), magnesium and nickel aluminosilicates (818), nickel molybdite (198), and bentonite clay (365).

d. Alkylation with n-butenes (Table 3)

Normal butenes and propene are similar in behavior, but under certain conditions the butenes undergo skeletal isomerization. Pines et al. (618) alkylated benzene with 2-butene over zinc chloride–alumina and phosphoric acid–kieselguhr at 200–250° and 40 atmospheres and obtained tertiary and secondary butylbenzenes in mole ratio of 2/98 and 13/87, respectively. Fluorided alumina at 360–370°, 40 atmospheres pressure, gave a monoalkylated product containing 5 to 6% t-butylbenzene (615). No isomerization occurred over silica–alumina at 250° and 40 atmospheres (618). It appears that isomerization occurs during alkylation since Pines et al. have shown that skeletal isomerization of butylbenzenes occurs only at higher temperatures.

F. Alkylation with n-Pentenes and Higher n-Olefins
(Tables 5–7, 13, 18, 22)

As mentioned before, 1-butene and 2-butene normally yield the same secondary carbonium ion which in alkylation reactions produces only 2-phenylbutane. However, with n-pentenes isomerization of the double bond would be expected to occur under the influence of the catalysts, producing two olefins or the corresponding secondary carbonium ions (25). Ipatieff, Pines, and Schmerling (341) furnished the first clear-cut evidence of this when they reported that the reaction of 1-pentene with benzene in the presence of 96% sulfuric acid yielded 65% of a mixture containing three parts of

2-phenylpentane and two parts of 3-phenylpentane. Nevertheless many authors reported obtaining only one phenylalkane isomer in similar reactions. Thus Brochet (78) indicated he had obtained a 50% yield of 2-phenylhexane from 1-hexene with sulfuric acid as catalyst. Spiegler and Tinker (779) reported 59%, 24%, and 50% yields of 3-phenylhexane by alkylating benzene with 3-hexene in the presence of hydrogen fluoride, $H_3BO_2F_2$, and sulfuric acid, respectively, as catalysts. Hunt (289) reported that alkylation of m-xylene with 1-decene in the presence of hydrogen fluoride had the same physical properties as 2-(2,4-dimethylphenyl)decane synthesized via Grignard reagents. Emerson et al. (185) claimed yields of 81% 2-phenyloctane and 88% of 2-phenyldecane in the sulfuric acid catalyzed alkylation of benzene with 1-octene and 1-decene, respectively. More recently Lenneman et al. (437) reported that the sulfuric acid catalyzed alkylation of benzene with the even-numbered terminal olefins from 1-octene to 1-octadecene yielded only 2-phenylalkanes and that no other isomers were formed. Their conclusions, based on certain infra-red data, were later criticized by Gray et al. (242) who studied the infra-red spectra of 1- and 5-phenylalkanes.

In the last few years, especially since the advent of improved analytical techniques including gas-liquid chromatography, workers have definitely established that isomerization occurs and that all possible phenylalkanes are produced except the 1-phenyl isomer.

Asahara and Takagi (24) reported that alkylation of benzene with 1-dodecene leads to a mixture containing mainly 2- and 3-phenyldodecanes and small amounts of 4- and 5-phenyldodecanes.

Tjepkema et al. (837) synthesized all five isomeric phenyldodecanes and found they could not be accurately differentiated by infra-red analysis. However, they were able to analyze mixtures of the isomers by mass spectrometry and so determined that alkylations of benzene with pure 1-dodecene carried out with various technical catalysts (not further identified) yielded products containing only 20% of 2-phenyldodecane, the rest being mixtures of roughly equal parts of 3-, 4-, 5-, and 6-phenyldodecanes.

Asinger and co-workers (25) determined that the sulfuric acid catalyzed alkylation of benzene with 1-heptene yielded all three possible secondary phenylheptanes in roughly equimolar proportion. Variations in the concentration of sulfuric acid catalyst did not materially affect the ratio of isomers.

A thorough study by Olson (582) of the alkylation of benzene with various terminal olefins indicated that hydrogen fluoride and aluminum chloride as well as sulfuric acid form mixtures of aryl-alkanes (see Table IV).

TABLE IV. Alkylation of benzene with 1-dodecene

Conditions	HF	AlCl$_3$	H$_2$SO$_4$
Catalyst			
Moles	50	0.1	5 ml. 98%
1-Dodecene, moles	5	2	0.15
Benzene, moles	50	10	1.5
Temp.	16° ± 3	30–53°	0–10°
Products			
% Monoalkylate	92	68	72
% Dialkylate	5	21	(9)
Ratio of isomers			
1-Phenyldodecane	0	0	0
2- ,,	20	32	41
3- ,,	17	22	20
4- ,,	16	16	13
5- ,,	23	15	13
6- ,,	24	15	13

Isomerization apparently occurs prior to alkylation with hydrogen fluoride or sulfuric acid since 2- and 6-phenyldecane were recovered unchanged after prolonged treatment with these catalysts under alkylation conditions. Olson suggested that the isomerization proceeds *via* addition of a molecule of acid to the 1-alkene by a carbonium-ion process and this is followed by repeated eliminations and additions of the acid to give a mixture of all the possible secondary carbonium ions. Alkylation with these carbonium ions yields the mixture of phenylalkanes found in the product.

Aluminum chloride could operate similarly *via* a series of prototropic shifts, but since this catalyst did have the power to convert the 2-isomer to the others it probably also operates *via* dealkylation, rearrangement of carbonium ion, and realkylation.

Olson reported similar results for the hydrogen fluoride catalyzed alkylation of toluene with 1-dodecene and the alkylation of *m*-xylene with 1-decene; a mixture of secondary arylalkanes was produced in each of these reactions.

Swisher, Kaelble, and Liu (820) confirmed the formation of all the possible phenyldecanes except the 1-phenyl isomer when 1-dodecene is alkylated with benzene in the presence of aluminum chloride–hydrogen chloride. The absence of the 1-phenyl isomer was attributed to the instability of the primary carbonium ion. They

suggested that the reaction proceeds *via* formation of a 2-dodecyl
π-complex (A) which may then rearrange along two paths:

(1) to a 2-dodecyl σ-complex (B) which eventually yields 2-phenyl-
dodecane and

(2) to the isomeric 3-, 4-, 5-, and 6-π-complexes which in turn yield
the 3-, 4-, 5-, and 6-phenyldodecanes.

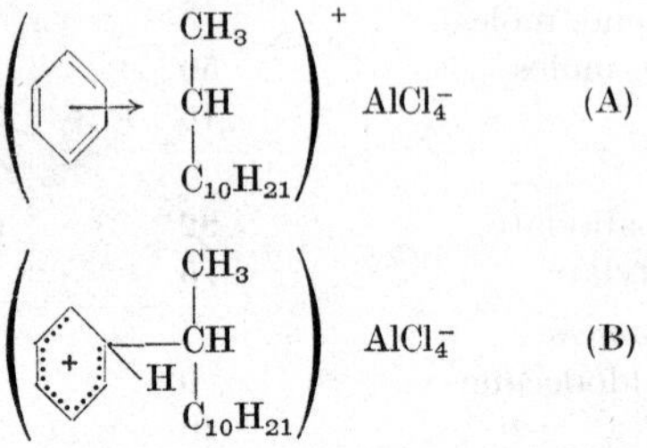

$$\left(\bigcirc\!\!\rightarrow\ \begin{array}{c} CH_3 \\ | \\ CH \\ | \\ C_{10}H_{21} \end{array}\right)^{+}\ AlCl_4^{-} \qquad (A)$$

$$\left(\begin{array}{c} CH_3 \\ | \\ \begin{array}{c}\\ + \end{array}\!\!\!\!\!—CH \\ H\ | \\ C_{10}H_{21} \end{array}\right)\ AlCl_4^{-} \qquad (B)$$

According to these authors, equilibrium is not reached during
alkylation. At the end of the time (15 minutes) required to add the
olefin, the ratio of 2-phenyl to 6-phenyl was about 3/1. After
prolonged aging or isomerization an equilibrium mixture of the
isomers was obtained, at which point the ratio was 2/1. It appeared
that the formation of all five phenyldodecanes in the alkylation
must be mainly a consequence of isomerization of the intermediate
π-complex, since once the phenyldecanes are formed, they undergo
relatively little isomerization under minimum alkylation conditions.
In fact, when the amount of aluminum chloride was doubled, only a
few per cent rearranged. Olson's success in effecting isomerization
with less catalyst may be attributed to his use of a water-promoted
aluminum chloride which is known (544a,700a) to be more active
than the anhydrous catalyst.

G. Alkylation with Isoolefins
(Tables 4–7, 12, 13, 17, 18, 22)

a. Steric factors

Where steric factors are not involved, as in the substitution of
alkylbenzenes at the *meta*- or *para*-position, isoolefins are quite
reactive—much more so than *n*-olefins.

Steric considerations do come into play in a minor way in alkylations of alkylbenzenes with propene and *n*-butenes (see Section
II-1-B), but this factor is a major one with isoolefins. The spatial
requirements of the *t*-alkyl groups are so great that the stability of

the *ortho* σ-complex must be smaller than the *meta*- and *para*-isomers (542). Further, the *ortho* end-product is less stable and subject to rapid isomerization; for example in *o-t*-butyltoluene the strain energy is about 6 kcal/mole and in *o-di-t*-butylbenzene it is estimated to be 25.5 kcal/mole (79a).

Several processes have been described which take advantage of steric hindrance in separating aromatic isomers. Schlatter (694), Corson *et al.* (140), and Schneider (716) separated *p*-dialkylbenzenes by selective alkylation of the *ortho*- and *meta*-isomers with isobutylene. Odioso (575) claimed the removal of trimethylindane and *o*-diisopropylbenzene from commercial diisopropylbenzenes by selective alkylation with isobutylene in the presence of sulfuric acid or hydrogen fluoride. Since the indane and the *ortho*-isomer normally act as inhibitors in a subsequent hydroperoxidation reaction, their removal makes the resulting mixture of *meta*- and *para*-isomers a better feed for that step.

It is claimed that mesitylene can be recovered unreacted in fairly high purity by treating mesitylene concentrates with isoamylene or isobutylene in the presence of aluminum chloride. All the other C_9 arenes including pseudocumene are apparently alkylated (158a). However, Wadsworth isolated unreacted pseudocumene of 95.3% purity by treating a C_9 arene concentrate containing 77.5% pseudocumene, with diisobutylene using boron fluoride monohydrate (909a). Schlatter (695) separated hemimellitine in high purity from its isomers by selective *t*-butylation in the presence of hydrogen fluoride, followed by removal of the *t*-butyl group as described in Section c (p. 43).

t-Butylation *ortho* to the methyl group of toluene takes place not at all or to a negligible extent. When the reaction is forced, so to speak, by employing a *para*-substituted toluene, *e.g.*, *p*-xylene (221) or *p*-cymene (692), a minor amount of substitution *ortho* to the methyl takes place. *t*-Amylation *ortho* to a methyl group is even less likely (219) because of the greater bulk of the *t*-amyl group.

b. Hydride transfer

t-Alkylation *ortho* to an isopropyl group is probably impossible. Where the *t*-cation is prevented or hindered from attacking the ring positions, it has ample opportunity to engage in another kind of reaction, namely hydride transfer. This involves removal of the *t*-hydrogen of the isopropyl side chain by the *t*-cation R$^+$ derived from the incoming isoolefin leading to the formation of RH, and arylindanes (A). This reaction was first described by Ipatieff, Pines, and Olberg (335).

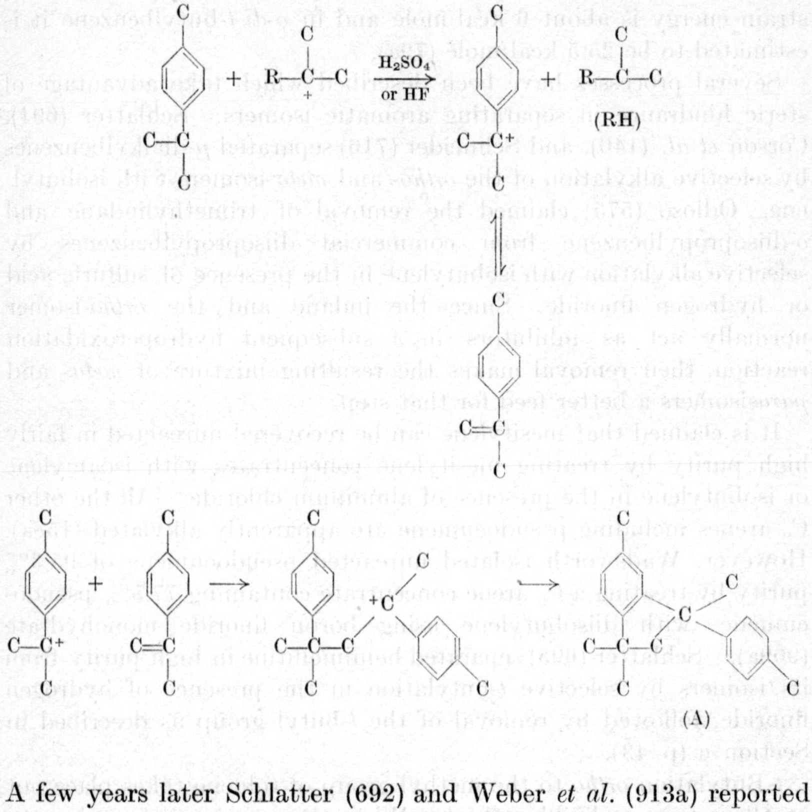

$$\text{(structure)} + \text{R—C—C} \xrightarrow[\text{or HF}]{\text{H}_2\text{SO}_4} \text{(structure)} + \text{R—C—C} \quad (\text{RH})$$

(A)

A few years later Schlatter (692) and Weber *et al.* (913a) reported that indanes of the type (B) were also produced in this reaction:

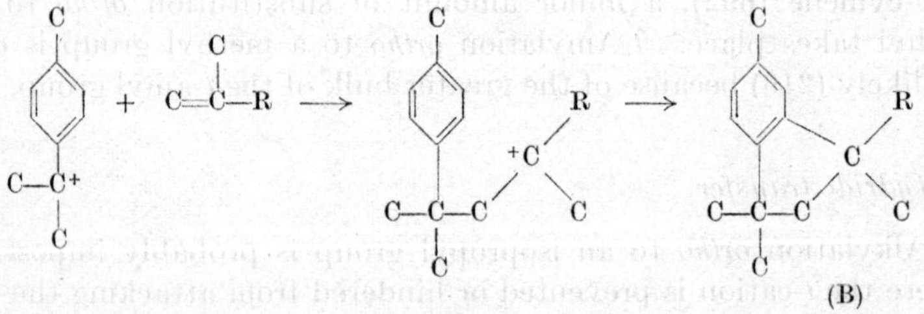

$$\text{(structure)} + \text{C=C—R} \longrightarrow \text{(structure)} \longrightarrow \text{(structure)}$$

(B)

Other examples and variations have been reported by Barclay *et al.* (43) and this phenomenon is more fully described by Barclay in Chapter XXII.

Similar reactions occur involving the ethyl and butyl groups in p-ethyltoluene and p-butyltoluene (620).

Even a methyl group, as in p-xylene (221,711*) or p-chlorotoluene (711*), undergoes hydride transfer. The resulting benzyl cation then attacks the ring of another molecule or aromatic forming diarylmethanes (C) and (E) in good yield. The formation of (E) is best explained by Schmerling's (711) mechanism which postulates cleavage of (C) to produce (D) which attacks p-xylene:

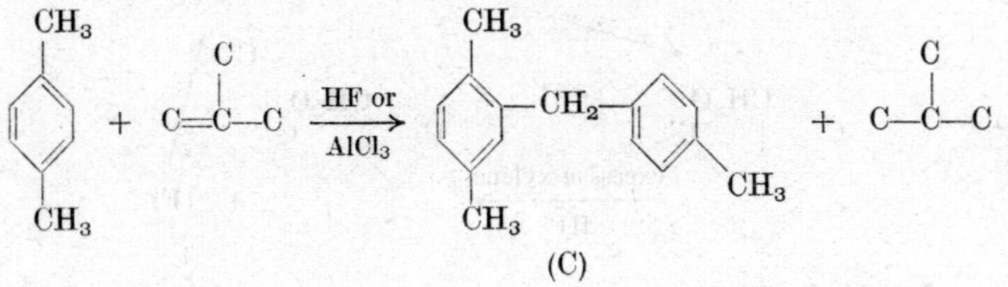

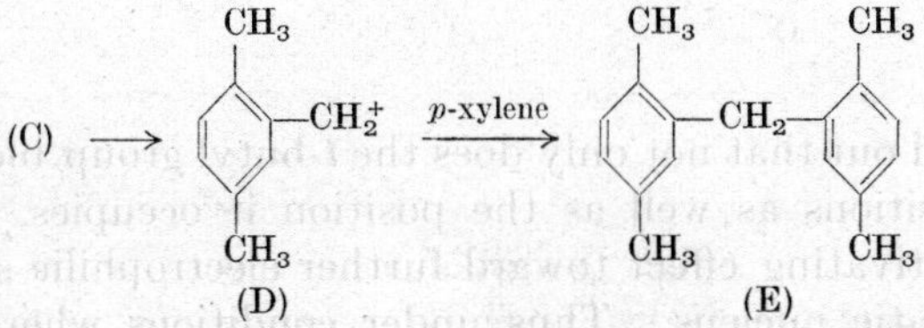

(C)

(D)   (E)

Similar results were obtained with p-cresol and isoamylenes (see Section III-2-C-b).

c. Selectivity, isomerization, and transalkylation

Isoolefins also appear to be more selective in substitution reactions. As discussed in Section II-1-B-b on orientation, high *para/meta* ratios (*e.g.*, 93/7–98/2) can be obtained in the alkylation of toluene with branched C_4 and C_5 olefins.

A complicating factor is the readiness with which t-alkyl groups undergo cleavage from the aromatic nucleus or migration to other positions on the ring. Schlatter and Clark demonstrated the great ease with which the p-t-alkyltoluenes are isomerized to the *meta*-isomers. Their definitive article cleared up the many discrepancies which had appeared in the literature in this field. In processes where he exploited the ability of the t-butyl group to act as a blocking group in directing an attacking substituent into the

---

* These authors employed alkyl halides instead of olefins.

desired position on the aromatic nucleus, Schlatter was able subsequently to remove the t-butyl group merely by stirring the substituted arene with an excess of the original arene in the presence of
hydrogen fluoride at 0° (690,690a).

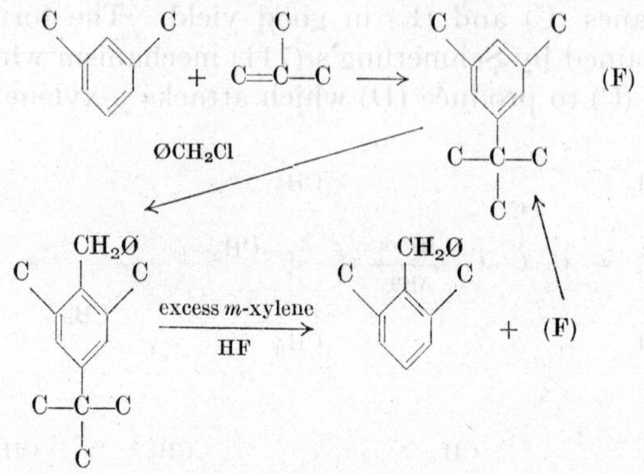

He pointed out that not only does the t-butyl group block the two
adjacent positions as well as the position it occupies, but it also
exerts an activating effect toward further electrophilic substitution
of the aromatic nucleus. Thus under conditions where hydrogen
fluoride effects ready alkylation of 1,3-dimethyl-5-t-butylbenzene
with ethylene, m-xylene reacts sluggishly, and toluene and benzene
not at all.

d. Skeletal isomerization in side chain

The branched pentenes provide still another complication—
skeletal isomerization in the side chain occurs concurrently with the
alkylation reaction. This was first reported by Boord and co-
workers (305) who prepared pure t-pentylbenzene by alkylation of
benzene with isoamylenes using sulfuric acid or ferric chloride catalysts, but obtained a mixture of isomeric amylbenzenes when they
employed aluminum chloride.

Schmerling and West (713) showed that this was a general phenomenon in alkylations with t-pentyl and t-hexyl chlorides catalyzed
by aluminum chloride. Others (218) confirmed the results with
t-pentyl chloride and extended the study to alkylations with isoamylenes and other catalysts.

Schmerling and West postulated a mechanism involving hydride
transfer and side-chain skeletal rearrangements:

$$
\underset{\text{(I)}}{C_6H_5\text{–}\overset{\displaystyle C}{\underset{\displaystyle C}{C}}\text{–}C\text{–}C}
\;+\;
C\text{–}\overset{+}{\underset{\displaystyle C}{C}}\text{–}C\text{–}C
\;\longrightarrow\;
\underset{\text{(II)}}{C_6H_5\text{–}\overset{\displaystyle C}{C}\text{–}\overset{+}{C}\text{–}C}
\;+\;
C\text{–}\overset{\displaystyle C}{C}\text{–}C\text{–}C
$$

$$
\underset{\text{(IV)}}{C_6H_5\text{–}\overset{\displaystyle C\;\;C}{C\text{–}C\text{–}C}}
\;+\;\text{II}\;\overset{\text{I}}{\longleftarrow}\;
\underset{\text{(III)}}{C_6H_5\text{–}\overset{\displaystyle C\;\;C}{C\text{–}\overset{+}{C}\text{–}C}}
$$

However, these authors were aware of an objection to this mechanism, namely, that hydrogen atoms attached to secondary carbon atoms are not readily abstracted under normal alkylation conditions. In a later paper (712) they indicated that this objection could be overcome by postulating that the neighboring phenyl group participates in the displacement of the hydride ion to form a phenonium ion (V):

$$
\underset{\text{(I)}}{C_6H_5\text{–}\overset{\displaystyle C}{\underset{\displaystyle C}{C}}\text{–}C\text{–}C}
\;+\;
C\text{–}\overset{+}{\underset{\displaystyle C}{C}}\text{–}C\text{–}C
\;\longrightarrow\;
\underset{\text{(V)}}{[\text{phenonium}]\overset{\displaystyle C\text{–}C}{\underset{\displaystyle C}{}}}
\;+\;
C\text{–}\overset{\displaystyle C}{C}\text{–}C\text{–}C
$$

When V abstracts a hydride ion from a fresh molecule of I, the reaction occurs at the tertiary carbon atom of V yielding compound IV and a new molecule of V.

This mechanism received support from the observation (713) that t-pentylbenzene and t-hexylbenzene are easily isomerized to branched secondary alkylates by treatment with the alkylating catalyst. Further support was provided by the fact that the isomerization reaction could be greatly diminished, or substantially eliminated, by employing sub-zero operating temperatures (218). Thus at $-40°$ aluminum chloride gave a satisfactory yield of fairly pure t-pentylbenzene. Conversely, catalysts such as hydrogen fluoride or boron fluoride alone which give only the tertiary derivative at 25°, yield a 70/30 and 80/20 mixture, respectively, of the two isomers I and IV at 100° and 119°, respectively. Ferric chloride and zirconium chloride also produce mixtures (10/90 and 85/15) of branched secondary and tertiary hexylbenzenes at 85° (713). Thus it is apparent that the isomerization reaction has a higher energy of activation than the alkylation reaction.

Difficulties were encountered (221), however, in applying Schmerling's mechanism to the alkylation of p-xylene with isoamylenes. This reaction produced a high yield of secondary isomer VII. As expected on the basis of steric considerations, none of the tertiary isomer VI could be detected. This made it seem unlikely that VI was the precursor of VII, and led to postulation of another mechanism to explain the formation of VII.

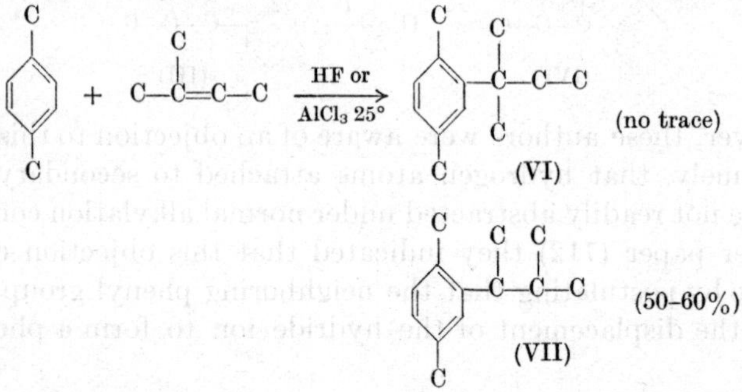

It was suggested (221) that the inability of the t-cation to attack the aromatic nucleus prolonged its life and provided ample time for

$$\text{C}$$
$$\text{|}$$
$$\text{C—C—}\overset{+}{\text{C}}\text{—C}$$

the formation of some secondary cation, C—C—$\overset{+}{\text{C}}$—C. Because the latter species has a much smaller steric requirement and readily attacks the p-xylene to form VII, it is removed as rapidly as formed and thus drains the equilibrium in its direction. Once formed, compound VII is stable under the alkylating conditions.

Another possible objection to Schmerling's mechanism is based on the assumption that if V is able to abstract a *secondary* hydride ion, especially one that is also sterically hindered, it certainly ought to be able to attack the excess unsubstituted or substituted arene present to form diarylpentanes (VIII).

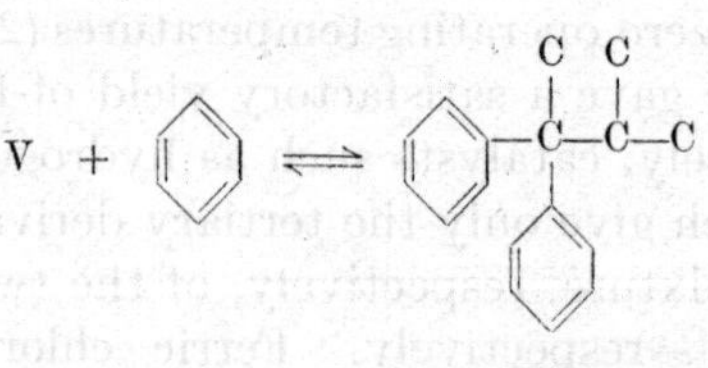

Condon and Matuszak (134) have shown that even the abstraction of a *tertiary* hydride ion (in isobutane) by a secondary carbonium ion, e.g., iso-$C_3H_7^+$, is only 0.00285 as fast as alkylation of benzene by the same carbonium ion. Since examination of the heavy ends by mass spectroscopy shows that diarylpentanes are not formed in the reaction of arenes with isoamylene at 0° or 20° (216), it may be argued that V could not have been present as a reaction intermediate. Perhaps this argument is weakened by the fact that the heavy ends do contain considerable material with a parent mass of 216 which corresponds to an indane such as IX.

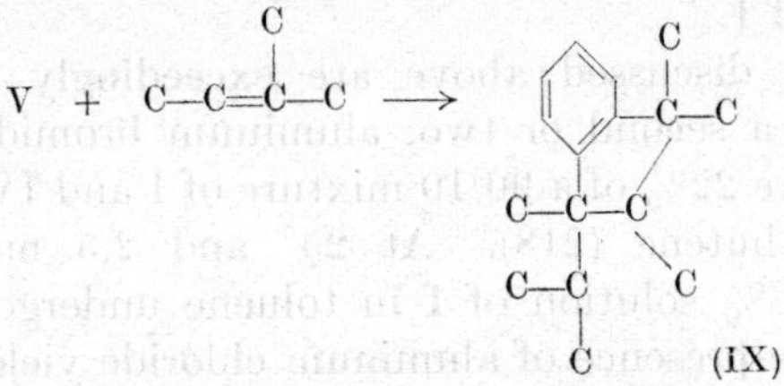

However, IX may not arise from the addition of V to isoamylene, but *via* addition of III (derived from IV through hydride abstraction by the *t*-amyl cation) to isoamylene followed by ring closure.   Thus the presence of the stable indane IX is no guarantee of the intermediacy of V.   But if IX were formed from III, then the absence of the diarylpentane, VIII, which could be formed by alkylation of benzene with III, must be attributed to the relative instability of VIII versus IX.   This line of reasoning is in accord with Streitwieser's demonstration of the high degree of reactivity of a 1,1-diarylalkane, *e.g.*, 1,1-ditolylethane (806b) in the presence of gallium bromide–hydrogen bromide.

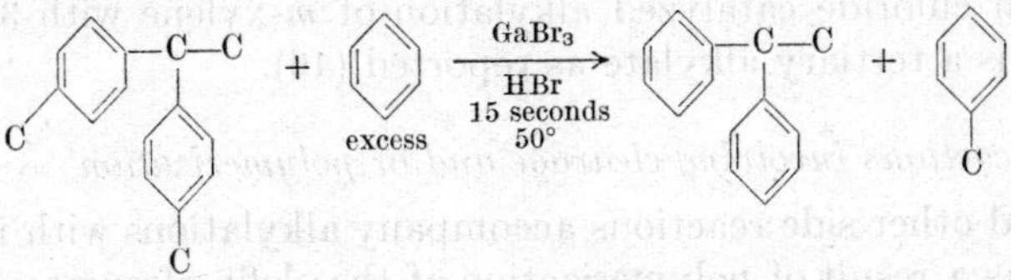

For alkylations not so affected by steric factors, *e.g.*, alkylation of benzene, it was possible to suggest a mechanism (221) based on the ease with which *t*-alkylarenes undergo dealkylation.

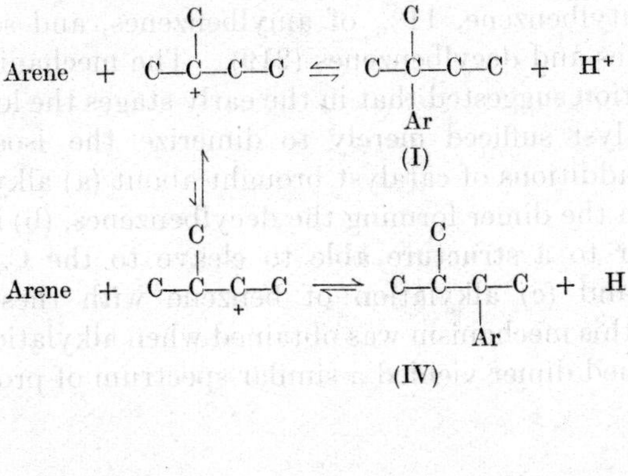

The initially formed tertiary derivative, *e.g.*, I, is in equilibrium with the tertiary cation, thus maintaining the supply of this species. The tertiary cation, in turn, is in equilibrium with a minor amount of secondary cation which attacks benzene to form IV. However, unlike I, compound IV is quite stable and builds up in concentration at the expense of I.

The reactions discussed above are exceedingly rapid; with a contact time of a second or two, aluminum bromide produced at room temperature 22% of a 90/10 mixture of I and IV from benzene and 2-methyl-2-butene (218). At 25° and 2.5 minutes contact time, a 4 molar % solution of I in toluene undergoes about 94% conversion in the presence of aluminum chloride yielding chiefly *m*- and *p-t*-amyltoluene and *m*- and *p*-(1,2-dimethylpropyl)toluene (217).

The failure of sulfuric acid to produce compound IV in alkylations with 2-methyl-2-butene may be ascribed (a) to the low severity, *e.g.*, low temperatures employed (to avoid sulfonation, etc.), or (b) to the possibility that the "alkyl cations in sulfuric acid may be a somewhat different species from those in aluminum halide media. . . . The cations could be bonded to the sulfuric acid similarly to the 'oxygen bonding' which has been postulated to interpret the activity coefficient behavior of arylmethyl cations." (157,157a).

In view of the above, it is not likely that the aluminum chloride–hydrogen chloride catalyzed alkylation of *m*-xylene with 3-ethyl-1-pentene is a tertiary alkylate as reported (46).

e. Side reactions involving cleavage and/or polymerization

Several other side reactions accompany alkylations with isoolefins mainly as a result of polymerization of the olefin often accompanied by subsequent cleavage reactions.

One example occurs when aluminum chloride is added slowly to a mixture of benzene and 2-methyl-2-butene. This procedure yielded 25% of *t*-butylbenzene, 11% of amylbenzenes, and some isomeric hexylbenzenes and decylbenzenes (219). The mechanism advanced for this reaction suggested that in the early stages the low concentration of catalyst sufficed merely to dimerize the isoamylene, but subsequent additions of catalyst brought about (a) alkylation of the benzene with the dimer forming the decylbenzenes, (b) isomerization of the dimer to a structure able to cleave to the C_6 and *t*-butyl fragments, and (c) alkylation of benzene with these fragments. Support for this mechanism was obtained when alkylation of benzene with preformed dimer yielded a similar spectrum of products. Also much earlier Tilicheev and Kuruindin (834) had obtained t-butyl, hexyl, and amyl derivatives from diamylene and benzene.

t-Butyl derivatives appear in the product of practically every alkylation with isoamylenes but apparently not with t-pentyl chloride (219). Alkylation of benzene with 2-methyl-2-butene over a silica–alumina or the U.O.P. "poly" catalyst (phosphoric acid–kieselguhr) in a flow reactor at 225° afforded a mixture of t-butyl-benzene, t-pentylbenzene (I), 2-methyl-3-phenylbutane (IV), and hexylbenzenes (216). The boron fluoride catalyzed alkylation of benzene with 3-methyl-2-butanol also afforded considerable t-butylbenzene (807). Weber, Spoelstra, and Polak (913a) observed formation of C_{14} indanes as well as the expected C_{15} indanes in alkylation of p-cymene with t-amyl alcohol.

Other examples of these types of side reaction are the formation of 1,3,3,6-tetramethyl-1-neopentylindane in the reaction of p-cymene with isobutylene (692); C_4, C_{12}, and C_{16} derivatives in alkylations with triisobutylene; and C_4, C_8, C_{12} derivatives in alkylations with tetraisobutylenes (682).

f. Migration of double bond

Beginning with the branched pentenes another complication arises, namely, migration of the double bond prior to alkylation to give the most branched type. Thus many years ago Ipatieff, Pines, and Schmerling (339) obtained t-pentylbenzene on alkylating benzene with 3-methyl-1-butene in the presence of sulfuric acid.

$$
\begin{array}{c}
\text{C} \\
| \\
\text{C—C—C=C}
\end{array}
\; + \; \bigcirc \; \longrightarrow \;
\begin{array}{c}
\text{C} \\
| \\
\text{C—C—C—C} \\
|
\end{array}
$$

Recently Shuikin et al. (746) obtained t-pentylbenzene in 74% yield in conducting these reactants over a nickel chloride–alumina catalyst.

No doubt the reaction proceeds via successive prototropic shifts to form the most stable (tertiary) carbonium ion

$$
\begin{array}{c}
\text{C} \\
| \\
\text{R—C—C—C} \\
+
\end{array}
$$

which attacks the arene to form a tertiary alkyl derivative. The substantial absence of secondary alkyl derivatives bespeaks a fast rate of the prototropic shift to the tertiary carbonium ion.

It would be of interest to see if some secondary alkylate were to be formed when the branched carbon is located at some distance from the double bond as in (A). The longer time required for the proto-tropic shifts to reach the branched carbon might provide an opportunity for alkylation by the various secondary carbonium ions:

$$
\begin{array}{c}
\overset{\displaystyle C}{\underset{\displaystyle |}{}} \\
C-C-(CH_2)_8-C=C \xrightarrow{\;C_6H_6\;} \quad
\end{array}
\qquad
\begin{array}{c}
\overset{\displaystyle C}{\underset{\displaystyle |}{}} \\
C-C-(CH_2)_8-C-C \\
\underset{C_6H_5}{|}
\end{array}
$$

(A)

$$
\begin{array}{c}
\overset{\displaystyle C}{\underset{\displaystyle |}{}} \\
C-C-(CH_2)_7-C-C-C \\
\underset{C_6H_5}{|}
\end{array}
$$

$$
\begin{array}{c}
\overset{\displaystyle C}{\underset{\displaystyle |}{}} \\
C-C-(CH_2)_6-C-C-C-C \quad \text{etc.} \\
\underset{C_6H_5}{|}
\end{array}
$$

Evidence on this point is lacking; however, Kelly and Lee (376) obtained results in hydride transfer reactions with 4-methyl-2-pentene and 4-methyl-1-pentene (their Table II) which led them to suggest that "an appreciable time is required for a series of hydride shifts leading to the formation of the t-carbonium ion structure."

H. Alkylation with Polymers of Isoolefins
(Tables 7, 13, 18, 22)

a. Depolyalkylation

This term was first introduced in 1936 by Ipatieff and Pines (329) to characterize the reactions they observed when benzene was alkylated with dimers and trimers of branched olefins. They reported that in the presence of 96% sulfuric acid at 0° the reaction of diisobutylene or triisobutylene with benzene or t-butylbenzene produced only t-butyl derivatives. Apparently the dimers and trimers undergo depolymerization yielding scission products which alkylated the arene. These authors stated that depolyalkylation also occurred with n-butene dimers (see Section b, p. 56).

Earlier Noelting (562) had noted that the reaction of toluene or m-xylene with diisobutylene in the presence of aluminum chloride or ferric chloride yielded t-butyl derivatives. A few years later Tilicheev et al. (834) condensed benzene with diamylene using aluminum chloride and obtained a mixture of scission products such as *t*-butyl- and amyl- as well as decylbenzenes. Simons and Archer (758) treated toluene with diisobutylene in the presence of hydrogen fluoride at 0° and obtained about 77% *t*-butyltoluene and 20% di-*t*-butyltoluene. Using 70% hydrogen fluoride, they were not able to prepare dodecylphenol by alkylating phenol with triiso-butylene. When Proell and co-workers (652,653) treated toluene with tetraisobutylene in the presence of alkanesulfonic acids, they obtained only *t*-butyltoluene and triisobutylene. With the same catalyst they obtained mainly *t*-octylphenol from phenol and tetraisobutylene.

Lee *et al*. (431) conducted an extensive survey of catalysts for the production of *t*-butyltoluene *via* the depolyalkylation of toluene with diisobutylene.   Ferric chloride and 99% sulfuric acid each gave only 10 to 30% *t*-butyltoluene, phosphoric acid–kieselguhr about 45%, and aluminum chloride and toluenesulfonic acid 66 to 68%. No catalyst approached the effectiveness of boron fluoride mono-hydrate which produced 80 to 90% of *t*-butyltoluene.   Benzene and *o*- and *m*-xylenes formed comparable yields of *t*-butyl derivatives. However, their report that phenol exhibited no measurable activity is subject to question in view of the results obtained by Topchiev *et al*. (864a) with this catalyst (see Section b-(2), p. 53).   The reaction of triisobutylene with toluene afforded excellent yields (78%) of *t*-butyltoluene, but tripropene gave only 1% of isopropyltoluene plus 6% *t*-butyl- and 14% amyltoluene (mostly *s*-amyltoluene) as well as 51% of intact alkylate.

b. *Intact alkylation*

(1) *With diisobutylene*. Many aromatics have been reported to yield intact alkylates, *i.e.*, *t*-octyl derivatives, when treated with diisobu-tylene.   These include the more reactive aromatic nuclei such as naphthalene (15,86), thiophenes (104,916), and phenols (39,125,552, 758).   Coleman and Rigterink (125) obtained a patent claiming the octylation and dioctylation of biphenyl with diisobutylene at 70–80° in the presence of aluminum chloride.   The authors of this review are inclined, however, to doubt that intact alkylate was obtained since one would expect depolyalkylation to predominate at such high temperatures.

In recent years data obtained as a result of an extensive study of catalysts and operating conditions showed that very good yields of intact alkylate could also be obtained from toluene and its homo-logs (679,680,681).   Temperature was found to be the critical variable; too low a temperature resulted in polymer formation, too high in depolyalkylation. Optimum temperatures found for toluene are given in the following table.

TABLE V. Optimum temperature for intact alkylation of toluene with diisobutylene (DIB)

Catalyst	Temp. °C	Wt. % DIB Converted to					
		t-C_4- Toluene	t-C_8-Toluene p/m		C_{12}-Toluene p/m		Polymer
$AlCl_3$–$C_6H_5NO_2$	25	<1	84	19	a		<1
$AlCl_3$–CH_3NO_2	25	15	71^b		a		15
H_2SO_4	5	10	69^b		10		a
$FeCl_3$	0	6	85^b		a		<1
RSO_3H–BF_3	−20	13	44	19	37	19	<1
$AlCl_3$	−35	6	79	7	a		a
$AlCl_3$–CCl_4	−35	6	45	3	21	3	c
HF	−40	<1	92	19	a		2
HF–BF_3	−60	12	79^b		<1		<1
$AlCl_3$–HCl	−65	3	72	5	24	1	2

^{a} None detected.

^{b} Contains octyl groups isomeric with 1,1,3,3-tetramethylbutyl-.

^{c} 26% Disubstituted C_{16}-toluene.

Contact time was another important variable; if stirring is continued for six minutes after addition of diisobutylene to toluene and aluminum chloride at −35°, the yield of t-octyltoluene is 79%; after sixty minutes the yield has dropped to 50% while C_{12}- and C_{16}-toluene derivatives have increased from < 1 to about 48%. Apparently the t-octyltoluene undergoes dealkylation, the resulting t-octyl cation disproportionates to furnish t-butyl, t-dodecyl, and hexadecyl fragments which in turn react with toluene to form the corresponding derivatives of toluene.

The results with benzene were much less satisfactory. No catalyst appeared to afford pure 1,1,3,3-tetramethylbutylbenzene; the octylbenzenes obtained were either contaminated with di-t-butylbenzene and/or polymer, or else they contained octyl groups isomeric with the expected 1,1,3,3-tetramethylbutyl group. These isomeric octyl groups no doubt result from acid-catalyzed skeletal rearrangements of the initial cation, derived from diisobutylene, to produce various isomeric C_8 cations as postulated by Condon (132):

$$
\begin{array}{ccc}
& \text{C} \quad \text{C} & \text{C} \quad \text{C} \\
& | \quad\ | & | \quad\ | \\
\text{C}-\overset{|}{\underset{|}{\text{C}}}-\text{C}-\overset{|}{\text{C}}-\text{C} \; \rightleftharpoons \; & \text{C}-\text{C}-\text{C}-\overset{|}{\text{C}}-\text{C} \; \rightleftharpoons
\end{array}
$$

$$
\left[
\begin{array}{c}
\overset{\displaystyle \text{CH}_2}{\diagup \ \ \ \diagdown} \\
\text{C} \quad \overset{\text{H}}{} \\
| \\
\text{C}-\text{C}-\text{CH}-\!\!-\!\!-\!\!-\text{CH}-\text{C} \\
| \\
\text{C}
\end{array}
\right]^{+}
\rightleftharpoons
\left[
\begin{array}{c}
\text{C} \qquad\quad \text{C} \\
| \qquad\qquad | \\
\text{C}-\text{C}-\!\!-\!\!-\text{CH}-\text{C}-\text{C} \\
\underset{\displaystyle\text{CH}_2}{\text{H}}
\end{array}
\right]^{+}
$$

$$
\begin{array}{cc}
\text{C} \ \ \text{C} \ \ \text{C} & \text{C} \qquad\ \text{C} \\
| \ \ \ | \ \ \ | & | \qquad\ | \\
\text{C}-\text{C}-\text{C}-\text{C}-\text{C} & \text{C}-\text{C}-\text{C}-\text{C}-\text{C}-\text{C} \\
\quad\ + & \quad\ +
\end{array}
$$

These in turn alkylate benzene to produce isomeric octylbenzenes.

Excellent yields of intact alkylate were also obtained from the reaction of o-xylene and 2-methylnaphthalene with diisobutylene using hydrogen fluoride as catalyst at $-20°$ and $-40°$ respectively. However, the yields of intact alkylate obtained from t-butylbenzene and t-octylbenzene were low (17% and 1%, respectively), a result which may be attributed to the decreased solubility of these higher mol. wt. arenes in the hydrogen fluoride catalyst.

Hearne et al. (266) also employed sulfuric acid (93% at 0°) to obtain the intact alkylate of toluene (50% yield) which was desired for conversion via oxidation to t-octyltoluic acid.

Schlatter (692) treated p-cymene with diisobutylene in the presence of hydrogen fluoride and obtained an indane which might be

$$
\begin{array}{c}
\text{C} \\
| \\
\text{C} \quad\ \text{C} \\
| \qquad | \\
\text{C}-\text{C}-\text{C}-\text{C} \\
| \qquad | \\
\text{C} \qquad \text{C} \\
\text{C}-\text{C} \\
| \\
\text{C}
\end{array}
$$

regarded as an intact alkylate. (This type of cyclization reaction is discussed in greater detail in Section II-1-G-b and in Chapter XXII.)

(2) *With tri- and tetraisobutylene.* Only a few instances have

been reported of intact alkylation with these olefins. Bruson and Stein (86) claimed formation of dodecyl- and hexadecylnaphthalenes by alkylation of naphthalene in the presence of sulfuric acid at 30°. However, they offered no proof of structure. Topchiev *et al.* (864a) produced dodecylphenol from phenol and triisobutylene using boron fluoride monohydrate at 50°.

In a recent publication, Sanford *et al.* (682) showed that by operating at proper conditions of temperature with certain catalysts, fair yields of intact alkylate could be obtained from toluene and triisobutylene. Depolyalkylation was the chief reaction, however. Thus at −40° aluminum chloride afforded 34% of dodecyltoluene and 27% of octyltoluene. Ferric chloride produced 20% and 47%, respectively, at 0°, and sulfuric acid 28% of each at −20°. Tetra-isobutylene yielded only 16% of hexadecyltoluene in the presence of aluminum chloride at −35°, the chief product (68%) being octyl-toluene. Sulfuric acid at −20° and hydrogen fluoride at −40° each afforded about 9% and 78% respectively of these products. Even with a more reactive aromatic, such as phenol, tetraisobutylene afforded mainly the octyl derivative (hydrogen fluoride at −40°). Similar results with phenol were obtained by Proell and Adams (653) who used alkanesulfonic acid catalysts.

I. Alkylation with Polymers of n-*Olefins*

(Tables 7, 13, 18, 22)

a. Propene polymers

Propene polymers are quite resistant to depolyalkylation. The dimer afforded 88% of hexyltoluene (266) when 93% sulfuric acid was used at 0–5°. Propene trimer gave excellent yields of nonyltoluene with aluminum chloride–hydrogen chloride at 98° (251) while sulfuric acid yielded 58 to 65% at 0–5° (266,468). Boron fluoride monohydrate, on the other hand, gave a fair amount of cleavage products at 75–80° (1% isopropyl-, 6% *t*-butyl-, and 14% amylbenzenes) in addition to 54% of the expected nonylbenzene (431).

Good yields (53–94%) of dodecyl derivatives were obtained by alkylating benzene and toluene with propene tetramer using aluminum chloride, sulfuric acid, hydrogen fluoride, and zirconium chloride. However, phosphoric acid–kieselguhr and sulfonic acid type exchange resin gave mediocre results (12–18%). Sulfuric acid was also satisfactory for the alkylation of *o*-xylene with the tetramer (266). Both propene tetramer and pentamer condensed with benzene to give good yields of intact alkylate in the presence of hydrogen fluoride, provided that a large amount of the catalyst, *e.g.*, 200–800 mol.%, was employed (441,442).

In view of the above data and in view of the ready availability of propene polymers from refinery polymer gasoline plants, it is not surprising to find that these olefinic stocks have been the main alkylating agent for producing phenylalkanes for the manufacture of synthetic detergents. Approximately 500 million lbs. of these alkylates are consumed per year for this purpose.

Propene tetramer normally employed for detergent manufacture boils in the range of 170–225°. The polymer is produced by polymerization of propene over the phosphoric acid on kieselguhr catalyst. Bloch and Hervert (59) have shown by chemical and infra-red analysis that propene tetramer has the following approximate distribution:

$$
\begin{array}{ll}
\text{I.} & R—CH{=}CH—R' \\
\text{II.} & R—CH{=}CH_2 \\
\end{array} \Bigg\} \; 10\text{–}15\%
$$

$$
\begin{array}{ll}
 & R' \\
 & | \\
\text{III.} & R—C{=}CH_2 \\[4pt]
 & R'\;\; R'' \\
 & |\quad| \\
\text{IV.} & R—C{=}CH \\[4pt]
 & R'\;\; R'' \\
 & |\quad| \\
\text{V.} & R—C{=}C—R''' \\
\end{array} \Bigg\} \; 85\text{–}90\%
$$

Meerkamp van Embden (506) reported that five different samples contained about 20% of I + II and about 80% of III + IV.

In the presence of Friedel-Crafts catalysts, types III and IV olefinic compounds, which resemble polyisobutylene structures, form carbonium ions that readily fragment by β-cleavage (441,442). Alkylation by these fragments yields undesirable lower boiling depolyalkylation products. As shown in Section II-1-H, di-, tri-, and perhaps tetraisobutylenes which contain large amounts of type III olefins, afford mainly cleavage products.

Sharrah and Feighner (735) reported that lower boiling saturate material containing about 12 carbon atoms was formed during the alkylation. They suggested that these products were the result of hydrogen transfer reactions and preferential cyclization of certain isomeric propene tetramer structures. However, no data were presented to verify the structure of these products or to shed further light on the mechanism of their formation.

The dodecylbenzene fraction (275–315°) which Sharrah and Feighner obtained by alkylation with propene tetramer contained more than 99% monoalkylbenzenes when the reaction was catalyzed by aluminum chloride or hydrogen fluoride. The sulfuric acid alkylate contained olefin polymers which were difficult to remove. High-boiling residues were obtained which were found to be mostly polysubstitution products of benzene.

The competing reactions which accompany alkylation, *e.g.*, fragmentation, hydrogen transfer (producing alkanes and diolefins), polymerization, cyclization of dodecene, and polyalkylation, were all reduced by using high ratios of benzene to propene tetramers. It was also necessary to avoid excessive temperatures to suppress fragmentation of the olefins. However, at low temperatures alkylation was slow and the yield of polymer relative to alkylate became high. Temperatures in the range of 0–10° were best for sulfuric acid and hydrogen fluoride and about 30° was optimum for aluminum chloride. Yields of about 80% could be obtained with each of these three catalysts.

Bloch and Hervert (59) investigated the structure and orientation of the alkyl side chains resulting from the alkylation of toluene with propene tetramer. They established by infra-red absorption spectra that the hydrogen fluoride and sulfuric acid catalyzed products were almost entirely *para*-substituted while aluminum chloride catalyzed products were 50% *meta*-substituted. These authors also believed that the alkylates obtained by catalysis with the proton acids were largely tertiary alkyltoluenes and that the alkylates formed by aluminum chloride catalysis were largely secondary. These conclusions were based on the olefin types present in the alkylating agent, the relative degree of branching of the alkylates as shown by infra-red absorption and the known isomerizing behavior of aluminum chloride (see Section II-1-G-d). As further evidence for these structures Bloch and Hervert pointed out that the sulfuric acid alkylate gave lower yields in subsequent sulfonation tests than did the aluminum chloride alkylate. They attributed this result to the fact that (1) the sulfuric acid alkylate is a *para*-substituted toluene and (2) the C_{12} group is largely tertiary. This type of group is susceptible to cleavage during sulfonation and is also very bulky, forcing the $-SO_3H$ group with its own fairly large steric requirement to attack at the positions *ortho* to the methyl side chain.

b. n-*Butene polymers*

n-Butene dimer yielded only scission products (*p*-di-*s*- and tri-*s*-butylbenzene) with sulfuric acid at 0° (325). Under suitable conditions intact alkylates would undoubtedly be obtained.

J. Alkylation with Aryl-substituted Olefins
(Tables 7, 13, 18, 22)

a. Styrene

Many aryl-substituted olefins undergo "normal" alkylation. The reaction of styrene and benzene yields 25% 1,1-diphenylethane in the presence of 93% sulfuric acid (780). Similarly in the presence of concentrated sulfuric acid toluene yields 65% of 1-phenyl-1-tolyl-ethane, pseudocumene gives 75% of 1-phenyl-1-pseudocumyltolyl-ethane, o-xylene gives 70% 1-phenyl-1-o-xylylethane, and p-xylene gives 1-phenyl-1-p-xylylethane (407). Aluminum chloride, however, gives mainly polystyrene (543).

b. α-Methylstyrenes

Because of the propensity of α-methylstyrene to dimerize in the presence of acids (610), alkylation with this olefin is very difficult. In attempts to alkylate toluene with the corresponding p-methyl-substituted α-methylstyrene (using sulfuric acid as catalyst) Coscia, Penniston, and Petroupoulis (144) obtained mainly the indane dimer (B′) instead of the alkylate (B). They found that the α,p-dimethylstyryl cation (A), in contrast to the carbonium ion derived from styrene, attacks the double bond of another α,p-dimethyl-styrene molecule in preference to the toluene nucleus:

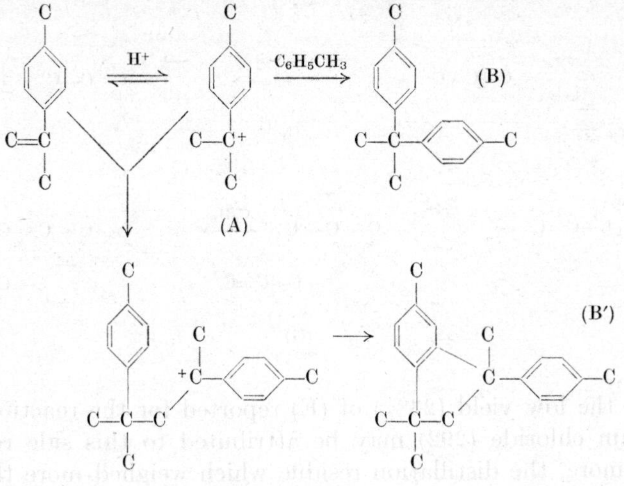

Oligomers of the olefin were the main by-product when aluminum chloride was used, and this was reduced from 74% to 40% when the catalyst was complexed with nitromethane.

Using a variety of catalysts and varying reaction conditions these workers were able to obtain only 1 to 4% of the desired alkylate (B). Only in one instance did they obtain a reasonably good yield (35%) and that was accomplished by adding the olefin dropwise to sulfuric acid dispersed in a very large excess (300/1) of toluene. However, when they employed the hydrochloride of the olefin, namely 2-chloro-2-(p-tolyl)propane, and used aluminum chloride complexed with nitromethane or nitrobenzene as the catalyst, a high yield (81%) of (B) was obtained.

c. *Unconjugated aryl-substituted olefins*

The reaction of allylbenzene with benzene was reported to proceed normally in the presence of hydrogen fluoride (757) or aluminum chloride (292) to form 1,2-diphenylpropane (E). No mention was made, however, of by-products such as (G) or (H) which might be expected to form *via* "self-alkylation."

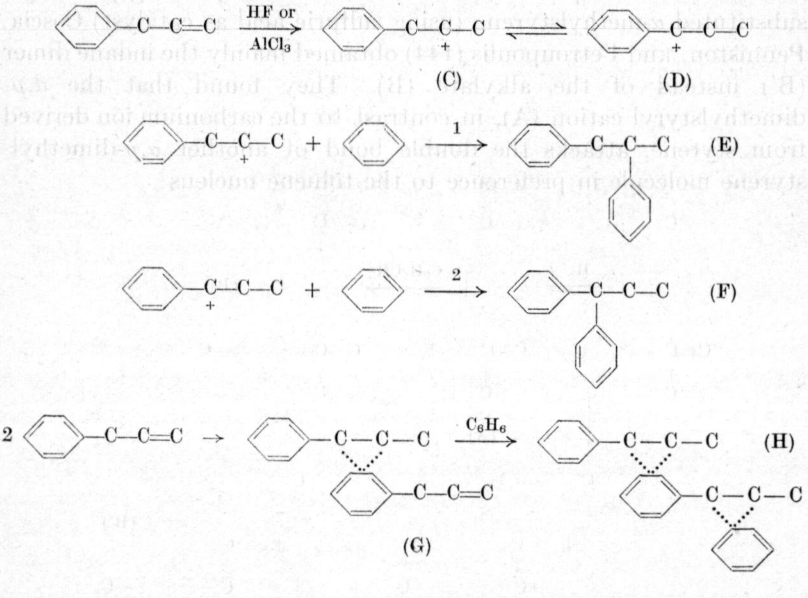

In fact, the low yield (23%) of (E) reported for the reaction using aluminum chloride (292) may be attributed to this side reaction. Furthermore, the distillation residue which weighed more than the amount of (E) recovered, may have contained by-products (G) and/or (H). No yields were given for the hydrogen fluoride catalyzed reaction.

It is somewhat unusual that 1,1-diphenylpropane (F) was not found since the benzylic carbonium ion (D) would be expected to be a more stable intermediate than (C).   It may be that (F) is subject to the same instability exhibited by 1,1-diarylethane (806b) resulting in reversal of reaction 2 to re-form (D) which equilibrates with (C). (C) is drained off in reaction 1 forming the more stable 1,2-diphenyl isomer (E).   However, a recent report by Lovina, Shabarov, and co-workers (439a) indicates that 1,1-diarylpropanes are quite able to survive contact with aluminum chloride.   These authors obtained, for example, 62% of 1-phenyl-1-p-tolylpropane by the reaction of phenylcyclopropane with toluene at 0–10° in the presence of aluminum chloride (see Section VIII-2).

Longer chain alkenylbenzenes tend to undergo ring closure, a reaction that is reviewed in Chapter XXII.   Apparently intramolecular (*ortho*) alkylation (reaction 3) has a much lower energy of activation than intermolecular alkylation (reaction 4):

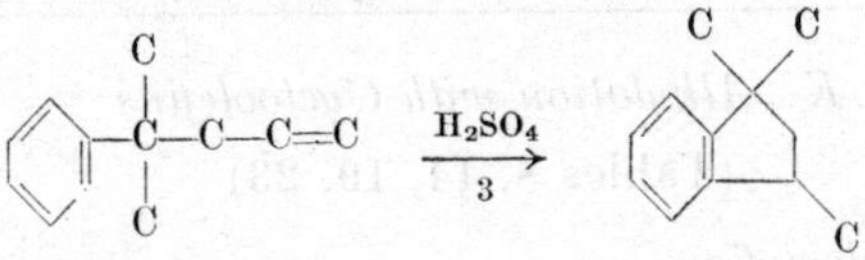

$$\text{(reaction 3)} \xrightarrow[\ 3\ ]{H_2SO_4} \quad 60\% \ (127)$$

$$2 \xrightarrow[\ 4\ ]{}$$

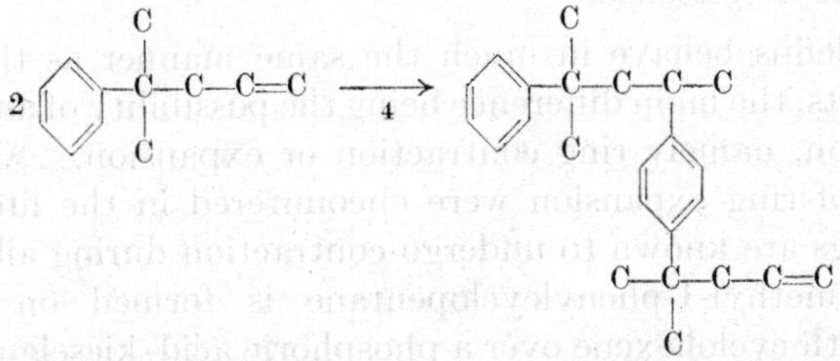

d. *Polyaryl-substituted olefins*

In some instances stilbene alkylates benzene in a normal fashion to give 1,1,2-triphenylethane in 49% yield (7), but in others dibenzyl is the only product isolated (7a).

A further complication is that alkylation of benzene with p-bromostilbene provides excellent yields of 1,1,2-triphenylethane (7).   The mechanism advanced for this transformation assumes a reversible addition of arene to the double bond:

$$C_6H_6 \ + \ p\text{-}BrC_6H_4CH=CHC_6H_5 \underset{AlCl_3\text{-}HCl}{\rightleftharpoons} p\text{-}BrC_6H_4CH-CH_2C_6H_5 \\ \qquad\qquad\qquad\qquad\qquad\qquad\qquad\qquad\qquad\qquad | \\ \qquad\qquad\qquad\qquad\qquad\qquad\qquad\qquad\qquad\quad C_6H_5$$

$$(C_6H_5)_2CH-CH_2C_6H_5 \xrightleftharpoons{\ C_6H_6\ } C_6H_5CH=CHC_6H_5 \ + \ C_6H_5Br$$

Since benzene is present in great excess, the final triarylethane will be substantially free from bromine. The results of Streitwieser and co-workers (806a,806b) lend support to the above mechanism.

Besides replacement of one aryl group with another, hydrogen transfer reactions occur leading to saturated products. Thus stilbene and benzene yield 20% of dibenzyl (7a). Both the replacement and hydrogen transfer reactions may occur as shown by the production of dibenzyl in condensation of benzene with the following compounds:

Starting material	Yield of dibenzyl	Ref.
$(C_6H_5)_2C{=}CHC_6H_5$	28%	7
$(p\text{-}ClC_6H_4)_2C{=}CHC_6H_5$	27%	7
$(C_6H_5)_2C{=}C(C_6H_5)_2$	54%	7
$p\text{-}ClC_6H_4CH{=}CHC_6H_4Cl\text{-}p$	70%	7a

K. Alkylation with Cycloolefins
(Tables 8, 14, 19, 23)

a. Unbranched cycloolefins

Cyclic olefins behave in much the same manner as their acyclic counterparts, the main difference being the possibility of an additional side reaction, namely ring contraction or expansion. Although no examples of ring expansion were encountered in the literature, C_6 and C_7 rings are known to undergo contraction during alkylation.

Thus 1-methyl-1-phenylcyclopentane is formed on alkylating benzene with cyclohexene over a phosphoric acid–kieselguhr catalyst (217a). Apparently the cyclohexene undergoes isomerization to methylcyclopentene prior to alkylation. A similar observation was mentioned by Pokrovskaya and Stepantseva (638) who noted that methylcyclopentylnaphthalene may have been formed in alkylations with cyclohexene in the presence of aluminum chloride.

Ring contractions occur quite readily in alkylations of benzene with cycloheptene or cycloheptanol. In the presence of aluminum chloride–hydrogen chloride, the monocycloalkyl product (39%) consisted mainly of methylphenylcyclohexanes (probably 1-methyl-3-phenylcyclohexane), the yield of cycloheptylbenzene being only about 3% (613). On the other hand, sulfuric acid and hydrogen fluoride afforded good yields (48 and 71% respectively) of cycloheptylbenzene. It is not known whether the rearrangement takes place before or after alkylation. Unfortunately no report was made of a test of the stability of cycloheptylbenzene under alkylation conditions.

Fused ring cycloolefins give low yields of alkylate (126).

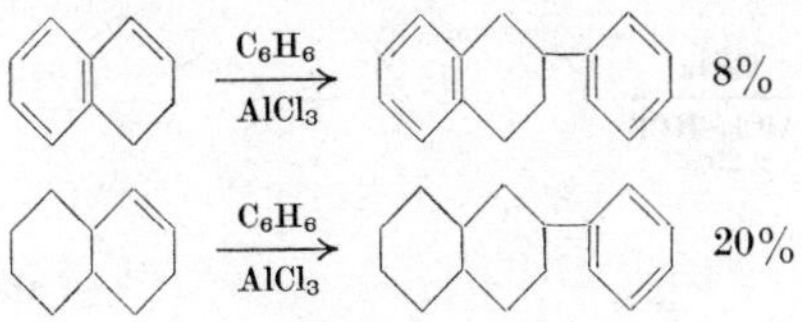

It would be of interest to see which of the various octalins would yield 9-phenyldecalin. Perhaps with sulfuric acid as catalyst, all of them would because of the great propensity of that catalyst to convert branched olefins to a tertiary carbonium ion.

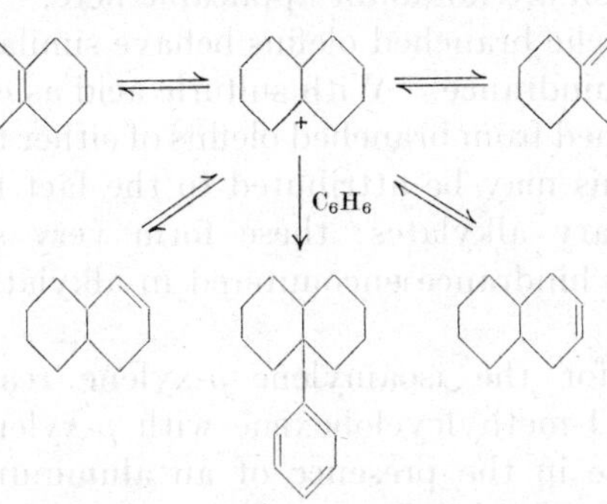

The spatial requirements involved in alkylations with cyclohexene and cyclopentene appear to be about the same as that for propene or butene. This is documented in Section II-1-B-b.

b. Branched cycloolefins

Double-bond migration occurs in alkylations with branched cycloolefins as it does in the acyclic series. Thus 4-methylcyclohexene yields the same tertiary alkylate as does 1-methylcyclohexene:

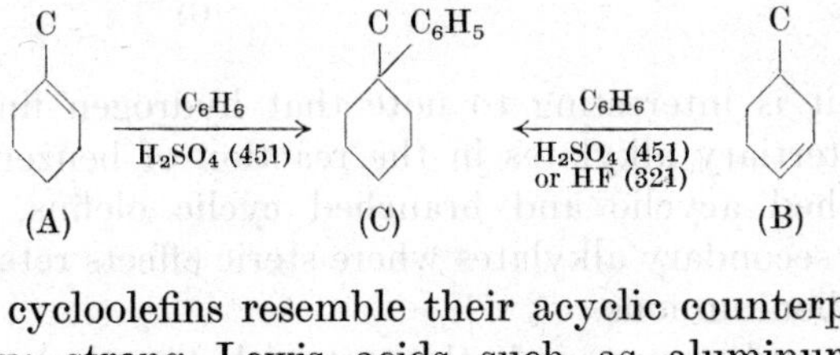

(A)   (C)   (B)

Branched cycloolefins resemble their acyclic counterparts in still another way; strong Lewis acids such as aluminum chloride–hydrogen chloride or boron fluoride–hydrogen fluoride, produce mainly the secondary alkylates, (D), (E) and (F) from 1-methyl-cyclohexene or 4-methylcyclohexene (220):

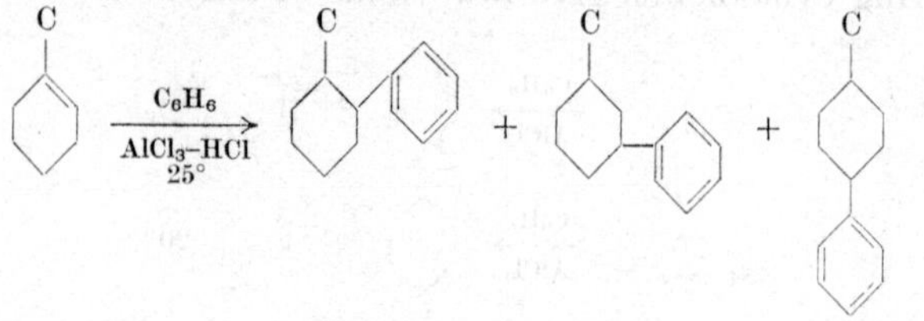

(D) 19%   (E) 49%   (F) 26%

Only 3% of the *t*-alkylate (C) was present. Mechanisms suggested (Section II-1-G-d) for the benzene–isoamylene isomerization–alkylation reaction are no doubt applicable here.

Cyclic and acyclic branched olefins behave similarly in alkylations involving steric hindrance. With sulfuric acid as catalyst, the yield of alkylate obtained from branched olefins of either type and *p*-xylene is very low. This may be attributed to the fact that this catalyst gives only tertiary alkylates; these form very slowly, if at all, because of steric hindrance encountered in alkylations *ortho* to ring substituents.

As reported for the isoamylene–*p*-xylene reaction (221), the condensation of 1-methylcyclohexene with *p*-xylene produces poor yields of alkylate in the presence of an aluminum chloride–nitro-methane–hydrogen chloride catalyst. Hydrogen fluoride and aluminum chloride–hydrogen chloride, on the other hand, give high yields of monoalkylate. Again paralleling the results obtained with isoamylene less than 5% of the alkylate (G) is tertiary:

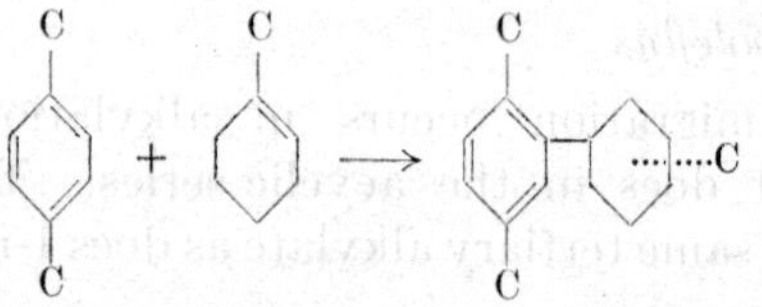

(G)

Here, too, it is interesting to note that hydrogen fluoride, which gives only tertiary alkylates in the reaction of benzene or toluene with branched acyclic and branched cyclic olefins, affords pre-dominately secondary alkylates where steric effects retard attack by tertiary carbonium ions.

o-Cymene and *m*-cymene both react with 4-methylcyclohexene in the presence of hydrogen fluoride to give the expected methylcyclohexyl derivatives, but *m*-cymene also gives products resulting from hydrogen transfer (622):

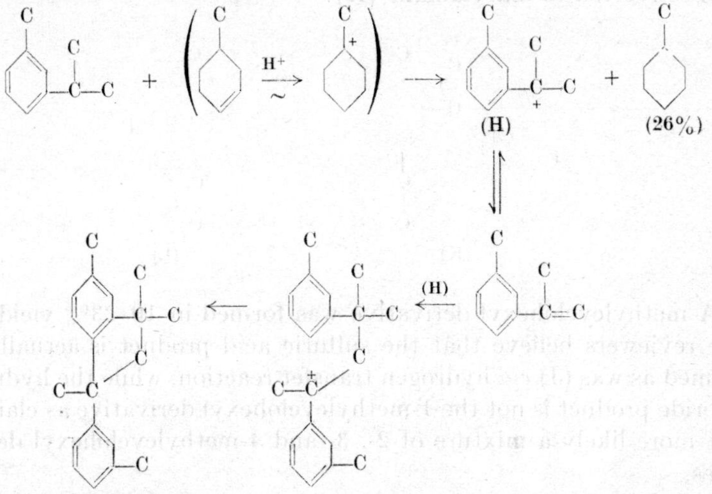

(H)   (26%)

(I) 25%

Steric hindrance greatly retards alkylation of *p*-cymene with 3-methylcyclohexene in the presence of either hydrogen fluoride or sulfuric acid. Only small amounts of alkylate (8–9%) are formed whereas a large amount of indane is formed *via* hydrogen transfer reaction (335). This indane, 1,3,3,6-tetramethyl-1-*p*-tolylindane, is formed in yields of 29–37% (based on olefin) by reactions similar to that giving rise to 1,3,3,5-tetramethyl-1-*m*-tolylindane (I).

Later workers (220) have pointed out that the so-called alkylate (335) from *p*-cymene and 3-methylcyclohexene must have consisted mainly of an indane since the elementary analyses clearly indicated a tricyclic structure such as (J) which they had obtained from *p*-cymene and 4-methylcyclohexene. Mass spectrographic data fully supported the indane structure for (J).

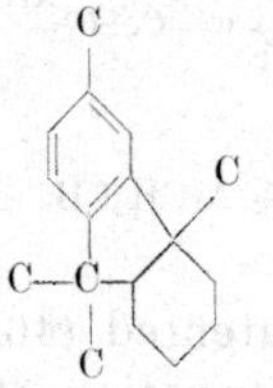

(J)

Similar hydrogen transfer reactions occurred with *p*-ethyltoluene and *p*-*n*-propyltoluene (620). Condensation of 4-methylcyclohexene with p-ethyltoluene in the presence of hydrogen fluoride or sulfuric acid produced 45–60% of methylcyclohexane while 65% of the arene was converted to diarylalkane (K):

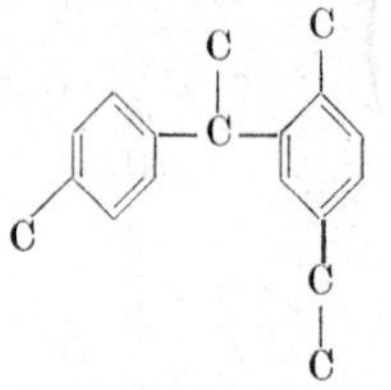

(K) 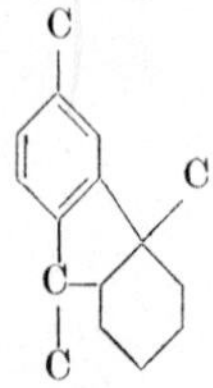   (L)

A methylcyclohexyl derivative was formed in 10–23% yield, but the reviewers believe that the sulfuric acid product is actually (L) formed as was (J) *via* hydrogen transfer reaction, while the hydrogen fluoride product is not the 1-methylcyclohexyl derivative as claimed, but more likely a mixture of 2-, 3- and 4-methylcyclohexyl derivatives.

L. Telemerization

When benzene and ethylene was heated under pressure with a nickel oxide–silica alumina catalyst at 225°, the product was mainly s-butylbenzene (62 vol. %). Ethyl-, hexyl-, and octylbenzene were produced in amounts ranging 10–15 vol. % each; a small amount (3 vol. %) of decylbenzene was also formed (38). At lower temperatures, *e.g.*, 110°, the product was mainly 1-butene with about 20% of a mixture of C_6 to C_{12} olefins. Toluene and ethylene gave similar results. Because the alkylbenzenes with C_6 and higher side chains were not characterized, it is not possible to tell if the reaction proceeded *via* (1) or (2) or both:

(1) $C{=}C + C{=}C \longrightarrow C{-}C{-}C{=}C \xrightarrow{\text{ArH}} Ar{-}\overset{\displaystyle C}{\underset{|}{C}}{-}C{-}C$

(2) $C{=}C + ArH \longrightarrow ArCH_2CH_3 \longrightarrow Ar{-}\overset{\displaystyle C}{\underset{|}{C}}{-}C{-}C$

Another novel process patented (461) for the synthesis of long-chain alkylarenes *via* telomerization of α-monoolefins involves the use of a combination catalyst consisting of (A) ethyl aluminum sesquihalides and (B) titanium halide. The titanium halide must be present in molar excess over the sesquihalide. A 1/2 mole ratio of (A)/(B) gave the best results:

$$\text{C}_6\text{H}_6 + \text{C}{=}\text{C} \xrightarrow[\substack{(B)\ \text{TiCl}_4(0.425) \\ 10\ \text{hrs. at } 40^\circ,\ 10\ \text{psig}}]{(A)\ \text{EtAlBr}_2/\text{Et}_2\text{AlBr}(0.2)} \text{C}_6\text{H}_5{-}\text{R}$$

$$(\text{R} = \text{C}_4\text{--}\text{C}_{20}, \text{ mainly } \text{C}_8\text{--}\text{C}_{12})$$

Equimolar mixtures of (A) and (B) yielded only polyethylene. A 1/1.25 mole ratio gave a considerable amount of polyethylene and some alkylate. Either (A) or (B) alone failed as catalyst for the telomerization reaction.

With a 1/2 mole ratio of A/B, benzene and ethylene yielded a product that was predominately dodecylbenzene. Some 7-phenyl-tridecane, 2-phenyloctane, and 9-phenylheptadecane was present.

Similar results were claimed for the telomerization of benzene with propene, toluene with isobutylene, 1-butene, or 1-pentene, and naphthalene with propene.

Aldridge and Hunter claimed a process for the synthesis of detergent arylalkanes which involved telomerizing certain C_5 to C_8 olefins with benzene or its homologs in the presence of small amounts of aluminum chloride containing trace amounts of moisture (6). By this means the alkyl group introduced into the nucleus of the arene contained from 2 to 15 monomer olefin units.

The olefins which telomerize in the desired manner are of the type $RCH{=}CH_2$ where R represents a saturated, branched alkyl radical or cycloalkyl radical. Olefins not falling in this category, such as 1-pentene and 4-methyl-2-pentene, give much less of the telomerate and more of the usual type of alkylate. Although the patent claims 0.1–10 wt. % of aluminum chloride (based on olefin), it appears that 2–3% gives the best results:

$$\text{C}_6\text{H}_6 + \text{C}{-}\text{C}{-}\text{C}{-}\text{C}{=}\text{C} \longrightarrow \text{Alkylate}$$
$$\text{mol. wt.} = 705$$
$$83\% \text{ C}_6\text{H}_5\text{R}$$

Even though the olefin is added gradually, free olefin may be present in relatively high concentration when a small amount of catalyst is employed, and therefore polymerization can occur prior to alkylation. With larger amounts of catalyst most of the olefin may be complexed by the catalyst, and alkylation would be favored by the high concentration of aromatic.

2. Halogenated and Nitrated Benzenes
(Tables 33, 34)

A. Halogenated Benzenes

It is well known that halogen atoms deactivate aromatic rings for electrophilic substitution and that substitution of haloaromatics generally occurs in *ortho-* and *para-*positions. Nevertheless, halo-aromatics, particularly the monosubstituted compounds, can be condensed with olefins. Typical Friedel-Crafts catalysts will catalyze the reaction. The *para-*derivative has been reported as the exclusive or predominant product in almost every case. However, isomeric mixtures have been indicated by Istrati (354) in 1885 and quite recently by Friedman and Morritz (219).

The reduced reactivity of halobenzenes such as bromobenzene and chlorobenzene is indicated by the tendency for 1-alkylcyclohexenes to undergo dimerization rather than alkylation. Monteils (530,531) found that in the presence of boron fluoride or aluminum chloride, 1-ethyl- and 1-butylcyclohexene dimerized almost exclusively. Under the same conditions a mixture of cyclohexylhalobenzenes and cyclohexene dimer was obtained when cyclohexene was used as the alkylating agent. However, substantial yields of alkylate were obtained when the milder catalyst, ferric chloride, was used. Martin (496) found that a 77% yield of alkylate could be obtained from the reaction of cyclohexene and chlorobenzene if very small amounts of aluminum chloride were used as catalyst.

Friedman and Morritz (219) found that 12% *t*-butyl- and 8% amylchlorobenzene was obtained from the aluminum chloride catalyzed condensation of chlorobenzene with isoamylene. With benzene only 5% *t*-butyl- and about 40% amylbenzene was formed. The alkylation of chlorobenzene is slower than the alkylation of benzene, thus providing more time for dimerization of isoamylene followed by isomerization and cleavage of the dimer. (The mechanism is discussed in Section II-1-G-e.)

In spite of the somewhat reduced reactivity of chlorobenzene, high yields of alkylate have been obtained by condensation with a variety of olefins in the presence of a number of catalysts. Chlorobenzene has been condensed with ethylene in the presence of aluminum chloride (354) or silica–alumina (493). An 84% yield of isopropylchlorobenzene and an 83% yield of *s*-butylchlorobenzene was obtained over an alumina silicate catalyst at 350° (492). Hydrogen fluoride catalyzed the condensation of 3-hexene and chlorobenzene at 5–10° (779). High yields of cyclopentyl- (529) and cyclohexylchlorobenzene (871) have been obtained with concentrated sulfuric acid at room temperature. Cyclohexyl derivatives of *o*-, *m*-, and *p*- chlorotoluenes were obtained in high yield by cyclohexylation in the presence of aluminum chloride (496,587a) or sulfuric acid–15% phosphorus pentoxide (875).

It is interesting to note that Mamedeliev (493) obtained a 16% yield of ethylchlorobenzene from ethylene and chlorobenzene in the presence of sulfuric acid containing 2% mercuric sulfate. The role of mercuric sulfate must be quite significant since benzene itself cannot be alkylated with ethylene in the presence of sulfuric acid (see Section II-1-D-b).

The introduction of a second halogen atom in a benzene ring drastically reduces the reactivity of the ring towards alkylation. *o*-Dichlorobenzene has been used as a solvent for the alkylation of aromatics such as polystyrene (527). However, Brown (365a) found in a study of the alkylation of benzene with ethylbromide in the presence of aluminum bromide that *o*-dichlorobenzene employed as solvent underwent alkylation to a significant extent. 1,2,4-Trichlorobenzene, on the other hand, was not appreciably attacked. In attempts to condense *o*-, *m*-, and *p*-dichlorobenzene with cyclohexene in the presence of sulfuric acid–phosphorus pentoxide, Truffault and Monteils (872) obtained only 5% yields of cyclohexyl derivatives of *o*- and *m*-dichlorobenzene and a 0% yield of cyclohexyl-*p*-dichlorobenzene. However, Martin and Coleman (496) claimed that with a small amount of aluminum chloride they obtained 46% yield of cyclohexyl-*o*-dichlorobenzene.

Zavgorodnii and co-workers (940,950) investigated the condensation of 2-butene with fluorobenzene, chlorobenzene, and bromobenzene in the presence of boron fluoride–phosphoric acid, or a solid derived by heating aluminum chloride and phosphoric acid ($AlCl_2 \cdot H_2PO_4$). The yields obtained from the three halobenzenes did not differ greatly but the data indicated the following order of reactivity: $C_6H_5F > C_6H_5Br > C_6H_5Cl$. A direct comparison of iodobenzene to the other halobenzenes has not been made. However, Mamedeliev *et al.* (479) found that sulfuric acid catalyzed the condensation of propene and butene with iodobenzene at room temperature. The high reactivity of fluorobenzene may be attributed to the greater ability of the first-row element to conjugate with the ring (653a).

The loss of halogen during alkylation has been noted at least twice. In an attempt to alkylate bromobenzene with ethylene in the presence of aluminum chloride, Berry and Reid (52) obtained high

4 + F.C. II

yields of alkylate, but almost half the product was ethyl- and diethylbenzene. Babakhanov (29) obtained *para*-dibromobenzene as well as isopropylbromobenzene, cumene and propane by condensing propene with bromobenzene over an aluminosilicate catalyst. *p*-Dibromobenzene was also obtained by passing bromobenzene over the same catalyst in the absence of propene.

B. Nitrated Benzenes

Only one instance of alkylation of a nitrated benzene with olefin has been reported, namely a patent claiming propylation of *o*-nitrotoluene in the presence of perchloric acid (159). However, Desseigne was able to alkylate *p*-nitrotoluene with isopropyl alcohol in the presence of sulfuric acid to obtain the 2-isopropyl- and 2,6-diisopropyl derivatives (158b).

3. Polycyclic Aromatic Hydrocarbons

The condensation of olefins with condensed ring systems and other polycyclic aromatic hydrocarbons has not been as extensively investigated as the reactions of olefins with benzene derivatives. Problems of identification of isomers in mono- and polysubstituted condensed ring systems are considerably more difficult than in the benzene system. Most identification work has been based on classical methods, such as separation and oxidation, and very little work has been reported in which modern instrumental analytical techniques were applied.

A. Naphthalenes
(Tables 25–29)

Electrophilic substitution on condensed ring systems is much more readily accomplished than substitution of benzene and its derivatives. De La Mare and Ridd (156) point out that in condensed ring systems the formation of a sigma-complex results in a much lower loss of stabilization energy. This is presumably reflected in the partial rate factors for nitration. Assuming a partial rate factor of 1 for benzene, Dewar *et al.* (160) found the partial rate factors for positions 1- and 2- in naphthalene to be 470 and 50, respectively. The rate of molecular chlorination in the 1-position of naphthalene (156) relative to benzene is 6.6×10^4. However, recent work of Olah (579) on nitration and alkylation indicates that an oriented π-bonded transition state may be more important than the σ-complex in many electrophilic reactions. Thus the relative reactivity of condensed

ring systems and benzene will depend on the mechanism of the
reaction and the nature of the intermediate electrophilic species.

Naphthalene has been alkylated with olefins in the presence of
metal halides and metal halide complexes, protonic acids and solid
oxide catalysts under conditions similar to those used in the alkylation of benzene.

Direct comparisons of the reactivity of naphthalene and other
condensed ring systems with benzene derivatives in Friedel-Crafts
alkylations have not been made. The reviewers have found no
reports of kinetic studies of these reactions in the literature. How·
ever, benzene has been used as a solvent for naphthalene alkylations
with cetene, pentene, and ethylene. The cetene and pentene
alkylations (532) were carried out in the presence of an aluminum
chloride–t-butyl chloride catalyst system; the naphthalene was
dissolved in a four- to five-fold molar excess of benzene. Benzene
was untouched, whereas high yields of alkylnaphthalenes were
obtained. The phosphoric acid catalyzed condensation of ethylene
with one mole of naphthalene dissolved in three moles of benzene was
accompanied by a small conversion of benzene (138).

Intact alkylation of naphthalene with diisobutylene in the presence
of sulfuric acid was claimed by Bruson and Stein (86), but the products were not characterized.   Although there are no published data
on the use of aluminum chloride for the reaction involving diisobutylene, Andreev and Petrov (15) reported intact alkylation with the
hydrochloride of diisobutylene at 0°.

In their study of intact alkylation (see Section II-1-H-b-(1))
Sanford et al. '(681) found that 1-methylnaphthalene was alkylated
with diisobutylene in the presence of hydrogen fluoride about as
readily as toluene and o-xylene. Substitution theory would predict
a much higher reactivity for 1-methylnaphthalene. However, the
bulky t-octyl cation or catalyst complex would encounter steric
resistance in attacking at the activated 4-position or the other open
α-positions. Therefore, it is not surprising that 1-methylnaphtha-
lene does not exhibit greater activity than toluene.

It is clear that the 1-position in naphthalene is considerably more
reactive than the 2-position for electrophilic substitution. However,
the majority of papers on Friedel-Crafts alkylation of naphthalene
with olefins as well as alkyl halides and alcohols report the exclusive
or predominant formation of the 2-isomer. For example, Price and
Ciskowski (647) and Pokrovskaya (638) report only 2-cyclohexyl-
naphthalene from boron fluoride and aluminum chloride catalyzed
condensation of cyclohexene and naphthalene. Enos (186) obtained

an α/β ratio of 1/24 on condensing propene and naphthalene in the presence of aluminum chloride at 100°. However, Topchiev *et al.* (844) obtained isopropylnaphthalenes having an α/β ratio of 4/1 by using silica–alumina. Increases in temperature resulted in larger amounts of the β-isomer along with increased disproportionation.

The preponderance of β-isomers generally reported is apparently a consequence of (1) isomerization of the initially formed α-isomers and (2) steric hindrance in the α-positions. Strong Friedel-Crafts catalysts such as aluminum chloride–hydrogen chloride would be expected to promote isomerization. Furthermore, catalyst–olefin complexes which are bulky would tend to favor attack at the β-position because of steric interference. However, the failure to report α-substitution in some cases may be attributed to insensitive analytical procedures.

Where steric hindrance at the α-position is a minor influence and mild catalysts and conditions are used, the predominant dialkylated naphthalene is the 1,4-disubstituted product. When, for reasons outlined above, monosubstitution at the β-position predominates, 2,6-dialkylnaphthalene is the major product. Pokrovskaya *et al.* (638) obtained a mixture of at least two dicyclohexylnaphthalenes from the aluminum chloride catalyzed condensation of cyclohexene and naphthalene. One of the two isomers was a high-melting solid which was dehydrogenated to diphenylnaphthalene (100). Price and Tomasek (648) proved by unambiguous synthesis that the structure of the diphenylnaphthalene obtained by Pokrovskaya *et al.* was the 2,6-isomer. Buu-Hoï and Cagniant (100) claimed to have synthesized only the 2,6-dicyclohexylnaphthalene in an aluminum chloride condensation. 1,4-Dicyclohexylnaphthalene was identified by Price and Ciskowski (647) as the product of alkylation of naphthalene with cyclohexanol in the presence of boron fluoride. This product was probably also present in the product mixture obtained by Pokrovskaya *et al.*

Unfortunately, other than the cyclohexylation studies discussed above, there appear to be no reports of isomer identification of dialkylates obtained with other olefins. However, Crawford and Glessman (145a) proved by unambiguous methods that 2,6- and 2,7-di-*t*-butylnaphthalenes were formed by alkylation of naphthalene with *t*-butyl chloride. Even though some of the other eight possible isomers may have been present and overlooked, it is unlikely that they would have been formed in substantial quantity because in these other isomers one or both of the *t*-butyl groups would occupy sterically hindered positions. Studies of isobutylene alkylation of naphthalene have not been reported, but the results should be similar to those obtained with t-butyl chloride. Although only the 1,4- and the 2,6-dialkyl products have been reported for the alkylation of naphthalene with cyclohexene, propene, or other normal olefins, it is believed that modern methods of analysis would reveal the presence of the 2,7-isomer.

The rule, established for benzene substitution, that no more than two secondary substituents derived from normal olefins can be introduced on adjacent aromatic carbon atoms is equally valid for naphthalene. In their classic work on hydrogen fluoride catalyzed condensations Calcott, Tinker, and Weinmayr (110), obtained a 98% yield of tetraisopropyl derivative on exhaustive propylation of naphthalene. Michel (517) reported the isolation of tetrabutyl- and tetraamylnaphthalenes from aluminum chloride condensations of 2-butene and 1-pentene with naphthalene.

Theoretically, as many as six groups could be introduced without placing three secondary alkyl groups adjacent to each other (I, II).

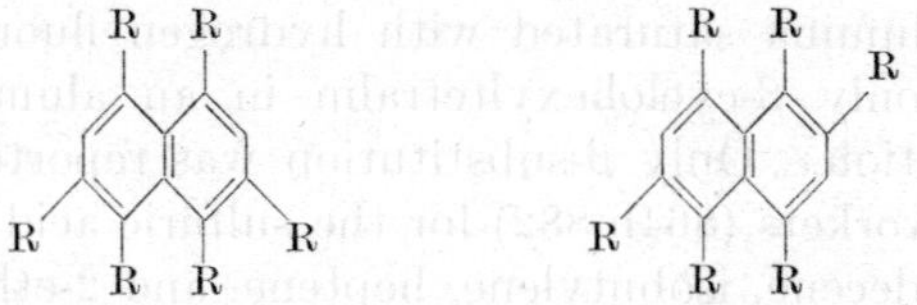

However, in these structures two adjacent secondary alkyl groups are positioned next to a fused carbon atom. This may involve steric effects somewhat similar to the 1,2-diisopropyl-3-methyl grouping in the benzene system, a grouping which has not as yet been demonstrated in benzene alkylation products.

Cyclohexylation of naphthalene follows the same rules as alkylation with acyclic olefins. Pokrovskaya and co-workers obtained products containing only four cyclohexyl groups on naphthalene (638) and three on 1-methylnaphthalene (633). They used aluminum chloride as the catalyst. However, this group of workers reported they had obtained pentacyclopentylnaphthalene (641) and tetracyclopentyl-1-methylnaphthalene (632) by alkylating tetracyclopentylnaphthalene and tricyclopentyl-1-methylnaphthalene with cyclopentene. The reviewers believe, however, these may have been products resulting from alkylation by dimers of cyclopentene or cyclohexene.

B. Tetralin and Indane
(Tables 24, 30)

Tetralin and indane have been alkylated by means of the usual Friedel-Crafts catalysts employing conditions normally used in alkylations of benzene. Olefins are reported to give better yields than alcohols or ethers (423). There are no published data on the relative reactivity of tetralin and indane. However, both of these compounds are sensitive to strong catalysts. Kutz and co-workers (423) found that extensive condensation side reactions occurred under the influence of alumina–silicate and aluminum chloride. Schroeter (722) reported that aluminum chloride converted tetralin into a variety of products including anthracene, hydrogenated phenanthrene, and ditetralyl.

Alkylation of indane or tetralin can take place in the α- or β-positions. There have been numerous reports in which only the β-substituted isomers were reported. Shuikin and co-workers (744,748) reported only β-substitutions of tetralin with nonene, heptenes, and amylenes in the presence of zinc chloride, silica–alumina, or alumina saturated with hydrogen fluoride. Bodroux (66) isolated only β-cyclohexyltetralin in an aluminum chloride catalyzed reaction. Only β-substitution was reported by Pokrovskaya and co-workers (864b,882) for the sulfuric acid catalyzed condensation of decene, isobutylene, heptene, and 2-ethylhexene with indane. However, Pokrovskaya and co-workers did isolate both isomers in the alkylation of tetralin with cyclohexene using aluminum chloride below room temperature.

Kutz and co-workers (423) investigated the alkylation of tetralin and indane with olefins and other alkylating agents in the presence of silica–alumina, phosphoric acid on kieselguhr, and hydrogen fluoride. All products were mixtures of the two possible isomers and the ratio of products depended on the catalyst, conditions and the olefin used. Because the data of these authors appear to be the most reliable, they are summarized in Table VI. The indane isomers were determined by ultraviolet adsorption analysis of the mixture of acids obtained by permanganate oxidation. The tetralins were dehydrogenated with sulfur and the products analyzed by infra-red and ultraviolet spectroscopy.

The distributions of ethyl- and isopropylindanes obtained under the conditions shown in Table VI are probably the equilibrium distributions at 300°. The large amount of 4-substituted indanes indicates that steric interference with the isopropyl group is not significant. On the other hand, the results of tetralin alkylation over a low alumina, silica–alumina catalyst, indicates considerable steric interference in introducing an isopropyl group in the 5-position

TABLE VI. Isomers formed from indane and tetralin

Product	Catalyst	Temp. (°C)	Pressure (psig)	Isomer distribution		
				−4	−5	−6
Ethylindane	25% Al_2O_3–75% SiO_2	300	400	26	74	
Isopropylindane	25% Al_2O_3–75% SiO_2	300	400	33	67	
Ethyltetralin	1% Al_2O_3–99% SiO_2	300	400		72	28
Isopropyltetralin	1% Al_2O_3–99% SiO_2	250	400		6	94
Isopropyltetralin	$AlCl_3$	20	15		1	99
Isopropyltetralin	95% H_2SO_4	10	15		45	55
Cyclohexyltetralin	1% Al_2O_3–99% SiO_2	250	400		53	47

of tetralin. The results with cyclohexene would seem to indicate that the cyclohexyl group has a much lower steric requirement than the isopropyl group, but isomerization may be the critical factor here. At low temperatures the equilibrium product must be almost entirely the 6-substituted tetralin. Almost complete isomerization of the 5- to the 6-substituted tetralin appears to have occurred with aluminum chloride. The milder sulfuric acid catalyst gave high yields of 5-isopropyltetralin.

Polyalkylation of tetralin and indane was investigated by Pokrovskaya and co-workers (638,639,640,641). Dicyclohexylindane obtained by aluminum chloride alkylation was identified as the 5,6-substituted product. The authors obtained the tricyclohexyla- ted product which they suggested was probably the 4,5,6-isomer (640). If true, this result is contrary to the rule that three secondary alkyl groups cannot be on consecutive positions on an aromatic ring. In similar alkylations with propene, 1-butene, and 2-methyl-2- butene, the maximum number of groups introduced into indane was three isopropyl groups, two s-butyl groups and one amyl group (two isomers), respectively.

A rather interesting result, reported by Pokrovskaya and Sushchik (641) was the synthesis of tetracyclopentyltetralin by the condensa- tion of tetralin and cyclopentene in the presence of aluminum chloride. This would mean that the substituents must be in the 5,6,7,8- positions. However, the reviewers believe the alternative possibility exists that the product may in fact be a disubstituted derivative formed *via* dimerization prior to alkylation:

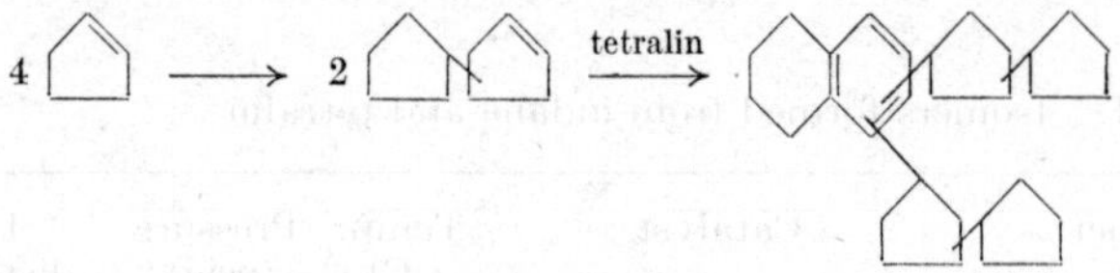

C. Tricyclics

(Table 32)

Only very few papers have been published on alkylation of tricyclic hydrocarbons. Fair yields of alkylate have been obtained at low and moderately high temperatures with aluminum chloride, sulfuric acid, phosphoric acid, boron fluoride–phosphoric acid, and activated clay. Severe conditions must be avoided because of the tendency of fused ring aromatics to undergo extensive condensation reactions. The tricyclics alkylated include acenaphthene, anthracene, phenanthrene, and fluorene.

There is a paucity of data on the distribution of isomers. It was suggested in one paper that cyclohexylation of anthracene in the presence of sulfuric acid, yields the 1- and 2-monosubstituted products (99). Dicyclohexylation of phenanthrene in the presence of aluminum chloride formed both 3,9- and 3,10-dicyclohexylphenanthrene (100). Substitution at the 5-position of acenaphthene was reported for both cyclopentylation and cyclohexylation with aluminum chloride (100,109).

D. Polyphenyl Derivatives

(Table 31)

Biphenyl has been alkylated in high yield with various aluminum chloride catalysts, boron fluoride–phosphoric acid, activated clay, and sulfuric acid.

Alkylation with 2-butene at 80° in the presence of a complex derived from aluminum chloride and phosphoric acid ($AlCl_2 \cdot H_2PO_4$) afforded 70% of *s*-butylbiphenyl (940), but the product obtained with a boron fluoride–phosphoric acid catalyst consisted of a 58/42 mixture of the *t*-butyl and *s*-butyl derivatives. Apparently some of the *n*-butene feed undergoes isomerization to isobutylene prior to alkylation. This phenomenon was noted by Pines *et al.* (618) when they used zinc chloride–alumina as a catalyst for alkylating benzene with

2-butene, and by Baev *et al.* (37) who employed a boron fluoride–phosphoric acid catalyst containing 5% of sulfuric acid.

A few alkylation experiments using standard catalysts have been carried out with terphenyl, diphenylmethane, bibenzyl, and polystyrene, but the products were poorly characterized.

III. Alkylation of Phenols and Derivatives

1. Theory

Because of the strong nucleophilic activity of the phenols, mild catalysts and operating conditions are usually employed for alkylating them with olefins. However, two or three complications are usually encountered. One is the ready formation of ethers, especially when mild conditions are employed. A second complication is the ease with which the phenol nucleus is attacked by certain catalysts, *e.g.*, sulfuric acid. A third is the tendency of the hydroxyl group to complex the catalyst.

Early workers (537,539,554) believed that nuclear alkylation of phenols involved the formation of an ether as an intermediate step followed by rearrangement of the alkyl group from the oxygen to the nucleus. As evidence for this they cited the easy formation of ethers using alkylation catalysts, and the fact that such ethers could be isomerized to give the corresponding alkyl phenol.

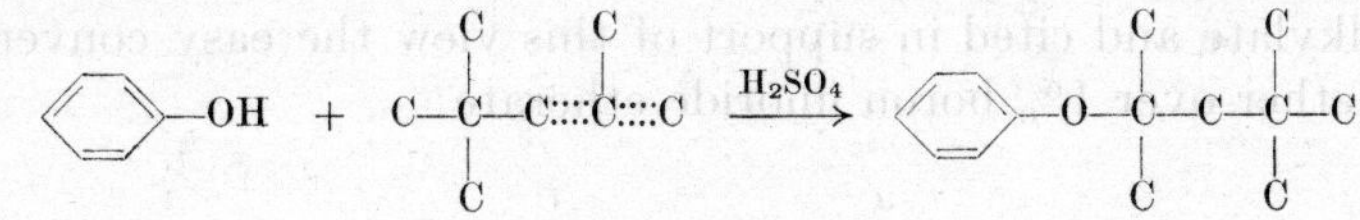

$$\langle\!\!\!\!\!\!\!\!\!\rangle\!\!-OH + C-\overset{C}{\underset{C}{C}}-C::::C::::C \xrightarrow{H_2SO_4} \langle\!\!\!\!\!\!\!\!\!\rangle\!\!-O-\overset{C}{\underset{C}{C}}-C-\overset{C}{\underset{C}{C}}-C \quad (556)$$

$$\langle\!\!\!\!\!\!\!\!\!\rangle\!\!-OH + C=C-C \xrightarrow[0°]{BF_3} \langle\!\!\!\!\!\!\!\!\!\rangle\!\!-O-\overset{C}{\underset{C}{C}}-C \quad (777)$$

$$(54\%)$$

$$\langle\!\!\!\!\!\!\!\!\!\rangle\!\!-O-\overset{C}{\underset{C}{C}}-\overset{C}{\underset{C}{C}}-C \xrightarrow[HCl]{ZnCl_2} C-\overset{C}{\underset{C}{C}}-C-\overset{C}{\underset{C}{C}}-\langle\!\!\!\!\!\!\!\!\!\rangle\!\!-OH \quad (537,554)$$

$$\langle\!\!\!\!\!\!\!\!\!\rangle\!\!-O-\overset{C}{C}-C \xrightarrow[75-85°]{BF_3} \langle\!\!\!\!\!\!\!\!\!\rangle\!\!-OH \quad (65\%) \quad (776)$$
with side chain $-\overset{C}{\underset{C}{C}}-C$

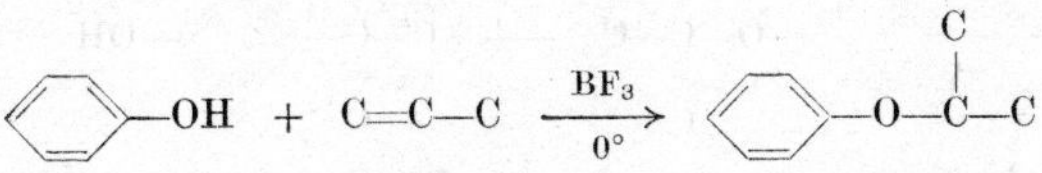

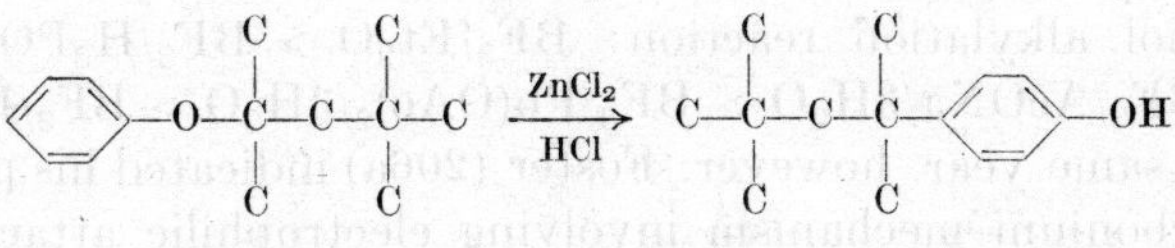

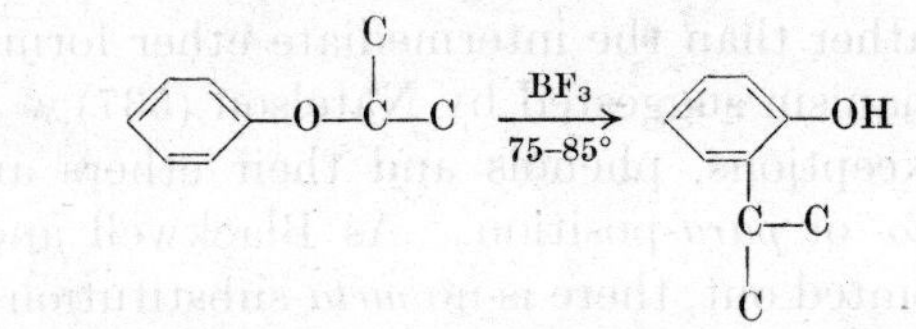

4*

However, later investigators reported evidence purporting to show that the alkyl group did not necessarily travel this route since they found that anisole condensed readily with propene in the presence of boron fluoride to form 2-isopropylanisole (778) and phenetole was propylated by employing phosphoric acid as catalyst (340). It was not long before it was generally accepted (552) that ether formation is not necessarily an intermediate step in nuclear alkylation with olefins. It is interesting, however, that the above lines of proof did not eliminate the possibility that ether formation could function as an intermediate as follows:

$$\text{C}_6\text{H}_5\text{—OH} + \text{C}=\overset{\text{C}}{\text{C}}\text{—C} \longrightarrow \text{C}_6\text{H}_5\text{—O—}\overset{\text{C}}{\underset{\text{C}}{\text{C}}}\text{—C}$$

$$\downarrow \overset{\text{C}}{\text{C}}=\text{C—C}$$

$$\text{C—}\overset{\text{C}}{\underset{\text{C}}{\text{C}}}\text{—C}_6\text{H}_4\text{—OH} + \text{C}=\overset{\text{C}}{\text{C}}\text{—C} \longleftarrow \text{C—}\overset{\text{C}}{\underset{\text{C}}{\text{C}}}\text{—C}_6\text{H}_4\text{—O—}\overset{\text{C}}{\underset{\text{C}}{\text{C}}}\text{—C}$$

Further uncertainty arose from the report of Topchiev and co-workers (863) who studied molecular combinations of boron fluoride for the alkylation of phenols with isobutylene. These authors appeared to accept the intermediacy of ethers in the formation of the final alkylate and cited in support of this view the easy conversion of the ether over 1% boron fluoride etherate:

$$\text{C}_6\text{H}_5\text{—O—}\overset{\text{C}}{\underset{\text{C}}{\text{C}}}\text{—C} \longrightarrow \text{C—}\overset{\text{C}}{\underset{\text{C}}{\text{C}}}\text{—C}_6\text{H}_4\text{—OH}$$

Incidentally, they found the following order of catalytic activity for the phenol alkylation reaction: $BF_3/Et_2O > BF_3/H_3PO_4 > BF_3/H_2O > BF_3/AcONa/3H_2O > BF_3/Pb(OAc)_2/3H_2O > BF_3/Pb(OAc)_2$.

In the same year, however, Foster (206a) indicated his preference for a carbonium mechanism involving electrophilic attack on the nucleus of phenol rather than the intermediate ether formation and rearrangement mechanism suggested by Natelson (537).

With but rare exceptions, phenols and their ethers are always attacked in the *ortho*- or *para*-position. As Blackwell and Hickinbottom (54) have pointed out, there is no *meta*-substitution in phenol alkylations "even with substituting groups which are extremely reactive by H. C. Brown's classification."

[*Note added in Proof:* However, a recent Belgian patent (122a) claims improved yields of *m*-derivatives by alkylating phenols with isobutylene or diisobutylene at 170–200° in the presence of Fuller's earth impregnated with concentrated sulfuric acid. In a slightly earlier patent (580a) Olin showed that *p*-secondary and *p*-tertiary alkylphenols could be converted to the *meta*-isomers by heating at 100–200° in the presence of a strong acid and an activated clay.]

2. Phenols, Cresols, and Dimethylphenols

A. Thermal Alkylation

When phenol is alkylated with cyclohexene at 350° without catalyst, the reaction produces, according to Skraup *et al.* (766), 2-cyclohexylphenol in rather poor yields, and a dicyclohexylphenol. The latter compound could not be identified as 2,6-dicyclohexylphenol. According to patents of the Rheinische Campherfabrik (765,767), thymol (3-methyl-6-isopropylphenol) is obtained when propene and *m*-cresol are heated under pressure without a catalyst at 330–350° for 20–24 hours. A patent of the N.V. Bataafsche Petroleum Mij. (568) claims that phenols have been alkylated with olefins ranging from C_7 to C_{22} without a catalyst, but the structure of the alkyl phenols was not reported.

Goldsmith, Schlatter, and Toland (237) recently reported on the results of a fairly extensive study of the uncatalyzed thermal alkylation of phenol with a variety of olefins. At 320° under pressures ranging from 34 to 248 atm., isobutylene, 1-butene, and cyclohexene gave largely the *ortho*-alkylate whereas ethylene and propene afforded a variety of products including di- and trialkylphenols and phenolic ethers. These authors indicate that *ortho*-alkylation *via* the alkyl phenyl ether is unlikely. They prefer a mechanism involving alkylation and transfer of the proton occurring as a concerted process through a transitory six-membered ring.

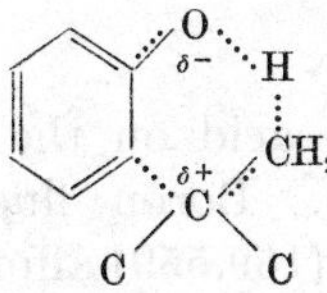

B. Alkylation with n-Olefins

a. Ethylene (Tables 35, 42)

Paralleling the situation with aromatic hydrocarbons, phenol has not been ethylated using sulfuric acid as catalyst (487). One patent reported ethylation and propylation of m-cresol using 40% fuming sulfuric acid, but with no yield data (55). No doubt at the high temperatures employed (90–160°) the cresol is sulfonated and the actual substrate consists of cresolsulfonic acids. m-Cresolsulfonic acid (654) and sulfonic acid ion exchange resins (148), however, will catalyze the propylation of phenols.

High yields of ethylphenols were obtained with aluminum halides at 60° (450), and fair yields with phosphoric acid at 225° (340), aluminum phenoxide at 300–320°, (396,397) and aluminum–barium chloride catalyst at 340° (815).

Missing from the usual list of metallic halide and protonic acid catalysts are these: ferric chloride, zinc chloride, hydrogen fluoride, boron fluoride ($\pm$ water or ether or phosphoric acid), and silica alumina.

Boron fluoride–hydrochloride was claimed (283) to give ethylated cresol ethers at 200°. Phosphoric acid gave a mixture of ethylated phenols, phenetole, and ethylated phenetole (340).

b. Propene (Tables 36, 42)

Several catalysts have been used for propylating phenol, the one really noticeable omission being the ferric halides. A few unusual catalysts may be mentioned: boric acid–oxalic acid was claimed for the propylation of m-cresol at 140° (883) and 70% perchloric acid at 75° (159).

At 0° boron fluoride gives a mixture of 41% 2-isopropylphenol and 54% isopropyl phenyl ether (777). At 20–40° the ether is further propylated, e.g.,

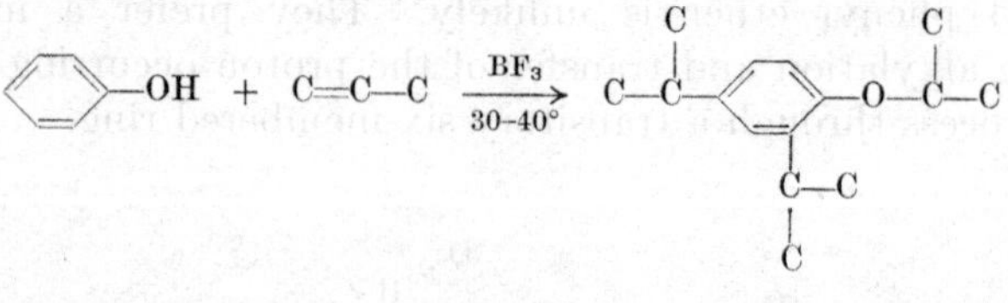

Boron fluoride–phosphoric acid on the other hand, gives 74% of monoisopropylphenol (28). Boron fluoride dihydrate (234) and dihydroxyfluoroboric acid (169,559) afford good yields of isopropylphenols. Aluminum chloride (450) affords a high yield (75%) of isopropylphenol while most other catalysts gave only fair yields.

The zinc and aluminum phenoxide catalysts which were used with a high propene–phenol ratio to produce good yields (53–61%) of 2,6-diisopropylphenol (194,396,397) could probably be used to good advantage with a lower ratio for the production of the 2-isopropyl derivative. Aluminum phenoxide was used in propylating m-cresol to afford 63% thymol (3-methyl-6-isopropylphenol) plus a small amount of the 3-methyl-2-isopropyl isomer. 3-Methyl-2,6-diisopropylphenol was also obtained in 14% yield (816). Magnesium phenoxide was patented for the ortho-isopropylation of o-cresol (194).

Among the solid catalysts, silica gel promoted with an alkyl halide gave a fairly good yield of the propylated isopropyl phenyl ether in a batch reactor at 150–200° (709), whereas silica–alumina produced 36% of 2-isopropylphenol at 160–238° in a flow reactor (729). Two other solid catalysts gave interesting results: nickel molybdite affording mono- and diisopropylphenol at 100–160° (198) and calcium dihydrogen phosphate giving 2-isopropylphenol and its isopropyl ether at 300° (684).

c. n-*Butene and higher* (Tables 37, 39, 40, 42)

Very few data are available on alkylations with n-butene and its higher homologs. Boron fluoride hydrate is reported to give good yields of mono- and higher s-butylphenols (234).

The reaction of 2-pentene and phenol catalyzed by boron trifluoride etherate at room temperature gave 68% of s-amyl phenyl ether, while at 52° the product consisted of s-amylphenol and its s-amyl ether (937).

The reaction of 1-nonene and phenol at 100–110° in the presence of a sulfonic acid cation exchange resin afforded 68% of nonylphenol (453).

When heated with the aluminum phenoxide catalyst at 300°, 1-decene and phenol produced 49% of "2-(2-decyl)-phenol" (397).

Another instance of preferential attack in the ortho-position is seen in the alkylation with 1-hexadecene using a fluoride-promoted silica–alumina catalyst at 180–190°. The monoalkylate, obtained in 53% yield, was claimed to have an ortho/para ratio of 92/8 (162).

C. Alkylation with Isoolefins

The usual array of catalysts has been investigated for the reaction of phenol and the cresols with isobutylene, isoamylene, and other monomeric branched olefins.

a. Phenol (Tables 38, 39, 40)

A great deal of work has been done with sulfuric acid catalysts. By varying the amount of acid, the temperature, and the contact time, high yields of one of the following are obtained from the corresponding isoolefins: *t*-butyl ethers of phenols (794), *t*-butyl-phenol (539,602,150), *t*-amylphenol (539) or 4-*t*-amylphenol (16,87). Topchiev *et al.* reported that boron fluoride, boron fluoride–phosphoric acid, boron fluoride etherate, aluminum chloride–sulfuric acid complex, aluminum chloride, and 75% sulfuric acid gave 95, 90, 89, 68, 64, and 68% respectively, of 4-*t*-amylphenol (857).

In most instances the 4-isomer is the main monoalkylation product, but it is possible to maximize the 2-isomer by using special conditions, *e.g.*, small amount of catalyst [sulfuric acid (71)] incomplete conversion [aluminum chloride (92)], or unusual catalyst [phosphorus oxychloride (87) or silica–alumina (730)].

It is possible to promote selective alkylation as shown by Dalin and co-workers (150). These authors were able, using 1% of concentrated sulfuric acid at 100°, to obtain an 80% yield of 4-*t*-butyl-phenol by selective alkylation of phenol with a feed containing only 5% isobutylene in admixture with 91% *n*-butene.

Toluenesulfonic acid (924) and various sulfonic acid ion exchange resins (898,148,453) have been used to good advantage in producing 4-*t*-butyl- and 4-*t*-amylphenols.

Several unusual catalysts have been claimed including iodine which gave 97% 4-*t*-butylphenol at 105° (288), fluorosulfonic acid producing the same product in 84% yield at 25° (72) and aluminum chloride–boric acid giving 64% at 35–80° (88).

Long aging favors the 2,4- over the 2,6-isomer which is formed preferentially earlier in the reaction catalyzed by aluminum chloride (92). Aluminum phenoxide gives very high yields of the 2,6-isomers (397) (see Section III-9).

Rosenwald (664) prepared *t*-butyl ethers of various phenols in yields up to about 33% by heating the phenols and isobutylene in an autoclave at 75° in the presence of chloroacetic, oxalic, and trinitrobenzoic acid as catalysts. However, Stevens (794) found sulfuric acid a very satisfactory catalyst for preparing *t*-alkyl aryl ethers in fairly high yields. He simply passed isobutylene at relatively low temperatures, *e.g.*, 25°, into phenol containing only a trace (*e.g.*, 0.00242 mole/mole phenol) of sulfuric acid. In this reaction the temperature is important with both dilute or concentrated sulfuric acid. Very little, if any, nuclear alkylation takes place at − 10°;

an appreciable amount occurs at 10°; and dialkylation becomes noticeable at 45–59°.

An abstract of Weingaertner's (914a) work on the boron fluoride catalyzed alkylation of phenol with various branched olefins indicated that (1) the *ortho*-alkyl derivative is formed initially regardless of catalyst concentration, (2) high concentrations of catalyst cause rapid rearrangement of the *ortho*-isomer to the *para* and (3) high concentrations cause disproportionation of the 2,4-dialkyl product to form *ortho*- and *para*-monoalkyl derivatives.

b. *Cresols and dimethylphenols* (Tables 42, 44)

Stevens (794) utilized very small amounts of sulfuric acid varying in concentration from 10% to 96% to obtain high yields of 6-*t*-butyl- or 4,6-di-*t*-butyl-*m*-cresol. Isagulyants (347) obtained 43–46% of 2,6-di-*t*-butyl-*p*-cresol by utilizing a cation exchange resin at 70–80°.

A few unusual catalysts have been mentioned. Perchloric acid (70%) catalyzed the reaction of 1-octene with *o*-cresol at 100° to give 80% of *s*-octyl-*o*-cresols (159). Aluminum perchlorate gave an excellent yield of 4-*s*-dodecyl derivative in the alkylation of *o*-cresol with dodecene at 90–95° (267).

Stevens (791) described a combination dialkylation–dealkylation process for separating *m*- and *p*-cresols, or mixtures of xylenols and ethylphenols. He dialkylated these phenolic mixtures with iso-butylene and separated the *t*-butylated phenols by fractional distillation with or without extraction with alkali. The individual parent phenols were then recovered by dealkylation. The alkylation step utilized 3 to 5% (based on phenol) of sulfuric acid as catalyst at a temperature of about 70°, and the debutylation step 0.2% at refluxing temperature. Other catalysts such as aromatic sulfonic acids or sulfuric acid esters were suggested as means to obtain faster dealkylation rates (801).

m-Cresol appears to undergo dialkylation more readily than *p*-cresol in competitive alkylation with isobutylene (791). This is in accord with results reported for competitive alkylations with *t*-butyl chloride–aluminum chloride (285) and with isobutyl alcohol–sulfuric acid (510). The explanation offered for this behavior is that first the hydroxy group directs substitution to the *para*-position, and secondly, since this position is already occupied in *p*-cresol, there is a preference for *m*-cresol alkylation. However, this ignores the role of steric hindrance. In view of the steric resistance encountered in *t*-butylation *ortho* to the methyl groups in toluene or *p*-xylene (see Section II-1-G-a), one would expect similar hindrance to the insertion of a *t*-butyl group in the 4-position in *m*-cresol.

Steric effects prevent the insertion of a *t*-butyl group between two methyl groups, or between a methyl and a hydroxyl group placed *meta* to each other (791). For example, 3,5-dimethylphenol is not alkylated by isobutylene (590b).

In the presence of aluminum chloride–hydrogen chloride, *m*-cresol and isobutylene react at 90° to yield 78% 6-*t*-butyl-*m*-cresol (88). Phosphorus oxychloride at 58–61° affords the same product in 60% yield (87). Furthermore, even when the *para*-position is completely unobstructed, as in *ortho*-cresol, sulfuric acid effects *t*-butylation extensively in the 6-position (797). Therefore, it may be concluded that (1) the tendency towards *para*-substitution is neither strong nor consistent, and (2) given a choice, the *t*-butyl will insert *ortho* to the hydroxyl rather than *ortho* to a methyl group.

The picture is complicated somewhat by the fact that *t*-butyl and *t*-amyl groups do attack *ortho* to a methyl group where this position on the ring is also activated by the hydroxy group:

(1)

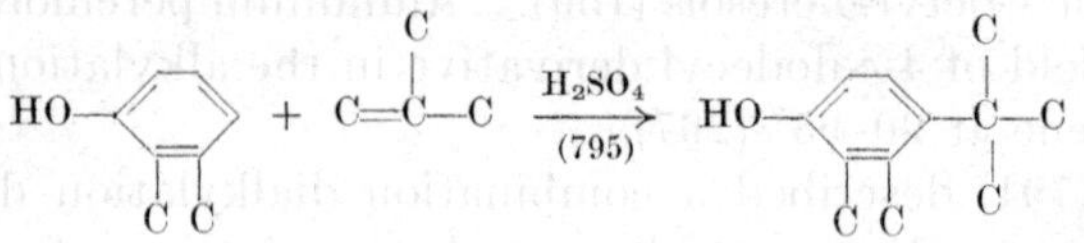

(2)

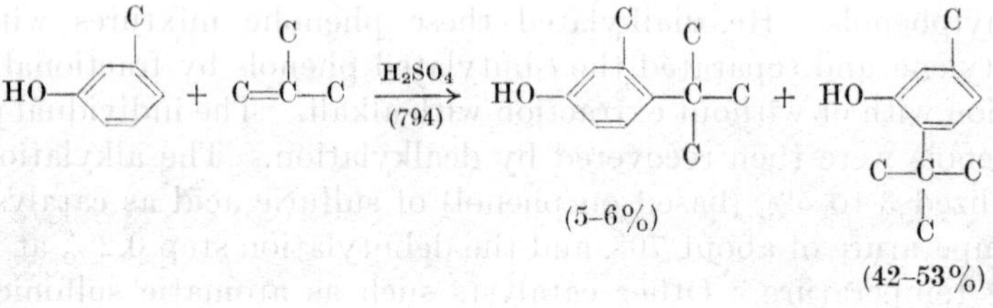

(5–6%)

(42–53%)

(3)

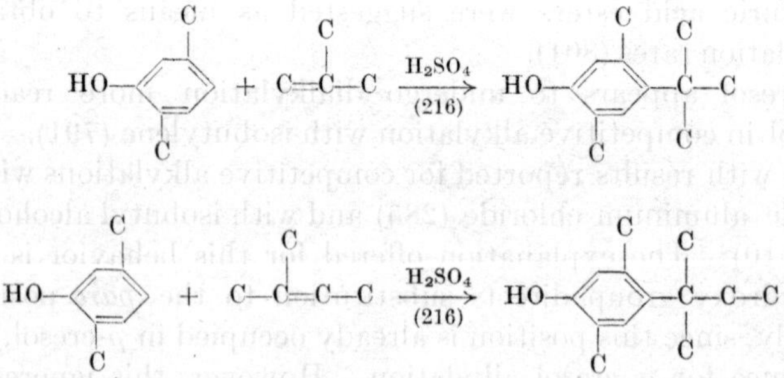

Reaction 1 was also studied by Parc (590b) who obtained 27% of the 4,6-di-*t*-butyl derivative as well as 55% of the 6-*t*-butyl derivative.

In Parc's hands (590a) reaction 2 yielded 73% of the 6-t-butyl derivative, which on further treatment with isobutylene afforded 26% of the 4,6-di-t-butyl derivative.

Thus in the production of the di-t-butylated cresols, the composition of the alkylate and the ratio of unreacted *meta*- and *para*-cresols seems not to be kinetically controlled but probably represents an equilibrium mixture resulting from the transalkylation ("homogenation") reaction taking place concurrently with the alkylation reaction.

Malchick and Hannan (471) clearly depicted the numerous side reactions which may occur in connection with sterically hindered alkylations. They obtained the 2-t-amyl derivative (A) in high yield when small or moderate amounts (1–25 mol. %) of boron fluoride were used in alkylating p-cresol with 2-methyl-2-butene. However, many of the side reactions noted earlier in p-xylene alkylation (see Section II-1-G) occurred when larger amounts (50 mol. %) of boron fluoride were used. These included side-chain isomerization giving rise to (B) and disproportionation of the olefin dimer resulting in (C).

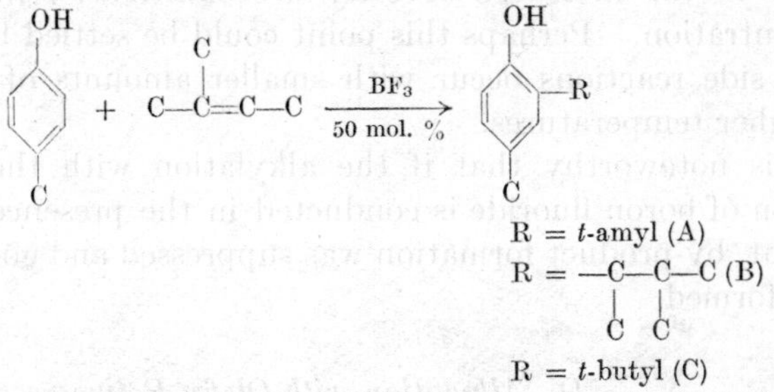

Hydrogen transfer, dealkylation, and realkylation result in the formation of (D), (E), (F), and (G).

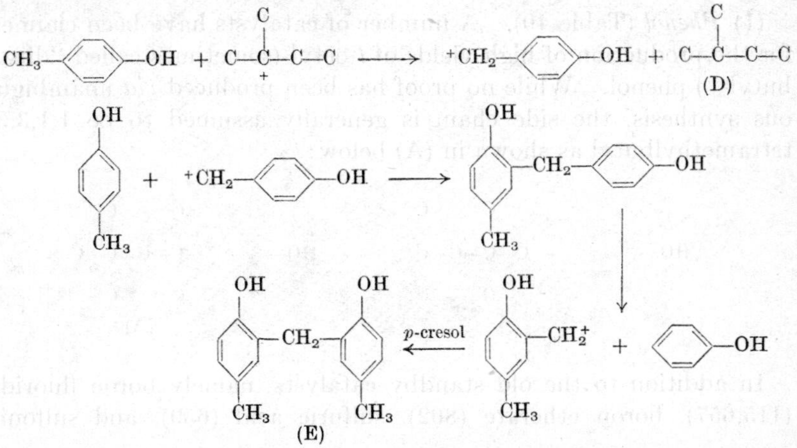

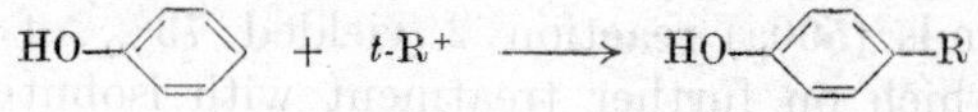

$$HO-\langle\!\!\!\!\!\bigcirc\!\!\!\!\!\rangle + \textit{t}\text{-R}^+ \longrightarrow HO-\langle\!\!\!\!\!\bigcirc\!\!\!\!\!\rangle-R$$

R = t-butyl (F)
R = t-amyl (G)

When p-$C^{14}H_3C_6H_4OH$ was employed in the reaction, the methylene carbon in (E) was radioactive, thus showing that it was originally the methyl carbon of p-cresol.

Malchick and Hannan suggested that high concentrations of boron fluoride inhibit normal alkylation by forming a complex with most of the p-cresol. The complexed p-cresol then undergoes hydrogen transfer and other side reactions. This assumption is supported by the observation that 2-t-amyl-p-cresol does not exhibit the rapid absorption of boron fluoride shown by phenol. Apparently the OBF_3 group cannot exist *ortho* to a t-alkyl group because of steric effects, and this prevents attack by a t-carbonium ion in the *ortho*-positions.

The reviewers believe that the side reactions may also be attributed to the increased severity of conditions, *e.g.*, high catalyst concentration. Perhaps this point could be settled by noting if the same side reactions occur with smaller amounts of boron fluoride at higher temperatures.

It is noteworthy that if the alkylation with the high concentration of boron fluoride is conducted in the presence of isopentane solvent, by-product formation was suppressed and good yields of (A) were formed.

D. Alkylation with Olefin Polymers

a. Diisobutylene

(1) *Phenol* (Table 40). A number of catalysts have been claimed for the production of high yields of t-octyl-(sometimes called "diisobutyl-") phenol. While no proof has been produced *via* unambiguous synthesis, the side chain is generally assumed to be 1,1,3,3-tetramethylbutyl as shown in (A) below:

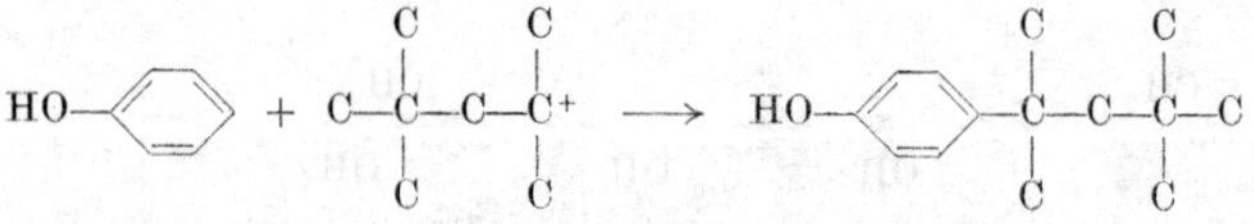

(A)

In addition to the old standby catalysts, namely boron fluoride (115,657), boron etherate (862), sulfuric acid (659), and sulfonic acid ion-exchange resins (250,453), other more novel ones such as cupric chloride (281), stannic chloride–hydrogen chloride (90), phosphorus oxychloride (206), tetraphosphoric acid on Fuller's earth (23), and boric acid–oxalic acid (39) give good yields of the t-octyl derivative, chiefly the para-isomer.

A number of workers who used sulfuric acid at room temperature obtained high yields of t-octylphenol; however, in one instance, only t-octyl phenyl ether was reported (556).

Under more severe conditions and/or with more active catalysts, cleavage ensues and the main product is t-butylphenol. This was observed with hydrogen fluoride at 0° (758), aluminum chloride at 80° (774), ferric bromide–hydrogen bromide or ferric chloride–hydrogen chloride at 120–150° (161), or with activated clay at 170–182° (607). However, this cleavage propensity can be controlled (a) by using lower temperatures, e.g., ferric chloride–hydrogen chloride at 90° gave 92% of (A) (88), or (b) by using lower concentrations of catalyst, e.g., 70% aqueous hydrogen fluoride afforded 4-t-octyl at 0° (758). No doubt aluminum chloride would also have yielded intact alkylate if used at temperatures lower than the 80° cited above.

With a high ratio of diisobutylene to phenol, one can obtain di-t-octylphenol in 55% yield (115). Aluminum phenoxide seems to be a mediocre catalyst (397).

(2) *Higher phenols* (Tables 42, 44). Sulfuric acid afforded t-octyl derivatives of *ortho*- (551) or *para*-cresol (277) and β-naphthol (4). With an excess of diisobutylene, boron fluoride etherate gave a fair yield of 2,6-di-t-octyl-p-cresol (384). Cleavage products, e.g., 4-t-butyl-o-cresol and 6-t-butyl-m-cresol were obtained from the respective cresols and diisobutylene by using ferric chloride–hydrogen chloride at 115–120° (161).

Roberts and Rose (654a) were able to separate 2,4-dimethylphenol from the 2,5-isomer by treatment with diisobutylene in the presence of sulfuric acid. Distillation afforded unreacted 2,5-isomer and octylated-2,4-dimethylphenol.

b. *Triisobutylene and tetraisobutylene* (Table 40)

Few data are reported involving alkylation of phenols with these oligomers, and all indicate cleavage. Triisobutylene in the presence of 70–100% hydrogen fluoride at 0° gave t-butylphenol (758). Even at −40° anhydrous hydrogen fluoride caused cleavage of tetraisobutylene giving excellent yields of t-octylphenol (682), a result paralleled by Proell et al. who used alkanesulfonic acid as catalyst at

70° (653). Other workers have employed boron fluoride (complexed with water, ether, or phosphoric acid) (864a) and sulfuric acid (659), but have not characterized their products.

c. Polypropenes (Table 40)

Sulfonic acids appear to be very satisfactory catalysts for alkylations with propene polymer. p-Toluenesulfonic acid monohydrate produced 92% of nonylphenol from the trimer (1), and mixed alkanesulfonic acids gave 68% of dodecylphenol from the tetramer and 78% of pentadecylphenol from the pentamer (653). Several other catalysts have been claimed to give good yields of alkylate from the tetramer. These include boron fluoride (469,534,787), its etherate (1), hydrogen fluoride (69) and aluminum chloride–sulfuric acid complex (21,386,387).

E. Alkylation with Cyclic Olefins
(Tables 41, 43, 44)

At 0° small amounts of aluminum chloride afforded 12–13% of alkylate and 17–21% of ethers from the reaction of cyclohexene and various cresols, but at water bath temperatures ether formation disappeared and the yield of alkylate increased to 44–64% (439). Larger amounts of aluminum chloride afforded good yields of cyclohexylphenol at 25° (66). However, the presence of carbon disulfide greatly reduced these yields. Carvacol and cyclohexene afforded minor amounts of alkylate and ether (66).

At 0° boron fluoride produces mainly the cyclohexyl ether of phenol (433,435) but at 40° good yields of mono-, di-, and tricyclohexylphenol may be obtained (434,438). This catalyst has been used at still higher temperatures, e.g., 150°, to produce the 6-cyclohexyl derivative from 2,4-xylenol (590a). Lefebvre and Levas (434) employed boron fluoride at 30°, 60°, and 150° for the alkylation of o- and p-cresol with cyclohexene and found that ethers were formed at the low and intermediate temperatures. Ethers were substantially absent at 150° where the yield of alkylate was of the order of 47–54%.

Kitchen (385) prepared isobornyl ethers in excellent yield by treating various phenols and phenolic derivatives with camphene in the presence of boron fluoride etherate at 0° ± 10°. Benzenesulfonic acid gave excellent yields of isobornyl 2,4-dimethylphenyl ether. 1-Norpinene and tricyclene formed ethers from 2,4-dimethylphenol.

Using concentrated hydrochloric acid as catalyst, Schrauth and

Quasebarth (721) alkylated phenol with octalin to produce decalyl-phenol in 70% yield.

Sulfuric acid and sulfonic acid ion exchange resins have been used to good advantage as catalysts for alkylation with cyclohexene or methylcyclohexene (250,581,721).

As with the acyclic olefins aluminum phenoxide promotes alkylation in the *ortho*-positions (see Section III-9). Thus reaction of phenol with cyclohexene at 224° yielded 42% 2-, 4% 4-, and 20% 2,6-dicyclohexylphenol (397). Iron phenoxide is also claimed for the production of 2- and 2,6-dicyclohexylphenol (194).

Perchloric acid (70%) catalyzed polyalkylation with cyclohexene to give large amounts of di- and tricyclohexylphenol (159).

It is interesting that a larger ring, namely cyclooctene, appears to encounter little steric resistance in attacking the *ortho*-position. The major product obtained with the boron fluoride–acetic acid catalyst at 60° was the 2-cyclooctylphenol (364). The same catalyst afforded a high *ortho/para* ratio of isobornylphenol from camphene (377) and a high yield of tetrahydronaphthylphenol from dihydronaphthalene (392).

Schrauth and Quasebarth (721) mentioned that the product (B) obtained in 55% yield by condensing 1-methylcyclohexene in the presence of sulfuric–acetic acid is also obtained in similar yields by

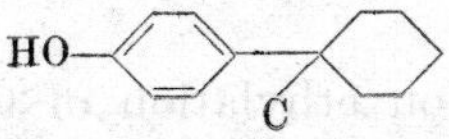

$$HO-\overline{}-\overline{} \quad (B)$$

condensing phenol with the other methylcyclohexene isomers. Apparently, as in the case of benzene alkylation, all these isomers rapidly form the same tertiary cation:

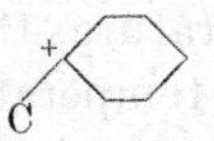

This reacts with phenol to form (B) (and presumably some of the unreported *ortho*-alkylate).

Niederl and Smith (558) reported, however, that 4-*t*-octylcyclo-hexene produced the 4-*t*-octyl-1-*p*-hydroxyphenylcyclohexane (C):

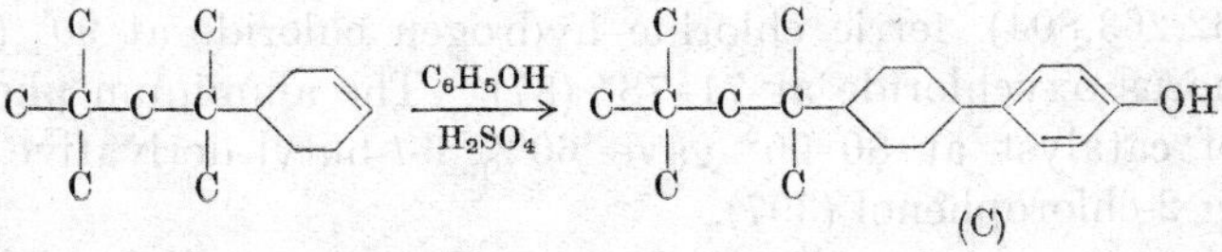

$$C-C-C-C-\overline{} \xrightarrow[H_2SO_4]{C_6H_5OH} C-C-C-C-\overline{}-\overline{}-OH$$

(C)

On the basis of the results of Schrauth and Quasebarth one would have expected the product to be a tertiary alkylate (D):

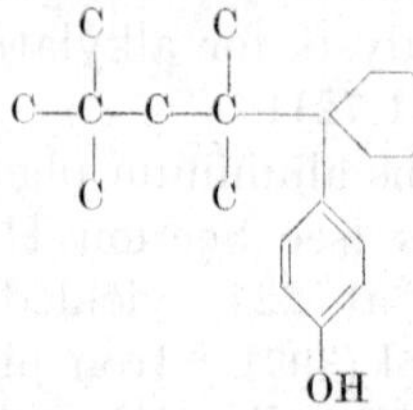

One explanation for the absence of (D) would be that steric blocking prevents its formation. However, this fails to explain why the 1,2- and 1,3-disubstituted cyclohexanes were not isolated in addition to the 1,4-isomer (C). Since Niederl and Smith gave neither yields nor proof of structure for the product labeled (C), their conclusion requires confirmation by additional studies.

3. Halogenated and Nitrated Phenols

A. Halogenated Phenols

(Tables 46, 47)

The presence of a halogen atom on the phenolic ring renders it somewhat more resistant to alkylation, and ether formation is often the result.

No one has reported on ethylation of the halogenated phenols, but considerable work has been done by Zavgorodnii and co-workers in alkylating 2- and 4-halophenols with propene, 2-butene, 1-pentene, 2-pentene, and cyclohexene using boron fluoride complexes as catalyst. By using a milder catalyst, e.g., boron fluoride etherate, or by employing more active catalysts such a boron fluoride–phosphoric acid at a little lower temperature, they obtained chiefly the ether (842,932,936,942); at higher temperatures with boron fluoride–phosphoric acid they were able to obtain mainly the alkylate (412,414).

Levas found boron fluoride an active catalyst at 30–35°; with it he produced 57% of alkylate from 2-chlorophenol and cyclohexene (438).

No difficulty was encountered in alkylations of halogenated phenols with isobutylene in high yields in the presence of sulfuric acid (261,262,263,804), ferric chloride–hydrogen chloride at 90° (88), or phosphorus oxychloride at 71–78° (87). The aluminum phenoxide type of catalyst at 80–90° gave 60% 6-t-butyl derivative of the starting 2-chlorophenol (397).

Activated clay was employed at 140–160°, 5–20 atm., to propylate 4-chloro-3-methylphenol in the 6-position (719); 70% perchloric acid afforded 70% s-dodecyl-4-chlorophenol from 4-chlorophenol and dodecene at 90–95° (159).

With diisobutylene as the alkylating agent it was possible to prepare the 2-t-octyl derivative of 4-chlorophenol using stannic chloride as catalyst, and both the 2-t-octyl and 2,6-di-t-octyl derivatives using boron fluoride etherate (5). However, ferric chloride–hydrogen chloride gave only the scission product, 4-t-butyl derivative of 2-chlorophenol (161).

Sulfuric acid was used to effect the alkylation of chlorophenol with diisoamylene (551).

The presence of a trifluoromethyl group greatly deactivates the nucleus (114):

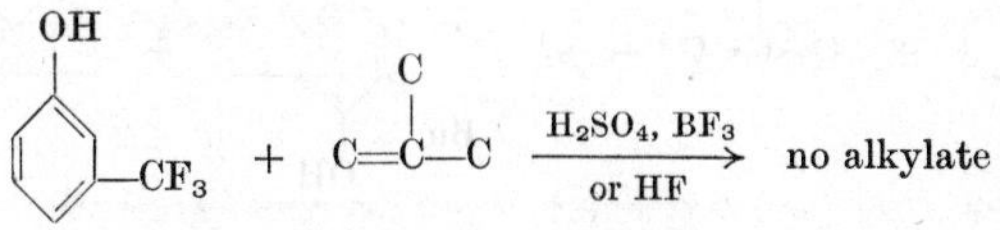

$$\underset{\text{CF}_3}{\text{OH}} \quad + \quad \text{C}=\overset{\overset{\text{C}}{|}}{\text{C}}-\text{C} \quad \xrightarrow[\text{or HF}]{\text{H}_2\text{SO}_4,\ \text{BF}_3} \quad \text{no alkylate}$$

B. Nitrophenols
(Tables 46, 47)

Only a few instances of nuclear alkylation of nitrophenols were found. 2-Nitrophenol was alkylated in 30% yield with propene using sulfuric acid at 100° (55). In this instance sulfonation occurred first, followed by isopropylation. The product was decomposed by steam to obtain the isopropyl nitrophenol. A 15% yield of 6-t-butyl-4-nitrophenol was obtained by treating 4-nitrophenol with isobutylene in the presence of phosphoric acid at 100° (332). Only 5% of the 2-cyclohexyl derivative was formed on alkylating 4-nitrophenol with cyclohexene in the presence of boron fluoride. Similarly the reaction with 2-butene afforded 10% of the s-butyl derivative (866a).

4. Higher Phenols
(Table 44)

t-Butylation of various dimethylphenols was discussed in Section III-2-C-b.

When heated at 145° over a zinc oxide–hydrogen chloride catalyst, 2,3,4-trimethylphenol condensed with propene tetramer to give the 6-dodecyl derivative (401).

Alkylation of o- and m-phenylphenol with diisobutylene in the presence of ferric chloride–hydrogen chloride at 115–120° gave cleavage products, e.g., 4-t-butyl-o-phenylphenol and t-butyl-m-phenylphenol, respectively (161). Aluminum chloride at 145–150° also gave cleavage products such as 4-t-butyl- and 2,4-di-t-butyl-o-phenylphenol (76).

The indanols are alkylated (533) in good yield by isobutylene in the presence of activated clay at 55–80°:

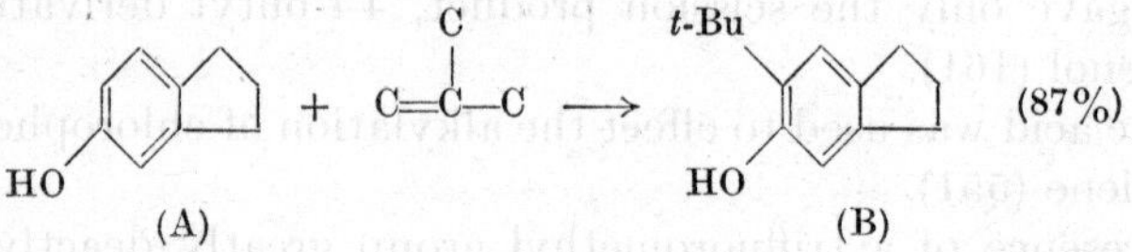

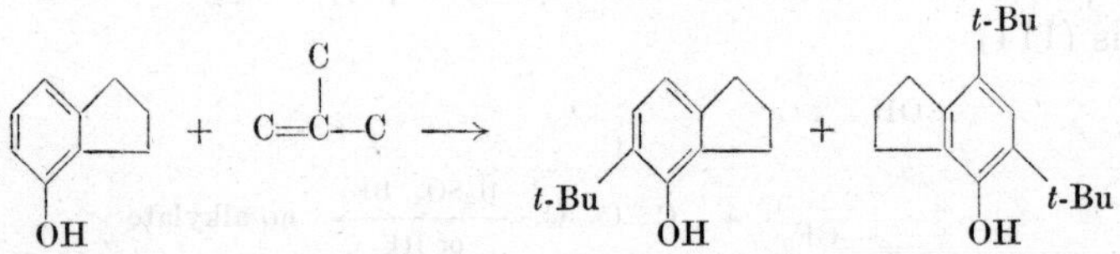

$$\text{(A)} + \text{C}=\text{C}-\text{C} \longrightarrow \text{(B)} \quad (87\%)$$

$$+ \quad \text{C}=\text{C}-\text{C} \longrightarrow$$

Benzene used as a solvent in this reaction was not alkylated. The alkylation of (A) with diisobutylene at 70–80° with sulfuric–acetic acid as catalyst produced the homolog of (B), namely 6-t-octyl-5-indanol (533).

p-Phenylphenol alkylated at 80° with isobutylene in the presence of 20% oleum gives 40% of the 2-t-butyl and 25% of the 2,4'-di-t-butyl derivatives (646).

2-Naphthol was converted to 1-ethyl-2-naphthol by reaction with ethylene over a zinc naphthoxide catalyst at 340–350° (194). An unusual catalyst, aluminum isopropoxide, afforded 54% of 2-isopropyl-1-naphthol from 1-naphthol and propene at 300–310° and 600–700 psig (397).

An aluminum phenoxide type catalyst produced 58% of the 6-s-butyl derivative from 2-ethylphenol and 1-butene at 215° and 200–500 psig (397).

5. Polyhydric Phenols and Bisphenols
(Table 51)

Sulfuric acid with or without acetic acid has been the most commonly used catalyst for alkylation of catechol, resorcinol, hydroquinone, or pyrogallol with diisobutylene (551,555,643), hexene (89), amylene (394,953), and isobutylene (70% sulfuric) (953). Other catalysts have been employed, e.g., hexene with aluminum chloride–acetic acid (551) or fluoroboric acid (779), isobutylene or propene with phosphoric acid (311,929), isobutylene with boron fluoride–phosphoric acid (28), and isobutylene or 1-octene with nickel molybdate (198), and styrene with perchloric acid–acetic acid (159).

Bisphenols such as 1,1-(4,4'-dihydroxy)diphenylethane were alkylated with isobutylene in the presence of boron fluoride–phosphoric acid (893). 4,4'-Dioxydiphenylmethane and phenol–formaldehyde resins have been alkylated by means of a 70% perchloric acid catalyst (159,268).

3-Mono-, 3,5-di-, and 3,6-diisopropylcatechol are obtained when catechol and propene are heated at 265–275° under pressure in the presence of aluminum isopropoxide (177).

6. Aromatic Ethers

(Tables 48, 49, 52)

Phenolic ethers are also strong nucleophiles, alkylation being accomplished quite easily with a majority of the same catalysts utilized in phenol alkylation.

Only one reference was found concerning alkylation with ethylene and this was the unsuccessful attempt by Mamedaliev and Mishiev (486) to ethylate anisole or phenetole using 85% sulfuric acid at 18°. They did, however, obtain good yields of alkylate from propene, butene, and isobutylene. Anisole was octylated with diisobutylene by the use of sulfuric acid (660).

Isagulyants et al. (348) employed an acid cationic exchange resin (KU-2) to obtain 50–57% of 4-t-butyl derivatives of anisole and phenetole. The 4-t-butyl derivative was prepared in a similar fashion from the benzyl ether of m-cresol.

Zavgorodnii and co-workers have utilized boron fluoride and its complexes to good advantage for alkylations with various olefins. At room temperature with 2-butene, boron fluoride afforded 46% ortho- and 27% para-s-butylanisole (940,941) while boron fluoride complexed with 75% phosphoric acid gave high yields of s-butyl derivatives, mostly mono-ortho. 2-Pentene and an anhydrous boron fluoride complex with phosphoric acid gave 49% para- and 10% ortho-pentylanisole (933,949). The complex with ethyl ether gave the para-isomer. These catalysts were effective for the butylation of phenetole (934). They also gave excellent yields of alkylate in the reaction with styrene (935):

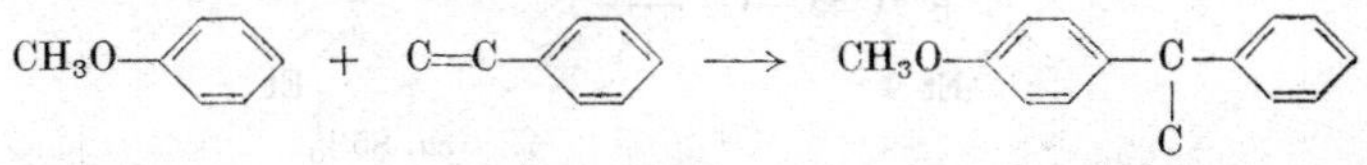

Some years earlier Lefebvre and Levas had used boron fluoride to obtain a 54/46 mixture of *o*- and *p*-cyclohexylanisole (434).   Boudroux, however, obtained a 75/25 ratio using aluminum chloride (66).

Phosphoric acid (85%) at 30–70° produced the 4-*t*-butyl derivative of 1,3-dimethoxybenzene in good yield and a small amount of the 4,6-di-butyl derivative (114).   At 25° the anhydrous acid afforded the *t*-butyl derivative of 2-methylanisole in which the *t*-butyl group is no doubt attached in the 4-position (826).

Hydrogen fluoride was used at 5–20° to alkylate diphenyl ether with 3-hexene in 61% yield (110).

Cullinane *et al.* reported that the titanium tetrachloride catalyzed reaction of anisole with 2-methyl-2-butene gave *p-t*-amylanisole in 61–67% yield (147).   The absence of *ortho*-substitution may seem unusual, especially in view of the facile synthesis of 4-*t*-butyl-1,3-dimethoxybenzene (114), but their observation received support from the fact that alkylation of anisole with isobutylene in the presence of hydrogen fluoride afforded *t*-butylanisole containing more than 98% of the *para*-isomer (216).   Further support is furnished by Zavgorodnii and Alisova (935) who obtained 71% of the *para*-derivative (A) on alkylation of anisole with α-methylstyrene at 60° using boron fluoride etherate:

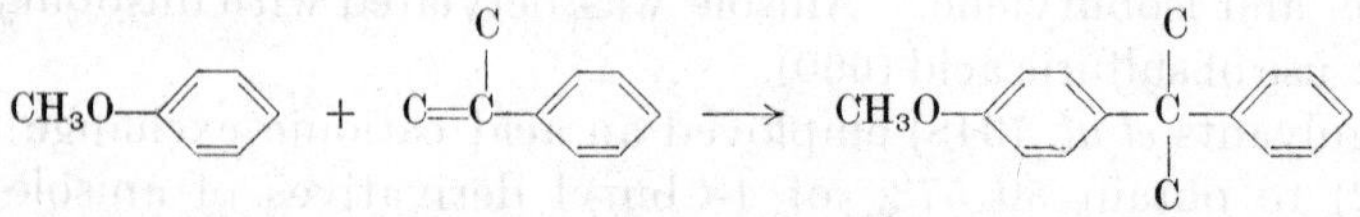

$$CH_3O-\langle\rangle + C=C-\langle\rangle \longrightarrow CH_3O-\langle\rangle-C-\langle\rangle$$

(A)

Alkylation with boron fluoride–phosphoric acid afforded lower yields of (A) and appears to induce the dimerization of the α-methylstyrene.

Alkylation of 4-methyl-, 4-ethyl- and 4-isopropylanisoles with isobutylene in the presence of 93% sulfuric acid at 22–30° introduced the *t*-butyl group *ortho* to the methoxy group (113,114).   A similar result was obtained with a 4-methylphenetole.   Aluminum chloride also effected *t*-butylation *ortho* to the methoxy group (455,921):

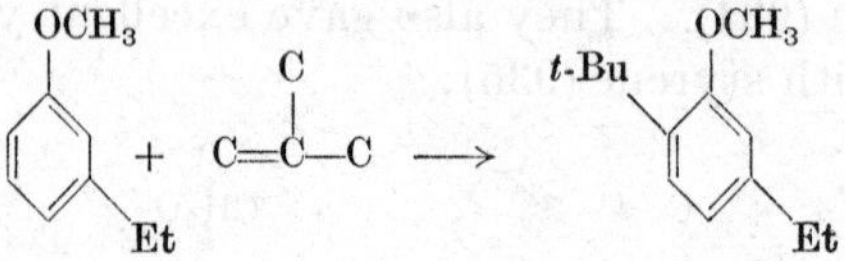

$$\text{(OCH}_3, \text{Et ring)} + C=C-C \longrightarrow \text{(OCH}_3, t\text{-Bu, Et ring)}$$

ca. 85%

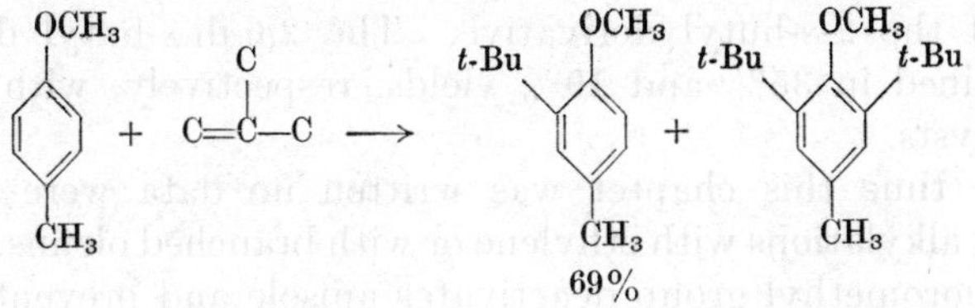

$$\text{OCH}_3 + \text{C}=\text{C}-\text{C} \longrightarrow \text{OCH}_3\ t\text{-Bu} + \text{OCH}_3\ t\text{-Bu}\ t\text{-Bu}$$

69%

Aluminum chloride has also been used in alkylating 1- and 2-methoxynaphthalene to produce 4-cyclohexyl-1-methoxynaphthalene and 6-cyclohexyl-2-methoxynaphthalene, respectively (126).

7. Methoxyphenols
(Table 52)

4-Methoxyphenol reacted readily with isobutylene at 50–60° in the presence of sulfuric or phosphoric acid. A high olefin to aromatic ratio yielded the 2,6-di-t-butyl derivative in 56% yield (137,665) and a 1:1 ratio afforded the 2-t-butyl derivative in 80% yield (663). Apparently the hydroxyl group has by far the strongest directing influence (665a). This is also borne out in alkylations with styrene (928).

On this basis one would predict that guaiacol (2-methoxyphenol) would alkylate in the 4- or 6-positions rather than the 5-position. Alkylations of guaiacol were performed using diisobutylene (551) and styrene (102) in the presence of sulfuric acid, but unfortunately the products were not fully characterized. Guaiacol was also alkylated with 2-butene at 100° in the presence of boron fluoride–phosphoric acid (934). The product consisted of 66–85% of s-butylguaiacol and its s-butyl ether.

8. Halogenated and Nitrated Aromatic Ethers
(Table 50)

Kryuchkova and Zavgorodnii have made extensive use of boron trifluoride–phosphoric acid as a catalyst for alkylating halogenated anisoles. With it they obtained high yields of 4-isopropyl, 4-s-butyl, and 4-cyclohexyl derivatives of 2-bromoanisole or 2-chloroanisole (843,415). The product from 2-chloroanisole and cyclohexene also contained the 6-cyclohexyl isomer.

In alkylation of 4-bromo-, 4-chloro-, and 4-fluoroanisoles they obtained good yields of the 2-alkyl derivative and in most instances fair yields of the 2,6-dialkyl derivative (411,411a,842).

Boron fluoride was more active than its phosphoric acid complex or its etherate for the reaction of 2-butene with 4-fluoroanisole (411a). At 80° these catalysts afforded 65, 59, and 26%, respectively, of the 2-s-butyl derivative. The 2,6-di-s-butyl derivative was obtained in 35% and 19% yields, respectively, with the first two catalysts.

At the time this chapter was written no data were available regarding alkylations with ethylene or with branched olefins.

A trifluoromethyl group deactivates anisole and prevents alkylation with isobutylene (114):

$$\text{(ring with OCH}_3\text{ and CF}_3) \quad + \quad C{=}C{-}C \quad \xrightarrow[\text{BF}_3/\text{H}_2\text{O}]{\text{H}_2\text{SO}_4 \text{ or}} \quad \text{no alkylation}$$

Similarly the introduction of one nitro group into the ring of 1,3-dimethoxybenzene sufficiently deactivated the compound so that alkylation with isobutylene could not be accomplished with either boron fluoride hydrate or with a 20 molar ratio of hydrogen fluoride as catalyst (114).

9. Phenoxide Catalysts

A very useful method for the selective alkylation of phenols in the ortho-positions was discovered and developed by the same two independent groups (397,814,816) who had developed the aniline ortho-alkylation process (see Section V). This synthesis involves a novel type of catalyst, the aluminum phenoxides. Excellent yields are obtained of mono- and di-ortho-alkylphenols. No p-alkylphenols can be detected in alkylates from ethylene, but small amounts are formed from propene (816) and considerable para-substitution may occur with isobutylene, especially at high temperatures. The reaction may be made very selective, e.g., 74% yield of 2,6-di-t-butylphenol, by taking advantage of the faster rate of formation of the ortho-alkylphenols and avoiding higher temperatures and longer reaction times which accelerate dealkylation of the ortho-isomers formed initially and favor the more thermodynamically stable para-isomer. Whereas the reactivity of olefins in the alkylation of aromatic amines decreases in the order ethylene > propene > butene, the inverse order holds for the alkylation of phenols (816).

It is not necessary to isolate the aluminum phenoxide to be used as the catalyst in the alkylation processes. This product is produced in a high-pressure autoclave from aluminum and phenol (in excess) before the olefin is added. Aluminum, in amounts of 1–2%, calculated on the basis of the weight of phenol, is used in the form of powder, shavings, or grits. The aluminum dissolves on heating to 120–140°, hydrogen is evolved and aluminum phenoxide is formed.

With cresols, the reaction begins at 150–180°. To obtain a smooth dissolution of aluminum, it can be "activated" by the addition of a small quantity of mercury (II) chloride. In alkylation of 1-naphthol the catalyst prepared by heating the naphthol with aluminum was not active, but a satisfactory one was obtained by heating the naphthol with aluminum isopropoxide (397).

The Ethyl group (397) suggest that the aluminum phenoxide probably complexes with a molecule of phenol to give an acid $HAl(OC_6H_5)_4$ which would be expected to exhibit acidic properties intermediate to the hypothetical acids formed from the aluminum alkoxides $(HAl(OR)_4)$ (507) and from the aluminum halides $(HAlCl_4)$ (83). As further evidence of the acidic nature of this catalyst, both groups of authors (397,816) point out that the reactivities of different types of olefins are typical of carbonium-ion type reactions $R_2C{=}CH_2 > RCH{=}CH_2 > RCH{=}CHR > CH_2{=}CH_2$. The German group (816) also cite as evidence the low "pH-value" of 1.0 found for a 1% solution of aluminum phenoxide in phenol. Phenol has a "pH-value" of 4.4–4.6 and a 1% solution of the lithium salt $[Al(OC_6H_5)_4]Li$ in phenol has a "pH-value" of 4.9.

The Ethyl group point out that the $HAl(OC_6H_5)_4$ complex possesses a geometry ideally suited for reaction with olefins in several six-membered ring concerted mechanisms:

(1) *Ether formation*

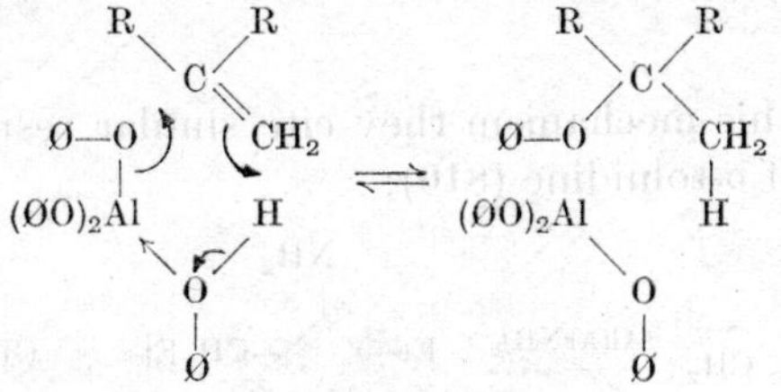

(2) *Ether rearrangement to* ortho-*alkylate*

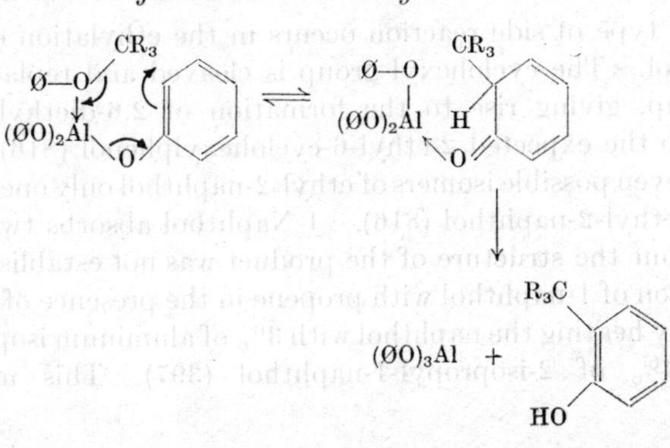

(3) Ortho-*alkylation*

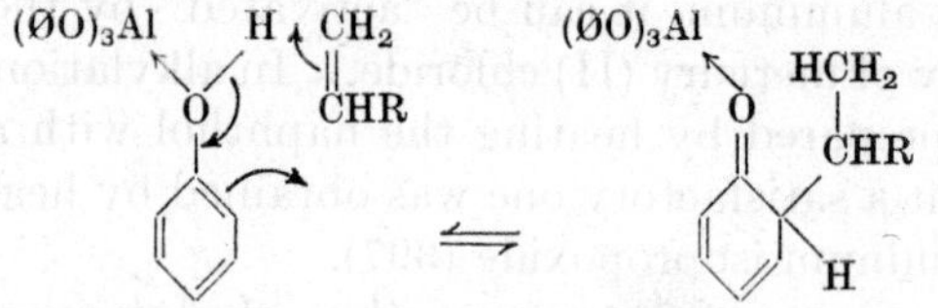

$$(\emptyset O)_3 Al \quad H \underset{\downarrow}{\overset{CH_2}{\text{ }}} \quad (\emptyset O)_3 Al \quad HCH_2$$

The German group found that atmospheric pressure treatment of *t*-butyl phenyl ether at 100° converts it partly into isobutylene and phenol and partly into 2-*t*-butylphenol. However, they suggest that these data do not fully support an ether intermediate mechanism.

When treated with ethylene at 320–340° at 200 atm. pressure, phenol absorbed two moles of ethylene yielding (816)

2-ethylphenol	32%
2,6-diethylphenol	39%
2-ethyl-6-*s*-butylphenol	17%

As in the ethylation of aniline, the *s*-butyl group may arise *via* prior dimerization of the ethylene. However, Stroh *et al.* (816) suggest the possibility of *C*-alkylation at the benzylic carbon in the initially formed 2-ethyl- or 2,6-diethylphenol:

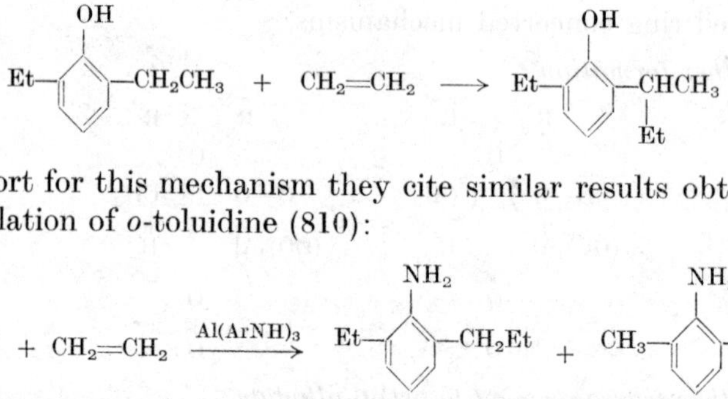

$$Et-\langle \rangle-CH_2CH_3 \;+\; CH_2{=}CH_2 \;\longrightarrow\; Et-\langle \rangle-CHCH_3$$

As support for this mechanism they cite similar results obtained in the ethylation of *o*-toluidine (810):

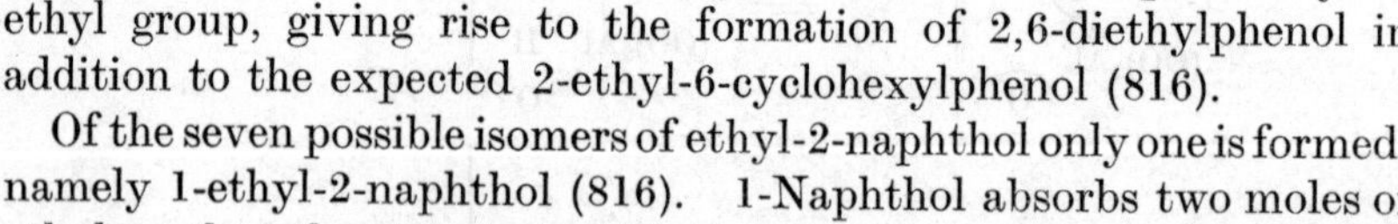

$$\langle \rangle-CH_3 \;+\; CH_2{=}CH_2 \xrightarrow{Al(ArNH)_3} Et-\langle \rangle-CH_2Et \;+\; CH_3-\langle \rangle-CHCH_3$$

Another type of side reaction occurs in the ethylation of *o*-cyclohexylphenol. The cyclohexyl group is cleaved and replaced by an ethyl group, giving rise to the formation of 2,6-diethylphenol in addition to the expected 2-ethyl-6-cyclohexylphenol (816).

Of the seven possible isomers of ethyl-2-naphthol only one is formed, namely 1-ethyl-2-naphthol (816). 1-Naphthol absorbs two moles of ethylene, but the structure of the product was not established (816).

Alkylation of 1-naphthol with propene in the presence of a catalyst prepared by heating the naphthol with 3% of aluminum isopropoxide, yielded 54% of 2-isopropyl-1-naphthol (397). This method of

preparing the phenoxide catalyst was employed in propylating catechol (177).

The German group has patented iron, magnesium, and zinc
phenoxides as *ortho*-alkylation catalysts for phenols, cresols, and
naphthols, etc. (194).

ortho-Propylation of the various chlorophenols proceeded satisfactorily in the presence of the phenoxide catalyst.   *m*-Chlorophenol
was able to absorb three moles of propene yielding 3-chloro-2,4,6-
triisopropylphenol.   *p*-Chlorophenol affords mainly the 2-isopropyl
and 2,6-diisopropyl derivatives, but the isopropyl ether of the
starting phenol was also obtained in 12% yield (816).

The phenoxide catalyzed *ortho*-alkylation of phenol with isobutylene
begins at 80–100° versus 200–230° for propene and 190–200° for
butene.   At 200°, isobutylene gives mainly the 4- and 2,4-di-*t*-butyl
derivatives.   On the other hand, *t*-butylation of hydroquinone seems
to require a temperature of 220–240°.

ortho-Alkylation with 2-methyl-2-butene proceeds at 120°. Diisobutylene affords 25% of the 4- as well as 11% of the 2-*t*-octyl isomer
(397).   *ortho*-Alkylation with styrene and α-methylstyrene can be
effected at atmospheric pressure because of the higher boiling point
of the olefins.

IV. Alkylation of Thiophenols and their Ethers
(Tables 53, 53A)

Tarbell *et al.* (825) have pointed out striking differences between
oxygen and sulfur compounds: first, the greater rate of splitting of an
ether compared to a sulfide by acidic reagents (260,824) and, second,
the greater effectiveness of the hydroxyl or alkoxyl group in promoting electrophilic substitution in the aromatic nucleus.   This has been
attributed to the electron-withdrawing effect resulting from resonance
structures such as (A) in which sulfur has expanded its valence
shell.

However, another explanation may be offered: The lower nucleophilic strength of the thio-compounds may be attributed to the
decreased ability of sulfur to form resonance structures such as (B)
via interaction of the sulfur $3p$ electrons with the attached π-system
(67,366,593,867).

It is therefore not surprising that only a few instances of nuclear alkylation of thiophenols with olefins have been mentioned in the literature. Contributing also to the difficulty of nuclear alkylation is the reactivity of the thiol group and the stability of the resulting alkyl sulfides (44). Thus when thiophenol and propene were heated under pressure with phosphoric acid at 120°, the sole product was n-propyl phenyl sulfide, the same addition product that was obtained in the absence of the catalyst (333). Similarly isobutylene yielded isobutyl phenyl sulfide in 50% yield at 120° with this catalyst, and in 90% yield at 33° in the absence of the catalyst.

Sulfuric acid was patented (548) for the alkylation of thiophenols with isobutylene, and Kreuz claimed the t-alkylation of thiophenols in the para-position using t-alcohols and t-mercaptans with aluminum halide catalysts (410).

Recently Bartkus, Hotelling, and Neuworth (44) succeeded in effecting ring alkylation of thiophenol and o-thiocresol with isobutylene using boron fluoride. The conversion of thiol was 71% in each instance. Substitution took place exclusively in the para-position; the yields of p-t-butyl derivative at 80° being 64% and 44%, respectively, of the thiol converted. t-Butyl ethers of thiophenol and its alkylate were also formed in 12% yield each, but o-thiocresol formed no ethers. Where the para-position was blocked as in p-thiocresol, t-butylation was unsuccessful. They also obtained p-t-butylthiophenols in good yield by a transalkylation reaction involving the appropriate t-butyl sulfide and the parent thiophenol.

In contrast, propene gave lower yields (19% and 25% respectively) of ring alkylate from thiophenol and p-thiocresol. It is of interest that the thiophenol alkylation with propene yielded only the ortho-isomer. Ethyl thiophenols could not be synthesized by the above techniques.

In 1960 Laufer presented a report of his very thorough study of the alkylation of thiophenol with unbranched acyclic and cyclic olefins (426f). He succeeded in alkylating thiophenol with ethylene, propene, 1-butene, 2-butene, 1-pentene, and cyclopentene in the presence of a variety of strong Lewis acid catalysts. The products consisted of 2-alkylthiophenols, 2,6-dialkylthiophenols, unreacted thiophenol, and the corresponding alkyl aryl sulfides. In every instance nuclear alkylation occurred ortho to the thiol group. Only in the dihydroxyfluoroboric acid catalyzed propylation of thiophenol was a substantial proportion (33%) of the para-alkylate obtained.

Low temperatures, e.g., < 30°, favored the ortho-alkylation of thiophenols whereas higher reaction temperatures favored ether formation. Thus at 100° the reaction of thiophenol with propene yielded only trace amounts of ring-propylated products. This contrasts with the report of Bartkus *et al.* (44) that tertiary nuclear alkylation of thiophenols occurs only at temperatures *above* 25°, the optimum being in the range of 75° to 100°. Perhaps at high temperatures the thiol group adds non-catalytically to propene at a rate faster than the cationic ring-alkylation reaction (see 333).

Using aluminum bromide, chloride, or iodide, Laufer almost doubled the yields of *o*-isopropylthiophenols previously reported for boron fluoride catalyzed isopropylations (44). The yield of alkylate decreased rapidly with increase in molecular weight of the olefins. 1-Butene gave a much greater proportion of alkylate than did *cis–trans* 2-butene. Cyclopentene gave several times more nuclear alkylation than did cyclohexene, a fact Laufer suggested might be attributed to the greater steric hindrance involved in the approach of the aplanar cyclohexene molecule to a position *ortho* to the sulfur atom (especially if the latter is complexed with the catalyst). On the basis of these steric considerations and considering that 1-methylcyclohexene, a branched olefin, readily alkylated thiophenol at the *para*-position, it was expected that *para*-substitution would be favored. Surprisingly, little if any *para*-substitution by the cyclo-hexyl group occurred. Cyclopropane yielded only 6% of *ortho-n*-propyl thiophenol, the major product being *n*-propyl phenyl sulfide.

In addition to boron fluoride, Laufer found that aluminum chloride, bromide, and iodide, zirconium tetrachloride, titanium tetrachloride, dihydroxyfluoboric acid, and a complex (BF_3–H_2O–HF) derived from aqueous hydrofluoric acid and boron fluoride were effective catalysts for the reaction. The BF_3–H_2O–HF catalyst was the only easily recoverable catalyst. It was separated as an immiscible liquid phase and re-saturated with boron fluoride before use. Superatmospheric pressure of boron fluoride had to be maintained to ensure the requisite concentration of that catalyst component. The metal halide catalysts dissolved readily in thiophenol and alkylations employing these catalysts were easily performed in glass equipment.

In discussing mechanism, Laufer suggested that the high *ortho*-selectivity of the reaction indicated the possible involvement of a directive influence operating *via* the initial formation of a ternary thiol–olefin catalyst complex which was followed by a quasi-cyclic transition state leading to the *o*-alkylthiophenol. He indicated that a typical carbonium-ion mechanism probably accounted for the

5+F.C. II

ether formation as well as for the occurrence of small amounts of *para*-alkylation.   This was in accord with previous reports that the alkylation of thiophenols with olefins, alcohols (410), halides, and mercaptans (410) which furnish *t*-carbonium ions proceeds exclusively *para* to the sulfhydryl group and could also proceed *via* migration of a *t*-alkyl group from sulfur to carbon (44).

It is worth noting that in almost all reported attempts to subject thiophenols to electrophilic substitution reactions, attack occurs at the sulfur atom and not on the aromatic ring (276) while the alkyl aryl sulfides, RSAr, undergo most electrophilic substitutions smoothly (see footnote 8 in ref. 276).   Nevertheless, Laufer states that the experimental evidence strongly suggests that the thioether by-products of the *ortho*-alkylation reaction are derived from the corresponding thiol and not to any great extent by the ring alkylation of an initially formed thioether.   Thus isopropyl phenyl sulfide was found to be quite stable in the presence of aluminum chloride and thiophenol at 0°.   He concluded that nuclear alkylation of thiophenols with primary or secondary alkyl groups cannot involve the isomerization of sulfides.   Therefore, both alkylation and ether formation must proceed concurrently and, probably, by basically different mechanisms.

Laufer's proposed reaction scheme is summarized as follows:

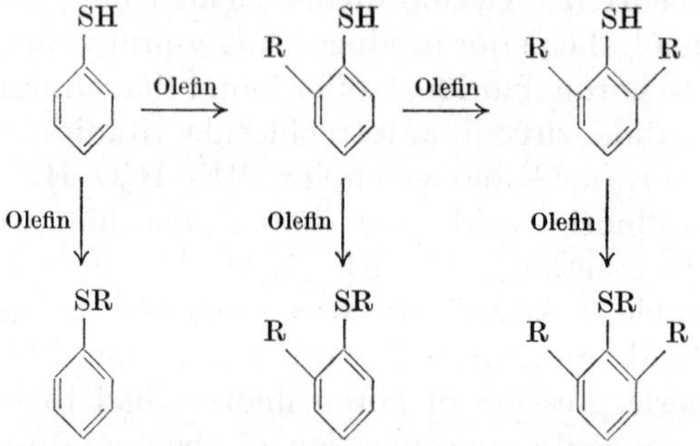

None of the steps is believed to be reversible under normal reaction conditions.   The beneficial effect of low temperatures on the yield of ring-alkylated products indicates that the previously postulated complex becomes less stable at higher temperatures.   Total conversion of the reactant thiol has not been achieved even in the presence of excess olefin, suggesting the progressive loss of catalyst to more stable, but ineffective, complexes with the products of the reaction, particularly the more basic sulfides.

Only minor amounts of 2,6-dialkylthiophenols, *i.e.*, derived from thiophenol *per se*, are produced except when the alkylations are carried out at Dry Ice–acetone temperatures. The dialkylated thiols are apparently more susceptible to ether formation than unsubstituted or mono-*ortho*-substituted thiophenols.

The aluminum halides on the one hand, and titanium and zirconium tetrachloride on the other, give quite different product distributions —particularly in regard to the major sulfide product obtained.

Apparently hydrogen fluoride has not been used as a catalyst for alkylation of thiophenols.

V. Alkylation of Aromatic Amines
(Tables 54, 55, 56, 57, 65)

In 1956 two groups of investigators, working independently, announced the discovery of a novel reaction by which primary and secondary aromatic amines are alkylated with olefins exclusively in the *ortho*-positions (when these are vacant). Both the Farben-fabriken Bayer group (809–816) (Stroh, Ebersberger, Haberland, Hahn, and Seydel) and the Ethyl group (179a,179b) (Ecke, Napoli-tano, Kolka, and Filbey) utilized an aluminum anilide catalyst which may be prepared by heating the amine with aluminum turnings until hydrogen evolution ceases. With this catalyst they alkylated aniline with ethylene to obtain excellent yields of the 2,6-diethyl derivative:

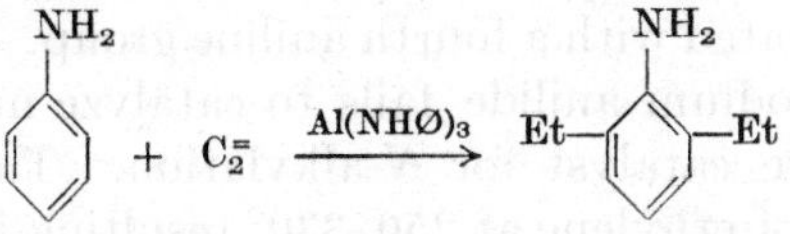

$$\text{NH}_2 \quad + \quad C_2^= \quad \xrightarrow{\text{Al(NH}\phi)_3} \quad \text{Et}-\overset{\text{NH}_2}{\bigcirc}-\text{Et}$$

Stroh (808) stated that *para*-substitution would occur in good yield if both *ortho*-positions were occupied:

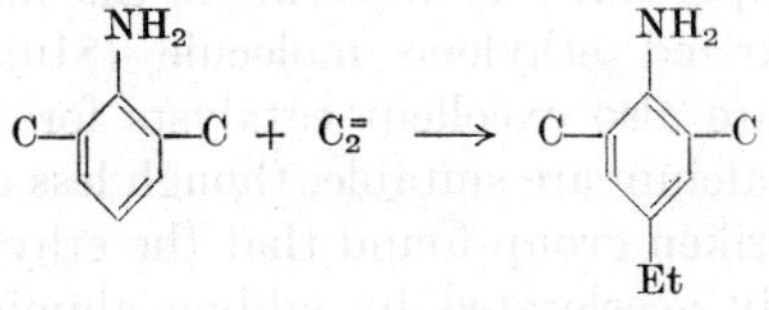

$$C-\overset{\text{NH}_2}{\bigcirc}-C \quad + \quad C_2^= \quad \longrightarrow \quad C-\overset{\text{NH}_2}{\underset{\text{Et}}{\bigcirc}}-C$$

The alkylation of aniline with higher olefins was more sluggish, resulting in a small yield of the branched monoalkylaniline as the sole product.

The Ethyl group suggested a cyclic mechanism in their first paper (179b) and elaborated on it in a later paper (179a). On the basis that the reactivities of the different types of olefins are those observed in carbanion reactions and are the inverse of those observed in carbonium-ion reactions, they assumed the reaction "although concerted was fundamentally a carbanion or free radical type of reaction."

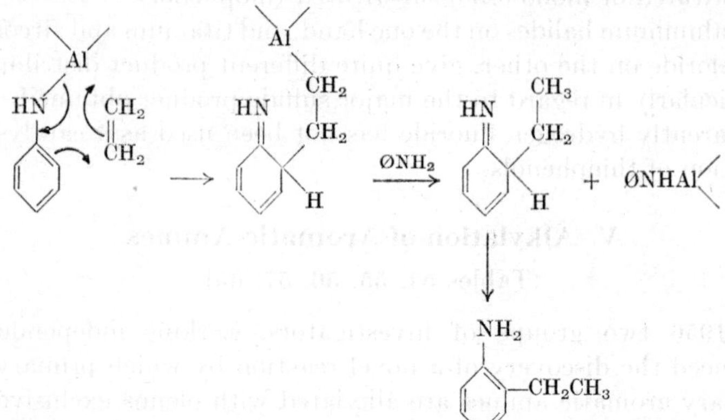

A cyclic mechanism was also postulated by the Farbenfabriken group (810) who emphasized the significance of the electron deficiency of the aluminum in aluminum trianilide. They found that if this deficiency is saturated, so to speak, with one mole of lithium or sodium, nuclear alkylation does not occur. To explain this deactivation by the alkali metal they suggested that a complex $Me^I[Al(NH\emptyset)_4]$ is formed, in which the electron deficiency of the aluminum is saturated with a fourth aniline group.

Even though sodium anilide fails to catalyze nuclear alkylation, it is a very active catalyst for N-alkylation. Thus one obtains a rapid absorption of ethylene at 250–330° resulting in a 96% yield of N-ethyl- and N-diethylaniline with no trace of nuclear alkylation. Here it is postulated that it is the electron pair of the nitrogen atom which plays an important role involving in this instance the positive end of the polarized ethylene molecule (810). Potassium and lithium anilides are also excellent catalysts for N-alkylation while magnesium and calcium are suitable, though less active, catalysts.

The Farbenfabriken group found that the ethylation of diphenylamine was greatly accelerated by adding aluminum chloride. In fact, if activated by aluminum chloride, even sodium anilide will give a 95% yield of 2,2'-diethyldiphenylamine.

One of the by-products isolated by both groups in the ethylation of aniline, etc., is a s-butyl derivative. This no doubt results from prior dimerization of the ethylene, as evidenced by the fact that the off-gas, in one instance, contained 0.8% butene (179a).

The *N*-alkylanilines were found to undergo nuclear alkylation at a lower temperature than aniline (179a), but only one alkyl group could be introduced:

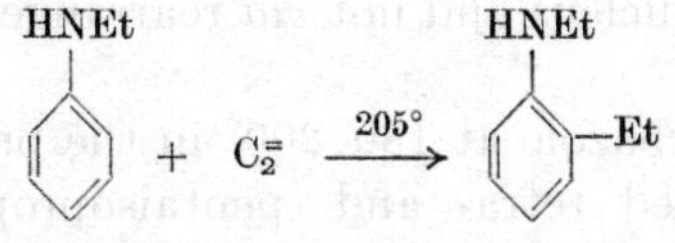

$$\text{HNEt} \quad + \quad C_2^= \quad \xrightarrow{205°} \quad \text{HNEt}\text{—Et}$$

It was suggested that the failure to react at the second *ortho*-position may result from steric hindrance between the *N*-alkyl and the existing *ortho*-alkyl group preventing rotation of the nitrogen atom to the angle required for the formation of the cyclic intermediate.

The aluminum–anilide catalyst system has been extended to include alkylations of various aniline derivatives, naphthylamine, aromatic diamines, phenthiazine, and benzidine (179a,195,810). The universal requirement was that there must be at least one hydrogen on the nitrogen atom. Stroh and Hahn (813) have reported on the nuclear *C*-alkylation of heterocyclics which contained a NH group in the ring. Carbazole for example yielded 1-ethylcarbazole:

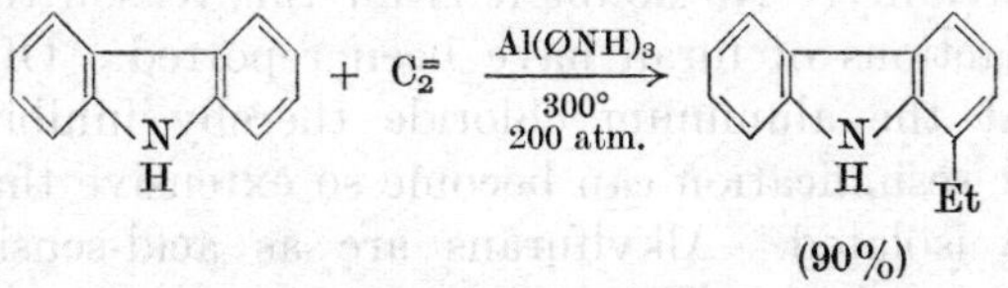

$$\text{[carbazole, N-H]} \quad + \quad C_2^= \quad \xrightarrow[\substack{300° \\ 200 \text{ atm.}}]{\text{Al}(\varnothing\text{NH})_3} \quad \text{[1-ethylcarbazole, N-H, Et]}$$

(90%)

No dialkylate, *e.g.*, 1,8-diethylcarbazole, was isolated. Substituted indoles were also alkylated to give 7-alkyl derivatives and 1,2,3,4-

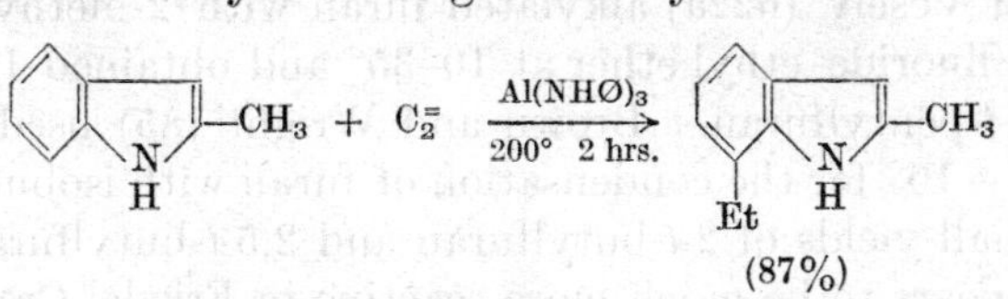

$$\text{[indole—CH}_3\text{, N-H]} \quad + \quad C_2^= \quad \xrightarrow[\substack{200° \quad 2 \text{ hrs.}}]{\text{Al(NH}\varnothing)_3} \quad \text{[alkylated indole—CH}_3\text{, Et, N-H]}$$

(87%)

tetrahydroquinoline to give 8-alkyl derivatives.

Apart from the anilides discussed above, only a few other catalysts are on record as being effective for aniline alkylations. These include activated clays (905), silica–alumina (426g), aniline hydrochlorides (278), cobalt chloride and cadmium chloride salts of aniline (905), and cerium phosphate (298).

Aluminum chloride was claimed (284) to effect alkylation in good yield with diisobutylene and styrene at 165–175°.

A very high yield (85–88%) of 4-*t*-butylaniline was obtained by using montmorillonite clay at 200°; only 0.2% of the 2-isomer was reported (75).

Hickinbottom (278) indicated that nuclear alkylates of aniline obtained by use of the hydrogen halide, cobalt chloride or cadmium chloride salts of aniline at 200–290° are produced by direct reaction of the olefin with the nucleus and not *via* rearrangement of an *N*-alkyl intermediate.

Propylation of carbazole at 180–200° in the presence of activated clay (Tonsil) afforded tetra- and pentaisopropylcarbazole (511). Aluminum chloride was claimed to yield diisopropylcarbazole at 90–100° (518).

Weinmayr (915) used hydrogen fluoride at 5–10° to obtain a moderate yield of isopropyl-*p*-anisidine by propylating *p*-anisidine.

Pyrrole was ethylated at 204–371° over a silica–alumina catalyst (910a).

VI. Alkylation of Furans and Thiophenes

1. Furans

(Table 65)

Resinification of furan in the presence of Friedel-Crafts catalysts occurs quite readily. No doubt it is for this reason that very few alkylation reactions of furan have been reported. Often resinous products coat the aluminum chloride thereby inhibiting further alkylation, or resinification can become so extensive that no simple products are isolated. Alkylfurans are as acid-sensitive as the unsubstituted nucleus. The resinification apparently occurs *via* the formation of an addition complex of furan and the catalyst (176).

Pines and Vesely (622a) alkylated furan with 2-methyl-2-butene using boron fluoride–ethyl ether at 10–35° and obtained 17% mono- and 3% di-*t*-pentylfuran. Brown and Wright (85) used the same catalyst at − 10° for the condensation of furan with isobutylene and obtained small yields of 2-*t*-butylfuran and 2,5-*t*-butylfuran.

Furan appears to be much more reactive in Friedel-Crafts alkylations than benzene. Fair yields of mono- and di-(1,1,3,3-tetramethylbutyl)furan were obtained from the reaction of furan and diisobutylene in the presence of boron fluoride–ether at 12° (85). It is interesting that 2-*t*-butyl-5-*t*-octylfuran was produced in 76% yield by alkylating 2-*t*-butylfuran with diisobutylene in the presence of boron fluoride–ether but was not formed in alkylation of 2-*t*-octylfuran with isobutylene in the presence of the same catalyst.

Gilman and Calloway (233) found that negatively substituted furans were easily alkylated with alkyl halides in the presence of aluminum chloride. Methyl-2-furoate was successfully alkylated with *t*-butyl bromide, *n*-butyl chloride, *s*-butyl bromide, and butene.

They reported obtaining in each instance a *t*-butyl derivative, namely methyl 5-*t*-butyl-2-furoate. However, on reinvestigation of the reaction Hurd and Oliver (291b) found that the monoalkylate obtained with *s*-butyl bromide and aluminum chloride was (by infra-red analysis) a 43/57 mixture of *t*- and *s*-butyl derivatives.

It is remarkable that where the alpha-position is blocked, as in 5-halo-2-furoate, profound cleavage of the alkyl groups occurred. Thus aluminum chloride catalyzed alkylations with *n*-octadecyl bromide, *n*-amyl bromide, *n*-amyl chloride, and *n*-hexyl bromide yielded the 4-*t*-butyl derivatives (233a). However, alkylation did not occur with butene, diisobutylene, *n*-amylene, or cyclohexene.

The aluminum chloride catalyzed reaction of dibenzofuran with ethylene afforded the 2-ethyl derivative (75a). Alkylation with α-methylstyrene over activated clay yielded α-phenylisopropyl derivatives (509).

2. Thiophenes
(Tables 59–64)

Apparently the alkylation of thiophene with olefins had not been accomplished prior to 1946 when Kutz and Corson (422) published their results. The discovery of this reaction was apparently delayed because of the tendency for thiophene to undergo resinification. In fact, Kutz and Corson were unable to alkylate thiophene with sulfuric acid, hydrogen fluoride, or Lewis acids, but they did accomplish the desired end by using a silica–alumina or phosphoric acid catalyst.

The manner in which the reactants and catalyst were mixed was the key to the successful alkylation of thiophene with strong acid catalysts. It was necessary to choose conditions that ensured the alkylation would occur before resinification could begin. Apparently the alkylated thiophenes are much more stable in acidic media than thiophene. The common alkylation procedure of adding the olefin to a mixture of the aromatic and catalyst was unsuccessful because contact of unreacted thiophene with the catalyst in the absence of olefin permitted resinification to occur.

Caesar (104) found that careful addition of 1-octene to 85–96% sulfuric acid prior to addition of thiophene gave a 55–60% yield of octylthiophene and much less resinification than the addition of sulfuric acid to a mixture of the reactants. A 67% yield of octyl-thiophenes, unaccompanied by resinification, was obtained by addition of aluminum chloride to a mixture of thiophene and diiso-butylene. Nevertheless, a small yield of alkylate was obtained if aluminum chloride was added to thiophene before addition of diiso-butylene. The catalyst became coated with thiophene resin, but remained active for alkylation but not for further resinification. Weinmayr (916) avoided violent polymerization of thiophene with hydrogen fluoride by the simultaneous addition of the olefin and thiophene to the catalyst.

It is interesting that there has not been a single report in the literature of a successful alkylation of thiophene with ethylene. The inability to effect ethylation must be a consequence of the fast rate of resinification of thiophene relative to alkylation, regardless of the catalyst used. High yields of alkylthiophenes are favored by the use of reactive olefins with mild catalysts (104). Further-more, alkylation with olefins rather than alcohols or ethers are pre-ferred because of their greater reactivity (916). While no mention was made of the utility of alkyl halides in this reaction (916), it would appear that at least the tertiary halides would give satisfactory results.

Caesar concluded that the choice of catalyst and conditions was determined by the reactivity of the alkylating agent and the pro-portion of mono- and dialkylthiophene desired. With reactive olefins such as isobutylene, 2-methyl-2-butene, and diisobutylene, one could use at moderate temperatures and atmospheric pressure such catalysts as 75% sulfuric acid, dihydroxyfluoboric acid, and boron fluoride complexes with ether, water, ethylacetate, ethyl alco-hol, and acetic acid. Concentrated sulfuric acid and aluminum chloride gave poor yields with the reactive olefins. On the other hand, the less reactive olefins, 1-pentene, 1-octene, or 1-hexadecene, gave the best yields with strong catalysts such as 90–96% sulfuric acid or boron fluoride hydrate. High ratios (up to 14/1) of mono- to dialkylthiophenes were obtained with 70–80% sulfuric acid or dihydroxyfluoboric acid. The ratios were reversed (as low as 1/10) when boron fluoride etherate was used. In general, a reaction temperature range of 25–85° was preferred for reactive olefins and 75–150° was required for unreactive olefins.

Pines and co-workers (617) confirmed the results obtained by Caesar with boron fluoride etherate and, in addition, they studied several other catalyst systems. Stannic chloride catalyzed the condensation of reactive olefins, such as isobutylene and isoamylene, with thiophene at 30–90°, but propene, 2-butene, 3-methyl-1-butene, cyclohexene, and 4-methylcyclohexene did not react. The activity of stannic chloride was, surprisingly, increased when complexed with nitromethane, and this complex successfully catalyzed the condensation of the less reactive olefins with thiophene. Phosphoric acid (85%) gave high yields of alkylate in the condensation of the more reactive olefins with thiophene at 70–80°. Under similar conditions only a small percentage of alkylate was obtained from propene, cyclohexene, styrene, and bicycloheptene. A mixture of equal volumes of 85% phosphoric acid and 96% sulfuric acid catalyzed the alkylation of thiophene at room temperature; however, some sulfonation of thiophene took place. Ethanesulfonic acid catalyzed the alkylation with 2-methyl-2-butene at room temperature.

Since, in the procedure used by Pines and co-workers, some of the thiophene was mixed with the catalyst prior to the addition of the mixture of thiophene and olefin, somewhat lower yields of alkylate and more resinification of thiophene might be expected than in the procedures of Weinmayr or Caesar which avoided such contact of thiophene with catalyst.

Thiophene appears to be substantially more reactive than benzene in Friedel-Crafts reactions. As indicated in previous paragraphs, very mild catalysts have been used to condense thiophene with isobutylene and isoamylene. For example, the alkylation of thiophene with isobutylene in the presence of 75% sulfuric acid is in sharp contrast with the alkylation of benzene where the main product was t-butyl sulfate (313). Intact alkylation of thiophene with diisobutylene can be accomplished using 80% sulfuric acid, boron fluoride, or a small amount of aluminum chloride, thus indicating that thiophene is about as reactive as phenol.

In contrast with the considerable evidence of the high reactivity of thiophene is the report by Weinmayr who alkylated benzene rather than thiophene when a solution of thiophene and benzene was treated with 1-octene in the presence of hydrogen fluoride. On the other hand, it has been reported that 1.5% thiophene was removed from toluene by t-butylation using a mixture of phosphoric acid and sulfuric acid as catalyst (895a). The results of Weinmayr seem the more remarkable when one notes that benzene has long been used as a solvent for the acylation of thiophene (781).

The introduction of an alkyl group on the thiophene nucleus gives the anticipated increase and the introduction of a halogen gives the expected decrease in reactivity. Depolyalkylation occurs in the reaction of thiophene with diisobutylene in the presence of hydrogen fluoride at 0°. Mono- and poly-t-butyl derivatives were produced (916). Under the same conditions, intact alkylation occurred with 3-methylthiophene, and depolyalkylation with 2-chlorothiophene.

5*

Much lower conversions of olefins were reported by Pines *et al.* (617) for the alkylation of 2-bromothiophene than in alkylations of thiophene.

Monosubstitution in the thiophene ring was believed by early workers to be invariably in the 2-position (264). Kutz and Corson (422) and Caesar (104) in their alkylation studies reported only 2-substitution. However, Appleby and co-workers (18) found that the monoisopropyl and mono-*t*-butyl derivatives they obtained using a phosphoric acid–kieselguhr catalyst at 288° were in fact mixtures of approximately 60% 2- and 40% 3-substituted thiophenes. They characterized their products by infra-red analysis of hydrocarbons obtained by the hydrogenation of the alkylthiophenes over a mixed tungsten and nickel sulfide catalyst. A similar analysis of the dialkylthiophenes labeled the principal products as the 2,5-isomers, but other isomers were present.

Using the conditions previously described, Appleby and co-workers obtained 37% 2-*t*-butyl, 23% 3-*t*-butyl, 33% di-*t*-butyl-thiophene, 5% di-*t*-butyldithienyl, and 2% unidentified product from the condensation of isobutylene and thiophene. The passage of thiophene over the phosphoric acid catalyst in the absence of alkylating agent indicated that thiophene undergoes decomposition forming hydrogen sulfide and carbonaceous material as well as coupling to form 2,2'- and 3,3'-dithienyl. The alkylation and decomposition data suggested that the following reactions were important in the alkylation of thiophene with isobutylene over phosphoric acid:

(1) Thiophene → H_2S + carbonaceous material

(2) Thiophene → dithienyl

(3) Thiophene + isobutylene → 2- and 3-*t*-butylthiophene

(4) *t*-Butylthiophene + isobutylene → di-*t*-butylthiophene

(5) *t*-Butylthiophene → di-*t*-butyldithienyl

(6) Isobutylene → polymer

(7) Disproportionation of isobutylene polymers

The ratio of isomers of 3- and 2-*t*-butylthiophenes was independent of pressure, mole ratio of thiophene/isobutylene, or space velocity. Only at low temperatures and low yield of monoalkylate was the ratio of 3-/2-*t*-butylthiophene less than 0.6. It would appear that at the space velocities used, isomerization equilibrium was attained at all conditions except at low conversion.

The ability of thiophene to accommodate bulky groups has been dramatically demonstrated by the formation of tetra-*t*-butylthiophene, obtained by Weinmayr (916) in 62% yield by the depoly-alkylation reaction of thiophene with diisobutylene in the presence of hydrogen fluoride at 0°. This lack of crowding may be explained on the basis that in the 5-membered rings such as thiophene and furan the divergence of adjacent C–R bonds is larger than in benzene. Schomaker and Pauling (720) calculated from electron-diffraction data the C—C=C and S—C=C bond angles in thiophene and found them to be 113° ± 3 and 112° ± 3 respectively, *i.e.*, much smaller than the benzene bond angle of 120°. This means the C–H (or C–R) valence bonds are directed further away from each other in thiophene. Because of this condition and the fact that the ring carbon–carbon bond distance in thiophene is greater than in benzene, bulky groups encounter less crowding.

VII. Alkylation of Aromatic Acids

(Table 58)

The presence of electron-withdrawing groups such as NO_2, CN, COOH, and SO_3H greatly reduces the nucleophilicity of the aromatic ring. It is therefore not surprising that no examples were found in the literature of alkylations of nitrobenzene, benzonitrile, benzoic acid, or benzenesulfonic acid with olefins. Isopropylation of benzoic acid with isopropyl ether was accomplished in the presence of hydrogen fluoride (110), but yields were not reported. Patents have been issued claiming alkylation of polycyclic aromatic sulfonic acids such as naphthalenesulfonic acid with olefins in the presence of sulfuric acid (112,642).

Introduction of a strongly activating group such as the OH group appears to offset the deactivating effect of the COOH group. Thus it is possible to alkylate *ortho-* *meta-*, and *para*-hydroxybenzoic acid with olefins in the presence of boron fluoride (146,300,789) or antimony chloride (821,822). It will be recalled that a similar effect was noted in the alkylation of *para*-nitrophenol (Section III-3-B).

Insertion of a CH_2 or OCH_2 group between the nucleus and the COOH group removes to a large extent the deactivating influence of that group. In fact, Steindorff *et al.* (789) claimed that phenylacetic acid is more easily alkylated in the presence of boron fluoride than is benzene. Several patents have been issued which claim excellent yields of alkylate from the reactions of phenoxyacetic acid with olefins at 60° in the presence of the same catalyst (40,300). Phenoxyacetic acid was also alkylated by means of a zinc chloride catalyst at 150° (300a). Naphthoxyacetic acid, cresoxyacetic acid, and phenoxybutyric acid have been alkylated with diisoheptylene in the presence of boron fluoride (300a).

VIII. Alkylation with Alkanes and Cycloalkanes

1. Alkanes

(Table 66)

There is general agreement that catalytic paraffin isomerization (see McCaulay (464a) for list of references, especially reference 64) and catalytic cracking (257) both involve a cationic mechanism based on the formation, reaction, and stabilization of carbonium-ion intermediates. These carbonium ions are generated by treatment of the paraffin under suitable conditions of temperature and pressure with Friedel-Crafts type catalysts or with silica–alumina type cracking catalysts, a process which usually involves a hydride extraction chain mechanism. In the presence of such catalysts the carbonium ions may, under suitable conditions, alkylate an aromatic compound if one is present.

The aluminum chloride catalyzed condensation of an aromatic with saturated hydrocarbons, (i.e., naphthalene with naphtha) was claimed in an early German patent (188). However, the chemistry and the full ramifications of the destructive alkylation reaction apparently was not understood until the pioneering papers and patents of Grosse, Ipatieff, and co-workers began to appear in 1935 (244,247, 248,319).

In their first paper these authors reported that condensation of benzene with 2,2,4-trimethylpentane in the presence of aluminum chloride–hydrogen chloride at 20–50° afforded 35% of t-butyl- and 25% of di-t-butylbenzene as well as considerable isobutane. Zirconium chloride–hydrogen chloride at 50–75° gave similar products. This reaction which they termed "destructive alkylation" probably proceeds as follows:

$$(1) \quad C-\overset{\overset{\displaystyle C}{|}}{\underset{\underset{\displaystyle C}{|}}{C}}-C-\overset{\displaystyle C}{|}-C \xrightarrow{-H} C-\overset{\overset{\displaystyle C}{|}}{\underset{\underset{\displaystyle C}{|}}{C}}-C-\overset{\displaystyle C}{\underset{+}{C}}-C$$

$$(A) \qquad\qquad\qquad (B)$$

$$(2) \quad C-\overset{\overset{\displaystyle C}{|}}{\underset{\underset{\displaystyle C}{|}}{C}}-C-\overset{\displaystyle C}{\underset{+}{C}}-C \longrightarrow C-\overset{\displaystyle C}{\underset{|}{C}}{}^{+} + C{=}\overset{\displaystyle C}{|}-C$$

$$(3) \quad C-\overset{\displaystyle C}{\underset{|}{C}}{}^{+} + ArH \longrightarrow Ar-\overset{\displaystyle C}{\underset{|}{C}}-C + H^{+}$$

$$\text{(4)} \quad C=\overset{\overset{\displaystyle C}{|}}{C}-C \; + \; H^+ \; \longrightarrow \; C-\overset{\overset{\displaystyle C}{|}}{\underset{\underset{\displaystyle C}{|}}{C^+}}$$

$$\text{(5)} \quad C-\overset{\overset{\displaystyle C}{|}}{\underset{\underset{\displaystyle C}{|}}{C^+}} \; + \; \text{(A)} \; \longrightarrow \; C-\overset{\overset{\displaystyle C}{|}}{\underset{\underset{\displaystyle C}{|}}{CH}} \; + \; \text{(B)}$$

Step 1, the initiation of the above chain of reactions, is probably brought about by traces of a polarized catalyst complex formed from traces of unsaturated or oxygenated hydrocarbon derivatives. These are present as impurities or formed by thermal cracking or oxidation. Step 2 is an example of the widely accepted beta-cleavage rule (920). Step 5 maintains the chain; for every mole of t-butylbenzene one should expect to find a mole of isobutane. This is borne out by the experimental results reported above.

It was later shown by the same authors that if the temperature were high enough (450°) phosphoric acid would give similar results. Furthermore, with the same catalyst they were able to condense benzene with normal paraffin, e.g., n-hexane, to obtain cumene and butylbenzene in moderate yields.

Hydride extraction from unbranched paraffins is more difficult, probably because of the lower stability of the resulting (secondary) carbonium ion. Therefore more severe conditions are required to effect alkylation with the unbranched or less branched paraffins. Thus with the aluminum chloride–hydrogen chloride catalyst destructive alkylations with n-pentane and isopentane required a temperature of 175°. Approximately 10% toluene, 25% ethylbenzene, and 8% n-propylbenzene was produced. 2-Methylpentane and the higher straight-chain paraffins such as hexane, heptane, octane, decane, and hexadecane gave similar results. The by-product gases consisted mainly of isobutane, some propane being found in most instances.

Triptane (2,2,3-trimethylpentane) afforded only t-butylbenzene (15 mol %) and isobutane (70 mol %); no information was given as to the fate of the balance of the triptane molecule.

The reaction with 2,2,4-trimethylpentane was extended with success to other arenes such as toluene and biphenyl leading to the production of 34–35% of t-butylarene and slightly more than one mole of isobutane per mole of reacting isooctane. Alkylations of ethylbenzene and p-xylene were complicated by migration of ethyl and methyl groups. Fluorene underwent hydrogen transfer to form some bifluorenyl. Naphthalene and pyrene seemed to poison the catalyst since neither the arene nor the isooctane underwent much reaction.

Others claimed 100% sulfuric acid at room temperature (399), hydrogen fluoride at 204° (48), and silica–alumina at 500–525° (850) for the destructive alkylation of benzene with 2,2,4-trimethyl-pentane. The hydrogen fluoride catalyst was claimed to yield 65% of t-butylbenzene. At 165° and 700–1070 psig, hydrogen fluoride-boron fluoride catalyzed the reaction of benzene with heptane to give about 30% of a mixture of toluene, ethylbenzene, diethyl-benzene, and ethyltoluene plus considerable C_3 to C_7 paraffins (48,444).

The non-catalytic thermal reaction of benzene with ethane at 605° and 2865 psig yields small amounts of toluene and ethylbenzene (213). Ipatieff and Monroe (322) employed nickel on silica–alumina at 372° and about 8000 psig to obtain about 21% of toluene. Silica-alumina alone gave only 5% toluene. The reaction of benzene with isobutane at 550–660° over silica–alumina produced 14–15% of toluene and its homologs (481). Nickel on kieselguhr catalyzed the reaction with propane at 350° and 900 psig to give 28% toluene and 8% of other homologs (368).

2. Cycloalkanes
(Table 67)

In 1937 Grosse and Ipatieff published their first paper (246) on "decycloalkylation"—the reaction involving formation of an alkyl-arene via reaction of the arene with a cycloparaffin.

With aluminum chloride–hydrogen chloride as catalyst (0–5°) these authors obtained as high as 65% of n-propylbenzene in the reaction of benzene with cyclopropane. By using a higher ratio of cyclopropane to benzene and operating at 25–30° they obtained considerable di-n-propyl- and the hitherto unknown hexa-n-propyl-benzene. Cyclobutane was not tested, but methylcyclobutane gave 25% of isoamylbenzene and its isomers. Cyclopentane reacted much less readily with benzene. When heated to 150° in the pre-sence of the above catalyst, it condensed with benzene to form small amounts of amylbenzene, cyclopentylbenzene, toluene, and ethyl-benzene.

Soon thereafter Ipatieff, Pines, and Corson reported that sulfuric acid was an effective catalyst for the decycloalkylation of benzene (326,331). At 5° cyclopropane afforded 35% of n-propylbenzene along with some n-propyl alcohol which could be isolated from the catalyst layer by dilution and steam distillation. Under the same alkylation conditions methylcyclobutane yielded 30% of amylbenzene (mainly t-amylbenzene) and some diamylbenzene, but cyclopentane was recovered unchanged.

In alkylation with cyclopropane at higher temperatures, 80% sulfuric acid apparently causes isomerization of the intermediate n-propyl cation to form the s-propyl cation, since isopropylbenzene is formed in 58% yield (341). This was not true for aluminum chloride since this catalyst produced high yields (48%) of n-propylbenzene even at 71°.

At about this time Simons and Archer reported they had obtained high yields of n-propylbenzene by using hydrogen fluoride as catalyst (756). Somewhat later Schmerling (700) showed that aluminum chloride–nitromethane would give as high as 70% of n-propylbenzene.

Alkylation with cyclopropane has been utilized to synthesize n-propyl derivatives of m-xylene, 2-methylnaphthalene, thiophene, and thiophenol.

A definitive study was made by Pines, Huntsman, and Ipatieff (614) of the reaction of benzene with various alkyl derivatives of cyclopropane. In the presence of hydrogen fluoride at 0–5° methylcyclopropane afforded 48% of pure s-butylbenzene. Ethylcyclopropane gave 42% of phenylpentanes; similar yields, 46% and 55% respectively, were obtained with sulfuric acid and aluminum chloride–hydrogen chloride. In all instances the ratio 2- to 3-phenylpentane was about 2 to 1.

The absence of t-alkylates is most interesting. The authors postulated the following steps for the reaction of ethylcyclopropane with benzene:

$$\underset{\displaystyle \text{CH}_2}{\text{CH}_2}\!\!\!\diagup\!\!\!\!\diagdown\!\!\!\text{CH}\!-\!\text{CH}_2\text{CH}_3 \;+\; (\text{H}^+)(\text{Y}^-) \rightarrow (\text{CH}_3\text{CH}_2\overset{+}{\text{C}}\text{HCH}_2\text{CH}_3)\text{Y}^-$$

$$\text{(I)}$$

$$\text{I} \xrightarrow{\text{hydride shift}} (\text{CH}_3\text{CH}_2\text{CH}_2\overset{+}{\text{C}}\text{HCH}_3)\text{Y}^-$$

$$\text{(II)}$$

$$\text{I} \;+\; \text{benzene} \rightarrow \text{3-phenylpentane}$$

$$\text{II} \;+\; \text{benzene} \rightarrow \text{2-phenylpentane}$$

The hydrogen fluoride catalyzed alkylation with 1,1-dimethylcyclopropane gave t-amylbenzene in 48% yield whereas a mixture of *cis*- and *trans*-1,2-dimethylcyclopropane gave a mixture of amylbenzenes. These results seem to indicate that alkyl substituents cause cleavage in the following manner:

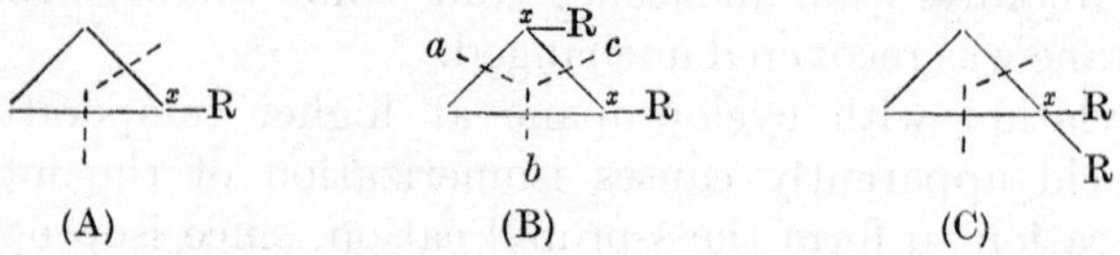

(A)   (B)   (C)

After cleavage, alkylation occurs at the position x. In (B) cleavage at (a) or (b) results in a tertiary alkylate whereas cleavage at (c) results in a secondary alkylate. As indicated by the composition of the alkylate the relative rate of cleavage is expressed by

$$\frac{a + b}{c} = \frac{10}{1}$$

Recently Levina, Shabarov, and co-workers (439a) found that in the alkylation of benzene, toluene, or anisole with phenylcyclopropane in the presence of aluminum chloride at 0–10° the ring opened as in (A) resulting in 52, 62 and 73%, respectively, of 1,1-diphenylpropane, 1-phenyl-1-*p*-tolylpropane and 1-phenyl-1-*p*-anisylpropane.

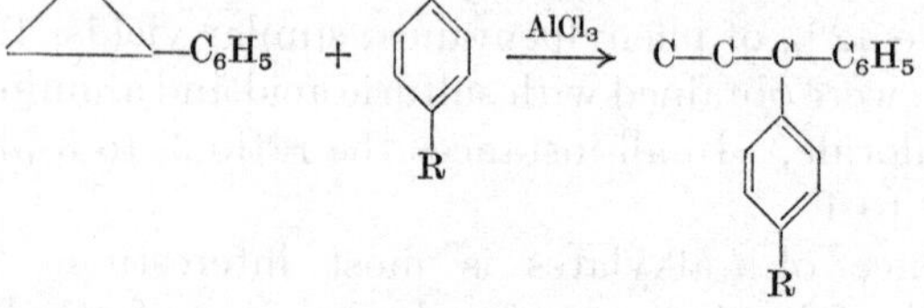

R = H, CH₃, or OCH₃

$R = H, CH_3,$ or OCH_3

p-Tolylcyclopropane and *p*-anisylcyclopropane appeared to undergo substantial polymerization and yielded less alkylate (34% and 6% respectively) on reaction with benzene. In a later paper (733) these authors reported that phenylcyclobutane was very resistant to decycloalkylation; 90% was recovered unchanged after reaction with anisole at 60°.

Alkylation with a 6-membered cycloparaffin has not been attained. A sort of destructive decycloalkylation of benzene with cyclohexane was achieved by using a zinc chloride–alumina catalyst at 400° and 267 atmospheres pressure. About 11% of C_3 to C_5 gases was formed plus toluene, C_8 and high aromatics (705).

Schneider (715) claimed a hydrogen transfer reaction involving methylcyclohexane to obtain 39% of s-methylcyclohexylbenzene (F):

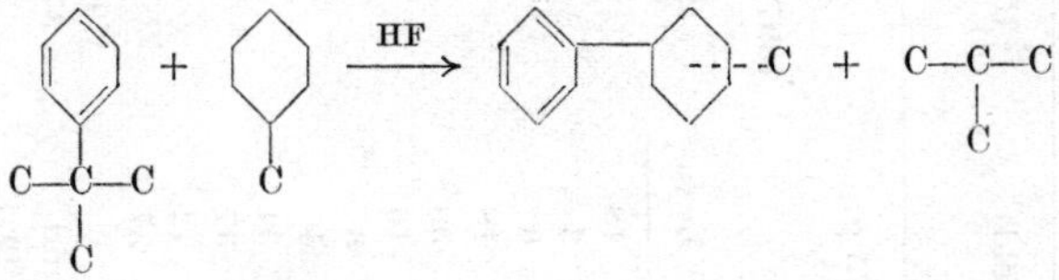

(D)   (E)   (F)

Apparently (D) is cleaved to form a t-butyl cation which abstracts a hydride from (E) forming a methylcyclohexyl cation which in turn attacks benzene forming (F). The assignment of a secondary structure to (F) is of interest, since the hydrogen fluoride catalyzed alkylation of benzene with various methylcyclohexenes yields only the tertiary alkylate (321,451). Results obtained in alkylations with isoamylene (220) make it seem unlikely that the temperature (60°) employed by Schneider was severe enough to produce mainly secondary alkylates with this catalyst, but this point needs to be checked.

Other examples of alkylation with paraffins and cycloparaffins via hydride transfer are discussed in Chapters XXII and XXV.

IX. Appendix (Tables)

TABLE 1. Benzene with ethylene

Benzene (Moles)	Ethylene (Moles)	Catalyst (Moles)	Temp. (°C)	Time (hrs.)	Ethylbenzene products (% Yield) Mono.[b]	di.[b]	tri.[b]	tetra.[b]	penta.[b]	hexa.[b]	Ref.
5	10	AlCl₃ (0.4)–HCl	70–90	—	Mono- (170 g.), di- (135 g.), tri- (75 g.)						a
0.8	—	AlCl₃ (0.5)	80	3–4	1,3,5-Tri- (70%)						(697,785)
1.5	—	AlCl₃ (1)	80–90 86 atm.	—	Hexa- (56–59%)						495
		AlCl₃–H₂O			Mono.[b]	di.[b]	tri.[b]	tetra.[b]	penta.[b]	hexa.[b]	
1	1.03[d]	0.75 —	75	—	27	24	18	—	11	18	
1	2.14[d]	0.75 —	75	—	9	45	28	13	2	3	
1	3.17[d]	0.75 —	75	—	0.3	9	56	25	4	6	
1	4.22[d]	0.75 —	75	—	—	1	17	37	27	18	
1	5.29[d]	0.75 —	75	—	—	—	—	11	39	50	
1	2.09[d]	0.75 —	55	—	9	28	27	9	11	16	
1	2.17[d]	0.75 —	95	—	8	45	41	3	0.3	3	
1	2–2.5[d]	0.75 —	75	—	8	44	35	7	2	4	
1	2–2.5[d]	0.75 0.05%	75	—	9	44	5	2	6	34	
1	2–2.5[d]	0.75 0.1%	75	—	11	22	19	8	3	37	
1	2–2.5[d]	0.75 0.2%	75	—	11	19	14	11	3	42	
1	2–2.5[d]	0.75 0.5%	75	—	10	22	19	11	1	37	
934[bb] g./hr.	139 g./hr.	AlCl₃	—		9,10-Dimethylanthracene						739a
		AlCl₃ (9 g./hr.)–HCl (1 g./hr.)	90	ee	Mono- (500 g./hr. 96%), di-, tri-, and tetra- (200 g./hr.)[cc], higher (5 g./hr.)						372
5	1	AlCl₃–C₂H₄–HCl	66	—	Mono- (12, 30, 96%)[c]						886 (355)
483	103	AlCl₃–EtCl (750 g.)	200 600 psi	0.16 flow	Mono- (86%)						77 (526)
80 pts.	—	AlCl₃–CH₃NO₂–HCl[e] 8/10/3	25–40–65[dd] 40 atm.	1–4–3[dd]	Mono- (12 pts.), higher alkylate (6 pts.)						699 (700)

400 ml.	400 psig	$AlCl_3$-NiO-SiO_2 (1.5% Ni)	225	2.25	Ethyl- (10%), s-butyl- (62%), hexyl- (15%), octyl- (10%), decyl-benzenes (3%) (all vol.%)	38
100 g.	50 atm.[g]	$AlCl_3$-V_2O_5 (5 g./10 g.)	250	5.5	Ethylbenzenes (10 g.)	457
100 g.	50 atm.[g]	$AlCl_3$-WO_3 (5 g./10 g.)	97	5.7	Ethylbenzenes (66 g.)	457
1.92	1	$AlCl_3$-NaCl-Pumice	268 / 200 psig	39.3 SV	Mono- (54%), di- (30%), higher (12%)	591 (592)
200 g.	50 g.	$AlCl_3$ (6 g.)-$SbCl_3$ (10 g.)	70	3	Ethyl derivatives	678
4.5	$C_2^=/C_3^=$ (1)	$AlCl_2 \cdot H_2PO_4$ (1)	9	—	Mono- (60%), cumene (98%)	940
100	10[f]	$AlBr_3$ (1)	9	—	Rates measured	282
66 lbs.	13 lbs.	$EtAlBr_2$-Et_2AlBr (0.21) $TiCl_4$ (0.42)	40	6	Octyl- to hexadecyl- (13 lbs.) mainly dodecyl- (some 7-phenyltridecane, 2-phenyloctane, and 9-phenyl-heptadecane)	461
200 g.	—	$FeCl_3$[y]	75-85	8	No reaction	224
—	—	$FeCl_3$-HCl-H_2O (2/2/5)		4	Mono- (4%)	306
145 g.	93.1 g.	$BeCl_2$ (6.62 g.)-HCl	200	60	Mono- (21%), di- (40%), tri- and higher (17%), hexa-(10%)	245
170 g.	47 g.	$CbCl_5$ (18.2 g.)-HCl	25	5	Mono- (24%), di- (10%), higher (200-245°, 6%), hexa- (8%)	245
152.7 g.	37.7 g.	$TaCl_5$ (19.7 g.)-HCl	25-50	6	Mono- (25%), di- (21%), higher (200-225° 12%), (225-245°, 7%), hexa- (14%)	245
148.8 g.	12.5 g.	$TiCl_4$ (17.1 g.)-HCl	120	6	Mono- (3%), higher (1%)	245
126.4 g.	58.0 g.	$ZrCl_4$ (12.37 g.)-HCl	25-50	29	Mono- (41%), di- (35%), higher (210-220°, 5%), (220°, 7%)	245
10	1	$ZnCl_2$-$Al(OH)_3$	250-300 / 30 atm.	—	Mono- (55-60%)	416
2	1	$ZnCl_2$-Al_2O_3 15-30%	300 / 40 atm.	—	Alkylate (16%): mono-, di-, (o-/m-/p- = 15.4/46.2/38.1), some toluene	740
865 g.	95 g.	$ZnCl_2$ (15-30%)-Silica gel	325 / 1700 psig	0.5	Mono- (66%), di- (17%), penta- (17%) Total 148 g.	578
865 g.	92 g.	$ZnCl_2$ (35 g.)-Silica gel (65 g.)-chloroform (12 g.)	325 / 1500 psig	0.5	Mono- (74%), di-, tri-, and tetra- (26%) Total 226 g.	578

Table continued

TABLE 1 (continued)

Benzene (Moles)	Ethylene (Moles)	Catalyst (Moles)	Temp. (°C)	Time (hrs.)	Ethylbenzene products (% Yield)	Ref.
100 g.	50 atm.[g]	ZrCl$_4$–WO$_3$ (5 g./10 g.)	200	5.5	Ethylbenzenes (44 g.)	457
100 g.	65 g.	TiCl$_3$–Al$_2$O$_3$	200	11	Mono- (19%), di- (20%), tri- (8%), poly- (40%)	908
26.3 g.	680 psig	Al–EtBr–I$_2$ 7.5 g./17.8 g./0.4 g.	176–220	—	Hexa- (17 g.)	45
26.5 g.	600 psig	Raney Ni alloy–EtBr–I$_2$ 12.8 g./17.7 g./0.3 g.	228–267	—	Hexa- (24%)	45
120 g.	2 l.	Al–BuCl (0.1 g./13 g.)	20–30	—	Mono- (48%)	751b
250 g.	60 atm.[g]	Al–TiCl$_4$ (3.5 g./2 g.)[ff]	140–150	6.5	Mono- (25%), di- (18%), tri- (5%), residue (25 g.)	702
100 g.	40 atm.[g]	B–TiCl$_4$ (5 g./2 g.)	250	6.5	Mono- (3%), di- (4%)	702
100 g.	40 atm.[g]	Fe–TiCl$_4$ (10 g./2 g.)	250	6.5	Mono- (16%), di- (4%)	702
100 g.	40 atm.[g]	Zr–TiCl$_4$ (10 g./2 g.)	250	5.5	Mono- (10%), di- (4%)	702
1	0.2	BF$_3$ (5.8%)	104	—	Mono- (86%)	94
3	0.9	BF$_3$–H$_2$O (0.25)	150 psi 20–25	8	Mono- (60%)	315(723,26 85a)
1.3	1	BF$_3$–Ni$_2$P$_2$O$_7$·4H$_2$O	70–80 270–640 psi	4.5	Mono- (28%), di- (5%)	374
2	—	BF$_3$–H$_2$SO$_4$ (11 g./82 g.)	10–20	—	Mono- (10.2 g.), di- (1.5 g.)	923[hh]
4.5	3	BF$_3$–85% H$_3$PO$_4$ (100 cc.)	25–38	—	Mono- (75–85%)[h], di- (15–20%)[h]	27(480,728, 858,840)
1	3.1	BF$_3$/H$_3$PO$_4$ (2 vol./vol. benzene)	100 psig 24	1.5–2	Mono- (28–35%), di- (19–22%), tri-, tetra-, and higher (14–40%), 83–88% conv. of benzene	770
1	3.1	BF$_3$ (0.5)–difluorophosphoric acid (2.4 vol./vol. benzene)	24	1.33	Mono- (21%), 1,2-di- (9%), 1,3-di- (9%), 1,4-di- (10%), tetra-, and penta- (18%), hexa- (25%)	771(840)

		Catalyst	Temp.	Ratio	Products	Ref.
1	3.1	BF₃ᵛ-difluorophosphoric acid (2.4 vol./vol. benzene)	24	0.5	Mono- (27%), 1,3-di- (5%), 1,3,5-tri- (34%), hexa- (29%)	771(840)
3.08	1.07	BF₃-FSO₃H (50 g./93 g.)	r.t. / 800 psi	—	Mono-, di-, tri-	320
87 g.	30 g.	BF₃-FeF₂ (20 g.) HF (123 g.)/(24 g.) C₆H₅NO₂	0-26	1.33	Mono- (27 g.), di-, and tri- (8 g.) hexa- (14 g.)	888
160 g.	38 g.	BF₃ (43 g.)-KHF₂ (40 g.)	300	4	Mono- (78 g.), di- (26 g.), higher (14 g.)	449
645	62.7^k	BF₃ (0.043)-Al₂O₃	121 / 37.4 atm.	—	Mono- (59.7 moles)^i	890(447)
5.3	1	BF₃-θ-Al₂O₃	150	1.50 L.H.S.V.	Mono- (74%)	275
1	3.6	HF (3)	165 / 500 psig	2	Mono- (49%)^f	783(211,212, 594,595,499)
87 g.	30 g.	HF (112 g.)-(24 g.) C₆H₅NO₂	0-5	1.55	Mono- (19 g.), di-, and tri- (6 g.)	888
88 g.	26 g.	HBr (137 g.)	150 / 375-400 psi	4	Ethylbromide (39 g.), mono- (19 g.), higher boiling (6.5 g.)	448
90 cc.	—	H₂SO₄ (90 cc.)-HgSO₄ (10-45 g.)	30	3	Bibenzyl (2.5-6.3 g.), phenylsulfonic acid	688
314 g.	^{aa}	85% H₃PO₄ (103 g.)	300	12	Mono-, di-, tri-^{i}	334
16	1	H₃PO₄	276	1.52 S.V.	Mono- (95%)^h	497
10	18.8	P₂O₅ (50 g.)-cresol (10 g.)- lampblack (24 g.)	250 / 27 atm.		Mono- (23%), di- (42%), tri- (24%), higher (9%)	472(870,45, 473)
1	0.26	H₃PO₄-CuO (1.5/1)	275-300 / 40 atm.		Mono- (89%)	881(879)
7.7	1	H₃PO₄-Sil-o-cel^m	270 / 400 psig	0.016	Mono-/poly- = 12.9/1 (75% conv. of ethylene)	678
15	1	H₃PO₄-Sil-o-cel^m	260-280 / 900 psig		Mono-/poly- = 20/1	678

Table continued

TABLE 1 (continued)

Benzene (Moles)	Ethylene (Moles)	Catalyst (Moles)	Temp. (°C)	Time (hrs.)	Ethylbenzene products (% Yield)	Ref.
10	1	H_3PO_4–kieselguhr	275 900 psi	2 L.H.S.V.	Mono-/di-/poly- = 38/1/0.3 moles di-$o/m/p$ ratio = 29/24/17 + 30% s-butylbenzene	424(343)
10	1^n	Polyphosphoric acid (160 g.) Diatomaceous earth $(43.2 \text{ g.})^p$	290 65 atm.	0.75 L.H.S.V.	Mono- (88%), higher (12%), 99% conv.^{q}	891
8	$1^{o,r}$	Polyphosphoric acid (160 g.) Diatomaceous earth $(43.2 \text{ g.})^p$	290–315 65 atm.	0.57 L.H.S.V.	77–83% conv.^{q}; Mono- (83%), di- (11%), s-butyl (1%), residue (5%)	891
10	1	Phosphate diatomite	325 40 atm.	—	80% Ethylene conversion; 97% to mono-	230
70 pts./hr.	14 pts./hr.	Calcined cupric phosphate (40 volumes)	408 600 psi	11	Mono- (18 pts./hr.), di- (7.2 pts./hr.)	706
80 pts.	—	$Ca(H_2PO_4)_2 \cdot H_2O$ 70 pts.	325 50 atm.	4	Mono- (10 pts.)	683
10	1	$FePO_4$	275 900 psi	2 L.H.S.V.	Mono-/di-/poly- = 25/1/0.3 moles di-/$o/m/p$ ratio = 25/20/14 + 41% s-butylbenzene	424
3.55	1	Fe_2O_3–P_2O_5–SiO_2–CuO (35.1%/67.5%/4.5%/ 0.65%)	300 300–400 psi	56 sec.	Mono- $(82\%)^h$ $(48\%)^w$, poly- (also)	139
2	1	Alumina	370	—	No alkylate	740
13.5 g./hr.	5 l./hr.	Bauxite	450	4	Mono- (9% on C_6H_6)	254
1.5	1	Silica gel	260–74 1000 psig	2 L.H.S.V.	Mono- (68%), poly- (32%)	728
—	—	SiO_2–Al_2O_3	30 20 atm	—	Mono- (16%)	490

		Catalyst	Temp., pressure	L.H.S.V.	Products	Ref.
10	1	SiO₂–Al₂O₃	275 / 900 psi	2 / L.H.S.V.	Mono-/di-/poly- = 10/1/3 moles; di-o/m/p ratio = 18/56/21 + 5% s-butylbenzene	424(725,728, 577,726,91, 254,480,792)
2.8	2.64	73% SiO₂–27% Al₂O₃ (56 g.)	150 / 1000 psi	5	Mono- (60%),[99] di- (20%),[99] tri- (12%)[99]	608
100 ml.	24 g.	Boria–alumina	200	18	Mono-	611
—	—	88% Al₂O₃–12% Cr₂O₃	550	—	Styrene (55%)	182
100 g.	20.41ˢ	Ni–Al₂O₃	350	0.25 / L.H.S.V.ᵗ	Toluene (5 g.)ᵘ	398
100 ml.	—	Al₂O₃ (14%)–SiO₂ (86%)– NaH (1.5 g.) or CaH or LiH	90–150 / 1000 psig	18	Ethylbenzenes (68% vol.) Mono-/di-/tri- = 75/20/5	207
6	1	Silica–alumina–zirconia (95/4/1)	260–276 / 800 psi	0.5	Mono- (81%)ᵏ	725(726,792)
400 ml.	—	1.9% Ni–SiO₂·Al₂O₃ (68.3 g.)	175 / 400 psig	2.75	Mono- (1%),[99] sec-butylbenzene (6%),[99] hexylbenzene (11%),[99] 1-butene, hexene, octene, decene, dodecene	38
3.3	1	Active natural clay–HOAc	243 / 820 psi	1–2	Mono- (16%), di- (5%), poly- (4%)	252
200	50 g.	Amalgamated Al (Al + HgCl₂)	75–85	8	Better catalyst than AlCl₃ Mono- (56 g.), di- (26 g.), higher (50 g.)	224

ᵃ See references 11, 52, 74, 122, 128, 152, 209a, 209b, 224, 229, 255, 379, 424, 523, 538, 662, 763, 782.   Ref. 210 has an extensive bibliography.
ᵇ % Ethylene as.
ᶜ For 60, 85, 75% AlCl₃, respectively.
ᵈ 268 cc./min./mole benzene.
ᵉ Omission of HCl results in low yields.
ᶠ Tagged with C¹⁴.
ᵍ Initial pressure.
ʰ Of alkylate.
ⁱ Also some cumene and ethylated cumene.

ʲ Of ethylene converted.
ᵏ Diluted with 72 H_2, 151 N_2 + CO, 281 CH_4, 96 C_2, 9.3 $C_3^=$, 4 C_3.
ˡ Benzene converted = 70%.
ᵐ About 62% P_2O_5 on diatomaceous earth.
ⁿ C_1 and C_2 present.
ᵒ 10% with N_2, H_2, CH_4.
ᵖ Mixture preheated to 170°, extruded, calcined 1 hr. at 560°.
𐞥 Of ethylene.

Footnotes continued

TABLE 1 (*footnotes continued*)

r 0.25% water based on feed.
s 37.5–50 S.V.
t On benzene.
u Author states ethylbenzene is intermediate.
v 500 psig.
w Of ethylene feed.
x Al–HgCl₂ (2 g./35 g.)
y Equimolar AlCl₃–FeCl₃ gives some alkylation.

aa 60 atm. at 21°.
bb Plus recycled di-, tri-, and tetraethylbenzenes.
cc Recycled.
dd Consecutive heating.
ee 3-Liter vessel.
ff No reaction even at 200° if Al omitted.
gg Volume %.
hh No alkylation when BF₃ is omitted.

TABLE 2. Benzene with propene

Benzene (Moles)	Propene (Moles)	Catalyst (Moles)	Temp. (°C)	Time (hrs.)	Isopropylbenzene products (% Yield)	Ref.
1	1	AlCl₃ (1 mol.%)	80	0.5	Mono- (61%), di- (31%), tri- (2%)	164(599b,180, 145b,52,77, 209)
1	2.4	AlCl₃ (1 mol.%)	80	0.5	Mono- (14%), di- (57%), tri- (27%) ($m/p = 65/35$),	164(29b,32)
1	4.19	AlCl₃ (12.8%)^a	67–72	0.57	Tri- (27%), 1,2,4,5-tetra- (57%), other tetra- (4%), poly- (13%)	895(30,33)
1^{cc}	0.47	AlCl₃	100	—	Mono- (95%)	955
2–X^b	1	AlCl₃ (15%)^{dd}	50	—	Mono- (145, 165, 161, 214, —, 214%)^{b,d} poly- (76, 40, 19, 62, −13, −47%)^{b,d} (0.379, 0.44, 0.464, 0.476, 0.48, —)^{b,c}	599b(855)

480 pts.	$AlCl_3$–HCl (25/25 pts.)	70–100	4	Di- (343 pts.), (m/p = 60/40), lower aromatics (112 pts.), higher (169 pts.)	118(356)
520 pts.				1,3,5-Tri- (98% of charge)	426a
1650 pts. 97.2 kg./hr.	$AlCl_3$–HCl (82.5/82.5 pts.)	70–100	5.5	Mono- (172.8 kg./hr.), m-di- (172.8 kg./hr.), tri- (54 kg./hr.)	372(123)
2575 pts. 49 kg./hr.	$AlCl_3$–HCl (1.5/0.4 kg./hr.)	85	3.66		
1700 pts.	$AlCl_3$ (9 pts.), iso-C_3H_7Cl (6.8 pts.)	65–100	2.5	Mono- (12%), di- (28%), tri- (50%), tetra- (2%)	519(426b,117)
15 g.	$AlCl_3$ (1 g.)–CH_3NO_2 (2.3 g.)	43	2.5	Mono- (61%), di- (35%), higher (5 g.)	700(129)
80 g. 24 g.	$AlCl_3$ (5 g.)–$C_2H_5NO_2$ (5.7 g.)	47	3	Mono- (45%), di- (35%), higher (7 g.)	700
40 g. 6 g.	$AlCl_3$ (5 g.)–iso-$C_3H_7NO_2$ (7.5 g.)	r.t.	—	Mono- (55%), di- (39%), higher (3 g.)	700
80 pts. 28.5	$AlCl_3$ (5 pts.)–1-chloro-1-nitropropane (10 pts.)	35	4	Mono- (30 pts.), di- (18 pts.), higher boiling (13 pts.)	698
100 pts. —	$AlCl_2$–Ac_2O 65/50 (20 pts.)	60	—	Mono:poly = 2:1 at 50% conv. of benzene	708
156 g. 15.4 g.	$AlCl_3$–H_3BO_3 (1/0.33 mole)–HCl (10 g.)	100	4	Mono-	501
80 g. 20 g.	$AlCl_3$ (0.038)–$NaCl$ (0.034)–CH_3NO_2 (10 cc.)	60 30 atm.	4	Mono- (14%), higher (6 g.)	700
80 g. 20 g.	$AlCl_3$–$NaCl$–CH_3NO_2 as above + HCl (2.5 g.)	60 30 atm.	4	Mono- (55%)	700
2	$AlCl_2$–HSO_4 (10%)[dd]	25		Mono- (54.4 g.), di- (o/p = 70/30)	845(599b)
80 pts. 21 pts.	$AlCl_3$–$ZnCl_2$	125	1.5	Mono- (128%)[d], di- (13%)[d]	57
80 pts. 21 pts.	$AlCl_2 \cdot H_2PO_4$ (5 pts.)	25	4	Mono- (25 pts.); high boilers > 163° (18 pts.)	344
100 3 l.	Al (0.15 g.)–iso-C_3H_7Br (3.5 g.)	20–23	—	Mono- (71%), di- and poly- (2.5 g.)	751b
1 2.7	$AlBr_3$–hydrocarbon complex (26 g.)	45 10 psig	0.8	Mono- (34%), di- (15%), tri- (3%)	241

Table continued

TABLE 2 (*continued*)

Benzene (Moles)	Propene (Moles)	Catalyst (Moles)	Temp. (°C)	Time (hrs.)	Isopropylbenzene products (% Yield)	Ref.
100 ml.	10 psig	Et_2AlBr–$EtAlBr_2$ (0.0013) $TiCl_4$ (0.0026)	40	8	Hexyl- to C_{30}-benzene, mainly C_{12}- to C_{18}-benzene (60 g.)	461
	—	$FeCl_3$ (0.3)	25	—	Mono- (91%)	645
80 g.	21 g.	$FeCl_3$ (15 g.)	350	4	Mono- (39 g.), di- (7.3 g.)	707
	1	$FeCl_3$–HCl–H_2O (2/2/5)	1500 psi (H_2)	4	Mono- (13%)	306
4–6	1[f]	$ZnCl_2$ (20–40%)–Al_2O_3	200, 5 atm.	0.45 S.V.	Mono- (75%)[d], di- (25%)	741
2	1	$ZnCl_2$–Al_2O_3	300	0.15 S.V.	Mono- (53%)	741(417)
4–6	1[f]	$ZnCl_2$ (20%)–SiO_2	200, 5 atm.	0.45 S.V.	Mono- (30%)	741
10	1	30% $ZnCl_2$ on $Al(OH)_3$ clay or silica gel	180–200	—	Mono- (50–70%)	416
	—	RMgCl–HCl		—	Alkylation	65
80 pts.	21 pts.	$MgCl_2$–Al_2O_3 (25/75)	350	4	Mono- (10 pts.), di- (5 pts.), higher (26 pts.)	704
285 g.	52 g.	BF_3 (13 g.) Air (0.75) (62 g. pentane)	100 atm. (H_2), 150	2	Mono- (21%), di- (5%), higher (2%)	906
4	3.77	BF_3–H_2O (1.0/1.5) (83 g.)	33–36	9	Mono- (92%)[g]	26(129,599b, 85a)
1	3	Dihydroxyfluoroboric acid (8.4 g.)		—	No alkylation	169
5.6	2	BF_3–CH_3OH (50 cc.)	27–32	h	Mono- (62%)[g], poly- (38%)[g]	727
		BF_3–C_2H_5OH (60 g.)	27–30	h	Mono- (51%)[g]	727
2.8	2.25	BF_3–iso-C_3H_7OH (40 g.)	30–33	h	Mono- (87%)[g]	727
6.2	451 g.	BF_3 (4 g.)–Phenol (6 g.)	i	—	Mono- (173 g.), di- (221 g.), tri- (126 g.), tetra- (88 g.)	769
1.93	—	BF_3 (9 g.)–HOAc (8 g.)	25	3.5	Mono- (2 g.)	769

		Catalyst	Temp.	Time	Products	Ref.
1.93	—	BF₃ (1.5 g.)-ClCH₂CO₂H (16 g.)	25	3.5	Mono- (9 g.)	769
1.93	—	BF₃ (1.5 g.)-Cl₃CCO₂H (29 g.)	25	3.5	Mono- (17 g.)	769
2	1.5	BF₃-H₂SO₄ 1.0/0.15	4	2	Mono- (50%), p-di- (30%). 1,2,4-tri- 82-95% Mono-	769(923,27)
1.5-4.0	1-3.5	60-98% BF₃-H₃PO₄ (50 cc.)^dd	25-30	8.7	Mono- (41-68%), di- (32-53%), some tri-	27(858,600, 854,599)
1		BF₃-H₂O (11.3%) + BF₃-H₃PO₄ (88.7%)^dd	50	—		846(599b)
2	1	40 cc. BF₃·H₂PO₃F, BF₃·HPO₂F₂, or BF₃·H₃PO₄	20	—	Mono- (89-91%)	841
1		BF₃-H₃PO₄ (3-4 vol.%)^j plus H₂SO₄^n	50-55	1-1.2^k	Mono- (42%)^g,l,m	37
629.8	9.3°	BF₃ (0.048)-Al₂O₃	121, 37.4 atm.	—	Mono- (7.3 moles)^p	890(58)
2-10	3-7	H₂SO₄ (1.5-3)	10	2	Mono- (32-78%), p-di- (33-18%), tri- (12%-0%), 1,2,4,5-tetra- (2%-0%), 1,2,4,5-Tetra- (34%)	313(13,923, 599b)
130-140 l.		H₂SO₄ (50 cc.)	0, 8	—		389
240 kg./hr.	48.6 kg./hr.	98% H₂SO₄ (55 kg./hr.)	8	—	Mono- (106 kg./hr.); higher mainly p-di- (20 kg./hr.)	786
	C₃=/C₂= (70/30)	H₂SO₄	—	—	Mono- and di-. (Ethylene is unchanged)	786
4	1	80-96% H₂SO₄ (0.75-1)	40-85	—	Mono- (76-96% propene converted)	142
5.2-6.2	1	88-90% H₂SO₄^q	35-40, 165 psig	0.55	Mono- (10-12 vol./vol.% acid)	462a
	18 (32C₂=)	84% H₂SO₄	45	9	Mono- (82%)	880
48.1 lbs.^r	2	88% H₂SO₄	30-40	—	Mono- (24.5 lbs.), di- (100 lbs.), tri- (47.4 lbs.), tetra- (1.8 lbs.), benzene (1.8 lbs.)	166

Table continued

TABLE 2 (continued)

Benzene (Moles)	Propene (Moles)	Catalyst (Moles)	Temp. (°C)	Time (hrs.)	Isopropylbenzene products (% Yield)	Ref.
117 pts.	126 pts.[bb]	80% H_2SO_4 (73.5 pts.)	50–80	—	Mono- (80.6 pts.), di- (95 pts.), $(o:m:p) = (2:4:6)$, tri- and tetra- (28 pts.)	187
2	1	BF_3–H_3PO_4, $AlCl_3$, $AlCl_2 \cdot HSO_4$, $BF_3 \cdot H_2O$, H_2SO_4	50	—	Mono- (82%, 58%, 49%, 88%, 71%, resp.), higher alkylate (8%, 26%, 36%, 4%, 15%, resp.)	599b(601)
1.12	1.35	CH_3SO_3H (or homologs)	65–75 40 psi	—	Mono- (46%), di- (28%), tri- (6%)	652
3.05	1	H_3PO_4	255 385 psi	35 S.V.	Mono- (88%)[g]	462a(497)
5.2	1	H_3PO_4 (100–106%) on quartz	150–200 250 psi	—	Mono- (94–98%), di- (3%)	426e(426d, 427)
150 g.	50 g.	P_2O_5–H_3PO_4 / $B_4O_7 \cdot (H_3P_2O_6)_2$ (25 g.)	80 / 275 175 atm.	— / 1.5	Mono- / Mono- (0.8 mole), di- (0.2 mole)	870 / 362
1	1	H_3PO_4–kieselguhr	237 255 psi	flow	Mono- (30 vol.%) (76%)[g] poly- (12 vol.%)	111(342, 509a,887s)
2.5	1	H_3PO_4–kieselguhr	90, 180, 200	0.4 S.V. 15 atm.	Mono- (39%, 61%, 64%),[t] poly- (10%, 16%, 24%)[t]	149
2.5	1	H_3PO_4–kieselguhr	180, 200, 220, 240, 270	2 S.V. 15 atm.	Mono- (30%, 36%, 48%, 51%, 55%),[t] poly- (11%, 11%, 18%, 20%, 19%)[t]	149
5.5–5.8	1	H_3PO_4–kieselguhr	180	0.37, 1, 2, 3, 4 S.V.	Mono- (61%, 54%, 44%, 40%, 35%),[u] poly- (16%, 16%, 11%, 10%, 6%)[u]	149
2–5	0.5–1	HF (5)	0	5	Mono- (84%)	110(211,753, 755)

Aromatic	Alkene/Alkane	Catalyst	Temp.	Pressure	Time	Products	Ref.
5	23	HF (25)	20		24	1,2,4,5-Tetra- (77%)	110
3.22	1	HF	45	102 psig	29 sec.	Mono- (85%)	95
8.3	$C_2^=$ (181 g.), $C_3^=$ (85 g.)	HF (1/1.3)[v]	48		0.33	Mono- (94 vol.%), di- (6 vol.%)	499(754)
875 g.	88 g.	HF (200g.)	r.t.		5–6	Mono- (96%)[aa]	595
441 g.	20 pts.	HBr (191 g.)	10	10–150 psi	4.25	Isopropylbromide (191 g.), cumene (9 g.), higher boiling (4 g.)	448
80 pts.	20 pts.	HCl (3 pts.)	300[ee]		4	Mono- (14 pts.), higher (5 pts.)	703
80 pts.	20 pts.	$Cu_2P_2O_7$ (10 pts.)	350	50 atm.	4	Mono- (35 pts.), higher boiling (5 pts.)	685(380)
80 pts.	20 pts.	$Cu_3(PO_4)_2 \cdot 3H_2O$ (10 pts.)	300	50 atm.	4	Mono- (56%)	706(879)
5	1	$Cu_2P_2O_7$—carbon	204–232	900 psi	flow	Propylated benzene	426h
80 pts.	20 pts.	Calcined cupric phosphate (10 pts.)	350	50 atm. N_2	4	Mono- (39 pts.), higher (10 pts.)	706
80 pts.	20 pts.	$Ca(H_2PO_4)_2 \cdot H_2O$ (10 pts.)	300		4	Mono- (33 pts.) higher (4 pts.)	683
80 pts.	20 pts.	$Ag_4P_2O_7$ (10 pts.)	300	50 atm.	4	Mono- (34 pts.), higher boiling (7 pts.)	685
27	1	Iron phosphate	250	400 psi	46 sec.	Mono- (91%)[g], polyisopropyl benzene (9%)[g], propene conv. (77%)	139
80 pts.	20 pts.	Al_2O_3—HCl	300[ee]		4	Mono- (12 pts.), higher (5 pts.)	703
4–6	1′	Al_2O_3—HCl	200	5 atm.	0.45 S.V.	No alkylation	741
80 pts.	20 pts.	Al_2O_3-ZnO—HCl (7/3/2.7 pts.)	300	100 atm. H_2	4	Mono- (56%), di- (23%), higher (3 pts.)	703
80 pts.	20 pts.	Silica gel (10 pts.) HCl (18 pts.)	200	100 atm. H_2	4	Mono- (21 pts.), di- (12 pts.), higher (3 pts.)	703
4–6	1	SiO_2—Al_2O_3	382–462	75–500 psig	0.33–0.5	Mono- (48–69%)	577(477,488, 724,830,831)

Table continued

TABLE 2 (*continued*)

Benzene (Moles)	Propene (Moles)	Catalyst (Moles)	Temp. (°C)	Time (hrs.)	Isopropylbenzene products (% Yield)	Ref.
2	1	Silica-alumina	177 400 psi	0.5	Mono- (40%), di- (13%)	725(569,972)
1	2	Aluminosilicate	350 20 atm.	0.5 L.H.S.V.	Di- (34%) $o/m/p = 5.8/57-65/30-36$	818
3.5	1	SiO_2–Al_2O_3	350 10–30 atm.	3.5–4.0 W.H.S.V.	Mono- (120–130%)[d]	167a
4	1	Silica-alumina[w]	300 10 atm.	0.5–1 S.V.	Alkylbenzene (90%)	817
1	2	SiO_2–Al_2O_3[dd]	149–204	0.5–4.0 S.V. upflow	1,3,5-Tri-	714
—	83%	SiO_2–Al_2O_3	20	upflow	Mono- (33%), di- (49%), tri- (10%), tetra- (8%)	849
			50	upflow	Mono- (44%), di- (41%), tri- (11%), tetra- (4%)	
			70–80	upflow	Mono- (54%), di- (25%), tri- (16%), tetra- (5%)	
1	2	SiO_2–Al_2O_3	30 2 atm.	—	Di- (36%)	490
48.4 g.	70 psig	SiO_2–Al_2O_3 (4 g.) $SiCl_4$ (9 g.)	85–134	0.5	Mono- and di-	238
(20 l.)	1600 g.	HF treated silica–Al_2O_3	250 500 psig	2 L.H.S.V.	Mono-	922
3 l.	350 g.	Filtrol-13 (100 g.)	90	8	Mono- (625 g.), poly-isopropylbenzene (305 g.)	20a(674)
1	0.45[x]	Activated clay	350 60 atm.	0.5 L.H.S.V.	Mono- (36%)	474(489)
4	1	Bentonite-type clay (14.2 wt.%)[a]	79–90	4.5	Mono- (34%), poly-isopropylbenzene (4%)	365
1	2	Magnesium aluminosilicate	350 20 atm.	0.5 L.H.S.V.	Di- (30%), $o/m/p = 5.8/57-65/30-36$	818

1	2	Nickel aluminosilicate	350 20 atm.	0.5 L.H.S.V.	Di- (30%), $o/m/p$ = 5.8/57–65/30–36	818
50 pts.	1	Nickel molybdite (5 pts.)	200	5	Mono- plus di- (58 pts.)	198
2		BF$_3$–H$_3$PO$_4$, AlCl$_3$, AlCl$_2$·HSO$_4$, BF$_3$–H$_2$O, H$_2$SO$_4$	50	—	Poly- (10, 35, 54, 6, 20%)^a (93/78, 60/90, 58/70, 93/80, 70/75)^{y,z}	599b
1	1	AlCl$_3$	50	—	Mono- (70%), di- (24%), tri- (5%), tetra- (2%)	849
1	1	SiO$_2$–Al$_2$O$_3$	50	—	Mono- (53%), di- (37%), tri- (8%), tetra- (2%)	849
1	1	AlCl$_2$·HSO$_4$	50	—	Mono- (58%), di- (24%), tri- (10%), tetra- (8%)	849
1	1	BF$_3$–H$_3$PO$_4$	50	—	Mono- (84%), di- (11%), tri- (5%), tetra- (1%)	849

^{a} Based on benzene.
^{b} Where X = 0, 0.25, 0.65, 0.9, and 1.0 moles recycled poly-. No advantage noted in recycling poly- with the H$_2$SO$_4$ or H$_3$PO$_4$–BF$_3$ catalysts.
^{c} Kg. alkylation product/1 of reactor space for each value of X.
^{d} Based on propene.
^{e} Plus recycled m-di- and tri-.
^{f} Diluted with N$_2$.
^{g} Of alkylate.
^{h} Propylene rate 90–95 ml./min.
^{i} Temp. allowed to rise to maximum.
^{j} Concentration of catalyst in reactor 38 mm. × 100 mm.
^{k} Contact time.
^{l} Versus 23–26% for AlCl$_3$.
^{m} Purer than AlCl$_3$ product.
^{n} 5 parts added per 95 parts catalyst to prevent corrosion of carbon–steel reactor.
^{o} Diluted with 72 H$_2$, 151 N$_2$ + CO, 281 CH$_4$, 62.7 C$_2^=$, 96 C$_2$, 4C$_3$.
^{p} Plus ethylated arenes.
^{q} 1 vol. per vol. hydrocarbon.   Optimum 86% H$_2$SO$_4$ at 50°, 88% at 40°.

Footnotes continued

TABLE 2 (*footnotes continued*)

r 24.5 lbs. mono-, 47.4 lbs. tri-, and 1.8 lbs. tetra- also included in feed.
s Water added with feed.
t For each catalyst, respectively.
u For each S.V., respectively.
v Vol. ratio to reactants.
w Fluidized bed.
x Feed = 16.7-19% C_3, 76.6-77.2% $C_3^=$, balance = C_2, $C_2^=$, C_4.

y Per cent di- in poly- fraction/per cent p in di-.
z For each catalyst, respectively.
aa Essentially all propene converted.
bb 3/1 $C_3^=/C_2^=$ mixture.
cc Includes 20% diisopropylbenzene.
dd See last four entries of this Table.
ee 100 atm. H_2 initial pressure.

TABLE 3. Benzene with *n*-butenes

Benzene (Moles)	Olefin (Moles)	Catalyst (Moles)	Temp. (°C)	Time (hrs.)	s-Butylbenzenes (% Yield)	Ref.
2	Butene (1)	$AlCl_3$ (15%)	—	—	Mono- (56%), poly- (15%)	847(854)
2	2-Butene (1)	$AlCl_3$ (0.2)	50	3.1[d]	Mono- (61%), di- (13%)	940
0.74	Butene (0.24)	$AlCl_2 \cdot HSO_4$ (0.075)	0-30	12-30	Mono-, p-di, and 1,3,5-tri- (total 78-86%)	752a
2	Butene (1)	$AlCl_2 \cdot HSO_4$ (15%)	50	6	Mono- (41%), higher (38%)	847
—	1-Butene	RMgCl–HCl	200	1	Alkylation	65
-.5	2-Butene (1)	$ZnCl_2$–Al_2O_3 (25/75)	40 atm.	L.H.S.V.	Butylbenzenes: mono- (43%) (t/s = 2/98), di- (32%)	618
2	Butene (1)	BF_3–H_2O (15%)	50	6	Mono- (87%), higher (5%)	847
1	Butene (3)	Dihydroxyfluoboric acid (8.4 g.)	—	—	Mono- (32%), poly- (14%)	169
1	Butene (32 g.)	Dihydroxyfluoboric acid (2 g.)	30-35	—	Mono- (18 g.), di- (5 g.)	559
2.8	2-Butene (1.4)[a]	BF_3–CH_3OH or BF_3–C_4H_9OH (47.5 g.)	27-30	—	Mono- (73-87%)[b]	727
2	2-Butene (1)	BF_3–H_3PO_4 (500 cc.)	30-32	—	Mono- (85%)[b]	27(847,854)

2	Butene (1)	88.7% BF_3–H_3PO_4 11.3% BF_3–H_2O	50	6	Mono- (85%), poly- (6%)	847
1	Butene (0.46)	$BF_3 \cdot H_3PO_4$–H_2SO_4 (95/5) (5–6 vol.%)	50–55	—	Mono- (56%) (t/s = 70/30), polymer (10–12%)	37
59 g.	Butene (25 l.)	H_2SO_4 (100 g.)	45 Stir	1.5	Mono-/di-/tri- = 30/57/10 (di-$o/m/p$ = 1/4/95)	925(313)
—	Butene	91–99% H_2SO_4	15–20	1	Mono- (92%)	876
—	1-Butene	H_2SO_4–H_3PO_4 (85%) 0/100 to 100/0	60	3	Best results with 40/60 ratio	309
1.25	2-Butene (0.5)	Silicophosphoric acid	255 40 atm.	1 L.H.S.V.	Butylbenzenes: mono- (75%) (t/s = 13/87); di- (8%)	618
2.5	2-Butene (1)	Al_2O_3/3.6%–8.2% F^c	360–370 40 atm.	1 L.H.S.V.	Dimer (20–25%), butylbenzene (31–35%) (t/s = 5/95 to 6/94), dibutylbenzene (18–28%)	615
6	2-Butene (1)	Silica-alumina (fluidized)	350	1 L.H.S.V.	Mono- (63%)	817(48,488, 725,945)
2.5	2-Butene (1)	Silica-alumina	250 40 atm.	1 L.H.S.V.	Mono- (56%), di- (18%)	618
—	Butene	Activated clay (18%)	454 1600 psi	0.5 L.H.S.V.	Alkylate to 210° (53%)	674(672)

6+F.C. II

ᵃ 90 ml./min.   ᵇ Of alkylate.   ᶜ Al_2O_3/0.0% F gives no product.   ᵈ l./hr.

TABLE 4. Benzene with isobutylene

Benzene (Moles)	Isobutylene (Moles)	Catalyst (Moles)	Temp. (°C)	Time (hrs.)	t-Butylbenzenes (% Yield)	Ref.
225 g.	230 g.	AlCl₃ (15 g.)–HCl	54–60	3	Mono- (18%),[b] m-di- (16%),[b] p-di- (22%),[b] higher (39%)[b]	357(105,133, 436[c])
100 g.	4 l.	Al–BuCl (0.2 g./3.7 g.)	40–45	—	Mono- (40%), di- and poly- (8 g.)	751b
		AlCl₂·H₂PO₄	—	—	Mono-	750
1	1	FeCl₃ (0.3)	25	—	Mono- (89%)	645
1	2	FeCl₃ (0.15)	25	—	p-Di-	645
		ZnCl₂–Al₂O₃	—	—	Mono-	417
4	3.8	BF₃–H₂O (92.5 g.) (1/1.04)	27–30	10.5	Mono- (50%)[a]	26(71)
4	3.8	BF₃–H₂O (92.5 g.) (1/1.04)	27–30	flow	Mono- (75%)[a]	26
2	1	BF₃–H₃PO₄ (25%)	50	—	Mono- (65%), higher (20%), (mostly p-di, no tri-)	847(27,750)
2	2.5	H₂SO₄ (1.5) (Cyclohexane)	15	1.2	Mono- (7%), p-di- (77%), tri- (8%)	313
	—	P₂O₅	200–240	2	Mono- (50%), p-di- (15%)	472
2.5	1	Silicophosphoric acid	250	1	Butylbenzenes: mono- (31%),	618
			40 atm.	L.H.S.V.	(t/s = 87/13), di- (2%)	
1	3	HF (400%)[b]	19	4	Mono- (2%), di- (14% m, 17% p), 1,3,5-tri- (19%), higher (40%)	464(753,754, 755)

[a] Of alkylate.

[b] Vol.%.

[c] Product reported (436) as 1-isopropyl-3-t-butylbenzene is no doubt 1,3-di-t-butylbenzene (see ref. 133).

TABLE 5.   Benzene with amylenes

Benzene (Moles)	Olefin (Moles)	Catalyst (Moles)	Temp. (°C)	Time (hrs.)	Alkylbenzenes (% Yield)	Ref.
5	1-Pentene (1)	AlCl₃ᶠ (2 g.)	5-27	1	Amylbenzene (87 g.), higher (27 g.) (mol. wt. = 298)	6
4	1-Pentene (1)	AlCl₃-t-C_4H_9Cl–HCl 2 pts./ 5 pts./-	30-40	1	Amyl- (mono- 56%, di- 4%, tri- 16%, penta- 16%)	532
390 g.	1-Pentene (280 g.)	$CuF_2 \cdot 2H_2O$–H_2O (35 g./900 g.)	304	2	Amyl-	838
2,4	1-Pentene (1)	30% $ZnCl_2$–Al_2O_3	350	0.5 L.H.S.V.	Alkylbenzene (26,42%)ʲ (85ʲ/15, 77ʲ/22)ʲ,ᵏ	742
0.4	1-Pentene (0.3)	H_2SO_4 (0.6)	40 atm. 5	1.2	2- and 3-Phenylpentanes (65%) (3/2 mixture)	341(313,389)
2.8	2-Pentene (2.8)	BF_3–CH_3OH (42 g.)	32-38	5	2-Phenylpentaneᵍ (68%)ᵈ	727
3	2-Pentene (2)	BF_3–H_3PO_4	30	—	2-Phenylpentaneᵍ (80%)ᵈ	27
240 pts.	2-Pentene (30 pts.)	HF (20 pts.)	0	3	2-Phenylpentaneᵍ (35 pts.)	753(755)
4	Pentene (1)	30% $ZnCl_2$–Al_2O_3	350 40 atm.	—	Alkylate (42%)	747
2	3-Methyl-1-butene (1)	88.7% BF_3–H_3PO_4 + 11.3% BF_3–H_2O (15%)	0, 30, 80	1.33	t-Amyl- (30, 42, 57%),ᵇ higher (47, 37, 25%)ᵇ	420
4	3-Methyl-1-butene (1)	30% $ZnCl_2$–Al_2O_3	350 40 atm.	—	Alkylate (74%)	747
5	3-Methyl-1-butene (1)	AlCl₃ᶠ (1 g.)	5-27	1	Heavy monoalkylate (100%)	6
5	3-Methyl-1-butene (1)	$AlCl_3$ (0.2)–HCl	0	0.68	Amyl-, (38, 42%),ᵇ (55/45, 11/87)ᵃ,ᵏ	218(341)
5	3-Methyl-1-butene (1)	HF (5)	21ᶠ 35 100	0.60 0.65 0.6	Amyl- (27%, 32%)ᵇ (100/1, 70/30)ᵃ t-butyl- (0%, 2%)ᵇ	218
5	3-Methyl-1-butene (3)	H_2SO_4 (1.8)	5	2	t-Amyl- (20%), di-t-amyl- (56%)	339(341)
4	3-Methyl-1-butene (1)	$NiCl_2$–Al_2O_3	300 40 atm.	0.5 L.H.S.V.	2-Methyl-2-phenylbutane (59%)	746

Table continued

TABLE 5 (continued)

Benzene (Moles)	Olefin (Moles)	Catalyst (Moles)	Temp. (°C)	Time (hrs.)	Alkylbenzenes (% Yield)	Ref.
10 pts.	2-Methyl-2-butene	$AlCl_3$	21	0.56	t-Amylbenzene (55%)[c]	834
5	2-Methyl-2-butene (1)	$AlCl_3$ (0.2)–HCl	0	0.5	Amyl- (42, 54, 39%),[b] (55/45, 75/25, 100/0)[a,b] t-butyl- (5, 1, 1%)[b]	219(218)
5	2-Methyl-2-butene (1)	$AlCl_3$ (3.5 g.)[e] (5 cc. t-$C_5H_{11}Cl$)	—40, 22	0.83, 1.6	t-Butyl- (25%), some amyl-, hexyl-, and decyl-	219
5	2-Methyl-2-butene (1)	$AlBr_3$ (27 g.)–HBr	25, 25	1 sec., 0.42	Amyl- (22, 21%)[m] 90/10, 70/30),[a] t-butyl- (17, 13%)[m]	219
0.55	2-Methyl-2-butene	$TiCl_4$ (0.1)	80	6	t-Amyl- (40%)	147
4	2-Methyl-2-butene (1)	30% $ZnCl_2$–Al_2O_3	350, 40 atm.	—	Alkylate (25%), t-amyl- (15.5 g.), 1- and 2-methyl-naphthalene (3 g.)	747
5	2-Methyl-2-butene (1)	BF_3 (1)	28, 119	0.65, 0.5	Amyl- (10, 11%)[b] (100/0, 80/20),[a] t-butyl- (6, 6%)[b]	218
5	2-Methyl-2-butene (1)	BF_3 (105 g.)–H_2O (36 g.)	24	0.5	Amyl- (54%) (approx. 100/0)[a]	218
1	2-Methyl-2-butene (0.5)	88.7% BF_3–H_3PO_4 / 11.3% BF_3–H_2O } 11.7 g.	50	2.5	Alkylate (88%) (t-amyl- 63%, di-t-amyl- 36%, bottoms 2%)	420
5	2-Methyl-2-butene (1)	BF_3–HF (27/100 g.)	0	0.3	Amyl- (51%) (75/25),[a] t-butyl- (7%)	218
5	2-Methyl-2-butene (1)	H_2SO_4 (185 g.)	0	1.11	Amyl- (4%) (100/0),[a] t-butyl- (2%)	218(305)
5	2-Methyl-2-butene (1)	HF (100 g.)	100	0.56	Amyl- (32%), (70/30),[a] t-butyl- (2%)	219(753,754, 755,759)
2.3	Amylene (0.7)	$AlCl_3$ (0.2)	80	—	t-Amyl-[c] (20%)	189
50 g.	Isoamylene (8.2 g.)	Al-iso-$C_5H_{11}Cl$ (0.2 g./1.85 g.)	75–80	—	t-Amyl-[c] (46%), di- and poly- (0.9 g.)	751b

				12/r.t. 1/20–30°	Amyl- (mono- 42%; di- 22%)	752a
70 g.	Isoamylenes (20 g.)	AlCl₃·HSO (14.3 g.)	0			
390 g.	Isoamylenes (175 g.)	H₂SO₄ (100 cc.)	—	452	t-Amyl- (18%), di-t-amyl- (50%)	339
3	Amylene (1)	Activated clay (25%)	1300 psi	0.58	Alkylate to 210° (31%)	674

[a] Ratio 2-phenyl-2-methylbutane to 2-phenyl-3-methylbutane.
[b] Results at the different temperatures.
[c] Reviewers believe this is a mixture of isomers listed in footnote a; see ref. 219.
[d] Of alkylate.
[e] Added portionwise.
[f] Much polymer at −40°.
[g] Probably mixture of 2- and 3-phenylpentanes (341).
[h] Literature value corrected by recent gas chromatography analysis.
[i] Trace of H₂O.
[j] For each mol. ratio feed, respectively.
[k] Ratio mono-/higher.
[l] t-Amyl, probably some 2-methyl-3-phenylbutane and 3-methyl-4-phenylbutane.
[m] For different contact times.

TABLE 6. Benzene with hexenes

Benzene (Moles)	Olefin (Moles)	Catalyst (Moles)	Temp. (°C)	Time (hrs.)	Products (% Yield)	Ref.
1	1-Hexene (1)	66° H_2SO_4 (0.1)	25	1	2-Phenylhexane[f] (50%)	78
1	1-Hexene (1, 2, 3)	H_2SO_4[a]	10	1	Hexylbenzenes (mono- 48–65%,[b] di- 26–52%,[c] tri- 10–20%)[d]	484
10	1-Hexene (1)	HF (10)	16	—	2- and 3-Phenylhexanes (37/63 ratio)	582
1	3-Hexene (0.66)	$H_3BO_2F_2$ (5 g.)	reflux, 140	0.65, 3–4	3-Phenylhexane[f] (24%)	779
1	3-Hexene (0.05)	H_2SO_4 (0.1)	25	—	3-Phenylhexane[f] (50%)	779
3	3-Hexene (2.07)	HF (10)	5–10	24	3-Phenylhexane[f] (59%), 1,4-di-(1'-ethylbutyl)benzene (24%)[g]	779
1	3-Hexene (3)	HF (10)	5–10	24	3-Phenylhexane[f] (13%), 1,4-di-(1'-ethylbutyl)benzene (41%)[g]	779
5	2-Methyl-1-pentene (0.5)	$AlCl_3$[e] (1.1 g.)	5–27	1	Light alkylate (7 g.); heavy alkylate (27 g.), mol.wt. 340, 10% C_6H_5R, 53% olefins	6
5	2-Methyl-2-pentene (0.5)	$AlCl_3$[e] (3.2 g.)	5–27	1	Light alkylate (18 g.); heavy alkylate (26 g.), mol.wt. 256, 23% C_6H_5R	6
5	4-Methyl-1-pentene (1)	$AlCl_3$[e] (1.8 g.)	5–27	1	Alkylate (91.5 g.), mol.wt. 705, 83% C_6H_5R	6
5	4-Methyl-1-pentene (0.5)	$AlCl_3$[e] (1.0 g.)	5–27	1	Alkylate (42.4 g.), mol.wt. 598, 65% C_6H_5R	6
5	4-Methyl-2-pentene (0.5)	$AlCl_3$[e] (4 g.)	5–27	1	Light alkylate (18 g.); heavy alkylate (9 g.), mol.wt. 246, 27% C_6H_5R, 69% olefins	6
2.56	2,3-Dimethyl-2-butene (0.48)	H_2SO_4 (80 g.)	2	2	2,3-Dimethyl-2-phenylbutane (17%), 1,4-bis-(1,1,2-trimethylpropyl)benzene (25%)	713
2.05	2,3-Dimethyl-2-butene (0.38)	HF (70 g.)	—	1	2,3-Dimethyl-2-phenylbutane (50%), 1,4-bis-(1,12-trimethylpropyl)benzene (32%)	713

[a] Equal amount.
[b] With 1/1 feed ratio.
[c] With 2/1 feed ratio.
[d] With 3/1 feed ratio.
[e] Traces of H_2O.
[f] Probably a mixture of phenylhexane isomers (582).
[g] Probably contains 1'-methylamyl side chains (582).

TABLE 7.   Benzenes with heptenes and higher olefins

Benzene (Moles)	Olefin (Moles)	Catalyst (Moles)	Temp. (°C)	Time (hrs.)	Benzene derivatives (Yield)	Ref.
—	C_5, C_6, C_7, or C_8 olefins[a]	$FeCl_3$	—	—	Amyl, hexyl, heptyl, or octyl- (68%)	421
10 pts.	C_5, C_6, C_7, C_8, C_9, C_{10}, C_{11}, or C_{16} olefins[a]	$AlCl_3$ or $AlBr_3$	—	—	Amyl- (69.3%), hexyl- (76%), heptyl- (68%), octyl- (72%), nonyl- (58%), decyl- (62%), undecyl- (44%), or octyl- (48%)	834
1	1-Heptene (0.2–0.25)	92–98% H_2SO_4 (40–50 g.)	3–4	0.75–1.16	2-, 3-, and 4-Phenylheptanes (72–79%)[b] in 1/1/1 ratio	25
1	1-Heptene (1, 2, 3)	H_2SO_4[d]	10	1	Heptyl- (48–65%),[e] di- (26–52%),[f] tri- (10–20%)[g]	484
1	1-Octene (1, 2, 3)	H_2SO_4[d]	10	1	Octyl- (48–65%),[e] di- (26–52%),[f] tri- (10–20%)[g]	484
390 g.	1-Octene (280 g.)	H_2SO_4 (100 cc.)	5–15	0.5	2-Phenyloctane (81%),[h] dioctyl- (8%)	185(313)
1.79	1-Octene (1)	HF (4)	240	4.5	Octyl- (52%), dioctyl- (18%), residue (19%)	739c
1	1-Octene (0.25)	HF (0.37, 0.75, 1.0) $CHCl_3$ (0.25)	0	0.75	Octyl- (3, 17, 85–89%)[i]	739c
1.79	1-Octene (1)	HF (4)	420	4.5	Cumene (5%)	739c
5	1-Octene (1)	HF (1.5, 3.0)	30	0.5	Octyl- (16/89–92%)[j,k]	739c
10	1-Octene (1)	HF (10)	16	—	2-, 3-, and 4-Phenyloctanes (33/32/35 ratio)[o]	582
100 pts.	Diisobutylene (112 pts.)	$AlCl_3$ (20 pts.)	0	—	t-Butyl- (major product)	325
23.4 pts.	Di-n-butene (29.4 pts.)	H_2SO_4 (105 pts.)	—	—	p-Di-s-butyl- (major product), some tri-s-butyl-	325
390 g.	Isooctenes (112 g.)	$AlCl_3$ (10 g.)	reflux	—	Mono-, di-, and tributyl- (20 g.), octyl- and some dodecyl- (106 g.)	762
80 g.	Diisobutylene (0.28)	$AlCl_3$ (10 g.)/iso-$C_3H_7 \cdot NO_2$ (15 g.)	35–40	16	t-Butyl- (6%), high boilers > 240°C (38 g.)	700(699)
97 g.	Diisobutylene (140 g.)	H_2SO_4 (100 cc.)	r.t.	1.5	t-Butyl-, p-di-t-butyl-, and tributyl- (total 214 g.)	329(325)

Table continued

TABLE 7 (continued)

Benzene (Moles)	Olefin (Moles)	Catalyst (Moles)	Temp. (°C)	Time (hrs.)	Benzene derivatives (Yield)					Ref.
					t-Butyl	di-t-butyl	t-octyl	C_4-C_6H_4-C_8	Dodecyl + Polymer	
5	Diisobutylene (1)	$AlCl_3$ (0.09)	−5	1.5	4%	<1%	17%[kk]	15%	49%	681(105, 222)
		$AlCl_3$ (0.09)–CCl_4 (3.17)	0	1.33	7	<1	20[kk]	16	<1	681
		$AlCl_3$ (0.06)–HCl[μ]	−35	1.25	5	11	33	<1	12	681
		$AlCl_3$ (0.9)–CH_3NO_2 (0.21)	25	1.5	7	13	28	28	5	681
		$FeCl_3$ (0.3)	20	2.0	7	22	18	20	<1	681
		H_2SO_4 (0.9)	−5	1.5	4	7	22	40	28	681
		HF (5)	−35	1.5	8	6	20	<1	29	681(679)
		BF_3 (0.04)–HF (1.5)	−50	1.5	18	1	40[kk]	<1	<1	681
		$AlCl_3$ (0.8)–$C_6H_5NO_2$ (0.29)	25	1.5	4	1	1	<1	73	680
4	Styrene (0.25)	$AlCl_3$ (0.01)	25	—	1,1-Diphenylethane (5%) (mainly polystyrene)					543
500 g.	Styrene (40 g.)	93% H_2SO_4 (40 g.)	30–35	2	1,1-Diphenylethane (25%)					780
34.5	Allylbenzene (11 g.)	$AlCl_3$ (6 g.)	25	—	1,2-Diphenylpropane (4.5 g.)					292
—	Allylbenzene	HF	—	—	1,2-Diphenylpropane					757
—	1-Decene	H_2SO_4	—	—	2-Phenyldecane (88%)[h]					185
1	1-Nonene (1, 2, 3)	H_2SO_4[d]	10	1	Nonyl- (48–65%),[e] di- (26–52%),[f] tri- (10–20%)[g]					484(313)
1	1-Decene (1, 2)	H_2SO_4[d]	10	1	Decyl- (48–65%),[e] di- (26–52%)[f]					484(389)
10	1-Decene (1)	HF (10)	16	—	2-, 3-, and 4-Phenyldecanes (23/22/17 ratio)[o]					582
5	Diisoamylene (0.75)	$AlCl_3$ (0.1)–HCl	25	1	Amyl- (39%), t-butyl- (17%), hexyl-, and decyl-					219(168, 834)
5	Amylene dimer (1)	H_2SO_4	10–20	2	Alkylate (140%)[i]					168
1	1-Undecene (1, 2)	H_2SO_4[d]	10	1	Undecyl- (48–65%),[e] di- (26–52%)[f]					484

5ʳ	C_{11}–C_{13} copolymer of propene and n-butene (1)	$AlCl_3$ᵍ–HCl (27%)ᵖ 0.2 H_2Oᵉ	13	—	Detergent alkylate (73%), degradation products (11%), polymer and heavy alkylate (16%)	452
10	1-Dodecene (2)	$AlCl_3$ (0.1)–H_2O (0.1 g.)	30	0.25ᵐ	Phenyldodecane (68%); (0, 32, 22, 16, 15, 15%)ⁿ didodecylbenzene (21%)	582
150 g.	Tetraphenyl-ethylene (7 g.)	$AlCl_3$–HCl (20 g.)	25	72	Dibenzyl (54%)	7
3.6	1-Dodecene (0.6)	$AlCl_3$ (0.027)–HCl	35–37	0.25 0.41 0.75	Phenyldecanes 2- 3- 4- 5- 6- 40 19 13 15 13 36 19 16 15 14 32 19 16 17 16	820
5.5	1-Dodecene (1)	$AlCl_3$ (0.044)–HCl	35–37	—	Dodecyl- (75%) di- and higher (9%), low boiler (3%)	820
6	1-Dodecene (1)	$AlCl_3(2)$–CCl_4	60	—	Dodecyl- (72%)	24
1.5	1-Dodecene (0.15)	98% H_2SO_4 (5 ml.)	0–10	2ᵐ	Phenyldodecane (72%); (0, 41, 20, 13, 13, 13%)ⁿ didodecylbenzene (9%)	582(313)
10	1-Dodecene (1)	HF (5)	16	—	Phenyldodecane (92%); (0, 20, 17, 16, 23, 24%)ⁿ didodecylbenzene (5%)	582
40 pts.	6-Dodecene (17 pts.)	HF (21 pts.)	0–5	18	6-Phenyldodecaneᵏ	291a
10	1-Dodecene (1)	HF (10)	16	—	2-, 3-, and 4-Phenyldodecanes (20/17/16 ratio)º	582
2500 pts.	Dodecene (1430 pts.)	$AlCl_3$ (20 pts.)	54	0.5	Detergent alkylate (3750 pts.)	232
10	1-Tridecene (1)	HF (10)	16	—	2-, 3-, and 4-Phenyltridecanes (17/15/12 ratio)º	582
—	Tetrapropyleneˢ b.p. 177–213°	$AlCl_3$	—	—	Dodecyl- (82%)ᵗ, low boilers (9%), high boilers (9%)	914
1000 pts.	Tetrapropene (320)ᵘ	$AlCl_3$ (11%)ᵘ–HCl (0.2–0.3%)	30–35	0.6	Dodecyl- (77%), intermediates (11%), higher (12%)	913
2	Propene tetramer (1)	$AlCl_3$ (4–5 g.)–HCl (0.3 g.) then HCl (1.6–1.8 g.)	12–14, 12–14	0.3, 0.3	Detergent alkylate, 270–320° (55%),ᶜ light alkylate (24%),ᶜ heavy alkylate (37%)ᶜ	253

6*

Table continued

TABLE 7 (continued)

Benzene (Moles)	Olefin (Moles)	Catalyst (Moles)	Temp. (°C)	Time (hrs.)	Benzene derivatives (Yield)	Ref.
20 cc.	Stilbene (1 g.)	$AlCl_3$ (1.5 g.)–HCl	r.t.	54	Dibenzyl (20%)	7a
20 cc.	p,p'-Dichlorostilbene (1 g.)	$AlCl_3$ (1.5 g.)–HCl	r.t.	16.5	Dibenzyl (70%)	7a
3–7	Polypropene (1) 110°/9 mm.	$AlCl_3$–HCl (10–15%)	8–10	4	20–25% alkylate	737
1000 g.	Polymer olefin (320 g.)	$AlCl_3$–HCl (10 g.)	60	1.33	Detergent alkane	426
7.5	Propene tetramer (1.5)	$AlCl_3$ (12 g.)–H_2O (0.1 g.)	55–60	0.75	Dodecyl- (238 g.), lower (43.2 g.), higher (57 g.)	735
585 g.	Hexene dimer (78.5 g.)	$AlCl_3$	70	—	Alkylbenzene, b.p. 157–175/12 mm.	686
5.7, 11.25, 15, 22.5	Propene tetramer (1.5)	$AlCl_3$ (12 g.) H_2O (0.1 g.)	55–60	—	Dodecyl- (219, 258, 277, 278 g.); interm., 138–228° (46, 41, 30, 33 g.),[f] botts. (67, 49, 48, 46)[aa]	735
5.7	Propene tetramer (1.5)	$AlCl_3$ (12 g.)–H_2O (1 g.)	55–60	0.33	Dodecyl- (211 g.)	735(828, 136)
1000 pts.	Tetrapropene (320)[u]	$AlCl_3$ (11)[u]–clay (2)[w]–HCl	30–35	0.6	Dodecyl- (79.5%), intermediates (9%), higher (12%)	913
1000 pts.	Tetrapropene (320)[u]	$AlCl_3$ (11)[u]–clay (2)[w]–HCl	30–35	0.6	Dodecyl- (85%),[x] intermediates (9%),[x] higher (6%)[x]	913(528)
1000 pts.	Tetrapropene (320)[u]	$AlCl_3$ (11)[u]–clay (2)[y]–HCl (0.2–0.3%)	30–35	0.6	Dodecyl- (80%), intermediates (9%), higher (12%)	913
1000 pts.	Propene tetramer (320 pts.)	$AlCl_3$ (11 pts.)–CH_3NO_2 (1 pt.) HCl (0.2–0.3%)	30–35	0.5	Dodecyl- (85%), intermediate boiling (9%), higher (6%)	528(583)
1000 pts.	Propene tetramer (320 pts.)	$ZrCl_4$ (18 pts.), Super-filtrol (2 pts.)	30–63	0.5	Dodecyl- (82%), intermediate boiling (3%), higher (15%)	528(913)
10	Propene tetramer (1)	98.5% H_2SO_4 (3 vol. n-heptane)	0	—	Dodecyl- (70%)[z]	61(564)

1.5	Propene polymer (b.p. 170–225°) (1)	98.6% H_2SO_4 (2)	3	0.66	Alkylate (60%)	274(60, 735)
5	Dodecene (1) 20% in cracked gasoline cut[v]	89% H_2SO_4 1 vol./vol. hydrocarbon feed	10	1.25	Alkylate (21%)	566
10	Propene tetramer (1) (170–225°)	H_2SO_4[gg] (1 vol.) n-C_7H_{16}[bb]	0	0.66	Dodecylbenzene (70%)[cc]	67(506)
11.25	Propene tetramer (1.5)	H_2SO_4 (80, 90, 94, 96.5, 97.6, 101.2%)[dd]	5–10	1.5	Dodecyl- (8, 16, 63, 70, 73, 69%)[i,ee]	735(303)
7.5	Propene tetramer (1.5)	H_2SO_4 (100 g., 200 g., 300 g., 367 g.)	5–10	1.5	Dodecyl- (51, 70, 81, 79, 72%)[i,ee]	735
80 g.	Tetrapropene (84 g.)	Amberlite IR-112[ff] (7%)	reflux	25	No reaction	453
11.25	Propene tetramer (1.5)	HF (6)	−10	1.5	Dodecyl- (67%), lower (21.9 g.), higher (62 g.)	735
			20	1.5	Dodecyl- (77%), lower (22.3 g.), higher (50 g.)	
10	Cracked olefins (C_{12}–C_{16}) (1)	HF	30	0.5	Alkylate (Av. mol. wt. 271)	286
87 g.	Propene tetramer (227 g.)	HF (270 g.)	0	4	Phenyldodecane (80.8%)	441(79, 442,735)
2	Polymer (C_{13}–C_{14})	H_2SO_4 (3)	35	1.2	Alkylate below b.p. 110°/10 mm. (26 pts.)	167b
10	1-Tetradecene (1)	HF (16)	16	—	2-, 3-, and 4-Phenyltetradecanes (18/14/14 ratio)[o]	582
234 pts.	Tetradecene (588 pts.)	BF_3–H_3PO_4 (196 pts.)	10–15	—	Tetradecyl- (91%)	300
150 cc.	Stilbene (10 g.)	$AlCl_3$–HCl (2 g.)	25	8	1,1,2-Triphenylethane (49%)	7
100 cc.	p-Bromostilbene (5 g.)	$AlCl_3$–HCl (0.5 g.)	25	8	1,1,2-Triphenylethane (37%)	7
10	1-Pentadecene (1)	HF (10)	16	—	2-, 3-, and 4-Phenylpentadecanes (18/14/14 ratio)[o]	582
10	$C_3^=$/$C_4^=$ Tetramer (1)	95% H_2SO_4 (1 vol.)	3	1	Monophenylalkane (18%) (C_8–C_{18} side chains)	567

Table continued

TABLE 7 (*continued*)

Benzene (Moles)	Olefin (Moles)	Catalyst (Moles)	Temp. (°C)	Time (hrs.)	Benzene derivatives (Yield)	Ref.
1	Dodecene (some Pentadecene) (1)	HF–AgF	10 20 psi	0.5	Dodecyl- and pentadecyl- (65%)	446
6	Propene pentamer (1)	HF (4)	0	4.75	Phenylpentadecane (56%)	442(79)
10	1-Hexadecene (1)	HF (10)	16		2, 3, and 4-Phenylhexadecanes (24/14/10 ratio)°	582
10	1-Heptadecene (1)	HF (10)	16		2, 3, and 4-Phenylheptadecanes (23/14/9 ratio)°	582
1.36	Propene polymer Av. mol. wt. 235 (0.68)	$AlCl_3$ (25 g.)–HCl (trace)	21	0.33	Alkylate (87%)	170
0.68	Propene polymer Av. mol. wt. 235 (0.68)	H_2SO_4 (450 g.)	10	15	Alkylate (75%)	170
10	1-Octadecene (1)	HF (10)	16	—	2, 3, and 4-Phenyloctadecanes (31/17/9 ratio)°	582
10	1-Hendecene (1)	HF (10)	16	—	2, 3, and 4-Phenylhendecanes (20/19/16 ratio)°	582
156 pts.	Octadecene (252 pts.)	HF (110 pts.)	5–10	3.5	Octadecyl- (225 pts.)	155(79)
4	Polyethylene (1) 110°/9 mm.	48– H_2SO_4 (78 g.)	5–10	0.5	Alkylate (8%)	736
396 g.	Polyethylene (94 g.) 48–110°/9 mm.	$AlCl_3$ (12.5 g.)	60–65	2.5	Alkylate (57%) mol. wt. 207	736
10	Olefins (C_8–C_{18})[h,h] (1)	HF[tt]	—	0.5	Alkylate (C_{10}–C_{14} side chain)	570
150 cc.	Triphenylethylene (5 g.)	$AlCl_3$–HCl (1 g.)	25	20	sym-Tetraphenylethane (70%)	7
150 cc.	1,1-Di-(p-chlorophenyl)-2-phenyl-ethylene (5 g.)	$AlCl_3$–HCl (10 g.)	25	20	Dibenzyl (27%)	7

a Cuts of thermally cracked gasoline containing about 50% olefins.
b Only 6.8% with 91% H_2SO_4.
c Vol.% based on vol. of olefin feed.
d "Equal amount."
e Olefin/benzene ratio was 1/l.
f Olefin/benzene ratio was 2/1.
g Olefin/benzene ratio was 3/1.
h Probably a mixture of phenylalkanes (582).
i For each catalyst amount respectively.
j 38, 34, 26, 17% non-aromatic.
k Get reproducible results only when reactor is not cleaned (just drained) after each test.
l Based on olefin.
m Stirred after addition of reagents.
n Per cent each of 1-, 2-, 3-, 4-, 5-, 6-phenyldecane.
o Ratio of isomers, balance consists of other possible secondary alkylbenzenes.
p Of $AlCl_3$ weight.
q 25 g./hr.
r 3.95 l./hr.

s Pretreated with spent catalyst.
t 80% if olefin pretreatment is omitted.
u Parts.
v Pretreated with 1.8% H_2SO_4 at room temperature.
w Parts Fuller's earth.
z Obtained when polyalkylate is recycled.
y Parts Superfiltrol.
aa Only 66% yield in absence of solvent. Branched paraffinic and naphthenic solvents give much lower yields than n-heptane.
aa 342-426°, 99% alkylbenzenes.
bb 43% based on benzene.
cc 66% in absence of heptane solvent.
dd 188.7 g., 113.3 g., 100 g., 100 g., 100 g., 100 g., respectively.
ee All alkylates contaminated with olefin.
ff Sulfonic acid type cation exchange resin, oven-dried.
gg Catalyst = used H_2SO_4 from paraffin alkylation process.
hh Not sulfated by 98% H_2SO_4.
ii Weight = hydrocarbon feed.
jj Added continuously.
kk Contains 1,1,3,3-tetramethylbutyl- and isomeric C_8 side chains.

TABLE 8. Benzene with cyclic olefins

Benzene (Moles)	Olefin (Moles)	Catalyst (Moles)	Temp. (°C)	Time (hrs.)	Benzene derivatives[e] (% Yield)	Ref.
0.9	Methylenecyclobutane and methylcyclobutene (0.45)	H_2SO_4 (30 g.)	4	1	Mono- (40%), 1,4-di- (49%) -(1′-methylcyclobutyl)-, tri-(methylcyclobutyl)- (11%)	330
70 cc.	Cyclopentene (15 g.)	$AlCl_3$ (2 g.)	0	0.16	Cyclopentyl-(major product), di- and tricyclopentyl-	109(536)
400 g.	Cyclohexene (120 g.)	$AlCl_3$ (60 g.)	r.t.	3	Mono- (44 g.), dicyclohexyl- (2 g.)	66(52)[a]
1	Cyclopentene (0.4)	$TiCl_4$ (0.3)–H_2O (0.3)	100	1	Cyclopentyl- (50%)[a]	588
5	Cyclohexene (1)	$AlCl_3$ (0.05)	40–50	—	Cyclohexyl- (79%)	496
1 pt.	Cyclohexene (3 pts.)	$AlCl_3$ (0.5 pt.)	0	—	Cyclohexyl-, p-di-, 1,3,5-tricyclohexyl	535
2	Cyclohexene (4), cyclohexane (150 g.)	$AlCl_3$ (60 g.)	3–20	3.5	Cyclohexyl- (20 g.), 1,4-di- (35 g.), 1,3,5-tri- (150 g.), 1,2,3,5-tetracyclohexyl- (80 g.)[b]	141
60 g.	Cyclohexene (8.2 g.)	Al (0.1 g.)–C_4H_9Cl (1 g.)	60	—	Cyclohexyl- (41%), di- and poly- (3 g.)	751b
1–1.5	Cyclohexene	$AlBr_3$	30–40	—	Cyclohexyl- (76%)	833
	Cyclohexene	Al–EtBr (0.01)	—	—	Cyclohexyl- (20%)	550
1	Cyclohexene (0.4)	$TiCl_4$ (0.3)–H_2O (0.3)	100	1	Cyclohexyl- (55%)[a]	588
—	Cyclohexene	$ZnCl_2$ (136 g.)–H_2O (27 g.)–HCl	75	6	Cyclohexyl- (43%)	306
39 g.	Cyclohexene (82 g.)	HCl–BF_3	100	—	Oil (114 g.) containing mono- and di-cyclohexyl-	283
2	Cyclohexene (3)	H_2SO_4 (92 g.)	ice-cooled	2	Cyclohexyl- (95 g.), p-dicyclohexyl- (71 g.)	141(99,870, 508,585)
6	Cyclohexene (2)	H_2SO_4 (92 g.)	60	—	Cyclohexyl- (78%), 1,4-dicyclohexyl- (50 g.)	101
25 cc.	Cyclohexene (25 cc.)	P_2O_5 (6 g.)	reflux	1	Cyclohexyl- (25%), dimer (75%)	869
200 pts.	Cyclohexene (50 pts.)	HF (120 pts.)	0	12.5	Cyclohexyl- (59 pts.)	753(755)
2	Cyclohexene (0.5)	HCl	208, 250 psi	25	Cyclohexyl- (37%), cyclohexyl chloride (27%)	760

10	1-Methylcyclohexene (1)	AlCl$_3$ (0.2)–HCl	25	1.11	Monoalkylate (44%) (3/19/49/46)^c	220
156 g.	1-Methylcyclohexene (34.6 g.)	H$_2$SO$_4$ (60 g.)	10–13	1.5	1-Methyl-1-phenylcyclohexane (51%), p-bis-(1-methylcyclohexyl)benzene (32%)	451
2.5	3-Methylcyclohexene (0.7)	AlCl$_3$ (0.25)	25	3	Methylphenylcyclohexane (33%), di-(methylcyclohexyl)benzene (12%)	66
5	4-Methylcyclohexene	AlCl$_3$ (0.2)–HCl	−20	0.95	Monoalkylate (trace)	220
5	4-Methylcyclohexene (1)	AlCl$_3$ (0.2)–HCl	0	0.76	Monoalkylate (30%) (44/trace/55/10)^c	220
5	4-Methylcyclohexene (1)	AlCl$_3$ (0.2)–HCl	20	1.45	Monoalkylate (45%) (7/28/40/16)^c	220
3	4-Methylcyclohexene (1.5)	HF (100 g.)	5	—	1-Methyl-1-phenylcyclohexane (75%), m-di-(1-methylcyclohexyl)-benzene (23%)	321(314)
5	4-Methylcyclohexene (1)	HF (103 g.)–BF$_3$ (saturated)	2	0.55	Monoalkylate (42%) (6/25/30/—)^c	220
5	4-Methylcyclohexene (1)	HF (80 g.)–BF$_3$ (132 g.)	25	0.41	Intractable mixture	220
45 g.	Cycloheptene (0.16)	AlCl$_3$ (5 g.)–HCl	5–8	1.5	Alkylate (29%) probably methyl-phenylcyclohexanes	613
31.2 g.	Cycloheptene (0.2)	H$_2$SO$_4$ (56 g.)	5	1.33	Cycloheptyl- (48%)	613
31.2 g.	Cycloheptene (0.2)	HF (30 g.)	5	0.75	Cycloheptyl- (71%)	613
50 g.	1-Ethyl-2-cyclopentene (8 g.)	AlCl$_3$ (10 g.)	—	—	1-Ethyl-3-phenylcyclopentane (20%), p-di-(3-ethylcyclopentyl)benzene (some)	126
2	Isopropylcyclohexene (0.1–0.5)	HF (10)	0–7	—	1-Isopropyl-1-phenylcyclohexane (70%)	312
50 cc.	1-Butyl-2-cyclopentene (15 g.)	AlCl$_3$ (10 g.)	40	—	1-Butyl-3-phenyl- and 1-butyl-2-phenyl cyclopentane (17%)	126
1.2	Menthene (0.3)	AlCl$_3$ (0.15)	25	3	Menthylbenzene	66

Table continued

TABLE 8 (*continued*)

Benzene (Moles)	Olefin (Moles)	Catalyst (Moles)	Temp. (°C)	Time (hrs.)	Benzene derivatives[e] (% Yield)	Ref.
50 cc.	1-Isoamyl-2-cyclo-pentene (15 g.)	AlCl$_3$ (10 g.)	—	—	1-Isoamyl-2-phenyl- and 1-isoamyl-3-phenylcyclopentane (10%)	126
1.5	1-Butylcyclohexene (1)	FeCl$_3$ (1)	—	—	Alkylate (40%)	530
2	1-Methyl-4-isopropyl-cyclohexene (0.1–0.5)	HF (10)	0–7	—	1-Methyl-1-phenyl-4-isopropylcyclo-hexane (60%)	312
1.1	1-Phenylcyclohexene (0.25)	AlCl$_3$ (0.1)	25	3	Diphenylcyclohexane (20%)	66
1.5	1-Phenylcyclohexene (1)	FeCl$_3$ (1)	—	—	Alkylate (35%)	530
100 cc.	1,2-Dihydronaphthalene (16 g.)	AlCl$_3$ (10 g.)	—	—	2-Phenyltetralin (2 g.)	126
—	2,3-Octalin	AlCl$_3$	—	—	2-Phenyldecalin (20%)	126
60 ml.	2,6-Dimethylbicyclo-(3,2,1]oct-2-ene (30 ml.)	H$_2$SO$_4$ (30 cc.)	4	1.5	2-Phenyl-2,6-dimethylbicyclo(3,2,1)-octane (70%)	326a

[a] Only 3% with anhydrous catalyst.
[b] Reviewer's note: m.p. 264–265° indicates it is instead the 1,2,4,5-isomer.
[c] Ratio 1-/2-/3-/4-methyl-1-phenylcyclohexane.
[d] At 55–80°.
[e] Or other product.

TABLE 9. Toluene with ethylene

Toluene (Moles)	Ethylene (Moles)	Catalyst (Moles)	Temp. (°C)	Time (hrs.)	Ethyltoluene products (% Yield)	Ref.
10	1	$AlCl_3$ (1%)	80	—	Mono-/poly- = 17/1 mono-($o/m/p$ = 11/64/25)	424(52, 12,68, 171)
1	0.5	$AlCl_3$	85	3–4	Mono- (70%) (m/p = 70/30), poly-(16%)[a]	741
0.6	—	$AlCl_3$ (0.5)	80–90	—	3,5-Di- (good yield)	226
2	1	$AlCl_3$ (0.03%)[f] (HCl)	−78, 15	1, 0.33[n]	Mono- ($o/m/p$ = 47/26/27)[m] (48/28/24)[n]	10
—	—	$AlCl_3$ (1, 2, 3, 4%)–HCl (or EtCl)[e]	80[g]	—	Mono- (23, 24, 24, 24%)[f], di- (6, 8, 10, 11%)[f] tri- (7, 16, 24, 32%)[f], toluene (64, 52, 42, 33%)[f]	227
24.7[i]	6.4	$AlCl_3$–EtCl (55 pts./4 pts.)	80	2	Mono- (720 pts.) ($o/m/p$ = 15/55/30), poly- (121 pts.)	240
7	3.36	$AlCl_3$ (0.168) iso-C_3H_7Cl (0.143)	80–90	—	Mono- (41%)[c] ($o/m/p$ = 22/43/35) di- (9%)[c], toluene (50%)[c]	181
200 g.	56 atm.[d]	Al/$TiCl_4$ (3 g./2 g.)	235	6	Mono- (27%), di- (27%), tri- (4%), tetra- (7%)	702
2	1 lbs.	$AlBr_3$ (0.017%)[f] (HBr)	15	0.33	Mono- ($o/m/p$ = 46/29/25)	10
66 lbs.	11 lbs.	Ethyl aluminum sesqui-bromide[i] (0.2-$TiCl_4$) (0.425)[i]	40 (10 psi)	6	Oils boiling above 110° (9 lbs.) Alkyl side chain C_8–C_{12} mainly C_{12}-	461
100 g.	—	Al (10 g.)–$SnCl_4 \cdot 2H_2O$ (20 g.)[b]	200–300 (40 psi)	4	Mono- (20 g.), di- (20 g.)	701
85 g.	84 g.	BF_3 (12 g.)–HCl (8 g.)	200	5	Liquid (160 g.)	283
2.3	1	BF_3 (90 g.) $CdSO_4$-H_2O (90 g.)	31–35 (210–360 psi)	5	Mono- (70%) ($o/m/p$ = 47/26/26), C_{11} aromatics (8%), C_{12}^+ aromatics (13%)	388
1380 g.	350 g.	BF_3 (90 g.)–$Fe_4(P_2O_7)_3$ (50 g.)	30–35 (170–400 psi)	4.5	Mono- (21%) ($o/m/p$ = 60/20/20), C_{11} aromatics (12%)	374
101 g.	50 atm.	BCl_3 (9 g.)–Boron (3 g.)–V_2O_5 (3 g.)	250 (124 atm.)	5.5	Mono- (15 g.), di- (7 g.)	458

Table continued

TABLE 9 (continued)

Toluene (Moles)	Ethylene (Moles)	Catalyst (Moles)	Temp. (°C)	Time (hrs.)	Ethyltoluene products (% Yield)	Ref.
1 l./hr.	(2)/hr.	Benzenesulfonic acid (sprayed)	150	—	Mono- (65%)	53
2.3	1	H_3PO_4–Sil-o-cel[k]	300 400 psig	0.012	Mono-/poly- = 7.9 (32% conv. of ethylene)	138
2	1	HF (2.0%)[f]	0	0.66	Mono- (o/m/p = 42/33/25)	10
10	1	H_3PO_4–kieselguhr	275 900 psi	2	Mono-/poly- = 9/1 (mono-o/m/p = 46/32/22)	424
1000 pts.	80 atm.	$Ce(PO_3)_3$ 100 pts.	300	L.H.S.V.	Oil (b.p. 150–180°)	298
10	1	$FePO_4$	275 900 psi	2	Mono-/poly- = 10/1 (mono-o/m/p = 48/30/22)	424
10	1	SiO_2–Al_2O_3	275 900 psi	L.H.S.V.	Mono-/poly- = 7/1 (mono-o/m/p = 29/50/21)	424
400 ml.	400 psig[d]	1.9% NiO on SiO_2–Al_2O_3 (75 g.)	175	3.75	s-Butyltoluene (38%), hexyltoluene (4%), aromatic residue (7%), 1-butene (24%), hexene (17%), octene (1%), decene (8%)	38[h]
—	—	Al_2O_3 (14%)–SiO_2 (86%) NaH (1.5 g.)	90–150 (500 psi)	5	Mono- (40 vol.%)	207

a Yields based on reacted toluene.
b $SnCl_2 \cdot 2H_2O$ also suitable.
c Of alkylate.
d Initial pressure.
e Sensitive to traces of water.
f Mol.%.
g Studied 0–90° range.
h Products, vol.%.

i Chloride is just as effective.
j With 0.2 m. $TiCl_4$ in catalyst mixture, product is 8 lbs. of polyethylene and 1.5 lbs. alkyltoluene.
k Diatomaceous earth.
l Plus 122 pts. of recycled polyethyltoluenes.
m At −78°.
n At 15°.

TABLE 10.   Toluene with propene

Toluene (Moles)	Propene (Moles)	Catalyst (Moles)	Temp. (°C)	Time (hrs.)	Products (% Yield)	Ref.
1	0.4–0.6	AlCl₃ (0.1–2 mole %)	110	1.5	m-Cymene (23–31%), p-cymene (10–14%), o-cymene (1–1.3%), diisopropyltoluene (3–8%)	272(52)
1	0.5	AlCl₃ (4%)	110^d	—	Cymenes (22%) ($o/m/p$ = 1–2/65–70/28–30)	402
7.0	84 g.	AlCl₃ (0.25)	50	—	Cymenes (22%) ($o/m/p$ = 3/66/33), poly-alkylate (22%)	293
276 g.	1.3^e	AlCl₃–HCl (13.1 g./6.0 g.) C₃H₇Cl (10 pts.)	0	1.5	Cymenes ($o/m/p$ = 34/25/41), conv. (53%)^a	764
600 pts.	290 pts.	AlCl₃ (20.9 pts.), iso-C₃H₇Cl (10 pts.)	75	0.5	Cymenes (44%) (o- 2%, m- 70%, p- 28%)	519
2	1	AlCl₃·2H₂O (1.3%)	55	1.5	Cymene ($o/m/p$ = 7/57/37) 26% conv.	10
2	1	AlCl₃·5H₂O (1.2%)	40	0.66	Cymene ($o/m/p$ = 48/17/36) 13% conv.	10
2	1	AlCl₃·4H₂O (1%)	40	0.4	Cymene ($o/m/p$ = 41/23/36) 23% conv.	10
0.368	0.13–0.3	AlCl₃ (0.012)–CH₃NO₂ (0.153)	5–65	—	Cymenes ($o/m/p$ = 38/27/35)	130(10, 129)
43 g.	50–68 psig	Al(iso-Bu)₃–SiCl₄ or Cl₂Si(CH₃)₂	115–150	2–4	Cymenes (mostly o and p)	239
3.5	1	Al–TiCl₄^c (0.013 to 0.004)	75–80	—	Cymenes (62–54%) ($o/m/p$ = 46/23/32) polyisopropyltoluene (19–25%)	293
2	1	AlBr₃ (0.1%) (HBr)	40	1.5	Cymenes ($o/m/p$ = 37/23/39) 5% conv.	10
98 ml.	10 psig	Et₂AlBr–EtAlBr₂ (0.0013) TiCl₄ (0.0026)	40	8	C₆- to C₂₄-toluenes (173 ml.)	461
3.5	12 g.	FeCl₃ (0.12)	75–80	—	Cymenes (14%) ($o/m/p$ = 49/16/35), poly-alkylate (5%)	293
2	1	FeCl₃ (5%) (HCl)	35	17.8	Cymene ($o/m/p$ = 42/20/38) 3% conv.	10
346 g.	0.5^e	FeCl₃ (50 g.)	70	1	Cymenes ($o/m/p$ = 45/21/34), conv. (18%)	764
43 g.	50–68 psig	EtMgBr–SiCl₄ or SnCl₄	120–160	1.25–8	Cymenes (o, m, p)	239

Table continued

TABLE 10 (continued)

Toluene (Moles)	Propene (Moles)	Catalyst (Moles)	Temp. (°C)	Time (hrs.)	Products (% Yield)	Ref.
43 g.	50 psig	LiAlH$_4$ (0.5 g.)–SnCl$_4$ (8.8 g.)	158	0.33	Cymenes (m, p), 3,5-diisopropyltoluene	239
42.3 g.	47 g.	Silica–alumina (4 g.)–SiCl$_4$ (8.9 g.)^f	120 20 psig	2	Cymenes (2%), diisopropyl- (16%), triisopropyltoluene (72%)	238
3.6	1	TiCl$_4$ (0.03)	70	—	Cymenes (20%) (o/m/p = 47/21/32), poly-alkylate	293
2	1	TiCl$_4$ (1%) (HCl)	80	0.82	Cymene (o/m/p = 42/22/35) 25% conv.	10
3.5	1	VCl$_4$ (0.075)	70–80	—	Cymenes (15%) (o/m/p = 41/18/40), poly-alkylate (4%)	293
3.5	55 g.	ZrCl$_4$ (0.03)	75–80	—	Cymenes (54%) (o/m/p = 20/45/31), poly-alkylate (19%)	293
276 g.	0.83^c	48% BF$_3$–Et$_2$O (25 ml.)	100	2	Cymenes (o/m/p = 42/22/35), botts. (9 g.), conv. 12%^{a}	764
0.3 (0.3 benzene)	0.084–0.15	BF$_3$–Et$_2$O (0.4)	5–65	—	Cymenes (o/m/p = 38/27/35)	130(129)
259 g.	37 g.	FeF$_2$–BF$_3$ complex (16 g.) HF (1 g.)	25	1.33	Cymenes and higher (96 g.)	888
—	—	BF$_3$–H$_2$SO$_4$	—	—	p-Cymene	769
400 g.	0.8^e	BF$_3$–85% H$_3$PO$_4$ (100 ml.)	25	2	Cymenes (o/m/p = 42/25/34), botts. (53 g.), conv. 45%^{a}	764
1	1	PF$_5$ (1 mole %) (based on C$_3^=$)	25	4.5	m- and p-Cymenes (equimolar) (22%), di-isopropyltoluenes (20%), C$_{16}$-alkylate (13%)	81
5	1	PF$_5$ (0.05 mole %) (on C$_3^=$)	24	1	Diisopropyltoluene (40%), polyalkylate (49%)	81
346 g.	0.55^e	H$_2$SO$_4$ (100 ml.)	5	1.5	Cymene (o/m/p = 48/20/33), conv. (35%)^a	764
—	1	H$_2$SO$_4$	15	—	p-Cymene (main product) diisopropyltoluene	313
2	1	90% H$_2$SO$_4$ (9%)	0	1	Cymene (o/m/p = 42/19/39) 10% conv.	10
1.9	5.1	CH$_3$SO$_3$H	104–130	—	Triisopropyltoluene (72%)	652

1	0.975	Amberlyst 15[b] (7.5 g.)	100–120	1.66	Isopropyltoluene (39%, mainly o-isomer, lesser amts. of m- and p-), 2,4-diisopropyl (6%), 2,4,6-triisopropyltoluene (3%)	661
460 g.	168 g.	$CuSO_4 \cdot 5H_2O-H_2O$ (25 g./900 g.)	288, 1925–142 psi	2	Cymene (95 g.) (o/m/p = 30/30/40)	461
9.4	16.6	P_2O_5 (0.3)	150	—	p-Cymene (50%)	472
1	0.83	P_2O_5 (15 g.) on activated carbon (7 g.), p-cresol (1 g.)	80	2	Cymenes (64% conversion)[a] (o/m/p = 31/14/55%) botts. (64 g.)	472
5.6	1	H_3PO_4-kieselguhr	400, 200 psig	2.0 V/V/hr.	Cymene (96% of alkylate)	426e
5.96	1	HF	32, 40–50 psig	0.66	Cymenes (o- 38%, m- 27%, p- 34%)	470(696)
460 g.	1	Boria–alumina (50 g.)	200	4	Cymenes (96.9 g.), (o/m/p = 36/19/45)	666
4	1	Filtrol Clay, Grade 13 (100 g.)	100	10	Cymenes (600 g.) o/m/p = 10/60/30), residue mostly polyisopropyltoluenes (185 g.)	20b
6.35	1	Montmorillonite sub-bentonite clay	200, 1000 psi	1.91	Cymenes (92%) (o/m/p = 4.1/64/31.9)	470
30 g.	30 g.	$NaBH_4$ (2 g.)–$SiCl_4$ (2 g.) on SiO_2–Al_2O_3	130–172	20	Cymenes (4 g.), 50 g. of diisopropyl- and triisopropyltoluene	238
3	1	SiO_2 (84.66%), Al_2O_3 (14.01%), Na_2O (0.36%), Fe_2O_3 (0.13%), CaO (0.6%)	300	0.45 L.H.S.V.	Cymenes (77%) trialkylbenzenes (3%)	589
9 pts.	32 pts.	Nickel molybdite (5 pts.)	200	5	Cymenes (13 pts.)	198

[a] Of toluene.
[b] Rohm and Haas sulfonic acid ion exchange resin.
[c] $AlCl_3$ + Al + $TiCl_4$ heated until atom ratios of Al/Ti/Cl = 1/3/12.

[d] Max. yield at 80° but o-cymene is increased.
[e] Mole ratio propene/toluene.
[f] Either component alone is inactive.

TABLE 11. Toluene with *n*-butenes

Toluene (Moles)	Olefin (Moles)	Catalyst (Moles)	Temp. (°C)	Time (hrs.)	s-Butyltoluene products (% Yield)	Ref.
5300 pts.	*n*-Butene (2000 pts.)	$AlCl_3$ (40 pts.), Al (200 pts.), HCl (10 vol. % of $C_4^=$)	90	—	Isomeric butyltoluenes (1500 pts.), higher butyltoluenes (1835 pts.)	835
2	2-Butene (1) 3.1 l./hr.	$AlCl_2 \cdot HPO_4$ (0.2)	30	—	Mono- (68%)	940
2	*n*-Butene (1)	BF_3–H_3PO_4 (0.2)	35–40	—	4- (81–84%)	939
5–10	*n*-Butene (1)	94% H_2SO_4 (1)	−5 to 0	2.33	Mono- (83%)	468
1000 pts.	*n*-Butene (1)	$Ce(PO_3)_3$ (100 pts.)	300	—	Butyl derivatives, b.p. 180–200°	298
4	1-Butene (1)	HF (8.6)	0–4	3.5	Mono- (92%)	696
4	2-Butene (1)	HF (8.6)	0–6	3.5	Mono- (89%)	696
100 cc.	2-Butene (30 g.)	Al_2O_3 (14%)–SiO_2 (86%) NaH (1.5 g.)	113	2	Mono- (70 vol. %), polybutyl (30 vol. %)	207
47.8 g.	1-Butene (30 psig)	SiO_2–Al_2O_3 (1 g.), $Al(iC_4H_9)_3$ (0.9 g.), $SiCl_4$ (1.5 g.)	77	16.5	Mono- (16.1 g.)	238
69 pts.	1-Butene (42 pts.)	Nickel molybdite (5 pts.)	200	5	Mono- (4.5 pts.)	198

TABLE 12. Toluene with isobutylene

Toluene (Moles)	Isobutylene (Moles)	Catalyst (Moles)	Temp. (°C)	Time (hrs.)	t-Butyltoluene products (% Yield)	Ref.
5 kg.	—	$AlCl_3$–HCl (200 g.)	10	—	Mono-	64(3)
1.4	1	$FeCl_3$ (0.036)	80–90	1.6	Mono- (33%) (m/p = 7/93)	696
404 pts.	100 pts.	$FeCl_3$ (12.9 pts.)–HCl (6.1 pts.)	15–25	1.75	Mono- (78%) (82% p-)	225
4	1	H_2SO_4 (92 g.)	<0	1	Mono- (95%) (m/p = 1.8/98)	597
2 kg.	350 l.	93% H_2SO_4 (500 g.)	−5 to 0	4	4-t-Butyl- (1895 g.)	114
4	1	93% H_2SO_4 (8)	0	few	4-t-Butyl- (90%)	266
4	1.2	Alkane–SO_3H (0.9)	70	1.3	Mono- (34%), triisobutene (66%)	653
460 g.	375 cc.	$CuSO_4 \cdot 5H_2O$ (25 g.)	277	<1	Mono- (20.6 g.) (o/m/p = 5/10/85)	838
460 g.	375 cc.	85% H_3PO_4/H_2O (25 g./450 g.)	315 / 2525 psi	2	Mono- (23.5 g.)	838[a]
5.5	1	UOP 2H_3PO_4–kieselguhr	170 / 300 psig	1.05 / L.H.S.V.	Mono- (53%) (m/p = 86/14)	696
4.5	1.44	HF (11.1)	−20	1.13	Mono- (o/m/p = 0/2/98)	696(693)
3	1	HF (0.6)	2–4	1.5	Mono- (53%) (m/p = 7/93)	696(693)
5	1	HF (5.5)	1–8	2	Mono- (87%) (m/p = 52/48)	696(693)
1104 pts.	898 pts.	HF (354 pts.)	0	6	Mono- (59%) 3,5-di- (26%)	689
3	1	HF (4)–H_2O (1.1)	0–5	2	Mono- (83%) (m/p = 7.7/92.3)	696(693)
460 g.	375 cc.	HCl/H_2O (0.25)–450 g.	315	2	Mono- (sl. > 23.5 g.)	838
—	—	Ni (thiophene modifier)	35 / 5–8 atm. H_2	—	3- and 4-t-Butyl- (35%)[b]	619
92 pts.	23 pts.	$HClO_4$	95–100	—	Di- (13%)	159

[a] No reaction without cat. after 2 hrs. at 330°, 1100 psig.   [b] 4% in the absence of thiophene.

TABLE 13. Toluene with higher olefins

Toluene (Moles)	Olefin (Moles)	Catalyst (Moles)	Temp. (°C)	Time (hrs.)	Products (% Yield)	Ref.
5.5	Amylene (3)	$AlCl_3$ (0.2)	25–100	—	3-t-Amyltoluene[x] (45%)	190
5	2-Methyl-2-butene (1)	$AlCl_3$ (3.5) 5 cc. t-$C_5H_{11}Cl$	25	1.36	Amyltoluene (46%), some C_6- and C_{10}-toluenes, t-butyltoluene (20%)	219
0.24	2-Methyl-2-butene	$TiCl_4$ (0.1)	20	3	4-t-Amyltoluene (33%)[i]	147
3	Amylene (1)	Activated clay (11%)	452	—	Alkylate (to 210°) (72%)	674
—	Amylene	Activated clay	2100 psi 449 1250 psi	0.75	Alkylate (100%)	672
1	Amylene	Activated clay	474	—	Alkylate (57%)	672
4	3-Hexene (0.66)	HF (3.3)	5–10	24	3-p-Tolylhexane (63%)[y]	779
5	Propene dimer (1)	H_2SO_4 (8)	0	few	4-t-Hexyltoluene (88%)	266
	4,4-Dimethyl-1-pentene	BF_3 (1.5 g.)	−30 to 0	1	Heavy alkylate (100%), mainly > C_{14} side chain	6
2 vol.	1-Octene (1 vol.)	$AlCl_3$	110	—	Octyl- (85%), dioctyl- (75%)	251
	1-Octene	HF	—	—	p-Octyl- (73%)	759
138	Octenes (336 pts.)[z]	HF (90 pts.)	0–10	1	Octyl- (138 pts.), dioctyl (236 pts.)	155
	Diisobutylene	$AlCl_3$	—	—	m-, some p-t-butyl	562
	Diisobutylene	$FeCl_3$	—	—	p-t-Butyl-	562
2	Diisobutylene (1)	BF_3–H_2O[o]	33–36	0.41	t-Butyl- (86%)[q] (p/m = 72/28), 3,5-di-t-butyl- (6%)[q,r]	431
2	Diisobutylene (1)	BF_3–H_2O modified with H_2O, acetone, or 2,4-dimethylhexa-1,3-diene	30–40	1	t-Butyl- (73, 85, 89%)[q,r], 3,5-di-t-butyl- (0, 0, 0.3%)[q,r]	431
644 g.	Diisobutylene (403 g.)	BF_3–EtH_2PO_4 (280 cc.)	30–40	1	t-Butyl- (63%)[q] (p/m = 87/13)	375
	Diisobutylene (1)	H_2SO_4,[p] 91% spent H_2SO_4,[p] $AlCl_3$–toluene–HCl complex[p]	33–37	3	t-Butyl- (28%, 33%, 66%)[q,r], 3,5-di-t-butyl- (0, 0,0.3%)[q,r]	431
2	Diisobutylene (1)	CH_3SO_3H	116	—	t-Butyl- (60%) (plus 18% high boilers)	652
2	Diisobutylene (1)	Toluenesulfonic acid	116–120	3	t-Butyl- (68%)[q] 3,5-di-t-butyl- (1%)[q]	431

	Reactant	Catalyst	Temp.	Ratio	t-Butyl-	t-Octyl-	Dodecyl-	Polymer	
5	Diisobutylene (1)	$AlCl_3$ (0.08)	−35	0.66	(6%)	(79%) (p/m = 7)[a]	—	—	681(222)
5	(1)	$AlCl_3$ (0.08)–CCl_4	−35	1.5	(6%)	(45%) (p/m = 3)[a]	21%	Higher (26%)	681
5	(1)	$AlCl_3$ (0.09)–HCl (0.09)	−65	1.5	(3%)	(72%) (p/m = 5)[a]	24%	—	681(222)
5	(1)	$AlCl_3$ (0.09)–CH_3NO_2 (0.92)	25	1.5	(15%)	(71%)	—	(15%)	681
5	(1)	$AlCl_3$ (0.085)–$C_6H_5NO_2$ (0.31)	25	1.5	(<1%)	(84%) (p/m = 19)[a]	—	—	681(696)
5	(1)	$FeCl_3$ (0.03)	0	1.5	(6%)	(85%)[b]	—	—	681(679)
5	(1)	HF (5)	−40	1.66	(<1%)	(92%) (p/m = 19)[a]	—	(2%)	681(679)
4.35	(2)	HF (5)	0–5	20	(77%)[d]				110
5	(1)	BF_3 (0.11)–HF (3.75)	−60	1.5	(12%)	(79%)[b] (p/m = 4)	—	—	681(679)
5	(1)	H_2SO_4 (0.9)	5	1.5	(10%)	(69%)[b]	10%	—	681(266, 404)
5	(1)	Alkane–SO_3H (50 g.)–BF_3 (saturated)	−20	0.6	(13%)	(44%) (p/m = 19)[a]	37%[h]	—	681
5	Styrene (0.4)	H_2SO_4	98	—	1-Phenyl-1-tolylethane (65%)				407
2 vol.	Propene trimer (1 vol.)	$AlCl_3$ (0.3%)–HCl (1.8%)	10	—	Nonyl- (90%)[w], dinonyl- and higher (10%)[w]				251
1.5	Tripropene (1)	BF_3–H_2O[o]	75–80	2.1	Nonyl- (54%)[g], isopropyl- (1%)[g], t-butyl- (6%)[g], amyl- (14%)[g]				431
2	Propene trimer (1)	94% H_2SO_4 (1)	0–5	2	Nonyl- (65%) (92% para-)				468(266, 564)
50 pts.	1-Decene (10 pts.)	HF (15 pts.)	0–10	18	2-(p-Methylphenyl)decane[e]				290
4	Isodecylene[j] (1)	H_2SO_4 (0.12)[n]	10	1	Alkylate (140%)[k] (b.p. 175–220° 12%; 220–300°, 84%; 300°, 2%)				406(403, 405)
1	α,p-Dimethylstyrene (1)	$AlCl_3$ (0.1)[s]	0	—	2,2-Ditolylpropane (1%), dimers[t] (26%), botts. (74%)				144
30	α,p-Dimethylstyrene (1)	$AlCl_3$–CH_3NO_2, 4 g./5 ml.	0	1	2,2-Ditolylpropane (4%), dimers[t] (26%), botts. (40%)				144
70	α,p-Dimethylstyrene (1)	H_2SO_4 (0.5)[s]	5	2	2,2-Ditolylpropane (4%), dimers[t] (80%)				144
300	α,p-Dimethylstyrene (1)	H_2SO_4 (20)[s]	0	6	2,2-Ditolylpropane (35%), dimers[t] (59%)				144

Table continued

TABLE 13 (continued)

Toluene (Moles)	Olefin (Moles)	Catalyst (Moles)	Temp. (°C)	Time (hrs.)	Products (% Yield)	Ref.
60	α,p-Dimethylstyrene (1)	70% H_2SO_4 (9)[s]	100	8	2,2-Ditolylpropane (1%), dimers[t] (71%)	144
30	α,p-Dimethylstyrene (1)	Me-, Et-, Pr-sulfonic acid (1)	27	3.5	2,2-Ditolylpropane (1%), dimers[t] (80%), botts. (20%)	144
1	1-Dodecene (1)	$AlCl_3$ (0.1)–$CHCl_3$ (0.05)	45	1	Dodecyl- (91%)	124
334 pts.	Dodecene (506 pts.)	H_2SO_4 (294 pts.)	<10	24	Liquid, b.p. 110–160 at 1.2–2.2 mm. (555 pts.)	155
10	1-Dodecene (1)	HF (10)	16	—	2-, 3-, 4-(4'-Methylphenyl)decanes (13/15/17%), 5- and 6-isomers (44%)	582(59)
5	Hexene dimer (1)	$AlCl_3$–HCl	46	1	Alkylate (115%)[k]	287
4–5	Diisohexylene (1)	97–98% H_2SO_4 (0.2)[l,m]	5–10	1.5	Alkylated toluene, b.p. > 250° (85–90%)	403
—	Propene tetramer	$AlCl_3$	—	—	Dodecyl- (56%)	49
3	Propene tetramer (1)	$AlCl_3$–HCl (0.034)[u]	33	0.75	s-Dodecyl- (54%) (p/m/o = 45/50/5)	59
2.5	Propene tetramer (1)	98.5% H_2SO_4 (4.42)[v]	2	1.33	t-Dodecyl- (92–4%) (p/m/o = 91/8/1)	59(63,155, 266,494, 564,886a)
0.4	Propene tetramer (0.2)	Amberlyst 15 (2 g.) HOAc (0.6)	123	6	Dodecyl- (18%)	661
5	Propene tetramer (1)	H_3PO_4–kieselguhr	300	0.5 L.H.S.V.	Alkylate (12%)	273
1.5	Propene tetramer (1)	HF (0.202)[u]	0	1	t-Dodecyl- (66%) (p-/m-/o- = 88/10/2)	59
5	Tetraisobutylene (1)	$AlCl_3$ (0.1)	−35	2	t-Butyl- (5%), octyl- (68%), dodecyl- plus butyl-, dodecyl- (10%), hexadecyl- plus dioctyl- (16%)	682(222)
3	Triisobutylene (1)	BF_3–H_2O[o]	24–38	0.9	t-Butyl- (78%)[q] (p-/m- = 62/38), 3,5-di-t-butyl- (4%)[q]	431
5	Triisobutylene (1)	Alkane-SO_3H (0.9)	75	5	t-Butyl- (20%), triisobutylene (60%), and tetraisobutylene (20%)	653

	Triisobutylene				*t*-Butyl-	Octyl-	Dodecyl-	C_4–C_7H_6–C_8	
5	(1)	$AlCl_3$ (0.08)	−40	1.83	(19%)	(27%)	(34%)	—	682(222)
5	(1)	$AlCl_3$ (0.1)–HCl	−60	3	(17%)	(30%)	(23%)[e]	(30%)	682
5	(1)	$AlCl_3$ (0.09)–CH_3NO_2 (0.25)	25	1.83	(37%)	(41%)	—	(21%)	682
5	(1)	$FeCl_3$ (0.2)	0	1.66	(16%)	(47%)	(20%)	—	682
5	(1)	96% H_2SO_4 (0.9)	−20	1.5	(18%)	(28%)	(28%)[e]	—	682
5	(1)	100% H_2SO_4 (0.9)	−20	3.16	(14%)	(22%)	(46%)	—	682
5	(1)	HF (5)	−40	1.5	(25%)	(48%)	(10%)[g]	—	682
—	Dodecene, pentadecene	HF–HgF_2	10	0.75	Dodecyl- (70%)		—	—	446
5	Tetraisobutylene (1)	$AlCl_3$ (0.9) CH_3NO_2 (0.25)	25	2.16	*t*-Butyl- (16%), *t*-octyl- (83%)[b]				682
5	Tetraisobutylene (1)	H_2SO_4 (0.9)	−20	3.16	*t*-Butyl- (5%), *t*-octyl- (78%), *p*-dodecyl- (9%)				682(679)
5	Tetraisobutylene (1)	HF (5)	−40	1.5	*t*-Butyl- (4%), *t*-octyl- (76%),[h] *p*-dodecyl- (9%)				682

[a] 1,1,3,3-Tetramethylbutyltoluene.
[b] Isomeric C_8 groups.
[c] Probably a mixture of tolyldecanes (see ref. 582).
[d] *Para*- (questionable in view of Schlatter, ref. 696), plus di-*t*-butyl- (19%).
[e] *Para-t-*.
[f] >91% *para-t-*.
[g] p/m = 90/10.
[h] p/m = 19/1.
[i] R. Pajeau (587b) obtained both *m*- and *p*-isomers in $TiCl_4$ catalyzed reaction of toluene with *t*-butylchloride.
[j] Phosphoric acid polymer of C_5 cut of thermal cracked gasoline.
[k] Based on wt. % olefin feed.
Vol. ratio acid/hydrocarbon.
[m] Added gradually.
[n] Volume ratio to hydrocarbons.
[o] 1 volume to 7 volumes of hydrocarbon.
[p] 1 volume to 4 volumes of toluene.
[q] Based on toluene reacting.
[r] Respective for each catalyst or catalyst modifier.
[s] Wt. ratio to olefin.
[t] 1,3,3,6-Tetramethyl-1-(*p*-tolyl)indane.
[u] Wt. ratio catalyst/hydrocarbon.
[v] Make-up ratio.
[w] Of alkylate.
[x] Probably contained other isomers; see Section II-1-G-d.
[y] 2-*p*-Tolylhexane probably also formed (582).
[z] B.p. 123–134°.

TABLE 14. Toluene with cyclic olefins

Toluene (Moles)	Cycloolefin (Moles)	Catalyst (Moles)	Temp. (°C)	Time (hrs.)	Toluene derivatives (% Yield)	Ref.
70 cc.	Cyclopentene (15 g.)	$AlCl_3$ (2 g.)	0	0.17	3-Cyclopentyl- (major), 4-cyclopentyl-, dicyclopentyl	109(631)
5	Cyclohexene (1.5)	$AlCl_3$ (0.45)	25	3	2- and 4- Cyclohexyl- (62%)	66(634)
5	Cyclohexene (1)	$AlCl_3$ (0.05)	38–42	0.25[a]	Cyclohexyl- (80%)	496
56 g.	Cyclohexene (23 g.)	$AlCl_3$ (10 g.)	—	—	Mono- and dicyclohexyl-	634
1 to 1.5	Cyclohexene	Al-EtBr (0.01)	—	—	Cyclohexyl- (21–26%), dicyclohexyl- (14–37%), polycyclohexyl- (19–40%)	550
6	Cyclohexene (1)	H_2SO_4 (50%)[c]	9–10	—	Cyclohexyl- (70–83%)	508
1.5	Cyclohexene (0.33)	HF (3.2)	r.t.	2	4-Cyclohexyl-	759
5	1-Methylcyclohexene (1)	$AlCl_3$ (0.2)—HCl	−50	0.50	Monoalkylate (19%) (90%)[b]	220
5	4-Methylcyclohexene (1)	$AlCl_3$ (0.2)—HCl	−50	0.65	Monoalkylate (28%) (37%)[b]	220
5	4-Methylcyclohexene (1)	HF (5)	5	0.83	Monoalkylate (89%) (90%)[b]	220
1.5	1-Butylcyclohexene	$FeCl_3$ (1)	—	—	Alkylate (65%)	530
736 g.	α-Pinene	$AlCl_3$ (20 g.)	110–118	11.3	Pinyl- "probably mixture of 3 isomers"	359

[a] Added stirring.
[b] Methyl-1-tolylcyclohexanes in monoalkylate.
[c] Based on toluene.

TABLE 15. C$_8$ aromatics with ethylene

Aromatic compound (Moles)	Ethylene (Moles)	Catalyst (Moles)	Temp. (°C)	Time (hrs.)	Products (% Yield)	Ref.
Ethylbenzene (10)	1	AlCl$_3$ (1%)	80	—	Ethylbenzenes (di-/poly- = 11/1) di-: $o/m/p$ = 3/64/33	424
Ethylbenzene (10)	1	H$_3$PO$_4$–kieselguhr	275 900 psi	2 L.H.S.V. 120	Ethylbenzenes (di-/poly- = 4/1) di-: $o/m/p$ = 43/29/28	424
Ethylbenzene (10)	1	FePO$_4$	275	2 L.H.S.V. 120	Ethylbenzenes (di-/poly- = 5/1) di-: $o/m/p$ = 43/30/27	424
Ethylbenzene (10)	1	SiO$_2$–Al$_2$O$_3$	275 900 psi	2 L.H.S.V. 120	Ethylbenzenes (di-/poly- = 4/1) di-: $o/m/p$ = 33/37/30	424
o-Xylene (1)	0.5	AlCl$_3$ (10%)	80–90	2	Dimethylethylbenzene, 1,3,5- (27%) 1,2,4- (15%)	676
o-Xylene (1)	1	AlCl$_3$ (15%)	85–90	2.5	Dimethylethylbenzene, 1,3,5- (13%) 1,2,4- (37%)	676
m-Xylene (1)	0.5	AlCl$_3$ (5%)	80–90	2	Dimethylethylbenzene, 1,3,5- (58%) 1,2,4- (8%)	676
m-Xylene (1)	1	AlCl$_3$ (10%)	85–95	2	Dimethylethylbenzene, 1,3,5- (25%) 1,2,4- (18%)	676
m-Xylene (1)	1.2	AlCl$_3$ (0.16)	85–90	4	85% Conv., 42% mono-, 14% di-, 13% heavier (24/47)[c]	383
		ditto + 0.002 H$_2$O	85–90	4	80% Conv., 43% mono-, 16% di-, 15% heavier (45/43)[c]	383
		ditto + 0.014 H$_2$O	85–90	4	37% Conv., 12% mono-, 1% di-, 6% heavier (53/37)[c]	383
m-Xylene (1)	1	BF$_3$–P$_2$O$_5$–kieselguhr	94–97 350–450 psig	5.3	60% Conv., 23% mono-, 4% di-, 15% heavier	383
p-Xylene (1)	1	AlCl$_3$ (10%)	80–85	2	Dimethylethylbenzene, 1,4,2- (56%)	676
Xylene (475 pts.) $o/m/p$ = 28/5/21	105 pts.	AlCl$_3$ (14.5 g.) EtCl (75 g.)	70–100	0.66	Xylene (28%), ethylxylenes (mono- 57%, di- 15%)	520

Table continued

TABLE 15 (*continued*)

Aromatic compound (Moles)	Ethylene (Moles)	Catalyst (Moles)	Temp. (°C)	Time (hrs.)	Products (% Yield)	Ref.
o-Xylene (1)	0.58	AlCl₃ (0.025)	90	0.58	3,4-Dimethyl-1-ethylbenzene (90%),[b] 2,3-dimethyl-1-ethylbenzene (5%),[b] 3,5-dimethyl-1-ethylbenzene (5%)[b]	183
m-Xylene (0.3)	—	AlCl₃ (0.2)	—	1.5	5-Ethyl-1,3-dimethylbenzene (50%)	226(520)
m-Xylene (2)	1	AlCl₃ (0.04)	95	0.5	Toluene 1, 2, 0%),[a] xylene (63, 34, 66%),[a] 3,5-dimethyl-1-ethylbenzene (11, 19, 7%),[a] 2,4-dimethyl-1-ethylbenzene (9, 12, 11%),[a] 2,5-dimethyl-1-ethylbenzene (0.6, 0, 0%),[a] 2,6-dimethyl-1-ethylbenzene (2.5, 2, 3%),[a] higher boiling (16, 13, 13%)[a]	184
(2)	1	(0.04)	95	18		
(2.5)	1	(0.46)	50	18		
m-Xylene (1)	1.1	BF₃ (1.2)–HF (9)	62	1	1,3,5-Ethylxylene (83, 81%),[a] diethylxylenes (11, 16%),[a] triethylxylenes (1, 2%)[a]	467a
	1.2	BF₃ (1.3)–HF (9)	16	66		
m-Xylene	1.1	BF₃ (1.6)–HF (9)	15	0.25	1,3,5-Ethylxylene (32%), 1,3,4-ethylxylene (12%), 1,2,3-ethylxylene (2%), diethylxylenes (22%), triethylxylenes (5%)	467a
m-Xylene	1	HF (9)	15	0.25	1,3,5-Ethylxylene (1%), 1,3,4-ethylxylene (15%), 1,2,3-ethylxylene (4%), diethylxylenes (6%), triethylxylenes (2%), tetraethylxylenes (10%)	467a

[a] Yields given for each set of operating variables.
[b] % of "ethylxylene product."
[c] Ratio 4-ethyl-m-xylene to 5-ethyl-m-xylene in monoalkylate.

TABLE 16. C_8 aromatics with propene

Aromatic (Moles)	Propene (Moles)	Catalyst (Moles)	Temp. (°C)	Time (hrs.)	Isopropyl derivative (% Yield)	Ref.
Ethylbenzene 330 pts.	170 pts.	AlCl₃ (24 pts.)	20–30	—	Ethyldiisopropylbenzenes	173
Ethylbenzene	—	AlCl₃ (1–7.7 mol. %) CH₃NO₂ (12.7–42 mol. %)	40	0.5–3	Alkylation rate = 1.81 × [benzene]	129
Ethylbenzene	—	BF₃–Et₂O (27 mol. % each)	40	2.5–5	Alkylation rate = 1.73 × [benzene]	129
Ethylbenzene (3)	(1)	BF₃–H₃PO₄ (0.3)	88–90	—	1-Ethyl-4-isopropylbenzene (69%)	947
Ethylbenzene (48 pts.) o- (39), m- (141), p-xylenes (72)	0.71ᶠ	HF (50 vol. %)	38	—	Conversions: ethylbenzene (82%), o- (59%). m- (57%), p-xylene (59%)	716
m-Xylene (1)	1.5	AlCl₃ (0.0128)	30–35	5.5	Conv. 99%; mono- 47% (11/88)ᵃ; di- (41%) isopropyl-m-xylenes	383
			90–95	5	Conv. 99%; mono- 53% (1/99)ᵃ; di- (34%) isopropyl-m-xylenes	
			125–130	4.7	Conv. 100%; mono- 64% (9/81)ᵃ; di- (26%) isopropyl-m-xylenes	

m-Xylene (1) | 1.3–1.5 | AlCl₃–H₂O | | | | 383 (Botts.)

Catalyst		Temp. (°C)	Time (hrs.)	Conv.	Mono-	Ratioᵃ	Diisopropyl-m-xylene	
0.013	0.0035	90–95	5.7	99%	49%	6/92	29%	12%
0.013	0.014	90–95	4.7	88%	50%	32/66	23%	8%
0.013	0.028	90–95	5.0	33%	16%	64/34	trace	3%

Aromatic (Moles)	Propene (Moles)	Catalyst (Moles)	Temp. (°C)	Time (hrs.)	Isopropyl derivative (% Yield)	Ref.
p-Xylene (1)	1	AlCl₃ (0.0128)	90–95	2.8	Conv. 86%; mono- (54%) (44ᶠ/41)ᵃ; di- (13%) isopropylxylenes	383
Xylenes (1)	1.5	AlCl₃ (1.6%)	90–95	5.5	Mono- (70%) 1/91ᵃ; di- (56%) isopropylxylenes (99–100% conv.)ᵈ	381

Table continued

TABLE 16 (*continued*)

Aromatic (Moles)	Propene (Moles)	Catalyst (Moles)	Temp. (°C)	Time (hrs.)	Isopropyl derivative (% Yield)	Ref.
Xylenes (1)	1.5	$AlCl_3$ (1.6%)–H_2O (0.06%)[e]	90–95	5.75	Mono- (63%) 6/92[a]; di- (52%) isopropylxylenes (99–100% conv.)[d]	383
Xylenes (1)	1.3	$AlCl_3$ (1.6%)–H_2O (0.3%)[e]	90–95	4.75	Mono- (70%) 22/66[a]; di- (40%) isopropylxylenes (89% conv.)[d]	381
Xylenes (1)	1.4	$AlCl_3$ (1.6%)–H_2O (0.5%)[e]	90–95	5	Mono- (23%) 64/34[a]; di- (1%) isopropylxylenes (33% conv.)[d]	381
Xylene	—	$AlCl_3$–(iso-C_3H_7Cl)	—	—	Isopropylxylenes	520
Xylenes (1)	0.7	BF_3 (saturation)	75–80	3	Mono- (29%), di- (8%) isopropylxylene	382
o-Xylene (1)	(0.5)	BF_3–H_3PO_4 (20%)	60	2	Mono- (90%); 88/12[b]; 4,5-di- (10%) isopropyl-o-xylene	865
o-Xylene (1)	(0.6)	BF_3–H_3PO_4 (10%)	20	4	Mono- (60%); 60/40[b]; 4,5-di- (23%) isopropyl-o-xylene	865
o-Xylene (1)	(0.5)	BF_3–H_3PO_4 (10%)	80	2	Mono- (85%); 96/4[b]; 4,5-di- (10%) isopropyl-o-xylene	865
m-Xylene (1)	(0.31)	BF_3–H_3PO_4 (10%)	60	1.5	Mono- (90%); 68/2/30[c]; 4,6- and 2,5-di- (9%) isopropyl-m-xylenes	865
m-Xylene (1)	(0.78)	BF_3–H_3PO_4 (10%)	60	3.1	Mono- (73%); 65/2/33[c]; 4,6- and 2,5-di- (25%) isopropyl-m-xylenes	865
m-Xylene (1)	0.5, 1.5[g]	BF_3–H_3PO_4	80–85	1.8, 5	Conversion 45, 91%, mono- (24, 48%) (65/34, 75/21)[c]; di- (4, 28%) isopropylxylenes	383(382)
p-Xylene (1)	(0.3)	BF_3–H_3PO_4 (10%)	50	2	Mono- (85%); 100/0/0[c]; 2,5-di- (7%) isopropyl-p-xylene	865
p-Xylene (1)	(0.5)	BF_3–H_3PO_4 (10%)	20	5	Mono- (60%); 100/0/0[c]; 2,5-di- (20%) isopropyl-p-xylene	865
o-Xylene (1)	1.1	BF_3–P_2O_5–kieselguhr	75–80	flow	Conv. 55%; mono- (26%) (50% 1,2,4); di- (10%) isopropylxylenes	383
m-Xylene (1)	0.2–0.9	BF_3–P_2O_5–kieselguhr	35–130	flow	Conversion 32–79%; mono- (14–47%) (65/34 to 80/13); di- (0–12%) isopropylxylenes	383

p-Xylene (1)	1.6	BF_3–P_2O_5–kieselguhr	75–80	flow	Conversion 88%; mono- (45%) (100/0)[a]; di- (32%) isopropylxylenes	383
m-Xylene (2.02)	1.97	BF_3 (4.36)–HF (35.6)	15	0.25	1,3,5-Isopropylxylene (81%), high boilers (19%)	467a
Xylenes (2.5)	1	BF_3[h]/P_2O_5–kieselguhr	75–80	1	Mono- (55%), di- (8%) isopropylxylene	382
m-Xylene (1)	1.5	BF_3 (20%)–Al_2O_3	75–80	flow	Conv. 77%; mono- (25%) (75/20)[a]; di- (36%) isopropylxylenes	383
o-Xylene (1)	0.5–0.7	H_2SO_4 (1)	ice	—	Dimethylisopropylbenzenes	635

[a] Ratio 1,2,4/1,3,5 isomers in monoalkylate.
[b] Ratio 1,2,4-/1,2,3-.
[c] Ratio 1,2,4-/1,2,3-/1,3,5-.
[d] Of xylene.
[e] Wt. % of arene.

[f] 2-Isopropyl-p-xylene.
[g] Yields given for each test.
[h] BF_3 must be fed continuously.
[i] Mol. ratio to ethylbenzene and o-xylene.

7+F.C. II

TABLE 17. C$_8$ aromatics with isobutylene

C$_8$ Aromatic (Moles)	Isobutylene (Moles)	Catalyst (Moles)	Temp. (°C)	Time (hrs.)	Products (% Yield)	Ref.
Ethylbenzene (1.1)	1	HF (1.1)	0–5	1.2	t-Butylethylbenzene (56%) (m/p = 15/85)	696
Ethylbenzene (1274 pts.)	900 pts. 150/hr.	HF (333 pts.)	0	6	t-Butylethylbenzene (41%), 3,5-di-t-butylethylbenzene (20%)	689(693)
Ethylbenzene (2.01)	1.03	HF (7.75)	100–105	1.5	t-Butylethylbenzene (0.26 mole), higher boiling (25 g.), iso-C$_4$H$_{10}$ (0.044), 1-phenyl-1-p-ethylphenylethane (0.05), benzene (0.37), ethylbenzene (0.59), diethylbenzene (0.26)	717
Ethylbenzene (64 pts.), o/m/p Xylene (52/188/96 pts.)	1.06	HF (50 vol. %)	13	—	Recovered arene feed: ethylbenzene (8.2 pts.) o/m/p xylene (24/148/96 pts.)	716
Xylene (o/m/p = 8/48/12), ethylbenzene (14%), paraffins (12%)	^{d}	HF	0–10	4	Alkylated 88% of o-, 84% of m-xylenes, and 94% of ethylbenzene. p-Xylene not affected	694
o-Xylene (1)	0.5	H$_2$SO$_4$ (1)	—	—	1,2-Dimethyl-4-t-butylbenzene (45%)	635
o-Xylene (9.4)	7.9	HF (6.9)	0–10	4.4	1,2-Dimethyl-4-t-butylbenzene (72%),^{a} higher (7%)^a	695
m-Xylene (100 g.)	(20 l.)	AlCl$_3$ (7.5 g.)	12–14	—	1,3-Dimethyl-5-t-butylbenzene (18%)	456(562)
m-Xylene (5000 pts.)	—	AlCl$_3$–iso-BuCl 200/50	>10	—	t-Butyl-m-xylene	64
m-Xylene (5 kg.)	—	AlCl$_3$–t-BuCl 200 g./50 g.	10	—	t-Butylxylene	3
m-Xylene	—	FeCl$_3$ (0.07)	0–10	1.5	sym-Butylxylene (very good yield)	562
Xylenes (1) (m/p = 50/50)	1	FeCl$_3$ (0.07)	0–10	1.5	No alkylate	140
Xylenes (1) (m/p = 50/50)	1	FeCl$_3$–HCl	0–10^b	1.5^b	Alkylate (39%), recovered xylenes (45%) (m/p = 6/94)	140
Xylenes (1) (m/p = 50/50)	0.7	HF (2.6)	0–5	1.5	Alkylate (48%); recovered xylenes (45%) (m/p = 3/97)	140

m-Xylene (0.98)	1	BF$_3$ (1.08)–HF (9.6)	5	0.5	1,3,5-t-Butylxylene (56%), higher (44%)	467a
m-Xylene (9.0)	8.0	HF (7.5)	0–5	6.2	1,3-Dimethyl-5-t-butylbenzene (76%),[a] higher (7%)[a]	695
p-Xylene (5)	1	AlCl$_3$ (0.2) 5 cc. t-BuCl	25	0.57	Toluene; 1,2,4-trimethylbenzene; t-butyltoluene; hydride transfer products, e.g., diarylmethanes	221
p-Xylene (5)	1	AlCl$_3$ (0.2) CH$_3$NO$_2$ (100 g.) t-BuCl (5 cc.)	25	0.75	t-Butyl-p-xylene (11%)	221
p-Xylene (2)	1	H$_2$SO$_4$ (1212 g.)	4	0.9	t-Butyl-p-xylene (7%)	221
Xylenes (1) o/m/p = 15/59/29	0.46, 1.1	H$_2$SO$_4$ (0.5)	0–10	—	Alkylate (22, 45%),[c] recovered xylenes (60, 33%)[c] (o/m/p = 0/63/37; 0/34/66)[c]	140(485)
p-Xylene (4.5)	4.0	HF (7.3)	0–3	4.9	1,4-Dimethyl-2-t-butylbenzene (11%),[a] higher (38%)[a]	695

[a] Per cent of product; balance is recovered xylene.
[b] Probable conditions.
[c] For respective mol. ratios of feed.
[d] Less than 1 mole/mole aromatics.

TABLE 18. C_8 aromatics with higher olefins

C_8 Aromatic (Moles)	Olefin (Moles)	Catalyst (Moles)	Temp. (°C)	Time (hrs.)	Products (% Yield)	Ref.
Ethylbenzene (2)	2-Butene (1)	$AlCl_2 \cdot H_2PO_4$ (0.2)	40	—	s-Butylethylbenzene (60.6%)	940
Ethylbenzene (1.5)	n-Butene (1)	$BF_3 \cdot H_3PO_4$ (0.2)	30	—	4-s-Butylethylbenzene (77%)	939(723a)
p-Xylene (2)	3-Methyl-1-butene (1)	$AlCl_3$–HCl (13 g.)	0	0.43	2-p-Xylyl-3-methylbutane (41%), isopentane (0.19 mole), some di-p-xylylmethane	221
p-Xylene (5)	3-Methyl-1-butene (1)	$AlCl_3$ (0.2)–CH_3NO_2 (100 g.)–t-Amyl Cl (5 cc.)	25	0.58	2-p-Xylyl-3-methylbutane (7%), t-butyl-p-xylene (8%), much polymer	221, 221
p-Xylene (3)	2-Methyl-2-butene (1)	$FeCl_3$–HCl (50 g.)	25	1.0	Very low yield	221
p-Xylene (3)	2-Methyl-2-butene (1)	BF_3 (continuous)	15	0.66	Low yield contaminated with polymer	221
p-Xylene (2)	3-Methyl-1-butene (1)	H_2SO_4 (184 g.)	0	1.1	Low yield contaminated with polymer	221
p-Xylene (2)	3-Methyl-1-butene (1)	HF (5.5)	23–25	1.43	2-p-Xylyl-3-methylbutane (34%)	221
p-Xylene (2)	2-Methyl-2-butene (1)	HF (4.25)	0	1.0	Low yield contaminated with polymer	221
p-Xylene (1.7)	2-Methyl-2-butene (1)	HF (5.7)	24–28	1.58	2-p-Xylyl-3-methylbutane (40%)	221
m-Xylene (1)	3-Hexene (0.75)	HF (3.3)	5–10	24	Hexylxylenes (89%)	779
o-Xylene	1-Heptene	H_2SO_4	—	—	1,2-Dimethyl-4-heptylbenzene	738
m-Xylene	1-Heptene	H_2SO_4	—	—	1,3-Dimethyl-4-heptylbenzene	738
p-Xylene	1-Heptene	H_2SO_4	—	—	1,4-Dimethyl-4-heptylbenzene	738
m-Xylene (0.5)	3-Ethyl-1-pentene (0.2)	$AlCl_3$–HCl (0.004)	25–50	3	3-Ethyl-3-(3,5-dimethylphenyl)-pentane (50%)[b]	46
o-Xylene (1)	n-Octenes (0.4)	$AlCl_3$ (15 g.)	heat	—	1,2-Dimethyl-4-isooctylbenzene	635
p-Xylene (7)	n-Octene (1)	H_2SO_4 (0.12)[c]	10	1	Alkylated xylene (162%)[d]	406
m-Xylene	Diisobutylene	$AlCl_3$	—	—	sym-Butylxylene	562
m-Xylene	Diisobutylene	$FeCl_3$	—	—	sym-Butylxylene	562
o-Xylene (2)	Diisobutylene (1)	BF_3/H_2O[e]	33–36	1.1	1,2-Dimethyl-4-t-butylbenzene (84%)[f]	431

m-Xylene (2)	Diisobutylene (1)	BF_3/H_2O[e]	33–36	1.05	5-t-Butyl-m-xylene (85.6%)[f]	431
m-Xylene (1)	Diisobutylene (2)	Toluenesulfonic acid	100	—	t-Butylxylene	909
o-Xylene (5)	Diisobutylene (1)	HF (5)	−20	1.16	4-t-Octyl-1,2-dimethylbenzene (96%),[a] t-butyl-1,2-dimethylbenzene (3%)	681(679)
o-Xylene (0.4)	Styrene (0.15)	H_2SO_4 (0.2)	cold	—	1-Phenyl-1-o-xylylethane (70%)	407
m-Xylene (5)	Styrene (0.3)	H_2SO_4 (0.5)	cold	—	1-Phenyl-1-m-xylylethane (65%)	407
p-Xylene	Styrene	H_2SO_4	cold	1	1-Phenyl-1-p-xylylethane	407
o-Xylene (7)	n-Nonene (1)	H_2SO_4 (0.12)[c]	10	1	Alkylated xylene (162%)[d]	406
p-Xylene (7)	n-Nonene (1)	H_2SO_4 (0.12)[c]	10	1	Alkylated xylene (147%)[d]	406
m-Xylene (10)	1-Decene (1)	HF (10)	16	—	2-, 3-, 4-, 5-(2,4-Dimethylphenyl)-decanes (20, 24, 20, 29%)	582
o-Xylene (7)	Isodecylene[g] (1)	H_2SO_4 (0.12)[c]	10	1	Alkylated xylene (161%)[d]	406
p-Xylene (7)	Isodecylene[g] (1)	H_2SO_4 (0.12)[c]	10	1	Alkylated xylene (81%)[d]	406
o-Xylene (4)	Propene tetramer (1)	93% H_2SO_4 (8)	0	few	1,2-Dimethyl-4-dodecylbenzene (92%)	266

[a] Contains 1.3% isomeric octyl-1,2-dimethylbenzenes.
[b] This tertiary structure for the C_7 group is open to question (see ref. 713).
[c] Volume ratio to hydrocarbon catalyzed.
[d] % Wt. of olefin.
[e] 1 Vol. to 7 vol. of hydrocarbon.
[f] Based on arene reacting.
[g] Phosphoric acid polymer of C_5 cut of thermal-cracked gasoline.

TABLE 19. C$_8$ aromatics with cyclic olefins

Arene (Moles)	Cycloolefin (Moles)	Catalyst (Moles)	Temp. (°C)	Time (hrs.)	Products (% Yield)	Ref.
Ethylbenzene (1)	Cyclohexene	AlEt$_2$Br–AlEtBr$_2$ (0.01)	100–120, 80–85	—, 4	Mono-, di-, and tricyclohexyl-ethylbenzenes	308
Ethylbenzene (1.5)	1-Butylcyclohexene (1)	FeCl$_3$ (1)	—	—	Alkylate (50%)	530
Ethylbenzene (6)	Cyclohexene (1)	H$_2$SO$_4$ (50%)ᵇ	9–10	—	Cyclohexyl derivatives (70–83%)	508
o-Xylene (70 cc.)	Cyclopentene (15 g.)	AlCl$_3$ (2 g.)	0	0.16	1,2-Dimethyl-4-cyclopentyl-benzene	530
m-Xylene (70 cc.)	Cyclopentene (15 g.)	AlCl$_3$ (2 g.) or FeCl$_3$	0	0.16	1,3-Dimethyl-5-cyclopentyl-benzene; dicyclopentyl-m-xylene	530
p-Xylene (70 cc.)	Cyclopentene (15 g.)	AlCl$_3$ (2 g.)	0	0.16	1,4-Dimethyl-2-cyclopentyl-benzene; 1,4-dimethyl-2,5-dicyclopentylbenzene	530(631)
m-Xylene (4)	Cyclohexene (1.5)	AlCl$_3$ (0.45)	25	3	5-Cyclohexyl-m-xylene (56%)	66
p-Xylene (2)	Cyclohexene (0.7)	AlCl$_3$ (0.2)	25	3	2-Cyclohexyl-p-xylene (33%); dicyclohexyl-p-xylene (5%)	66
o-Xylene (1–1.5)	Cyclohexene	Al–EtBr (0.01)	—	—	Mono-, di-, and polycyclo-hexyl-o-xylene (42/6/13%)	550
m-Xylene (1–1.5)	Cyclohexene	Al–EtBr (0.01)	—	—	Mono-, di-, and polycyclo-hexyl-m-xylene (40/12/15%)	550
p-Xylene (1–1.5)	Cyclohexene	Al–EtBr (0.01)	—	—	Mono-, di-, and polycyclo-hexyl-p-xylene (18/17/19%)	550
o-Xylene (6)	Cyclohexene (1)	H$_2$SO$_4$ (50%)ᵇ	9–10	—	Cyclohexyl derivatives (70–83%)	508
m-Xylene (6)	Cyclohexene (1)	H$_2$SO$_4$ (50%)ᵇ	9–10	—	Cyclohexyl derivatives (70–83%)	508
p-Xylene (6)	Cyclohexene (1)	H$_2$SO$_4$ (50%)ᵇ	9–10	—	Cyclohexyl derivatives (70–83%)	508

p-Xylene (2)	Cyclohexene	H_2SO_4 (184 g.)	0	0.82	Cyclohexyl-p-xylene (34%)	220
p-Xylene (5)	1-Methylcyclohexene (1)	$AlCl_3$ (0.1)–HCl	0	0.75	Monoalkylate (54%) (trace of 1-methyl-1-p-xylylcyclohexane)[a]	220
p-Xylene (5)	1-Methylcyclohexene (1)	$AlCl_3$ (0.2)–HCl CH_3NO_2 (100 g.)	25	1.10	Low yield	220
p-Xylene (5)	1-Methylcyclohexene (1)	HF (5)	4	0.83	Monoalkylate (76%) (<5% of 1-methyl-1-p-xylylcyclohexane)[a]	220(620)
p-Xylene (300 g.)	3-Methylcyclohexene (75 g.)	$AlCl_3$ (31 g.)	25	3	2-(3'- and 4'-Methylcyclohexyl)-p-xylene (19%)	66
m-Xylene (0.1)	4-Methylcyclohexene (0.05)	HF (5 g.)	ca 0	—	1,3-Dimethyl-5-(1-methylcyclohexyl)benzene	612
p-Xylene (2)	4-Methylcyclohexene (1)	$AlCl_3$ (0.1)–HCl	0	0.75	Monoalkylate (35%) (<5% 1-methyl-1-p-xylylcyclohexane)[a]	220
p-Xylene (5)	4-Methylcyclohexene (1)	H_2SO_4 (184 g.)	0	0.83	Monoalkylate (<5%)	220

[a] Balance consists of isomers with methyl group in 2-, 3-, or 4-positions. [b] Wt. % of arene feed.

TABLE 20. C$_9$ and higher aromatics with ethylene

Aromatic compound (Moles)	Ethylene (Moles)	Catalyst (Moles)	Temp. (°C)	Time (hrs.)	Products (% Yield)	Ref.
t-Butylbenzene (0.32 m.)	0.8	NaH–activated clay (2 g.)	150 910 psig	18	m- and p-Ethyl-t-butylbenzene (25%)	201
Diethylbenzene (2.24)	5.74	AlCl$_3$–HCl	70	—	Ethylbenzenes (tetra- 9%, penta- 1%, hexa- 91%)	52
1,3,5-Ethylxylene (0.5)	0.5	BF$_3$ (1)–HF (7.5)	25	0.25	1,3,5-Ethylxylene (40%) other ethylxylenes (di- 41%, tri- 13%, tetra- 6%)	467b
m- and p-Diethylbenzene (0.64), 1,3,5-ethyl-xylene (0.64)	0.64	BF$_3$ (2.14)–HF (10.9)	30	0.5	Ethylbenzene (2%), 1,3,5-ethylxylene (50%), -1,3,5-triethylbenzene (43%), higher (5%)	467b
p-Diisopropylbenzene (1000 pts.)	270 pts.	AlCl$_3$ (50 pts.) HCl (25 pts.)	75	1.75	1,2,4,5-Diethyldiisopropylbenzene (major)	677
Triethylbenzene (2.24)	5.24	AlCl$_3$–HCl	70	—	Ethylbenzenes (tri- 7%, tetra- 19%, penta- 2%, hexa- 72%)	52
1,3-Dimethyl-5-t-butyl-benzene (10)	9.5	HF (20.6)	0	7	1,3-Dimethyl-2-ethyl-5-t-butylbenzene (192 g.) (30%), 1,3-dimethyl-4-ethylbenzene (49 g.), 1,3-dimethyl-5-ethylbenzene (2 g.), triethyl-m-xylenes (21 g.), 1,3-dimethyl-2,4-diethylbenzene (53 g.), 1,3-dimethyl-2,5-diethylbenzene (some)	690

TABLE 21. C₉ and higher aromatics with propene

Aromatic (Moles)	Propene (Moles)	Catalyst (Moles)	Temp. (°C)	Time (hrs.)	Isopropylbenzene products (% Yield)	Ref.
Cumene (1)	1.97	$AlCl_3$ (0.1)	30	—	1,3,5- and 1,2,4-Tri- (3/1) (60%), di- (m/p = 2/1)	22(31,35)
Cumene (1)	0.98	$AlCl_3$ (7%)	60	7.5	Mono-, di-,[d,e] tri- (56%),[c] trimethylindane (0.2%)	253a(165)
Cumene (1700 pts.)	595 pts.	$AlCl_3$ (5.75 pts.)–iso-C_3H_7Cl (4.31 pts.)	70–100	2	Benzene (8%), mono- (12%), di- (28%), tri- (50%), tetra- (2%)	426c(180)
Cumene	—	$AlCl_3$ (1–7.7 mol. %)–CH_3NO_2 (12.7–42 mol. %)	40	0.5–3	Alkylation rate = 1.69 ± 0.05 × [benzene]	129
Cumene (35)	1	Al–$TiCl_4$ (0.03–0.015)	75	—	Dialkylate $o/m/p$ = 16–21/34–38/46	293
Cumene (189 g.)	—	Titanium subchlorides (66 g.)	146	2.25	Tri- (43%), higher alkylate (3%)	650
Cumene (3 kg.)	403 g.	BF_3–H_3PO_4 (414 g.)	100	3	1,4-Di- (73%), polyalkylate (8%)	948
Cumene (4340 pts.)	818 pts.	88% H_2SO_4 (3590 pts.)	49–52	5.5	Di- (1895 pts.), tri- (388 pts.), tetra- (94 pts.), higher boiling (106 pts.)	504
Cumene (480 g.)	0.91	Boria–alumina (50 g.)	200	4	Di- (o- 10%, m- 25%, p- 53% based on propene)[a]	666
Cumene (3)	1[l]	SiO_2–Al_2O_3	200 25 atm.	20 L.H.S.V.	Di-, $o/m/p$ = 12/32/56	571(34,206)
Cumene (3), triisopropylbenzene (0.3)	1	Alumina silicate (90 cc.)	250 60 atm.	5 L.H.S.V.	Di- (30%), (o- 2%, m- 45%, p- 53%)	371a
Cumene (5)	1 (60 atm.)	Aluminum silicate	120 160 240	2 L.H.S.V. 2 L.H.S.V. 2 L.H.S.V.	Conv. of C₃= (84%) p-isomer in di- (48%), Conv. of C₃= (99%) p-isomer in di- (53%), Conv. of C₃= (99%) p-isomer in di- (38%)	370

Table continued

7★

TABLE 21 (continued)

Aromatic (Moles)	Propene (Moles)	Catalyst (Moles)	Temp. (°C)	Time (hrs.)	Isopropylbenzene products (% Yield)	Ref.
Cumene^g (3)	(1) 25 atm.^{k}	Aluminum silicate	200 200 200 200	7.5 L.H.S.V. 15 L.H.S.V. 45 L.H.S.V. 135 L.H.S.V.	Conv. of $C_3^=$ (98%) polymer (0.1%) Conv. of $C_3^=$ (98%) polymer (0%) Conv. of $C_3^=$ (99%) polymer (0%) Conv. of $C_3^=$ (89%) polymer (10%)	370
Cumene (5)	—	SiO_2–Al_2O_3 (0.2% H_2O)	200	6 L.H.S.V.	p-Di-^{h} (372 g./l./hr.) 96% conv. of $C_3^=$	569(371)
Cumene (4)	1	WO_x–SiO_2	60 60 atm. 125	85 S.V. 85 S.V.	70% Conv. of $C_3^=$, di- (81%), $o/m/p$ = 15/28/57 99% Conv. of $C_3^=$, di- (77%), $o/m/p$ = 6/46/48	572
Pseudocumene (1)	0.7	BF_3–P_2O_5^{f}	75–80	2	62% Conv.; mono- (34%), di- (0%) isopropylpseudocumene, 10% bottoms	383
Mesitylene (1)	0.6	$AlCl_3$^{i}	—	—	1,2,5-Trimethyl-4-isopropylbenzene (85%)	635
Mesitylene (1)	2	$AlCl_3$^{i}	—	—	1,2,4-Trimethyl-3,5-diisopropylbenzene (84 g.)	635
Ethyltoluene (1) $o/m/p$ = 16/49/35	0.48	H_2SO_4 (0.5)	0–10	—	Alkylate (21%), recovered feed (61%) ($o/m/p$ = 15/55/30)	140
t-Butylbenzene	—	$AlCl_3$ (1–7.7 mol. %) CH_3NO_2 (12.7–42 mol. %)	40	0.5–3	Alkylation rate = 1.4 ± 0.16 × [benzene]	129
t-Butylbenzene	—	BF_3–Et_2O (27 mol. % each)	40	2.5–5	Alkylation rate = 1.23 ± 0.06 × [benzene]	129
t-Butylbenzene (100 cc.)	34 g.	Al_2O_3 (14%)–SiO_2 (86%) NaH (1.5 g.)	90–100	0.5	Isopropyl-t-butylbenzene (mono- 62 vol. %, di- 23 vol. %, poly- 15 vol. %)	207
Diethylbenzene (6780 g.)	3902 g.	$AlCl_3$ (454 g.)	20–30	—	Diethyldiisopropylbenzene (1300 g.)	173
Diisopropylbenzene	—	$AlCl_3$ (10 mole %)	65–70	—	1,3,5-Tri- (prac. quan. yield)	902

					Mono-, di-, tri-, and tetra-	
Diisopropylbenzene (1.0)	—	60	AlCl$_3$	—	Mono-, di-, tri-, and tetra-	34
p-Diisopropylbenzene (1000 pts.)	460 pts.	25	AlCl$_3$ (25 pts.) HCl (12.5 pts.)	1.75	1,2,4,5-Tetra- (major)	677
Diisopropylbenzene (3)	1[b] / 1.5 l./hr.	60	BF$_3$–H$_3$PO$_4$ (0.3)	0.66	Tri- (81%), (1,2,4-isomer 80–82%, 1,3,5-18–20%, 1,2,4,5-tetra- 9%)	951
p-Diisopropylbenzene (3)	1	60	BF$_3$–H$_3$PO$_4$ (0.5–0.7)	—	Tri- (81%), (1,2,4-/1,3,5- = 80/20); 1,2,4,5-tetra- (9–29%)	491
1,3,5-Triisopropylbenzene	—	16–17	85–92% H$_2$SO$_4$	—	1,2,4,5-Tetra-	714
Triethylbenzene	—	—	AlCl$_3$	—	Triethyldiisopropylbenzene	173
1,2-Dimethyl-4-t-butylbenzene (2)	2	ice	HF (8.5)	1.5	1,2-Dimethyl-3-isopropyl-5-t-butylbenzene (117 g.), probably some 1,2-dimethyl-4-t-heptylbenzenes	691
1,3-Dimethyl-5-t-butylbenzene (2)	2	ice	HF (8.5)	1.5	1,3-Dimethyl-2-isopropyl-5-t-butylbenzene (64 g.), some 1,3-dimethyl-5-t-heptylbenzene	691
Mono- (172.8 kg.), m-di- (172.8 kg.), triisopropylbenzenes (54 kg.), benzene (97.2 kg.)	—	80	AlCl$_3$–HCl 3 kg./0.4 kg.	—	Separate p-di- (81 kg.); recycle m-di- and tri-	373
1,3,5-Isopropylxylene (1)	0.7	75–80	BF$_3$–P$_2$O$_5$[g]	2	48% Conv., 43% monoalkylate, 15% bottoms	383
Tetraisopropylbenzene 15 l. (30 g.)	15 l.	0–160	BF$_3$–HCl	—	No reaction, decomposition at 160°	389
Tetraisopropylbenzene 15 l. (30 g.)	15 l.	—	H$_2$SO$_4$ (cyclohexane)	—	No reaction	389

[a] Polyphosphoric acid on kieselguhr yields less diisopropylbenzene containing 29% o-, 37% m-, and 34% p-.
[b] 80% C$_3^=$, 6% C$_2^=$, 1% i-C$_4^=$
[c] Of alkylate.
[d] m/p di- = 64.5/35.5.
[e] Substantially free of di-o- and indanes.
[f] Of catalyst.
[g] Recovered from previous reactions with same catalyst.
[h] 53% para- in di- fraction.
[i] Added gradually.
[j] On kieselguhr.
[k] Diluted with propane.
[l] 60% C$_3^=$/40% C$_3$.

TABLE 22. C$_9$ and higher aromatics with higher olefins

Aromatic (Moles)	Olefin (Moles)	Catalyst (Moles)	Temp. (°C)	Time (hrs.)	Products (% Yield)	Ref.
Cumene (3)	2-Butene (1)	AlCl$_3$·H$_3$PO$_4$ (0.3)	50	1.8	s-Butyl- (70%),[b] di-s-butylcumene (22%)	939
Cumene (3)	n-Butene (1) (3 l./hr.)	BF$_3$–H$_3$PO$_4$ (0.2–0.3)	50–60	—	s-Butylcumene (62–65%) (o/p = 9/91)	944
Cumene	Isobutylene	BF$_3$–H$_3$PO$_4$	—	—	p-t-Butylcumene (78%)	750
m- and p-Ethyltoluenes	Isobutylene	BF$_3$–H$_2$O	35	—	3-Ethyl-5-t-butyltoluene (98% purity)	10b
Ethyltoluenes (1) (o/m/p = 12/62/26)	Isobutylene (0.4)	H$_2$SO$_4$ (0.62)	0–10	—	Alkylate (20%), recovered ethyltoluenes (55%), (o/m/p = 0/61/39)	140
Ethyltoluene (1) (o/m/p = 12/62/26)	Isoamylene (0.36)	H$_2$SO$_4$ (0.75)	0–10	—	Alkylate (22%), recovered ethyltoluenes (49%, o/m/p = 0/60/40)	140
Hemimellitine (6)	Isobutylene (6.82)	HF (16.6)	0	2.5	5-t-Butylhemimellitine (75%)	695
Pseudocumene 80–85% in C$_9$ cut	Styrene (0.5)	H$_2$SO$_4$	Cold	—	1-Phenyl-1-pseudocumylethane (75%)	407
Pseudocumene and other C$_9$ arenes (4.15)	Diisobutylene	BF$_3$–H$_2$O (150g.)	25	0.5	Pseudocumene concentration in C$_9$ cut increased from 77.5% to 95.3%	909a
Mesitylene and other C$_9$ arenes (78 pts.)	Isoamylenes (28 pts.)	AlCl$_3$ (2 mol. %)	32–50	1.16	Mesitylene recovered unreacted in 93% purity (51 pts.)	158a
Mesitylene, pseudocumene and other C$_9$ arenes (5)	Isobutylene (1)	AlCl$_3$ (5%)[e]	—	—	Only mesitylene remained unalkylated	158a
s-Butylbenzene (3)	2-Butene (1)	AlCl$_3$·H$_3$PO$_4$ (0.3)	40	1.5	Di-s-butyl- (83%),[c] tri-s-butylbenzene (18%)	939
s-Butylbenzene (4)	Butylenes (1)[d]	BF$_3$–H$_3$PO$_4$	32–37	0.2	Di-s-butylbenzene; 1% C$^=$ unconv.	723a
t-Butylbenzene	Isobutylene	BF$_3$–H$_3$PO$_4$	—	—	p-Di-t-butylbenzene (56%)	750
t-Butylbenzene (200 g.)	2-Pentene (35 g.)	PF$_5$ (612 cc.)	85–107	48	Monoalkylate (13%)	81
t-Butylbenzene (3)	Diisobutylene (1)	HF (3)	–40	1.33	4-t-Octyl-t-butylbenzene (13%); isomers (4%); di-t-butylbenzene (7%); polymer (9%)	681

p-Cymene (2)	Isobutylene (1)	HF (3.5)	0-2	3.5	Indanes and isobutane by hydrogen transfer; minor amounts of 2-t-butyl derivatives	692
p-Cymene (2)	2-Methyl-2-butene (1)	HF (8.4)	0-7	0.5	t-Amyl-p-cymene (25%)[a]; 1,3,3,6-tetramethyl-1-p-tolylindane (46%)	335
p-Cymene (1)	Octene (0.5)	H$_2$SO$_4$ (0.6)	0-7	0.5	Octyl-p-cymene (72%)	335
Diethylbenzene (1)	Isobutene (0.32)	H$_2$SO$_4$ (0.56)	0-10	—	Alkylate (18%), recovered diethylbenzenes (65%), (o/m/p = 16/45/39)	140
Diisopropylbenzene (20) (o/m/p = 9/44/28; 19% tri-methylindane)	Isobutene (17.4)	H$_2$SO$_4$ (3.3)	0-10	8	100% of indane and 85% of o-di alkylated; m- and p-di recovered (69%)	575
1,2-Dimethyl-4-t-butylbenzene (2)	2-Butene (2)	HF (8.5)	ice	1.5	1,2-Dimethyl-3-s-butyl-5-t-butylbenzenes, some s-butyl-o-xylene, 4,5-di-s-butyl-o-xylene, and 4-t-octyl-o-xylene	691
1,3-Dimethyl-5-t-butylbenzene (1)	1-Decene (1)	HF (8.5)	ice	3.2	1,3-Dimethyl-2-decyl-5-t-butylbenzene (62 g.)	691
4-Methyl-1-cyclohexylbenzene (40 g.)	3-Methylcyclohexene (19 g.)	HF (75 g.)	10	2	Methylcyclohexane (30 g.); 1-p-tolyl-1-(2-methyl-5-cyclohexylphenyl)-cyclohexane plus higher polycyclic (30 g.)	328
t-Octylbenzene (5)	Diisobutylene (1)	HF (5)	-40	1.33	t-Octyl-t-butylbenzene (8%)	681
		H$_3$PO$_4$–BF$_3$ (25%)	50	—	Not alkylated	847
1,4-Di-s-butylbenzene	Butene	AlCl$_3$ (3.33 g.) iso-C$_3$H$_7$Cl (5 g.)	cooled	4	1,1,3,3,5,5,7,7-Octamethylhydrindacene (4 g.)	43
1,3,5-Triisopropylbenzene (5 g.)	Isobutylene	AlCl$_3$ (3.33 g.) iso-C$_3$H$_7$Cl (5 g.)	cooled	4	1,1,2,3,3,5,5,6,7,7-Decamethylhydrindacene (4 g.)	43
1,3,5-Triisopropylbenzene (5 g.)	2-Methyl-2-butene (4 g.)	AlCl$_3$ (1.5 g.) iso-C$_3$H$_7$Cl (5.6 g.)	-10	2	1,1,3,5,7,7-Hexamethyl-3,5-dineopentyl-hydrindacene (7 g.)	43
1,3,5-Triisopropylbenzene (10 g.)	2,4,4-Trimethyl-1-pentene (5.6 g.)					
Polystyrene (100 g.) m. wt. = 226,000 (1800 g. o-ClC$_6$H$_4$Cl)	Propene tetramer (237 g.)	AlCl$_3$ (0.1) C$_6$H$_5$NO$_2$ (100 g.)	—	3.5	Alkylation of aromatic ring	98

[a] This is probably 2-(2,3-dimethylpropyl)-p-cymene; see ref. 221.
[b] Chiefly para; 10-20% ortho.
[c] Chiefly para; only traces of ortho.
[d] 23% in C$_4$ feed.
[e] Based on aromatic feed.

TABLE 23. C_9 and higher aromatics with cyclic olefins

Aromatic (Moles)	Cycloolefin (Moles)	Catalyst (Moles)	Temp. (°C)	Time (hrs.)	Products (% Yield)	Ref.
Cumene (70 g.)	Cyclopentene (20 g.)	$AlCl_3$ (2 g.)	—	3	Dicyclopentylcumene[b]	634
Cumene (6)	Cyclohexene (1)	H_2SO_4 (50%)[c]	9–10	—	Cyclohexyl derivatives (70–83%)	508
Cumene	Cyclohexene	BF_3–H_3PO_4	0–7	—	Cyclohexylcumene (78%)	952a
p-Ethyltoluene (0.4)	4-Methylcyclohexene (0.2)	H_2SO_4 (35 g.)	0–7	—	2-(1-Methylcyclohexyl)-4-ethyltoluene and hydrogen transfer products	620
p-Ethyltoluene (2)	4-Methylcyclohexene (1)	HF (1.2)	0.5	—	Methylcyclohexyl-p-ethyltoluene (21 g.) and hydrogen transfer products	620
Mesitylene (70 cc.)	Cyclopentene (15 g.)	$AlCl_3$ (2 g.)	0	0.16	1,3,5-Trimethyl-2-cyclopentylbenzene	109(634)
Mesitylene (6)	Cyclohexene (1)	H_2SO_4 (50%)[c]	9–10	—	Cyclohexyl derivatives (62%)	508
Mesitylene (30 g.)	Cyclopentene (34 g.)	$AlCl_3$ (15 g.) (cyclohexane)	—	—	Dicyclopentylmesitylene	634
Mesitylene	Cyclopentene	$AlCl_3$	—	—	1,2,4-Trimethyl-5-cyclopentyl-benzene[d]	636
Mesitylene	Cyclopentene	H_2SO_4	—	—	1,3,5-Trimethyl-2-cyclopentylbenzene, 1,3,5-trimethyl-2,4-dicyclopentyl-benzene	636
Mesitylene	Cyclohexene	$AlCl_3$	Ice	—	1,2,4-Trimethyl-5-cyclohexyl-benzene,[d] 1,2,4-trimethyl-3,5-dicyclohexylbenzene	636
Mesitylene (2)	Cyclohexene (0.6)	$AlCl_3$ (0.2) CS_2	r.t.	3	Cyclohexylmesitylene (21%)	66
Mesitylene (2)	Cyclohexene (1)	H_2SO_4 (2)	Ice	—	1,3,5-Trimethyl-2-cyclohexylbenzene, 1,3,5-trimethyl-2,4-dicyclohexyl-benzene	636
Mesitylene (0.6)	4-Methylcyclohexene (0.3)	HF (75 g.)	0–10	—	1,3,5-Trimethyl-(x-methylcyclohexyl)-benzene	612
s-Butylbenzene (6)	Cyclohexene (1)	H_2SO_4 (50%)[c]	9–10	—	Cyclohexyl derivatives (70–83%)	508
Butylbenzene (1.5)	1-Methylcyclohexene (1)	$FeCl_3$ (1)	—	—	Alkylate (5%)	530
p-Cymene (60 g.)	Cyclopentene (15 g.)	$AlCl_3$ (5 g.)	—	—	Cyclopentyl-p-cymene (70%)	634

p-Cymene (1)	Cyclohexene (0.2)	AlCl₃ (0.1) (135 g. CS₂)	25	3	Cyclohexyl-p-cymene (46%), dicyclohexyltoluene (30%)	66
p-Cymene (268 g.)	Cyclohexene (125 g.)	H₂SO₄ (75 g.)	0–5	3	4-Isopropyl-2-cyclohexyltoluene (102 g.), dicyclohexyl-p-cymene (66 g.)	612
o-Cymene (0.5)	4-Methylcyclohexene (0.25)	HF (2.5)	0	—	2-Isopropyl-4-(1-methylcyclohexyl)- or 2-isopropyl-5-(1-methylcyclohexyl)-toluene (43 g.)	622
m-Cymene (1)	4-Methylcyclohexene (0.5)	HF (6.6)	0	—	2-(1-Methylcyclohexyl)-5-isopropyltoluene (49 g.), methylcyclohexane (12.2 g.), dimethyldicyclohexyl (3.5 g.), 1,3,3,5-tetramethyl-1-m-tolylindane (17.5 g.)	622(327)
p-Cymene (161 g.)	1-Methylcyclohexene (28.9 g.)	H₂SO₄ (56 g.)	0–2	1.5	Methylcyclohexane (69%) (72%),[a] 1,3,3,6-tetramethyl-1-p-tolylindane	451
p-Cymene (3)	4-Methylcyclohexene (1)	AlCl₃ (0.2)–HCl	20	0.58	Alkylate (<3%)	220
p-Cymene (4.8)	Methylcyclohexene (2)	H₂SO₄ (2.4)	0–7	0.5	Methylcyclohexyl-p-cymene (9%),[e] 1,3,3,6-tetramethyl-1-p-tolylindane (58%)	335
p-Cymene (2)	4-Methylcyclohexene (1)	H₂SO₄ (35 g.)	5	1	Indane type product (13%),	220
p-Cymene (0.8)	Dihydrolimonene (0.4)	HF (2.3)	0–7	0.5	5% Alkylated product, 1,3,3,6-tetramethyl-1-p-tolylindane (75%)	335
p-n-Propyltoluene (0.2)	4-Methylcyclohexene (0.1)	H₂SO₄ (10 g.)	0–7	—	2-(1-Methylcyclohexyl)-4-propyltoluene[a] (6.5 g.)	620
p-n-Propyltoluene (1.86)	4-Methylcyclohexene (0.93)	HF (12.5)	0–5	—	2-(1-Methylcyclohexyl)-4-propyltoluene (34 g.)[a]	620
Cyclopentylbenzene	Cyclopentene	AlCl₃	—	—	Dicyclopentylbenzene (m and p) 1,3,5-tricyclopentylbenzene (also a liquid isomer)	536
p-s-Butyltoluene (0.2)	4-Methylcyclohexene (0.1)	H₂SO₄ (18 g.)	0–7	—	4-s-Butyl-2-(1-methylcyclohexyl)-toluene (3.3 g.)[a]	621
p-s-Butyltoluene (1.1)	4-Methylcyclohexene (0.56)	HF (4)	0–5	—	4-s-Butyl-2-(1-methylcyclohexyl)-toluene (11.5 g.)[a]	621

Table continued

TABLE 23 (*continued*)

Aromatic (Moles)	Cycloolefin (Moles)	Catalyst (Moles)	Temp. (°C)	Time (hrs.)	Product (% Yield)	Ref.
p-Isobutyltoluene (2)	4-Methylcyclohexene (1)	HF (10)	0–5	—	Methylcyclohexyl-p-isobutyltoluene (64 g.)[a]	621
1,4-Dimethyl-2-isopropylbenzene (2)	Cyclopentene (1)	AlCl$_3$	—	—	1,4-Dimethyl-2-isopropyl-5-cyclopentylbenzene, dicyclopentyl-p-xylene	637
Trimethylisopropylbenzene (50 g.)	Cyclopentene (21 g.)	AlCl$_3$ (11 g.)	—	3	Trimethylisopropylcyclopentylbenzene	635
Cyclohexylbenzene (40 g.)	Cyclohexene (14 g.)	AlCl$_3$ (7 g.)	—	—	1,4-Dicyclohexylbenzene (some 1,3- and higher boilers)	535
Cyclohexylbenzene (1)	Cyclohexene (1.2)	H$_2$SO$_4$ (92 g.) cyclohexane (80 g.)	2–14	1	1,4-Dicyclohexylbenzene (23 g.), tetracyclohexylbenzene (12 g.)	141
1,2-Dimethyl-4-t-butylbenzene	Cyclopentene	AlCl$_3$	—	—	1,2-Dimethyl-4-t-butyl-6-cyclopentylbenzene	738
2,4-Diisopropyltoluene (36 g.)	4-Methylcyclohexene (10 g.)	HF (25 g.)	3–10	0.5	1,3,3,6-Tetramethyl-5-isopropyl-1-(4-methyl-3-isopropylphenyl)-indane (60%)	623
4-Isopropyl-2-cyclohexyltoluene (43 g.)	4-Methylcyclohexene (10 g.)	HF (25 g.)	3–10	0.5	1,3,3,6-Tetramethyl-5-cyclohexyl-1-(4-methyl-3-cyclohexylphenyl)-indane (60%)	623
1,4-Dimethyl-2-heptylbenzene	Cyclopentene	AlCl$_3$	—	—	1,4-Dimethyl-2-heptyl-5-cyclopentylbenzene	738
Dicyclopentylbenzene	Cyclopentene (15 g.)	AlCl$_3$ (7.5 g.)	—	—	Tetracyclopentylbenzene (12 g.)	536
Mono- and dicyclohexyltoluene (23 g.)	Cyclohexene (30 g.)	AlCl$_3$ (15 g.)	—	—	No tricyclohexyltoluene	634
Dicyclohexylbenzene (30 g.)	Cyclohexene (15 g.)	AlCl$_3$ (7.5 g.) CS$_2$	—	—	1,3,5-Tri- and tetracyclohexylbenzene	535

Dicyclohexylbenzene (0.24)	Cyclohexene (0.5)	AlCl$_3$ (20 g.) Cyclohexane (80 g.)	3–7	1	Cyclohexylbenzene (16 g.)	141(535)
1,3,5-Tricyclohexyl-benzene (0.1)	Cyclohexene (0.3)	AlCl$_3$ (20 g.) Cyclohexane (80 g.)	34–37	1	Tetracyclohexylbenzene (1 g.)	141(535)
Dicyclopentyl-mesitylene	Cyclopentene	AlCl$_3$	30	—	No tricyclopentyl derivative	634

[a] Plus hydrogen transfer products.
[b] Probably 1,3,5 because of high m.p. (134°).
[c] Of weight of arene.
[d] Note isomerization of methyl groups.
[e] See Section II-1-K-b.

TABLE 24. Indanes with olefins

Aromatic (Moles)	Olefin (Moles)	Catalyst (Moles)	Temp. (°C)	Time (hrs.)	Products (% Yield)	Ref.
Indane (25.4)	Ethylene (4)	SiO_2–Al_2O_3, 75/25 (60 g.)	250–300	16	Ethylindane (75%)	423
Indane	Propene[b]	$AlCl_3$ (0.25–0.5 pts.)[a]	0	—	Isopropylindanes (50%) (mono-, di-, and tri-)	861
Indane	1-Butene[b]	$AlCl_3$ (0.25–0.5 pts.)[a]	0	—	s-Butylindanes (mono- and di-)	861
Indane (2)	Isobutylene (1)	H_2SO_4 (1)	—	—	5-t-Butylindane (48%)	864b
Indane (3)	2-Methyl-1-2-butene (1)	$AlCl_3$ (0.25–0.5 pts.)[a]	0	—	Amylindanes (40%) (2 isomers)	861
Indane (3)	2-Methyl1-2-butene (1)	H_3PO_4–BF_3	0	—	Amylindane (20%) (single isomer)	861
Indane (2)	Cyclohexene (1)	$AlCl_3$	0	—	Cyclohexylindanes (mono- 25%, di- 15%)[d]	639(640)
Indane (2)	Heptene (1)	92% H_2SO_4 (1)	—	—	5-Heptylindane (70%)[c]	864b
Indane (2)	2-Ethylhexene (1)	H_2SO_4 (1)	—	—	5-Isooctylindane (47%)	864b
Indane (118 g.)	Decene (70 g.)	92% H_2SO_4 (98 g.)	ice	1.5	5-Decylindane (76%)	882
Indane (70 cc.)	Cyclopentane (15g.)	$AlCl_3$ (2 g.)	0	0.16	5-Cyclopentyl- and probably 5,6-dicyclopentylindane	109
Isopropylindane (22 g.)	Isobutylene (4 g.)	92% H_2SO_4	—	1.5	1-Isopropyl-5-t-butylindane (35%), some 1-isopropyl-5,7-di-t-butylindane	882
1,3,3-Trimethyl-1-phenylindane (3)	Butenes (6.1)	Retrol[e] (100 g.)	250	2	Mono- (156 g.), di- (75 g.), tri- (121 g.), poly- (142 g.) butyl derivatives	772a
1,3,3-Trimethyl-1-phenylindane (1.5)	Heptadecenes (1.5)	Retrol[e] (100 g.)	260	1.5	Mono- (263 g.) and poly- (84 g.) heptadecyl derivatives	772a
1,3,3-Trimethyl-1-phenylindane (3)	Cyclohexene (6.2)	Retrol[e] (100 g.)	210	0.5	Mono- (400 g.), di- (50 g.), poly- (138 g.) cyclohexyl derivatives	772a
1,3,3-Trimethyl-1-phenylindane (3)	Octene (3)	Retrol[e] (100 g.)	250	2	Mono-, di-, and trioctyl derivatives (315 g.)	772a

[a] Added slowly.   [b] Added 2–4 l./hr.   [c] 96% H_2SO_4 gives 20% yield.
[d] 34% Di- and some tri- with 1/1 indane/cyclohexene ratio.   [e] Activated clay.

TABLE 25. Naphthalene with ethylene

Naphthalene (Moles)	Ethylene (Moles)	Catalyst (Moles)	Temp. (°C)	Time (hrs.)	Ethylnaphthalene products (% Yield)	Ref.
128 kg.	38 kg.	$AlCl_3$–HCl (4 kg.)	100–200 20 atm.	4	Mono-, di-, poly-, also bi-naphthyl derivatives (110 kg.)	513(73,302, 512)
128 pts. (100 pts. decalin)	65 pts.	$AlBr_3$ (4 pts.)	80–90 20 atm.	5	Mono- and di- (130 pts.), poly- (55 pts.)	517
128 pts. (100 pts. decalin)	65 pts.	$AlBr_3$–HCl (4 pts./—)	80–90 20 atm.	—	Mono- and di- (135 pts.), poly-	73
—	—	$ZnCl_2$–Al_2O_3	—	—	Mono-	417
65 g.	112 g.	BF_3–HCl (10 g. each)	250	3	Oil (170 g.)[c]	283
600 pts.	300 pts.	BF_3–$2H_2O$ (100 pts.)	160–170 30 atm.	—	Mono- and di- (750 pts.)	299
100 g.	33 atm. at 20°	85% H_3PO_4 (50 g.)	300	14	Di- (23%)[a]	334
7.1	17.2	P_2O_5 (0.5)	250	—	Mono- and di-	472
1 (3 m. benzene)	1	H_3PO_4–Sil-o-cel[d]	300 400 psig	0.013	Ethylene conv. (20%), benzene conv. (3%), naphthalene conv. (12%)	138
1000 pts.	[e]	$Ce(PO_3)_3$ (100 pts.)[f]	300	—	Oil (only traces of naphthalene)	298
1.7 (cyclohexane) 1	1	$FePO_4$	300 900 psi	2 L.H.S.V.	Mono- (85%)[a], poly- (15%)[a]	139
4064 pts.[b]	62 pts.	SiO_2 (99%)–Al_2O_3 (1%)	300 500 psig	2.5 L.H.S.V.	Mono- (270 pts.) (80% β/20% α)	549(819)
1	1	Tonsil (20%)	230 20–40 atm.	Few	Mono- and poly- (10)	719

[a] Of alkylate.
[b] Plus 100 pts. ethylnaphthalene (α/β = 1/1).
[c] Contains ethylnaphthalene in low-boiling cut.
[d] Diatomaceous earth.
[e] Under pressure.
[f] May employ cerium metaborate or aluminum meta-arsenate at 400°.

TABLE 26. Naphthalene with propene

Naphthalene (Moles)	Propene (Moles)	Catalyst (Moles)	Temp. (°C)	Time (hrs.)	Isopropylnaphthalene products (% Yield)	Ref.
2	0.75–1.5	$AlCl_3$ (0.02)	100	0.66–0.83	Mono- (62–70%) $\beta/\alpha = 24/1$	186(271, 517,516)
128 pts. (150 pts. MCH)[d]	170 pts.	$AlCl_3$ (4 pts.)	80	—	Mono- and di- (80 pts.), tetra- (185 pts.)	73(295)
30 pts.	13.5 pts.	$AlCl_3$ (5 pts.) CH_3NO_2 (41 pts.)	30	1.5	Alkylated naphthalenes (31 pts.)	699
		$ZnCl_2$-Al_2O_3			Mono-	417
1	8	BF_3-$2H_2O$	100		Mono- and di- (106%)[c]	235(299)
0.34 (250 ml. CH)[d]	[a]	BF_3-CH_3OH (15 g.)	29–32	2	Isopropylnaphthalenes (88 g.)	727
600 pts.	660 pts.	BF_3-H_3PO_4	60, 5 atm.		Mono- (96%)	299(27)
2 (CCl_4)	1	BF_3-H_3PO_4 (10–35%)	25–95		Mono- (62–69%), higher alkylated naphthalenes (6–22%)	856
128 g.		H_2SO_4	60–70	8–11	Mono- (72 g.)	14(353)
40 g.	48 g.	Naphthalene-SO_3H (40 g.)	110–120		Di-, some mono-, tri-, tetra-; also sulfonic acid of di-	352
—	5.8	H_3PO_4	200	14	Mono-	334
		HF (25)	0–72	24	Tetra-	110
500 pts. (300 pts. decalin)	840 pts.	Fuller's earth (100 pts.)	120–150, 15–20 atm.		Tetra-[b] (1240 pts.)	296
1	(12 l./hr.)	Aluminosilicate (350 ml.)	50, 100, 150, 200		Mono- (30, 30, 37, 44%),[e,f] di- (24, 24, 23, 18%),[e] tri- (11, 11, 2, 6%),[e] tetra- (6, 6, 5, 8%)[e]	844

[a] 90–92 ml./minute.
[b] Apparently.
[c] Probably based on naphthalene.

[d] CH = cyclohexane; MCH = methylcyclohexane.
[e] For each temperature.
[f] Ratio 1-/2- = —, 80/20, 63/37, 56/44.[e]

TABLE 27. Naphthalene with higher olefins

Naphthalene (Moles)	Olefin (Moles)	Catalyst (Moles)	Temp. (°C)	Time (hrs.)	Naphthalene derivatives (% Yield)	Ref.
128 pts. (1000 pts. CH)[c]	2-Butene (24 pts.)	$AlCl_3$ (12 pts.)	20	—	Tetrabutyl- (300 pts.)	517(516,73)
2 (CCl_4)	Butene (1)	BF_3–H_3PO_4 (10–35%)	25–80	—	s-Butyl- (52–88%) polyalkyl- (8–22%)	856
0.5 (CCl_4)	Butene (1) (1.5–3 l./hr.)	BF_3–H_3PO_4 (146% by wt.)	r.t.	3	Mono- and di-s-butyl- (84%)	934(236)
	Isobutylene	BF_3–$2H_2O$	100	4	Monobutyl- (91%)	235
1.6	1-Pentene (0.8) (benzene, 3.25)	$AlCl_3$–t-BuCl (2 pts./5 pts.)	30–40	1	Monoamyl- (26%), di- (18%), tri- (31%), tetra- (20%)[d]	532
25.6 g.	2-Pentene (15.6 g.)	BF_3–Et_2O	w.b.	8	Alkylated product (3.3 g.)	934
16.2 g.	2-Pentene (19 g.)	BF_3–H_3PO_4 (17.3 g.) 131 cc. CCl_4	—	—	Alkylated product (8.2 g.)	934
128 pts.	Trimethylethylene (35 pts.)	70% $HClO_4$ (20 pts.)	100–110	—	t-Amyl-	159
1	Hexene (1)	BF_3–$2H_2O$	100	2	Hexyl- (61%)	235
1	3-Hexene (1)	HF (3.3)	5–10	24	3-Naphthylhexane[e] (30%), poly-hexylnaphthalene (28%)	779
25.6 g.	Diisobutylene (22.5 g.)	H_2SO_4 (5 g.)	30–50	8	[a]	86
80 g. (CCl_4)	Styrene (40 g.)	93% H_2SO_4	30–35	1	1-Phenyl-1-(β-naphthyl)ethane (20 g.)	780
1	Styrene (1)	$Ce(PO_3)_3$ (10%)	380[f]	2	Reddish oil (B.P. 300–360°)	298
1	1-Nonene (1)	BF_3–$2H_2O$	100	3	Nonyl- (27%)	235
600 pts.	Isononylene (380 pts.)	BF_3 (120 pts.)	190–200	—	Isononyl- (500 pts.) diisononyl- (100 pts.)	299
128 pts.	Diisohexylene (168 pts.)	BF_3–H_3PO_4 (68 pts./70 pts.)	50	17	Dodecyl-	300

Table continued

TABLE 27 (continued)

Naphthalene (Moles)	Olefin (Moles)	Catalyst (Moles)	Temp. (°C)	Time (hrs.)	Naphthalene derivatives (% Yield)	Ref.
1	Triisobutylene (1)	H_2SO_4 (0.2)	30	8	a	86
3–5	Cracked gasoline cuts	90–94% H_2SO_4 (230–250%)[b]	0	3	α-Mono- (main product) and some di- and trialkyl	475
1.2	Cetene (0.6) (benzene, 3.2)	$AlCl_3$–t.BuCl (2 pts./5 pts.)	30–40	1	Mono- (50%), dicetyl- (26%)	532
32 g.	Cetene (112 g.)	$SbCl_3$ (115 g.)–$FeCl_3$ (5 g.) aq. solution	90	4	Alkylate (61%)	821
1	Tetraisobutylene (1)	H_2SO_4 (0.2)	40–50	3	a	86
1	$C_{16}^=$ + $C_{18}^=$ (3)	BF_3–H_3PO_4 (256 g.)	80	1	Hexadecyl- and octadecyl-	236
1	$C_{19}^=$ + $C_{20}^=$ (3)	BF_3–H_3PO_4 (256 g.)	80	1	Eicosyl- (46%)	236

[a] Benzene is not alkylated.
[b] Of wt. of naphthalene.
[c] Cyclohexane.
[d] Product is sulfonated before isolation.
[e] Probably contains 2-naphthylhexane (see ref. 582).
[f] Under pressure.

TABLE 28. Naphthalene derivatives with olefins

Naphthalene (Moles)	Olefin (Moles)	Catalyst (Moles)	Temp. (°C)	Time (hrs.)	Naphthalene products (% Yield)	Ref.
1-Chloro- (300 pts.) (decalin 200 pts.)	Ethylene (100 pts.)	AlCl$_3$ (10 pts.)	100–120	—	Oils 165–185[b] (150 pts.), 185–210[b] (160 pts.), 210–250[b] (50 pts.)	517(73)
Methyl- (70% 1-) (1510 g.)	Isobutylene (excess)	H$_2$SO$_4$ (458 g.)	25–30 atm. 0–25	—	t-Butyl-1-methyl- (20%),[a] di-t-butyl-1-methyl- (45%)[a]	547
1-Methyl- (5)	Diisobutylene (1)	HF (5)	−40 −20	1.66 1.5	t-Octyl derivative (77%) t-Octyl- (54%), t-butyl derivative (12%)	681 681[c]
2-Methyl- (4)	1-Octene (1)	HF (1–2)	110–130 60 60	4 4 16	Alkylate (60–70%) Alkylate (15–30%) Alkylate (25–43%)	454
Methyl- (2) (4 moles benzene)	Propene trimer (1)	AlCl$_3$–t-BuCl (2 pts./5 pts.)	50–70	1	Nonyl- derivative (73%)[a]	532
Ethyl-	Ethylene	AlCl$_3$	50–160 20 atm.	—	Oil b.p. 200°–300°/12 mm.	302
Dimethyl[d] (1)	Propene (2.14) (48% in propane)	Toluene-SO$_3$H (8%)	260–265	92	Mono-/di-/polyisopropyl derivatives[e] = 17/11/7%	910
Dimethyl-[d] (1)	1-Butene (1.2)	Toluene-SO$_3$H (3)	130	80	Mono-/di-/polybutyl derivatives[e] = 39/60/18%	910
Diisopropyl- (1)	3-Hexene (1)	HF (3.3)	5–10	24	Mixture (67%)	779

[a] Of alkylate. [b] B.p. at 16 mm. [c] Unpublished data. [d] Hydroformer botts. [e] Wt. % based on charge.

TABLE 29. Naphthalene and derivatives and cyclic olefins

Aromatic (Moles)	Cycloolefin (Moles)	Catalyst (Moles)	Temp. (°C)	Time (hrs.)	Naphthalene products (% Yield)	Ref.
Naphthalene	Cyclopentene	$AlCl_3$	—	—	Mono-, di-, tri-, and tetra-cyclopentyl	514
Naphthalene (2)	Cyclohexene (1)	$AlCl_3$ (0.2) (CS_2)	35–45	—	Cyclohexyl- (43%)	66(516,638)
Naphthalene (50 g.)	Cyclohexene (50 g.)	$AlCl_3$	45	2	2,6-Dicyclohexyl-	779(66,517)
Naphthalene (200 g.)	Cyclohexene (120 g.)	$AlCl_3$ (26 g.) (60 g. CS_2)	c	0.33	2-, di.,[b] tri-, and tetra-cyclohexyl- (and liquid)[a]	638(771c)
Naphthalene (0.4)	Cyclohexene (0.6)	BF_3 (sparged 1.5 hrs.)	25	24	2-Cyclohexyl- (35%)	647
Naphthalene (1)	Cyclohexene (2.2)	Retrol (6.4 g.)	reflux	0.5	Mono-, di-, tri-, and higher cyclohexyl	771c
1-Bromo- (1.5)	Cyclopentene (1)	H_2SO_4 (2)	25	—	Cyclopentyl-1-bromo- (50%)	529
1-Bromo-	Cyclohexene (1)	H_2SO_4 (2) (SO_3/H_2O = 1/1.29)	30	—	Cyclohexyl-1-bromo- (38%)	873
1-Bromo- (1.5)	Cyclohexene	H_2SO_4 (2) 15% P_2O_5	—	—	Cyclohexyl-1-bromo- (57%)	872
1-Chloro- (5)	Cyclohexene (1)	$AlCl_3$ (0.1)	26–40	—	Cyclohexyl-1-chloro- (55%)	496
1-Methyl- (30 g.)	Cyclopentene (30 g.)	$AlCl_3$ (11 g.)	ice bath	—	Mono-, di-, tricyclopentyl derivatives	632
1-Methyl- (60 g.)	Cyclohexene (17 g.)	$AlCl_3$ (8 g.)	—	—	Mono- (36 g.) and dicyclohexyl derivatives	633
Mono-, di-, tri-cyclopentyl-1-methyl-naphthalenes	Cyclopentene	$AlCl_3$	—	—	Tetracyclopentyl derivative	632
Cyclohexyl-1-methyl- (31 g.)	Cyclohexene (36 g.)	$AlCl_3$ (10 g.)	e	—	Tricyclohexyl derivative[d]	633
Dicyclopentyl-	Cyclopentene	$AlCl_3$	—	—	Tri- and tetracyclopentyl-	641
Tetracyclopentyl-	Cyclopentene	$AlCl_3$	—	—	Pentacyclopentyl-	641

[a] Either 1-cyclohexyl- or methylcyclopentyl-.
[b] Shown to be 2,6-.
[c] With cooling.
[d] Max. number of cyclohexyl groups = 3.
[e] With cooling.
[f] Acid activated clay.

TABLE 30. Tetralins and halogenated tetralins with olefins

Tetralin (Moles)	Olefin (Moles)	Catalyst (Moles)	Temp. (°C)	Time (hrs.)	Tetralin derivatives (% Yield)	Ref.
132 kg.	Ethylene (30 kg.)	$AlCl_3$ (2 kg.)	100	4	Oil, b.p. 145–200° at 20 mm. (146 kg.)	515(513,512 302)
66 g.	Ethylene (122 g.)	BF_3—HCl (10 g. each)	20–30 atm. 250	3	Reaction product (156 g.)	283
—	Ethylene	H_3PO_4	300	—	Ethyl-, etc.	334
37.8	Ethylene (6.65)	Al_2O_3 (1%)–SiO_2	300[h]	24 (flow)	Monoethyl- (60% per pass)	423
1000 pts.	Ethylene	$Ce(PO_3)_{3/2}$ (1 pt.)	300[i]	—	Ethyl-, diethyl-	298
250 pts.	Propene (140 pts.)	$AlCl_3$ (12.5 pts.)	20–30	—	Oil b.p. 150–200° at 20 mm.	516(295)
264 pts.[d]	Propene (90 pts.)	$FeCl_3$ (50 pts.)	100–200 25 atm.	—	Oil b.p. 150–200° at 20 mm. (340 pts.)	517(73)
200 g.	Propene	H_2SO_4	60–70	8–11	Isopropyl- (93 g.)	14
1	Propene (5.3)	HF (28)	5–15	20	Isopropyl-	110
Chloro- (300 pts.)[e]	Propene (700 pts.)	$AlCl_3$ (50 pts.)	90–100	—	Propylated products	516
—	Amylenes	Aluminosilicate[b]	200–300 4 atm. N_2	—	β-Amyl (13%)	743
50 g.	Cyclopentene (25 g.)	$AlCl_3$ (12.5 g.)	0	—	Cyclopentyl- (40 g.), dicyclopentyl- (7 g.)	641
18 g.[f]	Cyclopentene (37 g.)	$AlCl_3$ (28 g.)	—	—	Di- and tricyclopentyl (both 1,2,3- and 1,2,4-	641
1.7	Cyclohexene (0.5)	$AlCl_3$ (0.15)	25	3	β-Cyclohexyl- (40%)	66(638)
200 g.	Cyclohexene (40 g.)	$AlCl_3$ (20 g.) (CS_2)	cooling	—	5- and 6-Cyclohexyl-, dicyclohexyl-	638
—	Cyclohexene (1)	H_2SO_4 (2)	25	—	Cyclohexylbromotetralin	529
Bromo- (1.5)	1-Heptene	HF–Al_2O_3	300 40 atm.	—	2-Heptyl- (9%),[c] 2,3-diheptyl- (some)	748
2	1-Heptene (1)	Aluminosilicate[b]	200 10 atm.	—	2-Heptyl- (24%), 2,3-diheptyl- (some)	748

Table continued

TABLE 30 (*continued*)

Tetralin (Moles)	Olefin (Moles)	Catalyst (Moles)	Temp. (°C)	Time (hrs.)	Tetralin derivatives (% Yield)	Ref.
0.25	1-Nonene	Al (0.1)–nonyl Br (0.3–0.6)	165–185	2	Mono- and dinonyl- (54%)	745
0.5	1-Nonene	$ZnCl_2$	250^g	0.25 S.V.	β-Nonyl- (34%)	744
2	1-Nonene (1)	30% $ZnCl_2$–Al_2O_3	270^g	0.25 S.V.	β-Nonyl- (48%)[a]	744
2	1-Nonene (1)	Al_2O_3–SiO_2	270^g	0.25	β-Nonyl- (25%)	744
264 pts.	Octalin (136 pts.)	70% $HClO_4$ (30 pts.)	90–100	8	Decalyl- (b.p. 222–227/10 mm.)	159
Dicyclopentyl-	Cyclopentene	$AlCl_3$	—	—	Tri- and tetracyclopentyl	641

[a] Lower yields with $ZnCl_2$ on SiO_2–Al_2O_3.   [b] Synthetic aluminosilicate, $AlCl_3$–H_3PO_4 and $ZnCl_2$–$AlCl_3$ are less effective.
[c] Some heptylnaphthalene formed *via* dehydrogenation.   [d] In 200 pts. pet. ether.   [e] In 200 pts. decalin.   [f] In hexane.   [g] 10 atm.
[h] Under 400 psig.   [i] 100–120 atm.

TABLE 31. Polyphenyl hydrocarbons with olefins

Aromatic compound (Moles)	Olefin (Moles)	Catalyst (Moles)	Temp. (°C)	Time (hrs.)	Products (% Yield)	Ref.
Biphenyl (310 g.)	Ethylene	$AlCl_3$ (70 g.)	100	—	m-Ethylbiphenyl, diethyl-biphenyl, m- and p-terphenyl	2
Biphenyl (4.68)	Propene (4.1)	$AlCl_3$ (35 g.)	90–95	0.5	Mono- (1.69 moles), di- (1.1 moles)-isopropylbiphenyl	440
Biphenyl (1000 pts.)	Propene (800 pts.)	Tonsil[a] (100 pts.)	150–200 5–10 atm.	—	Diisopropylbiphenyl (1200 pts.), some mono-	511
Biphenyl (3)	2-Butene (1) (2.9 l./hr.)	$AlCl_2 \cdot H_2PO_4$ (0.2)	80	—	s-Butylbiphenyl; mono- (70%), di- (13%)	940
Biphenyl (1)	2-Butene (1) (5–6 l./hr.)	BF_3–H_3PO_4 (0.2)	70, 90	2	Monobutylbiphenyl (46%, 47%),[b] (s-/t- = 81/19, and 58/42)[b]	946
Biphenyl (1.75)	2-Butene (1)	BF_3–H_3PO_4 (0.25)	90	2	Monobutylbiphenyl (58–60%)	946

Biphenyl (70 cc.)	Cyclopentene (15 g.)	$AlCl_3$ (2 g.)	0	0.16	p-Cyclopentylbiphenyl, p,p'-dicyclopentylbiphenyl	109
Biphenyl (0.7)	Cyclohexene (0.3)	$AlCl_3$ (0.1) (CS_2)	25	3	Cyclohexylbiphenyl (40%), dicyclohexylbiphenyl (5 g.)	66(496)
Biphenyl	Cyclohexene	H_2SO_4	50	—	4,4'-Dicyclohexylbiphenyl	99
Biphenyl (6)	Diisobutylene (6)	$AlCl_3$ (26 g.)	70–80	3.75	Mono- (273 g.), di- (155 g.), and tri-t-octylbiphenyl (91 g.)[c]	125
Diphenylmethane (1)	Cyclohexene (0.5)	$AlCl_3$ (0.15) (CS_2)	25	3	p-Cyclohexyldiphenylmethane (27%), p-benzylbiphenyl (3%)	66
Diphenylmethane (150 g.)	3-Methylcyclohexene (35 g.)	$AlCl_3$ (15 g.) (150 g. CS_2)	25	3	Methylcyclohexyldiphenyl-methane (18 g.)	66
Dibenzyl (80 pts.)	Propene (20 pts.)	$AlCl_3$ (7 pts.) CH_3NO_2 (13 pts.)	40	2	Propylated dibenzyls (approx. 20 pts.)	699
Dibenzyl (0.6)	Cyclohexene (0.4)	$AlCl_3$ (0.1) (CS_2)	25	3	Cyclohexyldibenzyl (30%), (2 isomers)	66
Terphenyl	Cyclohexene	H_2SO_4	50	—	Monocyclohexylterphenyls	99
Terphenyl (1)	Cyclohexene (1)	Retrol[a] (7 g.)	290	4	Waxy solid	772
Polystyrene (10 pts.) (250 pts. o-$C_6H_4Cl_2$)	Propene trimer (10 pts.)	$AlCl_3$ (2 pts.) $C_6H_5NO_2$ (10 pts.)	25–80	10	Alkylated product	527
Polystyrene (100 g.) (900 g. of $CH_2ClCHCl_2$)	Propene trimer (90 g.)	HF (80 g.)	0–5	1.5	"Polymer" (171 g.)	97
Polystyrene (CS₂, o-$C_6H_4Cl_2$, or $Cl_2C=CCl_2$)	1-Dodecene, 1-hexadecene, or 1-octadecene	$AlCl_3$	50–100	few	Alkylation (75–100%)	918a
Polystyrene (8.3 g.) (230 ml. $Cl_2C=CCl_2$)	1-Dodecene (20 g.)	HF (8.3 g.)	0	1	Alkylation (97%)	918a
Biphenyl (3)	Cyclohexene (9)	Retrol[a] (10 g.)	200	1	Tetracyclohexyl derivative	772b
as-Diphenylethane (728 g.)	Cyclohexene (390 g.)	Retrol[a] (100 g.)	200	2	Mono- (129 g.), mono- and di- (155 g.), di- (139 g.), di- and tri- (74 g.), poly- (100 g.) cyclohexyl derivatives	772c

[a] Activated clay.   [b] For respective temperatures.   [c] Probably t-butyl derivatives; see Section II-1-H-b.

TABLE 32. Tricyclic hydrocarbons with olefins

Aromatic (Moles)	Olefin (Moles)	Catalyst (Moles)	Temp. (°C)	Time (hrs.)	Products (% Yield)	Ref.
Acenaphthene (400 pts.) (Decalin 500 pts.)	Ethylene (50 pts.)	$AlCl_3$ (40 pts.)	110–130 30–40 atm.	—	Oil, b.p. 110–200°/12 mm. (1 part) Oil, b.p. 200–240°/12 mm. (1 part)	73(511)
Acenaphthene (450 pts.)	Propene (310 pts.)	$AlCl_3$ (45 pts.)	100–120 12 atm.	—	Oil, b.p. 150–210°/1 mm. (1 part) 200–210°/1 mm. (solid)	514(297)
Acenaphthene (1.26) (benzene, 5.5)	1-Pentene (0.65)	$AlCl_3$ complex, t-BuCl (5/2) (112.5 g.)	30–40	1	Amylacenaphthene (mono-18%, di- 5%, tetra- 64%), (benzene alkylation not significant)	532
Acenaphthene (70 cc.)	Cyclopentene (15 g.)	$AlCl_3$ (2 g.)	0	0.16	5-Cyclopentyldicyclopentyl-acenaphthene	109
Acenaphthene (50 g.)	Cyclohexene (50 g.)	$AlCl_3$ (20 g.)	45	2	5-Cyclohexyldicyclohexyl-acenaphthene	100
5-Bromoacenaphthalene (210 pts.)	Propene (85 pts.)	$AlCl_3$ (15 pts.)	100 15–18 atm.	—		297
Fluorene (27 g.)	Propene (40 g.)	89% H_3PO_4 (25 g.)	200	11	Isopropylfluorene (8 g.)	334
Fluorene (0.5) (200 pts. toluene)	α-Ethylstyrene (1)	Bleaching earth Tonsil AC (10 pts.)	70	1.5	α-Phenyl-s-butyl derivative (140 pts.)	509
Anthracene (450 pts.) (Decalin 500 pts.)	Ethylene (140 pts.)	$AlCl_3$ (330 pts.)	60 25 atm.	6	Oil, b.p. 200–300°/10 mm.	511(73)
Anthracene (350 pts.) (Decalin 600 pts.)	Propene (190 pts.)	$AlCl_3$ (35 pts.)	100	1	Oil, b.p. 90–200°/1 mm. (22%) 200–280°/1 mm. (70%)	73(514)
Anthracene (500 pts.) (43% crude)	Propene (200 pts.)	$AlCl_3$ (50 pts.)	120 20 atm.	—	Soft resin	514(297)
Anthracene (1)	3-Hexene (0.66)	$AlCl_3$	—	—	Di-s-hexylanthracene (20%)	779
Anthracene	Cyclohexene	H_2SO_4	—	—	Mono-, di-, and tricyclohexyl-anthracenes	99

Anthracene	Cracked gasoline	H_2SO_4 (90–92%)	0–10	3–4	Alkylation optimum at these conditions	482
Phenanthrene (500 pts.) (500 pts. decalin)	Propene (700 pts.)	$AlCl_3$ (50 pts.)	100 20 atm.	3	Viscous oil (11%), resinous distillate (87%)	514(511,73)
Phenanthrene (500 pts.)	Propene (270 pts.)	$AlCl_3$ (30 pts.)	110–130 15 atm.	2	140 pts. 140–200°/1 mm., 235 pts. 200–210°/1 mm., 390 pts. 210–215°/1 mm.	297
Phenanthrene (50 g.)	Cyclohexene (50 g.)	$AlCl_3$ (20 g.)	45	1	Cyclohexyl- (10 g.), 3,9- and 3,10-dicyclohexyl-phenanthrene (30 g.)	100(297)
Phenanthrene (178 pts.)	Isohexylene–iso-heptylene dimers (196 pts.)	BF_3 (68 g.)–H_3PO_4 (98 g.)	100	1.5	Alkylphenanthrenes (b.p. 225–260/5 mm.)	300
Phenanthrene (0.5) (200 cc. Xylene)	Styrene (1)	Bleaching earth (Bleichten G) (10 pts.)	70	3.5	α-Phenylethyl derivative	509
Phenanthrene (0.5) (200 cc. Xylene)	α-Methylstyrene (1)	Bleaching earth (Bleichten G) (10 pts.)	80	3	α-Phenylisopropyl derivative (200 pts.)	509
Phenanthrene (3.8)	iso-$C_5^=$ to iso-$C_{11}^=$ cracked gasoline (1)	90–92% H_2SO_4	—	3–4		483

TABLE 33.   Halogenated and nitrated benzenes and homologs with olefins

Aromatic (Moles)	Olefin (Moles)	Catalyst (Moles)	Temp. (°C)	Time (hrs.)	Products (% Yield)	Ref.
Bromobenzene (2.83)	Ethylene (1 equiv.)	$AlCl_3$ (0.37)	70	—	Ethylated bromobenzenes (b.p. 180–250°; 210 g.) ethyl- and diethylbenzene (135 g.)	52
Chlorobenzene (5)	Ethylene	$AlCl_3$ (1)	100	—	o-, m-, and p-Chloroethylbenzenes (2/3/1), chlorodiethylbenzenes, etc.	354
Chlorobenzene (3)	Ethylene (1)	H_2SO_4–2% Hg_2SO_4	10	3	Ethylchlorobenzene (16%)	493
Chlorobenzene (10 pts.)	Ethylene (100 atm.)	$Ce(PO_3)_3$ (1 pt.)	350	20	p-Chloroethylbenzene	298
Chlorobenzene (4)	Ethylene (1)	SiO_2–Al_2O_3	350–400 40 atm.	0.3 S.V.	Ethylchlorobenzene (46%)	493
Bromobenzene (1–4)	Propene (1)–propane (75.5/24.5 ratio)	Aluminosilicate	300–400 40 atm.	—	Isopropylbromobenzene (13–20%), cumene	478(29)
Chlorobenzene (4)	76.9% Propene (1)–22% propane	Aluminosilicate (0.3)	350 20 atm.	—	Isopropylchlorobenzene (84%)	492
Chlorobenzene (60 g.)	Propene (21 g.)	$Cu_3(PO_4)_2$ (5 g.)	350	4	Chloroisopropylbenzene (14 g.)	710
Fluorobenzene (3)	Propene (1)	BF_3–H_3PO_4 (0.3)	30, 60, 80	2	2-Mono- and 2,4-diisopropylfluorobenzenes (68, 78, 85%)[b]	894
Fluorobenzene (6.8)	Propene (1) (3 l./hr.)	Bentonite-type clay (7.4% of benzene)	82–95	7.5	4-Fluorocumene (16%), poly-isopropylfluorobenzene (5%)	365
Chlorobenzene (4)	Propene (1) $C_3^-/C_3^= = 77/23$	H_2SO_4 (1 vol.) 85, 90, 95%	40, 40, 10	3	Isopropylchlorobenzene (84, 86, 51%)[c] (o-/p- = 80/20)	492a
Iodobenzene (51 g.)	Propene (11.2 g.) (3 l./hr.)	95% H_2SO_4 (24.5 g.) or 92% H_2SO_4 (24.5 g.)	20 / 40	—	p-Isopropyliodobenzene (44%)	479
Bromobenzene (3)	2-Butene (1)	$AlCl_2 \cdot H_2PO_4$ (0.3)	60	1.2[c]	s-Butylbromobenzene (43%)	940

Aromatic	Alkene	Catalyst	Temp. (°C)	S.V.	Products (% yield)	Reference
Chlorobenzene (3)	2-Butene (1)	AlCl₂·H₃PO₄ (0.3)	60	2.4ᶜ	s-Butylchlorobenzene (33%)	940(950)
Chlorobenzene (3)	Butene (1)	BF₃–H₃PO₄ (0.4)	60	—	p-s-Butylchlorobenzene (20%)	950
Chlorobenzene (4)	2-Butene (1)	Aluminosilicate (0.3)	350	0.3 S.V.	s-Butylchlorobenzene (83%)	492
Fluorobenzene (3)	2-Butene (1)	AlCl₂·H₃PO₄ (0.3)	40 atm.	2.9ᶜ	s-Butylfluorobenzene (42%)	940(950)
Fluorobenzene (5)	Butene (1)	H₃PO₄–BF₃ (0.5)	60	—	p-s-Butylfluorobenzene (60%)	950
Chlorobenzene (4)	Butene (1)	H₂SO₄ (1 vol.) 85, 90, 95%ᵉ	40	3	s-Butylchlorobenzene (44, 73, 80%)ᵉ	492a
Iodobenzene (1)	Butene (1) (3 l./hr.)	H₂SO₄ (1)	20	—	s-Butyliodobenzene (17%)	479
Chlorobenzene (15)	2-Methyl-2-butene (1)	AlCl₃ (0.2)–HCl	24	1	Amylchlorobenzene (8%), t-butylchlorobenzene (12%)	219
Chlorobenzene (3)	3-Hexene (2.07)	HF (10)	5–10	24	3-(p-Chlorophenyl)hexaneᵃ (25%)	779
p-Dichlorobenzene (1)	Ethylene (0.5) (2 l./min.)	AlCl₃ (10%)	110	—	Ethyl derivatives (8%), polyethyl derivatives (30%)	149
p-Dibromobenzene (1)	Propene (1)	92% H₂SO₄ (1.5)	90	2	2,5-Dibromoisopropylbenzene (75%) (6% conv.)ᵈ	476a(476)
p-Bromochlorobenzene (1)	Propene (1)	92% H₂SO₄ (1.5)	70	2	Chlorobromoisopropylbenzene (74%) (13% conv.)ᵈ	476
p-Dichlorobenzene (1)	Propene (1)	92% H₂SO₄ (1.5)	60	2	2,5-Dichloroisopropylbenzene (74%) (23% conv.)ᵈ	476
o-Nitrotoluene (137 pts.)	Propene (21 pts.)	HClO₄ (20 pts.)	95–105	—	Isopropyl-o-nitrotoluene (95 pts.)	159
o-Dichlorocumene (147 pts.)	Propene (42 pts.)	AlCl₃ (15 pts.)	20–25	—	3,4-Dichlorocumene (95 pts.)	790

ᵃ Probably mixture of isomeric-p-chlorophenylhexanes (582).
ᵇ For each temperature.
ᶜ Liters/hour.
ᵈ Of arene.
ᵉ For each catalyst concentration.

TABLE 34. Halogenated and nitrated benzenes and homologs with cyclic olefins

Aromatic (Moles)	Olefin (Moles)	Catalyst (Moles)	Temp. (°C)	Time (hrs.)	Products (% Yield)	Ref.
Bromobenzene (1.5)	Cyclopentene (1)	H_2SO_4 (2)	25	—	4-Cyclopentyl-1-bromobenzene (50%)	529
Chlorobenzene (1.5)	Cyclopentene (1)	H_2SO_4 (2)	25	—	4-Cyclopentyl-1-chlorobenzene (55%)	529
Bromobenzene (1.5)	Cyclohexene (0.5)	$AlCl_3$ (8 g.)	cold	0.25	4-Cyclohexylbromobenzene (35 g.)	587a
Bromobenzene (1)	Cyclohexene (1)	H_2SO_4 (2)	—	—	4-Cyclohexylbromobenzene (50–60%)	871(205)
Chlorobenzene (5)	Cyclohexene (1)	$AlCl_3$ (0.05)	35–45	—	Cyclohexylchlorobenzene (77%)	496(587a, 531)
Chlorobenzene	Cyclohexene	$FeCl_3$	80	8	4-Cyclohexylchlorobenzene (30%)	531
Chlorobenzene	Cyclohexene	BF_3	—	—	Mixture of alkylate and dimer	531
Chlorobenzene (1.5)	Cyclohexene (1)	H_2SO_4 (0.25, 0.5, 0.75, 1.25, 2.0, 2.5, 3.5)	30	—	Cyclohexylchlorobenzene (12, 19, 26, 39, 42, 43, 44%)[a]	873(870a)
Chlorobenzene (1)	Cyclohexene (1)	H_2SO_4 (2)	—	—	4-Cyclohexylchlorobenzene (50–70%)	871(870a)
Chlorobenzene (1.5)	Cyclohexene (1)	H_2SO_4–P_2O_5 (15%)	0, 20, 40, 80	—	Cyclohexylchlorobenzene (25, 40, 42, 28%)[b] residue (14, 36, 48, 68 g.)[b]	873
Fluorobenzene (3)	Cyclohexene (1)	BF_3–H_3PO_4 (0.3)	17, 30, 60	2	p-Cyclohexylfluorobenzene (12, 62, 56%)[b]	894
Iodobenzene	Cyclohexene	$AlCl_3$	cold	0.25	Product decomposes on vac. distillation	587a
Bromobenzene (1.5)	1-Ethylcyclohexene (1)	$FeCl_3$ (1)	40	—	Products (40%) (condensation/ dimer = 70/30%)	530
Chlorobenzene (1.5)	1-Ethylcyclohexene (1)	$FeCl_3$ (1)	40	—	Products (50%) (condensation/ dimer = 92/8%)	530
Bromobenzene (1.5)	1-Butylcyclohexene (1)	$FeCl_3$ (1)	30–60	—	Products (40%) (condensation/ dimer = 70/30%)	530
Chlorobenzene	1-Butylcyclohexene	$AlCl_3$ or BF_3	—	—	Dimer only (70–80%)	531

Chlorobenzene (1.5)	1-Butylcyclohexene (1)	$FeCl_3$ (3)	40	—	4-(Butylcyclohexyl)chlorobenzene (50%)	531
Chlorobenzene (1.5)	1-Phenylcyclohexene (1)	$FeCl_3$ (1)	—	—	Products (20%) (condensation/dimer = 60/40%)	530
o-Dichlorobenzene (5)	Cyclohexene (1)	$AlCl_3$ (0.1)	38–42	—	Cyclohexyl-o-dichlorobenzene (46%)	496
o-Dichlorobenzene	Cyclohexene	H_2SO_4 (2)–P_2O_5 (15%)	—	—	Cyclohexyl-o-dichlorobenzene (5%)	872
m-Dichlorobenzene (1.5)	Cyclohexene	H_2SO_4 (2)–P_2O_5 (15%)	—	—	Cyclohexyl-m-dichlorobenzene (5%)	872
p-Chlorodiphenyl (2)	Cyclohexene (1)	$AlCl_3$ (0.15) (CS_2 500 cc.)	27–41	—	Cyclohexyl-p-chlorodiphenyl (61%)	496
p-Dichlorobenzene (1.5)	Cyclohexene	H_2SO_4 (2)–P_2O_5 (15%)	—	—	No reaction	872
Benzylchloride (1.5)	Cyclohexene	H_2SO_4 (2)–P_2O_5 (15%)	—	—	4-Cyclohexylbenzylchloride (30%)	872
o-Chlorotoluene (2.5)	Cyclohexene (0.5)	$AlCl_3$ (0.05)	40	—	Cyclohexyl-o-chlorotoluene (60%)	496(587a)
o-Chlorotoluene (1.5)	Cyclohexene	H_2SO_4 (2)–P_2O_5 (15%)	—	—	Cyclohexyl-o-chlorotoluene (60%)	872
m-Chlorotoluene (1.5)	Cyclohexene	H_2SO_4 (2)–P_2O_5 (15%)	—	—	Cyclohexyl-m-chlorotoluene (79%)	872
p-Chlorotoluene (1.5)	Cyclohexene (0.5)	$AlCl_3$ (8 g.)	cold	0.25	Cyclohexyl-p-chlorotoluene (50%), dicyclohexyl derivative (6 g.)	587a
p-Chlorotoluene (1.5)	Cyclohexene	H_2SO_4 (2)–P_2O_5 (15%)	—	—	Cyclohexyl-p-chlorotoluene (98%)	872
β-Bromoisopropyl-benzene (1.5)	Cyclopentene (1)	H_2SO_4 (2)	25	—	p-Cyclopentyl-β-bromoisopropyl-benzene (30%)	529
β-Bromoisopropyl-benzene (1.5)	Cyclohexene (1)	H_2SO_4 (2)	25	—	p-Cyclohexyl-β-bromoisopropyl-benzene (30%)	529
β-Chloroisopropyl-benzene (1.5)	Cyclohexene (1)	H_2SO_4 (2)	25	—	p-Cyclohexyl-β-chloroisopropyl-benzene (30%)	529
p-Methyl-β-bromoiso-propylbenzene (1.5)	Cyclohexene (1)	H_2SO_4 (2)	25	—	p-Methylcyclohexyl-β-bromoiso-propylbenzene (30%)	529
p-Chlorophenylcyclo-hexane (1.5)	Cyclohexene	H_2SO_4 (2)–P_2O_5 (15%)	—	—	Dicyclohexylchlorobenzene (45%)	872

a For each ratio of catalysts.   b For each temperature.

TABLE 35. Phenol with ethylene

Phenol (Moles)	Ethylene (Moles)	Catalyst (Moles)	Temp. (°C), pressure	Time hrs.	Ethylphenol products (% Yield)	Ref.
10 pts.[d]	3.2 pts.	$AlCl_3$–EtCl (1/0.4 pts.)	60	12	Ethylphenol (72%)	450
10 pts.[d]	3.2 pts.	$AlBr_3$–EtCl (1.5/0.3 pts.)	60	13	Ethylphenol (68%)	450
—	—	Al–$BaCl_2$	340	—	2- (10%), 2,6-Di- (37%)	815
300 g.	170 g.[a]	Al (6 g.)–$HgCl_2$ (2 g.)	340–350 200 atm.	6	2-, 2,6-Di-	194
300 g.	131 g.	Zn (6 g.)–$HgCl_2$ (0.2 g.)	340 200 atm.	6	2-, 2,6- Di-, and tri-	194
1	1 (50 atm.)[b]	H_3PO_4 (0.3)	225	22	2- and 4- (35%), Di- (25%), phenetole (7.9 g.), ethylphenetole (11.6 g.), diethylphenetole (30.9 g.)	340
—	—	Aluminum phosphate	280–400 40–100 atm.	—	Mono- and di-; mono- and diethylphenetole	731b
—	—	ThO_2	400	—	Phenetole (good yield), ethylbenzene (large amounts)	731b
600 g.	—	$Al(OC_6H_5)_3$ (0.16)	300–320 800 psig	10	2- (24%), 2,6-di- (8%), phenetole (1%)	397(396)
10 pts.	100 atm.	$Ce(PO_3)_3$ (1 pt.)	375	—	Nuclear alkylate, b.p. 230–260°	298
300 g.	170 g.	Al (3 g.)[c]	320–340 200 atm.	6	2- (32%), 2,6-Di- (39%), 2-ethyl-6-s-butyl-phenol	816

[a] Absorbed.   [b] Initial.   [c] As phenoxide.   [d] 100 pts. CCl_4.

TABLE 36.   Phenol with propene

Phenol (Moles)	Propene (Moles)	Catalyst (Moles)	Temp. (°C)	Time (hrs.)	Isopropylphenol products (% Yield)	Ref.
10 pts.[b]	4.9 pts.	$AlCl_3$–propyl chloride (1/0.5 pts.)	60–70	10	Mono- (75%)	450
40 g.	20 g.	Al (10 g.)/iso-C_3H_7Cl (5 g.)	150–200	4	Mono- (4 g.), isopropyl isopropylphenyl ether (33 g.)	709
1	0.5	BF_3 (0.08) (Benzene)	0	2	2- (41%), Isopropylphenyl ether (54%)	777
1	2	BF_3 (0.08) (Benzene)	15	2	2-Isopropylphenyl isopropyl ether (41%)	777
1	1	BF_3 (0.05)	20	2	2,4-Diisopropylphenyl isopropyl ether (30%)	777
1	excess	BF_3 (0.05)	30–40	—	2,4,6-Triisopropylphenyl isopropyl ether (92%)	777
94 g.	—	BF_3–$2H_2O$	—	—	92–99% yield, 52–87% mono-	234
—	25 g.	Dihydroxyfluoroboric acid (5 g.)	30–35	—	Mono- (45 g.)	559
1	28 g.	Dihydroxyfluoroboric acid (0.1)	—	—	2-Mono- (30%), 4-mono- (3%), phenol conv. = 37%	169
3	3	BF_3–H_3PO_4 (50 cc.)	35	1.5	Mono- (74%)	28
49 pts.[c]	—	Fuming H_2SO_4 (40%) (45 pts.)	90–110	12	Isopropylphenols[d]	55
96.5 pts.	224 pts.	Sulfonated styrene–divinyl-benzene resin (100 cc.)	100, 500 psi	4	Isopropylphenols (19.2%): 2- (92 pts.), 3- and 4- (40 pts.)	148
44.5 g.	56 g.	Naphthalenesulfonic acid (40 g.)	80–100	—	2-Mono- (20%), isopropyl cumyl ether (80%)	352
70 pts.	34 pts.	89% H_3PO_4 (30 pts.)	120–130	—	6% 85–205°, 43% 205–220°, 28% 220–230°, 11% 230–242°, 12% Higher	311
81 g.	20 g.	$Ca(H_2PO_4)_2$·H_2O (10 g.)	300, 110 atm.	4	2- (18.1 cc.), 2-Isopropylphenyl isopropyl ether	684
40 g.	20 g.	Silica gel (10 g.)–iso-C_3H_7Cl (5 g.)	150–200	4	Mono- (2 g.), isopropyl isopropylphenyl ether (37 g.)	709

Table continued

TABLE 36 (continued)

Phenol (Moles)	Propene (Moles)	Catalyst (Moles)	Temp. (°C)	Time (hrs.)	Isopropylphenol products (% Yield)	Ref.
2.3	1	SiO$_2$–Al$_2$O$_3$ (naphtha diluent)	160–238 400 psi	2.7–2.9 L.H.S.V.	2- (36%)	729
50 pts.	100 pts.	Nickel molybdite (5 pts.)	100–160	1	Mono- and di- (23 pts.)	198
2.12	4.45	Al (2 g.)[a]	220 70–10 atm.	2–3	2-Mono- (15%), 2,6-di- (73%)	816(397, 396)
600 pts.	30 atm.	Mg (6.5 pts.)[a]	323	2.5	2-Mono- (73%)	178
1	1.9	Zn (3 g.)[a]	320–340 362 atm.	19	2- (2.6%), 2,6-Di- (53%)	194

[a] Converted to phenoxide.   [b] 100 pts. CCl$_4$.   [c] As sulfonic acid.   [d] After hydrolysis.

TABLE 37. Phenol with n-butene

Phenol (Moles)	n-Butene (Moles)	Catalyst (Moles)	Temp. (°C)	Time (hrs.)	s-Butylphenols (% Yield)	Ref.
200 g.	190 g.	Fe (2 g.)	340 250 atm.	6	2-Mono- and 2,6-di-	194
1	2-Butene (1)	BF$_3$–Et$_2$O (10%)	53	3–5	Ether (32%), phenolics (30%)	931
		BF$_3$–2H$_2$O			92–99% Yield containing 52–87% mono-	234
300 g.	350 g.	Al (3 g.)[a]	190–200 45–5 atm.	0.75	2- (7%), 2,6-di- (73%)	816

[a] As phenoxide.

TABLE 38.   Phenol with isobutylene

Phenol (Moles)	Isobutylene (Moles)	Catalyst (Moles)	Temp. (°C)	Time (hrs.)	t-Butylphenol products (% Yield)						Ref.
					Phenol	2-	4-	2,4-	2,6-	2,4,6-	
2.7	1	AlCl$_3$ (1.25%)	57–64	—	2- (2%), 4- (95%)						87(602)
—	—	AlCl$_3$	100	—	4- (70%), Liquid product^a (24%)						346
1	4	AlCl$_3$ (0.02)	161–154	0.0							92
			630–260 psig	0.16	0.35	0.4	0.02	0.03	0.05	0.06	
				0.23	0.24	0.61	—	0.05	0.03	0.03	
				0.36	0.18	0.54	0.02	0.03	0.19	0.02	
				0.50	0.05	0.32	0.01	0.03	0.45	0.11	
				1.14	—	0.05	0.03	0.16	0.38	0.37	
				7.10	—	0.02	0.01	0.25	0.04	0.66	
10 pts. (100 pts. CCl$_4$)	6.5 pts.	AlCl$_3$–butyl chloride (1/0.7 pts.)	80	8	4- (80%)						450(346)
1	1	AlCl$_2$–HSO$_4$ (7.5%)	100	—	4- (41%), Liquid product^i (11%)						602(848)
2	1	FeCl$_3$ (0.019 g.); HCl (0.16 g.)	90	1.75	4- (92%)						88
10	1	POCl$_3$ (0.6% of phenol)	55–60	—	2- (61%), 4- (19%), di- (6%)						87
3.3	1	POBr$_3$ (0.2% of phenol)	55–60	—	2- (43%), 4- (25%), di- (17%)						87
1	1	BF$_3$ (3.7%)	100	—	4- (83%), Liquid product^a (13%)						602(848)
94 pts.	56 pts.	BF$_3$ (10 pts.)	40–50	1	4-^{e}						301
—	—	BF$_3$ (0.8%)	50,100	0.5	4- (30, 82%),^{d} Liquid product^a (58%, 13%)^d						346
50 g.	—	BF$_3$–H$_2$O	135–150	—	Mono- (52%)						862(234)
50 g.	—	BF$_3$–Et$_2$O (5%)	80	—	4- (Theor. yield)						862
3	2.7	BF$_3$–H$_3$PO$_4$ (50 cc.) (750 cc. pentane)	35	—	4- (80%)						28(862,602)
50 g.	—	BF$_3$–H$_3$PO$_4$ (5%, 10%)	40–50 135–150	—	Butyl phenyl ether, 4-t-butylphenol (52%, 62%)^h						862

Table continued

TABLE 38 (continued)

Phenol (Moles)	Isobutylene (Moles)	Catalyst (Moles)	Temp. (°C)	Time (hrs.)	t-Butylphenol products (% Yield)	Ref.
1.0	1.0	BF_3–H_3PO_4	100–120	0.5	4- (81%), Liquid product[l] (15%)	602(848)
—	—	75% H_2SO_4 (15 g.)	100	—	4- (65%), Liquid product[a] (19%)	848
2209	2320[b]	H_2SO_4 (20 cc.), then[c] $AlCl_3$ (60 g.)	r.t., 140	24, 2	2- (293 g.), 4- (2035 g.), Residue (445 g.)	580
66 g.	118 g.	H_2SO_4 (3.3 g.)	50	7	2,4,6-Tri- (150 g.)	805(775)
6	1	H_2SO_4 (2%)	45, 6	few	2- (22%), 2,4-di- (65%)	419(793)
1	0.8	H_2SO_4 (0.0005)	8	5.5	t-Butyl phenyl ether (69%)	797(581)
—	—	H_2SO_4 (5%)	70		4- ("exclusively")	71
—	—	H_2SO_4 (0.1%)	40–45		2- (main product)	71
3.2	4.5	H_2SO_4 (0.18)	90	1	2- (135 g.), 2- and 4- (65 g.), poly- (280 g.)	193
1	1	H_2SO_4 (1)	0–10, 65	0.5–1.0	Mono- (90%)	539
1	1	H_2SO_4 (7.5%)	100	—	4- (65%), Liquid product[l] (19%)	602
1	1[i]	100% H_2SO_4 (1%)	100	—	4- (80%)[n]	150
1	0.92	Cationic exchange resin (7%)[j]	80, 120	3, 4	2- (0, 4, 0, 0%),[k] 4- (37, 51, 57, 49%)[k]	453
740 pts.	140 pts.	Sulfonated styrene–divinylbenzene resin (10 pts.)	100	8	4- (51%)	148
470 pts.	140 pts.	"Zeo-Karb" (10 pts.)[f]	67–70	8	4- (24%)	148
94 pts.	108 pts.	Sulfonated polystyrene (10 pts.)	—	—	Alkylated phenol (82%) containing 2- (22.8 pts.), 4- (21.7 pts.), 2,4-di- (52.6 pts.), 2,4,6-tri- (67.9 pts.)	148
188 g. (400 g. C_6H_6)	132 g.	FSO_3H (26.2 g.)	25	4	2- (2.5%), 4- (84%)	72
3.3	3.3	H_3PO_4 (0.28)	75–80	1	Mono-	193
1	100 g.	89% H_3PO_4 (30 g.)	100	—	4- (40%), 2,4-Di- (30%)	332(602)

2	1	Boric acid (1.88 g.)—oxalic acid (5.64 g.)ᵍ	45	—	2- (25%)	883
2	1	Boric acid (1.88 g.)—oxalic acid (5.64 g.)ᵍ	140	1	4- (117 g.), Di- (22.7 g.)	883
6	6	I₂ (0.236)	105	1.5–2	4- (97%)	288
2.5	1 (4.5 iso-C₄H₁₀)	SiO₂–Al₂O₃	150–200, 1300 psig	4.8 L.H.S.V.	2- (22%), 4- (70%), Di- (6%)	730(729)
1	3.9	SiO₂–Al₂O₃	137, 250 psig	1.02 L.H.S.V.	2- (9%), 4- (7%), 2,4-Di- (53%), 2,4,6-tri- and higher (16%)	576
1	1	Aluminosilicate	100	flow	4- (43%), Liquid productˡ (44%)	602
			130	flow	4- (56%), Liquid productˡ (31%)	198
50 pts.	100 pts.	Nickel molybdite (5 pts.)	200	5	4- (31 pts.)	816
200	400 g.	Al (2 g.)ᵐ	200	6	2,4,6-Tri- (70%)	816
4	7.6	Al(OC₆H₅)₃ (0.13) (100 cc. toluene)	100, 240 psig	7	2- (9%), 2,6-Di- (74%), 2,4,6-tri- (9%)	397(191,396, 816)
470 pts.	—	Mg (6 pts.)ᵐ	325	1.5	2- (46%)	178

ᵃ Contains t-butyl ethers of phenol and t-butyl phenol, some di-t-butyl phenol, polymer.
ᵇ Contains n-butenes.
ᶜ Wash out H₂SO₄ and debutanize before adding second catalyst.
ᵈ At each temp.
ᵉ With 1 pt. BF₃ as catalyst 1/3 of the product is butylphenyl ether.
ᶠ Sulfonated coal cation exchange material (Permutit Co.).
ᵍ Mixture preheated 0.33 hours at 130°.
ʰ For the two catalyst concentrations.

ⁱ 5.1% In admixture with 91% n-butenes and 0.4% butane; also 3.5% butadiene (which did not react).
ʲ Must be oven-dried.
ᵏ Conversion with Amberlite IR-112, Permutit Q, Amberlite IR-120, and Dowex 50-X12, respectively.
ˡ Contains 75–85% 2,4-di-, 20–25% 2,4,6-tri-, and 2–3% 2-t-butylphenols.
ᵐ Converted to phenoxide.
ⁿ Purity 98–99.5%.

TABLE 39.   Phenol with amylenes

Phenol (Moles)	Amylene (Moles)	Catalyst (Moles)	Temp. (°C)	Time (hrs.)	Amylphenol products (% Yield)	Ref.
1	Isoamylenes (1)	1.6 g.-BF_3, H_3PO_4-BF_3, Et_2O-BF_3, $AlCl_3 \cdot HSO_4$, $AlCl_3$ or 17% H_2SO_4	100–120	0.5	4-t- (95, 90, 89, 68, 64, 68%),[e] Liquids[d] (3, 8, 6, 22, 25, 11%)[e]	857
10 pts. (100 pts. CCl_4)	Amylene (8.2 pts.)	$AlCl_3$-amyl chloride (1/0.9 pts.)	—	6	4-t- (85%)	450
0.497 (Cyclohexane)	Isoamylene (0.247)	$AlCl_3$-boric acid (12.96 g.)	35–80	2	4-t- (64%)	502
10 pts.	Amylene (8.2 pts.)	$AlBr_3$-amyl bromide (1.3/1 pts.)	60	5	4-t- (87–90%)	450
2	2-Methyl-2-butene	$FeCl_3$-HCl	90	2–4	4-t- (63%)	88
94 g.	3-Methyl-1-butene (70 g.)	BF_3 (1.8–26%)	100	0.5	4-t- (95–96%), "Liquid" products (2–3%)	857
1	2-Methyl-2-butene (1)	BF_3 (1.6%)	100–120	0.5	4-t- (95–96%), Di-t- (54%)	857
—	Isoamylene	BF_3	—	—	92–99% Yield, 52–58% mono-	234
—	Isoamylene	BF_3-$2H_2O$	—	—	92–99% Yield	862
50 g.	Isoamylene (38 g.)	BF_3-Et_2O (1–10%)	20–120	—	4-t- (92–99%)	937
23.5 g.	2-Pentene (26.5 g.)	BF_3-Et_2O (3 cc.)	52[a]	26	Ethers (40%)[f]	907
0.497 (Pet. ether)	Isoamylene (0.247)	BF_3-hydrocarbon O_2 complex	35–70	1.25	Isoamylphenol (64%)	
1880 g.	Amylenes (3000 g.) (i/n = 50/50)	H_2SO_4 (20 cc.), then[c] $AlCl_3$ (50 g.)	45; 130–140	—; 1	2-t- (51 g.), 4-t- (2015 g.), Residue (266 g.)	580
1880 g.	Amylene (3000 g.) (i/n = 50/50)	H_2SO_4 (20 cc.), then[c] $ZnCl_2$ (50 g.)-HCl	45; 140	—; 3	2-t- (162 g.), 4-t- (1740 g.), Residue (682 g.)	580
3	Isoamylene (1)	$POCl_3$ (1%)	100–110	1[b]	2-t- (52%), 4-t- (33%), di-t- (7%)	87
20	Amylenes (3000 g.) (i/n = 50/50)	H_2SO_4 (20 cc.)	140	4	2- and 4-t- (68 g.), 4-t- (2160 g.), Residue (394 g.)	580(151)

1	Isoamylene (1)	H₂SO₄ (1)	0-10	—	t-Amyl- (90%)	539
8*			65	0.5-1.0		
1880 g.	Mixed amylenes (2800 g.) (50% branched)	H₂SO₄ (20 cc.)	45-50	1.5	2- and 4-, Some di-t-	581
3670 lbs.	Isoamylene (1560 lbs.)	H₂SO₄ (7010 lbs.)	130-135	4	Mono-t- (2693 lbs.)	734(525)
0.15 (HOAc)	Isoamylene (0.15)	H₂SO₄ (0.12)	r.t.	96	4-t- (70%)	16
1	Isoamylene (1)	H₂SO₄–HOAc (1/1 vol.) (10 volumes)	r.t.	24-48	4-t-	391
0.1	Isoamylene (0.1)	p-Toluenesulfonic acid (0.0005)	100	6	4-t- (65%)	924
965 pts.	Amylene (375 pts.)	Sulfonated styrene–divinylbenzene resin	150-175	2	Mono- (52%), di- (18%)	148
47 g.	2-Methyl-2-butene (70 g.)	Sulfonated phenol–formaldehyde ion	60-90	L.H.S.V. 8	2,4-Di-t- (32%)	898
1	Amylene	KU-2 cation exchange resin (1)	135-140	—	4-t- (90-96%)	349
91.2 g.	Amylene (34 g.)	Boric acid (0.45 g.)–oxalic acid (3.2 g.)	150	0.75	Mono- (20 g.)	883
—	2-Methyl-2-butene	Al	120	—	2-t-	816

a At room temp. (72 hrs.) reaction gave 68% s-amylphenyl ether.
b Added stirring.
c Neutralize and depentanize before adding second catalyst.
d 15% Phenol, 55% t-amylphenyl ether, 5% di-t-amylphenol ether. 25% t-amyl ether of t-amylphenol.
e For respective catalysts.
f Mostly s-amyl-s-amylphenyl ether.

TABLE 40.   Phenol with higher olefins

Phenol (Moles)	Olefin (Moles)	Catalyst (Moles)	Temp. (°C)	Time, (hrs.)	Alkylated phenols (% Yield)	Ref.
47 pts.	Octene	H_2SO_4 (5 pts.)	40–42	—	Isooctyl- (73%)	901
	1-Octene (56 pts.)	Nickel molybdite	200	5	Octyl- (21 pts.)	198
1	Diisobutylene (0.5)	$AlCl_3$ (1.3)	80	6	4-t-Butyl- (67%), 4-t-octyl- (14%)	774(607)
2	Diisobutylene (1)	$FeCl_3$ (0.019 g.)–HCl (0.16 g.)	90	2–4	p-(1,1,3,3-Tetramethylbutyl)- (92%)	88
48.3	Diisobutylene (8)	$FeCl_3$ (0.07)–HCl (0.55)	145–150	4.6	t-Butyl- (88%)	161
3	Diisobutylene (0.5)	$FeBr_3$ (0.00086)–HBr (0.0115)	115–120	2.25	4-t-Butyl- (68%), 4-t-octyl- (18 g.)	161
1	Diisobutylene (1)	$SnCl_4$ (1%)–HCl	60–70	—	Tetramethylbutyl- (theor. yield)	90
1	Diisobutylene (1)	$POCl_3$ (0.15)	r.t.	12	Diisobutyl- (m.p. 83–84°)	277
1	Diisobutylene (1)	$CuCl_2$ (20 g.)	r.t., 60°[e]	4, 120–144	Diisobutyl- (47%)	281
170 pts.	Diisobutylene (410 pts.)	BF_3 (2%)	50–55	0.41	t-Octyl- (38%), di-t-octyl- (55%)	115(302a)
2577 pts.	Diisobutylene (3030 pts.)	BF_3 (53 pts.)	55–75	0.21	p-t-Octyl- (90–92%)	115(301,609, 657,868)
50 g.	Diisobutylene (30 g.)	BF_3–H_2O	50	2	4-t-Octyl- (38%)	864a(431)
50 g.	Diisobutylene (30 g.)	BF_3–Et_2O (5–10%)[e]	50	2	4-t-Octyl- (76%)	864a(862)
50 g.	Diisobutylene (30 g.)	BF_3–H_3PO_4 (1–5%)[e]	100	4	4-t-Octyl- (55%), higher (5%)	864a
0.5	Diisobutylene (0.5)	H_2SO_4 (0.5)	r.t. w.b.	168, 1	t-Octyl- (25%)	555(42,277, 332,539,551, 555)
2	Diisobutylene (2)	H_2SO_4 (78 g.)	85–0	16	4-t-Butyl- (8 cc.)	332
1	Diisobutylene (1)	H_2SO_4 (1)	0, r.t.	—, 168	t-Octyl phenyl ether	556
1	Diisobutylene (1)	H_2SO_4 (0.15)	20–25	1.5	Diisobutyl- (85–95%)	659(660)
31 pts.	Diisobutylene (33.6 pts.)	Amberlite IR-120[d] (3 pts.)	90	15	2- and 4-Octyl- (49%)	250(351)

92 g.	Diisobutylene (57 g.)	90% H_3PO_4 (50 g.)	150, 20 atm.[j]	6	p-(1,1,3,3-Tetramethylbutyl) (16 g.) 4-t-butyl- (4 g.)	332(425,528)
585 pts.	Diisobutylene (698 pts.)	Tetraphosphoric acid (12.4 pts.) Fuller's earth (57.5 pts.)	60–71	3.3	Octyl- (1220 pts.) (95%)	23
94 g.	Diisobutylene (1)	HF (121 g.)	0	24	t-Butyl- (88 g.)	758
47 g.	Diisobutylene (56 g.)	70% HF (20 g.)	0	48	4-t-Octyl- (35 g.)	758
91.2 g.	2,4,4-Trimethyl-2-pentene (54.4 g.)	Boric acid (0.45 g.)	100–135	0.25	2- (3 g.), 4-t-Octyl- (76.5 g.), higher (7 g.)	883(39)
2	Diisobutylene (1)	Oxalic acid (3.2 g.) Acid-activated clay (10–20% of phenol)	30–90	3–4	t-Octyl-	205
47 pts.	Diisobutylene (56 pts.)	Nickel molybdite (5 pts.)	200	5	Octyl- (10 pts.)	198
3	Diisobutylene (1)	Tonsil[a] (2.8 g.)	170–182	2.0	4-t-Butyl- (69.5)	607
2.38	Diisobutylene (2.42)	Al (4.5 g.)	280	1.5	2- (11%), 4- (1,1,3,3-Tetramethyl-butyl-) (25%), higher boiling (60 g.)	397
1	Styrene (2)	BF_3–Et_2O (0.4–0.6)	−5 r.t.[b]	1–2	1-(p-Hydroxyphenyl)-1-phenyl-ethane (46%)	952(229a)[k]
4	Styrene (1)	H_2SO_4 (0.74%)	reflux	576	α-Phenylethyl- (75–85%) (2-/4- = 40/60)	223(391,884)
1	Styrene (2)	25% H_2SO_4 (8 pts.)	135–145	4	4- (14%), 2,4-Di- (47%), 2,4,6-tri- (39%) (1-phenyl-1-ethyl)phenols	369
1.5	Styrene (3)	CH_3- or Et-sulfonic acid monohydrate (5 pts.)	135–145	2	Mono-, di-, and tri-(1-phenyl-1-ethyl)phenols (90%)	369
141 pts.	Styrene (312 pts.)	p-Toluenesulfonic acid monohydrate (5 pts.)	140	2	4-Mono- (14%), 2,4-di- (49%), 2,4,6-tri- (37%) (1-phenyl-1-ethyl)-phenols	369
—	Styrene	$HClO_4$–HOAc	25	2	o- and p-(1-Phenylethyl)-	206a
2	Styrene (1)	HCl (0.9%)	120–130	—	2- (32%), 4- (33%) (α-Phenylethyl)-	604
2	Chlorostyrene[g]	36% aq. HCl (0.5 g.)	145–165	3–4	4- (α-Phenylisopropyl)-2-chloro- (45%)	604

Table continued

TABLE 40 (*continued*)

Phenol (Moles)	Olefin (Moles)	Catalyst (Moles)	Temp. (°C)	Time (hrs.)	Alkylated phenols (% Yield)	Ref.
—	Styrene	HI	—	—	α-Phenylethyl- (2-/4- = 33/67)	806
2.2	Propene trimer (2)	p-Toluenesulfonic acid·H_2O (0.31)	110–115	6	Monononyl- (92%)	1
3	α-Methylstyrene (1)	BF_3–Et_2O (0.15)	80	6	2-(p-Hydroxyphenyl)-2-phenylpropane (60%), 1,1,3-trimethyl-3-phenylindane (2–3%)	952
141 pts.	α-Methylstyrene (354 pts.)	50% H_2SO_4 (4 pts.)	135–145	2	Aralkylated phenols (91%): 4-35%, 2,4-di- 60%, 2,4,6-tri- 5% (α-phenylisopropyl)phenols, α-methylstyrene dimer (7%)	369
141 pts.	α-Methylstyrene (354 pts.)	p-Toluenesulfonic acid (5 pts.)	135–145	2	Aralkylated phenols (89%) (mono-/di-/trisubstituted = 25/68/8%, α-methylstyrene dimers (31.5 pts.)	369
2	α-Methylstyrene (1)	36% aq. HCl (0.5 g.)	120–130	1.2	4-(α-Phenylisopropyl)- (92%)	604
3.2	1-Decene (1.28)	Al (4.5 g.)	300	1.5	"2-(2-Decyl)-" (49%)	397
141 pts.	α-p-Dimethylstyrene (354 pts.)	p-Toluenesulfonic acid (5 pts.)	135–145	2	4- (24%),[a] 2,4-Di- (70%),[a] 2,4,6-tri- (7%) (α-p-tolyliosopropyl)phenols	369
2	Ethylstyrene (1)[i]	36% aq. HCl (0.5 g.)	120–130	1.2	α-Ethylphenylethylphenols (72%)	604
94 g.	Anethole (74 g.) (100 mL. toluene)	H_2SO_4 (10 g.)	reflux	2	(α-Anisyl-n-propyl)phenol (60%)	102a
188 pts.	Isohexylene–isoheptylene dimer (392 pts.)	$AlCl_3$ (40 pts.)	25–30	1	Oil (b.p. 172–182°) (90%)	300
175 g.	Propene polymer (481 g.) (C_{12} average)	BF_3 (4.7 g.)	60–90	4	Alkylphenols (average 2.1 alkyl groups/phenol molecule)	787
2.32	Propene tetramer (2.1)	BF_3–Et_2O (0.122)	82–86	9.33	Monododecyl- (75%)	1

940 pts.	Isohexylene–isoheptylene dimer (1850 pts.)	BF_3 (67 pts.)–H_2O 36 pts.	40–45	2	C_{12}–C_{14} Alkylphenols (90%)	300
50 g.	Triisobutylene (30 g.)	BF_3–H_2O (10%)	50	4	Dodecyl- (80%)	864a
50 g.	Triisobutylene (30 g.)	BF_3–Et_2O (10%)	70	3	Dodecyl- (100%)	864a(862)
50 g.	Triisobutylene (30 g.)	BF_3–H_3PO_4 (10%)	100	3–4	Dodecyl- (80%)	864a
—	Propene tetramer	H_2SO_4	40–42	1–3	Dodecyl- (52%)	901
	Olefins	Acid cation exchanger	110–160		Monoalkyl phenols (90–99%)	345
100 g.	Triisobutylene (148 g.)	H_2SO_4 (40 g.)	r.t.	24	Oil, b.p. 120–170° at 3 mm. (120 g.)	659
3	Propene tetramer (1)	91% mixed alkane-sulfonic acids (100 g.)	45	2	Dodecyl- (68%)	653
1	Triisobutylene (1)	70–100% HF (122) (300 cc. CCl_4)	0	24	t-Butyl- (64 g.), high boilers	758
376 g.	Di- and triisobutylene (168 g.)	Tonsil[d] (8 g.)	157–182	2.5	4-t-Butyl- (248 g.)	607
282 pts.	Diisoheptylene (588 pts.)	BF_3 (3 pts.)	25–30	—	p-Tetradecyl-	300
100 pts.	C_{14}–C_{15} Olefin (150 pts.)	$ZnCl_2$ (15 pts.)	170–175	15	$R \cdot C_6H_4OH$ (R = C_{14} to C_{15} average, b.p. 150–225° at 7 mm.)	203
1	C_{14}–C_{18} Olefin (2.3)	$ZnCl_2$ (1.5%)–HCl (2.5%)		—	Alkylated phenol (75%)	400
—	Olefins	Sulfonated carbon		—	Alkylated phenol	307
1	C_{14}–C_{18} Olefin (525 g.)	ZnO–HCl (4 l./hr.)	145	3	Mono- and dialkyl- (84%) (mostly mono-)	573(565,401, 206)
2541 g.	Polybutenes (M.W. 360–380) (5000 g.)	BF_3 (45 g.)	50–60 105–110	1.5	Alkylated phenols	21
3	Propene pentamer (1)	91% mixed alkane-sulfonic acids (100 g.)	45	2	Pentadecyl- (78%)	653
50 pts.	Cetene (50 pts.)	$ZnCl_2$ (50 pts.)	Reflux	15	Oil (b.p. 238–252°/15 mm.)	203
1.1 (113 pts.)	1-Hexadecene (1) (224 pts.)	SiO_2 (80%)–Al_2O_3 (12%) (1% F.)	180–190	4	67% C_{16} conversion: mono-hexadecyl-isomers (53%), s-hexadecyl- (170 pts.) (2-/4- = 98/8)	162

Table continued

TABLE 40 (*continued*)

Phenol (Moles)	Olefin (Moles)	Catalyst (Moles)	Temp. (°C)	Time (hrs.)	Alkylated phenols (% Yield)	Ref.
5	Tetraisobutylene (1)	91% mixed alkanesulfonic acids (150 g.)	70	2	t-Octyl- (98%)	653
5	Tetraisobutylene (1)	HF^i (5)	−40	0.7	4-t-Octyl- (excellent yield)	682
2	1,1-Diphenylethylene (1)	36% aq. HCl (0.5 g.)	120–130	1.2	4-(α,α-Diphenylethyl)- (47%)	604
50 pts.	1,2-Heptadecene^h (50 pts.)	$ZnCl_2$ (50 pts.)	90–120	15	Heptadecyl- (b.p. 220–270°/15 mm.)	203
50 pts.	1,2-Heptadecene^h (50 pts.)	H_2SO_4 (10 pts.)	6–12	—	Heptadecyl- (b.p. 220–270°/15 mm.)	203
94 pts.	Isohexylene trimer (245 pts.)	BF_3 (2 pts.)	—	—	Alkylphenol (94%)	300
4	α-Methylstyrene dimer	H_2SO_4 (1%)	110	0.33	Cumyl- (59%)	243
15	Propene polymer (0.5) (b.p. 100–120°/1.5 mm.)	$AlCl_2 \cdot HSO_4$ (20%)	60–80	6	Alkylphenol (82%)	387(21)
3	Propene polymer (100–120°/1.5 mm.)	HF^i (5)	65	1	Alkylphenol (81%)	69
—	Propene polymer (295–325°)	BF_3 (3%)	30–50	—	Alkylphenol (side-chain average = 21 carbon atoms) (85%)	469

[a] Products in condensation product.
[b] Or heated 2–8 hours at 100°.
[c] Heated at daily intervals.
[d] Activated clay.
[e] On phenol.
[f] Same result with 1 ml. 52% aq. HBr.
[g] Mostly *para*.
[h] Probably 1-heptadecene.
[i] *Ortho*- and *meta*-.
[j] N_2.
[k] Uses BF_3 at 70°.

TABLE 41. Phenol with cyclic olefins

Phenol (Moles)	Olefin (Moles)	Catalyst (Moles)	Temp. (°C)	Time (hrs.)	Phenol derivatives (% Yield)	Ref.
5	Cyclohexene (1.5)	AlCl$_3$ (0.45)	25	3	2-Cyclohexyl- (56%), 4-cyclohexyl- (20%)	66
2	Cyclohexene (1.5)	AlCl$_3$ (0.45) (500 cc. CS$_2$)	25	3	2- (15%); 4-Cyclohexyl- (4%); cyclohexyl chloride (46 g.); cyclohexyl phenyl ether (12%)	66
1	Cyclohexene (2)	BF$_3$ (4–8 g.)	40	—	Cyclohexyl- (mono- 8%, di- 26%, tri- 40%)	438
3	Cyclohexene (61 g.)	BF$_3$ (4 g.)	19–36	—	Cyclohexyl- (58%) (o/p = 76/24)	434
5	Cyclohexene (1)	BF$_3$ (4–8 g.)	40	—	Cyclohexyl- (72%)	438
94 g.	Cyclohexene (41 g.)	BF$_3$ (6 g.)	0	0.66	Phenoxycyclohexane (61%), cyclohexyl-phenol (14%) (o/p = 80/20); cyclohexyl-phenoxycyclohexane (10%)	435(433)
3	Cyclohexene (3)	BF$_3$–H$_3$PO$_4$ (50 cc.) (C$_5$H$_{12}$)	36	4	Cyclohexyl- (50%)	28
290 g.	Cyclohexene (2.5)	H$_2$SO$_4$ (20 cc.)	reflux	3	2- and 4-Cyclohexyl- (mainly 4-)	581(721)
62.7 pts.	Cyclohexene (164 pts.)	70% HClO$_4$ (15 pts.)	60–70	—	Cyclohexyl- (16 pts.), dicyclohexyl- (58 pts.), tricyclohexyl- (90 pts.), residue (26 pts.)	159
3.2	Cyclohexene (3.0) (90 pts. Decalin)	Al (2.25 g.)	85, 224	several	2-Cyclohexyl- (42%), 4-cyclohexyl- (4%), 2,6-dicyclohexyl- (20%)	397
112 g.	Cyclohexene (196.8 g.)	Fe (2.3 g.)	320 62 atm.	7	2-Cyclohexyl-, 2,6-dicyclohexyl-	194
30 g.	1-Methylcyclohexene (20 g.)	H$_2$SO$_4$ (7.5 g.)	w.b.	15	Alkylate (32%), ether (30%)	721
0.15	1-Methylcyclohexene (0.15)	H$_2$SO$_4$ (0.1)–HOAc	w.b.	1	4-(Methylcyclohexyl)- (55%)	721
0.15	3-Methylcyclohexene (0.15)	H$_2$SO$_4$ (0.1)–HOAc	80	1	4-(Methylcyclohexyl)- (55%)	721
0.15	4-Methylcyclohexene (0.15)	H$_2$SO$_4$ (0.1)–HOAc	80	1	4-(Methylcyclohexyl)- (55%)	721
50 g.	Δ^5-1,3-Dimethylcyclohexene (10 g.)	HCl (conc.) (3 g.)	w.b.	5	1,3-Dimethyl-x-(p-hydroxylphenyl)cyclohexane (62%)	721
284 pts.	Cyclooctene (110 pts.)	BF$_3$–HOAc (7 pts.)	60	3	2-Cyclooctyl- (130 pts.), 4-cyclooctyl- (some)	364

Table continued

TABLE 41 (continued)

Phenol (Moles)	Olefin (Moles)	Catalyst (Moles)	Temp. (°C)	Time (hrs.)	Phenol derivatives (% Yield)	Ref.
186 g.	Pinene (227 g.)	H_2SO_4–HOAc (5 g./10 g.)	—	—	"Pinenephenol"	430
186 g.	Indene (235 g.)	H_2SO_4–HOAc (5 g./15 cc.)	—	—	"Indenephenol"	430
1 kg.	Camphene (715 g.)	BF_3 (72 g.)–HOAc	40, 80, 100	1, 2, 3	Isobornylphenols (60–65%) (o/p = 3.5/1)	377
50 pts.	Carvomenthene (50 pts.)	HF (12 pts.) (cyclo-hexane 50 pts.)	0–10	3	Solid resin (64 pts.); terpene-substituted phenol (64%); terpene phenyl ether (36%)	667
0.75	Pinene (0.15)	HCl	80	5	Addition product (86%)	721
28 g.	Dihydronaphthalene (40 g.)	H_2SO_4–HOAc (40 cc. ea.)	r.t.	24	Tetrahydronaphthyl- (70%)	392
40 g.	Octalin (9 g.)	Conc. HCl 4 g.	w.b.	5	Decalylphenol (70%)	721
6.3	1-Phenylcyclohexene (10.3 g.)	$AlCl_3$ (0.9 g.)	r.t. 50	72 4	1-p-Hydroxyphenyl-1-phenylcyclohexane	954
—	1-Benzylcyclohexene (5 g.)	$AlCl_3$	r.t. 50	24 4	1-p-Hydroxyphenyl-1-benzylcyclohexane	954
0.1	4-t-Octylcyclohexene-1 (0.1)	H_2SO_4 (2 cc.)	60 r.t.	16–20	4-(1',1',3',3'-Tetramethylbutyl)-1-p-hydroxyphenylcyclohexane[a] (1.6 g.)	558
—	Cyclohexene	Conc. HCl	w.b.	5	4-Cyclohexyl- (5%); ether (7.5%)	721

[a] No proof of structure given.

TABLE 42. Cresols with olefins

Cresol (Moles)	Olefin (Moles)	Catalyst (Moles)	Temp. (°C)	Time (hrs.)	Products (% Yield)	Ref.
Cresol (100 g.)	Ethylene (200 atm.)	3% BF_3–2% HCl	200	2	Oil (200 g.)[d]	283
o-Cresol	Ethylene	98% H_2SO_4 (5%)[r]	140–150	—	No alkylation	487
m-Cresol[t] (54 pts.)	Ethylene	40% fuming H_2SO_4 (50 pts.)	120	8	Ethyl-m-cresols[u]	55
p-Cresol (300 g.)	Ethylene	Al (6 g.)	340–350 100 atm.	—	2-Ethyl-p-cresol; 2,6-diethyl-p-cresol	194
m-Cresol (10 pts.) (100 pts. CCl_4)	Propene (4.4 pts.)	$AlCl_3$–propyl chloride (1/0.4 pts.)	>70	10	3-Methyl-x-isopropylphenol (69%)	450
o-Cresol (10 pts.) (100 pts. CCl_4)	Propene (4.4 pts.)	$AlBr_3$–propyl bromide (1.5/0.4 pts.)	70	10	2-Methyl-x-isopropylphenol (73%)	450
m-Cresol (108 pts.)	Propene (40–42 pts.)	$ZnCl_2$ (20 pts.)– H_2SO_4 (20 pts.)– P_2O_5 (15 pts.) or m-cresolsulfonic acid (15 pts.)	230 30 atm.	15	Thymol[s]	654(718)
o-Cresol	Propene	98% H_2SO_4 (5%)[r]	140–150	—	Isopropylation	487
m-Cresol[t] (54 pts.)	Propene	40% fuming H_2SO_4 (125 pts.)	160	—	Thymol (main product), 1,3,5-triisopropylcresol, and 1,3,4-triisopropylcresol (small amts.)	55[u]
m-Cresol (108 pts.)	Propene (48 pts.)	70% $HClO_4$ (16 pts.)	75	4–5	Light yellow liq. (81.3 pts.) b.p. 91–120°, dark yellow liq. (58.2 pts.) b.p. 120–134°, brown thick liq. (9.5 pts.) residue	159
m-Cresol (60 pts.)	Propene (32 pts.)	100% H_3PO_4 (30 pts.) (2 vol. cyclo-hexane)	120 30 atm.	12	Alkylate containing 5% ethers[g]	323

Table continued

TABLE 42 (continued)

Cresol (Moles)	Olefin (Moles)	Catalyst (Moles)	Temp. (°C)	Time (hrs.)	Products (% Yield)	Ref.
m-Cresol	Propene	Boric acid (1 g.)—oxalic acid (3 g.)	140	few	1-Methyl-3-hydroxy-4-isopropyl-benzene and isomers	883
m-Cresol (3)	Propene (3)	HF (27)	0–20	18	Isopropyl-m-cresols (408 g.)	110(836)
m-Cresol (108 pts.)	Propene (40–42 pts.)	Tonsil (10 pts.)	230 30 atm.	12	Thymol (60%), diisopropyl-m-cresol (5%)	654
m-Cresol (2.3)	Propene (97 g.)	Al (3 g.)[m]	200–230 80–12 atm.	3	3-Methyl-6-isopropylphenol (63%)[n], 3-methyl-2,6-diisopropylphenol (14%)[n]	816
o-Cresol (1)	Propene (1.95)	Mg (2 g.)	340	6	2-Methyl-6-isopropylphenol	194
o-Cresol	Butene	98% H_2SO_4 (5%)[r]	140–150	—	Butylation	487
o-Cresol (10 pts.) (50 pts. CCl_4)	Isobutylene (5.6 pts.)	$AlCl_3$—butyl chloride (1/0.5 pts.)	80	6–8	2-Methyl-x-t-butylphenol (73%)	450
m-Cresol (10 pts.) (100 pts. CCl_4)	Isobutylene (5–6 pts.)	$AlBr_3$—butyl bromide (1.5/0.5 pts.)	80	6	3-Methyl-x-t-butylphenol (74%)	450
o-Cresol (2)	Isobutylene (1)	$FeCl_3$-HCl	90	2–4	p-t-Butyl-o-cresol (92%)	88
m-Cresol (2)	Isobutylene (1)	$FeCl_3$-HCl	90	2–4	o-t-Butyl-m-cresol (78%)	88
o-Cresol (3)	Isobutylene (1)	$POCl_3$ (0.58% of cresol)	58–61	—	6-t-Butyl-o-cresol (60%)	87
o-Cresol (9.43)	Isobutylene (4.16)	H_2SO_4 (0.51 g.)	45–50	0.66	t-Butyl o-tolyl ether (226 g.) (35%), 6-t-butyl-2-methylphenol (151 g.), 4,6-di-t-butyl-2-methylphenol (77.5 g.)	797
o-Cresol (3,488 g.)	Isobutylene (450 g.)	H_2SO_4 (5%)	70–75	2.5	6-t-Butyl-o-cresol (35%),[k] 4-t-butyl-o-cresol (50%)[k]	545(487)
o-Cresol (216 g.) (heptane)	Isobutylene (201./hr.)	H_2SO_4 (6.5 g.)	50	2.5	4-t-Butyl- (6%), 6-t-butyl- (36%), 4,6-di-t-butyl- (24%) derivatives of 2-methylphenol	590a
m-Cresol (3)	Isobutylene (3)	BF_3—H_3PO_4 (50 cc.)	35	—	t-Butylcresol (62%)	28

Aromatic	Alkene	Catalyst	Temp.		Products	Ref.
m-Cresol (2.8)	Isobutylene (2.9)	H_2SO_4 (0.1)	20	0.6–1.3	4-t-Butyl- (33%),[n] dibutyl- (29%) m-cresol	193
m-Cresol (2)	Isobutylene (20 l./hr.)	H_2SO_4 (6.5 g.)	50	3.5	6-t-Butyl-3-methylphenol (73%)	590a

m-Cresol   Isobutylene H_2SO_4 (g.)

6-t-Bu[a]   4,6-di-t-Bu[a]   t-Butyl m-tolyl ether

m-Cresol	Isobutylene	H_2SO_4 (g.)	Temp.	6-t-Bu[a]	4,6-di-t-Bu[a]	t-Butyl m-tolyl ether	Ref.
270 g.	138.1 g.	96% (0.556)	23	64.1 g.	77.3 g.	28.3 g.	794(793)
270	139.9	75% (0.791)	23	42.1	16.0	37.5	
109.6	52.0	60% (0.372)	23	13.8	0.0	75.8	
107.7	49.1	40% (0.646)	23	11.2	0.0	69.6	
270	122.7	96% (0.142)	23	52.7	12.3	150.6	
270	109.7	96% (0.069)	23	26.7	0.0	163.7	
108	35.6	10% (2.35)	23	5.9	0.0	39.3	
108	43.1	10% (2.35)	100	71.3	17.9	0.0	

Aromatic	Alkene	Catalyst	Temp.		Products	Ref.
m-Cresol (1)	Isobutylene (35.6 g.)	10% H_2SO_4 (0.0024)	23	—	t-Butyl m-tolyl ether (80%), 6-t-butyl-3-methylphenol (6 g.)	797
m-Cresol (111 g.)	Isobutylene (41.2 g.)	100% H_2SO_4–glycerine (41.5% H_2SO_4)	23	—	t-Butyl m-tolyl ether (74%), 6-t-butyl-3-methylphenol (21 g.)	797
Cresols (180 g.) (40% p-, 60% m-)	Isobutylene (54 g.)	H_2SO_4 (0.12 g.)	–5	—	Mixed t-butyl ethers of cresols (75%)	797
m-Cresol (1)	Isobutylene (1)	Tetraphosphoric acid	60–66	—	t-Butyl-m-cresol (73%)	802
Cresols (250 g.) m- and p-	Isobutylene (197.5 g.)	H_2SO_4 (12.5 g.)	70	0.83	4-Methyl-2-t-butylphenol (15%),[l] 4-methyl-2,6-di-t-butylphenol (23%)[l] and 3-methyl-4,6-di-t-butylphenol (38%)[l] (total 484 g.)	791(800)
m- and p-Cresols	Isobutylene	Cation exchange resins KU-1 and KU-2	70–80	—	2,6-Di-t-butyl-4-methylphenol (43–46%)	347

Table continued

TABLE 42 (continued)

Cresol (Moles)	Olefin (Moles)	Catalyst (Moles)	Temp. (°C)	Time (hrs.)	Products (% Yield)	Ref.
m- and p-Cresols (1)	Isobutylene (2.5)	Silica–alumina	121 250 psig	1.02 L.H.S.V.	t-Butylcresols (53%) and 14% of di-t-butyl-p-cresol, di-t-butyl-m-cresol and higher boiling products	576
p-Cresol (108 g.)	Isobutylene	H_2SO_4 (2.4 g.)	40	16	2,6-Di-t-butyl-4-methylphenol	363(350, 799,917)
p-Cresol (0.2)	Isobutylene (0.54)	Polystyrene resin sulfonic acid (5 g.)	60	—	2-t-Butyl- (62%), 2,6-di-t-butyl- (26%) derivatives of 4-methylphenol	590a
p-Cresol (178 pts.)	Isobutylene (84 pts.)	Amberlite IR-120 (7 pts.)	50–150	—	4,6-Methyl-t-butylphenol (165.5 pts.)	250
p-Cresol	Isobutylene	Tetraphosphoric acid	40	8.5	2,6-Di-t-butyl-4-methylphenol (46%)	802
m-Cresol	1-Pentene	$ZnCl_2$–Al_2O_3	150	6	No information	749
m-Cresol (20)	1-Pentene (20)	Tin chloride (45 g.)	20–25 / 45–50 / 85–90 / 175–185 3–4 atm.	0.5 / 0.5–1 / 2 / 0.5	Oils, b.p. 146–154°/3.5 mm. (2568 g.), b.p. 143–145°/3.5 mm. (203 g.), b.p. 152–155°/4 mm. (2280 g.), 4-methylbutyl-m-cresol	70
o-Cresol (2950 g.)	Amylene (4096 g.) iso/n = 50/50	H_2SO_4 (25 cc.)[q] $AlCl_3$ (50 g.)	45 / 140	2 / 2	t-Amyl-o-cresol (1997 g.) residue (49 g.)	580
o-Cresol (200 g.)	Amylene (200 g.)	H_2SO_4 (400 cc.) (ether)	−15 to −5	2.5	Isomers of amyl-o-cresols (65 g.)	121(581)
m-Cresol	3-Methyl-1-butene	$ZnCl_2$–Al_2O_3	150 3–4 atm.	6	3-Methyl-6-isoamylphenol[o]	749
m-Cresol	2-Methyl-2-butene	$ZnCl_2$–Al_2O_3	150 3–4 atm.	6	3-Methyl-6-isoamylphenol[o]	749
m-Cresol (27 g.)	Mixed amylenes (17.5 g.)	BF_3–FeF_2 (8 g.)	27–30	2	2-Amyl-5-methylphenol	896(889)
p-Cresol (10 pts.)	Amylene (7.1 pts.)	$AlCl_3$–amyl chloride (1/0.7 pts.)	—	—	4-Methyl-x-t-amylphenol (78%)	450

p-Cresol (1)	Isobutylene (0.2)	H$_2$SO$_4$	81	slow addition	Conv. 22%; 2-t-Bu-^{b} 20%; 2,6-di-t-Bu.^{b} —%	791(800)
	(0.6)				Conv. 63%; 2-t-Bu-^{b} 61%; 2,6-di-t-Bu.^{b} 2%	
	(1.0)				Conv. 91%; 2-t-Bu-^{b} 82%; 2,6-di-t-Bu.^{b} 9%	
	(1.5)				Conv. 88%; 2-t-Bu-^{b} 49%; 2,6-di-t-Bu.^{b} 49%	
	(2.0)				Conv. 100%; 2-t-Bu-^{b} 17%; 2,6-di-t-Bu.^{b} 83%	
p-Cresol (1)	2-Methyl-2-butene (1)	BF$_3$ (1–25 mol. %)	r.t.	2–4	2-t-Amyl-4-methylphenol (high yield)^k	471
p-Cresol (1)	2-Methyl-2-butene (1)	BF$_3$ (50 mol. %)	r.t.	2–4	2-t-Amyl-4-methylphenol (20%), 4-t-C$_4$- and C$_5$-phenols, 2-s-iso-4-alkylphenols and 2,2'-bismethylene-diphenols, isobutane, isopentane, and methylpentane	471
p-Cresol (1)	2-Methyl-2-butene (1) (isopentane)	BF$_3$ (50 mol. %)	r.t.	2–4	2-t-Amyl-4-methylphenol (good yield)^k	471
p-Cresol	Isoamylene	H$_2$SO$_4$	—	—	2,6-Di-t-amyl-p-cresol	350
m-Cresol	Caprylene	H$_3$PO$_4$	—	8–10	Caprylcresol	827
Cresol (1000 cc.)	Hexene (1120 cc.)	H$_2$SO$_4$ (670 cc.)	r.t.	8	Alkylate (293 cc.), aryl alkyl ethers (816 cc.)	89
o-Cresol (108 pts.)	1-Octene (112 pts.)	70% HClO$_4$ (16 pts.)	80–90 / 100	1.5 / 4	s-Octyl-o-cresols (178 pts.)	159
o-Cresol (130 pts.)	Octene (22.4 pts.)	Al(ClO$_4$)$_3$·H$_2$O (5.5 pts.)	90–95	—	4-s-Octyl-o-cresol	267
o-Cresol (2.7)	Diisobutylene (0.45)	FeCl$_3$ (27 × 10^{-4})/ HCl (21.7 × 10^{-3})	115–118	2.3	4-t-Butyl-o-cresol (50 g.)	161
o-Cresol (0.5)	Diisobutylene (0.5)	H$_2$SO$_4$ (0.5)–HOAc	0–10	?	Diisobutyl-o-cresol^l (35%)	551(277, 42,551)
Cresylic acid (300 g.)	Butene dimer (474 g.)	Cresol-SO$_3$H	—	16	Octyl cresols (86%)	199
Cresols	Isooctylene	H$_2$SO$_4$	40–42	—	Isooctyl cresol (63%)	901
Cresylic acid (1)	Diisobutylene (1)	H$_2$SO$_4$ (4.6%)	25–30	5	Mono- and dioctylcresylic acid	42

Table continued

TABLE 42 (*continued*)

Cresol (Moles)	Olefin (Moles)	Catalyst (Moles)	Temp. (°C)	Time (hrs.)	Products (% Yield)	Ref.
o-Cresol (108 pts.)	Diisobutylene (112 pts.)	BF_3 (11 pts.)	30	—	Solid	301
o-Cresol (1)	Diisobutylene (1)	H_2SO_4 (0.3)	40	2	Alkylate	659(660)
m-Cresol (20)	Diisobutylene^c (10)	$AlCl_3$ (75 g.)	10–25 / 20–25 / 45–50 / 85–90 / 175–185	5 / 0.83 / 0.5–1 / 2 / 0.5	Isobutyl m-cresol ether, p-t-butyl-m-cresol, sym-isobutyl-m-cresol (total 78%)	70
m-Cresol (10)	Diisobutylene (5)	$FeCl_3$ (24 g.)	20–25 / 45–50 / 85–90 / 175–185	0.83 / 0.5–1 / 2 / 0.5	Oils b.p. 114–120°/4 mm. (114 g.), b.p. 135–138°/4 mm. (123 g.), b.p. 142–145°/3 mm. (840 g.)	70
m-Cresol (2.7)	Diisobutylene (0.45)	$FeCl_3$ (0.44)–HCl (0.58 g.)	115–120	6.2	6-t-Butyl-m-cresol (55.6 g.)	161
p-Cresol (214 g.)	Diisobutylene (896 g.)	45% BF_3 in ether (21 g.)	10–20	3.5	2,6-Di-(1′,1′,3′,3′-tetramethylbutyl)-4-methylphenol (81 g.); 2-mono-(283 g.); tetraisobutylene (581 g.)	384
p-Cresol (1)	Diisobutylene (1)	94% H_2SO_4 (0.3)	—	—	Diisobutyl-p-cresol^l	277
p-Cresol	Diisobutylene (1)	H_2SO_4 (0.3)	—	—	Alkylate	659
p-Cresol	Diisobutylene	H_2SO_4	—	—	2,6-di-t-octyl-p-cresol	350
o-Cresol (1)	Styrene (1.25) α-methylstyrene (0.75)	Bleaching clay (25 g.)	160–170	8	Alkylate	272a
o-, m-, p-Cresols (1)	Styrene (0.5)	H_2SO_4 (10 g.) (toluene)	reflux	—	α-Phenylethyl derivatives (80–86%)	102(393)
m-Cresol (177 pts.)	Styrene (312 pts.)	p-Toluene-SO_3H (5 pts.)	135–145	2	Aralkylated-m-cresol (93%), 5-methyl-2- (9%), 5-methyl-2,4- (or 2,6-) di- (81%), 3-methyl-2,4,6-tri- (10%)- (1-phenyl-1-ethyl)phenols	369
p-Cresol (177 pts.)	Styrene (312 pts.)	p-Toluene-SO_3H (5 pts.)	135–145	2	Aralkylated-p-cresols (94%), 2- (92%), 2,6-di- (2%) -(1-phenyl-1-ethyl)-p-cresols	369
Cresols	Propene tetramer	H_2SO_4	40–42	—	Dodecylcresol (44%)	901

o-Cresol (2)	α-Methylstyrene (1)	36% aq. HCl (5 g.)	20–40	15.4	4-(α-Phenylisopropyl)-o-cresol (129 g.)	604
o-Cresol (1)	1-Phenyl-1-propene (1)	H₂SO₄–HOAc (1)/400 g.	reflux	4	1-Phenyl-2-(4'-hydroxy-3'-methyl-phenyl)-propane	557
m-Cresol (2)	α-Methylstyrene (1)	36% aq. HCl (5 g.)	20–40	15.4	4-(α-Phenylisopropyl)-m-cresol (81%)	604
m-Cresol (177 pts.)	α-Methylstyrene (354 pts.)	p-Toluene-SO₃H (5 pts.)	135–145	2	2- (74%),[p] 2,4-di- (26%),[p] tri- (0.5%)[p] (α-Phenylisopropyl)-5-methyl-phenol	369
p-Cresol (2)	α-Methylstyrene (1)	36% aq. HCl (5 g.)	20–40	15.4	2-(α-Phenylisopropyl)-p-cresol (67%)	604
p-Cresol (177 pts.)	α-Methylstyrene (354 pts.)	p-Toluene-SO₃H (5 pts.)	135–145	2	2- (56%),[p] 2,6-di- (42%),[p] 2,3,6- (or 2,5,6-) tri- (3%),[p] (α-Phenyliso-propyl)-p-cresols	369
m-Cresol (192 g.)	Anethole (133 g.) (toluene)	H₂SO₄ (18 g.)	reflux	2	(α-Anisyl-n-propyl)-m-cresol (147 g.)	102a
p-Cresol (192 g.)	Anethole (133 g.) (toluene)	H₂SO₄ (18 g.)	reflux	2	(α-Anisyl-n-propyl)-p-cresol (67%)	102a
p-Cresol	Decene	ZnO–HCl	145	3	Decylocresol	401
m-Cresol (20)	2,6-Dimethyl-4-octene (20)	AlCl₃ (70 g.)	20–25 45–50 85–90 175–185	0.5 0.5–1 2 0.5	sym-Isoamyl-m-cresol[e] (2281 g.)	70
o-Cresol (130 pts.)	Dodecene (33.6 pts.)	Al(ClO₄)₃·H₂O[f]	90–95	—	4-s-Dodecyl-o-cresol (exc. yield)	267
o-Cresol (545 pts.)	Isohexyl-isoheptyl dimer (980 pts.)	BF₃ (30 pts.)	25–30	—	Tetradecyl-o-cresol (97%)	300

a Derivative of 3-methylphenol.
b Derivative of 4-methylphenol.
c Mixture of 2,4-dimethyl-3-hexene, 2,4,4-trimethyl-1-pentene and 2,4,4-trimethyl-2-pentene.
d 80% cresol ethers alkylated in nucleus and cresols alkylated in nucleus.
e Also prepared via m-cresol plus isoamylalcohol plus ZnCl₂.
f 43% H₂O; can use iron or lead perchlorates.
g 60% ethers if cyclohexane is omitted.
h Reduction in hydride transfer products.
i Probably 1,1,3,3-tetramethylbutyl derivative.
j 120 hours at r.t. and one hour on w.b.

k Based on converted o-cresol.
l Of product.
m As phenoxide.
n Structure not proven.
o Probably s-isoamyl- (reviewers' note).
p Per cent of alkylate.
q Neutralize and depentanize before using AlCl₃.
r Of cresol.
s Good yield.
t Substrate is actually cresolsulfonic acid.
u Product after hydrolysis.

TABLE 43. Cresols with cyclic olefins

Cresol (Moles)	Cycloolefin (Moles)	Catalyst (Moles)	Temp. (°C)	Time (hrs.)	Products (Yield)	Ref.
o-Cresol (1.5)	Cyclohexene (0.5)	AlCl₃ (22 g.)	w.b.	1.49	Alkylate (64%), ether (0%)	439
o-Cresol (1.5)	Cyclohexene (0.5)	AlCl₃ (22 g.) (100 cc. CS₂)	0	2	Alkylate (13%), 4-cyclohexyl-(30 pts.), 6-cyclohexyl-2-methyl-phenol (70 pts.), ether (17%)	439
o-Cresol (0.5)	Cyclohexene (1)	BF₃ (3.7 g.)	80	1	4,6-Dicyclohexyl derivative (64%)	590a
o-Cresol (4)	Cyclohexene (1.5)	BF₃ (8.6 g.)	80–85	1	6- (42%), 4-cyclohexyl deriva-tives (26%)	590a
o-Cresol (1.5)	Cyclohexene (0.5)	BF₃ (3–4 g.)	30/65/150	—	Cyclohexyl ether of o-cresol (37/25(trace) cyclohexyl-o-cresol (21/30/54%)ᵇ	434
m-Cresol (1.5)	Cyclohexene (0.5)	AlCl₃ (22 g.) (100 cc. CS₂)	0	2	Alkylate (12%) (mixture of iso-mers), ether (21%)	439
m-Cresol (1.5)	Cyclohexene (0.5)	AlCl₃ (22 g.) (100 cc. CS₂)	w.b.	0.7–0.8	Alkylate (44%) (mixture of iso-mers), ether (0%)	439
p-Cresol (1.5)	Cyclohexene (0.5)	AlCl₃ (22 g.)	w.b.	0.7–0.8	Alkylate (59%), ether (0%)	439
p-Cresol (1.5)	Cyclohexene (0.5)	AlCl₃ (22 g.) (100 cc. CS₂)	0	2	Alkylate (13%), 2-cyclohexyl 4-methylphenol; ether (23%)	439
p-Cresol (1.5)	Cyclohexene (0.5)	BF₃ (3–4 g.)	30/54/150	—	Cyclohexyl ether of p-cresol (6%/43%/(trace), cyclohexyl p-cresol (3, 8, 47%)ᵇ	434(438, 590)
p-Cresol (3.69)	Cyclohexene (1.23)	BF₃ (11.3 g.)	80	1	2-Cyclohexyl- (67%), 2,6-di-cyclohexyl derivatives (5%)	590a
p-Cresol (35.6 pts.)	Cyclohexene (25.2 pts.)	Amberlite IR-120ᶜ (3 pts.)	50–150	—	4-Methyl-2-cyclohexylphenol (7.8 pts.)	250
p-Cresol (35.6 pts.)	1-Methylcyclohexene (29.4 pts.)	Zeokarb 215ᵃ (3) or Amberlite IR-105ᶜ	90	16	2-(α-Methylcyclohexyl-4-methyl-phenol)	250
o-Cresol (270 g.)	Camphene (136 g.)	34% BF₃–HOAc (6.2 g.)	25, 40, 80, 95-100ᵉ	2,1, 2,4ᵉ	2-Methyl-4- (and 6-)ᵈ -isobornyl-phenol	378
Cresol (110 pts.)ᶠ	Dihydroterpene (105 pts.)	BF₃ (7.5 pts.)	10–20, 20–30	—	Viscous liquid, mol. wt. 227	668

ᵃ Nuclear sulfonated phenol resin.   ᵇ Yield at each temperature.   ᶜ Cationic exchange resin.
ᵈ 4-/6- = 1/1.9.   ᵉ Consecutive levels of temperature and time at each level.   ᶠ 55 pts. benzene.

TABLE 44. Higher phenol homologs with olefins

Aromatic (Moles)	Olefin (Moles)	Catalyst (Moles)	Temp. (°C)	Time (hrs.)	Products (%Yield)	Ref.
2-Ethylphenol (2.88)	1-Butene (200-500 psi)	Al (4 g.)	215	3	2-Ethyl-6-s-butylphenol (58%)	397
2,3-Dimethylphenol (0.25)	Isobutylene (20 g.)	H_2SO_4 (1.5 g.)	50	—	6-t-Butyl- (55%), 4,6-di-t-butyl derivatives (27%)	590b
3,4-Dimethylphenol (0.25)	Isobutylene (20 g.)	H_2SO_4 (1.5 g.)	50	—	6-t-Butyl derivative (79%)	590b
2,5-Dimethylphenol (0.2)	Isobutylene (10 l.)	H_2SO_4 (1.2 g.)	50	—	4-t-Butyl derivative	590b
2,4-Dimethylphenol (0.3)	Isobutylene (0.37)	Polystyrene resin sulfonic acid (5 g.)	—	—	6-t-Butyl derivative (49%)[b]	590b
2,4-Dimethylphenol (0.8)	Cyclohexene (0.4)	BF_3 (6.6 g.)	57, 140-150	—, 1.5	6-Cyclohexyl derivative (50 g.)	590a(590)
2,5-Dimethylphenol (2)	Diisobutylene (2.14)	H_2SO_4 (0.19)	5-r.t.	24	98.4% Aromatic recovered unchanged	654a
2,4- and 2,5-Dimethylphenol (2)	Diisobutylene (2.14)	H_2SO_4 (0.19)	5-r.t.	24	Octylated-2,4-dimethylphenol (235 g.). Recovered 2,5-dimethylphenol (95 g.)	654a
2,4- and 2,5-Dimethylphenol (3)	Diisobutylene (3.21)	Benzene-SO_3H (0.275)	—	—	2,4-Isomer is alkylated; 2,5-isomer is not	654a
2,4-Dimethylphenol (244 g.)	Camphene (272 g.)	70% Benzene-SO_3H (8 g.) (300 ml. toluene)	130	9.5	6-Isobornyl derivative (35%) 89%[c]	384
2,4-Dimethylphenol (632 g.)	l-Nopinene[d] (816 g.)	BF_3–Et_2O (7 ml.)	140	2	6-Isobornyl derivative (30%) 66%[c]	384
2-Methyl-5-ethylphenol	Isobutylene	ZnO–HCl	145	3	2-Methyl-4-t-butyl-5-ethylphenol	401
Mixed isopropylphenols (7306 g.)	Isobutylene (2458 g.)	60% H_2SO_4 (21.5 g.)	25	9.5	t-Butyl ethers of isopropylphenols (588 g.)	797
2,3,4-Trimethylphenol	Propene tetramer	ZnO–HCl	145	3	2,3,4-Trimethyl-6-dodecylphenol	401

Table continued

TABLE 44 (continued)

Aromatic (Moles)	Olefin (Moles)	Catalyst (Moles)	Temp. (°C)	Time (hrs.)	Products (% Yield)	Ref.
4-t-Butylphenol (1)	Isobutylene (1.3)	H_2SO_4 (0.15 g.)	100	4	t-Butyl ether of t-butylphenol (44%) (70.5 g.), 2,4-di-t-butyl-phenol (34.5 g.), high boilers (26.5 g.)[a]	797
2-t-Butylphenol (3)	Isobutylene (1) Hexane (4)	Silica-alumina	94 500 psig	5 S.V.	2,4-Di-t-butylphenol	22
4-Butylphenol (9.2 g.)	Isobutylene (6.9 g.)	H_2SO_4 (0.25 cc.)	—	—	4-Butyl-2,6-di-t-butylpheno (68%)	927
Thymol	Amylene	H_2SO_4–HOAc	25	—	4-t-Amyl-2-isopropyl-5-methyl-phenol (50%)	393
Carvacrol (1)	Cyclohexene (0.5)	$AlCl_3$ (0.15)	25	3	Carvacryl cyclohexyl ether (15%), cyclohexyl carvacrol (20%), cyclohexyl chloride (10 g.)	66
Thymol (1) (100 ml. toluene)	Styrene (0.5)	H_2SO_4 (10 g.)	reflux	6	3-Methyl-4-(α-phenylethyl)-6-isopropylphenol (75%)	102(393)
Thymol (160 g.)	Anethole (74 g.) (toluene)	H_2SO_4	reflux	2	p-(α-Anisyl-n-propyl)thymol (66%)	102a
6-t-Butyl-3-methyl-phenol (0.4)	Isobutylene (30 l.)	H_2SO_4	50	—	4,6-Di-t-butyl-3-methylphenol (26%)	590a
2-Phenylphenol (3)	Isobutylene (1)	$POCl_3$ (0.6%)[b]	70–78	—	2-t-Butyl-6-phenylphenol (45%), 4-t-butyl-2-phenylphenol (36%)	87
4-Hydroxydiphenyl (30 pts.)	Isobutylene (80 pts.)	H_2SO_4–$(NH_4)_2SO_4$ (1.5 pts.)	150 200 psi	—	2,6-Di-t-butyl-4-phenylphenol (52 pts.)	798, 801a
4-Phenylphenol (170 g.) (750 g. 3,5-dimethyl-phenol)	Isobutylene (130 g.)	20% Oleum (17 g.)	80	—	2-t-Butyl-4-phenylphenol (53%)	646
4-Phenylphenol (170 g.)	Isobutylene (232 g.)	20% Oleum (17 g.)	80	—	2- (40%), 2,4'-Di- (25%)-t-butyl-4-phenylphenol	646, 801a

2-Phenylphenol (10)	Diisobutylene (3)	AlCl$_3$ (0.5)	145–150	3	4-t-Butyl (903 g.), 2,4-di-t-butyl-, and t-octyl-6-phenylphenol (251 g.)	76
2-Phenylphenol (1.62)	Diisobutylene (0.27)	FeCl$_3$ (24 × 10^{-4})–HCl (24 × 10^{-3})	115–120	1.25	4-t-Butyl-2-phenylphenol (64 g.)	161(88)
3-Phenylphenol (3)	Diisobutylene (0.5)	FeCl$_3$ (0.77)–HCl (1.02 g.)	116–120	1.3	Mono-x-t-butyl-3-phenylphenol (50%)	161
2-Phenylphenol (2)	α-Methylstyrene (1)	Conc. HCl (1 ml.)	140–170	0.7	5-(α-Phenylisopropyl)-2-hydroxy-biphenyl	605
3-Phenylphenol (2)	α-Methylstyrene (1)	Conc. HCl (1 ml.)	140–170	0.7	6-(α-Phenylisopropyl)-3-hydroxy-biphenyl (70 g.)	605
2-t-Amyl-4-cresol (1)	Isobutylene (1–2)	H$_2$SO$_4$–boric acid	10–20	—	2-t-Butyl-4-methyl-6-t-amylphenol	803
2-Cyclohexylphenol	Isobutylene	Al	120	—	2-t-Butyl-6-cyclohexylphenol	816
2-Cyclohexylphenol (500 pts.)	Isobutylene	H$_2$SO$_4$ (25 pts.)	70	—	4,6-Di-t-butyl-2-cyclohexylphenol	798
4-Cyclohexylphenol (500 pts.)	Isobutylene	H$_2$SO$_4$ (25 pts.)	70	—	2,6-Di-t-butyl-4-cyclohexylphenol	798
2-Cyclohexylphenol (500 pts.)	2-Methyl-2-butene	H$_2$SO$_4$ (25 pts.)	70	—	4,6-Di-t-amyl-2-cyclohexylphenol	798
4-Cyclohexylphenol (500 pts.)	2-Methyl-2-butene	H$_2$SO$_4$ (25 pts.)	70	—	2,6-Di-t-amyl-4-cyclohexylphenol	798
4-Benzylphenol (1)	Isobutylene (2)	H$_2$SO$_4$–boric acid	60–80	—	2,6-Di-t-butyl-4-benzylphenol	803
2-Cyclohexyl-4-methyl-phenol (15.5 g.)	Isobutylene	H$_2$SO$_4$ (0.8 g.)	40–50	—	2-t-Butyl-4-methyl-6-cyclohexyl-phenol (60–70%)	590
2-Cyclohexyl-4-methyl-phenol (19 g.)	2-Methyl-2-butene	H$_2$SO$_4$ (1 g.)	70	—	2-t-Amyl-4-methyl-6-cyclohexyl-phenol (30–40%)	590
Nonylphenol (0.35)	Isobutylene (44 g.)	H$_2$SO$_4$ (0.09 g.)	3–5	1.5	t-Butyl ether of nonylphenol (51%)	797
2-t-Butyl-p-phenyl-phenol (113 g.)	Isobutylene (120 g.)	20% Oleum (5.7 g.)	120	—	2,4'-Di-t-butyl-p-phenylphenol (81 g.), 2,6,4'-tri-t-butyl-p-phenylphenol (65 g.)	646

[a] "Probably 2,4,6-tri-t-butylphenol."
[b] Based on phenolic feed.
[c] Based on phenolic consumed.
[d] No alkylate obtained using dipentene, BF$_3$–Et$_2$O at 60–82°.

TABLE 45. Indanols and naphthols with olefins

Aromatic (Moles)	Olefin (Moles)	Catalyst (Moles)	Temp. (°C)	Time (hrs.)	Products (% Yield)	Ref.
5-Indanol (67 g.)	Isobutylene (theor. amt.)	p-Toluene-SO₃H	—	—	6-t-Butyl-5-indanol (73%)	154
4-Indanol (100 ml. benzene)	Isobutylene	Retrol acid-activated clay	55–80	3.5	5-t-(15.9 g.), 5,7-di-t- (43.9 g.) butyl-4-indanol	533
5-Indanol (2) (400 ml. benzene)	Isobutylene	Retrol acid-activated clay	55–80	3.5	6-t-Butyl-5-indanol (87%)	533
5-Indanol (134 g.)	Diisobutylene (114 g.)	HOAc–H₂SO₄ 250 g./5 g.	70 / 70–90	2 / 9	6-Octyl-5-indanol (99 g.)	533
5-Indanol (134 g.) (200 ml. benzene)	Styrene	Retrol acid-activated clay (20 g.)	50	0.75	6-α-Methylbenzyl-5-indanol (132.5 g.)	533
2-Naphthol (300 g.)	Ethylene	Zn (6 g.)	340–350	—	1-Ethyl-2-naphthol	194
1-Naphthol (3.48)	Propene (600–700 psi)	Al (2.25 g.)ᵇ	300–310	3	2-Isopropyl-1-naphthol (54%), high boilers (51 g.)	397
2-Naphthol (10 pts.) (100 pts. CCl₄)	Isobutylene (4.4 pts.)	AlCl₃–C₄H₉Cl (1/0.4 pts.)	80	8	t-Butyl-2-naphthol (50%)	450
1-Naphthol	3-Hexene	—	—	—	8-Hexyl-α-naphthol (45–57%)	779
2-Naphthol	3-Hexene	—	r.t.	16	8-Hexyl-β-naphthol (45–57%)	779
2-Naphthol (288 pts.)	Isohexyl-isoheptyl dimer (392 pts.)	BF₃ (32 pts.)–HOAc (900 pt.) 40 pts. BF₃ added	85–90	6	b.p. 210–244°/3 mm.; some tetradecyl-acetyl-2-naphthol	300
2-Naphthol (1)	Diisobutylene (1)	94% H₂SO₄ (0.15)	70–78	0.16	Diisobutylnaphthol	659(4)
2-Naphthol	Styrene	H₂SO₄–HOAc	25	—	2-Hydroxy-1-(α-phenylethyl)-naphthalene	393
1-Naphthol (288 g.) (250 ml. toluene)	Styrene (104 g.)	H₂SO₄ (30 g.)	reflux	3	6-(α-Phenylethyl)-1-naphthol (90%)	102
2-Naphthol (288 g.) (250 ml. toluene)	Styrene (104 g.)	H₂SO₄ (30 g.)	reflux	3	6-(α-Phenylethyl)-2-naphthol (92%)	102
2-Naphthol (216 pts.)	Styrene (312 pts.)	p-Toluene-SO₃H (5 pts.)	135–145	2	Aralkylated naphthol (89%), 1-(17%), di-(84%), (α-phenylethyl)-2-naphthols	369

Aromatic	Olefin	Catalyst	Temp.	Time	Products (% Yield)	Ref.
2-Naphthol (216 pts.)	α-Methylstyrene (354 pts.)	p-Toluene-SO$_3$H (5 pts.)	135–145		1-(73%), Di-(27%)[a]-(α-Phenyl-isopropyl)-2-naphthols	369
2-Naphthol (2)	α-Methylstyrene (1)	Conc. HCl (1 ml.)	140–170	0.7	6-(α-Phenylisopropyl)-2-naphthol	605
2-Naphthol (144 pts.), decalin	5-(Methylcyclohexyl)-1-methylcyclohexene (96 pts.)	60% HClO$_4$ (25 pts.)	60–70 100	4	Resin	159
1-Naphthol (202 g.)	Anethole (104 g.) (toluene)	H$_2$SO$_4$	reflux	2	(α-Anisyl-n-propyl)-1-naphthol (57%)	102a
2-Naphthol (202 g.)	Anethole (104 g.) (toluene)	H$_2$SO$_4$	reflux	2	(α-Anisyl-n-propyl)-2-naphthol (61%)	102a

[a] Components in product.   [b] As isopropoxide.

TABLE 46. Halogenated phenols and nitrophenols with olefins

Aromatic (Moles)	Olefin (Moles)	Catalyst (Moles)	Temp. (°C)	Time (hrs.)	Products (% Yield)	Ref.
2-Bromophenol (3)	Propene (1)	BF$_3$–H$_3$PO$_4$ (0.2)	30	6.5	Isopropyl ether of 2-bromophenol (33%), 4-isopropyl-2-bromophenol (8%)	414
2-Bromophenol (2)	Propene (1)	BF$_3$–H$_3$PO$_4$ (0.2)	30	4	Isopropyl ether of 2-bromophenol (10%), 4-isopropyl-2-bromophenol	414
4-Bromophenol (2)	Propene (1)	BF$_3$–H$_3$PO$_4$ (0.2)	30 r.t.	4, 12	Isopropyl-4-isopropoxybromobenzene (14%), p-isopropoxybromobenzene (48%)	943
2-Chlorophenol (2.34)	Propene (100)	Al (3 g.)[b]	165–200 55–2 atm.	2	2-Isopropyl-6-chlorophenol	816
3-Chlorophenol (2.34)	Propene (100)	Al (3 g.)[b]	165–200 55 atm.	2	6-Isopropyl-3-chlorophenol	816
4-Chlorophenol (2.34)	Propene (100)	Al (3 g.)[b]	165–200 55 atm.	2	2-Isopropyl-4-chlorophenol, isopropyl ether of p-chlorophenol (12%)	816
4-Chlorophenol (3)	Propene	Al(OC$_6$H$_4$Cl)$_3$– (Toluene 100 cc.)	160–170 600 psig	2.5	2,6-Diisopropyl-4-chlorophenol	397

Table continued

TABLE 46 (continued)

Aromatic (Moles)	Olefin (Moles)	Catalyst (Moles)	Temp. (°C)	Time (hrs.)	Products (% Yield)	Ref.
4-Fluorophenol (5)	Propene (1)	BF_3–Et_2O	60	4	Only ethers	842
4-Fluorophenol (3)	Propene (1)	BF_3–H_3PO_4 (0.2)	60	4	3-Isopropyl-4-fluorophenol (6, 38%)[a] its isopropyl ether (33, 33%)[a]	842
			70	4	isopropyl ether of feed (52, 5%)[a]	
2-Nitrophenol[d] (70 pts.)	Propene (14 pts.)	100% H_2SO_4 (70 pts.)	100	—	Isopropyl-o-nitrophenol (17 pts.)[e]	55
2-Bromophenol	2-Butene	BF_3–ether	—	—	s-Butyl ether[c] (50%)	942
2-Bromophenol (16.7 g.)	2-Butene	BF_3–H_3PO_4 (3.1 g.)	30	7	s-Butyl ether[c] (12%)	942
4-Bromophenol	2-Butene	BF_3–ether	—	—	s-Butyl ether[c] (40%)	942
4-Bromophenol	2-Butene	BF_3–H_3PO_4	—	—	s-Butyl ether[c] (30–40%)	942
4-Bromophenol (0.5) (200 cc. benzene)	Isobutylene (2)	98% H_2SO_4 (4 cc.)	65	10	2,6-t-Butyl-4-bromophenol (35.6%), t-butyl-p-bromophenol (20%)	262(804)
4-Bromophenol (200 cc. p-xylene)	Isobutylene (2)	98% H_2SO_4 (4 cc.)	65	10	2,6-t-Butyl-4-bromophenol (47%), t-butyl-p-bromophenol (20%)	262
4-Bromophenol (121 g.)	Isobutylene (1)	H_2SO_4 (4 cc.)	60–70	5	4-Bromo-2-t-butylphenol (74%)	261
2-Chlorophenol (2)	Isobutylene (1)	$FeCl_3$–HCl	90	2–4	4-t-Butyl-2-chlorophenol (87%)	88
2-Chlorophenol (3)	Isobutylene (1)	$POCl_3$ (5%)	71–78	—	2-t-Butyl-6-chlorophenol (21%), 4-t-butyl-6-chlorophenol (32%)	87
2-Chlorophenol (5)	Isobutylene	Al (4.5 g.)	80–90	—	2-t-Butyl-6-chlorophenol (60%)	397
4-Nitrophenol (0.107)	Isobutylene (0.33)	90% H_3PO_4 (17.5 g.)	100	4	2-t-Butyl-4-nitrophenol (15%)	332
2-Bromophenol (69.4 g.)	1-Pentene (14 g.)	BF_3–Et_2O (8.9 g.)	15	71	s-Amyl ether of 2-bromophenol (43%) 4-s-amyl-2-bromophenol (18%)	414
2-Bromophenol (51.9 g.)	1-Pentene (7 g.)	BF_3–H_3PO_4 (4.1 g.)	40	3	4-s-Amyl-2-bromophenol (42%), s-amyl ether of 2-bromophenol (10%)	414

Aromatic	Alkene/Alkane	Catalyst	Temp.	Time	Products	Ref.
2-Bromophenol (4)	2-Pentene (1)	BF_3–Et_2O (0.2)	14–23 r.t.	10 / 38	4-s-Amyl-2-bromophenol (23%), s-amyl ether of 2-bromophenol (26%)	414
2-Bromophenol (4)	2-Pentene (1)	BF_3–H_3PO_4 (0.2)	14–23 r.t.	10 / 38	4-s-Amyl-2-bromophenol (17%), s-amyl ether of 2-bromophenol (23%)	414
4-Bromophenol (4)	2-Pentene (1)	BF_3–H_3PO_4 (0.2)	21	48	s-Amyl ether of 4-bromophenol (75%)	943
2-Chlorophenol (3)	1-Pentene (1)	BF_3–H_3PO_4 (0.1)	40	2	4-s-Amyl-2-chlorophenol (80–85%)	412
4-Chlorophenol (4)	1-Pentene (1)	BF_3–H_3PO_4 (0.2)	40	2	2-s-Amyl-4-chlorophenol (47–54%)	412
2-Chlorophenol (12.7 g.)	2-Pentene (6.4 g.)	BF_3–Et_2O (1.06 g.)	r.t.	120	Ether products (32%); alkylated product (8%)	936
2-Chlorophenol (12.7 g.)	2-Pentene (6.4 g.)	BF_3–Et_2O (1.06 g.)	95	4–16	Ether products (27–35%); alkylated product (12–27%)	936
4-Chlorophenol (257 g.)	Diisobutylene (336 g.)	$SnCl_4$ (50 g.)	60–65	2	2-t-Octyl-4-chlorophenol	5
4-Chlorophenol (1)	Diisobutylene (3)	BF_3–Et_2O (20 g.)	60–70	2	2-t-Octyl- and 2,6-di-t-octyl-4-chlorophenols	5
2-Chlorophenol (2.4)	Diisobutylene (0.4)	$FeCl_3$ (2.8×10^{-4})–HCl (1.6×10^{-3})	115–120	2.25	2-Chloro-4-t-butylphenol (11.5 g.)	161
2-Chlorophenol (2)	α-Methylstyrene (1)	36% aq. HCl (0.5 ml.)	145–165	3–4	4-(α-Phenylisopropyl)-2-chlorophenol (93%)	604
Chlorophenol	Diisoamylene	H_2SO_4–HOAc	0–10	—	Diisoamylchlorophenol	551
4-Chlorophenol (128.5 pts.) (250 pts. decalin)	Dodecene (84 pts.)	70% $HClO_4$ (20 pts.)	60 / 90–95	5	s-Dodecyl-4-chlorophenol (70%)	159
4-Chloro-3-methyl phenol (1)	Propene (1)	20% Tonsil activated clay	140–160 5–20 atm.	—	4-Chloro-3-methyl-6-isopropylphenol	719
4-Bromo-2-methyl-phenol (0.5) (30 ml. benzene)	Isobutylene (52.5 g.)	H_2SO_4 (6 g.)	65	—	6-t-Butyl derivative (42%)	590a
2-Methyl-4-bromo-phenol (140 g.) (200 cc. benzene)	Isobutylene	H_2SO_4 (5 cc.)	—	—	2-Methyl-4-bromo-6-t-butylphenol (70%)	263

a At resp. temperatures.   b As phenoxide.   c Of the bromophenol.   d As sulfonic acid.   e After hydrolysis.

TABLE 47. Halogenated phenols and nitrophenols with cycloolefins

Aromatic (Moles)	Cycloolefin (Moles)	Catalyst (Moles)	Temp. (°C)	Time (hrs.)	Products (% Yield)	Ref.
2-Bromophenol	Cyclohexene	BF_3–Et_2O	—	—	Cyclohexyl ether[b] (37%)	942
2-Bromophenol	Cyclohexene	H_3PO_4–BF_3	25	24	Cyclohexyl ether[b] (36%)	942
4-Bromophenol	Cyclohexene	BF_3–Et_2O	—	—	Cyclohexyl ether[b] (57–64%)	942
4-Bromophenol	Cyclohexene	BF_3–H_3PO_4	—	—	Cyclohexyl ether[b] (49–59%)	942
2-Chlorophenol (0.33)	Cyclohexene (1)	BF_3 (5 g.)	30–35	—	Cyclohexyl chlorophenol (57%)	438
2-Chlorophenol (12.07 g.)	Cyclohexene (16.45 g.)	BF_3–Et_2O (0.91 g.)	16–20	360	Cyclohexyl ether (16.2 g.)	932
2-Chlorophenol (12.18 g.)	Cyclohexene (14.88 g.)	BF_3–Et_2O (0.91 g.)	w.b.	8	Cyclohexyl ether (9.2 g.)[a]	932
4-Fluorophenol (3)	Cyclohexene (1)	BF_3–H_3PO_4 (0.2)	40	3	4-Fluorophenyl cyclohexyl ether (71%)	842
2-Nitrophenol	Cyclohexene	BF_3	100	—	No alkylation	866a
4-Nitrophenol	Cyclohexene	BF_3	100	—	2-Cyclohexyl derivative (5%)	866a
2-, 3-, or 4-Nitrophenol	Cyclohexene	BF_3–Et_2O	100	—	No alkylation	866a

[a] No change when heated 8 hours at 120–140° with 25% catalyst.   [b] Of the bromophenol.

TABLE 48. Anisole with olefins

Anisole (Moles)	Olefin (Moles)	Catalyst (Moles)	Temp. (°C)	Time (hrs.)	Products (% Yield)	Ref.
1–2	Ethylene (1)	85% H_2SO_4 (200%)[a]	18	0.33–0.5	No alkylate	486
1	Propene (1)	85% H_2SO_4 (200%)[a]	18	0.33–0.5	Isopropyl- (54%), polyisopropylanisole (5%)	486
350 pts.	Propene (150 pts.)	Nickel molybdite (10 pts.)	150	5	p-Isopropyl- (52 pts.), diisopropylanisole (5.5 pts.)	198
27.2 g.	2-Butene (17 g.)	BF_3 (10.8 g.)	r.t.	1.5	s-Butylanisoles (83%) (o- 46%, p- 27%, 2,4-di-)	941(933)

Anisole	Olefin	Catalyst	Temp. (°C)	Time (hr.)	Products	Ref.
27.2 g.	2-Butene (17 g.)	BF_3–H_3PO_4 (6.5/9.4)	r.t.	4	s-Butylanisole (74%)	941(940, 933)
1.2	n-Butene (1)	BF_3–Et_2O (10.8 g.)	r.t.	1.5	s-Butylanisole (82%)	940(933)
1–2	n-Butene (1)	85% H_2SO_4 (200%)[a]	18	2 l./hr.	s-Butyl- (64%), poly-s-butylanisole (2%)	486
108 g.	Isobutylene (1)	$AlCl_3$ (7 g.)	5–8	—	t-Butylanisole (48%)	456
1–2	Isobutylene (1)	85% H_2SO_4 (200%)[a]	18	0.33–0.5	t-Butyl- (71%), poly-t-butylanisole (4%)	486
0.3	Isobutylene (0.4)	KU-2 cation exchange resin (6.5 g.)	130	3	4-t-Butylanisole (57%)	348
5.4 g.	2-Pentene (3.5 g.)	BF_3–Et_2O (0.5)	96	4	4-s-Amylanisole (10%)	933(949)
27 g.	2-Pentene (35 g.)	BF_3 (5.2 g.)–H_3PO_4 (9.5 g.)	20	1.5	4- (49%), 2- (10%), Di- (4%)-s-amyl-anisoles	949(933)
0.32	Isoamylene (0.4)	20% $ZnCl_2$–80% $AlCl_3$	r.t.	14	4-t-Amyl/2,4-di-t-amylanisole = 51/8%	899
0.2	2-Methyl-2-butene	$TiCl_4$ (0.2)	200	6	p-t-Amylanisole (61–67%)	147
0.3	2-Methyl-2-butene (0.4)	KU.1 cation exchange resin (12.8 g.)	0–60	1	4-t-Amylanisole (14%)	899
70 cc.	Cyclopentene (15 g.)	$AlCl_3$ (2 g.)	95–100	6–8	4-Cyclopentyl-, 2-cyclopentyl- (small amount), and dicyclopentylanisole	109
1.5	Cyclohexene (0.5)	$AlCl_3$ (0.25)	0	0.16	o- and p-Cyclohexylanisole (50%, 3:1)	66
70 cc.	Cyclopentene (15 g.)	$AlCl_3$ (2 g.)	25	3	4-Cyclopentyl-, 2-cyclopentyl- (small amount), and dicyclopentylanisole	109
1.5	Cyclohexene (0.5)	$AlCl_3$ (0.25)	0	0.16	o- and p-Cyclohexylanisole (50%, 3:1)	66
1.5	Cyclohexene (0.5)	BF_3 (6 g.)	25	3	Cyclohexylanisole (56 g.) (46% p-, 54% o-)	434
1	Diisobutylene	H_2SO_4 (18 g.)	r.t.	24	Octylanisole	660
5	Styrene (1)	BF_3–H_3PO_4 (0.3) or BF_3–Et_2O (0.3)	60	1.75	4-Methoxydiphenylmethylmethane (88%)	935
—	Propene tetramer	$AlCl_3$	—	—	Dodecylanisole (47%)	49
5	α-Methylstyrene (1)	BF_3–Et_2O (0.5)	60	8.5	4-Methoxydiphenyldimethylmethane (71%)	935
5	α-Methylstyrene (1)	BF_3–H_3PO_4 (0.5, 0.2)	60	1.5	4-Methoxydiphenyldimethylmethane (51, 41%),[b] 1,1,3-trimethyl-3-phenylindane (8, 28%)[b]	935

[a] Based on wt. of anisole.   [b] For respective amounts of catalyst.

TABLE 49. Higher ethers with olefins

Aromatic (Moles)	Olefin (Moles)	Catalyst (Moles)	Temp. (°C)	Time (hrs.)	Products (% Yield)	Ref.
Phenetole (1–2)	Ethylene (1)	85% H_2SO_4 (200%)[a]	18	0.33–0.5	No alkylate	486
Phenetole (1)	Propene (1)	85% H_2SO_4 (200%)[a]	18	0.33–0.5	Isopropyl- (44%), polyisopropyl-phenetole (3.6%)	486
Phenetole (1.5)	Propene (1.5)	H_3PO_4 (0.6)	145	7	Isopropylphenetole (8%), di-isopropylphenetole (15%)	340
Phenetole (1–2)	n-Butene (1)	85% H_2SO_4 (200%)[a]	18	0.33–0.5	s-Butyl- (61%), poly-s-butyl-phenetole (3%)	486
Phenetole (12.5 g.)	2-Butene (5.6 g.)	BF_3–Et_2O (0.8 g.)	150	8	s-Butylphenetole (61%)	933
Phenetole	2-Butene	BF_3–Et_2O	—	—	Mono- and di-s-butylphenetole	934
Phenetole (27 g.)	2-Butene (25 g.)	BF_3 (5.6 g.)–75% H_3PO_4 (7.9 g.)	r.t.	3[d]	s-Butylphenetoles (82%) (mostly mono-ortho)	933
Phenetole	2-Butene	BF_3–H_3PO_4	—	—	Tri-s-butylphenetole	934
Phenetole (1–2)	Isobutylene (1)	85% H_2SO_4 (200%)[a]	18	0.33–0.5	t-Butyl- (69%), poly-t-butyl-phenetole (3%)	486
Phenetole (0.4)	Isobutylene (> 0.4)	KU-2[e] cation exchange resins	120–125	4	4-t-Butylphenetole (50%) (81%)[f]	348
Phenetole (0.32)	Isoamylene (0.4)	20% $ZnCl_2$–80% $AlCl_3$	200	6	4-t-Amyl/2,4-di t-amylphenetole = 47/5%	899
Phenetole (0.3)	2-Methyl-2-butene (0.4)	KU-1 cation exchange resin (12.8 g.)	95–100	6–8	4-t-Amylphenetole (20%)	899
o-Cresol methyl ether (366 g.)	Isobutylene (120 g.)	H_3PO_4 (180 g.)	25	—	t-Butyl-o-cresol methyl ether[b]	826
3-Methylanisole (100 g.)	Isobutylene (20 l.)	$AlCl_3$ (7.5 g.)	8–10	—	1-Methyl-3-methoxy-4(6)-t-butylbenzene (70%)	456(904)
m-Cresol methyl ether (366 g.)	Isobutylene (100 g.)	$AlCl_3$ (36 g.)	0	—	1-Methyl-3-methoxy-4-t-butylbenzene[c]	687(731a)
1-Methyl-4-methoxybenzene (150 g.)	Isobutylene (30 l.)	$AlCl_3$ (10 g.)	8–10	3.5	1-Methyl-3-t-butyl-4-methoxy-benzene (69%), 1-methyl-3-methoxy-4,6-di-t-butylbenzene	455(175)

Aromatic	Alkylating agent	Catalyst	Temp.	Time	Product	Ref.
p-Cresol methyl ether (366 g.)	Isobutylene (120 g.)	60% H_2SO_4 (2000 g.)	90	—	t-Butyl-p-cresol methyl ether[b]	826
p-Cresol methyl ether (1464 g.)	Isobutylene (330 l.)	93% H_2SO_4 (75 g.)	22–28	3	3-t-Butyl-4-methoxytoluene (2105 g.)	114(113)
Resorcinol dimethyl ether (100 pts.)	Propene (35 pts.)	Nickel molybdite (5 pts.)	150	5	Isopropylresorcinol dimethyl ether (23.5 pts.)	198
1,3-Dimethoxy-benzene	Isobutylene	$AlCl_3$ (5%)	—	—	4-t-Butyl- and 4,6-di-t-butyl-1,3-dimethoxybenzene	175
Resorcinol dimethyl ether (204 g.)	Isobutylene (83 g.)	85% H_3PO_4 (150 g.)	30–70	—	4-t-Butyl- (215 g.), 4,6-di-t-butyl-resorcinol dimethyl ether (11 g.)	114
1,4-Dimethoxy-benzene (50 g.)	Isobutylene (10 l.)	$AlCl_3$ (4 g.)-$C_6H_5NO_2$ (75 g.)	8–10	—	t-Butyl- and small amount of di-t-butyl-1,4-dimethoxybenzene	455
m-Ethylanisole (328 g.)	Isobutylene (50 l.)	$AlCl_3$ (10 g.)	19	—	3-Ethyl-6-t-butylanisole (340 g.)	921
p-Ethylanisole	Isobutylene	93% H_2SO_4 (5%)	25–30	—	t-Butylated ortho to ether group[c]	114
p-Cresol ethyl ether (204 g.)	Isobutylene (42 l.)	93% H_2SO_4 (9 g.)	22–28	1	3-t-Butyl-4-ethoxytoluene (224 g.)	114(113)
p-Isopropylanisole	Isobutylene	93% H_2SO_4 (5%)	25–30	—	t-Butylated ortho to ether group	114
1-Methoxy-naphthalene (40 g.)	Cyclohexene (20 g.)	$AlCl_3$	50–60	—	4-Cyclohexyl-1-methoxy-naphthalene (10%)	126
2-Methoxy-naphthalene (40 g.)	Cyclohexene (20 g.)	$AlCl_3$	40	—	6-Cyclohexyl-2-methoxy-naphthalene	126
Phenyl ether (80–85 g.)	Isobutylene (26–31 g.)	KU-2 (20, 40, 80 g.)	116	—	t-Butyl diphenyl ether (7, 4, 15%) (24, 15, 35%)[g,h]	348
Phenyl ether (0.6)	3-Hexene (1.8)	HF (6.5)	5–20	72	s-Hexyl phenyl ether (61%)	110
Diphenyl ether (3)	Styrene (2.65)	Retrol[i] (15 g.)	270	2.3	Probably isomeric mono-phenylethyl diphenyl ether (191 g.); isomeric polyphenyl-ethyldiphenyl ethers (147 g.)	773
Diphenyl ether (510 g.)	Cyclohexene (508 g.)	Retrol[i] (100 g.)	270	0.75	Mono- (188 g.), di- (88 g.), and poly- (225 g.) cyclohexyl derivatives	771a

Table continued

TABLE 49 (continued)

Aromatic (Moles)	Olefin (Moles)	Catalyst (Moles)	Temp. (°C)	Time (hrs.)	Products (% Yield)	Ref.
Diphenyl ether (56 g.)	3-Methylcyclohexene (124 g.)	Retrol[i] (1.7 g.)	200	4	Di-(3-methylcyclohexyl) derivative	771a
Diphenyl ether (110 g.)	1-Phenylcyclohexene (226 g.)	Retrol[i] (3.3 g.)	220	—	Mono-, di-, and poly-(1-phenyl cyclohexyl) derivatives	771a
Diphenyl ether (40 g.)	3-Cyclohexylcyclohexene (85 g.)	Retrol[i] (1.2 g.)	150–200	1	Di-(3-cyclohexylcyclohexyl) derivative	771a
Benzyl ether of m-cresol (60 g.)	Isobutylene (16 g.)	KU-2[j] (24 g.)	120	5.5	t-Butyl derivative and olefin polymer	348
t-Butylphenyl phenyl ether (1.52 m.)	Cyclohexene (3.3 m.)	Retrol[i] (10 g.)	200	3	Mono- and polycyclohexyl derivatives	771a
Phenyl diphenyl ether (3)	Cyclohexene (3)	Retrol[i] (23 g.)	200	12	Mono- and polycyclohexyl derivatives	771a
Phenyl diphenyl ether (2)	Styrene (1.73)	Retrol[i] (15 g.)	270	1.33	Probably isomeric monophenyl ethyl-[g] (161 g.); isomeric polyphenylethyl phenyldiphenyl ether (102 g.)	773
α-Naphthyl phenyl ether (50 g.)	Cyclohexene (33 g.)	Retrol[i] (1.2 g.)	200	0.33	Mono- and polycyclohexyl derivatives	771a
α,β-Dinaphthyl ether (28 g.)	Cyclohexene (18 g.)	Retrol[i] (1 g.)	200	0.5	Mono- and polycyclohexyl derivatives	771a

[a] Based on wt. of phenetole.
[b] Fair yield.
[c] Excellent yield.
[d] Stirred 2–6 hours longer.
[e] 44 Wt. % of phenetole.
[f] Based on phenetole charge.
[g] For each catalyst amount.
[h] Based on arene consumed.
[i] Activated clay.
[j] Cation exchange resin.

TABLE 50. Halogenated anisoles with olefins

Aromatic (Moles)	Olefin (Moles)	Catalyst (Moles)	Temp. (°C)	Time (hrs.)	Products (% Yield)	Ref.
2-Bromoanisole (3)	Propene (1)	BF_3–H_3PO_4 (0.3)	60	1.66	4-Isopropyl-2-bromoanisole (62%), resin (20 g.)	415
4-Bromoanisole (3)	Propene (1)	BF_3–H_3PO_4 (0.3)	30, 50, 60, 70	14–16	2-Isopropyl-4-bromoanisole (42, 51, 63, and 65%)[a]	411
2-Chloroanisole (3)	Propene (1)	BF_3–H_3PO_4 (0.2)	60 r.t.	2 12	4-Isopropyl-2-chloroanisole (96%)	843
4-Chloroanisole (3)	Propene (1)	BF_3–H_3PO_4 (0.2)	60	4	2-Isopropyl- (72%), 2,6-diisopropyl-4-chloroanisole (26%)	413
4-Fluoroanisole (2)	Propene (1)	BF_3–H_3PO_4 (0.4)	40, 60, 80	—	2-Isopropyl- (55, 63, 63%)[a] and 2,6-diisopropyl-4-fluoroanisole (40, 32, 32%)[a]	411a
2-Bromoanisole (3)	2-Butene (1)	BF_3–H_3PO_4 (0.3)	60	1.66	4-s-Butyl-2-bromoanisole (79%), resin (20 g.)	415
4-Bromoanisole (3)	Butene (1)	BF_3–H_3PO_4 (0.3)	30, 60	14–16	2-s-Butyl-4-bromoanisole (58, 51%)[a]	411
2-Chloroanisole (3)	2-Butene (1)	BF_3–H_3PO_4 (0.3)	60	3.5	4-s-Butyl-2-chloroanisole (96%)	843
4-Chloroanisole (3)	2-Butene (1)	BF_3–H_3PO_4 (0.2)	60	4	2-s-Butyl- (64%) 2,6-di-s-butyl-4-chloroanisole (30%)	413
4-Fluoroanisole (2)	2-Butene (1)	BF_3–H_3PO_4, BF_3 or BF_3–Et_2O (0.4)	80	—	2-s-Butyl- (59, 65, 26%)[b] and 2,6-di-sec-butyl-4-fluoroanisole (19, 35, —%)[b]	411a
2-Bromoanisole (3)	Cyclohexene (1)	BF_3–H_3PO_4 (0.3)	60	1.66	4-Cyclohexyl-2-bromoanisole (67%), resin	415
4-Bromoanisole (3)	Cyclohexene (1)	BF_3–H_3PO_4 (0.3)	20, 30, 50, 60	14–16	2- (46, 58, 59, 60%)[a]; 2,6-Di- (20, 24, 22, 22%)[a]-cyclohexyl-4-bromoanisole (56 g.)	411
2-Chloroanisole (3)	Cyclohexene (1)	BF_3–H_3PO_4 (0.3)	20, 30, 60 r.t.	3 16	4- and 6-Cyclohexyl-2-chloroanisole (92–94%) (4-/6- = 95/5)	843
4-Chloroanisole (4)	Cyclohexene (1)	BF_3–H_3PO_4 (0.3)	30	4	2-Cyclohexyl- (80%) 2,6-dicyclohexyl-4-chloroanisole	413
4-Fluoroanisole (2)	Cyclohexene (1)	BF_3–Et_2O (0.4)	80	—	2-Cyclohexyl- (31%), and 2,6-dicyclohexyl-(18%)-4-fluoroanisole	411a
4-Fluoroanisole (2)	Cyclohexene (1)	BF_3–H_3PO_4 (0.4)	40, 60, 80	—	2-Cyclohexyl- (61–64%) and 2,6-dicyclohexyl-4-fluoroanisole (38–34%)	411a

[a] At respective temperatures.   [b] With respective catalysts.

TABLE 51. Polyhydric phenols and bisphenols with olefins

Aromatic compound (Moles)	Olefin (Moles)	Catalyst (Moles)	Temp. (°C)	Time (hrs.)	Products (% Yield)	Ref.
Catechol (440 pts.) (toluene 272 pts.)	Propene	Aluminum (34) isopropoxide	265–275	3.66	3-Mono- (74 pts.), 3,6-di- (350 pts.), 3,5-di- (106 pts.) isopropylpyrocatechol	177
Catechol (1) (in C_5H_{12})	Isobutylene (1)	BF_3–H_3PO_4	500–700 psig 36	—	t-Butylcatechol (70%)	28
Resorcinol (2)	Isobutylene (4.5)	H_2SO_4 (0.2)	100	0.25	Alkylate contains 2 butyl groups	193
Hydroquinone (25 pts.)	Isobutylene (from 50 pts. t-butyl alcohol)	70% H_2SO_4	25–44	2.25	Dibutylhydroquinone[c]	953
Hydroquinone (147 g.) (500 cc. xylene)	Isobutylene (55 pts.)	85% H_3PO_4 (250 g.)	105	1	Butylhydroquinone (154 g.), hydroquinone,[d] and 2,5-di-t-butylhydroquinone[d]	929
Hydroquinone (55 g.) (300 cc. hexane)	Isobutylene (45 g.)	H_3PO_4 (15 g.)	50–75	1.25	Di-t-butylhydroquinone (58 g.), t-butylhydroquinone (<1 g.)	929
Hydroquinone (1)	Isobutylene (100 pts.)	Nickel molybdite (5 pts.)	200	2	2,5-Di-t-butyl-1,4-hydroquinone (1.9 pts.)	198
Hydroquinone (1)	Isobutylene (2)	Al	220–240	—	2,5-Di-t-butylhydroquinone	816
Catechol (0.03)	Amylene (0.08)	H_2SO_4–HOAc	25	120	Di-t-amylcatechol (15%)	394
Resorcinol (0.1)	Amylene (0.25)	H_2SO_4–HOAc	25	120	Di-t-amylresorcinol	394
Hydroquinone (25 pts.)	2-Methyl-2-butene (50 pts.)	65% H_2SO_4 (400 pts.)	26–45	2.55	Di-amylhydroquinone[c]	953
Hydroquinone (25 pts.)	Amylene (0.65)	H_2SO_4–HOAc, 50 cc./250 g.	25–38	24	2,5-Di-t-amylhydroquinone (50%)	394
Resorcinol	Hexene (0.5)	$AlCl_3$–HOAc	reflux	few	Hexylresorcinol[b]	551
Resorcinol (1)	3-Hexene (1)	$H_3BO_2F_2$ (5 g.)	reflux 140	0.66 3–4	Mono- (62%), di-s-hexylresorcinol (20%)	779
Resorcinol (200 g.)	Hexene (350 ml.)	H_2SO_4 (110 ml.)–CCl_4	—	—	Alkylated resorcinol	89
Catechol (0.5)	Diisobutylene (0.5)	H_2SO_4 (0.5), HOAc 15	r.t.	1.8 72	Diisobutylcatechol[a] (54%)	555(551)

Aromatic	Alkene/Alkane	Catalyst	Temp. (°C)	Time (hr.)	Product	Ref.
Catechol (110 g.)	Diisobutylene (448 g.)	H_2SO_4 (0.2 ml.)	105–115	2.5	4-t-Octylcatechol (75%)	644(643)
Catechol (1)	Styrene (0.5)	H_2SO_4 (10 g.) (toluene)	reflux	—	α-Phenylethyl derivatives (62%)	102
Resorcinol (50 pts.)	1-Octene (56 pts.)	Nickel molybdite (5 pts.)	200	5	Octylresorcinol (10.5 pts.)	198
Resorcinol (0.5)	Diisobutylene (0.5)	H_2SO_4 (0.5), HOAc	15 r.t.	1.8 72	Diisobutylresorcinol[a] (40%)	555(551)
Resorcinol (71 pts.)	Styrol (10 pts.)	25% $HClO_4$ (10 pts.), HOAc (10 pts.)	w.b.	2	Mono- (10.4 pts.), di- (6.6 pts.)-α-phenylethylresorcinol	159
Resorcinol (1)	Styrene (0.5)	H_2SO_4 (10 g.) (toluene)	reflux	—	α-Phenylethyl derivatives (72%)	102
Hydroquinone (0.5)	Diisobutylene (0.5)	H_2SO_4 (0.5), HOAc	15 r.t.	1.8 72	Diisobutylhydroquinone[a] (52%)	555(551)
Hydroquinone (27.5 pts.)	Styrene (52 pts.)	40% H_2SO_4 (250 pts.)	85	2	Diphenethylhydroquinone (68.3 pts.)	953
Hydroquinone (1)	Styrene (0.5)	H_2SO_4 (10 g.), (toluene)	reflux	—	α-Phenylethyl derivatives (62–86%)	102
Catechol (2)	α-Methylstyrene (1)	Conc. HCl (1 ml.)	120–150	1.1	4-(α-Phenylisopropyl)catechol (84%)	606
Resorcinol (2)	α-Methylstyrene (1)	Conc. HCl (1 ml.)	120–150	1.1	4-(α-Phenylisopropyl)resorcinol	606
Hydroquinone (2)	α-Methylstyrene (1)	Conc. HCl (3 ml.) (HOAc)	140	3	2-(α-Phenylisopropyl)hydroquinone	606
Pyrogallol (80 pts.)	Propene (27 pts.)	89% H_3PO_4 (30 pts.)	150	—	Alkylated pyrogallol	311
Pyrogallol	Amylene	H_2SO_4–HOAc	25	120	Di-t-amylpyrogallol	394
Pyrogallol (0.5)	Diisobutylene (0.5)	H_2SO_4 (0.5) HOAc	15 r.t.	1.8 72	Diisobutylpyrogallol[a] (40%)	555(551)
Pyrogallol (30 g.)	Diisobutylene (172 g.)	H_2SO_4 (0.2 cc.)	105–115	2.5	5-t-Octylpyrogallol (30.7 g.)	643(644)
4,4'-Dioxydiphenyl-methane (50 pts.) (300 pts. decalin)	Octalin (102 pts.)	70% $HClO_4$ (20 pts.)	80 90–100	— 4	Resin	159

Table continued

TABLE 51 (continued)

Aromatic compound (Moles)	Olefin (Moles)	Catalyst (Moles)	Temp. (°C)	Time (hrs.)	Products (% Yield)	Ref.
1,1-(4,4'-Di-hydroxyl)-diphenylethane (Et$_2$O)	Isobutylene[e] (1)	BF$_3$–H$_3$PO$_4$ (15%)	20	—	1,1-(4,4'-dihydroxy-5,5'-di-t-butyl)-diphenylethane	893
2,2-Bis-(4-hydroxy-phenyl) propane (215 pts.) (220 pts. triisobutylene)	Styrene (39 pts.) Isobutylene (179 pts.)	Act. clay (35 pts.)	70–80	—	Alkylated arylated bisphenols (100%)	135
Phenol–formaldehyde resin (300 pts.) (decalin 2000 pts.)	Butene	60% HClO$_4$ (50 pts.)	80–90	—	Hard brown butylphenol resin	268
Phenol–formaldehyde resin (300 pts.) (decalin 2000 pts.)	Isoamylene (70 pts.)	60% HClO$_4$ (50 pts.)	80–90	—	Viscous resin	268
Phenol–formaldehyde resin (100 pts.) (decalin 400 pts.)	Cyclohexene (120 pts.)	70% HClO$_4$	120	—	Red-brown hard resin	268
Phenol–formaldehyde resin (100 pts.) (decalin 400 pts.)	Diisobutylene (112 pts.)	70% HClO$_4$	80–120	—	Dark red soft resin	268

[a] Diisobutyl probably is t-octyl.
[b] Probably sec-hexyl.
[c] Excellent yield.
[d] Small amount.
[e] Two to three liters/hour.

TABLE 52. Methoxyphenols and dimethoxybenzenes with olefins

Aromatic (Moles)	Olefin (Moles)	Catalyst (Moles)	Temp. (°C)	Time (hrs.)	Products (% Yield)	Ref.
Guaiacol	2-Butene	BF_3–H_3PO_4	100	—	s-Butylguaiacols and s-butyl ethers thereof (66–85%)	934
4-Methoxyphenol (1) (45 cc. benzene)	Isobutylene (2.34)	H_2SO_4 (5 cc.)	50–60	—	2,6-Di-t-butyl-4-methoxyphenol (56%)	137(665)
4-Methoxyphenol (1) (1000 cc. hexane)	Isobutylene (1)	H_3PO_4 (300 g.)	50	1–1.5	t-Butyl-4-methoxyphenol (154 g.) (mono- 85%, di- 9%)	663
Guaiacol (0.5)	Diisobutylene (0.5)	H_2SO_4 ± HOAc	0–10	1.5	Diisobutylguaiacol[a] (70%)	551
Guaiacol (74 g.)	Styrene (52 g.)	H_2SO_4 (10 g.) (100 ml. Toluene)	reflux	1	α-Phenylethyl derivatives (58 g.)	102(393)
4-Methoxyphenol (1)	Styrene (1)	H_2SO_4 (2%)	50	2–4	2-(α-Phenylethyl)-4-methoxyphenol	928
2-Nitro-1,3-di-methoxy-benzene (92 g.)	Isobutylene (28 g.)	HF (200 g.) or BF_3–H_2O	10	—	No alkylation	114

[a] Diisobutyl probably means t-octyl.

9*

TABLE 53. Thiophenol with olefins[a]

Thiophenol (Moles)	Olefin (Moles)	Catalyst (Moles)	Temp. (°C)	Time (hrs.)	Conversion of thiol (Mole %)	Alkyl	Products (Mole % of converted thiol)				
							o-Alkyl thiophenol[b]	2,6-Dialkyl thiophenol	Alkyl aryl sulfide	Alkyl o-alkyl aryl sulfide	Alkyl 2,6-dialkyl aryl sulfide
5	Ethylene (3)	$AlCl_3$ (0.75)	20–32	3.5	36	Ethyl	25	<1	31	14	—
5	Propene (4)	$AlCl_3$ (0.25)	16–25	5	44	Isopropyl	34	2.8	16	12	13
5	Propene (4)	$AlCl_3$ (0.75) (CS_2)	−70 to −44	1	56	Isopropyl	43	17	15	7	2
5	Propene (2.7)	$AlBr_3$ (0.35) (CS_2)	−37 to +33	4.8	38	Isopropyl	41	3.6	20	12	9
2.5	Propene (1.9)	AlI_3 (0.26) (CS_2)	−20 to +23	5	43	Isopropyl	43	3	28	12	3
5	Propene (5)	$ZrCl_4$ (0.32)	25–38	1	48	Isopropyl	27	1.4	9	9	23
5	Propene (5)	$TiCl_4$ (0.53)	3–16	0.9	45	Isopropyl	33	2.8	4	3	31
5	Propene (5)	BF_3–H_2O–HF	2–5	1	59	Isopropyl	43	2.7	7	15	14
5	Propene (3.3)	$H_3BO_2F_2$	46–110	3.8	47	Isopropyl	13[c]		58	2.5	5
5	1-Butene (4)	$AlCl_3$ (0.41)	11–26	2.5	47	s-Butyl	16[d]		36	15	—
5	2-Butene (4)	$AlCl_3$ (0.41)	12–28	2.3	38	s-Butyl	10[d]		62	6	—
5	1-Butene (4)	$ZrCl_4$ (0.43)	−17 to −10	1.2	37	s-Butyl	17[d]		18	15	20
2.5	1-Pentene (2)	$AlCl_3$ (0.38)	−15 to −10	1.1	51	s-Amyl	24		29	22	10
2.5	Cyclopentene (2)	$AlCl_3$ (0.38)	−17 to −10	0.6	46	Cyclopentyl	16		32	21	9
5	Cyclohexene (4)	$AlCl_3$ (0.75)	−18 to −14	1	40	Cyclohexyl	4		67	3.5	—
1.1	Propene (1)	BF_3 (5%)	50	5	—	Isopropyl	19[e]		32	—	—
g	Isobutylene (excess)	H_2SO_4 (0.5–5%)[f]	50–100	flow	—	t-Butylthiophenol (85 g.), tri-t-butylphenol (18.2 g.)					

[a] All entries from ref. 426f.
[b] Typically 95–97.5% o-/2.5–5% p-/0% m-.
[c] o-/p- = 2/3.
[d] Exclusively ortho.
[e] Para- (ref. 44).
[f] Of thiophenol.
[g] Plus phenol (ref. 548).

TABLE 53A. Thiophenol homologs and ethers with olefins

Aromatic compound (Moles)	Olefin (Moles)	Catalyst (Moles)	Temp. (°C)	Time (hrs.)	Product (% Yield)	Ref.
m-Thiocresol (1)	Propene (1)	AlCl$_3$ (0.15) CS$_2$	−51 to −39	0.6	2-Isopropyl-5-methyl- (38%),[b] 2,6-diisopropyl-3-methylthiophenol (29%),[b] isopropyl phenyl sulfide (9%),[b] 2-isopropyl-5-methylphenyl isopropyl sulfide (5%)[b]	426f
p-Thiocresol (0.5)	Propene (1)	BF$_3$ (10%)	80	2	2-Isopropyl-4-methylthiophenol (25%), p-tolyl isopropyl sulfide (40%), 2-isopropyl-4-methylphenyl isopropyl sulfide (21%)	44
o-Thiocresol (0.8)	Isobutylene (1)	BF$_3$ (10%)	80	6	4-t-Butyl-2-methylthiophenol (44%)	44
o-Thiocresol (phenol)	Isobutylene (excess)	H$_2$SO$_4$	—	—	t-Butyl-o-thiocresol (75.4 g.), di-t-butylphenol (23.1 g.), tri-t-butylphenol (80 g.)	548
p-Thiocresol	Isobutylene	BF$_3$	—	—	No alkylation	44
Thioxylenols (m- and p-cresols)	Isobutylene (excess)	H$_2$SO$_4$ (0.5)	—	—	2,6-Di-t-butyl-p-cresol (25 vol. %), 4,6-di-t-butyl-m-cresol (29 vol. %), t-butylthioxylenols	548
4-t-Butylthiophenol (5)	Propene (4)	AlCl$_3$ (0.75)	−18 to −9	1	2-Isopropyl-4-t-butylthiophenol (43%),[c] isopropyl-4-t-butylphenyl sulfide (12%),[c] isopropyl 2-isopropyl-4-t-butylphenyl sulfide (18%),[c] isopropyl 2,6-diisopropyl-4-t-butylphenyl sulfide (9%)[c]	426f
2,6-Diisopropylthiophenol (46.6 g.)	Isobutylene (18.3 cc.)[a]	AlCl$_3$ (1.6 g.)	70–86	1	Diisopropylbenzene, disulfides, and H$_2$S	426f
Isopropyl phenyl sulfide (305 g.)	Propene (85 g.)	AlCl$_3$ (40 g.)	53–58	2.5	Isopropyl o-isopropylphenyl sulfide (7% based on 42% conversion)	426f

[a] Measured at −70°.   [b] Based on 68% converted thiol.   [c] Based on 56% converted thiol.

TABLE 54. Aniline with olefins

Aniline (Moles)	Olefin (Moles)	Catalyst (Moles)	Temp. (°C)	Time (hrs.)	Aniline derivatives (% Yield)	Ref.
300 pts.	Ethylene (0.5-1.5)	Al-HgCl₂ (7.5-0.3 pts.)	300 150-200 atm.	6	2-Ethyl- (22-72%), 2,6-diethyl- (33-55%)	809
300 g.	Ethylene (170 g.)	Al bronze (7.5 g.) HgCl₂, Al (2%) 1-10% bleaching clay, BF₃, or AlCl₃, etc.	200 (170 atm.)ᵇ	3	2-Ethyl-, 2,4-diethyl-, 2,4,6-triethyl-ᵃ	196
1	Ethylene (1-2)	6-8% AlCl₃ and 1-2% Na, Li, Cu, Mg, CaH₂, or Ca₂C	300 (200 atm.)ᵇ	1-4	2-Ethyl-, 2,6-diethyl-ᵃ	196
—	Ethylene	(ArNH)₃Al (3-4%)	330 (500-800 psi)ᵇ	9-24	Mono- and/or di-*ortho*-ethyl-(50-90% ult. yield)	179a(179b, 808,810, 395)
10 pts.	Ethylene (100 atm.)	Ce(PO₃)₃ (1 pt.)	375	—	Ring-alkylated aniline, b.p. 205-206°	298
300 g.	Ethylene (200 atm.)	Al grit (6 g.)-NiL₂ (2 g.)	280	3.5-5	2,6-Diethyl- (96%)	812
—	Propene (500-700 psig)	(ArNH)₃Al (3-4%)	330	5	2-Isopropyl- (4%)	179a(395)
1	Propene (1-3)	Al (2%) and 1-10% bleaching clay, BF₃, AlCl₃, or I₂	200-300 150-250 atm.	4	2-Isopropyl, 2,4-diisopropyl-, and 2,4,6-triisopropyl-	196(810)
100 pts.	Propene (100 pts.)	Al-HgCl₂ (5/0.3 pts.)	300-500 200 atm.	3	Propyl-	809
—	Propene	Al grit (6 g.)-NiL₂ (2 g.)	280	3.5-5	2-Isopropyl- (90%)	812
200 pts.	Propene	AlCl₃ (18 pts.)-Na (6 pts.)	300 250 atm.	—	2-Isopropyl- (38%), 2,6-diisopropyl- (18%)	811(196)
200 g.	n-Butene	Al (2%) and 1-10% bleaching clay, BF₃, or AlCl₃	200-300 150-250 atm.	—	2-Butyl-, 2,4-dibutyl-, 2,4,6-tributyl-ᵃ	196
1	n-Butene (1)	Syn. aluminosilicate	397 14.6 atm.	1.5 S.V.	4-Butyl-, N-butyl-; p-toluidine, and other cleavage products	426g

1	Isobutylene (1–3)	Al (2%) and 1–10% bleaching clay, BF_3, or $AlCl_3$	200–300 (150–250 atm.)	4	Mono-, di-, and tri-t-butyl.[a]	196(810)
—	Isobutylene (720 psig)	$(ArNH)_3Al$ (3–4%)	330	3	2-t-Butyl- (2%)	179a(395)
200 pts.	Isobutylene	$AlCl_3$ (18 pts.)–Na (6 pts.)	300 250 atm.	—	t-Butyl- (43%), di-t-butyl- (5%)	811(196)
1400 g.	Isobutylene (650 g.)	Montmorillonite clay (70 g.)	200	—	4-t-Butyl- (85–88%), 2-t-butyl- (0.2–0.3%), N-t-butyl-(0.3%), di-t-butyl-aniline- (2–3%)	75
80 g.	Isobutylene (5 g.)	$C_6H_5NH_2 \cdot HCl$ (10 g.)	220–240	22	Alkylated amines, secondary/primary = 0.61/1.45 g.	278
30 g.	Isoamylene (6 g.)	$C_6H_5NH_2 \cdot HCl$ (3 g.)	230–250	6.5	Amines, secondary/primary = 0.57/ 3.7 g.	278
100	Isoamylene (12 g.)	$C_6H_5NH_2 \cdot HCl$ (6 g.)	240–260	25	Amines, secondary/primary = 0.59/ 6.85 g.	278
100	Isoamylene (14.5)	$C_6H_5NH_2 \cdot \frac{1}{2}CoCl_2$ (8 g.)	245	24	Amines, secondary/primary = 0.37/ 2.71 g.	278
55 g.	3-Methyl-1-butene (20 g.)	Act. Kaolin (25 g.)	250–260 25 atm.	13.5	4-t-Amyl- (8.8 g.), mixed secondary amines (0.8 g.)	905
6	Hexene (3.5)	$C_6H_5NH_2 \cdot HCl$ (10 g.)	285–290	3.5	Amines, secondary/primary = trace/ 1.02 g.	278
50 g.	3-Ethyl-2-pentene (10 g.)	Aniline·HCl (8 g.)	230–260	12	Amines, secondary/primary = 0.35/ 1.22 g.	278
750 lbs.	Styrene (182 lbs.) DIB[c] (555 lbs.)	$AlCl_3$ (50 lbs.)	165–175	1.5	1260 lbs. amines: 4-t-octyldiphenyl- and 4-α-phenethyldiphenylamines (30%); 4,4'-di-t-octyldiphenyl-, 4,4'-di-α-phenethyldiphenyl- and 4-t-octyl-4'-α-phenethyldiphenylamines (70%)	284
5 g.	Styrene (5 g.)	Aniline·HCl (2 g.)	270	6	Amines, secondary/primary = trace/ 3.5 g.	278
50 g.	Styrene (9.1 g.)	Aniline·$CoCl_2$ (5.6 g.)	240	24	Amines, secondary/primary = 0.3/ 0.69 g.	278
50 g.	Styrene (7.2 g.)	Aniline·$CoCl_2$ (7.7 g.)	235	24	Amines, secondary/primary = 0.09/ 0.94 g.	278

[a] Excellent yields.   [b] Initial pressure.   [c] Diisobutylene.

TABLE 55. Aniline with cyclic olefins

Aniline (Moles)	Olefin (Moles)	Catalyst (Moles)	Temp. (°C)	Time (hrs.)	Products (% Yield)	Ref.
2	α-Pinene (1)	Aniline·HCl (1)	150–160	3	Condensation product (40%)	367
	α-Pinene	Aniline·HCl plus MgO, ZnO, or Al_2O_3	—	—	Condensation product (26, 45, 23%)[a]	367
93 g.	Cyclohexene (173 g.)	Al (4 g.)	340–350	24	2-Cyclohexylaniline	809
7.2 g.	Dihydronaphthalene (9.9 g.)	Aniline·HBr (13.3 g.)	220	6	Secondary/primary = nil/9.8 g.	278

[a] Respectively with each catalyst combination.

TABLE 56. Homologs and derivatives of aniline and phenylenediamine with olefins

Aromatic (Moles)	Olefin (Moles)	Catalyst (Moles)	Temp. (°C)	Time (hrs.)	Products (% Yield)	Ref.
p-Anisidine (123 pts.)	Propene	HF	5–10	5	Isopropyl-p-anisidine (30 pts.)	915
N-Methylaniline	Ethylene (500–800 psig)	(ArNH)$_3$Al (3–4%)	205	3	2-Ethyl derivative (86%)	179a(395)
o-Toluidine	Ethylene (600–800 psig)	(ArNH)$_3$Al (3–4%)	325	8	2-Methyl-6-ethylaniline (90%)	179a(395, 808,810)
n-Propylaniline	Ethylene	(ArNH)$_3$Al	235, 190 atm.	—	2-Ethyl-6-propylaniline (75%)	810
o-Toluidine (200 pts.)	Ethylene (50 pts.)	Al–HgCl$_2$ (10/1 pts.)		3	Ethyltoluidine	809
m-Toluidine (300 pts.)	Ethylene (151 pts.)	Al–HgCl$_2$ (6/0.3 pts.)	340–350 200 atm.	3.5	3-Methyl-2,6-diethylaniline (83%)	809(810)
p-Toluidine (1)	Ethylene (2)	Al–HgCl$_2$	340–350 200 atm.	3.5	2,6-Diethyl-4-methylaniline	809
p-Toluidine	Ethylene	Al grit, NiI$_2$	280	3.5–5	2,6-Diethyl-4-methylaniline (90%)	812

Aromatic	Alkene/Alkane	Catalyst	Temp. (°C)	Time (hr)	Product (yield)	Ref.
o-, m-, or p-Toluidine	Ethylene	Al–AlCl₃	300	—	Mono- and diethylation in ortho-positions[b]	196
o-, m-, p-Toluidine or sym.-o-Xylidine	Ethylene	AlCl₃–Na (6%/2%), or AlCl₃–Al	300, 200 atm.	—	Mono-, or diethylation in ortho-positions	196(811)
o-, m-, or p-Toluidine	Propene	Al–AlCl₃	300	—	Mono- and diisopropylation in ortho-positions	196(810)
N-Methylaniline	Propene (500–700 psig)	(ArNH)₃Al (3–4%)	235	4	2-s-Propyl derivative (54%)	179a(395)
o-Toluidine	Butene	Aniline–Al–AlCl₃	290, 250 atm.	8	2-Methyl-6-s-butylaniline (54%)	810
o-Toluidine	Isobutylene	Aniline–Al–AlCl₃	290, 250 atm.	8	2-Methyl-6-t-butylaniline (65%)	810
N-Methylaniline	Cyclohexene (280–300 psig)	(ArNH)₃Al (3–4%)	300	0.5	2-Cyclohexyl derivative (2%)	179a(395)
N-Methylaniline	Decene (90–100 psig)	(ArNH)₃Al (3–4%)	300	0.5	2-(1-Methylnonyl) derivative (35%)	179a(395)
N-Ethylaniline	Ethylene (600–800 psig)	(ArNH)₃Al (3–4%)	205	2.5	2-Ethyl derivative (86%)	179a(395)
N-Ethyl-m-chloroaniline	Ethylene (500–800 psig)	(ArNH)₃Al (3–4%)	200–300	—	2,6-Diethyl derivative (90%)	179a(395)
2,4-Dimethylaniline (1)	Ethylene (1)	Al (5 pts.)	330–360, 200 atm.	3	6-Ethyl-2,4-dimethylaniline (85%)	809(810)
2,6-Dimethylaniline	Ethylene	(ArNH)₃Al	—	—	4-Ethyl derivative (80%)	810(808)
3,5-Dimethylaniline (320 pts.)	Ethylene (142 pts.)	Al (5 pts.)	330–360, 200 atm.	3	3,5-Dimethyl-2,6-diethylaniline (79%)	809(810)
2-Ethylaniline	Propene	Aniline–Al–AlCl₃	290, 250 atm.	8	2-Ethyl-6-isopropylaniline (85%)	810
2-Ethylaniline	Butene	Aniline–Al–AlCl₃	290, 250 atm.	8	2-Ethyl-6-s-butylaniline (53%)	810
2-Ethylaniline (250 pts.)	Butene (180 pts.)	Al (5 pts.)	300–350 high pressure	9	2-Ethyl-6-butylaniline (30%)[d]	809
2-Ethylaniline	Isobutylene	Aniline–Al–AlCl₃	290, 250 atm.	8	2-Ethyl-6-t-butylaniline (41%)	810

Table continued

TABLE 56 (continued)

Aromatic (Moles)	Olefin (Moles)	Catalyst (Moles)	Temp. (°C)	Time (hrs.)	Products (% Yield)	Ref.
4-Methyl-2-ethyl-aniline	Butene	Aniline–Al–AlCl₃	290 250 atm.	8	4-Methyl-2-ethyl-6-s-butylaniline (51%)	810
1-Naphthylamine	Ethylene (500–800 psig)	(ArNH)₃Al (3–4%)	300	—	2-Ethyl derivative (30%)	179a
Diphenylamine	Ethylene	Al–AlCl₃–Aniline	280 100–150 atm.	—	2,2′-Diethyl derivatives[a]	196
Diphenylamine	Ethylene	(ArNH)₃Al	—	—	2,2′-Diethyl derivative (almost quan.)	808
Diphenylamine	Cyclohexene	Clay[e]	150–250	—	4-Mono- and 4,4′-dicyclohexyl-	771b
m-Phenylenediamine	Ethylene	Aniline–Al–AlCl₃	300 200 atm.	—	2-Ethyl (40%),[c] 4-ethyl (30%),[c] 2,4-diethyl (20%),[c] 2,4,6-triethyl (90%)[c] derivatives	810
Benzidine	Ethylene	Aniline–Al–AlCl₃	280 200 atm.	—	3,3′,5,5′-Tetraethylbenzidine (80%)	810
2,4-Tolyldiamine	Ethylene	Aniline–Al–AlCl₃	300 200 atm.	—	4-Methyl-2,6-diethyl-1,3-diamino-benzene (95%)[a]	196(810)
2,6-Tolyldiamine	Ethylene	Aniline–Al–AlCl₃	300 200 atm.	—	2-Methyl-4,6-diethyl-1,3-diamino-benzene (96%)[a]	196(810)
4,6-Dimethyl-1,3-diaminobenzene	Ethylene	Aniline–Al–AlCl₃	280 200 atm.	—	4,6-Dimethyl-2-ethyl-1,3-diamino-benzene (85%)	810

[a] Aniline also reacts.
[b] High yields.
[c] Up to this %.
[d] Based on 2-ethylaniline consumed.
[e] Acid activated.

TABLE 57.   Heterocyclic amines with olefins

Aromatic (Moles)	Olefins (Moles)	Catalyst (Moles)	Temp. (°C)	Time (hrs.)	Products (% Yield)	Ref.
2-Methylindole (200 g.)	Ethylene (140–145 g.) (200 atm.)	Al-anilide–aniline[a] (150 g.)	280–300	1.5–2	2-Methyl-7-ethylindole (87%), 2,6-diethylaniline (92%)[b]	813(195)
2-Methyl-2,3-dihydroindole (200 g.)	Ethylene (120 g.) (200 atm.)	Al-anilide–aniline[a] (150 g.)	280	6	2-Methyl-7-ethylindole (91%), 2,6-diethylaniline (91%)[b]	813
2,3-Dimethylindole (200 g.)	Ethylene (200 atm.)	Al-anilide–aniline[a] (150 g.)	280	1.5–2	2,3-Dimethyl-7-ethylindole (90%), 2,6-diethylaniline	813(195)
2,3,5-Trimethylindole (200 g.)	Ethylene (200 atm.)	Al-anilide–aniline[a] (150 g.)	280–300	72	2,3,5-Trimethyl-7-ethylindole (63%)	813
2-Phenylindole (200 g.)	Ethylene (130 g.) (200 atm.)	Al-anilide–aniline[a] (150 g.)	300–310	1	2-Phenyl-7-ethylindole (80–85%), 2,6-diethylaniline (88%)[b]	813(195)
1,2,3,4-Tetrahydroquinoline (200 g.)	Ethylene (130 g.) (200 atm.)	Al-anilide–aniline[a] (150 g.)	300	3.5	Monoethyl derivative (60–70%), 2,6-diethylaniline	813
1,2,3,4-Tetrahydroquinoline	Ethylene (200 atm. init.)	Al-anilide–aniline ± AlCl₃	300	0.5	8-Ethyl-1,2,3,4-tetrahydroquinoline (60–70%)	195
1,2,3,4-Tetrahydroquinoline	Ethylene (200 atm. init.)	AlCl₃ (8 pts.) Na (6 pts.)	270–280	0.5	8-Ethyl-1,2,3,4-tetrahydroquinoline (60–70%)	195
Carbazole (200 g.)	Ethylene (135 g.) (200 atm.)	Al-anilide–aniline[a] (150 g.) 8% AlCl₃	300	0.75	1-Ethylcarbazole (90%), 2,6-diethylaniline	813
Carbazole	Ethylene	Al-anilide–aniline + AlCl₃, AlI₃ or I₂	300 200 atm.	—	Ethylcarbazole	195
Carbazole (200 g.)	Ethylene (135 g.) (200 atm.)	Al-anilide–aniline[a] (150 g.)	300	1	1-Ethylcarbazole (90%), 2,6-diethylaniline	813
Carbazole (200 g.)	Propene (170 g.)	Al-anilide–aniline (150 g.)	290 200–500 atm.	2–3	1- (250 g.), 2- (50 g.), 2,6-di-(200 g.)-isopropylaniline	813
Carbazole (500 pts.) (decalin)	Propene (720 pts.)	AlCl₃ (25 pts.)	60 20 atm.	2	Resin, b.p. 200–260° (97%)	511

Table continued

TABLE 57 (continued)

Aromatic (Moles)	Olefins (Moles)	Catalyst (Moles)	Temp. (°C)	Time (hrs.)	Products (% Yield)	Ref.
Carbazole (500 pts.)	Propene (465–700 pts.)	Tonsil (100 pts.)	180–200 15–20 atm.	—	Tetra- and pentaisopropyl-carbazole	511
Carbazole (0.5) (400 pts. cumene)	α-Methylstyrene (1)	Act. bleach earth Tonsil AC (10 pts.)	80	3.5	α-Phenylisopropyl derivative (180 pts.)	509
9(N)-Ethylcarbazole (0.5)	α-Methylstyrene (1)	Act. bleach earth (15 pts.)	reflux	4	3,6-Di-(α-phenylisopropyl),9(N)-ethylcarbazole	509
Carbazole	Propene	Al-anilide–aniline–$AlCl_3$, AlI_3, or I_2	300	—	Propylcarbazole	195
Carbazole (334 pts.)	Propene (130 pts.)	HCl–Fuller's earth (35 pts.)	150 15 atm.	—	Resinous material, b.p. 210–240	518
Carbazole (334 pts.)	Propene (160 pts.)	$AlCl_3$ (16 pts.)	90–100 12 atm.	3	Resin (diisopropylcarbazole)	518
Phenothiazine (200 g.)	Ethylene (120 g.) (200 atm.)	Al-anilide–aniline[a] (150 g.)	300	2–3	Monoethyl derivative (86%)	813
Phenothiazine (200 g.)	Propene (130 g.)	Al-anilide–aniline (150 g.)–$AlCl_3$ (12 g.)	300	2–3	Mixture of feed, its mono-isopropyl derivative, and mono- and diisopropylaniline (210 g.)	813

[a] 2% Al.   [b] Based on aniline in reactor charge.

TABLE 58. Aromatic acids with olefins

Aromatic compound (Moles)	Olefins (Moles)	Catalyst (Moles)	Temp. (°C)	Time (hrs.)	Products (% Yield)	Ref.
Salicylic acid (35 g., 210 g. n-heptane)	Propene (1.25)	BF_3 (4 g.)	—	72	Isopropyl esters of 2-hydroxy-3-isopropyl and 2-hydroxy-3,5-diisopropyl benzoic acid	146
m-Hydroxybenzoic acid (207 g.)	Propene (156 g.)	BF_3 (34 g.) (781 g. CCl_4)	—	—	Isopropyl ester of 3-isopropoxy-4-isopropyl-benzoic acid	146
p-Hydroxybenzoic acid (0.5)	Propene (40 g.)	BF_3 (15 g.)	—	—	Isopropyl ester of 3-isopropyl-4-isopropoxy-benzoic acid	146
Salicylic acid (126 pts.)	Isohexyl-isoheptyl dimer (185 pts.)	BF_3 (35 pts.)–H_2O (19 pts.)	125	0.5	Alkyl salicylic acid	300
Salicylic acid (100 g.)	Cetene (400 g.)	$SbCl_3$ (625 g.)	90-95	4	Oily product (82%)	821(822)
Phenylacetic acid (34 pts.)	Isoheptene (49 pts.)	BF_3	70-80	15-20	Alkylate	789
Phenylacetic acid (34 pts.)	1-Dodecene (84 pts.)	H_2O (18 pts.) BF_3[a]	65-75	1-2	Mono- (some); mostly di-dodecylphenylacetic acid	789
Phenoxyacetic acid (152 pts. 500 pts. CCl_4)	Diisobutylene (112 g.)	BF_3 (8 pts.)	60, r.t.	2, 12	Isooctylphenoxyacetic (95%)	40(300b, 302a, 300a)
Phenoxyacetic acid (152 pts.) (CCl_4 800 pts.)	Isohexyl-isoheptyl dimer (168 pts.)	BF_3 (30 pts.)	60, r.t.	2, 12	Dodecylphenoxyacetic acid (87%)	300(300a)
Phenoxyacetic acid (152 pts.)	Tetradecene (196 pts.)	BF_3 (30 pts.)	60, r.t.	2, 15	Tetradecylphenoxyacetic acid (91%)	300
Phenoxyacetic acid (152 pts.)	Diisoheptylene (196 pts.)	$ZnCl_2$ (200 pts.)	150	0.25	Tetradecylphenoxyacetic acid	300a
α-Naphthoxyacetic acid (202 pts.)	Diisoheptylene (196 pts.)	BF_3 (35 pts.)	140	1.5-2	Tetrodecyl derivative	300a

Table continued

TABLE 58 (continued)

Aromatic compound (Moles)	Olefins (Moles)	Catalyst (Moles)	Temp. (°C)	Time (hrs.)	Products (% Yield)	Ref.
Cresoxyacetic acid (166 pts.)	Diisoheptylene (196 pts.)	BF_3 (25 pts.)	140	0.5	Tetradecyl derivative	300a
Phenoxybutyric acid (181 pts.)	Diisoheptylene	BF_3 (18 pts.)	110	1	Tetradecyl derivative	300a
Naphthalene-SO_3H	Propene (4.8)	H_2SO_4 (206 g.)	67–110 30–50 psi	2.25	Isopropylnaphthalene-sulfonic acids	112(642)
Naphthalene-SO_3H	2-Butene (6.7)	H_2SO_4	85–95 25–33 psi	5	Butylnaphthalenesulfonic acids	112
Naphthalene-SO_3H	n-Hexene (211 g.)	H_2SO_4 (100 g.)	90–100	4	Hexylnaphthalenesulfonic acids	112
Naphthalene-SO_3H (100 kg.)	Cyclohexene (135 kg.)	H_2SO_4 (285 kg.)	90	—	Condensation products (330 kg.)	642

[a] To saturation.

TABLE 59. Thiophene with propene

Thiophene (Moles)	Propene (Moles)	Catalyst (Moles)	Temp. (°C)	Time (hrs.)	Thiophene derivatives (% Yield)	Ref.
—	—	BF_3–Et_2O	85	—	Isopropyl- (mono-48%, di-36%)	617(258)
—	—	$SnCl_4$–CH_3NO_2 (1/1.5 pts.)	78	—	Isopropyl- (mono-14%, di-6%)	617
—	(27 g.)	$TiCl_4$–Ethyl orthophosphate	282	3	Isopropyl- (30.6 g.), diisopropyl- (8.8 g.)	358
(1)	(1)	BF_3–Dihydroxyfluoboric acid (80 pts.)	100	2	Propyl- (8 pts.), dipropylthiophene (5 pts.)	106
(294 g.)	(144 g.)	70% H_2SO_4 (1 kg.)	68	1.5	Isopropyl- (22%)	828a(108, 108a,675a[a])
(1)	(1)	HF	r.t.	20	Isopropyl- (19%)	916
(1)	(1)	H_3PO_4 (0.1%, H_2O)	285	4	Isopropyl- (40 vol. % of alkylate)	17
(1.1)	(1)	H_3PO_4–kieselguhr	300 psi 288 21.5 atm.	L.H.S.V. 3.6 W.H.S.V.	Isopropyl- (80%), mono- (40%) (2-/3- = 59/41), di- (significant amounts)	18(408,829)
(90 g.)	(15 g.)	Silica-alumina–$ZnCl_2$ (20 g.)	170–180 200–500 psi	1	Propyl- (16 g.)	107
(2.2)	(1)	Silica-alumina (60 g.) (Filtrol)	200 25 atm.	11	Isopropyl- (45%), (2-/3- = 76/24)	422
(1)	(3)	Silica-alumina–zirconia (88/10/2)	288 100 psi	1.7	Isopropyl- (26%)	829(408)

[a] No alkylation with 96% H_2SO_4.

TABLE 60. Thiophenes with butenes

Thiophene (Moles)	Olefin (Moles)	Catalyst (Moles)	Temp. (°C)	Time (hrs.)	Thiophene derivatives (% Yield)	Ref.
—	2-Butene	BF_3–Et_2O	80	—	s-Butyl- (mono- 48%, di- 27%)	617
—	2-Butene	$SnCl_4$–CH_3NO_2 (1/1.5 pts.)	65	—	s-Butyl- (mono- 11%, di- 2%)	617
(2.7)	Butene	H_2SO_4	—	—	No alkylation	675
	1-Butene (1)	Silica-alumina (60 g.) (Filtrol)	200 24 atm.	5	Butyl- (52%)	422
(84 g.)	Isobutylene (50 g.)	$AlCl_3$ (3 g.)	65–75	1	Butyl- (14 g.)	105(104)
(50.4 g.)	Isobutylene (17.5 g.)	$SnCl_4$ (23.3 g.)	50	1.25	t-Butyl- (18.5%), di-t-butyl- (50%)	152(617)
—	Isobutylene	$SnCl_4$–CH_3NO_2 (1/1.5 pts.)	50	—	t-Butyl- (mono- 31%, di- 17%)	617
(1)	Isobutylene (1)	BF_3–H_2O (dilute) (80 pts.)	65	2	t-Butyl- (42 pts.), di-t-butyl- (22 pts.)	106
(1)	Isobutylene (1)	BF_3–H_3BO_3–H_2O (4/1/3) (80 pts.)	75	2	t-Butyl- (22 pts.), di-t-butyl- (18 pts.)	106
(0.5)	Isobutylene (0.45)	Fluoboric acid (0.025)	40–45	—	t-Butyl- (35 pts.), di-t-butyl- (11 pts.)	106
(2)	Isobutylene (1.6)	Dihydroxyfluoboric acid (0.48)	30	1	t-Butyl- (40 pts.), di-t-butyl- (20 pts.)	106(104)
(3)	Isobutylene (3)	45% BF_3 in Et_2O (15 cc.)	25–30	1.5	Mono- (24%),b di- (42%),b tri- (3%)b-t-butyl-	258(104)
(2)	Isobutylene (1)	75% H_2SO_4a (15 g.)	67	4	t-Butyl- (mono- 56%, di- 41%)	104(108, 108a, 675, 828a)
(5.4) (400 cc.)	Isobutylene (1.8)	100% H_3PO_4 (100 g.)	60	4	t-Butyl- (20%), (2-/3- = 70/30)	422(17)
	Isobutylene (220 cc.)	85% H_3PO_4 (80 cc.)	< 43	—	Alkyl- (39%)	231
(1)	Isobutylene (1)	H_3PO_4–kieselguhr	270 21.5 atm.	4.3 W.H.S.V.	2-t-Butyl- (37%), 3-t-butyl- (23%), di-t-butyl- (33%), di-t-butyl-dithienyl (5%)	18

a 60°/82° gives no alkylate; 90%/−10° gives less alkylate.   b Vol. %.

TABLE 61. Thiophenes with amylenes

Thiophene (Moles)	Olefin (Moles)	Catalyst (Moles)	Temp. (°C)	Time (hrs.)	Thiophene derivatives (% Yield)	Ref.
(1)	1-Pentene (1)	BF_3–Et_2O (25 g.)	137	2	Amyl- (mono- 16%, di- 64%)	104(258)
(1)	1-Pentene (0.86)	HF–Boric acid (6/1)	100	3	Amyl- (21 pts.)	106
(1)	2-Pentene (18 g.)	FeF_2–BF_3 (17 g.)	30	2	Amyl- (3.7 g.)	889
(0.5)	Amylenes (2)	H_2SO_4 (0.44)	0 ± 5	1.5	Diamyl- (30%)	108(675)
(5.8)	Amylene (1)	Silica-alumina (50 g.) (Filtrol)	200, 17 atm.	5	Amyl- (65%)	422
(24 g.)	Amylene (50 g.)	Silica-alumina (25 g.)	180, 150 psig	0.16	Diamyl- (66%)	107
(28 pts.)	Amylene (9 pts.)	Silica-alumina	263	—	Propyl- and butyl- (2.7 pts.), amyl- (1.3 pts.), higher (1.4 pts.)	107
—	2-Methyl-2-butene	85% H_3PO_4–H_2SO_4 (1/1 vol.)	25	—	Amyl- (mono- 78%, di- 7%)	617
(840 g.)	2-Methyl-2-butene (350 g.)	70% H_2SO_4 (300 g.)	40–50	3	t-Amyl- (57%)	108(828a)
—	2-Methyl-2-butene	Ethanesulfonic acid	32	—	t-Amyl- (mono- 33%, di- 17%)	617
—	3-Methyl-1-butene	$SnCl_4$–CH_3NO_2 (1/1.5 pts.)	45	—	Amyl- (mono- 14%, di- 24%)	617
—	3-Methyl-1-butene	85% H_3PO_4	70	—	Amyl- (mono- 49%, di- 12%)	617
(84 g.)	Isoamylene (70 g.)	$AlCl_3$ (10 g.)	30	2	Amyl- (16 g.)	105
(42 g.)	Isoamylene (17.5 g.)	$AlCl_3$–Boric acid (12 g.)	33–37	2	Isoamyl- (21%)	503
(2)	Isoamylene (2)	45% BF_3 in Et_2O (20 cc.)	50–60	1	t-Amyl- (22%), di-t-amyl- (37%)	258(104)
(1)	Isoamylene (1)	$H_3BO_2F_2$ (20 g.)	62	3	Amyl- (mono- 75%, di- 14%)	104
(1)	Isoamylene (1)	75% H_2SO_4 (15 g.)	67	2	Amyl- (mono- 62%, di- 14%)	104(108)
(0.5)	Isoamylene (0.57)	H_2SO_4 (0.034)	25–40	—	Amyl- (50%),[a] diamyl- (25%)[a]	108a(108, 675)
(0.5)	Isoamylene (0.57)	Isopropylsulfate	70	—	Amyl-, mono- (30 g.), di- (32 g.)	108a

[a] Of alkylate.

TABLE 62. Thiophene with higher olefins

Thiophene (Moles)	Olefin (Moles)	Catalyst (Moles)	Temp. (°C)	Time (hrs.)	Thiophene derivatives (% Yield)	Ref.
(1)	1-Hexene (1.5)	HF	r.t.	20	Hexyl- (mono- 23%, di- 6%)	916
(1)	1-Octene (1)	42% Fluoboric acid–BF₃ (80 pts.)	76	2	Octyl- (31 pts.)	106
(0.5)	1-Octene (0.5)	H_2SO_4 (15 g.)	100	5	Octyl- (mono- 43%, di- 20%)	104(108, 108a)
(1)	1-Octene (1)	BF_3–H_2O (80 g.)	75	2	Octyl- (mono- 28%, di- 72%)	104(106)
	1-Octene	BF_3-ether	80	—	Octyl- (mono- 56%, di- 9%)	617
(1)	1-Octene (1)	Dihydroxyfluoboric acid–BF_3 (80 pts.)	70	2	Octyl- (23 pts.)	106
84 g.	Diisobutylene (55 g.)	$AlCl_3$ (1 g.)	70	0.5	Octyl-[a] (25 g.), dioctyl-[a] (40 g.)	105(104)
84 g.	Diisobutylene (56 g.)	$SnCl_4$ (10 g.)	70–80	4	Octyl-[a] (42 g.), dioctyl-[a] (25 g.)	105
(1)	Diisobutylene (2)	HF	r.t.	20	t-Butyl, tri- (11%), tetra- (62%)	916
	Diisobutylene	BF_3	33	4	Octyl-[a], (mono- 39%, di- 49%)	617
(2)	Diisobutylene (1)	BF_3-Et_2O (100 g.)	35	4	Octyl-[a], (mono- 25%, di- 54%)	104
(1)	Diisobutylene (1)	80% H_2SO_4 (120 g.)	35	4	Octyl-[a], (mono- 82%, di- 7%)	104 (108a)
(0.5)	Diisobutylene (0.5)	80% H_2SO_4 (0.32)	70–75	1	Dibutyl-[a], (45 g.)	108
	α-Methylstyrene	85% H_3PO_4	80	—	Mono- (54%), dialkylate (13%)	617
	α-Methylstyrene	BF_3-Et_2O	33	—	Mono- (11%), dialkylate (32%)	617
(2)	Diisoamylene (1.25)	45% BF_3 in ether (30 cc.)	50–60	1	Monoamyl (9%), diamyl-, and decyl- (44%) triamyl- and amyldecyl-thiophenes (12%)	258
(10)	Propene tetramer (5)	BF_3–$2H_2O$ (300 cc.)	50	3	b.p. 250–350° ≅ dodecyl-	445
(0.5)	Triisobutylene (0.5)	Fluoboric acid (50 pts.)	80	1	di-t-Butyl- and residue (74 pts.)	408
(1)	Propene tetramer (0.8)	HF	—	—	Dodecyl- (77%)	916
(1)	1-Hexadecene (1)	BF_3–H_2O (80 pts.)	75	2	Hexadecyl- (25 pts.)	106(104)

[a] Probably t-octyl.

TABLE 63. Thiophene with cyclic olefins

Thiophene (Moles)	Olefin (Moles)	Catalyst (Moles)	Temp. (°C)	Time (hrs.)	Thiophene derivatives (% Yield)	Ref.
—	Cyclohexene	$SnCl_4$–CH_3NO_2 (1/1.5 pts.)	51	—	Cyclohexyl- (mono- 30%, di- 14%)	617
—	Cyclohexene	BF_3–Et_2O	80	—	Cyclohexyl- (mono- 45%, di- 18%)	617
—	Cyclohexene	85% H_3PO_4–H_2SO_4 (1/1 vol.)	23	—	Cyclohexyl- (mono- 5%, di- 0%)	617
(2)	Cyclohexene (1)	Silica-alumina (35 g.) (Filtrol)	200 12 atm.	5	Cyclohexyl- (27%)	422
—	4-Methylcyclohexene	$SnCl_4$–CH_3NO_2 (1/7.5 pts.)	35	—	1-Methylcyclohexyl- (mono- 31%, di- 40%)	617
—	4-Methylcyclohexene	85% H_3PO_4	76	—	1-Methylcyclohexyl- (mono- 1%, di- 1%)	617
—	4-Methylcyclohexene	85% H_3PO_4–H_2SO_4 (1/1 vol.)	21	—	Methylcyclohexyl- (mono- 20%, di- 3%)	617
(34 g.)	Bicyclo-(2,2,1)-2-heptene (18.8 g.)	BF_3–Et_2O (10 cc.)	27–40	—	2-Monobicycloheptyl- (11 g.), 2,5-di-bicycloheptyl- (8 g.)	616

TABLE 64. Thiophene derivatives with olefins

Aromatic (Moles)	Olefin (Moles)	Catalyst (Moles)	Temp. (°C)	Time (hrs.)	Thiophene derivatives (% Yield)	Ref.
2-Bromothiophene	Isobutylene	BF_3–Et_2O	43	—	Monoalkyl-2-bromo- (38%)	617
2-Bromothiophene	2-Methyl-2-butene	$SnCl_4$	69	—	Monoalkyl-2-bromo- (58%)	617
Chlorothiophene	Isobutylene	70% H_2SO_4	32	0.5	t-Butylchloro- (28%)	828a(409)
2-Chlorothiophene (1)	Diisobutylene (1.7)	HF	r.t.	20	Dibutyl- (14%), tributyl-2-chlorothiophene (15%)	916
2-Methylthiophene (1)	2-Ethyl-1-butene (1.2)	HF	r.t.	20	Hexyl- (6%), dihexyl-2-methylthiophene (16%)	916
3-Methylthiophene (1)	Diisobutylene (1.7)	HF	r.t.	20	Octyl- (23%), dioctyl-3-methylthiophene (43%)	916
Isopropylthiophene (126 g.)	Propene (55 g.)	80% H_2SO_4 (425 g.)	68–71	1.5	Diisopropyl- (20%), triisopropyl- (assumed)	108(828a)
2-Acetylthiophene (1)	Propene	$AlBr_3$, $AlCl_3$, $FeCl_3$,[a] or HF[a]	Moderate 1 atm.	—	4-Isopropyl derivative (major), 5-isopropyl isomer (minor)	778a
Thianaphthene (201 g.)	Isobutylene (3)	100% H_3PO_4	—	—	3-t-Butylthionaphthene (75%)	143

[a] Poor yields with these catalysts.

TABLE 65. Furans, pyrrole and phenthiazine with olefins

Aromatic (Moles)	Olefin (Moles)	Catalyst (Moles)	Temp. (°C)	Time (hrs.)	Products (% Yield)	Ref.
Furan (68 g.) (200 cc. Et₂O)	Ethylene (2–3.5 l./hr.)	BF₃–Et₂O (14 g.) (charcoal bed)	—	—	2-Ethyl- (5–10%), diethyl-furan (2–3%)	279
Furan (68 g.)	Isobutylene (1)	BF₃–Et₂O (2.5 cc.)	−10	1.25	2-t-Butyl- (3.5 g.), 2,5-di-t-butyl-furan (3.6 g.)	85
Furan	Isoamylene	AlCl₃–Boric acid	—	—	Isoamylfuran (good yield)	503
Furan (34 g.)	Isoamylene (17 g.)	BF₃–Et₂O (2.5 cc.)	11–35	2.75	t-Amyl- (17%), di-t-amyl-furan (3%)	622a
Furan (2)	Diisobutylene (1)	BF₃–Et₂O (5 cc.)	12	0.5	2- (18%) and 2,5-di-(1'1',3',3'-tetramethylbutyl)-furan (14%)	85
2-t-Butylfuran (2.3 g.)	Diisobutylene (4.4 g.)	BF₃–Et₂O (0.5 cc.)	—	—	2-t-Butyl-5-(1',1',3',3'-tetramethylbutyl)-furan (3.6 g.)	85
Methyl-2-furoate	Butene	AlCl₃	—	—	5-t-Butyl-2-furoate	233
Ethyl-5-bromo-2-furoate (0.1)	$C_4^=$, $C_5^=$ DIB^a or cyclohexene (0.1)	AlCl₃ (0.2) (200 ml. CS₂)	r.t.	24	No alkylation, whereas alkyl halides produce 4-t-butyl derivatives	233a
Diphenylene oxide (0.5) (200 pts. xylene)	α-Methylstyrene (1)	Act. bleaching earth (10 pts.)	80	2.5	α-Phenylisopropyl derivatives	509
Pyrrole	Ethylene	SiO₂·Al₂O₃	204–371	—	Ethylpyrrole	910a
Phenthiazine	Ethylene (200 atm.)	Aluminum anilide–aniline–AlCl₃, or NiL₂ or I₂	300	—	4-Ethylphenthiazine (90%)	195
Phenothioxin	$C_2^=$, $C_3^=$, $C_4^=$, CH^b	Act. bleaching earth	—	—	Alkylation products	772a
Pyrrole (0.5)	Methyl vinyl ketone (1)	SO₂ (1 g.)–H₂O (50 g.)–C₆H₄O₂ (1 g.)	60	1.5	2,5-Bis-(3-oxobutyl)pyrrole (80%)	221
Dibenzofuran (4)	Ethylene (4) 500 psig	AlCl₃ (0.4)	80–90	Few	2-Ethyl derivative	75a

^{a} Diisobutylene. ^{b} Cyclohexene.

TABLE 66. Aromatics with alkanes

Aromatic (Moles)	Alkane (Moles)	Catalyst (Moles)	Temp. (°C)	Time (hrs.)	Products (% Yield)	Ref.
Benzene (1)	Methane (9.1)	SiO_2–Al_2O_3 (15%)	600 232 atm.	—	Toluene (5%)	322
Benzene	Methane	Ni–SiO_2	372 545 atm.	—	Toluene (21%)	322
Benzene (88.9%)	Ethane (11.1%)	None	605 2865 psi	—	Ethylbenzene–toluene = 5.5/1	213
Benzene	Propane	Ni–kieselguhr	350 60 atm.	0.18	Toluene (28%),[a,b] C_8 aromatics (3%),[a] cumene (1%),[a] higher (3%),[a] methylcyclopentane (some)	368
Benzene	Isobutane	SiO_2–Al_2O_3	550–660	—	Butyl-, isopropylbenzene and lower (14–15%)	481
Benzene (1.3)	n-Pentane (0.7)	$AlCl_3$–HCl (0.06)	175	8	Toluene (10%), ethylbenzene (25%), n-propylbenzene (8%)[c]	247
Benzene (118 g.)	Pentane (109 g.)	Aluminosilicate (46%)	400–450 420–510 atm.	—	Toluene, ethylbenzene, xylenes, cumene, n-propylbenzene, etc. (total 35%)	839(673)
Benzene (1.3)	Isopentane (0.7)	$AlCl_3$–HCl (0.06)	175	8	Toluene (10%), ethylbenzene (25%), n-propylbenzene (8%)[c]	247
Benzene (1.2)	n-Hexane (0.6)	$AlCl_3$–HCl (0.06)	175	8	Toluene (10%), ethylbenzene (25%), n-propylbenzene (6%)[c]	247
Benzene (0.6)	n-Hexane (0.6)	H_3PO_4 (0.2)	450	10	Cumene (15%), butylbenzene (10%), C_3, C_2, H_2	319(318)
Benzene (100 g.)	2-Methylpentane (55 g.)	$AlCl_3$ (8.5 g.)–HCl (1.75 g.)	125	8	Toluene (5.8 g.), ethylbenzene (28.3 g.)[c]	247
Benzene (1)	n-Heptane (51 g.)	$AlCl_3$ (6.7 g.)–HCl (0.06 g.)	125	8	Toluene (1.4 g.), ethylbenzene (7.4 g.)	247
Benzene (1)		$AlCl_3$ (6.6 g.)–HCl (0.2 g.)	175	8	n-propylbenzene (3.3)[c]; Toluene (1.6 g.), ethylbenzene (12.7 g.), n-propylbenzene (3.9)	247

Aromatic	Alkane	Catalyst	Temp.	Pressure		Products	Ref.
Benzene (232 pts.)	Heptane (229 pts.)	HF–BF$_3$ (373 pts./19 pts.)	165	700–1070 psig	0.83	32% C$_4$- (33% C$_3$, 67% iso-C$_4$); 68% C$_5$ + (10% iso-C$_5$, 3% C$_6$, 26% C$_7$, 25% benzene); toluene (8%) C$_6$H$_4$Et$_2$ (3%), ethylbenzene (14%), ethyltoluene (7%), bottoms (7%)	444(48)
Benzene (39 g.)	2,2,3-Trimethylpentane (28.5 g.)	AlCl$_3$ (3.3 g.)–HCl (0.4 g.)	80–90		11	t-Butylbenzene (15%), isobutane (70%)	247
Benzene	n-Heptane, 2,2,4-tri-methylpentane, or n-hexadecane	Syn. aluminosilicate	500–25	15 atm.	—	Some destructive alkylation occurs	850
Benzene (1)	n-Octane (57 g.)	AlCl$_3$ (6.7 g.)–HCl (2.3 g.)	125		10	Toluene (2.6 g.), ethylbenzene (9.8 g.), n-propylbenzene (4 g.)[c]	247
Benzene (1.63)	2,2,4-Trimethylpentane (1.4)	AlCl$_3$–HCl (0.07)	20–50		4	t-Butylbenzene (35%), di-t-butyl-benzene (25%), isobutane (70%)	244(247, 316)
Benzene (63 g.)	2,2,4-Trimethylpentane (78.5 g.)	ZrCl$_4$ (16.7 g.), HCl (8 g.)	50 75 r.t.		1.5 2 10	t-Butylbenzene (24.7 g.), di-t-butylbenzene, isobutane (40.4 g.)	244
Benzene	2,2,4-Trimethylpentane	100% H$_2$SO$_4$, 100 vol.				Butylbenzenes and higher alky-late (60 vol. %)	399
Benzene (0.7)	2,2,4-Trimethylpentane (0.5)	100% H$_3$PO$_4$ (0.15)	450		6	t-Butylbenzene (20%)[c]	319
Benzene (4.2)	2,2,4-Trimethylpentane (2.1)	HF (4.5)	204	1300 psi	5	t-Butylbenzene (65%)	48
Benzene (48 g.)	n-Decane (36 g.)	AlCl$_3$ (3.3 g.)–HCl (2.7 g.)	125		23	Toluene (0), ethylbenzene (4.9 g.)[c]	247
Benzene (1)	n-Hexadecane (113 g.)	AlCl$_3$ (6.7 g.)–HCl (0.9 g.)	125		8	Toluene (2.2 g.), ethylbenzene (5.8 g.), n-propylbenzene (2.2 g.)	247
Toluene	n-Pentane	SiO$_2$–Al$_2$O$_3$	500		—	Catalyzate (17%) contg. 14 pts. ethylbenzene, 12 pts. o-, 47 pts. m-, 27 pts. p-xylenes	93

Table continued

TABLE 66 (*continued*)

Aromatic (Moles)	Alkane (Moles)	Catalyst (Moles)	Temp. (°C)	Time (hrs.)	Products (% Yield)	Ref.
Toluene (0.9)	2,2,4-Trimethylpentane (0.6)	$AlCl_3$–HCl (0.045/0.034)	96	8	Butyltoluene (17.3 g.), iso-C_4 (22.1 g.), nC_4 (1.4 g.)	248
Naphthalene (91.8%)	Ethane (8.2%)	None	—	—	Methylnaphthalene, ethyl-naphthalene	213
Naphthalene (50 g.)	Naphtha (b.p. 60–90°) (200 cc.)	$AlCl_3$ (50 g.)	50	5	80% Naphthalene consumed	188
Biphenyl (0.8)	2,2,4-Trimethylpentane (0.4)	$AlCl_3$–HCl (0.04/0.018)	90–95	2.2	Butylbiphenyls (35%), iso-C_4 (24.9 g.)	248
Phenol (1)	2,4-Dimethylhexane (1)	$AlCl_3$ (85%)	80	6	4-t-Butylphenol (75%)	586
Phenol (1)	2,4-Dimethylhexane (1)	$TiCl_4$ (200%)	115–120	—	4-t-Butylphenol (30%)	586
Phenol (1)	2,4-Dimethylhexane (1)	$ClC_6H_4SO_3H$ (28%)	>130	6	4-t-Butylphenol (28%)	586

[a] Based on benzene.   [b] 9% when propane is omitted from feed.   [c] Propane and isobutane gases also produced.

TABLE 67. Aromatics with cycloalkanes

Aromatic (Moles)	Cycloalkane (Moles)	Catalyst (Moles)	Temp. (°C)	Time (hrs.)	Products (% Yield)	Ref.
Thiophene	Cyclopropane	BF_3–Et_2O	90	—	Propylthiophenes (mono- 39%, di- 16%)	153
Thiophenol (5)	Cyclopropane (4)	$AlCl_3$ (0.75)	15–39	1.3	2-Propylthiophenol (6%),[a] propylphenylsulfide (56%)[a] propyl-o-propylphenylsulfide (1%)[a]	424
Benzene	Cyclopropane	$AlCl_3$ (10%)	15	—	n-Propylbenzene (mono-50%, di- 25%, hexa- 5%)	892
Benzene (78 g.)	Cyclopropane (21.3 g.)	$AlCl_3$ (10 g.)	71	6	n-Propylbenzene (48%)	341
Benzene (1)	Cyclopropane (1)	$AlCl_3$–HCl (8.9 g./0.3 g.)	25–30	3	n-Propylbenzene (29%), di-n-propylbenzene (13%), hexa-n-propylbenzene (6%)	246
Benzene (2.3)	Cyclopropane (1)	$AlCl_3$–HCl (8.8 g./0.8 g.)	0–5	5	n-Propylbenzene (65%)	246
Benzene (62 g.)	Cyclopropane (6 g.)	$AlCl_3$ (5 g.)–CH_3NO_2 (5.7 g.)	r.t.	4	Propylbenzene (70%), high boilers (2.5 g.)	700
Benzene (80 g.)	Cyclopropane (23.5 g.)	80% H_2SO_4 (400 cc.)	50	2	Isopropylbenzene (58%)	341
Benzene (1.1)	Cyclopropane (0.6)	80% H_2SO_4 (3)	65	5	Cumene (58%)	341
Benzene (90 pts.)	Cyclopropane (18 pts.)	H_2SO_4 (45 pts.)	65	5	n-Propylbenzene (35%)	326(331)
Benzene	Cyclopropane	HF	5	1	n-Propylbenzene (42%), di-n-propylbenzene (20%)	756
Benzene (2.4)	Cyclopropane (0.1)	HF (0.5)	0	—	n-Propylbenzene (29%)	614
Benzene (0.3)	Methylcyclobutane (0.15)	$AlCl_3$–HCl (1.35 g./0.3 g.)	25	22	Isoamylbenzene also probably 2-phenylpentane (5 ml.)	246
Benzene (1.2)	Methylcyclobutane (0.4)	H_2SO_4 (0.9)	2	2.5	t-Amylbenzene (2%)	331
Benzene (90 pts.)	Methylcyclobutane (30 pts.)	H_2SO_4 (90 pts.)	4	2.5	Amylbenzene (30%)	326

Table continued

TABLE 67 (continued)

Aromatic (Moles)	Cycloalkane (Moles)	Catalyst (Moles)	Temp. (°C)	Time (hrs.)	Products (% Yield)	Ref.
Benzene (1.5)	Cyclopentane (0.7)	$AlCl_3$–HCl (9.97 g.)/ (0.8 g.)	150	8	Amylbenzenes (5.2 g.) cyclopentyl-benzene (1.7 g.) also toluene, ethylbenzene	246
Benzene (1)	Ethylcyclopropane (0.25)	$AlCl_3$ (0.1)–HCl	5–12	—	Phenylpentanes (50–55%)[b]	614
Benzene (1)	Ethylcyclopropane (0.24)	H_2SO_4 (20 cc.)	5–10	—	Phenylpentanes (46%)[b]	614
Benzene (1.2)	Ethylcyclopropane (0.1)	HF (0.5)	0–5	—	Phenylpentanes (42%)[b]	614
Benzene (0.8)	1,1-Dimethylcyclopropane (0.07)	HF (0.34)	0–5	—	t-Amylbenzene (48%)	614
Benzene (1.86)	1,2-Dimethylcyclopropane (0.16)	HF (0.9)	0–5	—	Amylbenzenes (42.5%) (t/s = 83–87/10–14; also 2–3% 2-phenyl-3-methylbutane)	614
Benzene (1 pt.)	Cyclohexane (1 pt.)	$AlCl_3$ (0.4 pts.)/HCl 30 atm. H_2	80	24	Ethylbenzene (15%), cyclohexyl-benzene	317
Benzene (80 pts.)	Cyclohexane (52 pts.)	$ZnCl_2/Al_2O_3$ (25/75) (15 pts.)	400 267 atm.	4	Liquids (113 pts.): toluene, xylenes, ethylbenzene and higher. Gases (6 pts.): C_3/iso-C_4/n-C_4/C_5 = 21.4/32.6/15.4/30.6	705
Benzene (1)	Phenylcyclopropane (0.3)	$AlCl_3$ (0.09)	0–10	5	1,1-Diphenylpropane (52%)	439a
Benzene	p-Tolylcyclopropane	$AlCl_3$	—	—	1-Phenyl-1-p-tolylpropane (34%)	439a
Benzene	p-Anisylcyclopropane	$AlCl_3$	—	—	1-Phenyl-1-p-anisylpropane (6%)	439a
Toluene	Phenylcyclopropane (0.3)	$AlCl_3$	—	—	1-Phenyl-1-tolylpropane (62%)	439a
Anisole	Phenylcyclopropane (0.3)	$AlCl_3$	—	—	1-Phenyl-1-anisylpropane (73%)	439a
m-Xylene (120 g.)	Cyclopropane (22 g.)	$AlCl_3$ (4.4 g.)	0–5 15	4.5 0.5	1,3-Dimethyl-4-n-propylbenzene (40%)	560(561)
m-Xylene (1)	Cyclopropane (0.5)	$FeCl_3$ (0.06)	—	—	4-n-Propyl-m-xylene (19%)	561
t-Butylbenzene (40 g.)	Methylcyclohexane (117 g.)	HF (90 g.)	25, 60	1.5, 0.5	s-Methylcyclohexylbenzene (39%)	715
2-Methylnaph-thalene (0.6)	Cyclopropane (0.5)	$ZrCl_4$–HCl (0.02)	30–35	4	Propyl-2-methylnaphthalene (15%)	246

a Based on 38% conversion of thiol.   b 2-/3- = 63/37.

References

1. Abadir, B. Y., U.S. Pat. 2,865,966 (Dec. 23, 1958).
2. Adam, Paul, *Ann. Chim. Phys.*, (6), **15**, 224 (1888); *Bull. Soc. Chim. France*, (2), **49**, 98 (1888).
3. Aktien-Gesells. für Anilin-Fabrik., Germ. Pat. 184,230 (Feb. 2, 1906).
4. Albert, H. E., U.S. Pat. 2,537,635 (Jan. 9, 1951).
5. Albert, H. E., U.S. Pat. 2,560,044 (July 10, 1951).
6. Aldridge, C. L. and E. A. Hunter, U.S. Pat. 3,014,081 (Dec. 19, 1961).
7. Alexander, L. L. and R. C. Fuson, *J. Am. Chem. Soc.*, **58**, 1745 (1936).
7a. Alexander, L. L., A. L. Jacoby, and R. C. Fuson, *J. Am. Chem. Soc.*, **57**, 2208 (1935).
7b. Allen, R. H., *J. Am. Chem. Soc.*, **82**, 4856 (1960).
8. Allen, R. H., T. Alfrey, and L. D. Yats, *J. Am. Chem. Soc.*, **81**, 42 (1959).
9. Allen, R. H., and L. D. Yats, *J. Am. Chem. Soc.*, **81**, 5289 (1959).
10. Allen, R. H., and L. D. Yats, *J. Am. Chem. Soc.*, **83**, 2799 (1961).
10b. Allen, R. H., L. D. Yats, and D. S. Erley, *J. Am. Chem. Soc.*, **82**, 4853 (1960).
11. Amos, J. L., U.S. Pat. 2,225,543 (Dec. 17, 1941).
11a. Axe, W. N., U.S. Pat. 2,430,660 and 2,430,661 (Nov. 11, 1947).
12. Amos, J. L., and K. E. Coulter, U.S. Pat. 2,763,702 (Sept. 18, 1956).
13. Anderson, J., E. F. Bullard, and S. H. McAllister, U.S. Pat. 2,396,144 (Mar. 5, 1946).
14. Andreev, D. N., A. P. Meshcheryakov, and A. D. Petrov, *J. Appl. Chem. U.S.S.R.*, **19**, 705 (1946).
15. Andreev, D. N., and A. D. Petrov, *J. Appl. Chem. U.S.S.R.*, **21**, 134 (1948).
16. Anschutz, R., and H. Beckerhoff, *Ann.*, **327**, 218 (1903).
17. Appleby, W. G., L. L. Lovell, and M. P. L. Love, U.S. Pat. 2,429,575 (Oct. 21, 1947).
18. Appleby, W. G., A. F. Sartor, S. H. Lee, and S. W. Kapranos, *J. Am. Chem. Soc.*, **70**, 1552 (1948).
19. Arbuzov, B. A., and E. V. Kuznetsov, *Compt. rend. acad. sci. U.R.S.S.*, **39**, 311 (1943).
20a. Aries, R. S., U.S. Pat. 2,930,819 (Mar. 29, 1960).
20b. Aries, R. S., U.S. Pat. 2,930,820 (Mar. 29, 1960).
21. Arnold, G. B., and H. D. Kluge, U.S. Pat. 2,789,143 (Apr. 16, 1957).
21a. Arnold, J. C., Brit. Pat. 581,907 (Oct. 29, 1946).
22. Arnold, P. M., U.S. Pat. 2,553,538 (May 22, 1951).
23. Arvin, J. A., and J. V. Hunn, U.S. Pat. 2,415,069 (Feb. 4, 1947).
24. Asahara, T., and Y. Takagi, *J. Chem. Soc. Japan, Ind. Chem. Sect.*, **58**, 147 (1955).
25. Asinger, F., G. Geiseler, and W. Beetz, *Ber.*, **92**, 755 (1959).
26. Axe, W. N., U.S. Pat. 2,403,963 (July 16, 1946).
27. Axe, W. N., U.S. Pat. 2,412,595 (Dec. 17, 1946).
28. Axe, W. N., U.S. Pat. 2,544,818 (March 13, 1951).
29. Babakhanov, R. A., *Tr. Pyatoi Nauchn. Konf. Aspirantov Akad. Nauk Azerb. S.S.R.*, 39 (1957).

29a. Babin, E. P., *Khim. Prom.*, 381 (1961).
29b. Babin, E. P., V. G. Plyusnin, and I. A. Alekseeva, *Izv. Sibirsk. Otd. Akad. Nauk S.S.S.R.*, No. 1, 75 (1960).
30. Babin, E. P., V. G. Plyusnin, and M. I. Nasakina, *Izv. Sibirsk. Otd. Akad. Nauk S.S.S.R.*, No. 11, 28 (1958); *C.A.*, **53**, 16026h (1959).
31. Babin, E. P., V. G. Plyusnin, and M. I. Nasakina, *Izv. Sibirsk. Otd. Akad. Nauk S.S.S.R.*, No. 1, 72 (1959).
32. Babin, E. P., V. G. Plyusnin, and M. I. Nasakina, *Izv. Sibirsk. Otd. Akad. Nauk S.S.S.R.*, No. 3, 50 (1960).
33. Babin, E. P., V. G. Plyusnin, M. I. Nasakina, and N. M. Rodigin, *Zh. Fiz. Khim.*, **34**, 1389 (1960).
34. Babin, E. P., V. G. Plyusnin, M. I. Nasakina, and N. M. Rodigin, *Zh. Fiz. Khim.*, **34**, 1671 (1960).
35. Babin, E. P., V. G. Plyusnin, M. I. Zelentsova, and N. M. Rodigin, *Izv. Sibirsk. Otd. Akad. Nauk S.S.S.R.*, No. 11, 57 (1959).
36. Baddeley, G., G. Hart, and D. Voss, *J. Chem. Soc.*, 101 (1952).
37. Baev, N. P., A. V. Topchiev, Y. M. Paushkin, and M. V. Kurashev, *Khim. Pererabotka Neft. Uglevodorodov, Tr. Vses. Soveshch. po Kompleksn. Khim. Pererabotke Neft. Gaz.*, 422 (1956); *C.A.*, **51**, 17782d (1957).
38. Bailey, G. C., and J. A. Reid, U.S. Pat. 2,519,099 (Aug. 15, 1950).
39. Bakelite Ltd., Brit. Pat. 560,908 (Apr. 26, 1944).
40. Balle, G., and H. Schild, Germ. Pat. 745,802 (Apr. 25, 1944).
41. Balsohn, M., *Bull. Soc. Chim. France*, (2), **31**, 539 (1879).
42. Bann, B., and R. D. Thrower, *Compt. rend. 27e Congr. intern. chim. ind. Brussels*, 2 (1954).
43. Barclay, L. R. C., J. W. Hilchie, A. H. Gray, and N. D. Hall, *Can. J. Chem.*, **38**, 94 (1960).
44. Bartkus, E. A., E. B. Hotelling, and M. B. Neuworth, *J. Org. Chem.*, **25**, 232 (1960).
45. Bataafsche, N. V., Fr. Pat. 782,194 (May 31, 1935).
46. Battegay, M., and M. Kappeler, *Bull. Soc. Chim. France*, (4), **35**, 989 (1924).
47. Becke, F., and H. Bittermann, *Chem. Ber.*, **93**, 2344 (1960).
48. Becker, S. B., U.S. Pat. 2,433,020 (Dec. 23, 1947).
49. Beltrame, P., *Chim. Ind. (Milan)*, **39**, 270 (1957).
50. Benesi, H. A., *J. Phys. Chem.*, **61**, 970 (1957).
51. Bergel, F., A. M. Copping, A. Jacob, A. R. Todd, and T. S. Work, *J. Chem. Soc.*, 1382 (1938).
52. Berry, T. M., and E. E. Reid, *J. Am. Chem. Soc.*, **49**, 3142 (1927).
53. Biller, E., Brit. Pat. 839,501 (June 29, 1960).
54. Blackwell, J., and W. J. Hickinbottom, *Chem. and Ind.*, 1569 (1961).
55. Blagden, J. W., Brit. Pat. 214,866 (June 12, 1923).
56. Blanding, F. H., U.S. Pat. 2,385,187 (Sept. 18, 1945).
57. Bloch, H. S., U.S. Pat. 2,426,665 (Sept. 2, 1947).
58. Bloch, H. S., U.S. Pat. 2,971,992 (Feb. 14, 1961).
59. Bloch, H. S., and G. L. Hervert, Am. Chem. Soc., Chicago Meeting, Div. Petrol. Chem., Gen. Papers, No. 30, 57 (1953).
60. Bloch, H. S., and G. L. Hervert, U.S. Pat. 2,703,330 (Mar. 1, 1955).
61. Bloch, H. S., and G. L. Hervert, U.S. Pat. 2,887,518 (May 19, 1959).
62. Bloch, H. S., and G. L. Hervert, Brit. Pat. 844,042 (Aug. 10, 1960).

63. Bloch, H. S., J. M. Mavity and D. H. Belden, Brit. Pat. 666,642 (Feb. 13, 1952).

63a. Bloch, H. S., H. Pines, and L. Schmerling, *J. Am. Chem. Soc.*, **67**, 914 (1945).

64. Bloxam, A. G., Brit. Pat. 28,147 (July 25, 1907).

65. Blues, E. T., and D. Bryce-Smith, *Proc. Chem. Soc.*, 245 (1961).

66. Bodroux, D., *Ann. Chim. (Paris)*, (10), **11**, 511 (1929).

67. Böhme, H., N. Fischer, and R. Frank, *Ann.*, **563**, 54 (1949).

68. Bondarenko, A. V., M. I. Bogdanov, and M. I. Farberov, *J. Appl. Chem. U.S.S.R.*, **30**, 822 (1957).

69. Bos, L. B., U.S. Pat. 2,698,867 (Jan. 4, 1955).

70. Bowles, A. F., U.S. Pat. 2,618,645 (Nov. 18, 1952).

71. Bowman, R. S., D. R. Stevens, and W. E. Baldwin, *J. Am. Chem. Soc.*, **79**, 87 (1957).

72. Braidwood, C. A., U.S. Pat. 2,523,939 (Sept. 26, 1950); Brit. Pat. 640,485 (July 19, 1950).

73. Brit. Pat. 323,100 (Dec. 3, 1928).

74. Brit. Pat. 597,223 (Jan. 21, 1948).

74a. Brit. Pat. 769,383 (Mar. 6, 1957).

75. Brit. Pat. 846,226 (Aug. 31, 1960).

75a. British Thomson-Houston Co., Brit. Pat. 635,631 (April 12, 1950).

76. Britton, E. C., G. H. Coleman, and R. P. Perkins, U.S. Pat. 2,248,401 (July 8, 1941).

77. Britton, E. C., and J. C. Vander Weele, U.S. Pat. 2,403,785 (July 8, 1946).

78. Brochet, A., *Compt. rend.*, **117**, 115, 235 (1893).

78a. Brooks, B. T., *Chemistry of Petroleum Hydrocarbons*, Vol. III, Chapter 55, Reinhold Publishing Corp., New York, 1955.

79. Brooks, L. F., Can. Pat. 520,517 (Jan. 10, 1956).

79a. Brown, H. C., *J. Chem. Educ.*, **36**, 424 (1959).

80. Brown, H. C., and J. D. Brady, *J. Am. Chem. Soc.*, **74**, 3570 (1952).

81. Brown, H. C., and W. S. Higley, U.S. Pat. 2,767,230 (Oct. 16, 1956).

81a. Brown, H. C., and H. Jungk, *J. Am. Chem. Soc.*, **77**, 5579 (1955).

82. Brown, H. C., and K. L. Nelson, *J. Am. Chem. Soc.*, **75**, 6292 (1953).

83. Brown, H. C., and H. W. Pearsall, *J. Am. Chem. Soc.*, **74**, 191 (1952).

84. Brown, H. C., and R. C. Smoot, *J. Am. Chem. Soc.*, **78**, 6256 (1956).

84a. Brown, H. C., and R. C. Smoot, *J. Am. Chem. Soc.*, **78**, 2176 (1956).

85. Brown, W. H., and G. F. Wright, *Can. J. Chem.*, **35**, 236 (1957).

85a. Bruner, F. H., L. A. Clarke, and R. L. Sawyer, U.S. Pat. 2,376,119 (May 15, 1945).

86. Bruson, H. A., and Otto Stein, U.S. Pat. 2,072,153 (Mar. 2, 1937).

87. Bryner, F., U.S. Pat. 2,655,547 (Oct. 13, 1953); Brit. Pat. 725,873 (Mar. 9, 1955).

88. Bryner, F., U.S. Pat. 2,726,270 (Dec. 6, 1955).

89. Buc, H. E., U.S. Pat. 2,104,412 (Jan. 4, 1938).

90. Buc, H. E., U.S. Pat. 2,332,555 (Oct. 26, 1938).

91. Buell, C. K., and R. G. Boatright, U.S. Pat. 2,431,166 (Nov. 18, 1947).

92. Buls, V. W., and R. S. Miller, U.S. Pat. 2,923,745 (Feb. 2, 1960).

93. Bunigat-Zade, A. A., A. M. Belkina, A. A. Bakshi-Zade, and L. N. Petukhova, *Uch. Zap. Azerb. Gos. Univ., Ser. Fiz. Mat. i Khim. Nauk*, No. 1, 91 (1960); *C.A.*, **56**, 360e (1962).

93a. Burk, R. E., *Twelfth Catalysis Report*, John Wiley and Sons, New York, p. 266, 1940.

94. Burk, R. E., and E. C. Hughes, U.S. Pat. 2,399,662 (May 7, 1946).

95. Burk, R. E., and E. C. Hughes, U.S. Pat. 2,442,342 (June 1, 1948).

96. Burton, H., and P. F. G. Praill, *Chem. and Ind.*, 90 (1954).

97. Butler, J. M., U.S. Pat. 2,569,400 (Sept. 25, 1951).

98. Butler, J. M., U.S. Pat. 2,661,335 (Dec. 1, 1953).

99. Buu-Hoï, Ng. Ph., and P. Cagniant, *Compt. rend.*, **216**, 381 (1943).

100. Buu-Hoï, Ng. Ph., and Paul Cagniant, *Compt. rend.*, **220**, 326 (1945).

101. Buu-Hoï, Ng. Ph., P. Cagniant, and C. Mentzer, *Bull. Soc. Chim. France*, (5), **11**, 127 (1944).

102. Buu-Hoï, Ng. Ph., H. LeBihan, and F. Binon, *J. Org. Chem.*, **17**, 243 (1952).

102a. Buu-Hoï, Ng. Ph., H. LeBihan, F. Binon, and P. Maleyran, *J. Org. Chem.*, **17**, 1122 (1952).

103. Buu-Hoï, Ng. Ph., and Dat Xuong, *Bull. Soc. Chim. France*, 751 (1948).

104. Caesar, P. D., *J. Am. Chem. Soc.*, **70**, 3623 (1948).

105. Caesar, P. D., U.S. Pat. 2,552,769 (May 15, 1951).

106. Caesar, P. D., G. C. Johnson, and J. W. Brooks, U.S. Pat. 2,527,794 (Oct. 31, 1950).

107. Caesar, P. D., and A. N. Sachanen, U.S. Pat. 2,448,211 (Aug. 31, 1948).

108. Caesar, P. D., and P. G. Waldo, U.S. Pat. 2,482,084 (Sept. 20, 1949).

108a. Caesar, P. D., and P. Waldo, U.S. Pat. 2,550,769 (May 1, 1951).

109. Cagniant, P., A. Deluzarche, and G. Chatelus, *Compt. rend.*, **224**, 1064 (1947).

110. Calcott, W. S., J. M. Tinker, and V. Weinmayr, *J. Am. Chem. Soc.*, **61**, 1010 (1939).

111. Carmody, D. R., and H. E. Huber, U.S. Pat. 2,396,683 (Mar. 19, 1946).

112. Carnes, J. J., U.S. Pat. 2,433,316 (Dec. 23, 1947).

113. Carpenter, M. S., and W. M. Easter, U.S. Pat. 2,476,815 (July 19, 1949); 2,450,877 (Oct. 12, 1948).

114. Carpenter, M. S., W. M. Easter, and T. F. Wood, *J. Org. Chem.*, **16**, 586 (1951).

115. Centre de Technologie Chimique, French Pat. 1,209,863 (Mar. 4, 1960).

116. *Chem. Eng. News*, Nov. 6 (1961), 25.

117. Chempatents, Inc., Brit. Pat. 763,155 (Dec. 5, 1956).

118. Chempatents, Inc., Brit. Pat. 762,763 (Dec. 5, 1956).

119. Chirkov, N. M., and Kh. R. Rustamov, *Zh. Fiz. Khim.*, **32**, 219 (1958).

120. Choi, S. U., and H. C. Brown, *J. Am. Chem. Soc.*, **81**, 3315 (1959).

121. Christiansen, W. G., and W. A. Lott, U.S. Pat. 1,922,153 (Aug. 15, 1933).

122. Cline, E. L., and E. E. Reid, *J. Am. Chem. Soc.*, **49**, 3150 (1927).

122a. Coalite and Chemical Products, Ltd., Belg. Pat. 609,029 (open Feb. 1, 1962).

123. Coats, R. R., and N. H. Keir, Brit. Pat. 773,502 (Apr. 24, 1957).

124. Cohen, C. A., and C. W. Muessig, U.S. Pat. 2,521,344 (Sept. 5, 1950).

125. Coleman, G. H., and R. H. Rigterink, U.S. Pat. 2,617,837 (Nov. 11, 1952).

126. Colomb, Mlle., *Ann. Min. Carb. Document Fr.*, **135**, 545 (1946).

127. Colonge, J., and P. Garnier, *Bull. Soc. Chim. France*, 436 (1948).

128. Compagnie Française de Raffinage, Brit. Pat. 631,874 (Nov. 11, 1949).

129. Condon, F. E., *J. Am. Chem. Soc.*, **70**, 2265 (1948).

130. Condon, F. E., *J. Am. Chem. Soc.*, **71**, 3544 (1949).
131. Condon, F. E., U.S. Pat. 2,653,980 (Sept. 29, 1953).
132. Condon, F. E., *J. Org. Chem.*, **21**, 761 (1956).
133. Condon, F. E., and E. E. Burgoyne, *J. Am. Chem. Soc.*, **73**, 4021 (1951).
134. Condon, F. E., and M. P. Mutuszak, *J. Am. Chem. Soc.*, **70**, 2539 (1948).
135. Conklin, L. H., and R. A. McPherson, U.S. Pat. 2,978,515 (Apr. 4, 1961); Brit. Pat. 831,828 (May 14, 1957).
136. Continental Oil Co., Brit. Pat. 816,610 (July 15, 1959).
137. Cook, C. D., R. G. Inskeep, A. S. Rosenberg, and E. C. Curtis, *J. Am. Chem. Soc.*, **77**, 1672 (1955).
138. Corson, B. B., and L. J. Brady, U.S. Pat. 2,417,454 (Mar. 18, 1947).
139. Corson, B. B., and L. J. Brady, Brit. Pat. 616,260 (Jan. 19, 1949).
140. Corson, B. B., W. J. Heintzelman, R. C. Odioso, H. E. Tiefenthal, and F. J. Pavlik; *Ind. Eng. Chem.*, **48**, 1180 (1956).
141. Corson, B. B., and V. N. Ipatieff, *J. Am. Chem. Soc.*, **59**, 645 (1937).
142. Corson, B. B., and W. M. Kutz, U.S. Pat. 2,572,701 (Oct. 23, 1951).
143. Corson, B. B., H. E. Tiefenthal, G. R. Atwood, W. J. Heintzelman, and W. L. Reilly, *J. Org. Chem.*, **21**, 584 (1956).
144. Coscia, A. T., J. T. Penniston, and J. C. Petroupoulis, *J. Org. Chem.*, **26**, 1398 (1961).
145a. Crawford, H. M., and M. C. Glessman, *J. Am. Chem. Soc.*, **76**, 1108 (1954).
145b. Crisp, E. T., and N. H. Keir, Brit. Pat. 794,570 (May 7, 1958).
145c. Crosby, J. N., University Microfilms Publ. 352 (1941) Ph.D. Thesis, Pennsylvania State College.
146. Croxall, W. J., F. J. Sowa, and J. A. Nieuwland, *J. Am. Chem. Soc.*, **56**, 2054 (1934); **57**, 1549 (1935).
147. Cullinane, N. M., and D. M. Leyshon, *J. Chem. Soc.*, 2942 (1954).
148. D'Alelio, G. F., U.S. Pat. 2,802,884 (Aug. 13, 1957).
149. Dalin, M. A., P. I. Markosov, R. I. Shenderova, and G. V. Prokof'eva, *Alkylation of Benzene with Olefins*, Gosudarst. Nauch.-Tekh. Izdatel. Khim. Lit., Moscow, 1957; through *C.A.*, **52**, 15563h (1958).
150. Dalin, M. A., R. E. Spivak, and E. F. Burmistrov, *Azerb. Khim. Zh.*, No. 6, 21 (1960).
151. Dalin, M. A., R. E. Spivak, E. F. Burmistrov, and L. M. Vyazmitinov, *Khim. Prom.*, 3, 21 (1961).
152. Danforth, J. D., U.S. Pat. 2,410,151 (Oct. 29, 1961).
153. Dat-Xuong, N., N. P. Buu-Hoï, and B. Khac-Diep, *Bull. Soc. Chim. France*, 1136 (1961).
154. Dean, R. E., A. Midgley, E. N. White, and D. McNeil, *J. Chem. Soc.*, 2773 (1961).
155. de Benneville, P. L. R., and L. H. Bock, Brit. Pat. 659,353 (Oct. 24, 1951).
156. De La Mare, P. B., and J. H. Ridd, *Aromatic Substitution*, Academic Press, Inc., New York, pp. 169–185, 1959.
157. Deno, N. C., H. E. Berkheimer, W. L. Evans, and H. J. Peterson, *J. Am. Chem. Soc.*, **81**, 2344 (1959).
157a. Deno, N. C., H. J. Peterson, and G. S. Saines, *Chem. Rev.*, **60**, 7 (1960).
158. Denton, W. I., and C. H. Schlesman, U.S. Pat. 2,392,466 (Jan. 8, 1946).
158a. De Pierre, W. G., Jr., W. R. Edwards, and H. G. Boynton, U.S. Pat. 3,052,741 (Sept. 4, 1962).

158b. Desseigne, G., *Bull. Soc. Chim. France*, (5), **2**, 617 (1935).

159. Deutsche Hydrierwerke A-G, Brit. Pat. 469,548 (July 23, 1937).

160. Dewar, M. J. S., T. Mole, and E. N. T. Warford, *J. Chem. Soc.*, 3581 (1956).

161. Dietzler, A. J., and F. Bryner, U.S. Pat. 2,784,239 (Mar. 5, 1957).

162. Dijkstra, R., U.S. Pat. 2,874,193 (Feb. 17, 1959).

163. Dillingham, W. B., and E. E. Reid, *J. Am. Chem. Soc.*, **60**, 2606 (1938).

164. Distillers Company, Ltd., Brit. Pat. 763,179 (Dec. 12, 1956).

165. Distillers Company, Ltd., Brit. Pat. 763,181 (Dec. 12, 1956).

166. Distillers Company, Ltd., Brit. Pat. 763,182 (Dec. 12, 1956).

167a. Doladugin, A. I., Yu. L. Khmel'nitskii, and A. V. Guseva, *Neft. Khoz.*, **24**, No. 3/4, 44 (1946).

167b. Donleavy, J. J., and M. M. Baizer, U.S. Pat. 2,439,457 (Apr. 13, 1948).

168. Dorogochinskii, A. Z., V. I. Lavrent'ev, A. V. Lyuter, N. P. Melnikova, and V. A. Kupriyanov, *Dokl. Akad. Nauk S.S.S.R.*, **131**, 367 (1960).

169. Dorris, T. B., F. J. Sowa, and J. A. Nieuwland, *J. Am. Chem. Soc.*, **60**, 656 (1938).

169a. Dorris, T. B., P. J. Sowa, and J. A. Nieuwland, *J. Am. Chem. Soc.*, **56**, 2689 (1934).

170. D'Ouville, E., and D. E. Burney, U.S. Pat. 2,450,585 (Oct. 5, 1948).

171. D'Ouville, E. L., and B. L. Evering, U.S. Pat. 2,338,711 (Jan. 11, 1944).

172. Dow, W., *Ind. Eng. Chem.*, **34**, 1267 (1942).

173. Dreisbach, R. R., U.S. Pat. 2,149,762 (Mar. 7, 1939).

174. Dreisbach, R. R., U.S. Pat. 2,078,238 (Apr. 27, 1937); Brit. Pat. 474,414 (Nov. 1, 1937).

174a. Dreisbach, R. R., and G. B. Heusted, U.S. Pat. 2,183,552 (Dec. 19, 1939).

175. Dubinin, B. M., *Compt. rend. acad. sci. U.S.S.R.*, **3**, 263 (1935).

176. Dunlop, A. P., and F. N. Peters, *The Furans*, Reinhold Publishing Corp., New York, p. 64, 1953.

177. Ecke, G. G., and A. J. Kolka, U.S. Pat. 2,831,817 (Apr. 22, 1958).

178. Ecke, G. G., and A. J. Kolka, U.S. Pat. 2,831,898 (Apr. 22, 1958).

179a. Ecke, G. G., J. P. Napolitano, A. H. Filbey, and A. J. Kolka, *J. Org. Chem.*, **22**, 639 (1957).

179b. Ecke, G. G., J. P. Napolitano, and A. J. Kolka, *J. Org. Chem.*, **21**, 711 (1956).

180. Egbert, R. B., U.S. Pat. 2,883,438 (Apr. 21, 1959).

181. Egbert, R. B., R. Landau, and A. Saffer, U.S. Pat. 2,920,119 (Jan. 5, 1960).

182. Egloff, G., U.S. Pat. 2,383,179 (Aug. 21, 1945).

182a. Ellis, C., *The Chemistry of Petroleum Derivatives*, Vol. I, Chemical Catalogue Co., New York, 1934; Vol. II, Reinhold Publishing Corp., New York, 1937.

183. Elwell, W. E., U.S. Pat. 2,578,294 (Dec. 11, 1951).

184. Elwell, W. E., and A. J. Castro, U.S. Pat. 2,563,826 (Aug. 14, 1951).

185. Emerson, W. S., V. E. Lucas, and R. E. Heimsch, *J. Am. Chem. Soc.*, **71**, 1742 (1949).

186. Enos, H. I., Germ. Pat. 936,089 (Dec. 7, 1955).

187. Enos, H. I., U.S. Pat. 2,817,687 (Dec. 24, 1957).

188. Ernst, O., and H. Lange, Germ. Pat. 494,429 (Aug. 27, 1925).

189. Essner, J. C., *Bull. Soc. Chim. France*, (2), **36**, 212 (1881).
190. Essner, J. C., and E. Gossin, *Bull. Soc. Chim. France*, (2), **42**, 213 (1884).
191. Ethyl Corporation, Brit. Pat. 856,458 (Dec. 14, 1960).
192. Evans, A. G., *Disc. Faraday Soc.*, **8**, 302 (1950).
193. Evans, T., and K. R. Edlund, U.S. Pat. 2,051,473 (Aug. 18, 1936).
193a. Evans, A. G., and G. W. Meadows, *J. Polymer Soc.*, **4**, 359, 376 (1949).
193b. Evans, A. G., and G. W. Meadows, *Trans. Faraday Soc.*, **46**, 327 (1950).
193c. Evans, A. G., and M. Polanyi, *J. Chem. Soc.*, 252 (1947).
194. Farbenfabriken Bayer A.-G., Brit. Pat. 776,204 (June 5, 1957).
195. Farbenfabriken Bayer A.-G., Brit. Pat. 807,668 (Jan. 21, 1959).
196. Farbenfabriken Bayer A.-G., Brit. Pat. 823,223 (Nov. 11, 1959).
197. Farbwerke Hoechst Akt. G-S, Brit. Pat. 822,009 (Oct. 21, 1959).
198. Fawcett, F. S., and B. W. Hawk, U.S. Pat. 2,572,019 (Oct. 23, 1951).
199. Fearey, J. E., Brit. Pat. 630,487 (Oct. 14, 1949).
200. Fedor, W. S., *Chem. Eng. News*, **39**, No. 12, 116 (1961).
201. Field, E., and M. Feller, U.S. Pat. 2,780,660 (Feb. 5, 1957).
202. Fischer, F., and W. Schneider, *Ges. Abhandl. Kennt. Kohle*, **1**, 227 (1917).
203. Flett, L. H., U.S. Pat. 2,134,712 (Nov. 1, 1938).
204. Fontana, B. J., *J. Am. Chem. Soc.*, **73**, 3348 (1951).
205. Foote, J. K., U.S. Pat. 2,732,408 (Jan. 24, 1956).
206. Fortuin, J. P., M. J. Waale, and R. P. Van Oosten, *Petrol. Refiner*, **38**, No. 6, 189 (1959).
206a. Foster, G. L., *J. Chem. Soc.*, 2788 (1954).
207. Fotis, P., and D. L. Esmay, U.S. Pat. 2,852,576 (Sept. 16, 1958).
208. Francis, A. W., *Chem. Rev.*, **43**, 257 (1948).
209a. Francis, A. W., and E. E. Reid, U.S. Pat. 2,364,203 (Dec. 5, 1944).
209b. Francis, A. W., and E. E. Reid, U.S. Pat. 2,397,542 (Apr. 2, 1946).
210. Francis, A. W., and E. E. Reid, *Ind. Eng. Chem.*, **38**, 1194 (1946).
211. Frey, F. E., U.S. Pat. 2,372,320 (Mar. 27, 1945).
212. Frey, F. E., U.S. Pat. 2,394,905 (Feb. 12, 1946).
213. Frey, F. E., and J. P. Jones, U.S. Pat. 2,373,303 (Apr. 10, 1945).
214. Friedel, C., and J. M. Crafts, *Bull. Soc. Chim. France*, (2), **27**, 530 (1877).
215. Friedel, C., and J. M. Crafts, *Ann. Chim. Phys.*, (6), **14**, 449 (1884).
216. Friedman, B. S., unpublished results.
217. Friedman, B. S., and L. Joo, unpublished data.
217a. Friedman, B. S., and S. M. Kovach, unpublished results.
218. Friedman, B. S., and F. L. Morritz, *J. Am. Chem. Soc.*, **78**, 2000 (1956).
219. Friedman, B. S., and F. L. Morritz, *J. Am. Chem. Soc.*, **78**, 3430 (1956).
220. Friedman, B. S., F. L. Morritz, and C. J. Morrisey, *J. Am. Chem. Soc.*, **79**, 1465 (1957).
221. Friedman, B. S., F. L. Morritz, C. J. Morrisey, and R. Koncos, *J. Am. Chem. Soc.*, **80**, 5867 (1958).
222. Friedman, B. S., and R. A. Sanford, U.S. Pat. 2,810,769 (Oct. 22, 1957).
223. Frisch, K. C., *J. Org. Chem.*, **15**, 587 (1950).
224. Gallay, W., and G. S. Whitby, *Can. J. Res.*, **2**, 31 (1930).
224a. Gal'pern, G. D., M. M. Kusakov, and N. A. Shimanko, *Tr. Inst. Nefti, Akad. Nauk S.S.S.R.*, **13**, 11 (1959).
225. Gardner, C., and J. L. Forryan, Brit. Pat. 774,716 (May 15, 1957).
225a. Garner, F. R., and R. L. Iverson, *Oil Gas J.*, Oct. 25, 86 (1954).

226. Gattermann, L., S. Fritz, and K. Beck, *Ber.*, **32**, 1122 (1899).
227. Gau, G., Ph.D. Thesis, University of Minnesota, 1956.
228. Gayer, F. H., *Ind. Eng. Chem.*, **25**, 1122 (1933).
229. Gaylor, P. T., U.S. Pat. 2,384,295 (Sept. 4, 1945).
229a. Geiger, L. M., U.S. Pat. 2,502,003 (March 28, 1950).
230. Gel'bshtein, A. I., A. A. Zansokhova, and G. G. Shcheglova, *Khim. Prom.* 284 (1958).
231. Gerald, C. F., and G. R. Donaldson, U.S. Pat. 2,570,542 (Sept. 9, 1951).
232. Gieser, P. E., U.S. Pat. 2,806,875 (Sept. 17, 1957).
233. Gilman, H., and N. O. Calloway, *J. Am. Chem. Soc.*, **55**, 4197 (1933).
233a. Gilman, H., and J. A. V. Turck, *J. Am. Chem. Soc.*, **61**, 473 (1939).
234. Gilyarovskaya, L. A., *Izv. Vysshikh Uchebn. Zavedenii, Neft i. Gaz*, No. 8, 63 (1959).
235. Gilyarovskaya, L. A., and S. L. Lyubimova, *Tr. Mosk. Inst. Tonkoi Khim. Tekhnol.*, No. 8, 21 (1958).
236. Gilyarovskaya, L. A., and N. I. Sokolova, *Tr. Mosk. Inst. Tonkoi Khim. Tekhnol.*, No. 8, 27 (1958).
237. Goldsmith, E. A., M. J. Schlatter, and W. G. Toland, *J. Org. Chem.*, **23**, 1871 (1958).
238. Gordon, L. B., and T. P. Motte, U.S. Pat. 2,927,085 (Mar. 1, 1960).
239. Gordon, L. B., and T. P. Motte, U.S. Pat. 2,927,086 (Mar. 1, 1960).
240. Gorham, W. F., and J. A. Stenstrom, U.S. Pat. 2,778,862 (Jan. 22, 1957).
241. Gorin, M. H., and L. G. Sharp, U.S. Pat. 2,438,211 (Mar. 23, 1948).
242. Gray, F. W., I. F. Gerecht, and I. J. Krems, *J. Org. Chem.*, **20**, 511 (1955).
243. Griffin, W. D., and G. G. Joris, U.S. Pat. 2,882,322 (Apr. 14, 1959); Can. Pat. 616,365 (Mar. 14, 1961).
244. Grosse, A. V., and V. N. Ipatieff, *J. Am. Chem. Soc.*, **57**, 2415 (1935).
245. Grosse, A. V., and V. N. Ipatieff, *J. Org. Chem.*, **1**, 559 (1936).
246. Grosse, A. V., and V. N. Ipatieff, *J. Org. Chem.*, **2**, 447 (1937).
247. Grosse, A. V., J. M. Mavity, and V. N. Ipatieff, *J. Org. Chem.*, **3**, 137 (1938).
248. Grosse, A. V., J. M. Mavity, and V. N. Ipatieff, *J. Org. Chem.*, **3**, 448 (1938).
249. Grote, H. W., and C. F. Gerald, *Chem. Eng. Progr.*, **56**, No. 1, 60 (1960).
250. Groves, L. H., A. Lambert, and H. Palfreeman, Brit. Pat. 731,270 (June 8, 1955).
251. Habeshaw, J., Brit. Pat. 633,985 (Dec. 30, 1949).
252. Haensel, V., U.S. Pat. 2,418,028 (Mar. 25, 1947).
253. Hakala, T. H., U.S. Pat. 2,886,609 (May 12, 1959).
253a. Hall, R. H., and W. Webster, Brit. Pat. 785,607 (Oct. 30, 1957).
253b. Hammett, L. P., *Physical Organic Chemistry*, McGraw-Hill, New York, p. 311, 1940.
254. Hammick, D. L., and M. Roberts, *J. Chem. Soc.*, 73 (1948).
255. Hanai, S., *J. Chem. Soc. Japan*, **62**, 1208 (1941).
256. Hansford, R. C., *Ind. Eng. Chem.*, **39**, 849 (1947).
257. Hansford, R. C., Chapter 1, "Chemical Concepts of Catalysis," Vol. IV, *Advances in Catalysis*, Academic Press, New York, 1952.
258. Hansford, R. C., and P. D. Caesar, U.S. Pat. 2,469,823 (May 10, 1949).
258a. Hansford, R. C., C. G. Myers, and A. N. Sachanen, *Ind. Eng. Chem.*, **37**, 671 (1945).

259. Hansford, R. C., P. G. Waldo, L. C. Drake, and R. E. Honig, Joint Symposium on the Use of Isotopes in Petroleum Chemistry, 118th Meeting, American Chemical Society, Chicago, Sept. 1950.
260. Harnish, D. P., and D. S. Tarbell, *Chem. Rev.*, **49**, 1 (1951).
261. Hart, H., *J. Am. Chem. Soc.*, **71**, 1966 (1949).
262. Hart, H., and F. A. Cassis, *J. Am. Chem. Soc.*, **73**, 3179 (1951).
263. Hart, H., and E. A. Haglund, *J. Org. Chem.*, **15**, 396 (1950).
264. Hartough, H. D., *Thiophene and Its Derivatives*, Interscience, New York, p. 143, 1952.
265. Hartough, H. D., *ibid.*, p. 170.
266. Hearne, G. W., T. W. Evans, V. W. Buls, and C. G. Schwarzer, *Ind. Eng. Chem.*, **47**, 2311 (1955).
267. Henkel and Cie., Brit. Pat. 484,151 (May 2, 1938).
268. Henkel and Cie., Brit. Pat. 486,972 (June 14, 1938).
269. Hennion, G. F., and J. G. Anderson, *J. Am. Chem. Soc.*, **68**, 424 (1946).
270. Hennion, G. F., A. J. Driesch, and P. L. Dee, *J. Org. Chem.*, **17**, 1102 (1952).
271. Hercules Powder Co., Brit. Pat. 754,673 (Aug. 8, 1956).
272. Hercules Powder Co., Brit. Pat. 754,872 (Aug. 15, 1956).
272a. Herdieckerhoff, E., and P. Schneider, Brit. Pat. 864,696 (April 6, 1961).
273. Hervert, G. L., and H. S. Bloch, U.S. Pat. 2,589,253 (Mar. 18, 1952).
274. Hervert, G. L., and H. S. Bloch, U.S. Pat. 2,821,562 (Jan. 28, 1958).
275. Hervert, G. L., and C. B. Linn, U.S. Pat. 2,939,890 (June 7, 1960).
276. Herz, A. H., and D. S. Tarbell, *J. Am. Chem. Soc.*, **75**, 4657 (1953).
277. Hester, W. F., U.S. Pat. 2,008,017 (July 16, 1935); 2,060,573 (Nov. 10, 1936).
278. Hickinbottom, W. J., *J. Chem. Soc.*, 404 (1937).
279. Hillers, S., A. Berzina, and L. Lauberte, *Latvijas PSR Zinatnu Akad. Vestis*, No. 4, 71 (1958); *C.A.*, **53**, 325c (1959).
280. Hindin, S. G., G. A. Mills, and A. G. Oblad, *J. Am. Chem. Soc.*, **73**, 278 (1951).
281. Hodges, P. W., M.S. Thesis, New York University, May, 1935.
282. Hodnett, E. M., and C. F. Feldman, Jr., *J. Am. Chem. Soc.*, **81**, 1638 (1959).
283. Hoffman, F., and C. Wulff, Brit. Pat. 307,802 (Mar. 13, 1928); U.S. Pat. 1,898,627 (Feb. 21, 1933).
284. Hollis, A. L., U.S. Pat. 2,530,769 (Nov. 21, 1950).
285. Honel, H., U.S. Pat. 2,058,797 (Oct. 27, 1936).
286. Hoog, H., and A. Schaafsma, U.S. Pat. 2,871,254 (Jan. 27, 1959).
287. Horeczy, J. T., U.S. Pat. 2,612,531 (Sept. 30, 1952).
288. Huett, G., and W. O. Ranky, U.S. Pat. 2,900,418 (Aug. 18, 1959).
289. Hunt, M., U.S. Pat. 2,467,131 (Apr. 12, 1949).
290. Hunt, M., V. Weinmayr, and M. F. Sartori, U.S. Pat. 2,467,130 (Apr. 12, 1949).
291a. Hunt, M., V. Weinmayr, and A. V. Willett, Jr., U.S. Pat. 2,467,132 (Apr. 12, 1949).
291b. Hurd, C. D., and G. L. Oliver, *J. Am. Chem. Soc.*, **76**, 50 (1954).
292. Huston, R. C., and D. D. Sager, *J. Am. Chem. Soc.*, **48**, 1955 (1926).
293. I.C.I., French Pat. 1,252,801 (Dec. 26, 1960).
294. I. G. Farben, A.G., Brit. Pat. 265,601 (Aug. 3, 1928).

10*

295. I. G. Farben A.G., Brit. Pat. 295,990 (Aug. 1, 1928).
296. I. G. Farben A.G., Brit. Pat. 316,951 (Sept. 4, 1928).
297. I. G. Farben A.G., Brit. Pat. 326,500 (Dec. 11, 1928).
298. I. G. Farben A.G., Brit. Pat. 327,382 (Nov. 28, 1928).
299. I. G. Farben A.G., Brit. Pat. 453,422 (Sept. 4, 1936).
300. I. G. Farben A.G., Brit. Pat. 481,909 (Apr. 18, 1938).
300a. I. G. Farben A.G., Brit. Pat. 490,416 (Aug. 9, 1938).
300b. I. G. Farben A.G., Brit. Pat. 497,487 (Dec. 21, 1938).
301. I. G. Farben A.G., Brit. Pat. 497,721 (Dec. 22, 1938).
302. I. G. Farben A.G., French Pat. 628,440 (Oct. 10, 1927).
302a. I. G. Farben A.G., French Pat. 823,486 (Jan. 20, 1938).
303. I. G. Farben A.G., French Pat. 793,250 (Jan. 20, 1936).
304. Imaev, M. G., *Izv. Vysshikh Uchebn. Zavedenii, Neft i Gaz*, No. 6, 77 (1960).
305. Inatome, M., K. W. Greenlee, J. M. Dorfer, and C. E. Boord, *J. Am. Chem. Soc.*, **74**, 292 (1952).
306. Inst. Franç. du Pétrole, des Carburants et Lubrifiants, Brit. Pat. 870,772 (June 21, 1961).
307. Ioffe, I. I., and V. A. Kambulova, U.S.S.R. Pat. 121,133 (July 15, 1959).
308. Iovu, M., and E. Isvoranu, *Analele Univ. "C. I. Parhon" Bucuresti, Ser. Stiint Nat.*, No. **21**, 73 (1959).
309. Ipatieff, V. N., U.S. Pat. 2,006,695 (July 2, 1935).
310. Ipatieff, V. N., U.S. Pat. 2,046,900 (July 7, 1936).
311. Ipatieff, V. N., U.S. Pat. 2,099,738 (Nov. 23, 1937).
312. Ipatieff, V. N., H. R. Appell, and H. Pines, *J. Am. Chem. Soc.*, **72**, 4260 (1950).
313. Ipatieff, V. N., B. B. Corson, and H. Pines, *J. Am. Chem. Soc.*, **58**, 919 (1936).
314. Ipatieff, V. N., J. E. Germain, and H. Pines, *J. Am. Chem. Soc.*, **75**, 6056 (1953).
315. Ipatieff, V. N., and A. V. Grosse, *J. Am. Chem. Soc.*, **58**, 2339 (1936).
316. Ipatieff, V. N., and A. V. Grosse, U.S. Pat. 2,088,598 (Aug. 3, 1937).
317. Ipatieff, V. N., and A. V. Grosse, U.S. Pat. 2,104,424 (Jan. 4, 1938).
318. Ipatieff, V. N., and V. I. Komarewsky, U.S. Pat. 2,098,045 (Nov. 2, 1937).
319. Ipatieff, V. N., V. I. Komarewsky, and H. Pines, *J. Am. Chem. Soc.*, **58**, 918 (1936).
320. Ipatieff, V. N., and C. B. Linn, U.S. Pat. 2,428,279 (Sept. 30, 1947).
321. Ipatieff, V. N., E. E. Meisinger, and H. Pines, *J. Am. Chem. Soc.*, **72**, 2772 (1950).
322. Ipatieff, V. N., and G. S. Monroe, *J. Am. Chem. Soc.*, **69**, 710 (1947).
323. Ipatieff, V. N., and H. Pines, U.S. Pat. 2,147,256 (Feb. 14, 1939).
324. Ipatieff, V. N., and H. Pines, A.C.S. National Meeting, Boston, Sept., 1939 (M-21).
325. Ipatieff, V. N., and H. Pines, U.S. Pat. 2,187,034 (Jan. 16, 1940).
326. Ipatieff, V. N., and H. Pines, U.S. Pat. 2,199,564 (May 7, 1940).
326a. Ipatieff, V. N., and H. Pines, U.S. Pat. 2,480,268 (Aug. 30, 1949).
327. Ipatieff, V. N., and H. Pines, U.S. Pat. 2,519,577 (Aug. 22, 1950).
328. Ipatieff, V. N., and H. Pines, U.S. Pat. 2,631,174 (Mar. 10, 1953).
329. Ipatieff, V. N., and H. Pines, *J. Am. Chem. Soc.*, **58**, 1056 (1936).
330. Ipatieff, V. N., and H. Pines, *J. Am. Chem. Soc.*, **61**, 3374 (1939).

331. Ipatieff, V. N., H. Pines, and B. B. Corson, *J. Am. Chem. Soc.*, **60**, 577 (1938).
332. Ipatieff, V. N., H. Pines, and B. S. Friedman, *J. Am. Chem. Soc.*, **60**, 2495 (1938).
333. Ipatieff, V. N., H. Pines, and B. S. Friedman, *J. Am. Chem. Soc.*, **60**, 2731 (1938).
334. Ipatieff, V. N., H. Pines, and V. I. Komarewsky, *Ind. Eng. Chem.*, **28**, 222 (1936).
335. Ipatieff, V. N., H. Pines, and R. C. Olberg, *J. Am. Chem. Soc.*, **70**, 2123 (1948).
336. Ipatieff, V. N., H. Pines, and R. E. Schaad, *J. Am. Chem. Soc.*, **66**, 816 (1944).
338. Ipatieff, V. N., H. Pines, and L. Schmerling, *J. Am. Chem. Soc.*, **58**, 912 (1936).
339. Ipatieff, V. N., H. Pines, and L. Schmerling, *J. Am. Chem. Soc.*, **60**, 353 (1938).
340. Ipatieff, V. N., H. Pines, and L. Schmerling, *J. Am. Chem. Soc.*, **60**, 1161 (1938).
341. Ipatieff, V. N., H. Pines, and L. Schmerling, *J. Org. Chem.*, **5**, 253 (1940).
342. Ipatieff, V. N., and R. E. Schaad, U.S. Pat. 2,382,318 (Sept. 14, 1945).
343. Ipatieff, V. N., and L. Schmerling, *Ind. Eng. Chem.*, **38**, 400 (1946).
344. Ipatieff, V. N., and L. Schmerling, U.S. Pat. 2,402,051 (June 11, 1946).
345. Isagulyants, V. I., *Tr., Mosk. Inst. Neftekhim. i Gaz. Prom.*, **28**, 68 (1960).
346. Isagulyants, V. I., and P. P. Bagryantseva, *Neft. Khoz.*, No. 2, 36 (1938).
347. Isagulyants, V. I., N. A. Favorskaya, and V. N. Tishkova, *Zh. Prikl. Khim.*, **34**, 693 (1961).
348. Isagulyants, V. I., and E. V. Panidi, *Zh. Prikl. Khim.*, **34**, 1578 (1961).
349. Isagulyants, V. I., and N. A. Slavskaya, *Zh. Prikl. Khim.*, **33**, 953 (1960).
350. Isagulyants, V. I., V. N. Tishkova, and N. A. Favorskaya, *Tr. Groznensk. Neft. Inst., Sb.*, No. 23, 132 (1960).
351. Isagulyants, V. I., V. N. Tishkova, and S. K. Ivanov, *Tr. Groznensk. Neft. Inst., Sb*, No. 23, 137 (1960).
352. Isham, R. M., U.S. Pat. 2,014,766 (Sept. 17, 1935).
353. Isham, R. M., U.S. Pat. 2,017,803 (Oct. 15, 1935).
354. Istrati, C. I., *Bull. Soc. Chim. France*, **42**, 111 (1884); *Ann. Chim. (Paris)*, (6), **6**, 395 (1885).
355. Iwai, Shinji, *J. Soc. Chem. Ind. Japan*, **45**, Suppl. Binding, 53 (1942).
356. Iwai, Shinji, *J. Soc. Chem. Ind. Japan*, **45**, Suppl. Binding, 97 (1942).
357. Johnson, C. E., and C. E. Adams, U.S. Pat. 2,521,850 (Sept. 12, 1950).
358. Johnson, E. C., and W. J. Zimmerschied, U.S. Pat. 2,839,474 (June 17, 1958).
359. Johnson, G. C., and J. Kellett, U.S. Pat. 2,487,338 (Nov. 8, 1949).
360. Johnson, M. F. L., and J. S. Melik, *J. Phys. Chem.*, **65**, 1146 (1961).
361. Johnson, O., *J. Phys. Chem.*, **59**, 827 (1955).
362. Johnstone, W. W., U.S. Pat. 2,652,434 (Sept. 15, 1953).
363. Joklik, O. F., *J. Prakt. Chem.*, **10**, 499, 563 (1959).
364. Jones, W. O., Brit. Pat. 743,153 (Jan. 11, 1956); Brit. Pat. 861,792 (Feb. 22, 1961).

364a. Jordon, D. O., and F. E. Treloar, *J. Chem. Soc.*, 737 (1961).

365. Joris, G. G., U.S. Pat. 2,945,072 (Apr. 11, 1956).

365a. Jungk, H., C. R. Smoot, and H. C. Brown, *J. Am. Chem. Soc.*, **78**, 2185 (1956).

366. Karle, J., and L. O. Brockway, *J. Am. Chem. Soc.*, **66**, 574 (1944).

367. Kawamoto, T., *J. Chem. Soc. Japan*, **61**, 383 (1940).

368. Kazanskii, B. A., M. I. Rozengart, and Z. F. Kuznetsova, *Dokl. Akad. Nauk S.S.S.R.*, **126**, 571 (1959).

369. Kehe, H. J., U.S. Pat. 2,714,120 (July 26, 1955).

370. Keizer, A. de, U.S. Pat. 2,881,227 (Apr. 7, 1959).

371. Keizer, A. de, and N. Max, Dutch Pat. 86,350 (Sept. 16, 1957).

371a. Keizer, A. de, C. P. Van Dijk, and A. A. Gips, U.S. Pat. 2,870,229 (Jan. 20, 1959).

372. Keller, R., E. Kissel, and G. Wenner, Brit. Pat. 868,163 (May 17, 1961).

373. Keller, R., E. Kissel, and G. Wenner, Germ. Pat. 1,060,371 (July 2, 1959).

374. Kelly, J. T., and H. M. Knight, U.S. Pat. 2,824,146 (Feb. 18, 1958).

375. Kelly, J. T., and H. M. Knight, U.S. Pat. 2,898,390 (Aug. 4, 1959).

376. Kelly, J. T., and R. J. Lee, *Ind. Eng. Chem.*, **47**, 757 (1955).

377. Kheifits, L. A., G. I. Moldovanskaye, E. V. Broun, and V. N. Belov, *J. Gen. Chem. U.S.S.R.*, **30**, 1705 (1960).

378. Kheifits, L. A., L. M. Shulov, E. V. Broun, and V. N. Belov, *Zh. Obshch. Khim.*, **31**, 672 (1961).

379. Kimberlin, C. N. Jr., U.S. Pat. 2,373,030 (Apr. 3, 1945).

380. King, C. C., U.S. Pat. 2,787,648 (Apr. 2, 1957).

381. Kirkland, E. V., U.S. Pat. 2,740,819 (Apr. 3, 1956).

382. Kirkland, E. V., U.S. Pat. 2,754,341 (July 10, 1956).

383. Kirkland, E. V., O. P. Funderburk, and F. T. Wadsworth, *J. Org. Chem.*, **23**, 1631 (1958).

384. Kitchen, L. J., *J. Am. Chem. Soc.*, **70**, 1290 (1948); U.S. Pat. 2,445,735 (July 20, 1948).

384a. Kitchen, L. J., U.S. Pat. 2,537,636 (Jan. 9, 1951).

385. Kitchen, L. J., U.S. Pat. 2,581,916 (Jan. 8, 1952).

386. Kluge, H. D., and F. W. Moore, U.S. Pat. 2,868,823 (Jan. 13, 1959).

387. Kluge, H. D., and F. W. Moore, U.S. Pat. 2,671,117 (Mar. 2, 1954).

388. Knight, H. M., and J. T. Kelly, U.S. Pat. 2,824,150 (Feb. 18, 1958).

389. Koch, H., and H. Steinbrink, *Brennstoff-Chem.*, **19**, 277 (1938).

390. Koelsch, C. F., and F. J. Lucht, *J. Am. Chem. Soc.*, **65**, 1240 (1943).

391. Koenigs, W., *Ber.*, **23**, 3145 (1890).

392. Koenigs, W., *Ber.*, **24**, 179 (1891).

393. Koenigs, W., and R. W. Carl, *Ber.*, **24**, 3889 (1891).

394. Koenigs, W., and C. Mai, *Ber.*, **25**, 2649 (1892).

395. Kolka, A. J., G. G. Ecke, and R. D. Closson, U.S. Pat. 2,814,646 (Nov. 26, 1957).

396. Kolka, A. J., J. P. Napolitano, and G. G. Ecke, *J. Org. Chem.*, **21**, 712 (1956).

397. Kolka, A. J., J. P. Napolitano, A. H. Filbey, and G. G. Ecke, *J. Org. Chem.*, **22**, 642 (1957).

398. Komarewsky, V. I., *J. Am. Chem. Soc.*, **59**, 2715 (1937).

399. Komarewsky, V. I., U.S. Pat. 2,333,866 (Nov. 9, 1944).

400. Kooijman, E. C., Dutch Pat. 64,991 (Dec. 15, 1949).

401. Kooijman, E. C., U.S. Pat. 2,567,848 (Sept. 11, 1951).
402. Kozik, B. L., I. S. Vol'fson, *et al.*, *Khim. i Tekhnol. Topliv i Masel*, **6**, No. 10, 9 (1961).
403. Kozorezov, Y. I., and A. Z. Dorogochinskii, *Izv. Vysshikh Uchebn. Zavedenii, Neft. i Gaz.*, No. 8, 45 (1959).
404. Kozorezov, Y. I., and A. Z. Dorogochinskii, *Izv. Vysshikh Uchebn. Zavedenii, Neft. i Gaz.*, No. 5, 49–54 (1959).
405. Kozorezov, Y. I., and A. Z. Dorogochinskii, *Dokl. Akad. Nauk S.S.S.R.*, **123**, 857 (1959).
406. Kozorezov, Y. I., and A. Z. Dorogochinskii, *Izv. Vysshykh Uchebn. Zavedenii, Khim. i Khim. Teckhnol.*, **4**, No. 1, 133 (1961).
407. Kraemer, G., A. Spilker, and P. Eberhardt, *Ber.*, **23**, 3269 (1890).
408. Kreuz, K. L., U.S. Pat. 2,531,280 (Nov. 21, 1950).
409. Kreuz, K. L., and R. T. Sanderson, U.S. Pat. 2,529,298 (Nov. 7, 1950).
410. Kreuz, K. L., U.S. Pat. 2,753,378 (July 3, 1956).
411. Kryuchkova, V. G., and S. V. Zavgorodnii, *Zh. Obshch. Khim.*, **30**, 1929 (1960).
411a. Kryuchkova, V. G., and S. V. Zavgorodnii, *Dokl. Akad. Nauk S.S.S.R.*, **130**, 775 (1960).
412. Kryuchkova, V. G., and S. V. Zavgorodnii, *Zh. Obshch. Khim.*, **30**, 3869 (1960).
413. Kryuchkova, V. G., and S. V. Zavgorodnii, *Izv. Vysshykh Uchebn. Zavedenii, Khim. i Khim. Tekhnol.*, **4**, No. 1, 92 (1961).
414. Kryuchkova, V. G., and S. V. Zavgorodnii, *Zh. Obshch. Khim.*, **31**, 374 (1961).
415. Kryuchkova, V. G., and S. V. Zavgorodnii, *Zh. Obshch. Khim.*, **31**, 731 (1961).
416. Kuchkarev, A. B., *Dokl. Akad. Nauk Uz. S.S.R.*, No. 1, 21 (1957).
417. Kuchkarev, A. B., *Izv. Akad. Nauk Uz. S.S.R., Ser. Khim. Nauk*, No. 3, 67–80 (1957); *C.A.*, **55**, 27150i (1961).
418. Kundiger, D. C., and H. Pledger, *J. Am. Chem. Soc.*, **78**, 6098, 6101 (1956).
419. Kunz, W., Brit. Pat. 701,264 (Dec. 23, 1953).
420. Kurashev, M. V., A. V. Topchiev, and Ya. M. Paushkin, *Proc. Acad. Sci. U.S.S.R., Chem. Sect.*, **107**, 203 (1956).
421. Kuryndina, V. S., V. I. Voevodova, and T. A. Rasskazova, *J. Appl. Chem. U.S.S.R.*, **10**, 877 (1937).
422. Kutz, W. M., and B. B. Corson, *J. Am. Chem. Soc.*, **68**, 1477 (1946); **71**, 1503 (1949).
423. Kutz, W. M., J. E. Nickels, J. J. McGovern, and B. B. Corson, *J. Am. Chem. Soc.*, **70**, 4026 (1948).
424. Kutz, W. M., J. E. Nickels, J. J. McGovern, and B. B. Corson, *J. Org. Chem.*, **16**, 699 (1951).
425. Kyrides, L. P., U.S. Pat. 2,189,805 (Feb. 13, 1940).
426. Kyrides, L. P., U.S. Pats. 2,232,117, 2,232,118 (Feb. 18, 1941).
426a. Landau, R., U.S. Pat. 2,814,652 (Nov. 26, 1957).
426b. Landau, R., R. B. Egbert, and A. Saffer, U.S. Pat. 2,855,430 (Oct. 7, 1958).
426c. Landau, R., A. Saffer, and R. B. Egbert, Brit. Pat. 841,424 (July 13, 1960).

426d. Langlois, G. E., U.S. Pat. 2,695,324 (Nov. 23, 1954).

426e. Langlois, G. E., U.S. Pat. 2,713,600 (July 19, 1955).

426f. Laufer, R. J., 137th National Meeting, Am. Chem. Soc., Cleveland, 1960, p. 61o.

426g. Lavrovskii, K., A. Mikhnovskaya, and L. Olen'chenko, *Dokl. Akad. Nauk S.S.S.R.*, **64**, 345 (1949).

426h. Layng, E. T., U.S. Pat. 2,414,206 (Jan. 14, 1947).

427. Layng, E. T., U.S. Pat. 2,498,607 (Feb. 21, 1950).

428. Lebedev, N. N., *J. Gen. Chem. U.S.S.R.*, **24**, 1751 (1954).

429. Lebedev, N. N., I. K. Kolchin, and I. S. Markovich, *Trudy Moskov. Khim. Tekhnol. Inst. im D. I. Mendeleeva*, No. 23, 52 (1956); *C.A.* **53**, 9104 (1959).

430. Lee, W. M., and H. Clark, U.S. Pat. 2,050,188 (Aug. 4, 1936).

431. Lee, R. J., J. T. Kelly, and H. M. Knight, *Ind. Eng. Chem.*, **50**, 1001 (1958); U.S. Pats. 2,836,634 (May 27, 1958) and 2,918,504 (Dec. 22, 1959).

432. Lee, R. J., H. M. Knight, and J. T. Kelly, U.S. Pat. 2,918,504 (Dec. 22, 1959).

433. Lefebvre, H., and E. Levas, *Compt. rend.*, **220**, 782 (1945).

434. Lefebvre, H., and E. Levas, *Compt. rend.*, **220**, 826 (1945).

435. Lefebvre, H., and E. Levas, *Compt. rend.*, **221**, 301 (1945).

436. Legge, D. I., *J. Am. Chem. Soc.*, **69**, 2079 (1947).

437. Lenneman, W. L., R. D. Hites, and V. I. Komarewsky, *J. Org. Chem.*, **19**, 463 (1954).

438. Levas, E., *Ann. Chim. Phys.*, (12), **3**, 145 (1948).

439. Levas, E., *Bull. Soc. Chim. France*, 469 (1948).

439a. Levina, R. Y., Y. S. Shabarov, and I. M. Panazarova, *Zh. Obshch. Khim.*, **29**, 44 (1959).

440. Levine, A. A., and O. W. Cass, Brit. Pat. 497,284 (June 15, 1937).

441. Lewis, A. H., U.S. Pat. 2,477,382 (July 26, 1949).

442. Lewis, A. H., U.S. Pat. 2,477,383 (July 26, 1949).

443. Lien, A. P., and D. A. McCaulay, *J. Am. Chem. Soc.*, **75**, 2407 (1953).

444. Lien, A. P., and B. H. Shoemaker, U.S. Pat. 2,430,516 (Nov. 11, 1947).

445. Linn, C. B., U.S. Pat. 2,624,742 (Jan. 6, 1953).

446. Linn, C. B., and G. L. Hervert, U.S. Pat. 2,639,303 (May 19, 1953).

447. Linn, C. B., and G. L. Hervert, U.S. Pat. 2,995,611 (Apr. 3, 1959).

448. Linn, C. B., and R. J. Newman, U.S. Pat. 2,563,050 (Aug. 7, 1951).

449. Linn, C. B., and V. N. Ipatieff, U.S. Pat. 2,411,047 (Nov. 12, 1946).

450. Linner, F., U.S. Pat. 1,892,990 (Jan. 3, 1933).

451. Linsk, J., *J. Am. Chem. Soc.*, **72**, 4257 (1950).

452. Lippincott, S. B., and H. L. Yowell, U.S. Pat. 2,695,326 (Nov. 23, 1954).

453. Loev, B., and J. T. Massengale, *J. Org. Chem.*, **22**, 988 (1957).

454. Lottes, J. C., Ph.D. Thesis, Purdue University, June, 1949.

455. Lur'e, S. I., *J. Gen. Chem. U.S.S.R.*, **16**, 145 (1946).

456. Lur'e, S. I., and A. Ya. Golovacheva, *J. Gen. Chem. U.S.S.R.*, **13**, 189(1943).

457. Luvisi, J. P., and L. Schmerling, U.S. Pat. 2,882,325 (Apr. 14, 1959).

458. Luvisi, J. P., and L. Schmerling, U.S. Pat. 2,910,515 (Oct. 27, 1959).

459. Lysenko, A. P., and V. G. Plyusnin, *Zh. Fiz. Khim.*, **32**, 1074 (1958).

460. Maatman, R. W., R. M. Lago, and C. D. Prater, *Advances in Catalysis*, Vol. IX, Academic Press, Inc., New York, p. 531, 1951.

461. McCall, M. A., and H. W. Coover, Jr., U.S. Pat. 2,824,145 (Feb. 18, 1958).

462. McAllister, S. H., *The Chemistry of Petroleum Hydrocarbons*, Vol. 3, Chapter 57, Reinhold, New York, 1955.

462a. McAllister, S. H., J. Anderson, and E. F. Bullard, *Chem. Eng. Progr.*, **43**, 189 (1947).

463. McCaulay, D. A., *J. Am. Chem. Soc.*, **81**, 6437 (1959).

464. McCaulay, D. A., U.S. Pat. 2,908,729 (Oct. 13, 1959).

464a. McCaulay, D. A., *J. Am. Chem. Soc.*, **81**, 6437 (1959).

465. McCaulay, D. A., and A. P. Lien, *J. Am. Chem. Soc.*, **73**, 2013 (1951).

466. McCaulay, D. A., and A. P. Lien, *J. Am. Chem. Soc.*, **74**, 6246 (1952).

467a. McCaulay, D. A., and A. P. Lien, *J. Am. Chem. Soc.*, **77**, 1803 (1955); U.S. Pat. 2,766,307 (Oct. 9, 1956); U.S. Pat. 2,803,682 (Aug. 20, 1957); U.S. Pat. 2,803,683 (Aug. 20, 1957).

467b. McCaulay, D. A., and A. P. Lien, U.S. Pat. 2,803,687 (Aug. 20, 1957).

468. McLean, A., J. Habeshaw, and W. J. Oldham, Can. Pat. 613,048 (Jan. 24, 1961).

469. McNulty, G. M., and T. Cross, U.S. Pat. 2,655,544 (Oct. 13, 1953).

470. Mahan, J. E., U.S. Pat. 2,564,488 (Aug. 14, 1951).

471. Malchick, S. P., and R. B. Hannan, *J. Am. Chem. Soc.*, **81**, 2119 (1959).

472. Malishev, B., *J. Am. Chem. Soc.*, **57**, 883 (1935); U.S. Pat. 2,141,611 (Dec. 27, 1938).

473. Malishev, B., U.S. Pat. 2,238,594 (Apr. 15, 1941).

474. Mamedaliev, Yu. G., *Izv. Akad. Nauk S.S.S.R., Otd. Khim. Nauk*, 458 (1946).

475. Mamedaliev, Yu. G., and S. T. Akhmedov, *Uch. Zap. Azerb. Gos. Univ.*, No. 1, 23 (1955); *C.A.*, **54**, 7120d (1960).

476. Mamedaliev, Yu. G., and R. S. Alimardanov, *Dokl. Akad. Nauk S.S.S.R.*, **140**, 381 (1961).

476a. Mamedaliev, Yu. G., and R. S. Alimardanov, *Dokl. Akad. Nauk Azerb. S.S.R.*, **17**, 7, 575 (1961).

477. Mamedaliev, Yu. G., V. S. Aliev, and S. A. Sultanov, *Dokl. Akad. Nauk Azerb. S.S.R.*, **14**, 681 (1958).

478. Mamedaliev, Yu. G., and R. A. Babakhanov, *Izv. Akad. Nauk Azerb. S.S.R.*, No. 8, 41 (1957).

479. Mamedaliev, Yu. G., and R. A. Babakhanov, *Uch. Zap. Azerb. Gos. Univ.*, No. 1, 19 (1957).

480. Mamedaliev, Yu. G., and A. A. Bakhshi-Zade, *Dokl. Akad. Nauk Azerb. S.S.R.*, **11**, No. 3, 161 (1955); *C.A.*, **51**, 4293d (1957).

481. Mamedaliev, Yu. G., and A. A. Bakhshi-Zade, *Dokl. Akad. Nauk Azerb. S.S.R.*, **12**, 819 (1956); *C.A.*, **51**, 7317d (1957).

482. Mamedaliev, Yu. G., and D. G. Gasanov, *Uch. Zap. Azerb. Gos. Univ.*, No. 1, 3 (1956).

483. Mamedaliev, Yu. G., and D. G. Gasanov, *Uch. Zap. Azerb. Gos. Univ.*, No. 4, 47 (1957); *C.A.*, **53**, 8605a (1959).

484. Mamedaliev, Yu. G., A. G. Khanlarova, Sh. A. Mirzoeva, and F. A. Mekhtieva, *Uch. Zap. Azerb. Gos. Univ.*, No. 7, 23 (1956); *C.A.*, **55**, 5381i (1961).

485. Mamedaliev, Yu. G., and D. D. Kichieva, *Dokl. Akad. Nauk Azerb. S.S.R.*, **14**, 595 (1958); *C.A.*, **53**, 2122h (1959).

486. Mamedaliev, Yu. G., and D. E. Mishiev, *Uch. Zap. Azerb. Gos. Univ.*, No. 8, 31 (1957).

487. Mamedaliev, Yu. G., and D. E. Mishiev, *Tr. Inst. Nefti, Akad. Nauk Azerb. S.S.R.*, **5**, 138 (1958).

488. Mamedaliev, Yu. G., and S. A. Sultanov, *Azerb. Neft. Khoz.*, 28 (1957); *C.A.*, **53**, 9628c (1959).

489. Mamedaliev, Yu. G., and S. A. Sultanov, *Azerb. Neft. Khoz.*, 33 (1957); *C.A.*, **53**, 8602g (1959).

490. Mamedaliev, Yu. G., and S. A. Sultanov, *Azerb. Neft. Khoz.*, 34 (1958); *C.A.*, **53**, 11273f (1959).

491. Mamedaliev, Yu. G., A. V. Topchiev, and S. M. Aliev, *Izv. Akad. Nauk S.S.S.R., Otd. Khim. Nauk*, 1794 (1959).

492. Mamedaliev, Yu. G., and Sh. V. Veliev, *Dokl. Akad. Nauk S.S.S.R.*, **92**, 573 (1953).

492a. Mamedaliev, Yu. G., and Sh. V. Veliev, *Dokl. Akad. Nauk S.S.S.R.*, **92**, 325 (1953).

493. Mamedaliev, Yu. G., and Sh. V. Veliev, *Uch. Zap. Azerb. Gos. Univ.*, No. 4, 7 (1955).

494. Mammen, H. E., U.S. Pat. 2,718,526 (Sept. 20, 1955).

495. Marks, E. M., J. M. Almand, and E. E. Reid, *J. Org. Chem.*, **9**, 13 (1944).

496. Martin, L. F., and G. H. Coleman, U.S. Pat. 1,969,984 (Aug. 14, 1934).

497. Mattox, W. J., *Trans. Am. Inst. Chem. Engrs.*, **41**, 463 (1945).

498. Mattox, W. J., and W. F. Arey, U.S. Pat. 2,904,607 (Sept. 15, 1959).

499. Matuszak, M. P., U.S. Pat. 2,408,173 (Sept. 24, 1946).

500. Matuszak, M. P., U.S. Pat. 2,456,435 (Dec. 14, 1948).

501. Mavity, J. M., U.S. Pat. 2,467,326 (Apr. 12, 1949).

502. Mavity, J. M., U.S. Pat. 2,480,254 (Aug. 30, 1949).

503. Mavity, J. M., U.S. Pat. 2,639,286 (May 19, 1953).

504. Max, N., and Y. Schaafsma, U.S. Pat. 2,730,557 (Jan. 10, 1956); Brit. Pat. 755,956 (Aug. 29, 1956).

505. Masuo, F., and S. Hattori, *J. Soc. Chem. Ind. Japan*, **48**, 55 (1945).

506. Meerkamp van Embden, I. C., *Fette, Seifen, Anstrichmittel*, **63**, 456 (1961).

507. Meerwein, H., and T. Bersin, *Ann.*, **476**, 113 (1929).

508. Mekhtiev, S. D., and T. A. Pashaev, *Azerb. Khim. Zh.*, No. 2, 39 (1959).

509. Meis, H., and H. Sauer, U.S. Pat. 2,983,731 (May 9, 1961).

509a. Melpolder, F. W., J. E. Woodbridge, and C. E. Headington, *J. Am. Chem. Soc.*, **70**, 935 (1948).

510. Meyer, H., and K. Bernhauer, *Monatsh.*, **53/54**, 721 (1929).

511. Michel, R., Germ. Pat. 550,494 (Dec. 9, 1927).

512. Michel, R., U.S. Pat. 1,667,214 (Apr. 24, 1928).

513. Michel, R., U.S. Pat. 1,741,472 (Dec. 31, 1929).

514. Michel, R., U.S. Pat. 1,741,473 (Dec. 31, 1929).

515. Michel, R., U.S. Pat. 1,766,344 (June 24, 1930).

516. Michel, R., U.S. Pat. 1,767,302 (June 24, 1930).

517. Michel, R., U.S. Pat. 1,878,963 (Sept. 20, 1932).

518. Michel, R., U.S. Pat. 1,972,232 (Sept. 4, 1934).

519. Mid-Century Corp., Brit. Pat. 807,650 (Jan. 21, 1959).

520. Mid-Century Corp., Brit. Pat. 843,601 (Aug. 4, 1960).

521. Milligan, C. H., and E. E. Reid, *J. Am. Chem. Soc.*, **44**, 206 (1922).

522. Milliken, T. H. Jr., G. A. Mills, and A. G. Oblad, *Disc. Faraday Soc.*, **8**, 279 (1950).

523. Mills, E. J. Jr., U.S. Pat. 2,388,758 (Nov. 13, 1945).

524. Mills, G. A., E. R. Boedeker, and A. G. Oblad, *J. Am. Chem. Soc.*, **72**, 1554 (1950).
525. Monsanto Chemical Co., Brit. Pat. 452,335 (Aug. 20, 1936).
526. Monsanto Chemical Co., Brit. Pats. 640,040 (July 12, 1950) and 639,873 (July 5, 1950).
527. Monsanto Chemical Co., Brit. Pat. 640,566 (July 26, 1950).
528. Monsanto Chemical Co., Brit. Pat. 813,214 (May 13, 1959) (see L. J. Weaver, U.S. Pat. 2,853,533).
529. Monteils, Y., *Bull. Soc. Chim. France*, 637 (1951).
530. Monteils, Y., *Bull. Soc. Chim. France*, 747 (1953).
531. Monteils, Y., *Bull. Soc. Chim. France*, 749 (1953).
532. Moore, R. J., U.S. Pat. 2,541,882 (Feb. 13, 1951).
533. Morris, R. E., U.S. Pat. 2,948,704 (Aug. 9, 1960).
534. Mulligan, J. G., U.S. Pat. 3,000,964 (Sept. 19, 1961).
535. Nametkin, S. S., and J. S. Pokrovskaya, *J. Gen. Chem. U.S.S.R.*, **7**, 69 (1937).
536. Nametkin, S. S., and J. S. Pokrovskaya, *J. Gen. Chem. U.S.S.R.*, **8**, 699 (1938).
537. Natelson, S., *J. Am. Chem. Soc.*, **53**, 272 (1931).
538. Natelson, S., *Ind. Eng. Chem.*, **25**, 1391 (1933).
539. Natelson, S., *J. Am. Chem. Soc.*, **56**, 1584 (1934).
540. Nauta, W. Th., and D. Mulder, *Rec. Trav. Chim.*, **58**, 514 (1939).
541. Nelson, K. L., *J. Org. Chem.*, **21**, 145 (1956).
542. Nelson, K. L., and H. C. Brown, *Chemistry of Petroleum Hydrocarbons*, Vol. III, Chapter 56, Reinhold Publishing Corp., New York, 1955.
543. Nenitzescu, C. D., D. A. Isacescu, and C. N. Ionescu, *Ann.*, **491**, 210 (1931).
544. Nenitzescu, C. D., *Angew. Chem.*, **52**, 231 (1939).
544a. Nenitzescu, C. D., *Experientia*, **16**, 333 (1960).
545. Neuworth, M. B., and E. A. Depp, U.S. Pat. 2,836,627 (May 27, 1958).
546. Newton, A., *J. Am. Chem. Soc.*, **65**, 320 (1943).
547. Nickels, J. E., U.S. Pat. 2,598,715 (June 3, 1952).
548. Nickels, J. E., U.S. Pat. 2,686,815 (Aug. 17, 1954).
549. Nickels, J. E., and W. M. Kutz, U.S. Pat. 2,570,263 (Oct. 9, 1951).
550. Nicolescu, I. V., M. Iovu, and G. I. Nikishin, *Izv. Akad. Nauk S.S.S.R., Otd. Khim. Nauk*, 94 (1960).
551. Niederl, J. B., U.S. Pat. 2,008,032 (July 16, 1935); Brit. Pat. 431,487 (1935); Can. Pat. 370,468 (Dec. 14, 1937).
552. Niederl, J. B., *Ind. Eng. Chem.*, **30**, 1269 (1938).
553. Niederl, J. B., and R. Casty, *Monatsh.*, **51**, 86, 1038 (1929).
554. Niederl, J. B., and S. Natelson, *J. Am. Chem. Soc.*, **53**, 1928 (1931).
555. Niederl, J. B., S. Natelson, and E. McK. Breekman, *J. Am. Chem. Soc.*, **55**, 2571 (1933).
556. Niederl, J. B., and S. Natelson, *J. Am. Chem. Soc.*, **53**, 272 (1931).
557. Niederl, J. B., and C. H. Riley, *J. Am. Chem. Soc.*, **56**, 2412 (1934).
558. Niederl, J. B., and R. A. Smith, *J. Am. Chem. Soc.*, **59**, 715 (1937); U.S. Pat. 2,121,472 (June 21, 1938).
559. Nieuwland, J. A., and F. J. Sowa, U.S. Pat. 2,192,015 (Feb. 27, 1940).
559a. Nightingale, D. V., *Chem. Rev.*, **25**, 329 (1939).
560. Nightingale, D. V., and B. J. Carton, *J. Am. Chem. Soc.*, **62**, 280 (1940).

561. Nightingale, D. V., R. G. Taylor, and H. W. Smelser, *J. Am. Chem. Soc.*, 63, 258 (1941).
562. Noelting, E., *Chim. Ind.* (*Paris*), 6, 719 (1921).
563. Norris, J. F., and D. Rubinstein, *J. Am. Chem. Soc.*, 61, 1163 (1939).
563a. Norrish, R. G., and K. E. Russell, *Trans. Faraday Soc.*, 48, 91 (1952).
564. Norwood, S. L., and T. W. Sauls, U.S. Pat. 2,838,564 (June 10, 1958).
565. N. V. de Bataafsche Petroleum Maatschappij, Brit. Pat. 649,305 (Jan. 24, 1951).
566. N. V. de Bataafsche Petroleum Maatschappij, Brit. Pat. 661,383 (Nov. 21, 1951).
567. N. V. de Bataafsche Petroleum Maatschappij, Brit. Pat. 706,653 (Mar. 31, 1954).
568. N. V. de Bataafsche Petroleum Maatschappij, Brit. Pat. 746,407 (Mar. 14, 1956).
569. N. V. de Bataafsche Petroleum Maatschappij, Brit. Pat. 778,014 (July 3, 1957).
570. N. V. de Bataafsche Petroleum Maatschappij, Brit. Pat. 787,950 (Dec. 18, 1957).
571. N. V. de Bataafsche Petroleum Maatschappij, Brit. Pat. 799,186 (Oct. 8, 1959).
572. N. V. de Bataafsche Petroleum Maatschappij, Dutch Pat. 87,523 (Feb. 15, 1958).
573. N. V. de Bataafsche Petroleum Maatschappij, Germ. Pat. 831,842 (Feb. 18, 1952).
574. Oblad, A. G., T. H. Milliken, Jr., and G. A. Mills, *Advances in Catalysis*, Vol. III, Academic Press, Inc., New York, p. 199, 1951.
575. Odioso, R. C., U.S. Pat. 2,810,771 (Oct. 22, 1957).
576. Offut, W. C., U.S. Pat. 2,684,389 (July 20, 1954).
577. O'Kelly, A. A., J. Kellett, and J. Plucker, *Ind. Eng. Chem.*, 39, 154 (1947).
578. O'Kelly, A. A., and R. H. Work, U.S. Pat. 2,436,151 (Feb. 17, 1948).
579. Olah, G. A., private communication.
579a. Olah, G. A., and S. J. Kuhn, *J. Am. Chem. Soc.*, 80, 6535 (1958).
579b. Olah, G. A., and S. J. Kuhn, *J. Am. Chem. Soc.*, 80, 6541 (1958).
579c. Olah, G. A., S. J. Kuhn, and S. H. Flood, *J. Am. Chem. Soc.*, 84, 1688 (1962).
580. Olin, J. F., U.S. Pat. 2,107,060 (Feb. 1, 1938).
580a. Olin, J. F., U.S. Pat. 3,014,079 (Dec. 19, 1961).
581. Olin, J. F., and J. L. Tetley, U.S. Pat. 2,337,123 (Dec. 21, 1943).
582. Olson, A. C., *Ind. Eng. Chem.*, 52, 833 (1960).
583. O'Neill, R. J., and L. J. Weaver, Can. Pat. 613,137 (Jan. 24, 1961).
584. *Org. Syn.*, Coll. Vol. 2, John Wiley and Sons, New York, p. 151, 1943.
585. *Org. Syn.*, Vol. 19, John Wiley and Sons, New York, p. 36, 1939.
586. Ostronmova, L. E., Z. M. Meshcheryokova, and I. I. Bondarevskaya, *Lakokrasochnye Materialy i ikh Primenenie*, No. 2, 16 (1960); *C.A.*, 55, 433e (1962).
587a. Pajeau, R., *Compt. rend.*, 213, 655 (1941).
587b. Pajeau, R., *Compt. rend.*, 247, 935 (1958).
588. Pajeau, R., *Compt. rend.*, 252, 3060 (1961).
589. Panchenkov, G. M., and I. M. Kolesnikov, *Zh. Obshch. Khim.*, 30, 3846 (1960).

590. Parc, G., Brit. Pat. 804,121 (Nov. 5, 1958).
590a. Parc, G., *Rev. Inst. Franc. Petrole Ann. Combust. Liquides*, **15**, 567 (1960).
590b. Parc, G., *ibid.*, **15**, 680 (1960).
591. Pardee, W. A., and B. F. Dodge, *Ind. Eng. Chem.*, **35**, 273 (1943).
592. Pardee, W. A., and B. F. Dodge, U.S. Pat. 2,388,077 (Oct. 30, 1945).
593. Parham, W. E., I. Gordon, and J. D. Swalen, *J. Am. Chem. Soc.*, **74**, 1824 (1952).
594. Passino, H. J., U.S. Pat. 2,396,966 (Mar. 19, 1946).
595. Passino, H. J., U.S. Pat. 2,545,671 (Mar. 20, 1951).
596. Patinkin, S. H., and R. A. Sanford, unpublished results.
597. Patinkin, S. H., and R. A. Sanford, U.S. Pat. 2,867,674 (Jan. 6, 1959).
598. Patinkin, S. H., and R. A. Sanford, U.S. Pat. 2,915,568 (Dec. 1, 1959).
599a. Paushkin, Ya. M., and M. V. Kurashev, *Izv. Akad. Nauk S.S.S.R., Otd. Khim. Nauk*, 133 (1954).
599b. Paushkin, Ya. M., and M. V. Kurashev, *Bull. Acad. Sci. U.S.S.R., Div. Chem. Sci.*, 1027 (1956).
600. Paushkin, Ya. M., and A. V. Topchiev, *Zh. Prikl. Khim.*, **21**, 1065 (1948).
601. Paushkin, Ya. M., A. V. Topchiev, and M. V. Kurashev, *Dokl. Akad. Nauk S.S.S.R.*, **91**, 1141 (1953).
602. Paushkin, Ya. M., A. V. Topchiev, and M. V. Kurashev, *Dokl. Akad. Nauk S.S.S.R.*, **130**, 1033 (1960).
603. Pederson, C. J., and V. M. Weinmayr, U.S. Pat. 2,275,311 (Mar. 3, 1942).
604. Perkins, R. P., and F. Bryner, U.S. Pat. 2,247,402 (July 1, 1941).
605. Perkins, R. P., and F. Bryner, U.S. Pat. 2,247,403 (July 1, 1941).
606. Perkins, R. P., and F. Bryner, U.S. Pat. 2,247,404 (July 1, 1941).
607. Perkins, R. P., and H. S. Nutting, U.S. Pat. 2,091,565 (Aug. 31, 1937).
608. Peters, E. F., U.S. Pat. 2,773,108 (Dec. 4, 1956).
609. Peters, T. J., U.S. Pat. 2,739,172 (Mar. 20, 1956).
610. Petropoulos, J. C., and J. J. Fisher, *J. Am. Chem. Soc.*, **80**, 1938 (1958).
611. Pfefferle, W. C., and P. N. Rylander, U.S. Pat. 2,972,642 (Feb. 21, 1961).
612. Pines, H., and J. T. Arrigo, *J. Am. Chem. Soc.*, **80**, 4369 (1958).
613. Pines, H., A. Edeleanu, and V. N. Ipatieff, *J. Am. Chem. Soc.*, **67**, 2193 (1945).
614. Pines, H., D. W. Huntsman, and V. N. Ipatieff, *J. Am. Chem. Soc.*, **73**, 4343 (1951).
615. Pines, H., and V. N. Ipatieff, U.S. Pat. 2,584,103 (Feb. 5, 1952).
616. Pines, H., and B. Kvetinskas, U.S. Pat. 2,553,785 (May 22, 1951).
617. Pines, H., B. Kvetinskas, and J. A. Vesely, *J. Am. Chem. Soc.*, **72**, 1568 (1950).
618. Pines, H., J. D. LaZerte, and V. N. Ipatieff, *J. Am. Chem. Soc.*, **72**, 2850 (1950).
619. Pines, H., and W. S. Postl, *J. Am. Chem. Soc.*, **79**, 1769 (1957).
620. Pines, H., D. R. Strehlau, and V. N. Ipatieff, *J. Am. Chem. Soc.*, **71**, 3534 (1949).
621. Pines, H., D. R. Strehlau, and V. N. Ipatieff, *J. Am. Chem. Soc.*, **72**, 1563 (1950).
622. Pines, H., D. R. Strehlau, and V. N. Ipatieff, *J. Am. Chem. Soc.*, **72**, 5521 (1950).

622a. Pines, H., and J. A. Vesely, U.S. Pat. 2,532,515 (Dec. 5, 1950).
623. Pines, H., A. Weizmann, and V. N. Ipatieff, *J. Am. Chem. Soc.*, **70**, 3859 (1948).
624a. Plank, C. J., and D. M. Nace, *Ind. Eng. Chem.*, **47**, 2374 (1955).
624b. Plesch, P. H., M. Polanyi, and H. A. Skinner, *J. Chem. Soc.*, 257 (1947).
625. Plyusnin, V. G., and E. P. Babin, *Zh. Fiz. Khim.*, **34**, 78 (1960).
626. Plyusnin, V. G., E. P. Babin, M. I. Nasakina, and N. M. Rodigin, *Zh. Fiz. Khim.*, **34**, 267 (1960).
627. Plyusnin, V. G., and A. P. Lysenko, *Zh. Fiz. Khim.*, **31**, 2464 (1957).
628. Plyusnin, V. G., and A. P. Lysenko, *Zh. Fiz. Khim.*, **32**, 1262 (1958).
629. Plyusnin, V. G., A. P. Lysenko, and E. P. Babin, *Zh. Fiz. Khim.*, **31**, 2066, 2229, 2464 (1957).
630. Plyusnin, V. G., and N. M. Rodigin, *Zh. Fiz. Khim.*, **31**, 2066 (1957).
631. Pokrovskaya, E. S., *Compt. rend. acad. sci. U.R.S.S.*, **39**, 25 (1943).
632. Pokrovskaya, E. S., *J. Gen. Chem. U.S.S.R.*, **13**, 579 (1943).
633. Pokrovskaya, E. S., *J. Gen. Chem. U.S.S.R.*, **16**, 435 (1946).
634. Pokrovskaya, E. S., *Tr. Inst. Nefti, Akad. Nauk S.S.S.R.*, **1**, No. 2, 264 (1950).
635. Pokrovskaya, E. S., *Tr. Inst. Nefti, Akad. Nauk S.S.S.R.*, **13**, 5 (1959).
636. Pokrovskaya, E. S., and N. A. Shimanko, *Dokl. Nauk S.S.S.R.*, **123**, 109 (1958).
637. Pokrovskaya, E. S., and M. V. Shishkina, *Dokl. Akad. Nauk S.S.S.R.*, **125**, 1269 (1959).
638. Pokrovskaya, E. S., and T. G. Stepantseva, *J. Gen. Chem. U.S.S.R.*, **9**, 1953 (1939).
639. Pokrovskaya, E. S., and T. G. Stepantseva, *Compt. rend. acad. sci. U.R.S.S.*, **55**, 829 (1947).
640. Pokrovskaya, E. S., and T. G. Stepantseva, *Tr. Inst. Nefti, Akad. Nauk S.S.S.R.*, **1**, No. 2, 300 (1950).
641. Pokrovskaya, E. S., and R. Y. Sushchik, *J. Gen. Chem. U.S.S.R.*, **9**, 2291 (1939).
642. Pospiech, F., U.S. Pat. 1,787,408 (Dec. 30, 1930).
643. Pospisil, J., Czech. Pat. 89,933 (May 15, 1959).
644. Pospisil, J., and V. Ettel, *Collection Czech. Chem. Commun.*, **24**, 729 (1959).
645. Potts, W. M., and L. L. Carpenter, *J. Am. Chem. Soc.*, **61**, 663 (1939).
646. Preston, R. W. G., U.S. Pat. 2,990,428 (June 27, 1961); Brit. Pat. 833,022 (April 21, 1960).
647. Price, C. C., and J. M. Ciskowski, *J. Am. Chem. Soc.*, **60**, 2499 (1938).
648. Price, C. C., and A. J. Tomisek, *J. Am. Chem. Soc.*, **65**, 439 (1943).
649. Price, C. C., *Org. Reactions*, **3**, John Wiley, New York (1946).
650. Prill, E. J., U.S. Pat. 2,965,686 (Dec. 20, 1960).
651. Proell, W., *J. Org. Chem.*, **16**, 178 (1951); U.S. Pat. 2,564,077 (Aug. 14, 1951).
652. Proell, W. A., and C. E. Adams, *Ind. Eng. Chem.*, **41**, 2217 (1949).
653. Proell, W. A., C. E. Adams, and B. H. Shoemaker, *Ind. Eng. Chem.*, **40**, 1129 (1948).
653a. Remick, A. E., *Electric Interpretations of Organic Chemistry*, John Wiley and Sons, New York, p. 103, 1949.
654. Rhein, Kampfer-Fabrik Ges., Brit. Pat. 298,600 (Oct. 12, 1927).
654a. Roberts, E., and M. P. Rose, Brit. Pat. 645,446 (Nov. 1, 1950).

655. Rodigin, N. M., E. P. Babin, and V. G. Plyusnin, *Zh. Fiz. Khim.*, **34**, 726 (1960).

656. Rodigin, N. M., E. P. Babin, and V. G. Plyusnin, *Zh. Fiz. Khim.*, **34**, 966 (1960).

657. Rogers, D. T., and H. Feldhusen, U.S. Pat. 2,398,253 (June 20, 1944).

658. Rohm & Haas Co., Brit. Pat. 659,353 (Oct. 24, 1951).

659. Rohm & Haas Co., Germ. Pat. 616,786 (Aug. 5, 1935).

660. Rohm & Haas Co., Germ. Pat. 665,514 (Sept. 27, 1938).

661. Rohm & Haas Co., Pamphlet on Amberlyst 15, June, 1960, p. 8; also July, 1960.

662. Rosenquist, E. N., and R. W. Sudhoff, U.S. Pat. 2,403,124 (July 2, 1946).

663. Rosenwald, R. H., U.S. Pat. 2,470,902 (May 24, 1949).

664. Rosenwald, R. H., U.S. Pat. 2,477,091 (July 26, 1949).

665. Rosenwald, R. H., U.S. Pat. 2,908,718 (Oct. 13, 1959).

665a. Rosenwald, R. H., and J. A. Chenicek, Abstracts, p. 73o, Am. Chem. Soc., Chicago, Sept. 6, 1953.

666. Rosenwald, R. H., and E. H. Volance, U.S. Pat. 2,950,335 (Aug. 23, 1960).

667. Rummelsburg, A. L., U.S. Pat. 2,471,453 (May 31, 1949).

668. Rummelsburg, A. L., U.S. Pat. 2,471,454 (May 31, 1949).

669. Rustamov, Kh. R., and N. M. Chirkov, *Zh. Fiz. Khim.*, **29**, 2113 (1955).

670. Rustamov, Kh. R., and N. M. Chirkov, *Zh. Fiz. Khim.*, **30**, 20 (1956).

671. Rustamov, I. Kh. R., T. A. Kudryavtseva, and N. M. Chirkov, *Zh. Fiz. Khim.*, **29**, 1945 (1955).

672. Sachanen, A. N., U.S. Pat. 2,242,960 (May 20, 1941).

673. Sachanen, A. N., and S. B. Davis, U.S. Pat. 2,234,984 (Mar. 18, 1941).

674. Sachanen, A. N., and A. A. O'Kelly, *Ind. Eng. Chem.*, **33**, 1540 (1941).

675. Sadykhov, I. D., *Azerb. Khim. Zh.*, No. 3, 89 (1960).

676. Sadykh-Zade, S. I., and A. K. Askerov, *Azerb. Khim. Zh.*, No. 6, 39 (1960).

677. Saffer, A., and R. Landau, U.S. Pat. 2,909,575 (Oct. 20, 1959).

678. Sandlar, E., Germ. Pat. 699,607 (Dec. 3, 1940).

679. Sanford, R. A., and B. S. Friedman, U.S. Pats. 2,810,769 and 2,810,770 (Oct. 22, 1957).

680. Sanford, R. A., S. M. Kovach, and B. S. Friedman, *J. Am. Chem. Soc.*, **75**, 6326 (1953).

681. Sanford, R. A., S. M. Kovach, and B. S. Friedman, *Ind. Eng. Chem.*, **51**, 1455 (1959).

682. Sanford, R. A., S. M. Kovach, and B. S. Friedman, *Ind. Eng. Chem.*, **52**, 679 (1960).

683. Schaad, R. E., U.S. Pat. 2,290,211 (July 21, 1942).

684. Schaad, R. E., U.S. Pat. 2,371,550 (Mar. 13, 1945).

685. Schaad, R. E., U.S. Pat. 2,412,229 (Dec. 10, 1946).

686. Schering, A. G., French Pat. 1,258,585 (Mar. 6, 1961).

687. Schering-Kohlbaum Aktiengesellschaft, Brit. Pat. 373,896 (June 2, 1932).

688. Schikawawa, H., H. Tozaki, I. Veki, and H. Shingu, *J. Chem. Soc. Japan, Pure Chem. Sect.*, **72**, 267 (1951).

689. Schlatter, M. J., U.S. Pat. 2,635,114 (April 14, 1953).

690. Schlatter, M. J., *J. Am. Chem. Soc.*, **76**, 4952 (1954).

690a. Schlatter, M. J., Symposium on Petrochemicals in the Postwar Years, Am. Chem. Soc., Div. Petrol. Chem., Chicago, Sept. 9, 1953, p. 79.

691. Schlatter, M. J., Joint Symposium on Synthetic Fuels and Chemicals, Am. Chem. Soc., Div. Petrol. Chem., Cincinnati, Sept. 12–15, 1955, p. 5.

692. Schlatter, M. J., Am. Chem. Soc., Div. Petrol. Chem., Preprints Symposia 1, No. 2 (Chemicals from Petrol.) 77 (1956).

693. Schlatter, M. J., U.S. Pat. 2,768,985 (Oct. 30, 1956).

694. Schlatter, M. J., U.S. Pat. 2,801,271 (July 30, 1957).

695. Schlatter, M. J., U.S. Pat. 2,816,940 (Dec. 17, 1957).

696. Schlatter, M. J., and R. D. Clark, J. Am. Chem. Soc., 75, 361 (1953).

697. Schleicher, A., and E. Buttgenbach, J. Prakt. Chem., 105, 355 (1923 ; Chem. Zentr., III, 835 (1923).

698. Schmerling, L., U.S. Pat. 2,302,721 (Nov. 24, 1937).

699. Schmerling, L., U.S. Pat. 2,385,303 (Sept. 18, 1945).

700. Schmerling, L., Ind. Eng. Chem., 40, 2072 (1948).

700a. Schmerling, L., Ind. Eng. Chem., 45, 1447 (1953).

701. Schmerling, L., U.S. Pat. 2,849,505 (Aug. 26, 1958).

702. Schmerling, L., U.S. Pat. 3,009,003 (Nov. 14, 1961).

703. Schmerling, L., and A. M. Durinski, U.S. Pat. 2,357,978 (Sept. 12, 1944).

704. Schmerling, L., and V. N. Ipatieff, U.S. Pat. 2,329,858 (Sept. 21, 1943).

705. Schmerling, L., and V. N. Ipatieff, U.S. Pat. 2,361,065 (Oct. 24, 1944).

706. Schmerling, L., and V. N. Ipatieff, U.S. Pat. 2,375,041 (May 1, 1945).

707. Schmerling, L., and V. N. Ipatieff, U.S. Pat. 2,402,847 (June 25, 1946).

708. Schmerling, L., and V. N. Ipatieff, U.S. Pat. 2,404,536 (July 23, 1946).

709. Schmerling, L., and V. N. Ipatieff, U.S. Pat. 2,430,190 (Nov. 4, 1947).

710. Schmerling, L., and V. N. Ipatieff, U.S. Pat. 2,442,878 (June 8, 1948).

711. Schmerling, L., J. P. Luvisi, and R. W. Welch, J. Am. Chem. Soc., 81, 2718 (1959).

712. Schmerling, L., R. W. Welch, and J. P. Luvisi, J. Am. Chem. Soc., 79, 2636 (1957).

713. Schmerling, L., and J. P. West, J. Am. Chem. Soc., 76, 1917 (1954).

714. Schmidl, A. J., U.S. Pat. 2,945,901 (July 19, 1960).

715. Schneider, A., U.S. Pat. 2,681,373 (Aug. 18, 1953).

716. Schneider, A., U.S. Pat. 2,648,713 (Aug. 11, 1953).

717. Schneider, A., U.S. Pat. 2,742,514 (Sept. 22, 1953).

718. Schollkopf, K., Germ. Pat. 586,150 (Oct. 13, 1927).

719. Schollkopf, K., U.S. Pat. 2,115,884 (May 3, 1938); Germ. Pat. 638,756 (Nov. 21, 1936); Brit. Pat. 319,205 (Sept. 17, 1928).

720. Schomaker, V., and L. Pauling, J. Am. Chem. Soc., 61, 1769 (1939).

721. Schrauth, W., and K. Quasebarth, Ber., 57, 854 (1924).

722. Schroeter, G., Ber., 57, 1990 (1924).

723. Schulze, W. A., U.S. Pat. 2,378,040 (June 12, 1945).

723a. Schulze, W. A., U.S. Pat. 2,382,506 (Aug. 14, 1945).

724. Schulze, W. A., U.S. Pat. 2,395,198 (Feb. 19, 1946).

725. Schulze, W. A., U.S. Pat. 2,419,599 (Apr. 29, 1947).

726. Schulze, W. A., U.S. Pat. 2,419,796 (Apr. 29, 1947).

727. Schulze, W. A., and W. M. Axe, U.S. Pat. 2,425,839 (Aug. 19, 1947).

728. Schulze, W. A., and J. P. Lyon, U.S. Pat. 2,395,199 (Feb. 19, 1946); 2,416,022 (Feb. 18, 1947).

729. Schulze, W. A., and J. E. Mahan, U.S. Pat. 2,516,152 (July 25, 1950).

730. Schulze, W. A., and C. E. Stoops, U.S. Pat. 2,514,419 (July 11, 1950).
731a. Seide, O. A., and B. M. Dubinin, Chem. Zentr., I, 603 (1933).
731b. Semerano, G., C. Beggi, and L. Fillipi, Atti. mem. accad. sci. Podova, 57, 19 (1942); Chem. Zentr., I, 721 (1943).
732. Sergeev, P. G., Khim. Prom., 144 (1956).
733. Shabarov, Yu. S., N. I. Vasilev, and R. Y. Levina, J. Gen. Chem. U.S.S.R., 31, 1693 (1961).
734. Sharples Solvents Corp., Brit. Pat. 420,636 (Dec. 5, 1934).
735. Sharrah, M. L., and G. C. Feighner, Ind. Eng. Chem., 46, 248 (1954).
736. Shikhalieva, R. A., and M. J. Movsumzade, Izv. Vysshikh Uchebn. Zavedenii, Neft i Gaz, No. 1, 57 (1959); No. 5, 97 (1958).
737. Shikhalieva, R. A., M. M. Movsumzade, and L. S. Dedusenko, Izv. Vysshikh Uchebn. Zavedenii, Neft i Gaz, No. 4, 85 (1960).
738. Shimanko, N. A., and E. S. Pokrovskaya, Dokl. Akad. Nauk S.S.S.R., 129, 1313 (1959).
739a. Shishido, K., J. Soc. Chem. Ind. Japan, 45, Suppl. Binding, 169B (1942).
739b. Shishido, K., and S. Ando, J. Soc. Chem. Ind. Japan, 44, Suppl. Binding, 361 (1941); C.A., 44, 7761 (1950).
739c. Shreve, R. N., and H. E. Marsh, Jr., A.C.S. Chicago, Sept. 3–8, 1950 (H. E. Marsh, Jr., Ph.D. Thesis, Purdue, Feb., 1950).
740. Shuikin, N. I., A. B. Kuchkarev, and N. A. Pozdnyak, Bull. Acad. Sci. U.S.S.R., Div. Chem. Sci., 783 (1954).
741. Shuikin, N. I., and N. A. Pozdnyak, Bull. Acad. Sci. U.S.S.R., Div. Chem. Sci., 713 (1957).
742. Shuikin, N. I., and N. A. Pozdnyak, Bull. Acad. Sci. U.S.S.R., Div. Chem. Sci., 279 (1959).
743. Shuikin, N. I., and N. A. Pozdnyak, Izv. Akad. Nauk S.S.S.R., Otd. Khim. Nauk, 1094 (1960).
744. Shuikin, N. I., and N. A. Pozdnyak, Izv. Akad. Nauk S.S.S.R., Otd. Khim. Nauk, 326 (1961).
745. Shuikin, N. I., and N. A. Pozdnyak, Izv. Akad. Nauk S.S.S.R., Otd. Khim. Nauk, 1156 (1961).
746. Shuikin, N. I., N. A. Pozdnyak, and Y. P. Egorov, Izv. Akad. Nauk S.S.S.R., Otd. Khim. Nauk, 10, 1239 (1958).
747. Shuikin, N. I., N. A. Pozdnyak, and Y. P. Egorov, Izv. Akad. Nauk S.S.S.R., Otd. Khim. Nauk, 1988 (1959).
748. Shuikin, N. I., N. A. Pozdnyak, and V. A. Shlyapochnikov, Izv. Akad. Nauk S.S.S.R., Otd. Khim. Nauk, 1254 (1960).
749. Shuikin, N. I., E. A. Viktorova, and V. P. Litvinov, Vestn. Mosk. Univ. Ser. II: Khim., 12, No. 5, 121 (1957); C.A., 53, 1211a (1959).
750. Shvetsova, L. S., Tr. Voronezhsk. Gos. Univ., 60, 23 (1957).
751a. Sidorova, N. G., and I. P. Tsukervanik, J. Gen. Chem. U.S.S.R., 1543 (1957).
751b. Sidrova, N. G., I. P. Tsukervanik, and E. Pak, Zh. Obshch. Khim., 24, 94 (1954).
752a. Sidorova, N. G., and E. A. Vdovtsova, J. Gen. Chem. U.S.S.R., 19, 299 (1949).
752b. Sidorova, N. G., and E. A. Vdovtsova, Soviet Research in Catalysis, VI, 153 (1957).
753. Simons, J. H., U.S. Pat. 2,423,470 (July 8, 1947).

754. Simons, J. H., and S. Archer, *J. Am. Chem. Soc.*, **60**, 986 (1938).

755. Simons, J. H., and S. Archer, *J. Am. Chem. Soc.*, **60**, 2952 (1938).

756. Simons, J. H., S. Archer, and E. Adams, *J. Am. Chem. Soc.*, **60**, 2955 (1938).

757. Simons, J. H., and S. Archer, *J. Am. Chem. Soc.*, **61**, 1521 (1939).

758. Simons, J. H., and S. Archer, *J. Am. Chem. Soc.*, **62**, 451 (1940).

759. Simons, J. H., and G. C. Bassler, *J. Am. Chem. Soc.*, **63**, 880 (1941).

760. Simons, J. H., and H. Hart, *J. Am. Chem. Soc.*, **66**, 1309 (1944).

761. Simons, J. H., and H. Hart, *J. Am. Chem. Soc.*, **69**, 979 (1947).

762. Sinnova ou Sadic, French Pat. 954,945 (Jan. 3, 1950).

763. Sisido, K., *J. Soc. Chem. Ind. Japan*, **44**, Suppl. Binding 104 (1941); *Chem. Zentr.*, I, 1110 (1943).

764. Skinner, D. A., and W. L. Wasley, U.S. Pat. 2,777,007 (Jan. 8, 1957).

765. Skraup, S., Germ. Pat. 489,364 (July 11, 1927); Brit. Pat. 293,753 (Sept. 6, 1928).

766. Skraup, S., and W. Beifuss, *Ber.*, **60**, 1070 (1927).

767. Skraup, S., K. Schollkopf, and A. Serini, U.S. Pat. 1,886,311 (Nov. 11, 1932).

768. Skripnik, E. I., *Transactions of the Grozny Petroleum Institute*, Symposium, **6**, 73 (1948).

769. Slanina, S., F. Sowa, and J. A. Nieuwland, *J. Am. Chem. Soc.*, **57**, 1547 (1935).

770. Slaughter, J. I., and D. A. McCaulay, U.S. Pat. 2,906,788 (Sept. 29, 1959).

771. Slaughter, J. I., and D. A. McCaulay, U.S. Pat. 2,908,728 (Oct. 13, 1959).

771a. Smith, F. B., U.S. Pat. 2,195,383 (Mar. 26, 1940).

771b. Smith, F. B., and H. W. Moll, U.S. Pat. 2,194,079 (Mar. 19, 1940).

771c. Smith, F. B., and H. W. Moll, U.S. Pat. 2,229,018 (Jan. 14, 1941).

772. Smith, F. B., and H. W. Moll, U.S. Pats. 2,233,964 (Mar. 4, 1941); 2,221,819 (Nov. 19, 1940).

772a. Smith, F. B., and H. W. Moll, U.S. Pat. 2,221,271 (Nov. 12, 1940).

772b. Smith, F. B., and H. W. Moll, U.S. Pat. 2,263,448 (Nov. 18, 1942).

772c. Smith, F. B., and H. W. Moll, U.S. Pat. 2,246,988 (June 24, 1941).

773. Smith, F. B., and H. W. Moll, U.S. Pat. 2,281,252 (Apr. 28, 1942).

774. Smith, R. A., and C. J. Rodden, *J. Am. Chem. Soc.*, **59**, 2353 (1937).

775. Somers, B. G., and C. D. Cook, *J. Chem. Educ.*, **32**, 312 (1955).

776. Sowa, F. J., H. D. Hinton, and J. A. Nieuwland, *J. Am. Chem. Soc.*, **54**, 2019 (1932).

777. Sowa, F. J., H. D. Hinton, and J. A. Nieuwland, *J. Am. Chem. Soc.*, **54**, 3694 (1932).

778. Sowa, F. J., H. D. Hinton, and J. A. Nieuwland, *J. Am. Chem. Soc.*, **55**, 3402 (1933).

778a. Spaeth, E. C., Abstracts, Am. Chem. Soc., Chicago, Sept. 6, 1953, p. 12o.

779. Spiegler, L., and J. M. Tinker, *J. Am. Chem. Soc.*, **61**, 1002 (1939).

780. Spilker, A., and W. Schade, *Ber.*, **65B**, 1686 (1932).

781. Stadnikoff, G., and I. Goldfarb, *Ber.*, **61**, 2341 (1928).

782. Stahly, E. E., U.S. Pat. 2,373,062 (Apr. 3, 1945).

783. Standard Oil Development Co., Brit. Pat. 581,907 (Oct. 29, 1946).

784. Standard Oil Co., French Pat. 821,688 (Dec. 10, 1937).

785. Stanley, H. M., *J. Soc. Chem. Ind.*, **49**, 349T (1930).

786. Stanley, H. M., and J. E. Youell, U.S. Pat. 2,143,493 (Jan. 10, 1939).
787. Stayner, R. A., R. P. Stayner, and L. H. Dimpfl, U.S. Pat. 2,786,745 (Oct. 7, 1947).
788. Steegmuller, R., *Chim. Ind. (Paris)*, **60**, 441 (1948).
789. Steindorff, A., C. Platz, and J. Rosenbach, Germ. Pat. 738,198 (Aug. 31, 1943).
790. Stempel, G. H., Brit. Pat. 652,618 (Apr. 25, 1951).
791. Stevens, D. R., *Ind. Eng. Chem.*, **35**, 655 (1943).
792. Stevens, A. H., Brit. Pat. 613,926 (Dec. 7, 1948).
793. Stevens, D. R., U.S. Pat. 2,603,662 (July 5, 1952).
794. Stevens, D. R., *J. Org. Chem.*, **20**, 1232 (1955).
795. Stevens, D. R., private communication.
796. Stevens, D. R., and R. S. Bowman, U.S. Pat. 2,560,666 (July 17, 1951).
797. Stevens, D. R., and R. S. Bowman, U.S. Pat. 2,655,546 (Oct. 13, 1953).
798. Stevens, D. R., and W. A. Gruse, U.S. Pat. 2,248,827 (July 8, 1941).
799. Stevens, D. R., and W. A. Gruse, U.S. Pat. 2,265,582 (Dec. 9, 1941).
800. Stevens, D. R., and C. J. Livingstone, U.S. Pat. 2,297,588 (Sept. 29, 1942).
801. Stevens, D. R., and J. B. McKinley, U.S. Pats. 2,290,602 and 2,290,603 (July 21, 1942).
801a. Stevens, D. R., and J. E. Nickels, U.S. Pat. 2,181,823 (Nov. 28, 1939).
802. Stillson, G. H., U.S. Pat. 2,428,745 (Oct. 7, 1947).
803. Stillson, G. H., and D. W. Sawyer, U.S. Pats. 2,248,830 and 2,248,831 (July 8, 1941).
804. Stillson, G. H., and D. W. Sawyer, U.S. Pat. 2,459,597 (Jan. 18, 1949).
805. Stillson, G. H., D. W. Sawyer, and C. K. Hunt, *J. Am. Chem. Soc.*, **67** 303 (1945).
806. Stoermer, R., and O. Kippe, *Ber.*, **36**, 3992 (1903).
806a. Streitwieser, A., *J. Am. Chem. Soc.*, **82**, 5003 (1960).
806b. Streitwieser, A., and W. J. Downs, *J. Org. Chem.*, **27**, 625 (1962).
807. Streitwieser, A., D. P. Stevenson, and W. D. Schaeffer, *J. Am. Chem. Soc.*, **81**, 1110 (1959).
808. Stroh, R., *Angew. Chem.*, **68**, 387 (1956).
809. Stroh, R., J. Ebersberger, and H. Haberland, U.S. Pat. 2,762,845 (Sept. 11, 1956); Brit. Pat. 756,538 (Sept. 5, 1956); Germ. Pat. 951,501 (Oct. 31, 1956); Germ. Pat. 1,048,277 (Jan. 8, 1959).
810. Stroh, R., J. Ebersberger, H. Haberland, and W. Hahn, *Angew. Chem.*, **69**, 124 (1957).
811. Stroh, R., J. Ebersberger, H. Haberland, and W. Hahn, Germ. Pat. 1,056,138 (Apr. 30, 1959).
812. Stroh, R., H. Haberland, and W. Hahn, Germ. Pat. 1,044,097 (Nov. 20, 1958).
813. Stroh, R., and W. Hahn, *Ann.*, **623**, 176 (1959).
814. Stroh, R., and R. Seydel, Germ. Pat. 944,014 (June 7, 1956).
815. Stroh, R., and R. Seydel, Germ. Pat. 1,044,825 (Nov. 27, 1958).
816. Stroh, R., R. Seydel, and W. Hahn, *Angew. Chem.*, **69**, 699 (1957).
817. Sultanov, S. A., Yu. G. Mamedaliev, and A. B. Terteryan, *Sb. Tr. Nauchn.-Issled. Inst. po Pererabotke Nefti, Min. Neft. Prom. Azerb. S.S.R.*, No. 3, 296 (1958).
818. Sultanov, S. A., and M. A. Mardanov, *Azerb. Neft. Khoz.*, **37**, No. 10, 32 (1958).

819. Swietoslawski, W., U.S. Pat. 2,428,102 (Sept. 30, 1947).
820. Swisher, R. D., E. F. Koelble, and S. K. Liu, *J. Org. Chem.*, **26**, 4066 (1961).
821. Tadema, H. J., U.S. Pat. 2,510,937 (June 6, 1950).
822. Tadema, H. J., and N. V. de Bataafsche, Dutch Pat. 65,640 (May 15, 1950).
823. Tamale, M. W., *Disc. Faraday Soc.*, **8**, 270 (1950).
824. Tarbell, D. S., and D. P. Harnish, *J. Am. Chem. Soc.*, **74**, 1862 (1952).
825. Tarbell, D. S., and J. C. Petropoulos, *J. Am. Chem. Soc.*, **74**, 244 (1952).
826. Tchitchibabin, A. E., U.S. Pat. 1,933,775 (Nov. 7, 1933).
827. Tchitchibabin, A., *Compt. rend.*, **198**, 1239 (1934).
828. Tegge, B. R., and W. J. Paltz, U.S. Pat. 2,667,519 (Jan. 26, 1954).
828a. Texaco Development Co., Brit. Pat. 625,173 (Jan. 23, 1949).
829. Texaco Development Co., Brit. Pat. 641,944 (August 23, 1950).
829a. Thomas, C. A., *Anhydrous Aluminum Chloride in Organic Chemistry*, Reinhold Publishing Co., New York, 1941.
830. Thomas, C. L., and V. Haensel, U.S. Pat. 2,410,111 (Oct. 29, 1946).
831. Thomas, C. L., and V. Haensel, U.S. Pat. 2,448,160 (Aug. 31, 1948).
832. Thompson, K. M., U.S. Pat. 2,875,257 (Feb. 24, 1959).
833. Tilecheev, M. D., *J. Appl. Chem. U.S.S.R.*, **12**, 735 (1939).
834. Tilicheev, M. D., and K. S. Kuruindin, *Neft. Khoz.*, **19**, 586 (1930).
835. Timbrol, Ltd., Australian Pat. 149,032 (Nov. 17, 1952).
836. Tinker, J. M., and V. Weinmayr, U.S. Pat. 2,275,312 (Mar. 3, 1942).
837. Tjepkema, J. J., B. Pavlis, and H. W. Huijser, Proc. Fifth World Petr. Congr., Sect. IV, Paper 21, New York, 1959.
838. Toland, W. G., Jr., U.S. Pat. 2,793,239 (May 21, 1957).
839. Tolchinskii, I. M., B. A. Krentsel, and A. V. Topchiev, *Bull. Acad. Sci. U.S.S.R., Div. Chem. Sci.*, 451 (1955).
840. Topchiev, A. V., and V. N. Andronov, *Proc. Acad. Sci. U.S.S.R., Sect. Chem.*, **112**, 107 (1957).
841. Topchiev, A. V., and V. N. Andronov, *Proc. Acad. Sci. U.S.S.R., Sect. Chem.*, **112**, 137 (1957).
842. Topchiev, A. V., V. G. Kryuchkova, and S. V. Zavgorodnii, *Dokl. Akad. Nauk S.S.S.R.*, **131**, 329 (1959).
843. Topchiev, A. V., V. G. Kryuchkova, and S. V. Zavgorodnii, *Dokl. Akad. Nauk S.S.S.R.*, **133**, 617 (1960).
844. Topchiev, A. V., M. V. Kurashev, and I. F. Gavrilenko, *Dokl. Akad. Nauk S.S.S.R.*, **139**, 124 (1961).
845. Topchiev, A. V., M. V. Kurashev, and B. A. Krentsel, *Zh. Prikl. Khim.*, **28**, 976 (1955).
846. Topchiev, A. V., M. A. Kurashev, and Ya. M. Paushkin, *Dokl. Akad. Nauk S.S.S.R.*, **93**, 839 (1953).
847. Topchiev, A. V., M. V. Kurashev, and Ya. M. Paushkin, *Proc. Acad. Sci. U.S.S.R., Sect. Chem.*, **107**, 191 (1956).
848. Topchiev, A. V., M. V. Kurashev, and Ya. M. Paushkin, *Izv. Akad. Nauk S.S.S.R., Otd. Khim. Nauk*, 307 (1961).
849. Topchiev, A. V., M. V. Kurashev, Ya. M. Paushkin, and I. F. Gavrilenko, *Dokl. Akad. Nauk S.S.S.R.*, **131**, 587 (1960).
850. Topchiev, A. V., G. M. Mamedeliev, and S. M. Aliev, *Izv. Akad. Nauk S.S.S.R., Otd. Khim. Nauk*, 1971 (1959).

851. Topchiev, A. V., and Ya. M. Paushkin, *Boron Fluoride Compounds as Catalysts in Alkylation, Polymerization, and Condensation Reactions*, Moscow, 1949.
852. Topchiev, A. V., and Ya. M. Paushkin, *Usp. Khim.*, **6**, 664 (1947).
853. Topchiev, A. V., and Y. M. Paushkin, Reports 4th World Petrol. Congr., Rome, 1955, Section IV, p. 341.
854. Topchiev, A. V., Ya. M. Paushkin, I. F. Baev, M. V. Kurashev, and O. I. Shuleshov, *Tr., Mosk. Inst. Neftekhim. i Gaz Prom.*, No. 24, 269 (1959).
855. Topchiev, A. V., Ya. M. Paushkin, and M. V. Kurashev, *Proc. Akad. Sci. U.S.S.R.*, **88**, 849 (1953).
856. Topchiev, A. V., Ya. M. Paushkin, and M. V. Kurashev, *Proc. Acad. Sci. U.S.S.R., Sect. Chem.*, **108**, 219 (1956).
857. Topchiev, A. V., Ya. M. Paushkin, and M. V. Kurashev, *Dokl. Akad. Nauk S.S.S.R.*, **130**, 559 (1960).
858. Topchiev, A. V., Ya. M. Paushkin, and L. I. Sergaeva, *Dokl. Akad. Nauk S.S.S.R.*, **64**, 81 (1949).
859. Topchiev, A. V., Ya. M. Paushkin, T. P. Vishnyakova, and M. V. Kurashev, *Dokl. Akad. Nauk S.S.S.R.*, **80**, 381 (1951).
860. Topchiev, A. V., Ya. M. Paushkin, T. P. Vishnyakova, and M. V. Kurashev, *Dokl. Akad. Nauk S.S.S.R.*, **80**, 611 (1951).
861. Topchiev, A. V., E. S. Pokrovskaya, and T. G. Stepantseva, *Dokl. Akad. Nauk S.S.S.R.*, **119**, 1164 (1958).
862. Topchiev, A. V., and B. M. Tumerman, *Tr., Mosk. Inst. Neftekhim. i Gaz Prom.*, No. 23, 9 (1958).
863. Topchiev, A. V., B. M. Tumerman, V. N. Andronov, and L. I. Korshunova, *Neft. Khoz.*, **32**, No. 7, 65 (1954).
864a. Topchiev, A. V., B. M. Tumerman, and T. A. Fedorova, *Dokl. Akad. Nauk S.S.S.R.*, **120**, 90 (1958).
864b. Topchiev, A. V., N. E. Tsytovich, and E. S. Pokrovskaya, *Dokl. Akad. Nauk S.S.S.R.*, **128**, 558 (1959).
865. Topchiev, A. V., R. L. V. Volkov, and S. V. Zavgorodnii, *Dokl. Akad. Nauk S.S.S.R.*, **134**, 844 (1960).
866. Topchiev, A. V., R. N. Volkov, and S. V. Zavgorodnii, *Dokl. Akad. Nauk, S.S.S.R.*, **134**, 1101 (1960).
866a. Topchiev, A. V., S. V. Zavgorodnii, and Ya. M. Paushkin, *Boron Fluoride and its Compounds as Catalysts in Organic Chemistry*, Pergamon Press, New York, 1959.
866b. *Ibid.*, pp. 131–138.
867. Toussaint, J., *Bull. Roy. Soc. Liège*, **13**, 111 (1944).
868. Trigo, G. Gonzalez, 32nd Intern. Ind. Chem. Congr. (1960); Abstr. in *Chim. Ind. (Paris)*, **84**, 173 (1960).
869. Truffault, R., *Bull. Soc. Chim. France*, (5), **1**, 391 (1934).
870. Truffault, R., *Compt. rend.*, **202**, 1286 (1936).
870a. Truffault, R., *Compt. rend.*, **207**, 676 (1938).
871. Truffault, R., and Y. Monteils, *Bull. Soc. Chim. France*, (5), **6**, 726 (1939).
872. Truffault, R., and Y. Monteils, *Bull. Soc. Chim. France*, 241 (1948); 97 (1951).
873. Truffault, R., and Y. Monteils, *Bull. Soc. Chim. France*, 230 (1951).
874. Tsukervanik, I. P., *Vopr. Khim. Kinetiki, Kataliza, i Reaktsionnoi Sposobnosti, Akad. Nauk S.S.S.R., Otd. Khim. Nauk*, 608 (1955).

875. Tsukervanik, I. P., *Usp. Khim.*, **26**, 1036 (1957).
876. Tsunoda, Y., *Tokai Denkyoku Giho*, **17**, No. 2, 16 (1956).
877. Tsunoda, Y., *Tokai Denkyohu Giho*, **18**, No. 1, 23 (1957).
878. Tsutsumi, S., Japan. Pat. 56' 8274 (Sept. 24, 1956).
879. Tsutsumi, S., Japan. Pat. 57' 1719 (Mar. 15, 1957).
880. Tsutsumi, S., Japan. Pat. 57' 5162 (July 19, 1957).
881. Tsutsumi, S., T. Yoshijima, and K. T. Koyama, *T. Fuel Soc. Japan*, **34**, 145 (1955).
882. Tsytovich, N. E., and E. S. Pokrovskaya, *Dokl. Akad. Nauk S.S.S.R.*, **134**, 1119 (1960).
883. Turkington, V. H., L. R. Whiting, and L. P. Rankin, U.S. Pat. 2,353,282 (July 11, 1944).
884. Underwood, J. W., U.S. Pat. 2,432,356 (Dec. 9, 1947).
885. Universal Oil Products Co., Brit. Pat. 498,260 (Jan. 5, 1939).
886. Universal Oil Products Co., Brit. Pat. 615,624 (Jan. 10, 1949).
886a. Universal Oil Products Co., Brit. Pat. 669,657 (April 9, 1952).
887. Universal Oil Products Co., Brit. Pat. 769,383 (Mar. 6, 1957).
888. Universal Oil Products Co., Brit. Pat. 794,153 (April 30, 1958).
889. Universal Oil Products Co., Brit. Pat. 795,574 (May 28, 1958).
890. Universal Oil Products Co., Brit. Pat. 827,830 (Feb. 10, 1960).
891. Universal Oil Products Co., Brit. Pat. 863,539 (Mar. 22, 1961).
892. Universal Oil Products Co., French Pat. 830,037 (July 19, 1938).
893. Vaiser, V. L., and V. D. Ryabov, *Dokl. Akad. Nauk S.S.S.R.*, **125**, 547 (1959).
894. Vakhtin, V. G., and S. V. Zavgorodnii, *J. Gen. Chem. U.S.S.R.*, **30**, 116 (1960).
895. Van Winkle, J. L., and R. D. Vaughan, Can. Pat. 624,459 (July 25, 1961).
895a. Vesely, J. A., U.S. Pat. 2,563,687 (Aug. 7, 1951).
896. Vesely, J. A., and C. B. Linn, U.S. Pat. 2,891,966 (Dec. 23, 1958).
897. Viktorova, E. A., N. I. Shuikin, and B. G. Bubnova, *Izv. Akad. Nauk S.S.S.R., Otd. Khim. Nauk*, 1657 (1961).
898. Viktorova, E. A., N. I. Shuikin, and G. S. Korosteleva, *Izv. Akad. Nauk S.S.S.R., Otd. Khim. Nauk*, 1510 (1960).
899. Viktorova, E. A., N. I. Shuikin, G. S. Korosteleva, and N. G. Baranova, *Izv. Akad. Nauk S.S.S.R., Otd. Khim. Nauk*, 1518 (1961).
900. Vinik, M. I., Cand. Dissertation, 1952, Institute for Chemical Physics of the Academy of Science, U.S.S.R.
901. Voicu, O., and F. Popescu, *Acad. Rep. Populare Romine, Studii Cercetari Chim.*, **7**, 587 (1959); *C.A.*, **54**, 19556d (1960).
902. Volkov, R. N., and S. V. Zavgorodnii, *J. Gen. Chem., U.S.S.R.*, **29**, 3630 (1959).
903. Volkov, R. N., and S. V. Zavgorodnii, *Dokl. Akad. Nauk S.S.S.R.*, **133**, 843 (1960).
904. Vonderwahl, E., U.S. Pat. 1,927,053 (Sept. 19, 1933).
905. Vorozhtsov, N. N., and I. I. Ioffe, *Zh. Obshch. Khim.*, **21**, 1659 (1951).
906. Wackher, R. C., and C. B. Linn, U.S. Pat. 2,488,752 (Nov. 22, 1949).
907. Wackher, R. C., and C. B. Linn, U.S. Pat. 2,647,931 (Aug. 4, 1953).
908. Wade, R. C., U.S. Pat. 2,951,885 (Sept. 6, 1960).
909. Wadsworth, F. T., U.S. Pat. 2,881,226 (April 7, 1959).
909a. Wadsworth, F. T., U.S. Pat. 2,929,856 (Mar. 22, 1960).

910. Wadsworth, F. T., and R. J. Lee, U.S. Pat. 2,462,792 (Feb. 22, 1949).

910a. Wagner, C. R., U.S. Pat. 2,393,132 (Jan. 15, 1946).

911. Wakaboyashi, S., and Y. Matsubara, *Nippon Kagaku Zasshi*, **80**, 1179 (1959).

912. Walling, C., *J. Am. Chem. Soc.*, **72**, 1164 (1950).

913. Weaver, L. J., U.S. Pat. 2,853,533 (Sept. 23, 1958); (see Monsanto, Brit. Pat. 813,214).

913a. Weber, S. H., D. B. Spoelstra, and E. H. Polak, *Rec. Trav. Chim.*, **74**, 1179 (1955).

914. Weaver, L. J., U.S. Pat. 2,949,492 (Aug. 16, 1960).

914a. Weingaertner, E., *Brennstoff-Chem. Abstract*, **42**, 361 (1961).

915. Weinmayr, V. M., U.S. Pat. 2,285,243 (June 2, 1941).

916. Weinmayr, V. M., *J. Am. Chem. Soc.*, **72**, 918 (1950).

917. Weinrich, W., *Ind. Eng. Chem.*, **35**, 264 (1943).

918. Weil-Malherbe, H., and J. Weiss, *J. Chem. Soc.*, 2164 (1948).

918a. Welch, L. M., U.S. Pat. 2,651,628 (Sept. 8, 1953).

919. Wertyporoch, E., and T. Firla, *Ann.*, **500**, 287 (1933).

920. Whitmore, F. C., and E. E. Stahly, *J. Am. Chem. Soc.*, **55**, 4153 (1933).

921. Wood, T. F., U.S. Pat. 2,493,797 (Jan. 10, 1950).

922. Woodle, R. A., U.S. Pat. 2,909,574 (Oct. 20, 1959).

923. Wunderly, H., F. Sowa, and J. Nieuwland, *J. Am. Chem. Soc.*, **58**, 1007 (1936).

924. Wuyts, H., *Bull. Soc. Chim. Belges*, **26**, 308 (1912).

925. Yamashita, G., and K. Ogata, Japan. Pat. 61' 757 (Feb. 17, 1961).

926. Yeo, A. A., and A. J. M. Wenham, Brit. Pat. 863,148 (Mar. 15, 1961).

927. Yoke, G. R., E. O. Blodgett, and W. F. Loranger, *J. Am. Chem. Soc.*, **71**, 2273 (1949).

928. Young, D. W., and F. W. Banes, U.S. Pat. 2,730,436 (Jan. 10, 1956).

929. Young, D. S., and G. F. Rodgers, U.S. Pat. 2,722,556 (Nov. 1, 1955).

930. Yur'ev, Yu. K., N. S. Zefirov, A. A. Shteĭnman, and V. M. Gurevich, *J. Gen. Chem. U.S.S.R.*, **30**, 434 (1960).

931. Zavgorodnii, S. V., *J. Gen. Chem. U.S.S.R.*, **16**, 1495 (1946).

932. Zavgorodnii, S. V., *J. Gen. Chem., U.S.S.R.*, **22**, 2045 (1952).

933. Zavgorodnii, S. V., *Dokl. Akad. Nauk S.S.S.R.*, **97**, 257 (1954).

934. Zavgorodnii, S. V., *Tr. Voronezhsk. Gos. Univ.*, **57**, 117 (1959).

935. Zavgorodinii, S. V., and E. V. Alisova, *Dokl. Akad. Nauk S.S.S.R.*, **139**, 1367 (1961).

936. Zavgorodnii, S. V., and E. M. Faustova, *Zh. Obshch. Khim.*, **23**, 1651 (1953).

937. Zavgorodnii, S., and K. Fedoseeva, *J. Gen. Chem. U.S.S.R.*, **16**, 2006 (1946); *C.A.*, **42**, 144a (1948).

938. Zavgorodnii, S. V., T. G. Fedoseeva, and A. Ya Shumakher, *Tr. Voronezhsk. Gos. Univ.*, **57**, 107 (1959).

939. Zavgorodnii, S. V., T. B. Gonsovskaya, L. S. Shvetsova, V. I. Sidel'nikova, and V. G. Vakhtin, *Zh. Obshch. Khim.*, **31**, 726 (1961).

940. Zavgorodnii, S. V., and M. M. Gostev, *Soviet Research in Catalysis*, VI, 187 (1954).

941. Zavgorodnii, S. V., and M. M. Gostev, *Zh. Obshch. Khim.*, **24**, 2002 (1954).

942. Zavgorodnii, S. V., and V. G. Kryuchkova, *Zh. Obshch. Khim.*, **27**, 330 (1957).

943. Zavgorodnii, S. V., and V. G. Kryuchkova, *J. Gen. Chem. U.S.S.R.*, **29**, 1315 (1959).
944. Zavgorodnii, S. V., and L. S. Shvetsova, *J. Gen. Chem. U.S.S.R.*, **28**, 2695 (1958).
945. Zavgorodnii, S. V., L. S. Shvetsova, and B. S. Khromykh, *J. Gen. Chem. U.S.S.R.*, **26**, 2435 (1956).
946. Zavgorodnii, S. V., and V. I. Sidel'nikova, *Proc. Acad. Sci. U.S.S.R.*, **118**, 9 (1958).
947. Zavgorodnii, S. V., and V. I. Sigova, *Izv. Vysshikh Uchebn. Zavedenii, Khim. i Khim. Tekhnol.*, **4**, 99 (1961).
948. Zavgorodnii, S. V., O. V. Sigov, and I. F. Baev, *Zh. Obshch. Khim.*, **28**, 1279 (1958).
949. Zavgorodnii, S. V., and V. G. Vakhtin, *Tr. Voromezh. Univ.*, **42**, 37 (1956).
950. Zavgorodnii, S. V., and V. G. Vakhtin, *Sb. Tr. Voronezhsk. Otd. Vses. Khim. Obshchestva*, 195 (1957).
951. Zavgorodnii, S. V., and R. N. Volkov, *J. Gen. Chem. U.S.S.R.*, **29**, 1421 (1959).
952. Zavgorodnii, S. V., B. A. Zaitsev, and D. B. El'chinov, *Zh. Obshch. Khim.*, **30**, 2196 (1960).
952a. Zavgorodnii, S. V., and V. L. Zavgorodnyaya, *Dokl. Akad. Nauk S.S.S.R.*, **129**, 113 (1959).
953. Zerbe, R. O., U.S. Pat. 2,832,808 (Apr. 29, 1958).
954. Zinke, A., F. Hanus, and E. Ziegler, *J. Prakt. Chem.*, **156**, 169 (1940).
955. Zollner, G., I. Wurdits, and J. Marton, *Magy. Kem. Lapja*, **9**, 199 (1954).

CHAPTER XV

Alkylation of Aromatics with Dienes and Substituted Alkenes

ROBERT KONCOS and B. S. FRIEDMAN

Sinclair Research, Inc., Harvey, Illinois

I. Introduction

Four years after Friedel and Crafts announced their pioneering studies on the alkylation of aromatics with alkyl halides, and in the same year (1879) that Balsohn had described the alkylation of aromatics with olefins, Silva (183) reported alkylation with a substituted olefin, namely allyl chloride and Demole (49) alkylation

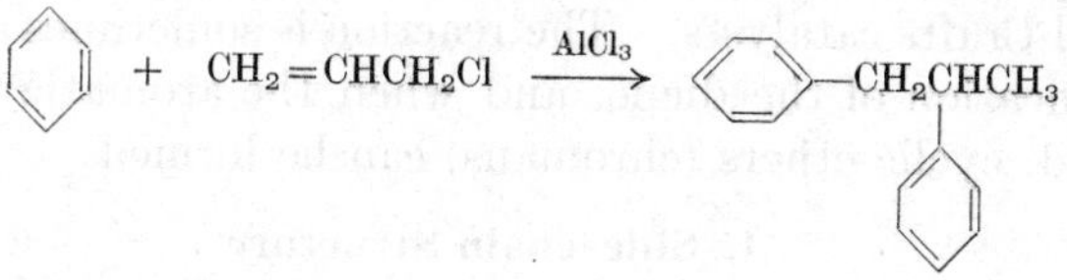

$$\bigcirc + \ CH_2=CHCH_2Cl \ \xrightarrow{AlCl_3} \ \bigcirc-CH_2CHCH_3$$

with 1,1-dibromoethylene.

Other types of substituted olefins as well as dienes were subsequently utilized as alkylating reagents. The substituted olefins included unsaturated ketones, esters, acids, alcohols, and ethers. In some instances, e.g., unsaturated halides or acyl halides, reaction took place only with the substituent group; in other instances with both this group and the double bond.

Several other competing or complicating reactions were noted; e.g., hydrogen transfer, migration of the double bond away from the functional group prior to alkylation, replacement of one aryl group by another, and cyclialkylation. Apparently, these side reactions could be controlled in certain instances by adjusting reaction conditions.

While they have been invaluable in laboratory syntheses, the reactions described in this chapter have found relatively little large-scale commercial application. The cost and availability of the unsaturated reactants have undoubtedly been major deterrents. At

289

one time, however, phenylstearic acids were manufactured *via* alkylation of benzene with oleic acid, for use as lubricant additives.

Alkylation with functionally substituted olefins or with dienes has not been investigated to the same extent as olefin alkylation. Much remains to be done in extending the synthetic scope of this reaction as well as the elucidation of the reaction mechanisms.

Most of the literature covered in this chapter deals with the descriptive chemistry of the reaction with the exception of some notable contributions toward the elucidation of reaction mechanisms. In general, only representative examples are discussed and the reader is referred to the tables at the end of the chapter for a more complete source of references. The reviewers have strived to make these tables as complete as possible up to the end of 1960. In addition many articles and patents published in 1961 were covered, especially if they were indexed in the 1961 volume of *Chemical Abstracts*.

II. Dienes

Alkenyl aromatics, polyalkenyl aromatics, and diarylalkanes are formed by the condensation of aromatics with dienes in the presence of Friedel-Crafts catalysts. The reaction is sometimes accompanied by resinification of the diene, and when the aromatic is a phenolic compound, cyclic ethers (chromans) can be formed.

1. Side-chain Structure

The main products of alkenylation have been shown in almost all cases to result from the 1,4-addition of the aromatic to the diene. In most instances the side-chain skeletal structure of the product was determined by hydrogenation of the double bond. The position of the double bond was determined by oxidation, ozonization, or isomerization of the double bond and by infra-red spectra.

Proell (160) condensed butadiene with benzene, toluene, *p*-xylene, naphthalene, methylnaphthalene, and phenol using low molecular weight alkanesulfonic acids as the catalyst. In the presence of 5% catalyst at 0 to 40° the benzene condensation product was 1-phenyl-2-butene (I). The benzene homologs yielded mixtures of position isomers but the same side-chain skeletal structure was assumed. At 40–150° in addition to arylbutenes, diarylbutanes and more complex products were formed. Moeller (125) reported that the major products of butenylation of benzene, toluene, and xylene with 95% phosphoric acid were the 1,4-addition products. Ipatieff, Pines, and Schaad (87a) used stronger acids, sulfuric and hydrogen fluoride, as catalysts at 0–20°; they identified 1,2-diphenylbutane (II) as the lowest boiling product. Compound II is probably the product of the alkylation of benzene with the initially formed 1-phenyl-2-butene (I) (87a).

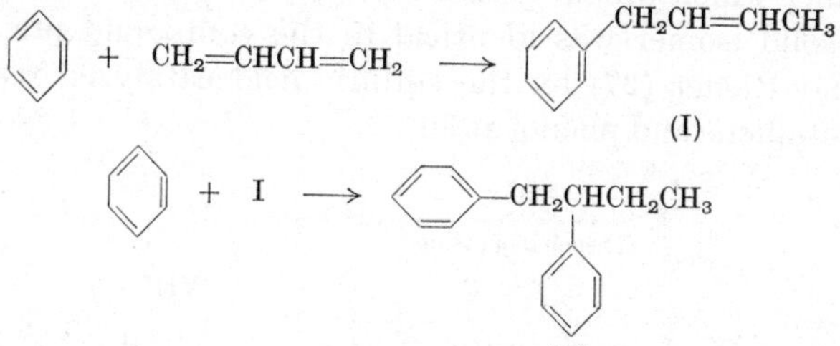

$$\bigcirc + CH_2=CHCH=CH_2 \longrightarrow \bigcirc-CH_2CH=CHCH_3$$

(I)

$$\bigcirc + I \longrightarrow \bigcirc-CH_2CHCH_2CH_3$$

(II)

Ipatieff and co-workers (87a) reported a 59% yield of phenyl-butenes, mostly 1-phenyl-1-butene, when a 4.5/1 molar ratio of benzene and butadiene was passed over solid phosphoric acid at 27 atmospheres and 216°. The reviewers believe that the formation of 1-phenyl-1-butene at these severe conditions must have been the result of isomerization of the initially formed 1-phenyl-2-butene.

Pines and co-workers (154) investigated the reactions of butadiene and isoprene with thiophene in the presence of 85% phosphoric acid. It is interesting that the authors reported obtaining only 2-(3-methyl-2-butenyl)thiophene (III) from isoprene, but they report both 2-(2-butenyl)thiophene (IV) and 2-(3-butenyl)thiophene (V), the latter compound being the major component, in the butadiene reaction.

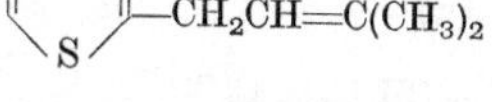

$$\bigcirc_S -CH_2CH=C(CH_3)_2 \quad \bigcirc_S -CH_2CH=CHCH_3 \quad \bigcirc_S -CH_2CH_2CH=CH_2$$

(III) 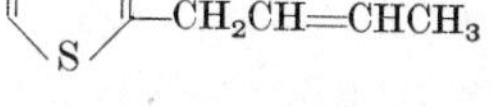 (IV) 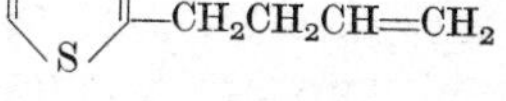 (V)

Intense infra-red bands observed at 910 cm.$^{-1}$ and 970 cm.$^{-1}$ for the butadiene product were considered indicative of a vinyl group and therefore consistent with V. A band of moderate intensity at 960 cm.$^{-1}$ was assigned to the internal double bond of IV.

Bader (16) considered the formation of V unlikely from a mechanistic point of view and pointed out that 970 cm.$^{-1}$ (10.3μ) was too long a wavelength for a vinyl group. He suggested that the product identified as V might have been the cis-isomer of IV.

p-2-Cyclopentenylphenol (VI) was identified by Bader (14) as the major product of the condensation of cyclopentadiene and phenol in the presence of phosphoric acid at room temperature. When refluxed with a catalytic amount of phosphoric acid, dicyclopentadiene (VII), and phenol yielded some *o*-2-cyclopentenylphenol (VIII) and solid phenoxydihydro-*exo*-dicyclopentadiene (IX or X), and a liquid isomer which probably had the alternative structure of IX or X. The solid isomer was identical to the compound prepared by Bruson and Riener (27) by the sulfuric acid catalyzed reaction of dicyclopentadiene and phenol at 30°.

(VI)

(VII) (IX) (X) (VIII)

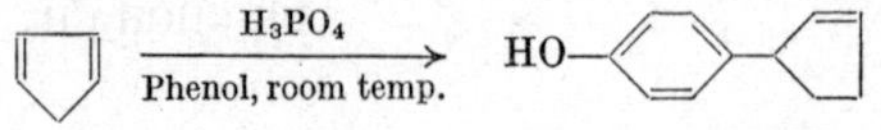

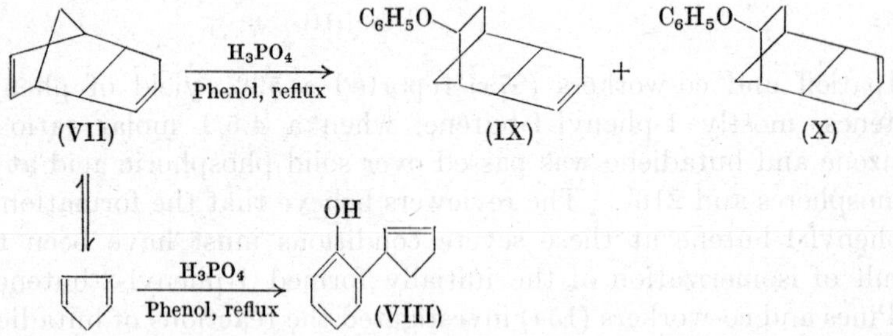

Bader (16) obtained mixtures of *ortho*- and *para*-2-butenylphenols by condensing phenol and butadiene using a number of catalysts. Dilute phosphoric acid (71%) promoted the reaction of isoprene and phenol yielding six products (17). The products of alkenylation were the 1,4-addition products *p*- and *o*-(3-methyl-2-butenyl)phenol (XI and XII). Along with these compounds two tertiary alcohols (XIII and XIV) were formed and two chromans (XV and XVI). 2,2-

(XI) (XII)

(XIII) (XIV)

(XV) (XVI)

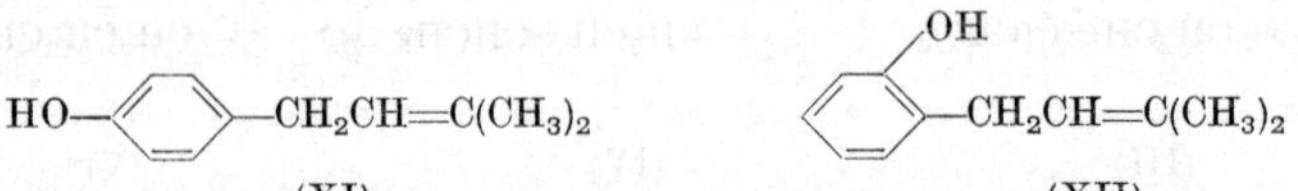

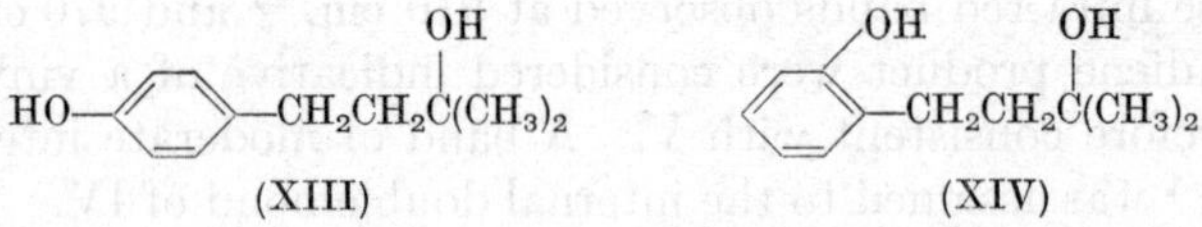

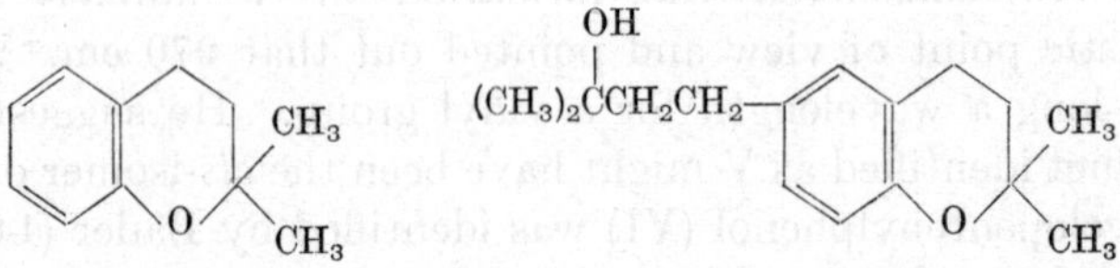

Dimethylchroman (XV) was originally prepared by Claisen (36a) by the condensation of phenol and isoprene and identified by the ring closure of the tertiary alcohol (XIV) prepared by the action of methyl magnesium iodide on ethyl dihydrocoumarate.

4-(p-Methoxyphenyl)-2-pentene (XVII) and 4-(p-hydroxyphenyl)-2-pentene (XVIII) were the major products identified by Vdovtsova and co-workers (211,213) as the products of the reaction of anisole and phenol respectively with piperylene. The structure of the side chain was independent of the catalyst or conditions used.

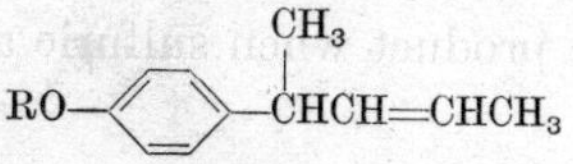

$$RO\!-\!\!\langle\ \rangle\!-\!\overset{\overset{\textstyle CH_3}{|}}{C}HCH\!=\!CHCH_3$$

(XVII) R = CH$_3$
(XVIII) R = H

The reactions of dienes, including butadiene, isoprene, and 2,3-dimethylbutadiene with substituted phenols to form chromans have been of considerable interest because the products are related to tocopherol and Vitamin K$_1$. The formation of chromans was first noted by Claisen (36a) and repeated with phenol and p-cresol by Smith and co-workers (195) who condensed these compounds with isoprene in the presence of hydrogen chloride or zinc chloride to obtain compounds XV and XIX. Smith *et al.* also condensed iso-

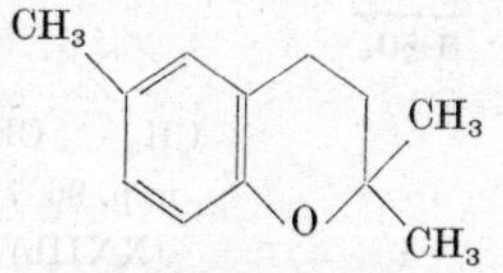

(XIX) 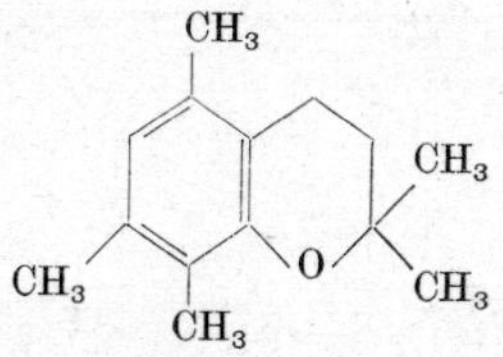   (XX)

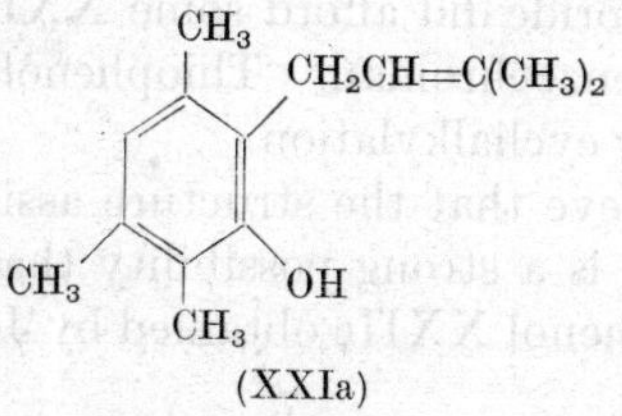

(XXIa)

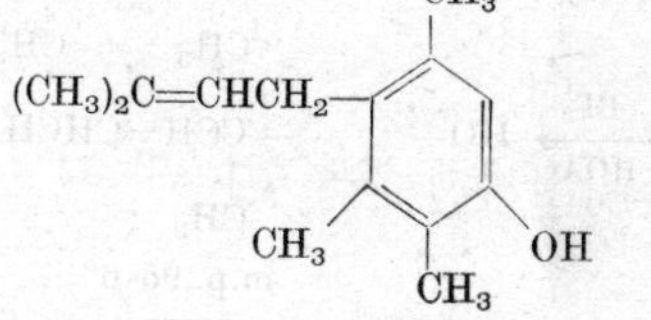

(XXIb) 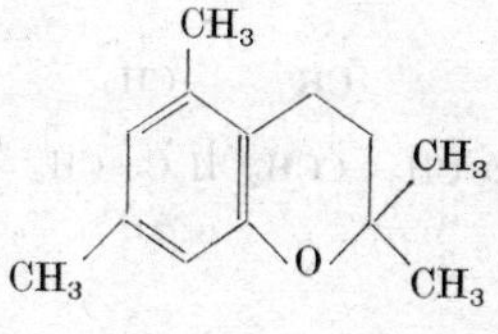   (XXII)

prene with 2,3,5-trimethylphenol in the presence of hydrogen chloride and obtained compounds XX and XXI. The latter was assumed to be XXIa instead of XXIb because of its alkali insolubility. 3,5-Dimethylphenol formed 2,2,5,7-tetramethylchroman (XXII) when condensed with isoprene under the same conditions. In all of these reactions with isoprene, the product was the 3-methyl-2-butenyl derivative and/or the corresponding cyclic ether.

Bruson and Kroeger (26) have studied the reaction of 2,5-dimethyl-1,5-hexadiene with various aromatics. Phenol gave the cyclialkylated product XXIIa with aluminum chloride but the indanol XXIIb was assumed to be the product when sulfuric acid or boron trifluoride was used.

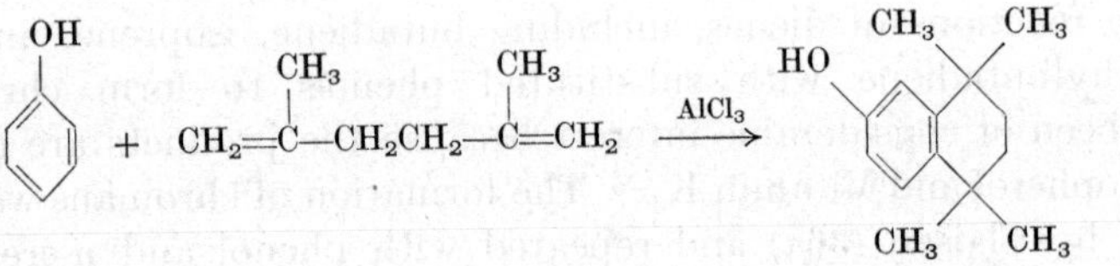

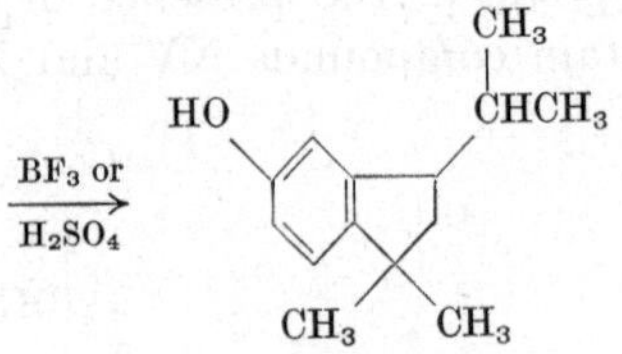

At 0°, boron trifluoride did afford some XXIIa as well as XXIIb together with a benzochroman. Thiophenol forms dithioethers instead of undergoing cyclialkylation.

The reviewers believe that the structure assigned to XXIIb may be incorrect. There is a strong possibility that XXIIb is identical to the unsaturated phenol XXIIc obtained by Jones and Schick (92).

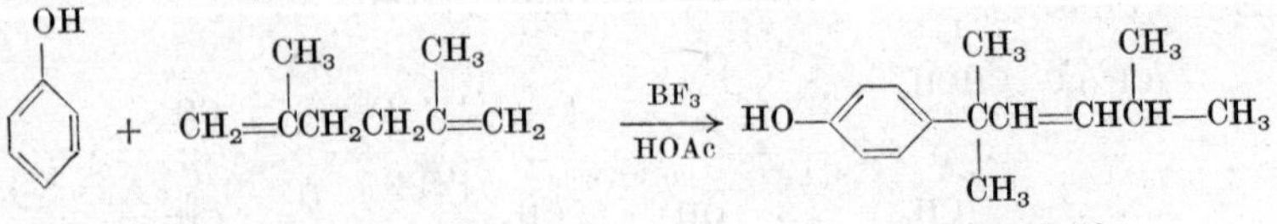

Other instances of cyclialkylation are discussed by Barclay in Chapter XXII.

Although hydroquinone was unreactive under the conditions used above to form chromans, Smith and co-workers (195) found that the monomethyl ether and methylated hydroquinones could be made to react with dienes to form cyclic ethers. p-Methoxyphenol reacted readily with 2,3-dimethylbutadiene in acetic acid and dry hydrogen chloride to form 2,2,3-trimethyl-6-methoxychroman (XXIII), and with isoprene to give the halogen compound (XXIV) which could be cyclized to 2,2-dimethyl-6-methoxychroman (XXV) with alcoholic potassium acetate. Trimethylhydroquinone, the most reactive of the hydroquinones examined by these investigators, condensed with isoprene in acetic acid containing zinc chloride and sulfuric acid to form the chroman (XXVI). Butadiene (190), on the other hand, formed only the 2-butenyl derivative (XXVII) and would not undergo cyclization.

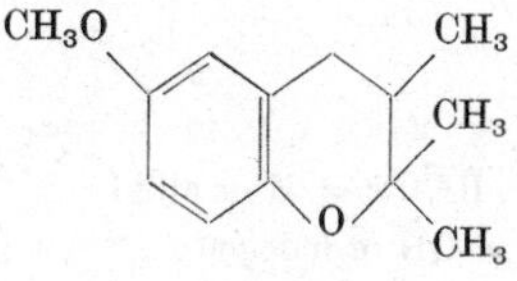

(XXIII)

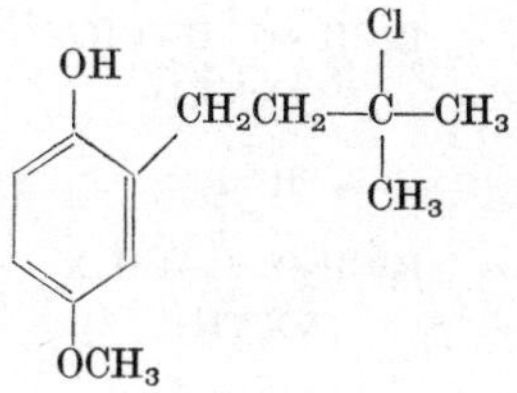

(XXIV)

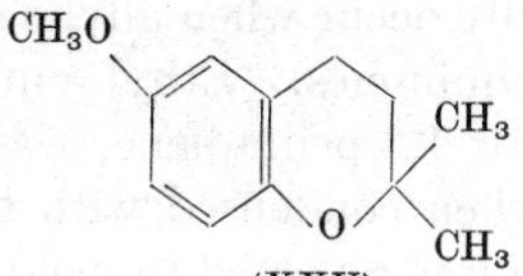

(XXV)

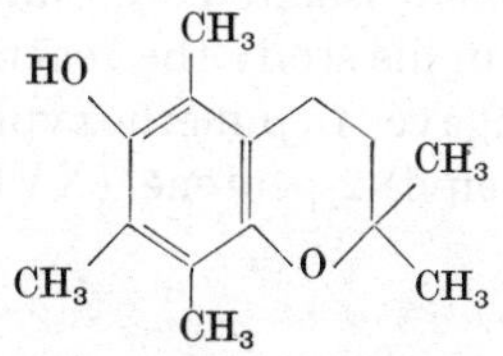

(XXVI)

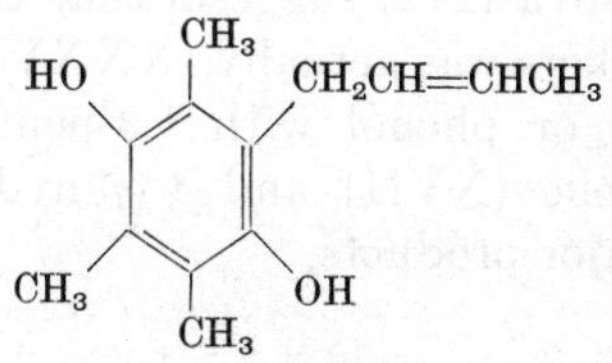

(XXVII)

In their study of the synthesis of compounds related to Vitamin K$_1$, Fieser and co-workers (62) condensed methylnaphthohydroquinone with 2,3-dimethyl-1,3-butadiene in the presence of anhydrous oxalic acid. As in the work of Smith et al. 1,4-addition products (XXVIII) and the corresponding cyclic ethers (XXIX) were obtained.

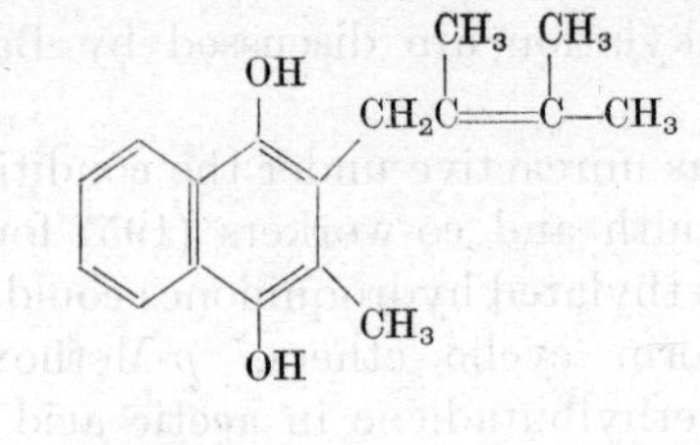

CH$_3$ CH$_3$

OH

CH$_2$C=C—CH$_3$

HO   CH$_3$ CH$_3$

CH$_3$

CH$_3$

CH$_3$

OH

(XXVIII) 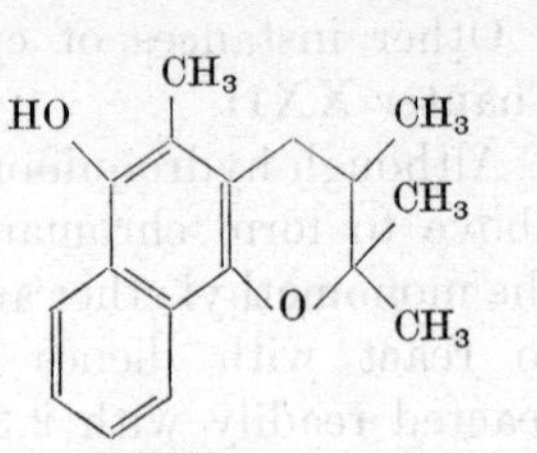   (XXIX)

Hydroquinones, specifically trimethylhydroquinone, were reported by Smith and co-workers (196) to condense with 1,3-pentadiene, isoprene, 2,3-dimethylbutadiene, phytadiene, and other similarly constituted dienes with terminal CH$_2$ groups (XXXI) to give the same product that would be obtained by using the allylic halide or alcohol (XXXII).

R^2 R^3

R^{1}CH=C—C=CH$_2$ R^1, R^2, R^3 = H or alkyl

(XXXI)

R^2 R^3

R^{1}CH$_2$C=C—CH$_2$X   R^1, R^2, R^3 = H or alkyl

(XXXII)   X = OH or halogen

These authors showed, however, that the intermediate formation of dienes did not necessarily occur when allylic alcohols or halides were condensed with hydroquinones. Ethyl vinyl carbinol (XXXIII), which can dehydrate to 1,3-pentadiene, was reported to form the coumaran (XXXIV) when condensed with trimethylhydroquinone, whereas 1,3-pentadiene was reported to yield the chroman (XXXV). Vdovtsova (212) suggests that the chroman isolated by Smith and co-workers was actually (XXXVI) since in his study the reactions of anisole or phenol with 1,3-pentadiene gave 4-(*p*-methoxyphenyl)-2-pentene (XVII) and 4-(*p*-hydroxyphenyl)-2-pentene (XVIII) as the major products.

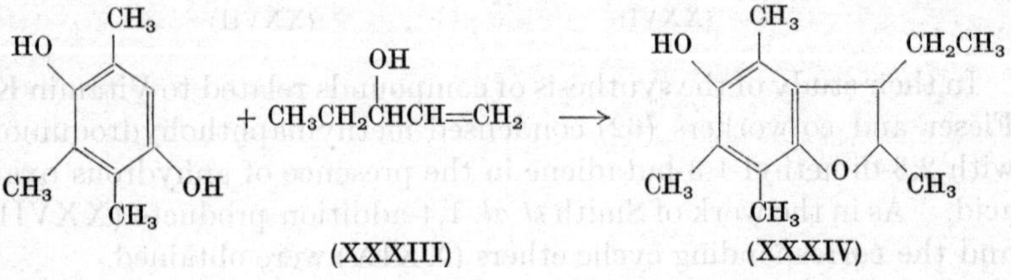

CH$_3$

HO

OH

+ CH$_3$CH$_2$CHCH=CH$_2$ →

CH$_3$ OH

CH$_3$

HO   CH$_3$ CH$_2$CH$_3$

CH$_3$ CH$_3$ CH$_3$

(XXXIII)   (XXXIV)

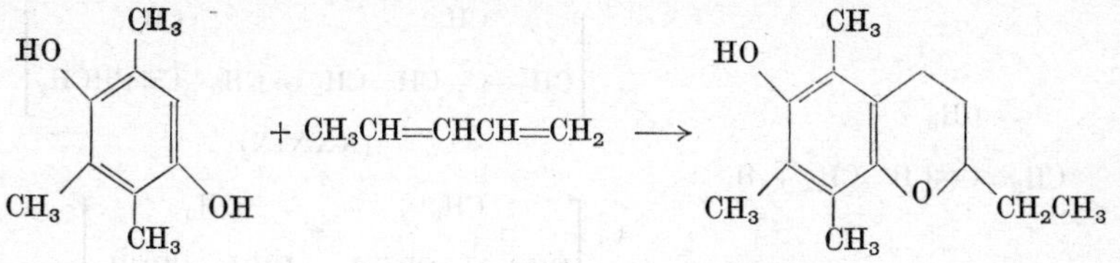

(XXXV)

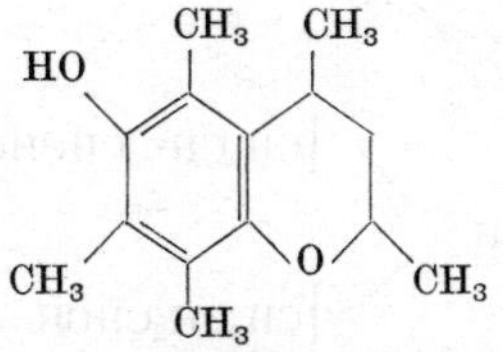

(XXXVI)

The results discussed in the preceding paragraphs overwhelmingly indicate that the reaction of dienes with aromatic compounds involves the formation of a resonance-stabilized allyl cation (XXXVIII) reaction intermediate. More accurately the intermediate is probably an ion pair composed of the allyl cation and an anion formed from the Friedel-Crafts catalyst.

$$\underset{\text{(XXXI)}}{R^1CH{=}\overset{R^2}{\overset{|}{C}}-\overset{R^3}{\overset{|}{C}}{=}CH_2} \xrightarrow{H^+} \underset{\text{(XXXVIII)}}{\left[R^1CH{=}\overset{R^2}{\overset{|}{C}}-\underset{+}{\overset{R^3}{\overset{|}{C}}}-CH_3 \leftrightarrow R^1\underset{+}{CH}\overset{R^2}{\overset{|}{C}}{=}\overset{R^3}{\overset{|}{C}}-CH_3\right]}$$

In his discussion of the mechanism of the phenol–diene reaction, Bader (17) suggested that a resonant allylic cation is formed and that the products of alkenylation are derived from the resonance hybrid of the carbonium ion which is "spatially most accessible," presumably not the *t*-allylic cation. The reviewers believe, however, that the preponderance of evidence cited in the literature (see Chapter XIV, Section III-2-C) tends to discount the importance of steric effects in phenol alkylations. Furthermore, even if attack at the *ortho*-position of phenol were sterically hindered, certainly the *para*-position would offer no steric problems. Perhaps an alternative explanation for the absence of *t*-alkylenates is that they may not survive because their susceptibility to dealkylation is much greater than that of primary alkylenates.

It appears to the reviewers that the carbonium ion produced is always the most stable of the cations which theoretically can be formed, namely, XXXIX or XLI. In no case has a product been identified which could have been derived from the resonant ions XL or XLII in alkenylations with isoprene or piperylene respectively.

$$CH_2=\overset{\overset{\displaystyle CH_3}{|}}{C}-CH=CH_2 + H^+$$

$$\left[CH_3-\overset{\overset{\displaystyle CH_3}{|}}{\underset{+}{C}}-CH=CH_2 \leftrightarrow CH_3-\overset{\overset{\displaystyle CH_3}{|}}{C}=CH\overset{+}{C}H_2\right]$$

(XXXIX)

$$\left[CH_2=\overset{\overset{\displaystyle CH_3}{|}}{\underset{+}{C}}-CHCH_3 \leftrightarrow \overset{+}{C}H_2\overset{\overset{\displaystyle CH_3}{|}}{C}=CHCH_3\right]$$

(XL)

$$CH_3CH=CHCH=CH_2 + H^+$$

$$\left[CH_3CH=CH\overset{+}{C}HCH_3 \leftrightarrow CH_3\overset{+}{C}HCH=CHCH_3\right]$$

(XLI)

$$\left[CH_3CH_2\overset{+}{C}HCH=CH_2 \leftrightarrow CH_3CH_2CH=CH\overset{+}{C}H_2\right]$$

(XLII)

The failure to isolate t-alkyl substitution products in alkenylation with isoprene and 2,3-dimethylbutadiene is probably the result of the greater thermodynamic stability of the primary substituted products. It is possible that t-alkyl substitution does occur, but the product may rapidly isomerize to the more stable primary isomer.

2. The Effect of Catalysts and Conditions on the Alkenylation Reaction

With unreactive aromatics, such as benzene, relatively strong Friedel-Crafts catalysts give high yields of alkenyl aromatics. For example, Axe (11) obtained an 80% yield of phenylbutenes from benzene and butadiene using phosphoric acid saturated with boron fluoride. Schulze and Axe (172) obtained a 90% yield using a boron fluoride–methanol complex. Aluminum chloride apparently leads to considerable resinification of the diene (124a). In order to minimize this, a high ratio of aromatic to diene is required. However, with sulfuric acid and hydrogen fluoride the product of the benzene–butadiene reaction was 1,2-diphenylbutane even when high (3.7/1 and 5.4/1, respectively) benzene to butadiene mole ratios were used (87a).

Fair yields of phenylbutenes have been obtained with fixed-bed catalysts including "solid phosphoric acid" (87b) and zinc chloride on alumina at temperatures over 200° (164). High benzene to butadiene ratios (4.5 and 8.0/1) and high pressures (27 and 40 atmospheres) were employed. The high pressures are apparently necessary to maintain the liquid phase and to prevent catalyst deactivation by resins depositing on the catalyst surfaces.

Milder catalysts and conditions than those used with benzene are required for the more reactive phenols. The yields of monoalkenyl-phenols are highly dependent on the nature of the catalyst. Bader (16) found that phosphoric acid saturated with boron fluoride, aluminum chloride, and concentrated sulfuric acid were too vigorous for the reaction of butadiene and phenol; ethers (probably chromans) and resinous materials were formed. The preferred catalysts for this reaction were: (a) a mixture of equal weights of 85% phosphoric acid saturated with boron fluoride and 85% phosphoric acid; and (b) an equal weight mixture of 85% phosphoric acid and concentrated sulfuric acid. These two catalysts gave high yields of butenyl-phenols and small amounts of ethers and higher phenols. Bader (16) also found that 65% sulfuric acid, aluminum chloride alcoholate and etherate, mixtures of polyphosphoric acid with phosphoric acid, titanium tetrachloride, arenesulfonic acids, and alkanesulfonic acids also catalyze the monobutenylation at 15–25°.

Viktorova and co-workers (216a) reported that only coumarones and chromans were formed when p-cresol was condensed with piperylene in the presence of ethylsulfonic acid or zinc chloride on alumina. On the other hand, the sulfonic acid cationic exchange resin, KU-2, considered by these investigators to be a weaker acid, formed high yields of pentenylcresols.

Vdovtsova and Zavgorodnii (214) found similar relationships among various catalysts in the condensation of piperylene and anisole. These authors found that anhydrous orthophosphoric acid was the best catalyst giving a maximum yield of 92.2% of the monosubsti-tuted product at a piperylene/anisole/catalyst mole ratio of 1/4/0.25. Stronger catalysts in general produced lower yields because of the formation of higher boiling products. To improve yields with strong Friedel-Crafts catalysts it was necessary to increase the anisole/piperylene ratio (4/1) or to increase the amount of catalyst (0.07 aluminum chloride). However, if the anisole to butadiene ratio was increased, it was generally necessary to increase the catalyst concen-tration to obtain the maximum yield. The maximum yields ob-tained with the catalysts studied were in the order 100% H_3PO_4 > $BF_3 \cdot H_3PO_4$ > $AlCl_2 \cdot H_2PO_4 \simeq AlCl_3 \simeq BF_3$.

The reactivity of the diene is also significant with regard to choice of catalyst. Bader (14) obtained a 70% yield of monocyclopentenyl-phenols when he used 85% phosphoric acid to catalyze the conden-sation of cyclopentadiene with phenol at 25°. Isoprene reacted readily with phenol in the presence of 71% phosphoric acid (17). On the other hand the reaction with butadiene required tempera-tures above 100°. Vdovtsova and Romanikhin (213) preferred

11*

100% phosphoric acid for the condensation of piperylene and phenol, which afforded 78% of pentenylphenols.

In general, alkenylations of phenols give products which are mixtures of *ortho*- and *para*-isomers. Bader (16) reported that the temperature and the nature of the catalyst influence the distribution of position isomers. *para*-Substitution predominated at 15–20° with phosphoric acid saturated with boron fluoride or with alkane-sulfonic acids, whereas with 68% aqueous sulfuric acid as catalyst, 60% of the monobutenyl phenols was the *ortho*-isomer. When used at suitably high temperatures, weaker catalysts such as 85% phosphoric acids were effective promoters, affording mainly *ortho*-substituted products. Bader (16) suggested that alkenylations do not involve simply the electrophilic attack of the free resonant carbonium ion on phenol; the product distribution appears to depend on the negative ion associated with the carbonium ion.

Bader (16) also found that the range of effective catalyst mixtures was quite narrow. With anthraquinone as the Hammett indicator, catalysts effective at 15–25° (excluding sulfuric acid) were found to have acidity functions, H_0, ranging from -6 to -7. This value of H_0 corresponds to 77–83% sulfuric acid rather than the experiment-ally determined effective range of 68–70%. This discrepancy is probably a consequence of the tendency of sulfuric acid to promote oxidation above 70%. Aqueous sulfuric acid at a concentration of less than 68% is apparently unable to catalyze the butadiene–phenol condensation.

3. Summary

The alkylation of aromatic nuclei with dienes can lead to alkenyl substituted products, diaryl alkanes, or cyclized products. *Ortho*- and *para*-substituted isomers are obtained and the *ortho/para* ratio can be varied within wide limits with reactive nuclei (*e.g.*, phenols). A mild acid catalyst, relatively unreactive aromatic, and a low temperature favor the formation of alkenylaromatics resulting from the 1,4-addition of the aromatic to the diene. With increasing acid strength, a more active nucleus, and higher temperatures, dialkylation and cyclization are favored.

III. Unsaturated Halides

1. Vinyl Halides

A. Monohalides

Unsaturated halides may react with an aromatic nucleus at either of the two reactive sites. Vinyl halides, having a relatively strong carbon–chlorine bond, tend to react at the double bond in the presence of a metal or metal halide catalyst.   The resulting benzyl type halide is now a more active alkylating species than the original vinyl halide and further reaction with an additional mole of aromatic leads to a 1,1-diarylethane as shown in equations 1–4.

$$H^+ \ + \ CH_2{=}CHX \rightarrow CH_3{-}\overset{+}{C}HX \tag{1}$$
$$X = Cl, \ Br$$

$$CH_3{-}\overset{+}{C}HX \ + \ ArH \rightarrow \underset{\underset{Ar}{|}}{CH_3{-}CH} \ + \ H^+ \tag{2}$$

$$\underset{\underset{Ar}{\diagdown}}{CH_3{-}\overset{\diagup X}{CH}} \ \xrightarrow{AlCl_3} \ CH_3{-}\overset{+}{C}H{-}Ar \ + \ X^- \tag{3}$$

$$CH_3{-}\overset{+}{C}H{-}Ar \ + \ ArH \rightarrow CH_3{-}CH{-}(Ar)_2 \ + \ H^+ \tag{4}$$

1,1-Diphenylethane has been obtained in yields as high as 60% when using vinyl chloride with an aluminum–mercuric chloride catalyst at 0° (25).

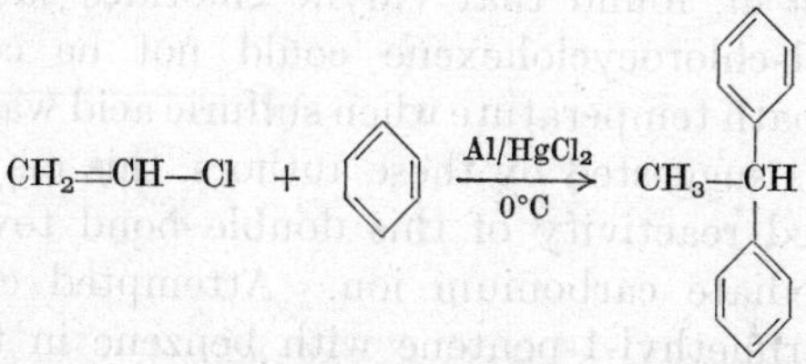

$$CH_2{=}CH{-}Cl \ + \ \bigcirc \ \xrightarrow[0°C]{Al/HgCl_2} \ CH_3{-}CH\Big\langle$$

Other workers have used aluminum chloride with vinyl chloride or bromide and obtained the same product (3,6,48,121).

Variations in the structure of the vinyl halide, particularly when a tertiary carbonium ion can be formed, give rise to different products. 1-Chloro- or 1-bromo-2-methyl-1-propene and benzene gave the corresponding 2-halo-1,1-dimethylethylbenzene (I) when treated with sulfuric acid (70,166).

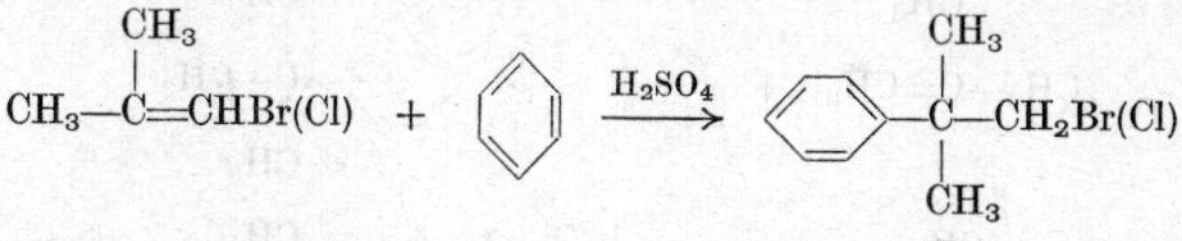

$$\underset{}{\overset{CH_3}{\underset{|}{CH_3{-}C}}{=}CHBr(Cl)} \ + \ \bigcirc \ \xrightarrow{H_2SO_4} \ \bigcirc{-}\overset{\overset{CH_3}{|}}{\underset{\underset{CH_3}{|}}{C}}{-}CH_2Br(Cl)$$
$$(I)$$

The primary bromide I, for example, does not react further under these conditions. With aluminum chloride, however, it cannot be isolated, since it reacts further with benzene to form a diaryl derivative (209).

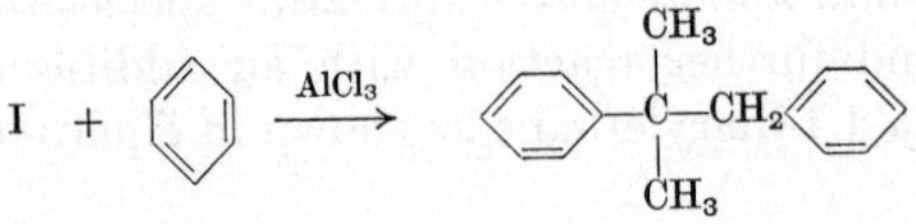

The reaction of toluene with vinyl chloride has only recently been investigated (210). In the presence of a low concentration of aluminum chloride, 1,1-ditolylethane was formed in 68% yield.

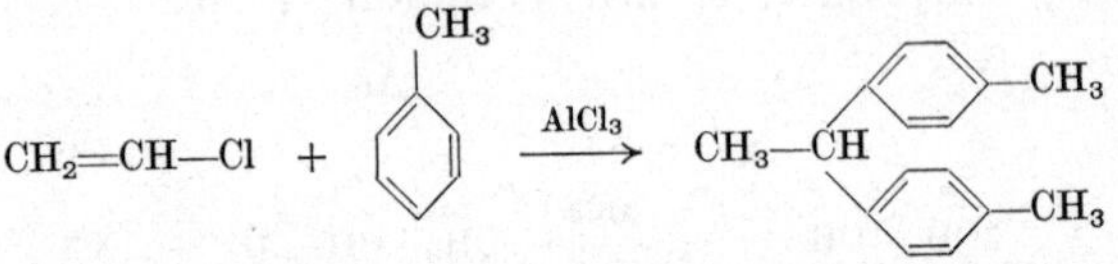

Also of recent interest, 1,1-di-p-anisylethane was obtained by Tsukervanik et al. in the reaction of anisole with vinyl chloride or bromide (210). At 0° vinylchloride gave the highest yield (42%) of product. With longer contact times and a higher temperature, 4-ethylanisole was also found. This product is undoubtedly formed by a hydrogen transfer reaction which will be discussed later in this section.

Schmerling et al. found that vinylic chlorides such as 2-chloropropene and 1-chlorocyclohexene could not be condensed with benzene at ice-bath temperature when sulfuric acid was used as a catalyst (168a). As suggested by these authors, this may be attributed to the decreased reactivity of this double bond toward formation of the intermediate carbonium ion. Attempted condensation of 1-chloro-2,4,4-trimethyl-1-pentene with benzene in the presence of sulfuric acid resulted in cleavage of the chloroolefin prior to alkylation. (2-Chloro-1,1-dimethylethyl)benzene and t-butylbenzene were the final products.

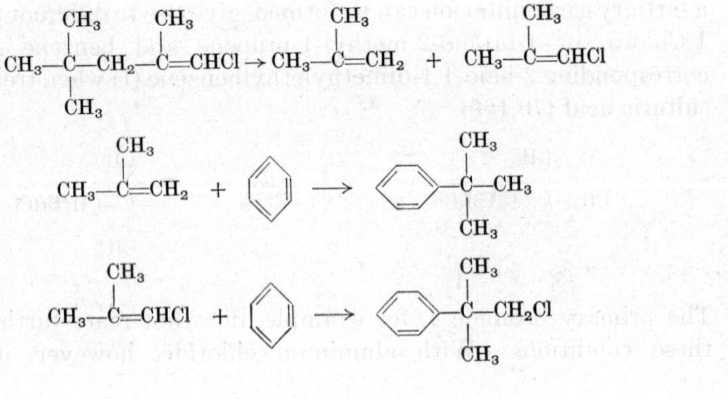

B. Polyhalides

1,1-Dihaloethylenes yield 1,1-diphenylethylene as one of the major products when treated with a relatively high ratio of aluminum chloride and benzene (49,104).

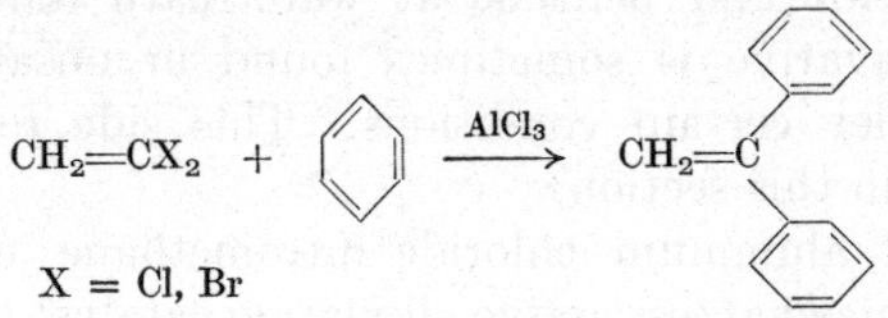

$$CH_2{=}CX_2 \; + \; \bigcirc \xrightarrow{AlCl_3} \; CH_2{=}C\Big\langle \quad (II)$$

$$X = Cl, Br$$

A possible pathway for the formation of (II) is shown in equations 5–8.

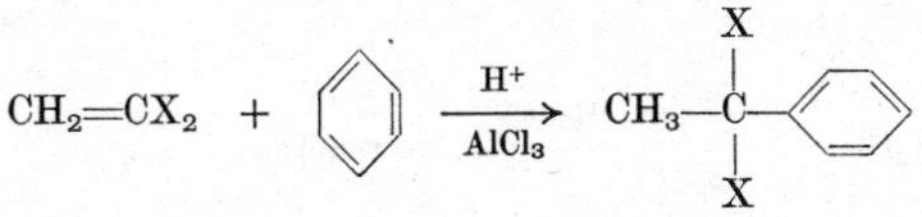

$$CH_2{=}CX_2 \; + \; \bigcirc \xrightarrow[AlCl_3]{H^+} \; CH_3{-}\underset{X}{\overset{X}{C}}{-}\bigcirc \tag{5}$$

$$CH_3{-}\underset{X}{\overset{X}{C}}{-}\bigcirc \xrightarrow{AlCl_3} \; CH_2{=}\overset{X}{C}{-}\bigcirc \; + \; HX \tag{6}$$

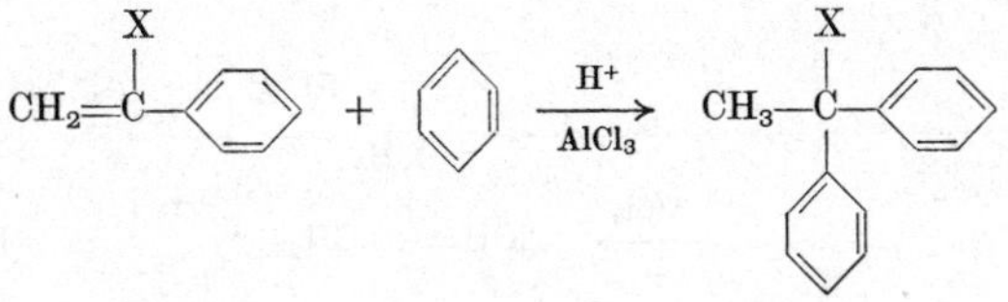

$$CH_2{=}\overset{X}{C}{-}\bigcirc \; + \; \bigcirc \xrightarrow[AlCl_3]{H^+} \; CH_3{-}\overset{X}{\underset{\bigcirc}{C}}{-}\bigcirc \tag{7}$$

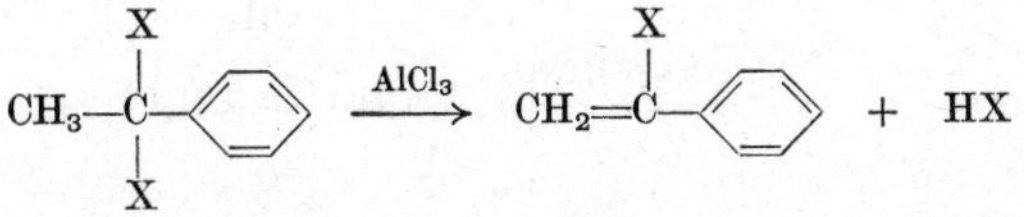

$$CH_3{-}\overset{X}{\underset{\bigcirc}{C}}{-}\bigcirc \xrightarrow{AlCl_3} \; CH_2{=}C{-}\bigcirc \; + \; HX \tag{8}$$

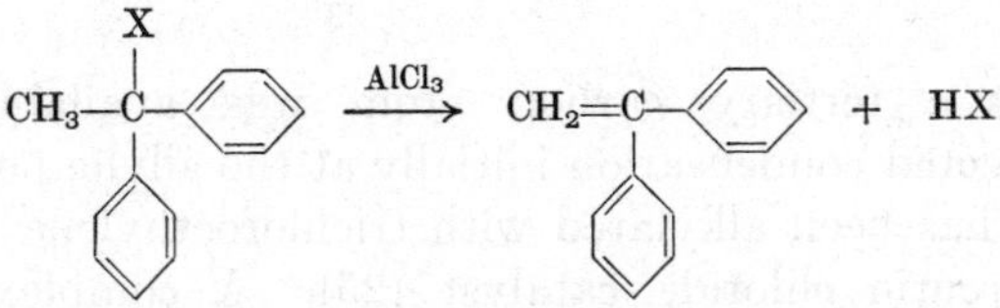

A mixture of *cis-* and *trans*-1,2-dichloroethylene, when treated with an aluminum–mercuric chloride catalyst and benzene, gave a mixture of di-, tri-, and tetraphenylethane (25).

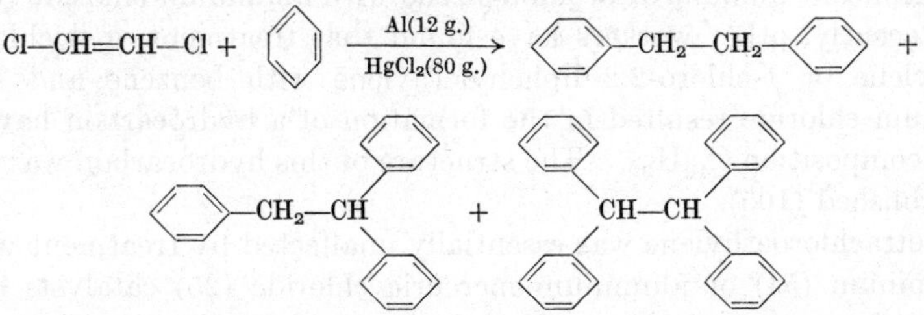

$$Cl{-}CH{=}CH{-}Cl \; + \; \bigcirc \xrightarrow[HgCl_2(80\ g.)]{Al(12\ g.)} \; \bigcirc{-}CH_2{-}CH_2{-}\bigcirc \; + $$

$$\bigcirc{-}CH_2{-}CH\Big\langle \quad + \quad \underset{}{CH{-}CH}\Big\rangle$$

As the ratio of aluminum/mercuric chloride was increased to 60/90 g., no tetraphenylethane was formed. Demole (49) reported the formation of anthracene, 1,2-diphenylethane, and bromobenzene when acetylene dibromide (1,2-dibromoethylene) was heated with aluminum chloride and benzene at water-bath temperature. An anthracene derivative is sometimes found in unsaturated halide alkylations under certain conditions. This side reaction will be discussed later in this section.

A complexed aluminum chloride–nitromethane catalyst is an effective but somewhat less active alkylation catalyst than aluminum chloride. Schmerling carried out a short catalyst study on the reaction of 1,3-dichloro-2-methylpropene with benzene (168a) and found a different product with the nitromethane modified catalyst.

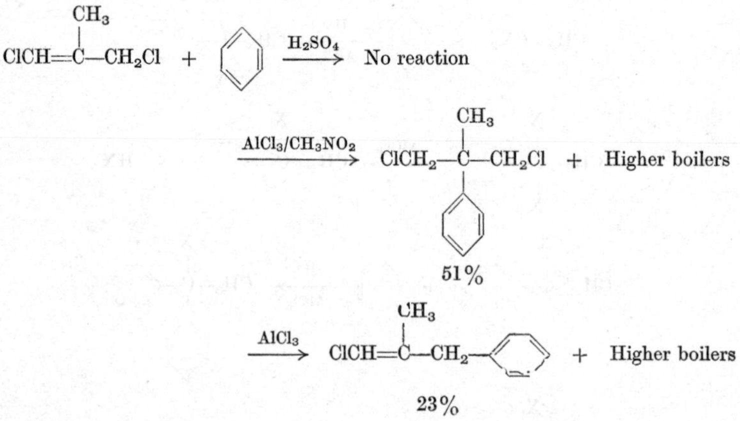

Even when a tertiary carbon atom was available, aluminum chloride effected condensation initially at the allylic position.

Benzene has been alkylated with trichloroethylene using an aluminum–mercuric chloride catalyst (25). A complex mixture of products was obtained from which 1,1- and 1,2-diphenylethane as well as some tetraphenylethane were isolated in low yields. Tribromoethylene gave 1,1-diphenylethylene, 1,2-diphenylethane, and a significant amount of bromobenzene with aluminum chloride (6).

Recently, other workers have found that treatment of trichloroethylene or 1-chloro-2,2-diphenylethylene with benzene and aluminum chloride resulted in the formation of a hydrocarbon having the composition $C_{40}H_{32}$. The structure of this hydrocarbon was not established (105).

Tetrachloroethylene was essentially unaffected by treatment with aluminum (54) or aluminum–mercuric chloride (25) catalysts and benzene. A large quantity of anthracene was obtained when aluminum chloride was used (127).

C. Side Reactions

Intermolecular alkylation and hydrogen transfer are the two major side reactions to be considered.   9,10-Dimethyl-9,10-dihydro-anthracene* has been reported by several workers (3,6,25,48,121) together with small amounts of ethylbenzene in some cases.   Based on Nenitzescu's (137) work with allyl halides, one may explain the formation of these products by the following route:

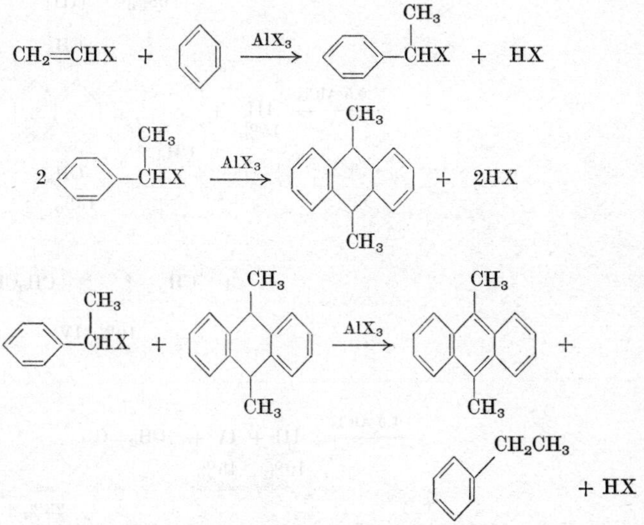

Styrene has occasionally been isolated in trace quantities and can function as the hydrogen acceptor.

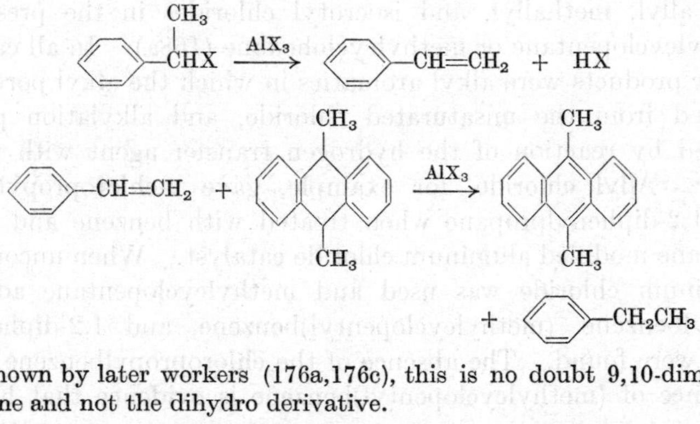

* As shown by later workers (176a,176c), this is no doubt 9,10-dimethyl-anthracene and not the dihydro derivative.

In one of the few systematic studies on the effect of catalyst concentration on product distribution, an anthracene was obtained at intermediate catalyst concentrations whereas a 1,1-diarylethylene was found at high concentrations (210). These results are summarized in equations 9–11.

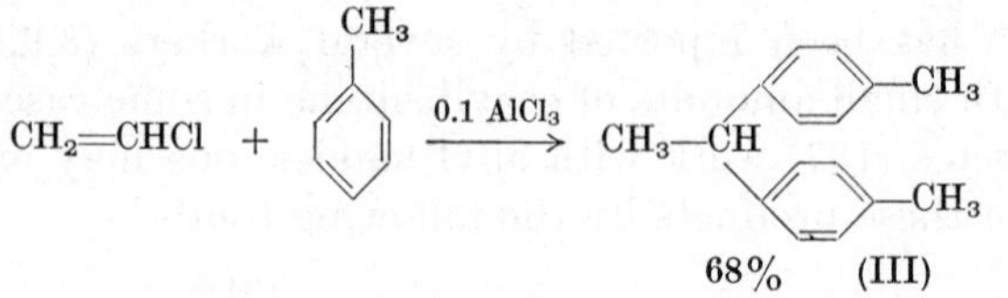

$$CH_2=CHCl + \underset{}{\text{(toluene)}} \xrightarrow{\text{0.1 AlCl}_3} CH_3-CH\underset{68\%\quad(III)}{\langle\text{ditolyl}\rangle} \tag{9}$$

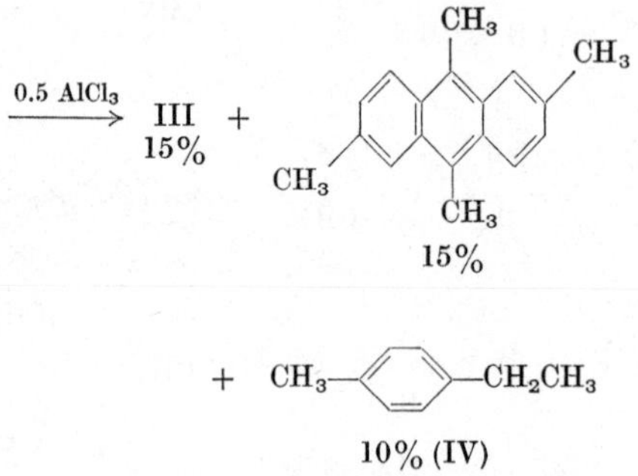

$$\xrightarrow{\text{0.5 AlCl}_3} \underset{15\%}{III} + \underset{15\%}{\langle\text{tetramethylanthracene}\rangle} \tag{10}$$

$$+ \quad CH_3-\langle\text{aryl}\rangle-CH_2CH_3$$
$$10\% \text{ (IV)}$$

$$\xrightarrow{\text{1.0 AlCl}_3} \underset{10\%}{III} + \underset{45\%}{IV} + CH_2=C\underset{23\%}{\langle\text{ditolyl}\rangle} \tag{11}$$

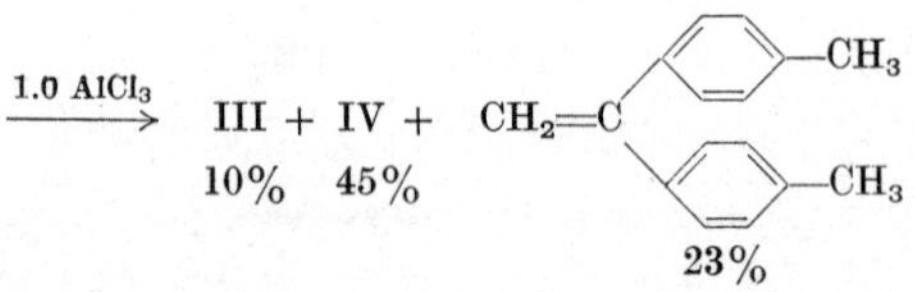

1,1-Ditolylethylene probably arises from III *via* hydrogen transfer. Hydrogen transfer reactions were investigated by Schmerling *et al.* with allyl, methallyl, and isocrotyl chlorides in the presence of methylcyclopentane or methylcyclohexane (168a). In all cases, the major products were alkyl aromatics in which the alkyl portion was derived from the unsaturated chloride, and alkylation products formed by reaction of the hydrogen transfer agent with the aromatic. Allyl chloride, for example, gave 2-chloropropylbenzene and 1,2-diphenylpropane when treated with benzene and a nitromethane modified aluminum chloride catalyst. When uncomplexed aluminum chloride was used and methylcyclopentane added, *n*-propylbenzene, (methylcyclopentyl)benzene, and 1,2-diphenylpropane were found. The absence of the chloropropylbenzene and the presence of (methylcyclopentyl)benzene is evidence that hydrogen transfer has occurred.   It is interesting that the (methylcyclopentyl)-benzene was mainly the 3-isomer rather than the tertiary compound.

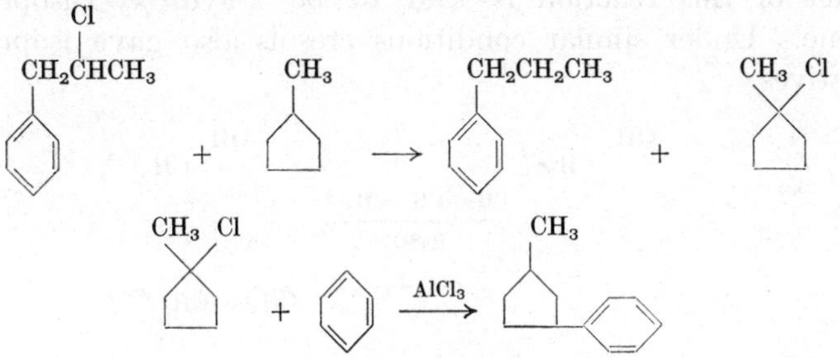

2. Allyl Halides

A. Monohalides

Allyl halides react either at the double bond or at the allylic position.   With proton donor type catalysts (sulfuric acid) allyl chloride or bromide reacts only at the double bond (206,207).   The reaction undoubtedly involves addition of a proton to the halide followed by alkylation.

$$CH_2{=}CH{-}CH_2X \xrightarrow{H^+} CH_3{-}\overset{+}{C}H{-}CH_2X$$

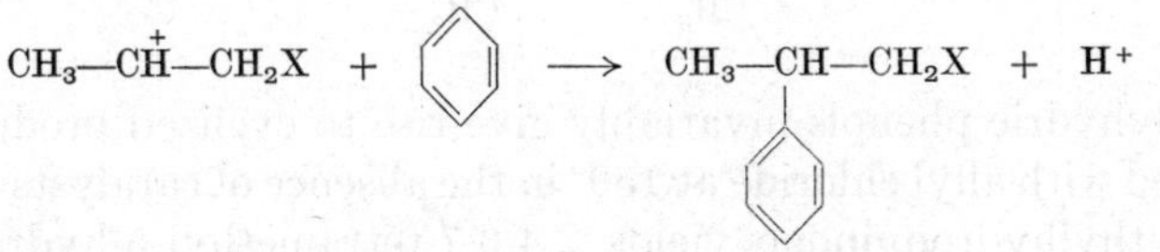

$$X = Cl\ 20\%$$
$$X = Br\ 58{-}60\%$$

(2-Chloropropyl)benzene is also formed when less active metal halide catalysts (e.g., $ZnCl_2$, $FeCl_3$) (137) or aluminum chloride modified by nitromethane are used (224).

Some alkylbenzenes have been treated with allyl chloride or bromide and sulfuric acid (126,206).   In all cases, the aromatic is alkylated mostly in the para-position as expected.   Only small amounts of meta-substituted products were found by some workers.

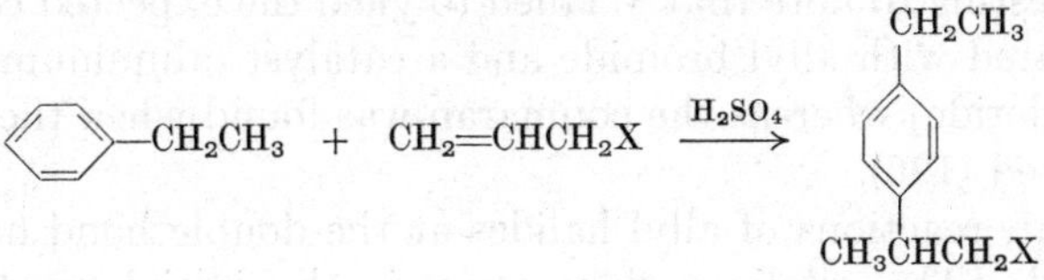

$$X = Cl\ 5\%$$
$$X = Br\ 17\%$$

Allyl chloride is reported to alkylate phenol after prolonged contact (6 months) with sulfuric acid at room temperature (197). The product of this reaction is said to be 2-hydroxy-1-isopropenyl benzene. Under similar conditions cresols also gave isopropenyl derivatives.

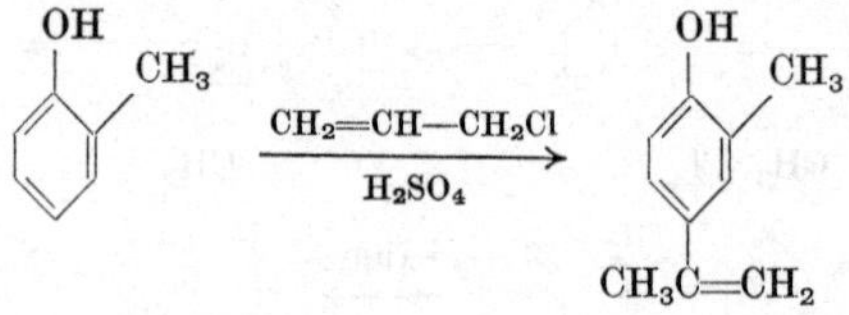

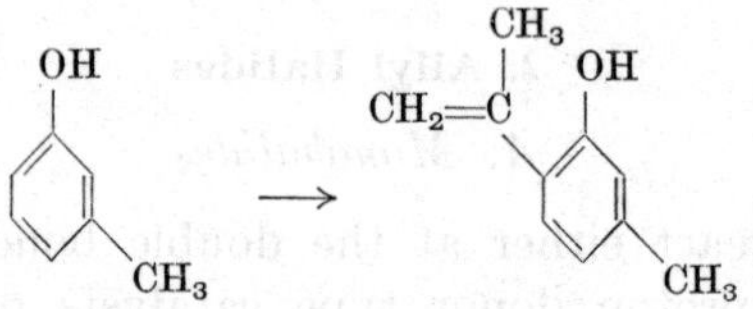

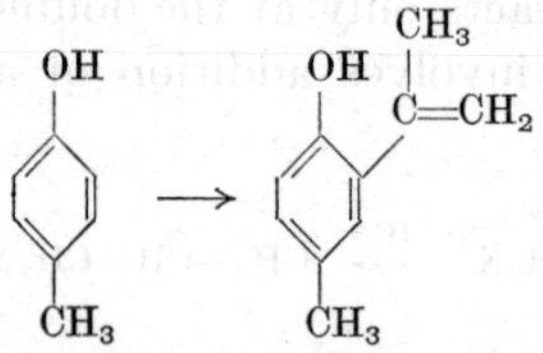

$$ \text{(o-cresol)} \xrightarrow[\ \text{H}_2\text{SO}_4\ ]{\ \text{CH}_2\!=\!\text{CH}\!-\!\text{CH}_2\text{Cl}\ } \text{(product with } \text{CH}_3\text{C}\!=\!\text{CH}_2 \text{ group)} $$

$$ \text{(m-cresol)} \longrightarrow \text{(product with } \text{CH}_2\!=\!\overset{\text{CH}_3}{\text{C}} \text{ group)} $$

$$ \text{(p-cresol)} \longrightarrow \text{(product with } \overset{\text{CH}_3}{\text{C}}\!=\!\text{CH}_2 \text{ group)} $$

Polyhydric phenols invariably give rise to cyclized products when treated with allyl chloride at 150° in the absence of catalysts (194,196). Trimethylhydroquinone yields 2,4,6,7-tetramethyl-5-hydroxycoumaran when heated with allyl chloride.

$$ \text{(V, trimethylhydroquinone)} \ + \ \text{CH}_2\!=\!\text{CHCH}_2\text{Cl} \xrightarrow{\ 150°\ } \text{(tetramethylhydroxycoumaran)} $$

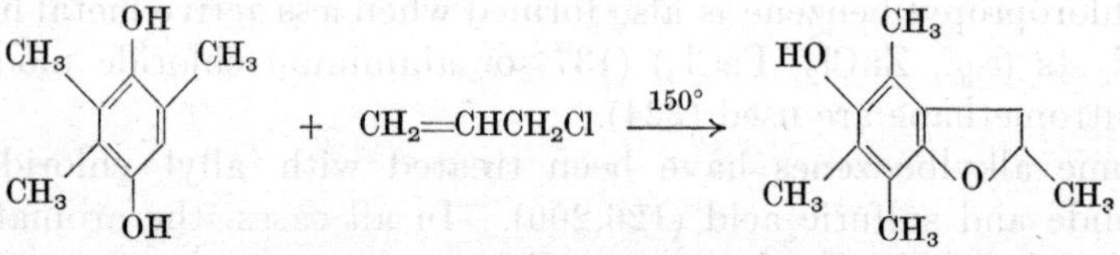

(V)

It is interesting to note that V failed to yield the expected coumaran when treated with allyl bromide and a catalyst (aluminum chloride or zinc chloride) whereas the coumaran was found when the catalyst was omitted (196).

Thus far, reactions of allyl halides at the double bond have been considered. The allylic carbon atom is the initial reactive site, however, when alkylations are catalyzed by metals or metal halides.

Nenitzescu and Isacescu (137) investigated the effect of several catalysts on the reaction of allyl chloride with benzene.

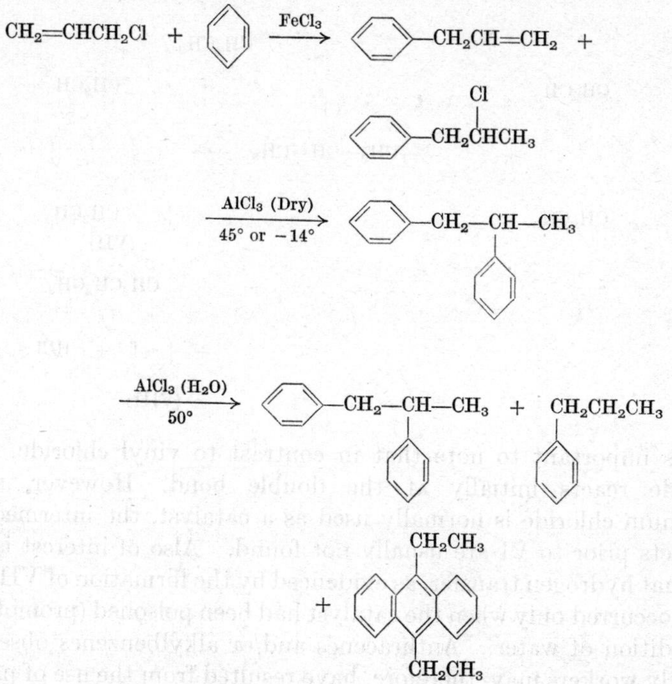

$$CH_2=CHCH_2Cl \ + \ \bigcirc \ \xrightarrow{FeCl_3} \ \bigcirc-CH_2CH=CH_2 \ +$$

$$\bigcirc-CH_2\overset{\overset{\displaystyle Cl}{|}}{C}HCH_3$$

$$\xrightarrow[45° \text{ or } -14°]{AlCl_3 \text{ (Dry)}} \ \bigcirc-CH_2-CH-CH_3$$

$$\xrightarrow[50°]{AlCl_3 \text{ (H}_2\text{O)}} \ \bigcirc-CH_2-CH-CH_3 \ + \ CH_2CH_2CH_3$$

$$+ \quad \bigcirc\bigcirc\bigcirc \quad \begin{matrix} CH_2CH_3 \\ \\ CH_2CH_3 \end{matrix}$$

These products have also been observed by other workers (54,116,227, 228).

Nenitzescu and Isacescu suggest that the observed products result from the reactions shown in equations 12–16.

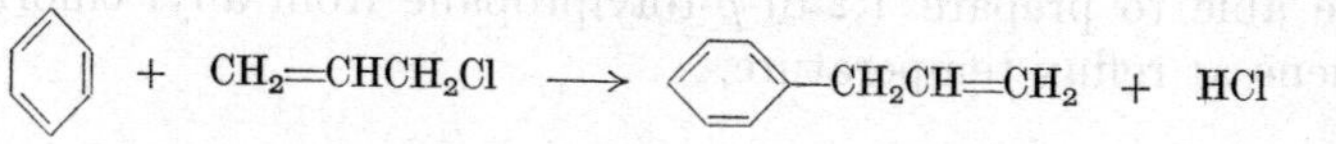

$$\bigcirc \ + \ CH_2=CHCH_2Cl \ \longrightarrow \ \bigcirc-CH_2CH=CH_2 \ + \ HCl \quad (12)$$

$$\bigcirc-CH_2CH=CH_2 \ + \ HCl \ \longrightarrow \ \bigcirc-CH_2\overset{\overset{\displaystyle Cl}{|}}{C}H-CH_3 \quad (13)$$

$$\bigcirc-CH_2\overset{\overset{\displaystyle Cl}{|}}{C}H-CH_3 \ + \ \bigcirc \ \longrightarrow \ \bigcirc-CH_2CH-CH_3 \ + \ HCl \ (14)$$

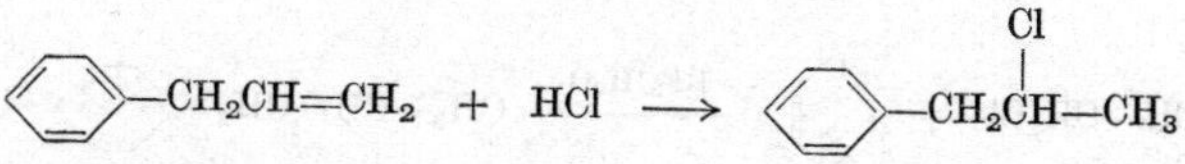

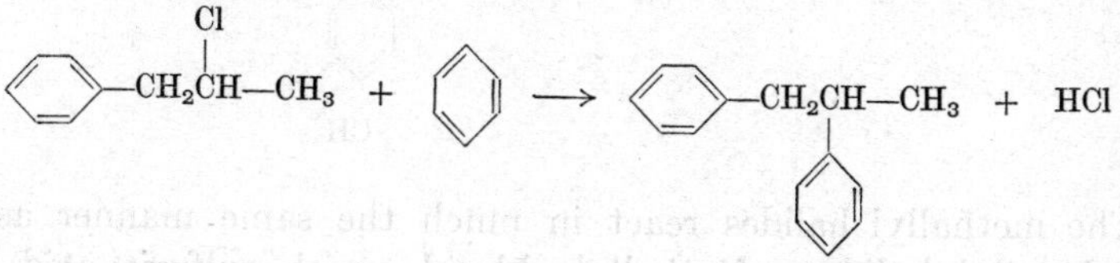

$$\text{(VI)}$$

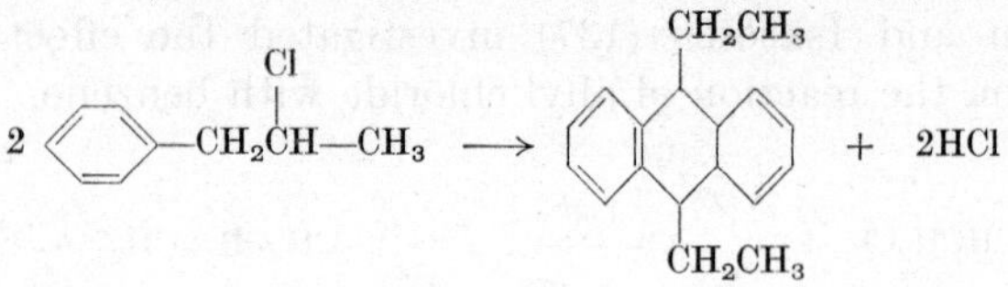

$$2 \quad \langle\rangle-CH_2CH-CH_3 \longrightarrow \quad (anthracene) \quad + \quad 2HCl \qquad (15)$$

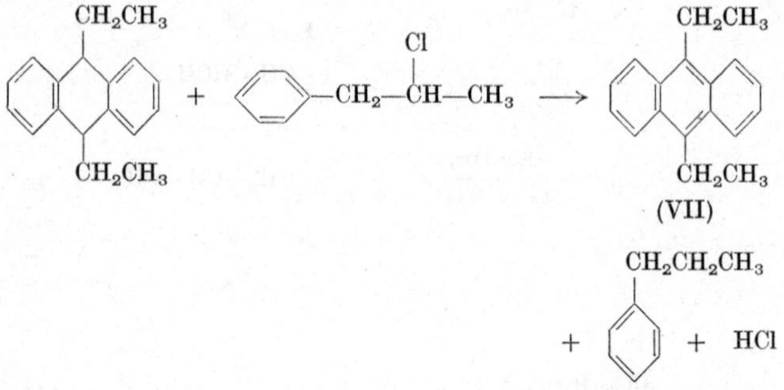

with Cl substituent on CH; product bearing CH_2CH_3 groups top and bottom.

$$\text{(structure with } CH_2CH_3\text{)} \quad + \quad \langle\rangle-CH_2-CH-CH_3 \quad \longrightarrow \quad \text{(VII)} \qquad (16)$$

$$+ \quad \overset{CH_2CH_2CH_3}{\langle\rangle} \quad + \quad HCl$$

(VIII)

It is important to note that in contrast to vinyl chloride, allyl chloride reacts initially at the double bond. However, since aluminum chloride is normally used as a catalyst, the intermediate products prior to VI are usually not found. Also of interest is the fact that hydrogen transfer, as evidenced by the formation of VII and VIII, occurred only when the catalyst had been poisoned (promoted?) by addition of water. Anthracenes and/or alkylbenzenes observed by early workers may, therefore, have resulted from the use of partly hydrated catalysts.

With zinc metal as catalyst, allyl bromide and benzene gave 1,2-diphenylpropane and n-propylbenzene (171,181), whereas zinc chloride and toluene gave only 1,2-ditolylpropane (171).

With a boron fluoride hydrate catalyst Hennion and Kurtz (77) were able to prepare 1,2-di-p-tolylpropane from allyl chloride and toluene at reflux temperature.

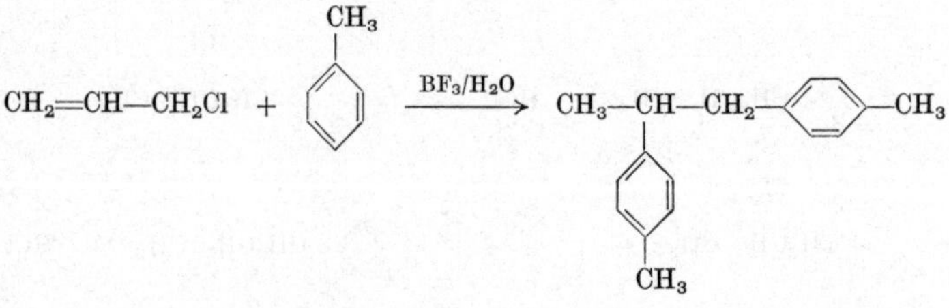

$$CH_2{=}CH{-}CH_2Cl \quad + \quad \overset{CH_3}{\langle\rangle} \quad \xrightarrow{BF_3/H_2O} \quad CH_3{-}CH{-}CH_2{-}\langle\rangle{-}CH_3$$

The methallyl halides react in much the same manner as the simple allyl halides. Methallyl chloride, with sulfuric acid as a catalyst, gave (2-chloro-1,1-dimethylethyl)benzene in 74% yield (70,166).

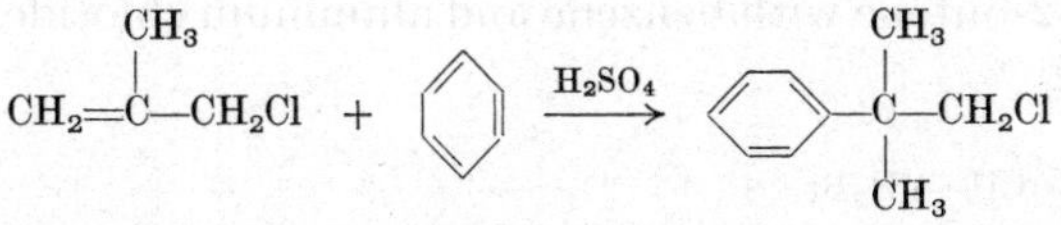

$$CH_2\!\!=\!\!\underset{\underset{CH_3}{|}}{C}\!\!-\!\!CH_2Cl \;+\; \bigcirc \;\xrightarrow{H_2SO_4}\; \bigcirc\!\!-\!\!\underset{\underset{CH_3}{|}}{\overset{\overset{CH_3}{|}}{C}}\!\!-\!\!CH_2Cl$$

Methallyl bromide gave the corresponding bromo derivative in 35% yield (70). Small amounts of dialkylated product were also observed.

In the alkylation of *t*-butylbenzene with methallyl chloride or bromide, Gramenitskaia *et al.* (70) used 100% sulfuric acid as the catalyst. Most of the product was *para*-substituted. Although some *meta* was suspected, these workers could not establish its presence by an oxidative degradation procedure.

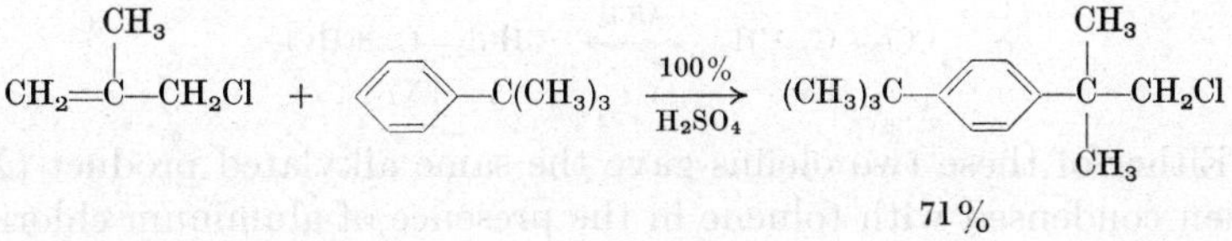

$$CH_2\!\!=\!\!\underset{\underset{CH_3}{|}}{C}\!\!-\!\!CH_2Cl \;+\; \bigcirc\!\!-\!\!C(CH_3)_3 \;\xrightarrow[H_2SO_4]{100\%}\; (CH_3)_3C\!\!-\!\!\bigcirc\!\!-\!\!\underset{\underset{CH_3}{|}}{\overset{\overset{CH_3}{|}}{C}}\!\!-\!\!CH_2Cl$$

71%

Toluene, ethylbenzene, cumene, and neopentylbenzene were also investigated and found to undergo *para*-substitution, as expected, to give the corresponding (2-chloro-1,1-dimethylethyl)benzene.

Thiophene is the only heterocyclic compound which has been alkylated with methallyl halides. Boron fluoride etherate or ethanesulfonic acid catalyst afforded a 2-substituted thiophene in 50% yield (153) whereas sulfuric acid (108) gave only 6%.

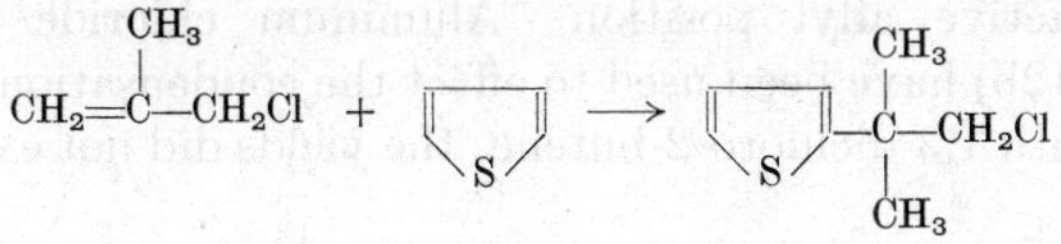

$$CH_2\!\!=\!\!\underset{\underset{CH_3}{|}}{C}\!\!-\!\!CH_2Cl \;+\; \underset{S}{\bigcirc} \;\longrightarrow\; \underset{S}{\bigcirc}\!\!-\!\!\underset{\underset{CH_3}{|}}{\overset{\overset{CH_3}{|}}{C}}\!\!-\!\!CH_2Cl$$

Metal or metal halide catalysts have not been widely used in reactions of benzene with methallyl halides (54,209). 2-Methyl-1,2-diphenylpropane and *t*-butylbenzene were the major products when aluminum or aluminum chloride was used. Crotyl chloride afforded 1,2-diphenylbutane and a small amount of *s*-butylbenzene (209).

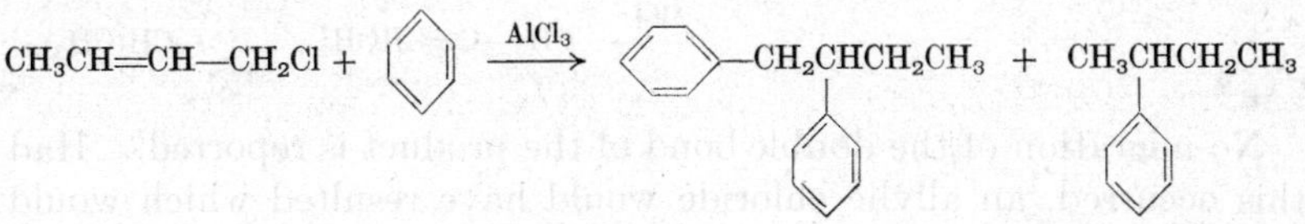

$$CH_3CH\!\!=\!\!CH\!\!-\!\!CH_2Cl \;+\; \bigcirc \;\xrightarrow{AlCl_3}\; \bigcirc\!\!-\!\!CH_2CHCH_2CH_3 \;+\; CH_3CHCH_2CH_3$$

B. Polyhalides

Shishido and Nozaki invariably found cyclized products when using a 1,4-dihalo-2-butene with benzene and aluminum chloride (176d).

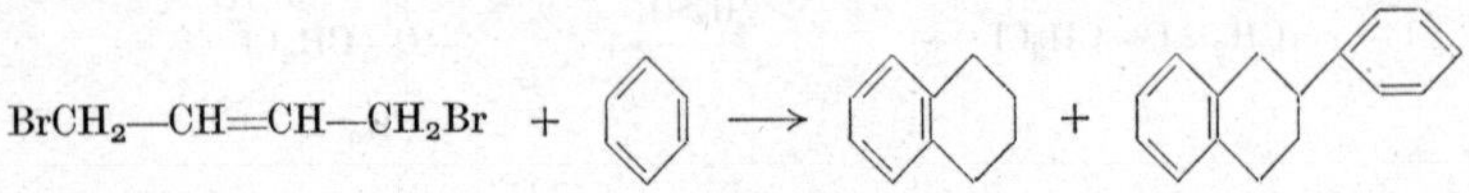

$$BrCH_2—CH=CH—CH_2Br \ + \ \bigcirc \longrightarrow \ \text{[bicyclic]} \ + \ \text{[bicyclic with phenyl]}$$

No phenyl-substituted butanes were detected.

While investigating the reaction between 1,1,1-trichloro-2-methyl-2-propanol with aromatics, Kundiger and Pledger (108a) showed that the olefin (IX) derived from this alcohol quantitatively rearranged to 1,3,3-trichloro-2-methyl-1-propene (X) in the presence of aluminum chloride.

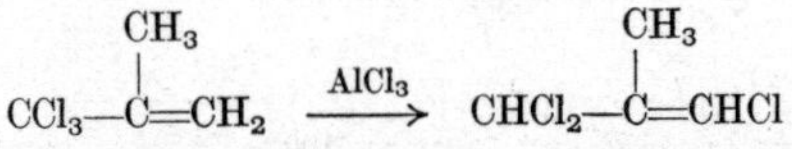

$$\underset{\text{(IX)}}{CCl_3—\overset{\overset{\displaystyle CH_3}{|}}{C}=CH_2} \ \xrightarrow{AlCl_3} \ \underset{\text{(X)}}{CHCl_2—\overset{\overset{\displaystyle CH_3}{|}}{C}=CHCl}$$

Either of these two olefins gave the same alkylated product (XI) when condensed with toluene in the presence of aluminum chloride.

$$\text{(IX) or (X)} \ + \ \underset{}{\overset{\overset{\displaystyle CH_3}{|}}{\bigcirc}} \ \longrightarrow \ CH_3—\bigcirc—CH_2\overset{\overset{\displaystyle CH_3}{|}}{C}=CCl_2$$

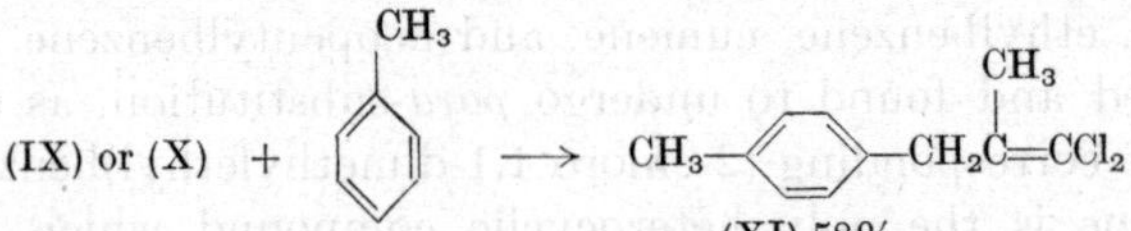

$$\text{(XI) 58\%}$$

It is interesting to note that with this catalyst, no reaction occurs at the double bond of XI.

Compounds having both allylic and vinylic halides react only at the more active allyl position. Aluminum chloride (12b) and aluminum (12b) have been used to effect the condensation of various aromatics with 1,3-dichloro-2-butene; the yields did not exceed 50%.

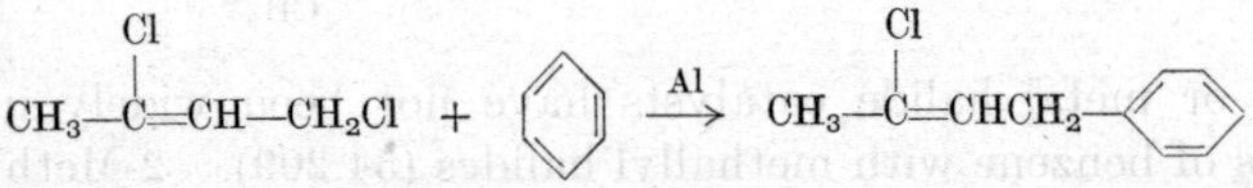

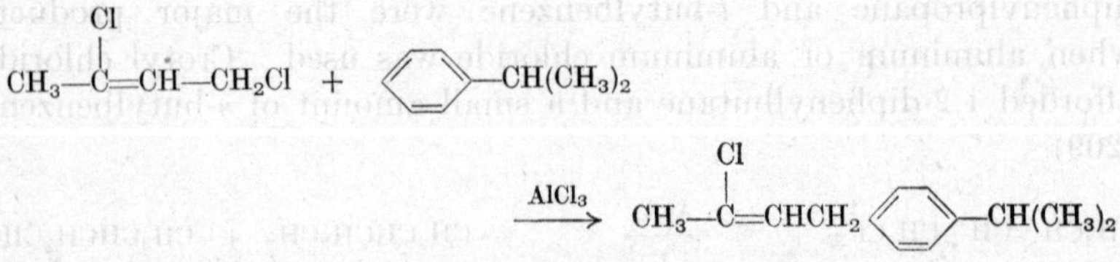

$$CH_3—\overset{\overset{\displaystyle Cl}{|}}{C}=CH—CH_2Cl \ + \ \bigcirc \ \xrightarrow{Al} \ CH_3—\overset{\overset{\displaystyle Cl}{|}}{C}=CHCH_2—\bigcirc$$

$$CH_3—\overset{\overset{\displaystyle Cl}{|}}{C}=CH—CH_2Cl \ + \ \bigcirc—CH(CH_3)_2$$

$$\xrightarrow{AlCl_3} \ CH_3—\overset{\overset{\displaystyle Cl}{|}}{C}=CHCH_2—\bigcirc—CH(CH_3)_2$$

No migration of the double bond of the product is reported. Had this occurred, an allylic chloride would have resulted which would have undergone further alkylation.   Dialkylated products, however, were not isolated.

1,3-Dichloro-2-methyl-1-propene gave the expected 1,3-dichloro-2-methyl-2-phenylpropane in 6% yield with sulfuric acid (70).

3. Miscellaneous Halides

Benzosuberan derivatives were reported as products when compounds such as 2-chloro-2-methyl-5-hexene or 2-chloro-2,3,3-trimethyl-6-heptene underwent cyclialkylation with benzene in the presence of aluminum chloride (40).

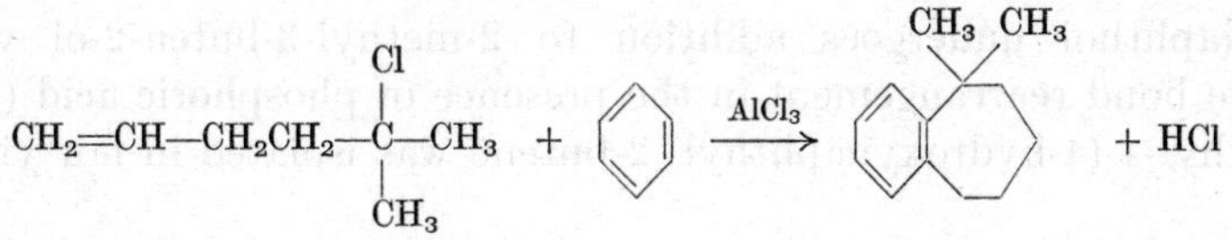

$$CH_2=CH-CH_2CH_2-\underset{\underset{CH_3}{|}}{\overset{\overset{Cl}{|}}{C}}-CH_3 \; + \; \bigcirc \; \overset{AlCl_3}{\longrightarrow} \; \text{(benzosuberan)} \; + \; HCl$$

However, Barclay (Chapter XXII) has shown that this product is actually a tetralin derivative.

4. Summary

Vinyl and allyl halides can be made to react preferentially at the double bond in the presence of proton donor type catalysts (*e.g.*, sulfuric acid).   Since the halogen atoms are not involved, this method represents a simple synthetic route to aromatic compounds having a halo-substituted side chain.   With more active catalysts (*e.g.*, aluminum chloride), reaction occurs both at the double bond and at the halogen atoms to yield polyaryl-substituted alkanes.   If the compound possesses both allylic and vinylic halides, aluminum chloride effects condensation at the allylic position.

The most important side reactions appear to be intermolecular alkylation of certain intermediate products followed by hydrogen transfer.   An anthracene and an alkyl aromatic are undoubtedly products of these processes.

IV. Unsaturated Alcohols and Ethers

1. Unsaturated Alcohols

The reaction of allyl alcohol with benzene gave 1,2-diphenyl-propane when using aluminum chloride (84), sulfuric acid (185), or hydrogen fluoride (32) as a catalyst.   With a 10 molar excess of hydrogen fluoride, the diphenylpropane was obtained in 53% yield.

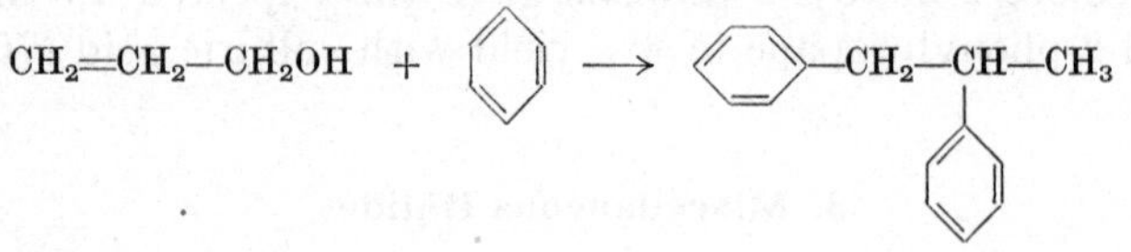

$$CH_2=CH_2-CH_2OH + \bigcirc \longrightarrow \bigcirc-CH_2-CH-CH_3$$

An aluminum chloride–nitropropane catalyst, however, gave 2-chloro-1-phenylpropane (224) which is produced by the addition of hydrogen chloride to the intermediate allylbenzene found by some workers (84,118,185).

1-Naphthol undergoes addition to 2-methyl-3-buten-2-ol with double bond rearrangement in the presence of phosphoric acid (93). 2-Methyl-4-(4-hydroxynaphthyl)-2-butene was isolated in fair yield.

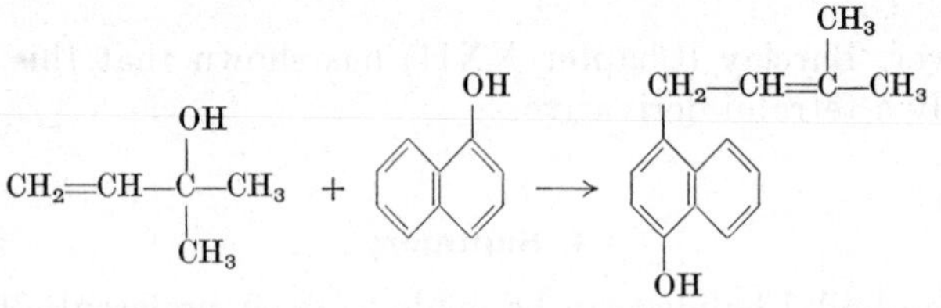

$$CH_2=CH-\overset{OH}{\underset{CH_3}{\overset{|}{C}}}-CH_3 + \bigcirc\bigcirc \longrightarrow$$

It is interesting to note that alkylation at the tertiary carbon atom is not reported. Failure to isolate t-alkylates may account for the low yield in this reaction.

Phenol ethers are reported to react only at the allylic carbon atom. Thus, it is reported that anisole and 4-hydroxy-2-hexene give 4-(p-methoxyphenyl)-2-hexene in 76% yield when treated with a small amount of sulfuric acid (201).

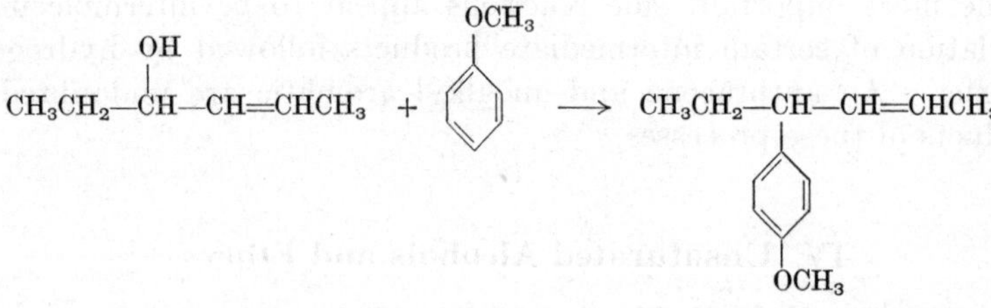

$$CH_3CH_2-\overset{OH}{\overset{|}{CH}}-CH=CHCH_3 + \bigcirc \longrightarrow CH_3CH_2-CH-CH=CHCH_3$$

The double bond has not rearranged into conjugation with the benzene ring as one would have expected.

A catalyst consisting of a mixture of sulfuric and fuming sulfuric acids is claimed to yield 2,2-dipseudocumylpropane from allyl alcohol and pseudocumene (107).   This could be formed as follows:

$$CH_2{=}CHCH_2OH \;+\; ArH \;\xrightarrow{H^+}\; \underset{\underset{Ar}{|}}{CH_3{-}CHCH_2OH}$$

$$\underset{\underset{Ar}{|}}{CH_3{-}CHCH_2OH} \;\xrightarrow{H_2SO_4(SO_3)}\; \underset{\underset{Ar}{|}}{CH_3{-}C{=}CH_2} \;+\; H_2O$$

$$\underset{\underset{Ar}{|}}{CH_3{-}C{=}CH_2} \;+\; ArH \;\xrightarrow{H^+}\; \overset{\overset{Ar}{|}}{\underset{\underset{Ar}{|}}{CH_3{-}C{-}CH_3}}$$

(I)

ArH = pseudocumene

It is to be noted, however, that the structure of I was not adequately established by chemical means.

Ring closure to form substituted coumarans is the favored reaction between β,γ-unsaturated alcohols and phenols (145).

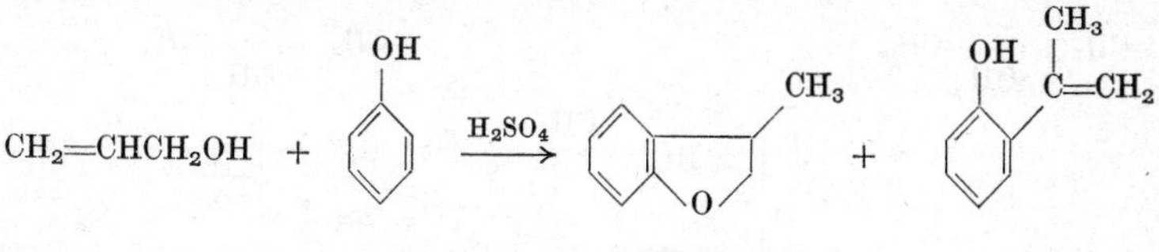

(II)   (III)

The coumaran is apparently formed as shown in equations 1–3.

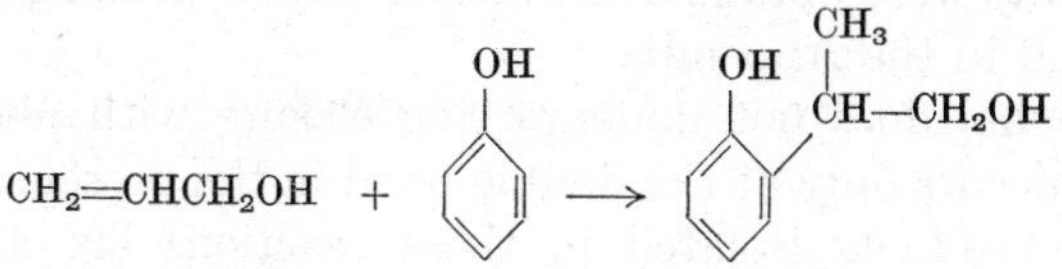

(1)

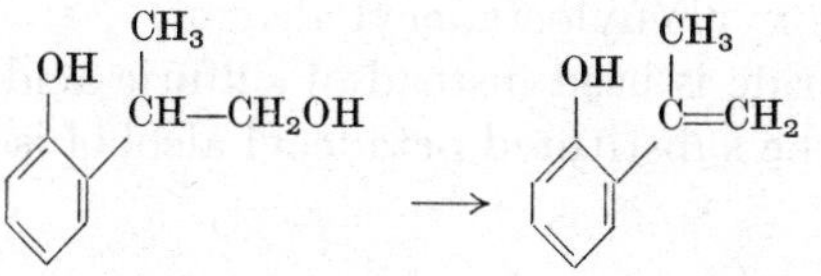

(2)

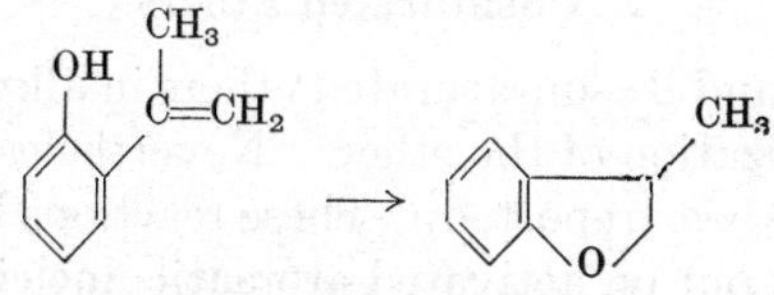

(3)

Compounds having the general structure (IV) have been prepared by the following reaction (145):

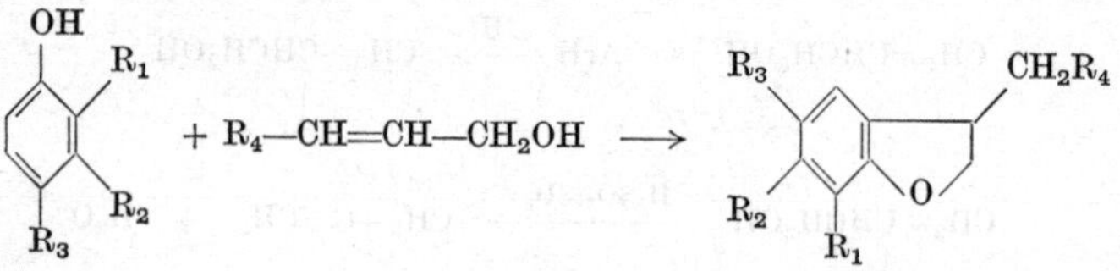

$$\text{(structure with OH, R}_1, R_2, R_3\text{)} + R_4-CH=CH-CH_2OH \longrightarrow \text{(structure IV with R}_3, R_2, R_1, CH_2R_4, O\text{)}$$

(IV)

In all cases, the alkenyl phenol corresponding to product (III) was also isolated.

In contrast to the protonic acids, metal halides effect alkylation at the allylic carbon atom. For example, with zinc chloride as a catalyst (193), trimethylhydroquinone and allyl alcohol gave 2,4,6,7-tetramethyl-5-hydroxycoumaran and not the 3,4,6,7-tetramethyl derivative.

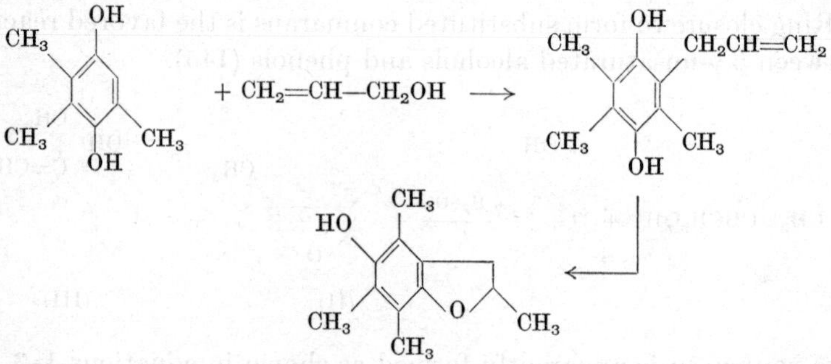

$$\text{(trimethylhydroquinone structure)} + CH_2=CH-CH_2OH \longrightarrow \text{(substituted product)}$$

$$\downarrow$$

$$\text{(2,4,6,7-tetramethyl-5-hydroxycoumaran structure)}$$

Similar results were obtained with other allylic alcohols. Examples can be found in the Appendix.

Oleyl alcohol does not undergo ring closure with phenols (141). Alkylation occurs only at the double bond in the presence of sulfuric acid. The products isolated in these reactions are sulfuric acid esters of a hydroxyphenyloctadecyl alcohol.

If cupric chloride is used instead of sulfuric acid, there is no ester formation and the substituted octadecyl alcohol is obtained directly (141).

2. Unsaturated Ethers

The use of α,β- and β,γ-unsaturated ethers in alkylations is complicated by polymerization of the ether. Nevertheless, a few examples of alkylation have been reported. These reactions have, for the most part, been carried out on activated aromatic nuclei (e.g., phenols).

Benzene has been added to butyl vinyl ether to give a 20% yield of 1-butoxy-1-phenylethane. In addition, a 33% yield of a butyl-phenol was reported (208).

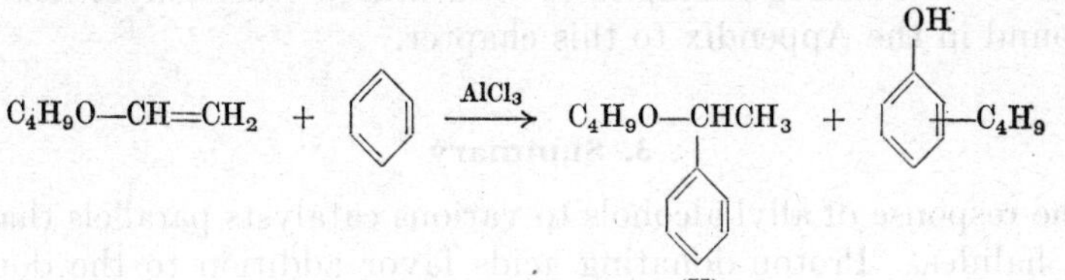

$$C_4H_9O-CH=CH_2 \;+\; \bigcirc \xrightarrow{\text{AlCl}_3} \; C_4H_9O-CHCH_3 \;+\; \overset{OH}{\bigcirc}-C_4H_9$$

(V)

The addition product (V) is formed *via* the carbonium ion (VI) which is undoubtedly stabilized by resonance involving the oxygen atom.

$$C_4H_9O-CH=CH_2 \xrightarrow{H^+} C_4H_9\overset{+}{O}-\overset{+}{C}H-CH_3 \leftrightarrow C_4H_9-\overset{+}{O}=CHCH_3$$

(VI)

The formation of the phenol product in this reaction merits further investigation.

Phenol adds to butyl vinyl ether in the presence of phosphoric acid at 50° to give 1-phenoxy-1-butoxyethane (112).

Ether cleavage was observed in the reaction of ethyl vinyl ether and anisole when hydrogen chloride was used as a catalyst (208). The fate of the ethoxy group was not determined.

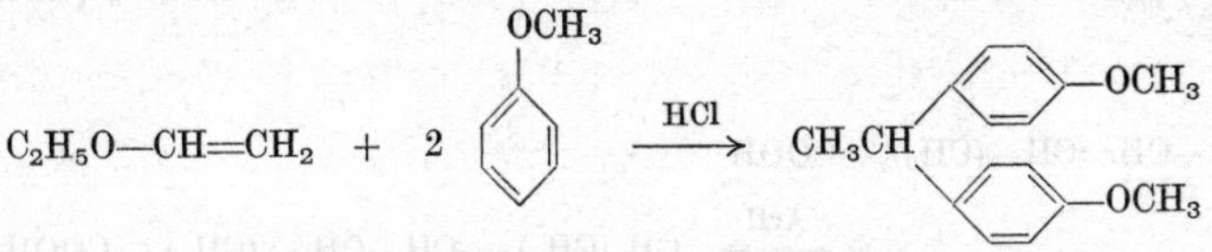

$$C_2H_5O-CH=CH_2 \;+\; 2 \; \overset{OCH_3}{\bigcirc} \xrightarrow{\text{HCl}} \; CH_3CH \overset{\bigcirc-OCH_3}{\underset{\bigcirc-OCH_3}{}}$$

Methallyl methyl ether and phenol gave a good yield of VII in a reaction catalyzed by aluminum phenoxide (57).

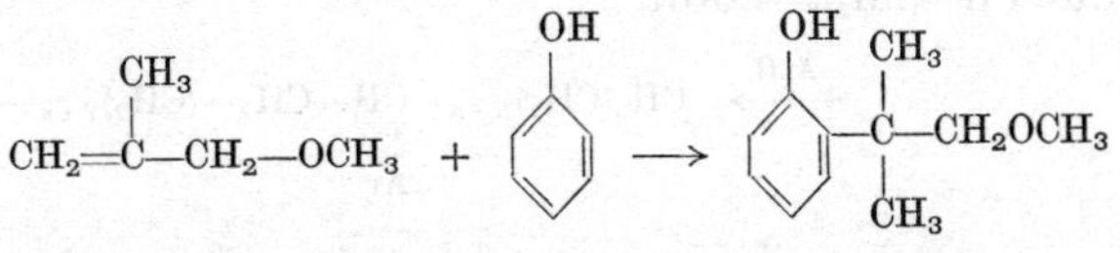

$$\overset{CH_3}{\underset{}{CH_2=C-CH_2-OCH_3}} \;+\; \overset{OH}{\bigcirc} \longrightarrow \; \overset{OH}{\bigcirc}\overset{CH_3}{\underset{CH_3}{-C-CH_2OCH_3}}$$

(VII)

An isopropenyl group was found intact when allyl ether or allyl ethyl ether was treated with sulfuric acid and phenol (144).

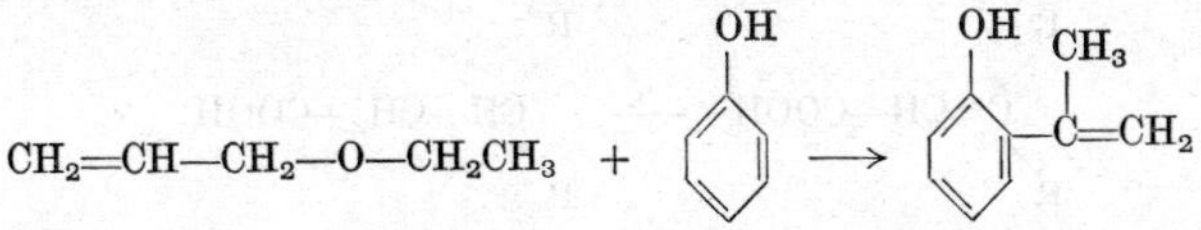

$$CH_2=CH-CH_2-O-CH_2CH_3 \;+\; \overset{OH}{\bigcirc} \longrightarrow \; \overset{OH}{\bigcirc}\overset{CH_3}{-C=CH_2}$$

These reactions may proceed *via* addition of a proton to the double bond, attack of the resulting carbonium ion on the aromatic nucleus, and dealkylation of the side-chain ether.

The few remaining examples of unsaturated ether alkylations can be found in the Appendix to this chapter.

3. Summary

The response of allyl alcohols to various catalysts parallels that of allyl halides. Proton-donating acids favor addition to the double bond whereas metal halide catalysts effect reaction at the allylic carbon atom. Ring closure is common when the benzene ring is activated by one or more hydroxy groups.

In the few examples reported, allyl ethers have been found to react at the double bond. Vinyl ethers react at the α-position unless the β-carbon atom is tertiary. In addition, products resulting from ether cleavage and from alkoxy group displacement have been observed.

V. Unsaturated Acids

The Friedel-Crafts catalyzed reaction of unsaturated acids with aromatic compounds involves addition, rearrangement, replacement, and hydrogen transfer reactions as shown in the general equations 1–4.

$$CH_3(CH_2)_x—CH{=}CH—(CH_2)_Y—COOH$$

$$\xrightarrow{\text{ArH}} \quad CH_3(CH_2)_x—\underset{\underset{Ar}{|}}{CH}—CH_2—(CH_2)_Y—COOH \quad (1)$$

$$CH_3(CH_2)_x—CH{=}CH—(CH_2)_Y—COOH$$

$$\xrightarrow{\text{ArH}} \quad CH_3(CH_2)_{x-n}—\underset{\underset{Ar}{|}}{CH}—CH_2—(CH_2)_{Y+n}—COOH \quad (2)$$

$$X—Ar—CH{=}CH—COOH \xrightarrow{\text{ArH}} \quad \overset{Ar}{\underset{Ar}{\diagdown\diagup}}CH—CH_2—COOH \quad + \quad X—ArH \quad (3)$$

$$\overset{R}{\underset{R}{\diagdown\diagup}}C{=}CH—COOH \quad \longrightarrow \quad \overset{R}{\underset{R}{\diagdown\diagup}}CH—CH_2—COOH \quad (4)$$

1. Addition

Eijkman first reported the addition of benzene and toluene to many α,β-unsaturated acids (58,59).

Acrylic acid yielded β-phenylpropionic acid (81).

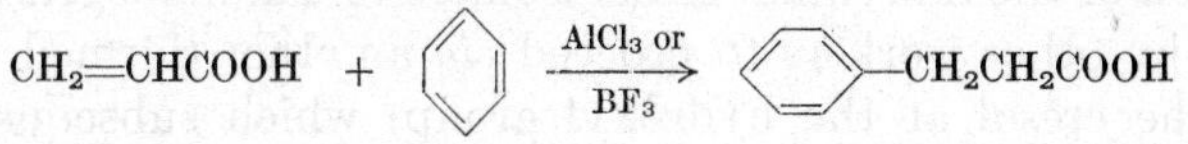

$$CH_2{=}CHCOOH \; + \; \bigcirc \xrightarrow[\text{BF}_3]{\text{AlCl}_3 \text{ or}} \bigcirc{-}CH_2CH_2COOH$$

β,β-Dimethylacrylic acid gave a β-phenyl addition product with benzene (20,159) and m-xylene (72,137).

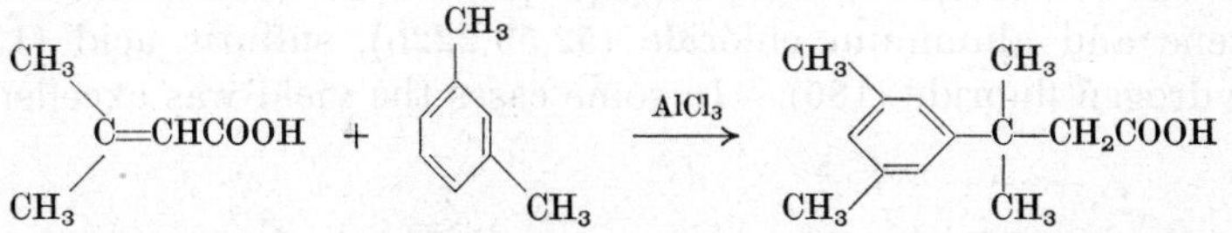

A dibasic acid, 2-phenyl-2,4,4-trimethylpentane-3,5-dicarboxylic acid, found as a by-product in one instance, was probably formed *via* dimerization of the β,β-dimethylacrylic acid followed by alkylation (20).

Oleic acid has been extensively used to alkylate aromatic nuclei (see Appendix). In most references, the addition to the double bond is claimed to give a mixture of 9- and 10-arylstearic acids (75).

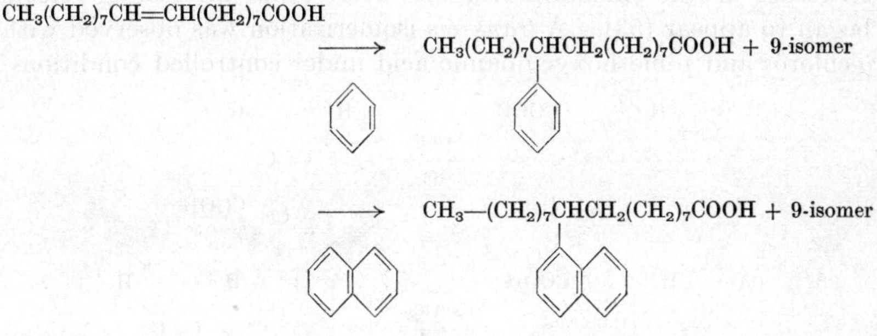

$$CH_3(CH_2)_7CH{=}CH(CH_2)_7COOH$$

Most of the condensations have been carried out with aluminum chloride used in an amount equivalent to the unsaturated acid. These conditions, together with an excess of benzene, are claimed by Schmidt (169) to give the fastest reaction. A large excess of aromatic to oleic acid (7:1 ratio) was also found desirable by other workers (200).

Phenol gave *O*- and *C*-alkylations with oleic acid when 70% perchloric acid was used as a catalyst (50). Oxyphenylstearic acid and oxyphenylenedistearic acid were reported to be the products. *m*-Cresol is thought to undergo *O*-alkylation in the presence of the sulfuric–acetic acid catalyst to give an intermediate which is unstable and rearranges to a 2-hydroxy-4-methylphenylstearic acid (143,182). A mixture of cresols and oleic acid gave a viscous oil when boron fluoride was used as a catalyst (23).

Addition of the individual cresol isomers to chaulmoogric acid was assumed by other workers to proceed *via* an ether (formed by reaction of the cresol at the hydroxyl group) which subsequently rearranged to the corresponding hydroxy-*o*(*m*,*p*)-tolyldihydrochaulmoogric acid (146).

Cinnamic acid gave β,β-diphenylpropionic acid when treated with benzene and aluminum chloride (52,59,222b), sulfuric acid (115), or hydrogen fluoride (185). In some cases the yield was excellent.

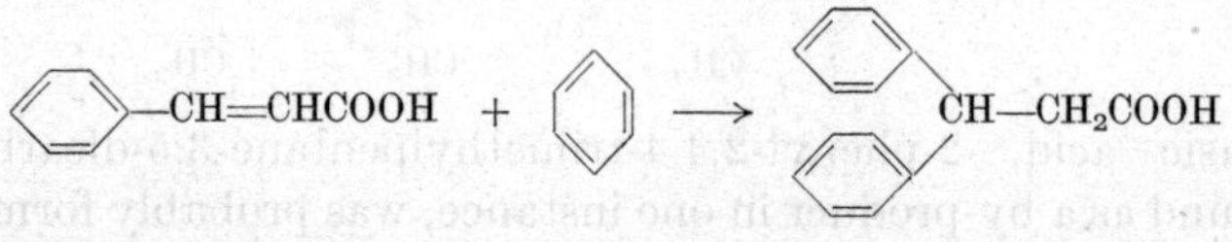

Ethylbenzene has been added to cinnamic acid (149). An aluminum chloride–nitromethane catalyst afforded an 82% yield of β-phenyl-β-(4-ethylphenyl)propionic acid.

Dippy and Young found normal β-addition products in the reaction of cinnamic acid with substituted benzenes (52). On varying the structure of the cinnamic acid, however, other interesting effects began to appear (53). A *trans–cis* isomerization was observed with *o*-chloro- and *p*-methoxycinnamic acid under controlled conditions.

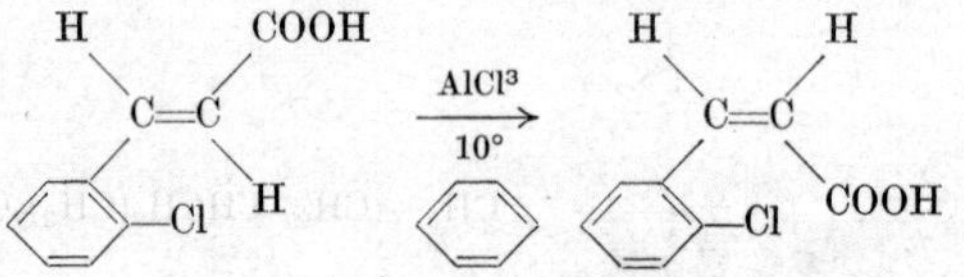

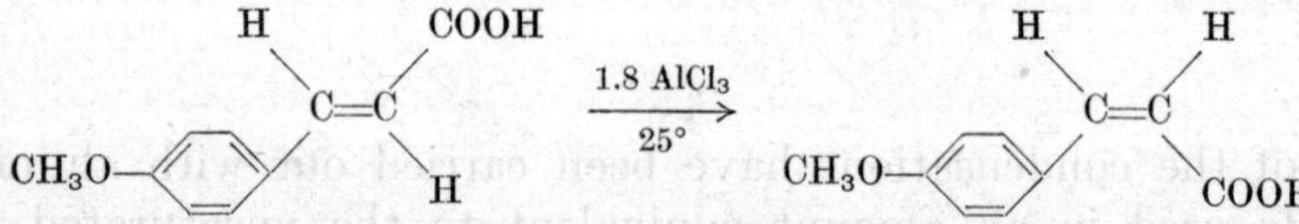

When the mole ratio of aluminum chloride/acid was increased from 1.8 to 5/1, *p*-methoxycinnamic acid underwent a cleavage rearrangement of the methoxy group as well as alkylation at the double bond.

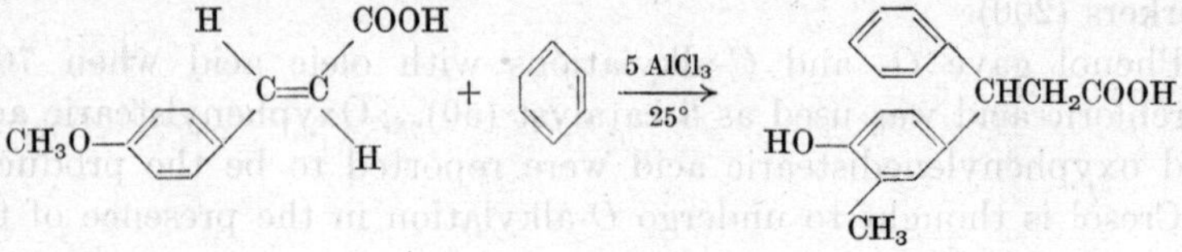

In alkylating the higher methylbenzenes, it was discovered that the aromatic suffered a loss of one methyl group and rearrangement of another. Pseudocumene, hemimellitine, durene, isodurene, and prehnitene all gave a single addition product, β-(3,4,5-trimethyl-phenyl)isovaleric acid, on reaction with β,β-dimethylacrylic acid and aluminum chloride (188,191).

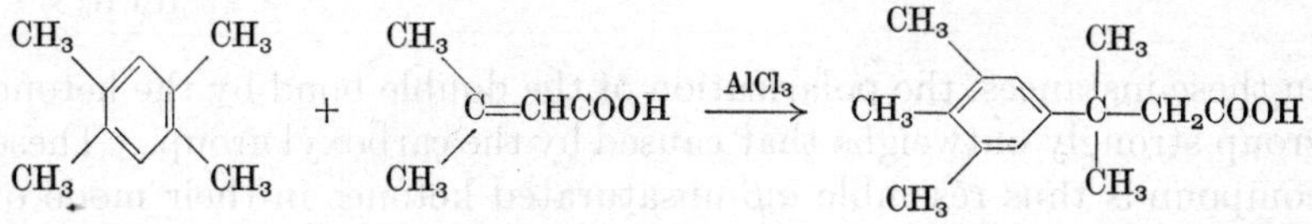

Methyl group displacement occurs because of the inability of the entering t-alkyl group to be easily accommodated in existing vacant positions flanked by two methyl groups. Pentamethylbenzene, isolated in some instances, accounts for the lost methyl group. The presence of isovaleric acid in some products indicates a concurrent hydrogen transfer reaction. Mesitylene gave a dimethylphenyliso-valeric acid (I) which was not identical to the β-(2,5-dimethylphenyl)-isovaleric acid obtained from p-xylene (191). However, the reviewers note that compound I had the same melting point as β-(3,5-dimethylphenyl)isovaleric acid (II) and may in fact be this compound.

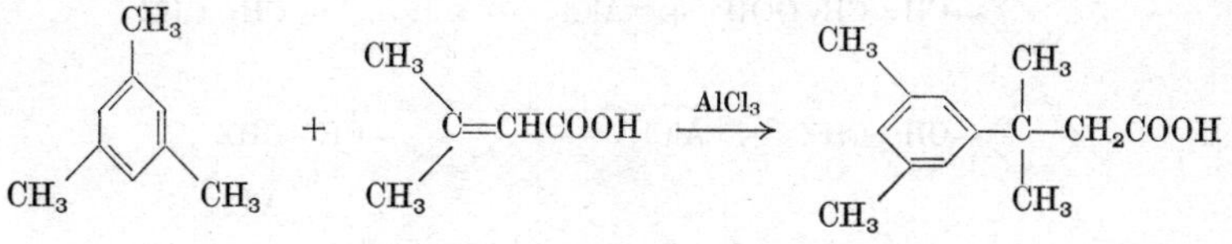

(II)

Other examples of β-addition may be found in the Appendix.

α-Addition can occur when the double bond polarity is altered by some structural feature present in the acid. α-Phenylacrylic acid provides one example (53,59).

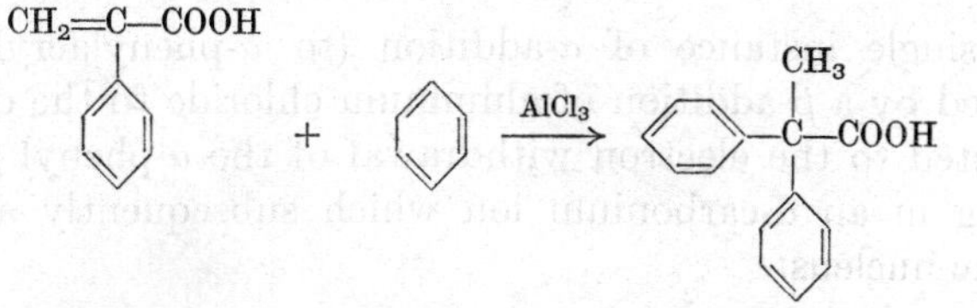

When β-benzoyl- or β-toluylacrylic acids were treated with toluene and aluminum chloride, addition occurred *alpha* to the carboxyl group (161).

$$\text{C}_6\text{H}_5\text{-CO-CH=CHCOOH} + \text{C}_6\text{H}_5\text{CH}_3 \xrightarrow{\text{AlCl}_3} \text{C}_6\text{H}_5\text{-CO-CH}_2\text{-CH(COOH)(C}_6\text{H}_4\text{CH}_3)$$

In these instances, the polarization of the double bond by the ketone group strongly outweighs that caused by the carboxyl group. These compounds thus resemble α,β-unsaturated ketones in their mode of addition.

Eijkman (58) reported finding an α-addition product in the reaction between benzene and β,β-dimethylacrylic acid, but other workers have shown it to be in fact a β-addition product (53).

Dippy and Young have proposed a reasonable scheme for the addition of aromatics to α,β-unsaturated acids based on work with cinnamic acid and substituted acrylic acids (52,53). An interaction between the carboxyl group and aluminum chloride is assumed (designated by Z and not definitely specified) which in the presence of the excess catalyst forms a carbonium ion (III or IV). These reactive species then engage in an electrophilic attack on the aromatic nucleus.

$$\text{C}_6\text{H}_5\text{-CH=CHCOOH} + \text{AlCl}_3 \longrightarrow \text{C}_6\text{H}_5\text{-CH=CHZ}$$

$$\text{C}_6\text{H}_5\text{-CH=CHZ} + \text{AlCl}_3 \longrightarrow \text{C}_6\text{H}_5\text{-}\overset{+}{\text{C}}\text{H-CHZ}(\text{AlCl}_3^-)$$

$$\text{C}_6\text{H}_5\text{-}\overset{+}{\text{C}}\text{H-CHZ}(\text{AlCl}_3^-) \xrightarrow{\text{AlCl}_3} \text{C}_6\text{H}_5\text{-}\overset{+}{\text{C}}\text{H-CHZ}(\text{AlCl}_2) + \text{AlCl}_4^- \quad \text{(III)}$$

$$\xrightarrow{\text{HCl}} \text{C}_6\text{H}_5\text{-}\overset{+}{\text{C}}\text{H-CH}_2\text{Z} + \text{AlCl}_4^- \quad \text{(IV)}$$

The single instance of α-addition (to α-phenylacrylic acid) is explained by a β-addition of aluminum chloride to the double bond (attributed to the electron withdrawal of the α-phenyl group) thus resulting in an α-carbonium ion which subsequently alkylates an aromatic nucleus.

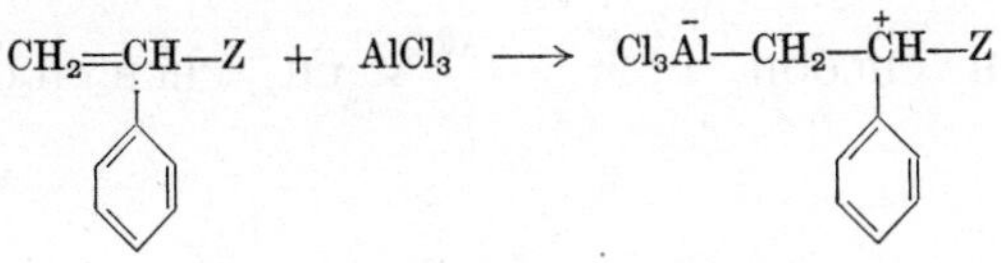

$$CH_2=CH-Z \ + \ AlCl_3 \ \longrightarrow \ Cl_3\bar{Al}-CH_2-\overset{+}{C}H-Z$$

2. Rearrangement

The reaction of Δ^1-cyclohexenylacetic acid and benzene in the presence of aluminum chloride is reported to yield the expected 2-phenylcyclohexaneacetic acid (67).

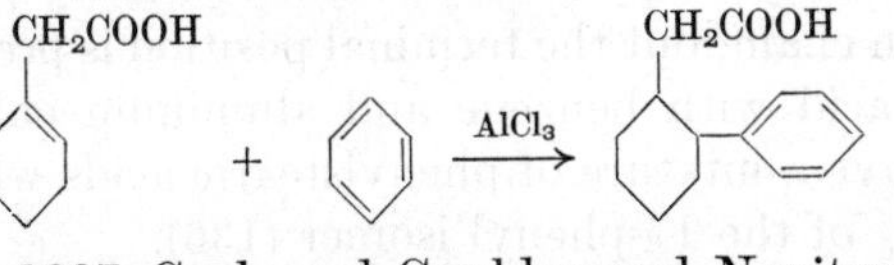

However, in 1937, Cook and Goulden and Nenitzescu and Gavat isolated 4-phenylcyclohexaneacetic acid from the same reaction (45,46,134). Nenitzescu and Gavat proved the structure by independent synthesis.

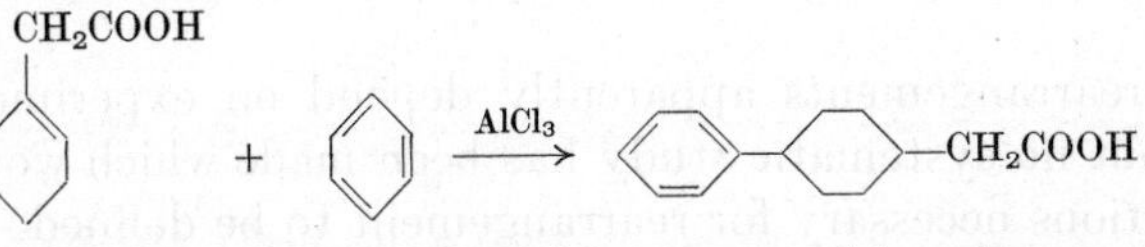

Cook pointed out that a 2-phenyl isomer would undergo cyclization when treated with sulfuric acid. Treatment of the addition products with sulfuric acid resulted in sulfonation (not cyclization) and thus it was concluded that the 2-phenyl isomer was not present in the reaction products.

β-Cyclohexylacrylic acid (134) and cyclohexene-1-carboxylic acid (133) also gave rearranged products.

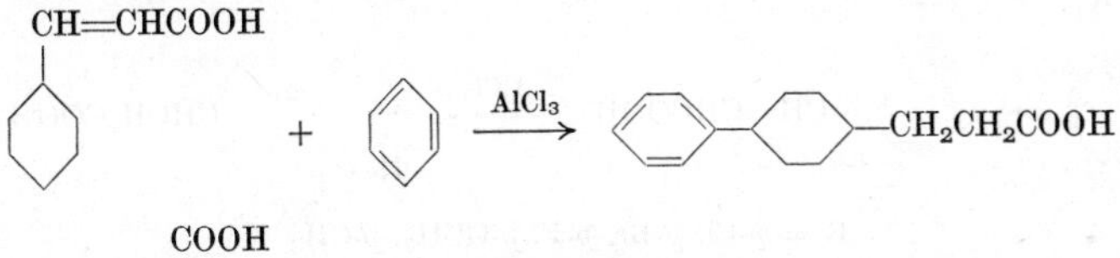

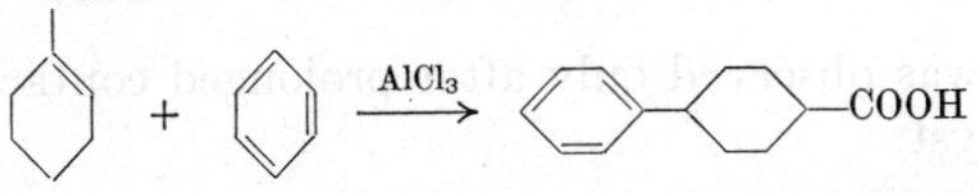

Similar rearrangements have been reported with 2-pentenoic acid (136), 2-hexenoic acid, and 3-methyl-2-hexenoic acid (135). For example, Nenitzescu et al. found only a single (migrated) addition product from the aluminum chloride catalyzed addition of benzene to 2-hexenoic acid.

12+F.C. II

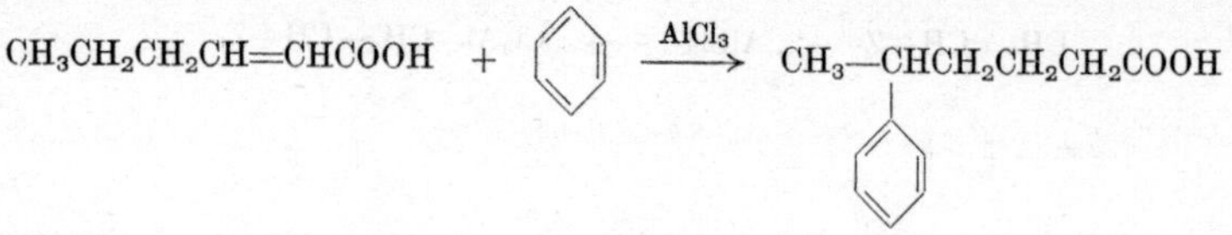

$$CH_3CH_2CH_2CH{=}CHCOOH \ + \ \bigcirc \xrightarrow{AlCl_3} \ CH_3{-}\underset{\overset{|}{\bigcirc}}{CH}CH_2CH_2CH_2COOH$$

Nenitzescu *et al.* proposed a series of eliminations and additions of hydrogen chloride to explain a double bond migration, but attempts to isolate the intermediate chloroacids for this scheme were essentially unsuccessful.

The double bond can apparently migrate to every possible position in a long carbon chain, but the terminal position is preferred. Treatment of oleic acid with benzene and aluminum chloride at reflux temperature gave a mixture of phenylstearic acids which is reported to contain 50% of the 17-phenyl isomer (136).

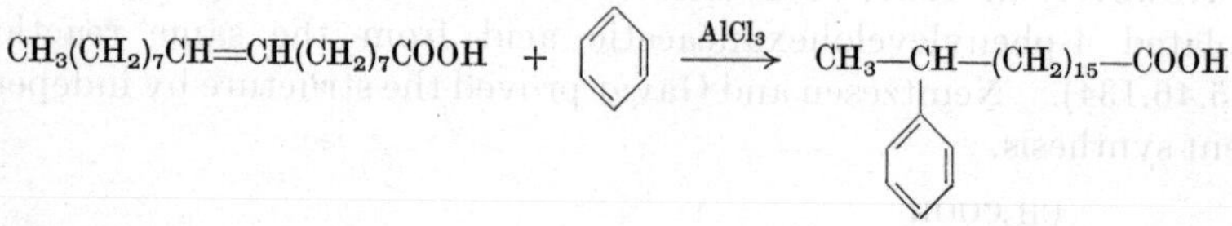

$$CH_3(CH_2)_7CH{=}CH(CH_2)_7COOH \ + \ \bigcirc \xrightarrow{AlCl_3} \ CH_3{-}\underset{\overset{|}{\bigcirc}}{CH}{-}(CH_2)_{15}{-}COOH$$

These rearrangements apparently depend on experimental conditions, but no systematic study has been made which would enable the conditions necessary for rearrangement to be defined.

3. Replacement

Replacement of aryl groups in β,β-diarylpropionic acids occurs less readily than with β,β-diarylketones. Thus, Dippy and Young were able to add various monosubstituted benzenes to cinnamic acid and obtain only addition products as shown in equation 5 (52).

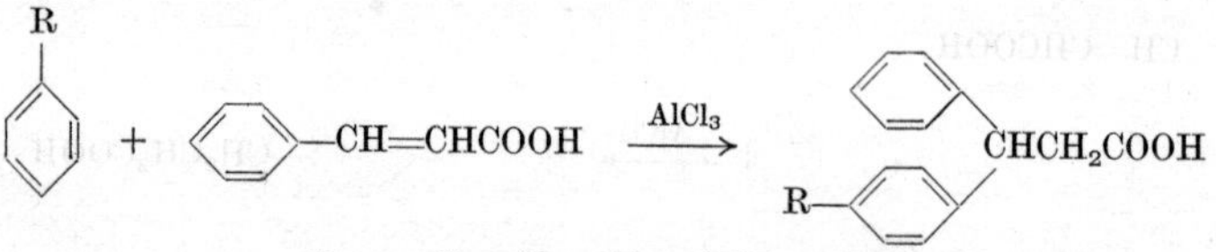

$$\underset{R}{\bigcirc} \ + \ \bigcirc{-}CH{=}CHCOOH \xrightarrow{AlCl_3} \ \underset{R{-}\bigcirc}{\overset{\bigcirc}{}}CHCH_2COOH \qquad (5)$$

$$R = p\text{-Cl}, \ p\text{-Br}, \ p\text{-F}, \ p\text{-OCH}_3, \ p\text{-CH}_3$$

Replacement was observed only after prolonged contact (2–3 days) with the catalyst.

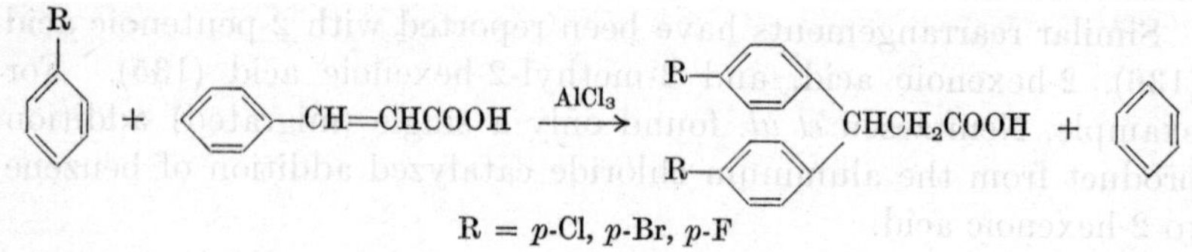

$$\underset{R}{\bigcirc} \ + \ \bigcirc{-}CH{=}CHCOOH \xrightarrow{AlCl_3} \ \underset{R{-}\bigcirc}{\overset{R{-}\bigcirc}{}}CHCH_2COOH \ + \ \bigcirc$$

$$R = p\text{-Cl}, \ p\text{-Br}, \ p\text{-F}$$

Various substituted cinnamic acids were also used by these workers (53). For example, p-methylcinnamic acid also gave a replacement product, β,β-diphenylpropionic acid, when treated with benzene and aluminum chloride at room temperature for 2–3 days.

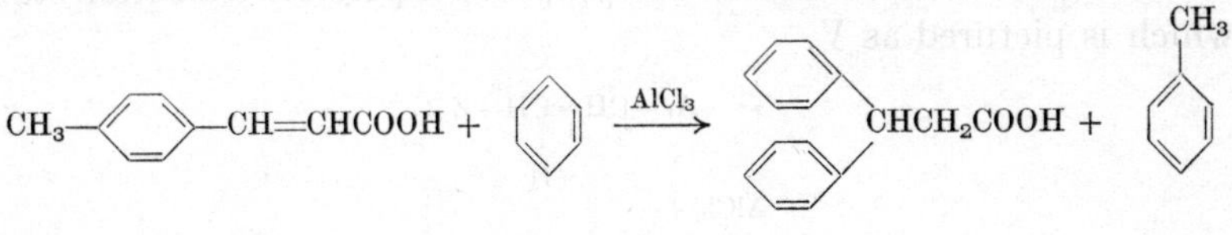

The reversibility of the replacement reaction with acids was shown by Fuson *et al.* (66a). These experiments are outlined in Chart I.

Chart I

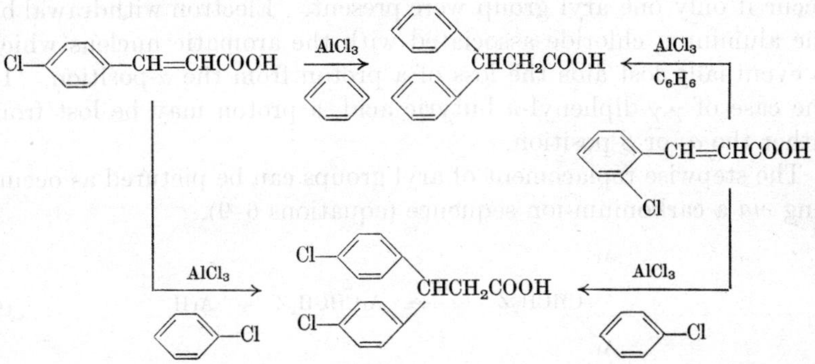

The fate of the displaced aryl group(s) was shown by Dippy and Young who treated β,β-diphenylpropionic acid with chlorobenzene in the presence of a large amount of an aluminum chloride–hydrogen chloride catalyst and found benzene in the solvent (52).

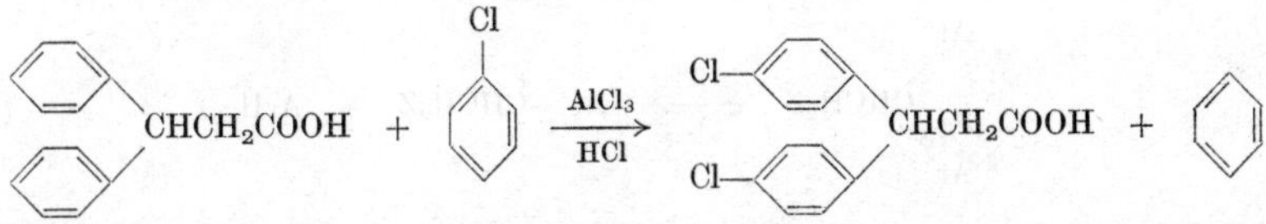

However, the benzene could have been formed *via* disproportionation of the chlorobenzene. Under these conditions, the phenyl groups of γ,γ-diphenyl-n-butyric acid were also replaced by chlorobenzene.

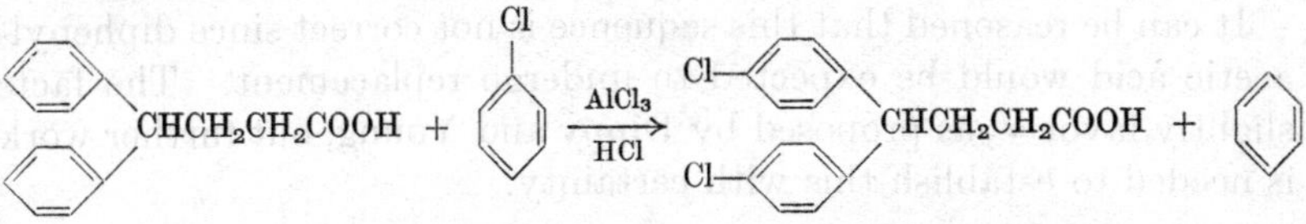

In this reaction, the benzene released was not isolated. Phenylacetic, diphenylacetic, or β-phenylpropionic acids were unaffected when treated in the same manner.

Dippy and Young (53) have summarized the facts known to date on the replacement reaction and proposed a possible transition state which is pictured as V.

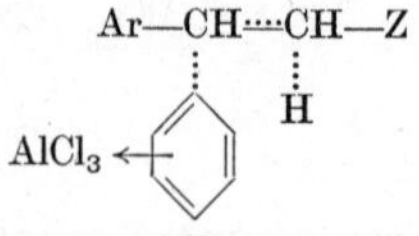

(V)

They reasoned that the *gem*-diaryl group is needed to stabilize the incipient double bond and that no replacement reaction would occur if only one aryl group were present. Electron withdrawal by the aluminum chloride associated with the aromatic nucleus which is eventually lost aids the loss of a proton from the α-position. In the case of γ,γ-diphenyl-n-butyric acid, a proton may be lost from either the α- or β-position.

The stepwise replacement of aryl groups can be pictured as occurring *via* a carbonium-ion sequence (equations 6–9).

$$(Ar)_2CHCH_2Z \overset{H^+}{\rightleftharpoons} Ar\overset{+}{C}HCH_2Z + ArH \qquad (6)$$

$$Ar{-}\overset{+}{C}HCH_2Z + Ar'{-}H \rightleftharpoons (Ar')(Ar)CHCH_2Z + H^+ \qquad (7)$$

$$(Ar')(Ar)CHCH_2Z \overset{H^+}{\rightleftharpoons} Ar'{-}\overset{+}{C}HCH_2Z + ArH \qquad (8)$$

$$Ar'{-}\overset{+}{C}HCH_2Z + Ar'{-}H \rightleftharpoons (Ar')_2CHCH_2Z + H^+ \qquad (9)$$

It can be reasoned that this sequence is not correct since diphenylacetic acid would be expected to undergo replacement. The facts slightly favor V, as proposed by Dippy and Young, but further work is needed to establish this with certainty.

4. Hydrogen Transfer

Instances of hydrogen transfer have been reported when the β-carbon atom is substituted by bulky groups (*e.g.*, β,β-diphenyl). Hydrogen transfer was readily observed when β,β-diphenylacrylic acid was treated with benzene and aluminum chloride (53). β,β-Diphenylpropionic acid was the only product isolated. Apparently it is impossible to form β,β,β-triarylpropionic acid this way.

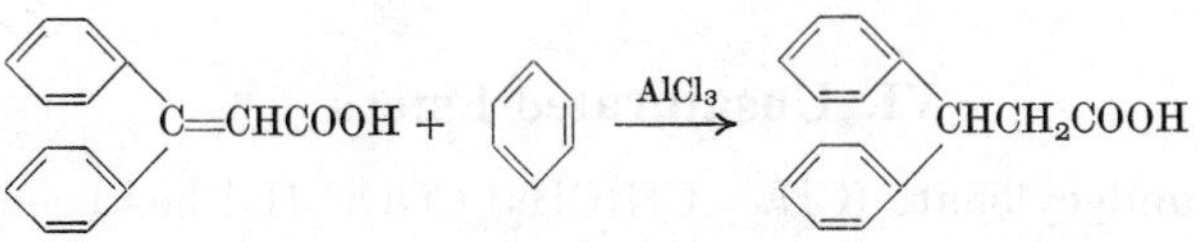

Addition of benzene to β-methyl-β-phenylacrylic acid was reported to yield β,β-diphenylbutyric acid (normal addition) (20) but other workers observed mainly hydrogen transfer (53).

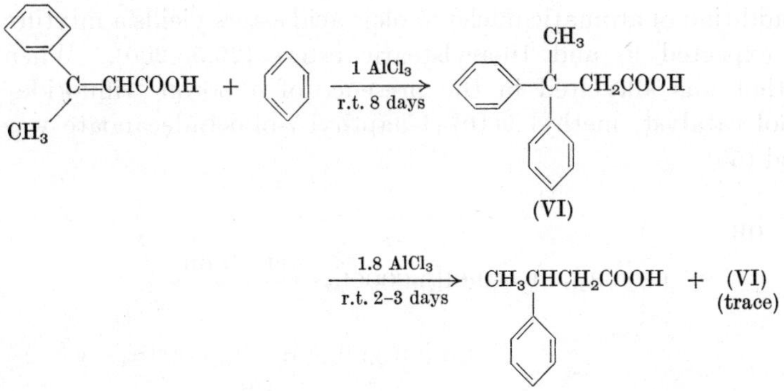

These differences probably result from variations in experimental procedures.

5. Summary

Four processes can occur in the aluminum chloride catalyzed reaction of an aromatic nucleus with an unsaturated acid: (1) normal β-addition to the double bond (this is by far the most common, but α-addition is possible when certain structural features are present in the acid), (2) rearrangement of the double bond away from the carboxyl group followed by addition, (3) replacement of an existing aryl group, and (4) hydrogen transfer. Even though protonic acids have been used in a few instances as catalysts for the alkylation reaction, most investigators employed aluminum chloride.

In view of the conflicting reports concerning normal versus rearranged addition, it appears that rearrangement (when it can occur) is mainly a function of experimental conditions. Replacement of one aryl group by another occurs less readily than in alkylations with unsaturated ketones and may be controlled by selection of proper experimental conditions. As is true in reactions with unsaturated ketones, hydrogen transfer is governed largely by the "bulk" of the substituents at the β-carbon atom.

VI. Unsaturated Esters

Ethyl undecylenate ($CH_2{=}CH(CH_2)_8COOC_2H_5$) has been treated with various aromatic nuclei and aluminum chloride. A mono-adduct is formed in most cases but under forcing conditions the monoalkylated aromatic undergoes further alkylation leading to disubstituted products, namely phenylenediundecanoic acid diethyl ester (63).

The addition of aromatic nuclei to oleic acid esters yields a mixture of the expected 9- and 10-arylstearic esters (26,55,200). When 2-naphthol was alkylated in the presence of a boron trifluoride–methanol catalyst, methyl 9(10)-(1-napthyl-7-ol)octadecanoate was obtained (55).

$$\text{(naphthol)} + CH_3(CH_2)_7CH{=}CH(CH_2)_7COOCH_3 \xrightarrow{BF_3/CH_3OH}$$

$$CH_3(CH_2)_7CH{-}CH_2(CH_2)_7COOCH_3 + \text{9-isomer}$$

Similar results were obtained with phenol.

Di- and trisubstituted benzenes were found when methyl oleate and benzene were treated with aluminum chloride (29). Alkylation of benzene with oleyl acetate gave 9- and 10-phenylstearyl acetate (186).

Vinyl acetate is claimed to yield o-vinylphenol with phenol (144), β-phenylethyl acetate with benzene (81), and a mixture of diphenyl-ethane and 9,10-dimethyl-9,10-dihydroanthracene* with benzene (106).

---

* Probably 9,10-dimethylanthracene (176a,176c).

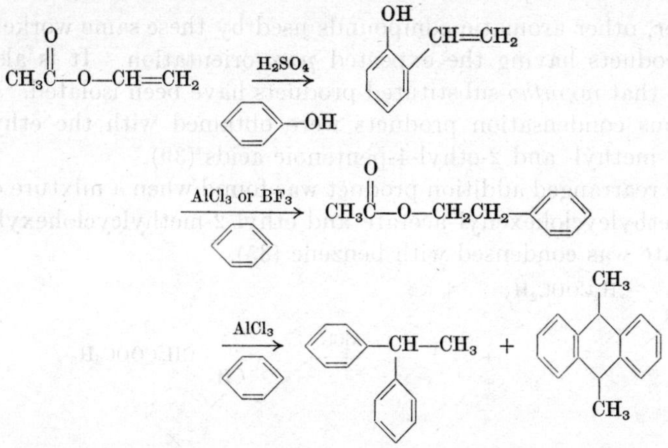

$$CH_3\overset{\overset{\textstyle O}{\|}}{C}\text{—O—CH=}CH_2 \quad \xrightarrow{H_2SO_4}$$

(phenol with OH, CH=CH$_2$, and —OH substituents)

$$\xrightarrow{AlCl_3 \text{ or } BF_3} \quad CH_3\overset{\overset{\textstyle O}{\|}}{C}\text{—O—}CH_2CH_2\text{—}$$

$$\xrightarrow{AlCl_3} \quad \text{—CH—CH}_3 \quad + \quad \text{(anthracene-type structure with two } CH_3 \text{ groups)}$$

The work with vinyl acetate needs considerable clarification. For example, attempted duplication by other workers (15) of the reaction with phenol resulted in polymer formation. The divergent reports with respect to benzene addition remain unresolved.

Alkylations of aromatics with ethyl 4-pentenoate have been investigated by several workers. It is generally agreed that addition to the double bond occurs normally to give ethyl 4-arylvalerate derivatives. It is interesting that double bond migration toward the ester group is not observed.

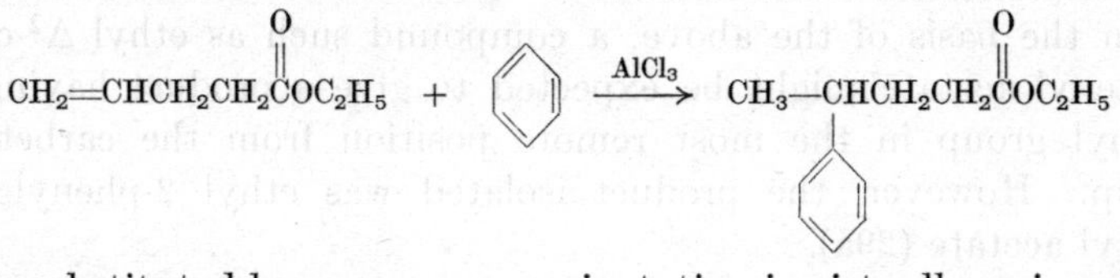

$$CH_2\text{=}CHCH_2CH_2\overset{\overset{\textstyle O}{\|}}{C}OC_2H_5 \quad + \quad \xrightarrow{AlCl_3} \quad CH_3\text{—}CHCH_2CH_2\overset{\overset{\textstyle O}{\|}}{C}OC_2H_5$$

With substituted benzenes, *para*-orientation is virtually universal.

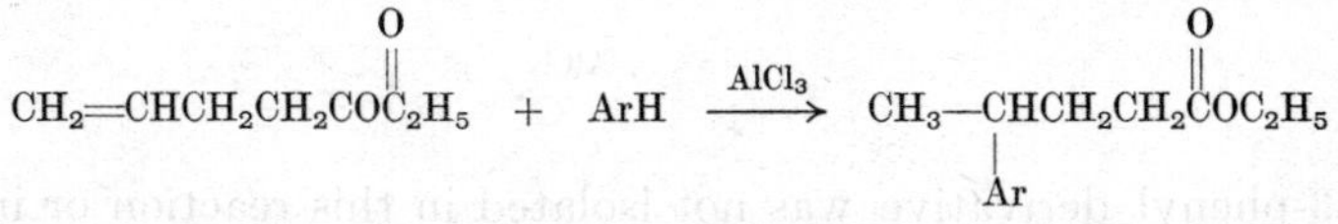

$$CH_2\text{=}CHCH_2CH_2\overset{\overset{\textstyle O}{\|}}{C}OC_2H_5 \quad + \quad ArH \quad \xrightarrow{AlCl_3} \quad CH_3\text{—}CHCH_2CH_2\overset{\overset{\textstyle O}{\|}}{C}OC_2H_5$$
$$\overset{\textstyle |}{Ar}$$

$Ar = p\text{-}CH_3C_6H_4,\ 3,4\text{-}(CH_3)_2C_6H_3,\ p\text{-}FC_6H_4,\ p\text{-}ClC_6H_4,\ p\text{-}Br\text{-}C_6H_4,\ p\text{-}CH_3OC_6H_4,$
$$3\text{-}CH_3\text{-}4\text{-}CH_3OC_6H_3$$

One instance of *meta*-substitution has been reported with toluene (131).

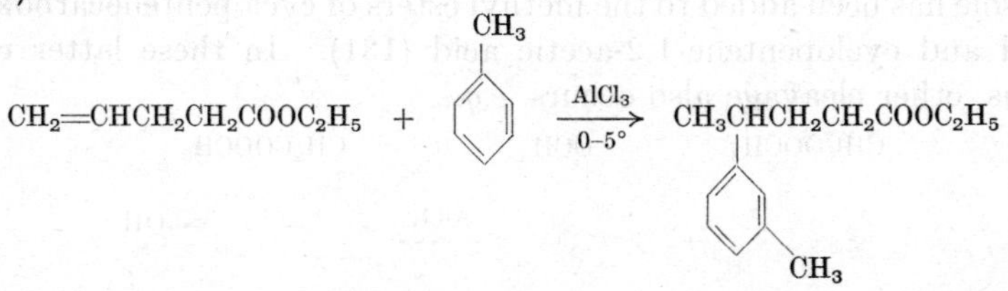

$$CH_2\text{=}CHCH_2CH_2COOC_2H_5 \quad + \quad \xrightarrow[0-5°]{AlCl_3} \quad CH_3CHCH_2CH_2COOC_2H_5$$

However, other aromatic compounds used by these same workers yielded products having the expected *para*-orientation. It is also of interest that no *ortho*-substituted products have been isolated.

Analogous condensation products were obtained with the ethyl esters of 2-methyl- and 2-ethyl-4-pentenoic acids (39).

A single rearranged addition product was found when a mixture of ethyl 2-methylcyclohexenyl acetate and ethyl 2-methylcyclohexylidene acetate was condensed with benzene (35).

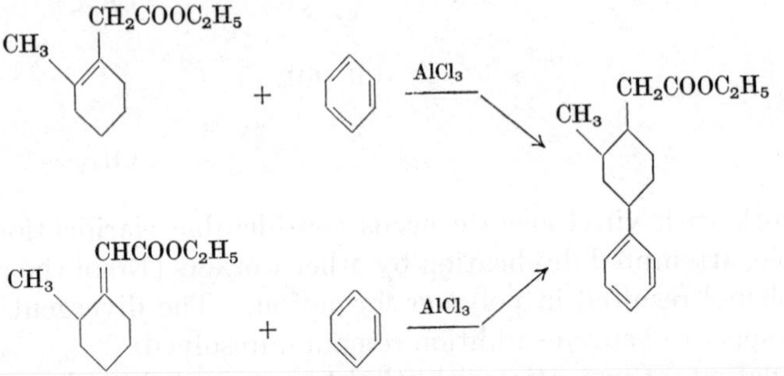

The tertiary carbonium ion which is expected to form at positions 1 or 2 of the cyclohexane ring is apparently not stable in this system and is rearranged to the 4-position. Rearrangement to the distal position has not been noted with acyclic esters but is well established with acyclic unsaturated acids.

On the basis of the above, a compound such as ethyl Δ^2-cyclopentenyl acetate might be expected to give a product having the phenyl group in the most remote position from the carbethoxy group. However, the product isolated was ethyl 2-phenylcyclopentyl acetate (29a).

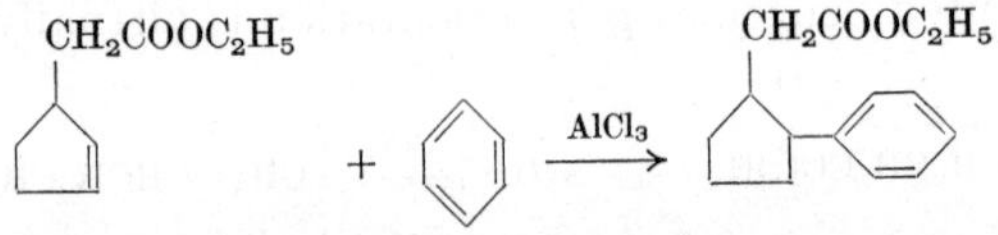

A 3-phenyl derivative was not isolated in this reaction or in the analogous reactions with toluene, the xylene isomers, or acenaphthene. It is also strange that active nuclei such as anisole and veratrole failed to react (30,31) especially in view of the fact that anisole has been added to the methyl esters of cyclopentenecarboxylic acid and cyclopentene-1,2-acetic acid (131). In these latter reactions, ether cleavage also occurs, *e.g.*,

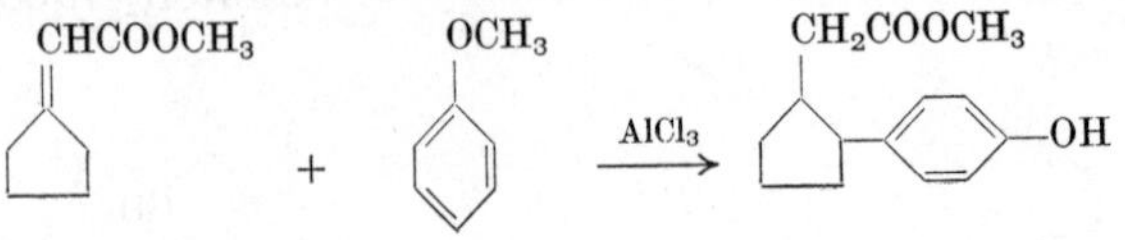

Treatment of allylorthoborate with benzene (or cumene) in the presence of a ferric chloride catalyst has been claimed to give allylarenes (199).

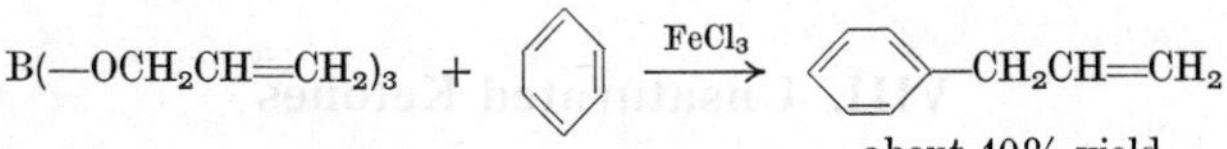

$$B(-OCH_2CH=CH_2)_3 \;+\; \text{(benzene)} \xrightarrow{FeCl_3} \text{(benzene)}-CH_2CH=CH_2$$

about 40% yield

The fate of the boron was not established.

1. Summary

Unsaturated esters undergo catalyzed addition of aromatics to the double bond whether the unsaturation be in the acid or alcohol part of the ester.   The ester function in general remains intact and is not cleaved during the reaction.   Prior rearrangement of the double bond followed by addition of the aromatic can give rise to abnormal products.   This has been substantiated with certain cyclohexene and cyclohexylidene derivatives, but not apparently with acyclic compounds.

The ester linkages of allylorthoborate do not survive in the attempted addition of an aromatic to the double bonds.   Allylbenzene was the only product reported.

VII. Unsaturated Aldehydes

Furan adds readily to acrolein; even a weak acid such as aqueous sulfur dioxide functions as a catalyst for this reaction (175).   Low yields of β-(α-furyl)propionaldehyde and β,β-(α,α-furyl)dipropionaldehyde were reported.

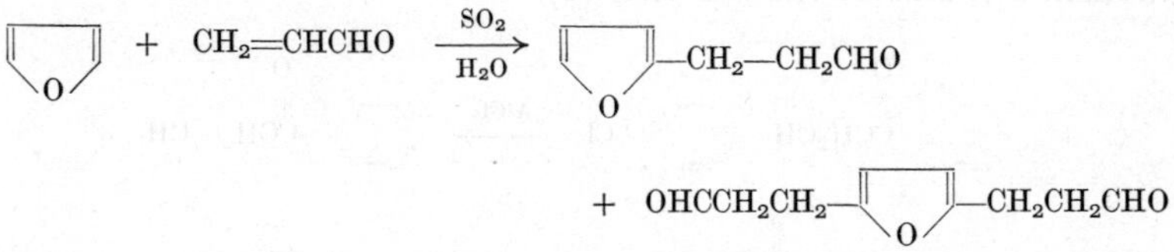

$$\text{(furan)} + CH_2=CHCHO \xrightarrow[\text{H}_2\text{O}]{SO_2} \text{(furyl)}-CH_2-CH_2CHO$$

$$+ \; OHCCH_2CH_2-\text{(furyl)}-CH_2CH_2CHO$$

2-Methylfuran and crotonaldehyde gave some β-(5-methylfuryl-2)-butyraldehyde (1) in the presence of methyl tolylsulfinate.

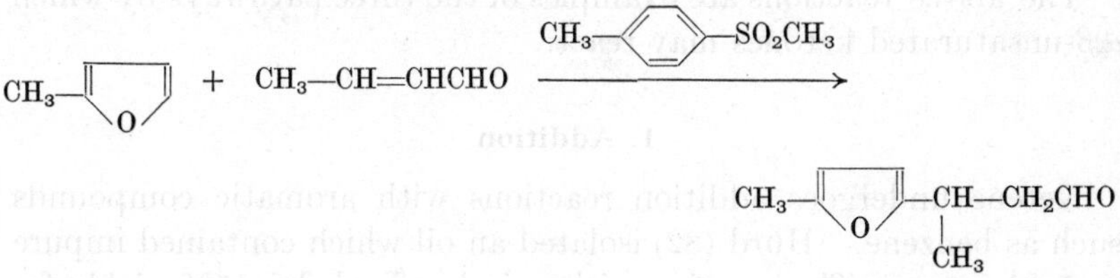

$$CH_3-\text{(furan)} + CH_3-CH=CHCHO \xrightarrow{CH_3-\text{(benzene)}-SO_2CH_3} $$

$$CH_3-\text{(furyl)}-CH-CH_2CHO$$
$$\underset{CH_3}{|}$$

24%

One might wonder how the sulfinate ester functions as a catalyst. It may be that some hydrolysis occurred liberating sulfinic acid which then functioned as the catalyst.

VIII. Unsaturated Ketones

The catalyzed addition of an aromatic compound to an α,β-unsaturated ketone was first reported by Vorlander and Friedberg (219). They found that 3,3-diphenylpropiophenone was formed in 76–85% yields when excess benzene was treated with benzalacetophenone and aluminum chloride.

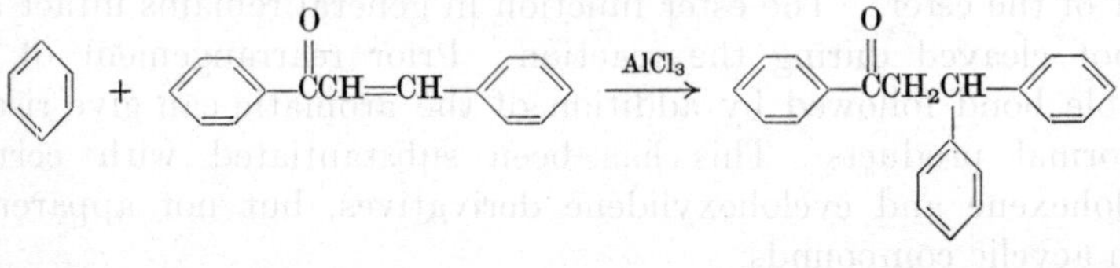

However, some types of unsaturated ketones yield only hydrogenated products (2).

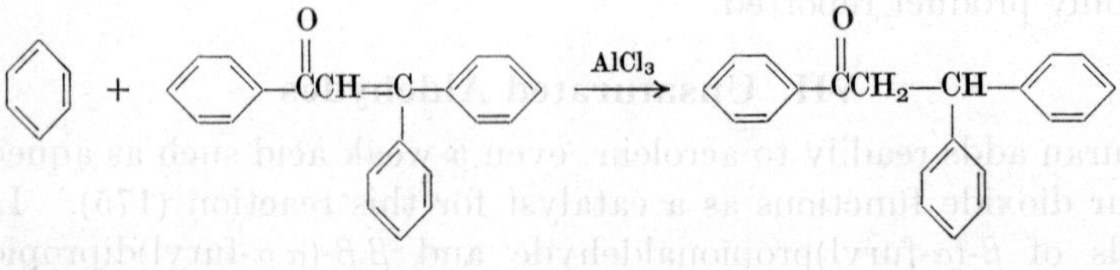

Replacement of one aryl group by another is also now a well-established course of the reaction (2).

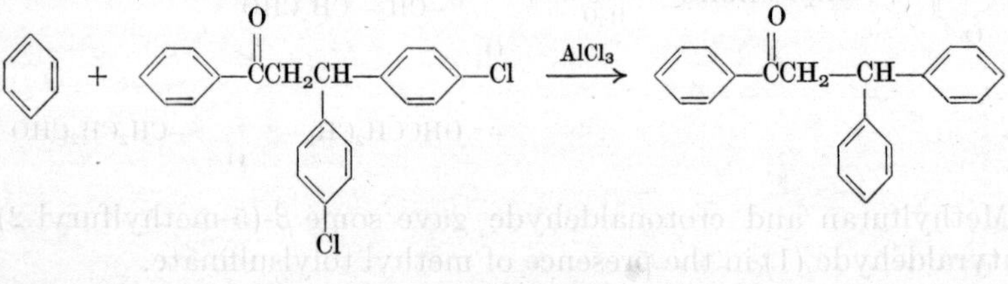

The above reactions are examples of the three pathways by which α,β-unsaturated ketones may react.

1. Addition

Ketene undergoes addition reactions with aromatic compounds such as benzene. Hurd (82) isolated an oil which contained impure acetophenone. The reaction with anisole afforded a 45% yield of a mixture of ketones containing approximately 66% *para-* and 33% *ortho*-isomers.

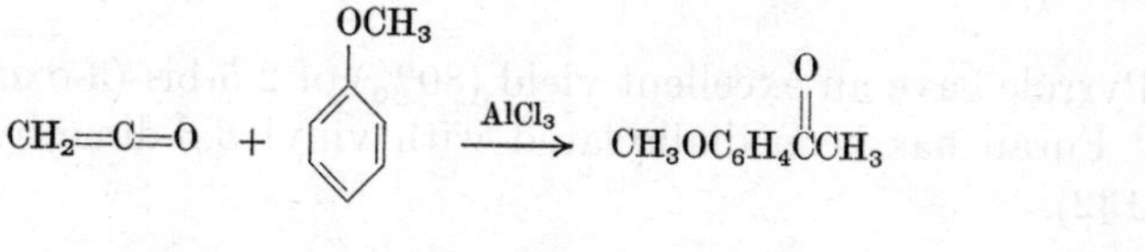

$$CH_2{=}C{=}O \ + \ \underset{}{\overset{OCH_3}{\bigodot}} \ \xrightarrow{AlCl_3} \ CH_3OC_6H_4\overset{O}{\overset{\|}{C}}CH_3$$

Naphthalene gave a mixture of 1- and 2-naphthylmethyl ketones (81). Acetyl ketene gave a low (10%) yield of benzoylacetone when treated with benzene and aluminum chloride (64).

Methyl vinyl ketone reacts with benzene, toluene, phenol, anisole, thiophene, furans, and pyrrole to give β-substituted ketones as final products (1,7,221).   Phenol, for example, afforded *p*-hydroxybenzylacetone.

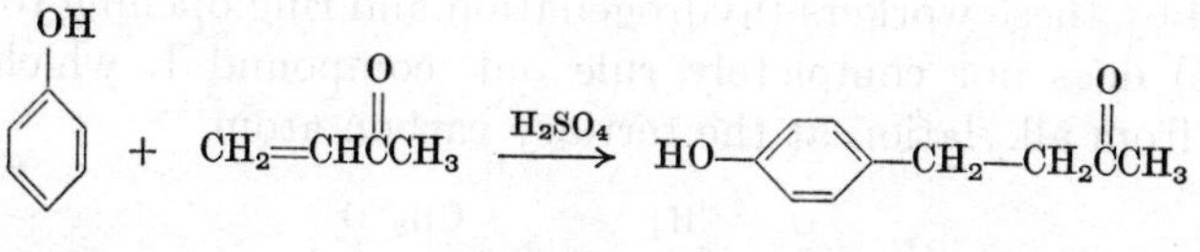

$$\underset{}{\overset{OH}{\bigodot}} \ + \ CH_2{=}CHC\overset{O}{\overset{\|}{C}}CH_3 \ \xrightarrow{H_2SO_4} \ HO{-}\bigodot{-}CH_2{-}CH_2\overset{O}{\overset{\|}{C}}CH_3$$

Aniline, *p*-toluidine, or *p*-anisidine (as the hydrochlorides) undergo cyclization under the conditions necessary to effect a condensation (33).

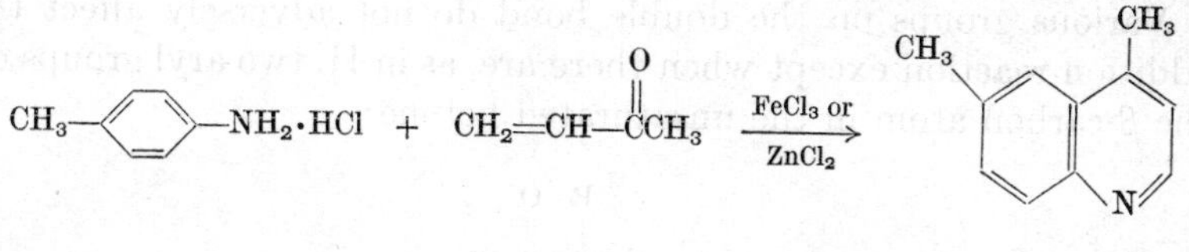

$$CH_3{-}\bigodot{-}NH_2{\cdot}HCl \ + \ CH_2{=}CH{-}\overset{O}{\overset{\|}{C}}CH_3 \ \xrightarrow[ZnCl_2]{FeCl_3 \ or}$$

A study of the effect of various protonic acid catalysts on the reaction of 2-methylfuran with methyl vinyl ketone has been made (1).   The product in all instances was 5-methylfurfurylacetone.

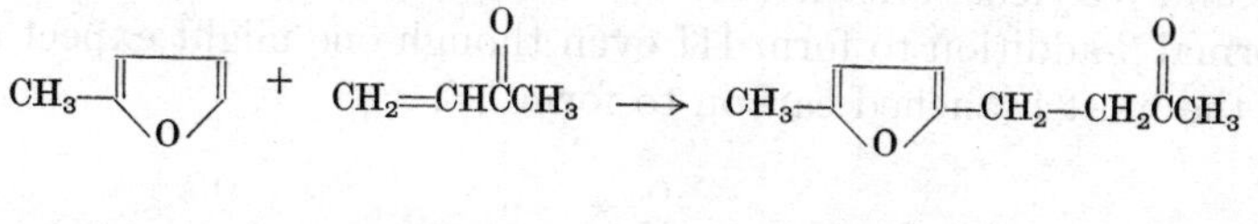

$$CH_3{-}\overset{}{\underset{O}{\bigcirc}} \ + \ CH_2{=}CHC\overset{O}{\overset{\|}{C}}CH_3 \ \longrightarrow \ CH_3{-}\overset{}{\underset{O}{\bigcirc}}{-}CH_2{-}CH_2\overset{O}{\overset{\|}{C}}CH_3$$

Traces of saturated aqueous sulfur dioxide or sulfuric acid gave 40–65% yields (1,232).   When the blocking methyl group was not present a dialkylated product was formed (1,221).

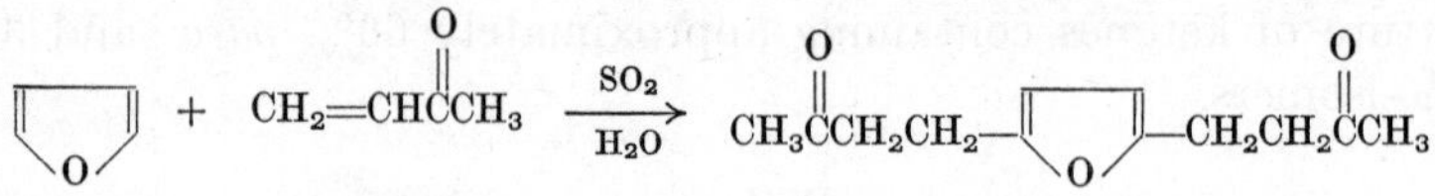

$$\text{(furan)} + CH_2{=}CHCCH_3 \xrightarrow[H_2O]{SO_2} CH_3CCH_2CH_2{-}\text{(furan)}{-}CH_2CH_2CCH_3$$

Pyrrole gave an excellent yield (80%) of 2,5-bis-(3-oxobutyl)pyrrole.

Furan has been dialkylated with vinyl β,β-dimethylvinyl ketone (132).

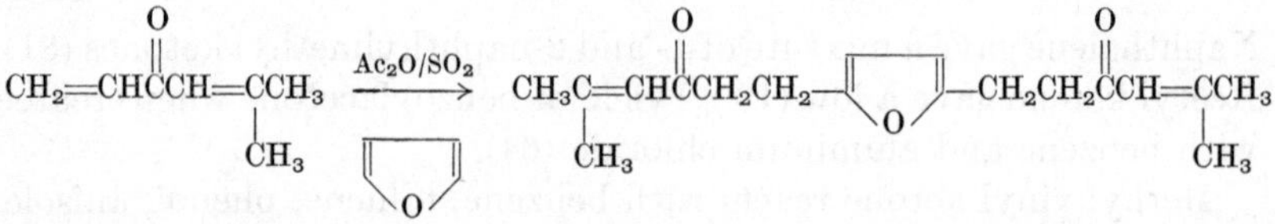

$$CH_2{=}CHCCH{=}CCH_3 \xrightarrow{Ac_2O/SO_2} CH_3C{=}CHCCH_2CH_2{-}\text{(furan)}{-}CH_2CH_2CCH{=}CCH_3$$

It is interesting that reaction occurs only at the unsubstituted vinyl group, especially in view of the many reported alkylations with mesityl oxide. In the opinion of the reviewers the structure proof offered by these workers (hydrogenation and ring opening to a tetraketone) does not completely rule out compound I, which would result from alkylation at the tertiary carbon atom.

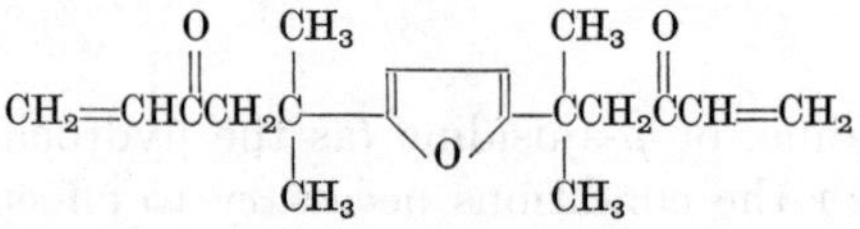

$$CH_2{=}CHCCH_2C{-}\text{(furan)}{-}CCH_2CCH{=}CH_2$$

(I)

Various groups on the double bond do not adversely affect the addition reaction except when there are, as in II, two aryl groups on the β-carbon atom in the unsaturated ketone:

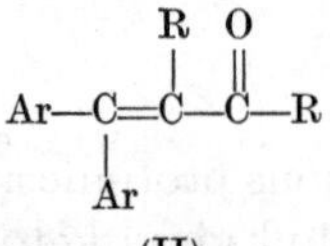

$$Ar{-}C{=}C{-}C{-}R$$

(II)

Condensation of 3-methyl-3-buten-2-one with benzene, toluene, m- and p-xylene, anisole (41,42), and 2-methylfuran (109) results in normal β-addition to form III even though one might expect attack at the most branched carbon to form IV.

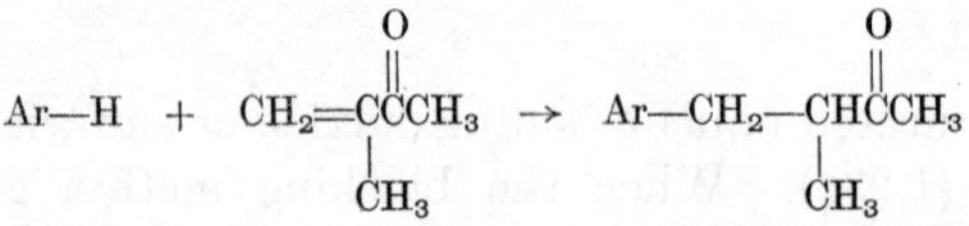

$$Ar{-}H + CH_2{=}CCCH_3 \rightarrow Ar{-}CH_2{-}CHCCH_3$$

(III)

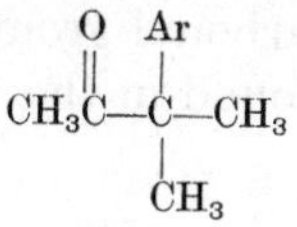

$$\underset{(IV)}{CH_3\overset{\overset{O}{\|}}{C}-\overset{\overset{Ar}{|}}{\underset{\underset{CH_3}{|}}{C}}-CH_3}$$

Similar behavior was observed in condensations with 3-methyl-3-penten-2-one (41).

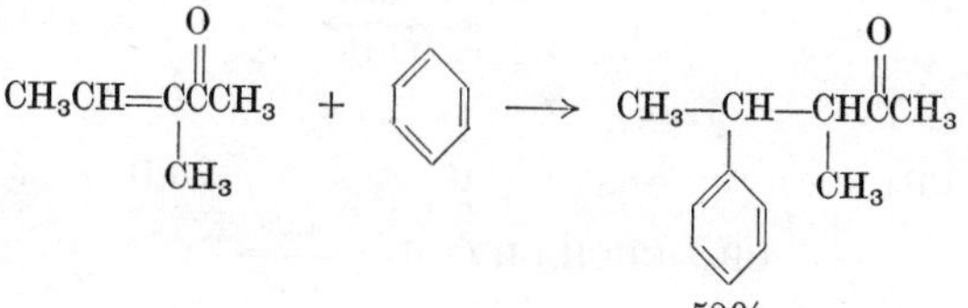

$$\underset{\underset{CH_3}{|}}{CH_3CH=}\overset{\overset{O}{\|}}{C}CH_3 \ + \ \bigcirc \longrightarrow CH_3-\underset{\bigcirc}{CH}-\underset{\underset{CH_3}{|}}{CH}\overset{\overset{O}{\|}}{C}CH_3$$

58%

Also, 3-penten-2-one yields the expected addition products with benzene, toluene, and 2-methylfuran (41,109).

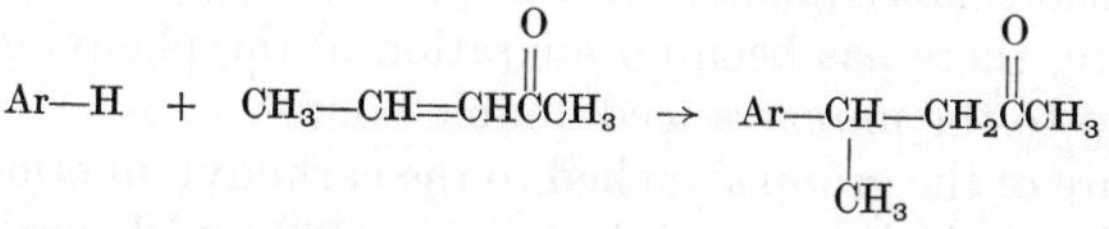

$$Ar-H \ + \ CH_3-CH=CH\overset{\overset{O}{\|}}{C}CH_3 \ \rightarrow \ Ar-\underset{\underset{CH_3}{|}}{CH}-CH_2\overset{\overset{O}{\|}}{C}CH_3$$

(V)

It is interesting to note that with benzene, the yield of V could be noticeably increased (from 25 to 74%) if the catalyst (aluminum chloride) was promoted by addition of hydrogen chloride (41).

2-Cyclohexen-1-one and benzene gave phenylcyclohexanone (41). The yield of this product was improved (from 5% to 45%) by preliminary treatment of the ketone with hydrogen chloride prior to reaction with benzene and aluminum chloride.

Mesityl oxide has been extensively used in addition reactions. The addition of an aromatic occurred normally with benzene (41,228), toluene (87), the halobenzenes (47), and furan derivatives (109). With benzene, 4-methyl-4-phenyl-2-pentanone was formed in 25-31% yield when the reaction temperature was varied in ten-degree increments from 0-30°. With a more active aromatic nucleus, cyclized products were frequently found. The higher methyl benzenes gave substituted indenes (42,191) and phenols yielded substituted chromanols (140).

An unsaturated ketone having an isolated double bond gives the product resulting from a normal olefin alkylation unaffected by any

directive influence of the carbonyl group.   A few specific examples
are shown; others may be found in the Appendix.

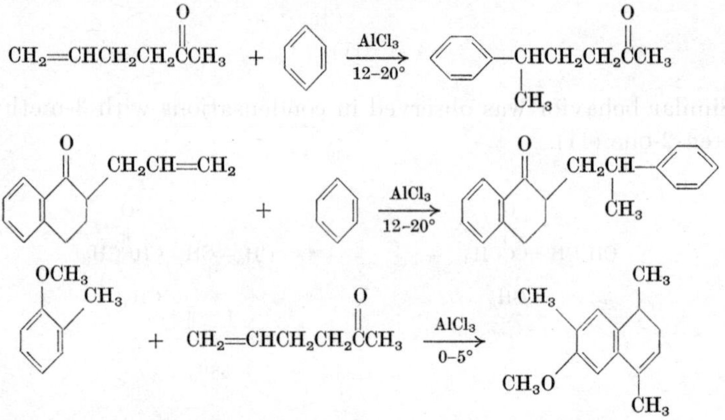

It is noteworthy that in these examples there has been no migration
of the double bond to the conjugated position which would give rise
to substitution subsequently at the position *beta* to the carbonyl.
Furthermore, there has been no migration of the phenyl group once
it has added to the unrearranged double bond.

The nature of the group attached to the carbonyl function does not
appear to be critical.   Benzalpinacolone (223) and benzalmenthone
(219) treated with benzene and aluminum chloride gave normal
addition products.

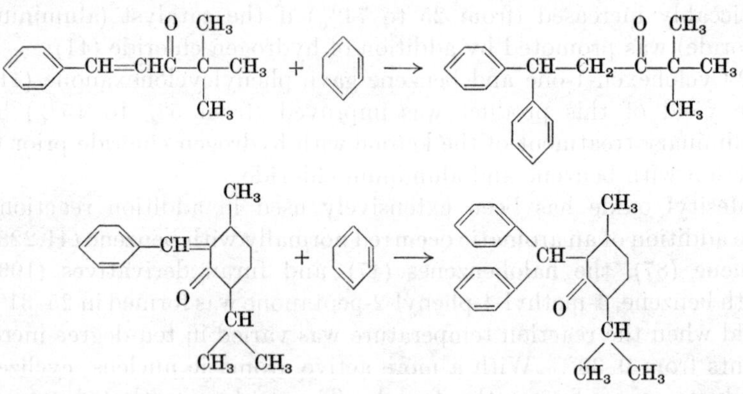

However, not much work has been done on the effect of this structure
variation.

Alkylation with phorone is a logical extension of the work with
mesityl oxide.   The addition reactions of phorone take place at both

double bonds to give diaryldimethylheptanone derivatives, as shown in equations 1 and 2.

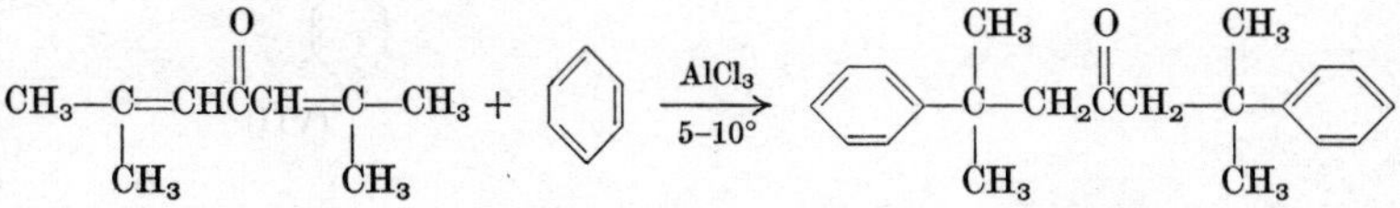

(Ref. 42)

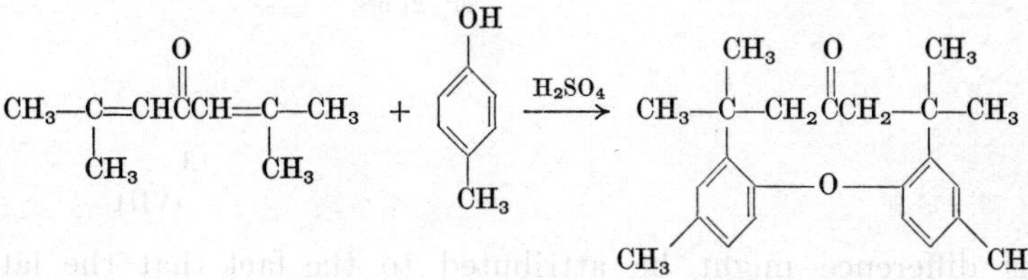

(Ref. 142a)

No instance of substitution (replacement) reactions with phorone type compounds has been reported.

Compounds of the general type represented by VI represent an intermediate class. For example, the reaction of benzalaceto-phenone and chlorobenzene proceeded *via* addition at short contact times, but substitution occurred when the reaction time was prolonged (51).

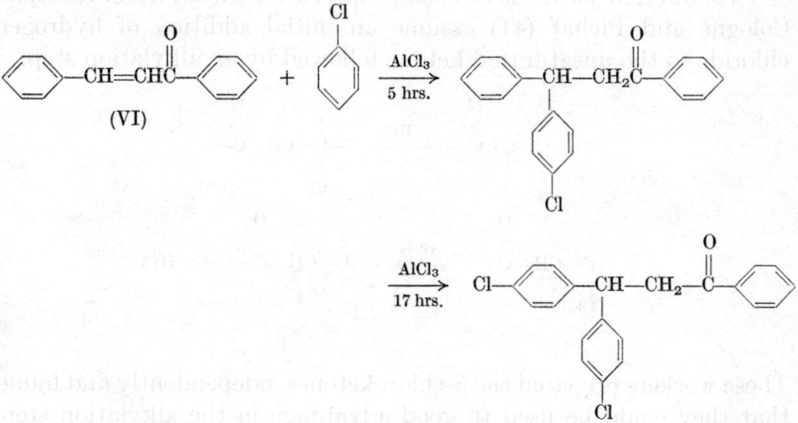

Conflicting reports are found in the case of *m*-chlorobenzalaceto-phenone. Fuson *et al.* (56) report substitution with benzene yielding VII while Dippy and Palluel (51) isolated an addition product (VIII).

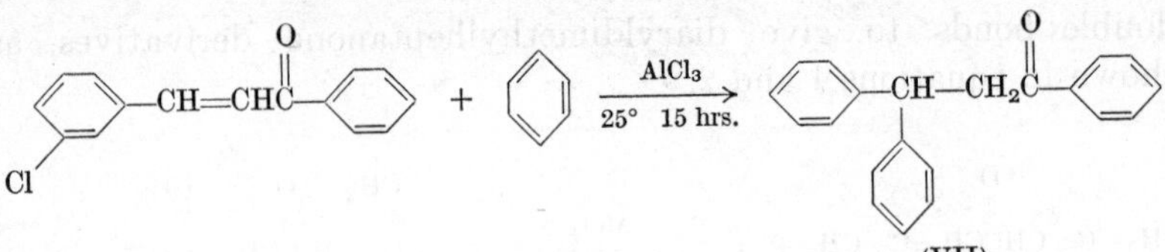

(VII)

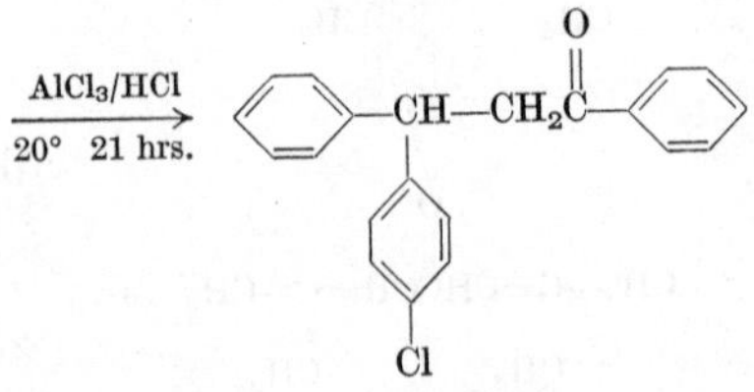

(VIII)

This difference might be attributed to the fact that the latter added hydrogen chloride to their catalyst. But this explanation is undermined by the fact that the reaction of p-chlorobenzalacetone with aluminum chloride–hydrogen chloride results in replacement of the p-chlorophenyl group (229).

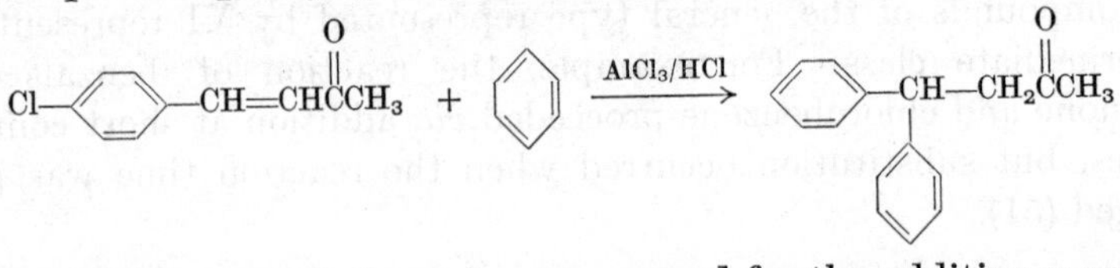

Two different paths have been proposed for the addition reaction. Cologne and Pichat (41) assume an initial addition of hydrogen chloride to the unsaturated ketone followed by an alkylation step.

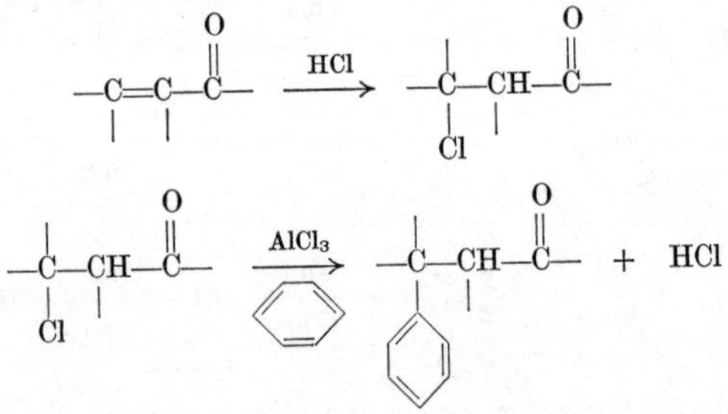

These workers prepared the β-chloroketones independently and found that they could be used to good advantage in the alkylation step. As Dippy et al. point out, however, this does not prove that a β-chloroketone is necessarily an intermediate.

Dippy and Palluel (51) proposed the route outlined in equations 3–7.

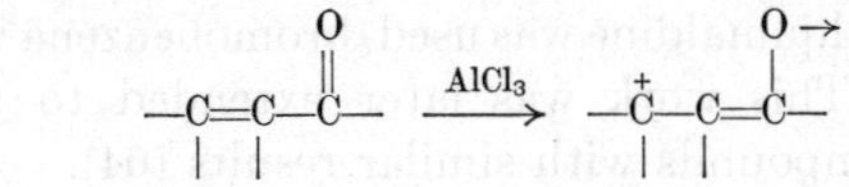

$$\underset{\substack{|\\ \end{}}{-C}=\underset{}{C}-\overset{O}{\underset{}{\overset{\|}{C}}}- \xrightarrow{AlCl_3} -\overset{+}{\underset{}{C}}-C=\overset{O \rightarrow AlCl_3^-}{\underset{}{C}}- \tag{3}$$

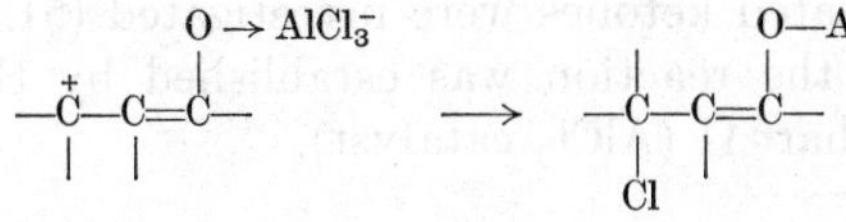

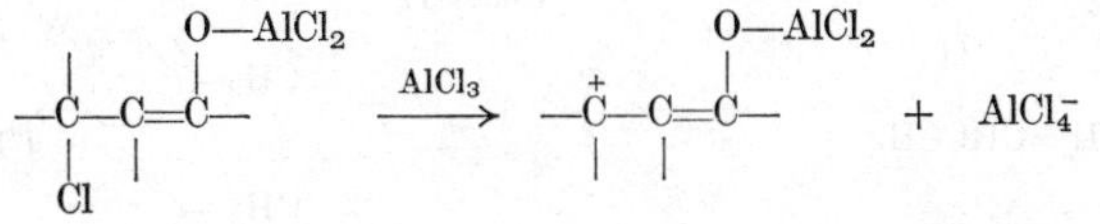

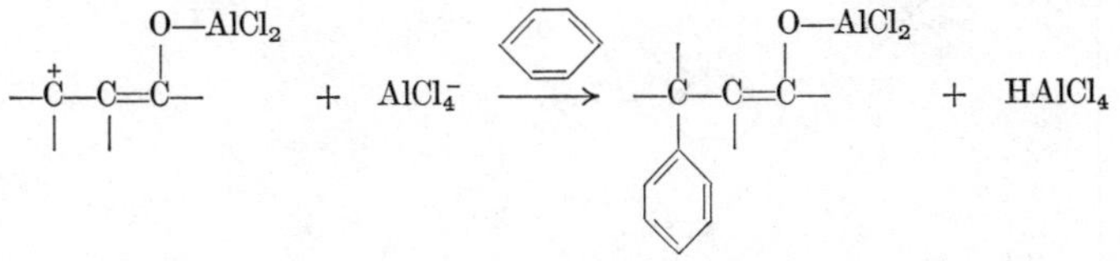

$$-\overset{+}{\underset{}{C}}-\underset{}{C}=\overset{O \rightarrow AlCl_3^-}{\underset{}{C}}- \longrightarrow -\underset{\substack{|\\ Cl}}{C}-C=\overset{O—AlCl_2}{\underset{}{C}}- \tag{4}$$

$$-\underset{\substack{|\\ Cl}}{\overset{O—AlCl_2}{C}}-C=C- \xrightarrow{AlCl_3} -\overset{+}{\underset{}{C}}-C=\overset{O—AlCl_2}{\underset{}{C}}- + AlCl_4^- \tag{5}$$

$$-\overset{+}{\underset{}{C}}-C=C- + AlCl_4^- \;\;\;\longrightarrow\;\;\; -\underset{\substack{|\\ C_6H_5}}{C}-C=\overset{O—AlCl_2}{\underset{}{C}}- + HAlCl_4 \tag{6}$$

$$-\underset{\substack{|\\ C_6H_5}}{C}-C=\overset{O—AlCl_2}{\underset{}{C}}- + HAlCl_4 \longrightarrow -\underset{\substack{|\\ C_6H_5}}{C}-CH-\overset{O}{\underset{}{\overset{\|}{C}}}- + 2AlCl_3 \tag{7}$$

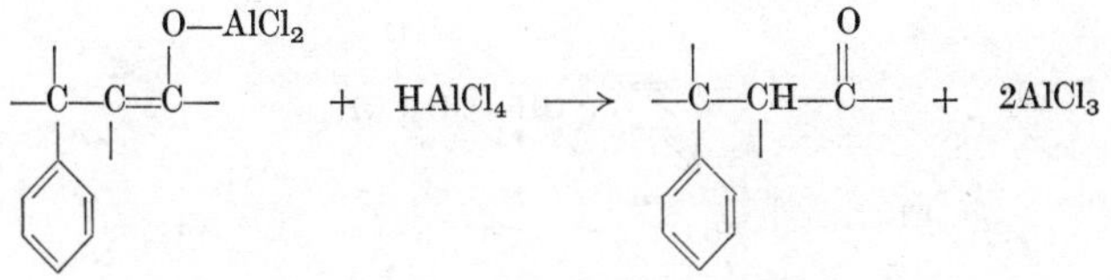

This route adequately accounts for the fact that (a) the optimum aluminum chloride/ketone ratio was 2/2.5; (b) added hydrogen chloride was unnecessary in most cases; (c) stannic chloride (a weaker electron acceptor) was ineffective as a catalyst; and (d) a 1 : 1 aluminum chloride–ketone complex was isolated in one instance and would undergo alkylation only upon addition of another mole of aluminum chloride.

This seems to be the most acceptable version of the path by which the reaction proceeds.

2. Replacement

Many instances of replacement of one aryl group by another have been noted. Fuson *et al.* initially reported the replacement of aromatic nuclei from benzalquinaldine derivatives (66a,80).

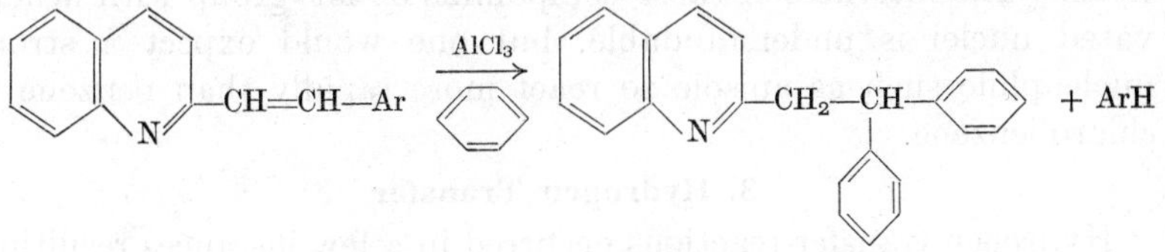

$$Ar = C_6H_5,\ p\text{-}ClC_6H_4,\ p\text{-}BrC_6H_4,\ m\text{-}BrC_6H_4$$

When p-bromobenzalquinaldine was used, bromobenzene was isolated from the solvent. This work was later extended to the benzal-lepidine series of compounds with similar results (64).

Later, α,β-unsaturated ketones were investigated (51,56,223) and the reversibility of the reaction was established by the series of reactions shown in Chart II ($AlCl_3$ catalyst).

Chart II

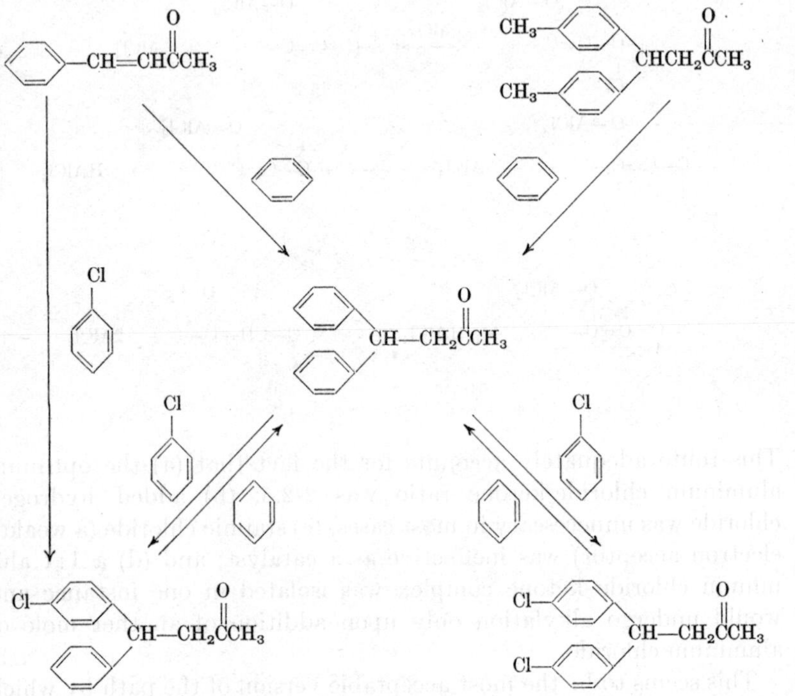

Similar replacement reactions were performed with acetophenone and pinacolone derivatives (51,223).

Dippy and Palluel (51) stated that anisole, nitrobenzene, ethyl-benzoate, or pyridine do not undergo the addition reaction (or presumably replacement) under their standardized reaction conditions. The inertness of those compounds of this group with deactivated nuclei is understandable, but one would expect a strong nucleophile such as anisole to react more rapidly than benzene or chlorobenzene.

3. Hydrogen Transfer

Hydrogen transfer reactions occurred in a few instances resulting, in effect, in the hydrogenation of the unsaturated feed. This process is observed when there is considerable bulk at the β-carbon of the vinyl group as in 1,1-diphenyl-2-benzoylethylene (2) and 1,1-diphenyl-2-trimethylacetylethylene (64).

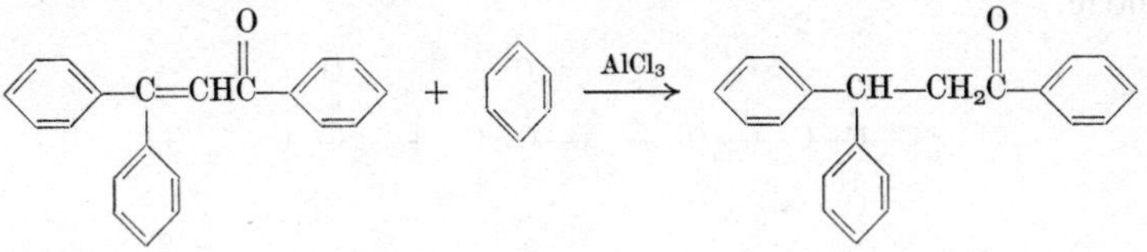

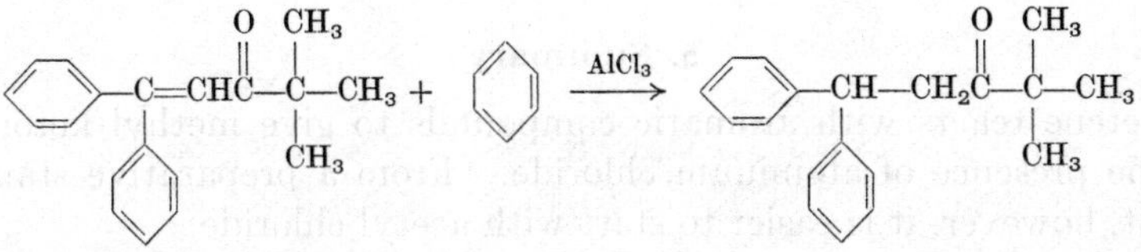

β-Phenylcrotonophenone gave products resulting both from addition and hydrogen transfer (51).

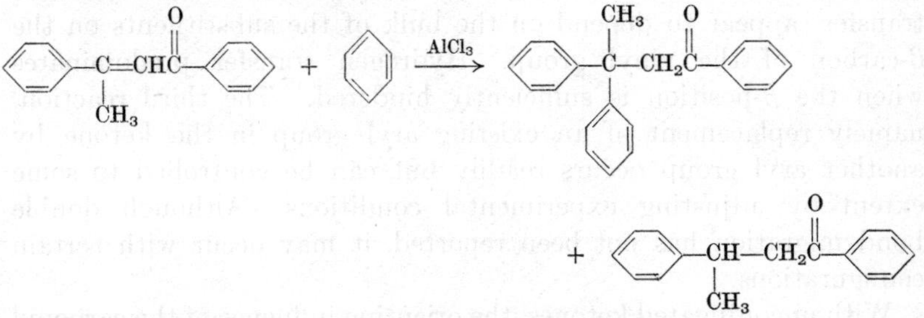

4. Miscellaneous Reactions

In the presence of hydrogen fluoride the reaction of mesityl oxide with benzene or toluene (151) resulted in an unexpected cleavage of the mesityl oxide. The major product was a t-butyl substituted aromatic. Toluene also afforded a methyl ketone.

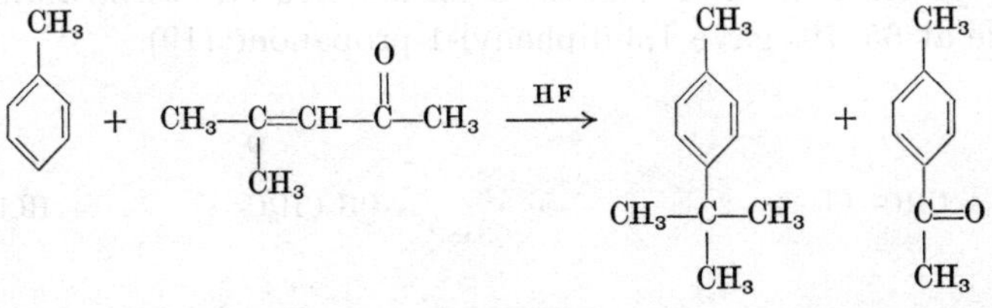

A zinc chloride promoted alumina catalyst gave similar products in the vapor-phase alkylation of benzene with mesityl oxide (167). t-Butylbenzene was formed in 26% yield together with polyalkylated benzenes and acetic acid.

These products can be explained by assuming cleavage of the intermediate carbonium ion to form isobutylene and an acetyl cation, followed by subsequent reaction of these fragments with the aromatic.

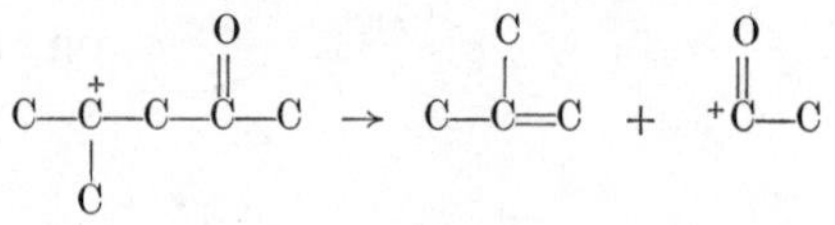

$$
\underset{\underset{C}{\overset{|}{\underset{\quad}{}}}{C-\overset{+}{C}-C-\overset{\overset{O}{\parallel}}{C}-C} \;\rightarrow\; C-\overset{\overset{C}{|}}{C}{=}C \;+\; \overset{+}{C}-\overset{\overset{O}{\parallel}}{C}
$$

5. Summary

Ketene reacts with aromatic compounds to give methyl ketones in the presence of aluminum chloride. From a preparative standpoint, however, it is easier to start with acetyl chloride.

Three reactions have been reported to take place when aluminum chloride, an aromatic, and an α,β-unsaturated ketone are mixed. Two of these reactions, addition to the double bond and hydrogen transfer, appear to depend on the bulk of the substituents on the β-carbon of the vinyl group. Hydrogen transfer predominates when the β-position is sufficiently hindered. The third reaction, namely replacement of an existing aryl group in the ketone by another aryl group occurs readily but can be controlled to some extent by adjusting experimental conditions. Although double bond migration has not been reported, it may occur with certain configurations.

With unconjugated ketones, the orienting influence of the carbonyl group is negligible, and the resulting products are those of normal olefin alkylation.

IX. Unsaturated Acid Chlorides

Acrylyl chloride and excess benzene treated with aluminum chloride at 65–70° gave 1,3-diphenyl-1-propanone (19).

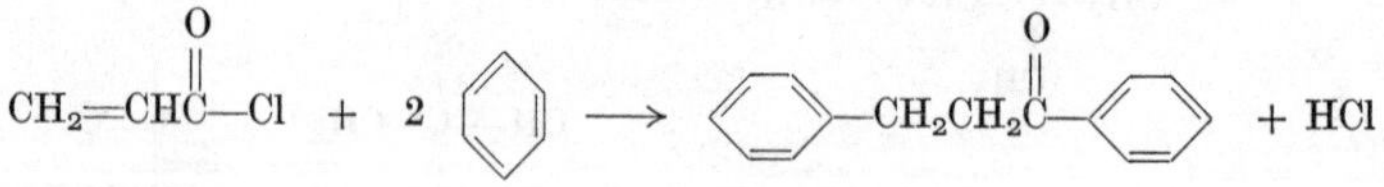

$$
CH_2{=}CH\overset{\overset{O}{\parallel}}{C}{-}Cl \;+\; 2\; \bigcirc \;\longrightarrow\; \bigcirc{-}CH_2CH_2\overset{\overset{O}{\parallel}}{C}\bigcirc \;+\; HCl
$$

Anisole gave the corresponding di-p-methoxy compound (19). The course of the reaction might be assumed to proceed via acylation followed by addition of a second mole of aromatic to the resulting α,β-unsaturated ketone system. This assumption is supported by the fact that at a lower temperature the reaction of crotonyl chloride with benzene yielded 1-phenyl-2-buten-1-one (101).

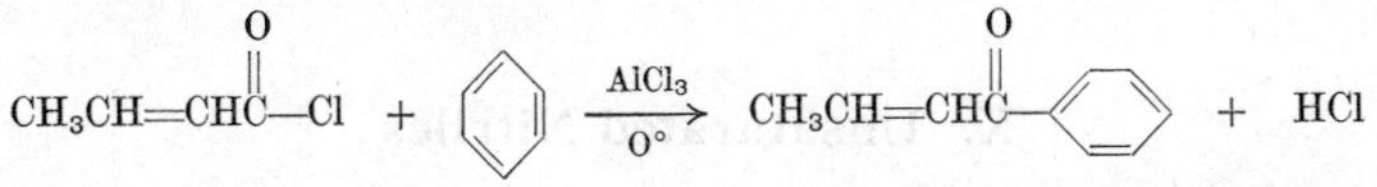

$$CH_3CH{=}CH\overset{\overset{\textstyle O}{\|}}{C}{-}Cl \;+\; \bigcirc \;\xrightarrow[0°]{AlCl_3}\; CH_3CH{=}CH\overset{\overset{\textstyle O}{\|}}{C}{-}\bigcirc \;+\; HCl$$

Pseudocumene did not undergo addition to the double bond of β,β-dimethylacryloyl chloride in the presence of aluminum chloride (191). This may be attributed to steric effects, since the addition would introduce a t-group ortho to a methyl group. Reaction occurred only at the more reactive acid chloride site.

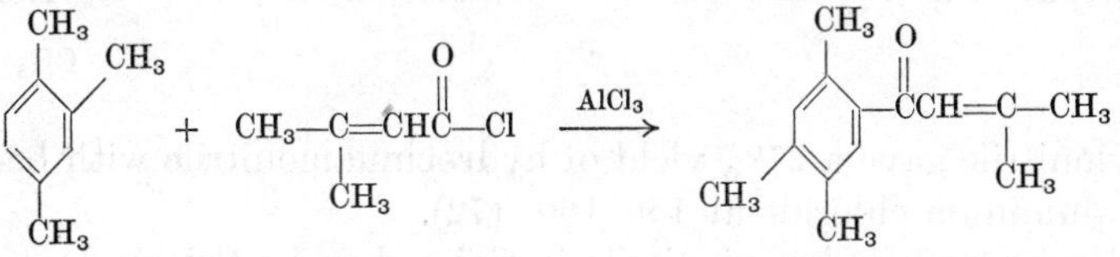

$$\text{(pseudocumene)} \;+\; CH_3{-}\underset{\underset{\textstyle CH_3}{|}}{C}{=}CH\overset{\overset{\textstyle O}{\|}}{C}{-}Cl \;\xrightarrow{AlCl_3}\; \text{(product)}$$

Cinnamoyl chloride apparently can react initially at either the double bond or the acid chloride group. β-Chloro-β-phenylpropiophenone (102) and β,β-diphenylpropionic acid (119) have been isolated as well as the expected β,β-diphenylpropiophenone.

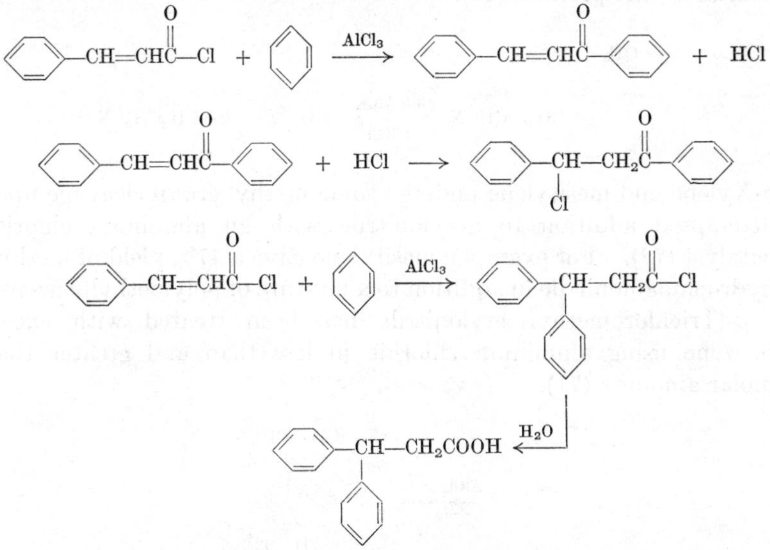

$$\bigcirc{-}CH{=}CH\overset{\overset{\textstyle O}{\|}}{C}{-}Cl \;+\; \bigcirc \;\xrightarrow{AlCl_3}\; \bigcirc{-}CH{=}CH\overset{\overset{\textstyle O}{\|}}{C}{-}\bigcirc \;+\; HCl$$

$$\bigcirc{-}CH{=}CH\overset{\overset{\textstyle O}{\|}}{C}{-}\bigcirc \;+\; HCl \;\longrightarrow\; \bigcirc{-}\underset{\underset{\textstyle Cl}{|}}{CH}{-}CH_2\overset{\overset{\textstyle O}{\|}}{C}{-}\bigcirc$$

$$\bigcirc{-}CH{=}CH\overset{\overset{\textstyle O}{\|}}{C}{-}Cl \;+\; \bigcirc \;\xrightarrow{AlCl_3}\; \bigcirc{-}\underset{\underset{\textstyle \bigcirc}{|}}{CH}{-}CH_2\overset{\overset{\textstyle O}{\|}}{C}{-}Cl$$

$$\bigcirc{-}\underset{\underset{\textstyle \bigcirc}{|}}{CH}{-}CH_2COOH \;\xleftarrow{H_2O}\;$$

This reaction has also been reported (102) to yield a cyclized product (3-phenyl-1-indanone). Attempted addition of bromobenzene to the double bond in cinnamoyl chloride resulted in cyclization (to an indanone) and formation of benzal-p-bromoacetophenone (102).

3-Methyl-2-butenoyl chloride and *m*-xylene gave a cyclialkylated product, 3,3,5,7-tetramethyl indanone, in 58% yield (42).

X. Unsaturated Nitriles

A mixture of β- and γ-phenylbutyronitriles was obtained when 3-butenonitrile and benzene were contacted in the presence of aluminum chloride (58).

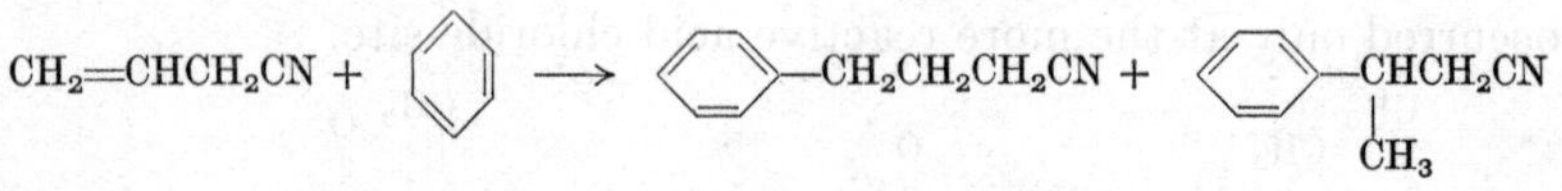

$$CH_2{=}CHCH_2CN + \underset{}{\bigcirc} \longrightarrow \underset{}{\bigcirc}{-}CH_2CH_2CH_2CN + \underset{}{\bigcirc}{-}\underset{\underset{CH_3}{|}}{CH}CH_2CN$$

Acrylonitrile gave a 27% yield of hydrocinnamonitrile with benzene and aluminum chloride at 150–160° (72).

o-Hydroxyphenylpropionitrile is claimed to be the product when phenol and acrylonitrile were treated with a catalyst having an aluminum chloride/hydrogen chloride mole ratio of 0.5/1. When this ratio was increased to 3.5/1, *p*-hydroxyphenylpropionitrile is said to be the product (91).

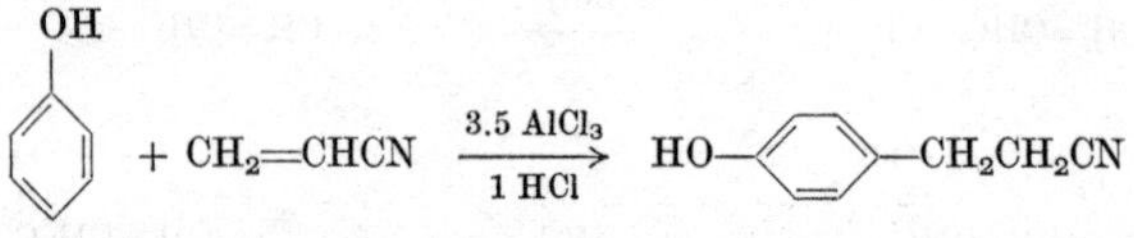

$$\underset{}{\overset{OH}{\bigcirc}} + CH_2{=}CHCN \xrightarrow[\text{1 HCl}]{\text{3.5 AlCl}_3} HO{-}\underset{}{\bigcirc}{-}CH_2CH_2CN$$

o-Xylene and mesitylene undergo some methyl group cleavage upon attempted addition to acrylonitrile with an aluminum chloride catalyst (72). For example, mesitylene gave a 47% yield of methyl-hydrocinnamonitrile in addition to a mixture of polymethylbenzenes.

β-(Trichloromethyl)acrylonitrile has been treated with excess benzene using aluminum chloride in less than and greater than molar amounts (71).

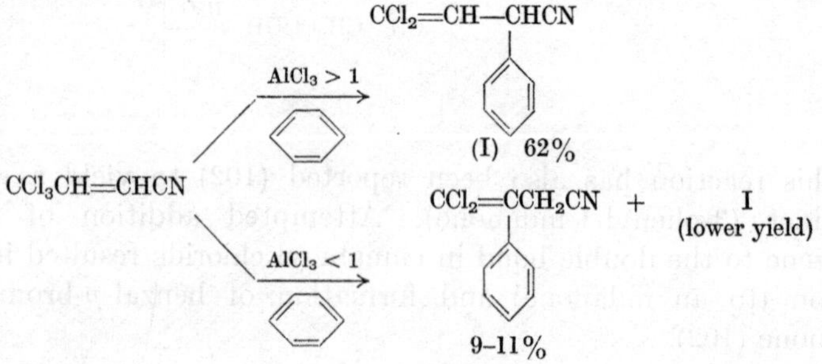

On the basis of Kundiger's work (108a) with trichloro-2-methyl propanol, the formation of these products could be explained by a prior rearrangement to II and III followed by alkylation.

$$CCl_3CH{=}CHCN \xrightarrow{H^+} CCl_2{=}CCH_2CN + CCl_2{=}CH{-}CHCN$$

$$\underset{(II)}{\underset{\mid}{Cl}} \qquad\qquad \underset{(III)}{\underset{\mid}{Cl}}$$

XI. Miscellaneous Unsaturated Alkylating Agents

N-Allylacetamide has been found to undergo β-addition with benzene or toluene (162) in the presence of aluminum chloride. Good yields (66–80%) of β-arylpropylamine derivatives were obtained.

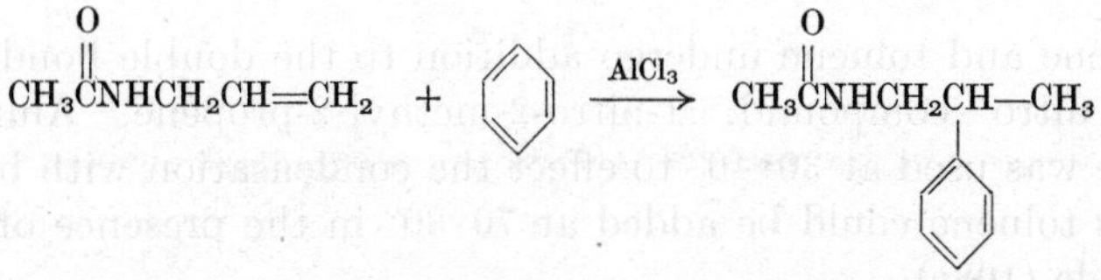

$$CH_3\overset{O}{\overset{\|}{C}}NHCH_2CH{=}CH_2 + \langle\text{benzene}\rangle \xrightarrow{AlCl_3} CH_3\overset{O}{\overset{\|}{C}}NHCH_2CH{-}CH_3$$

The addition of aromatics to α,β-unsaturated sulfones was found by Truce *et al.* to be catalyzed by sulfuric acid (203).

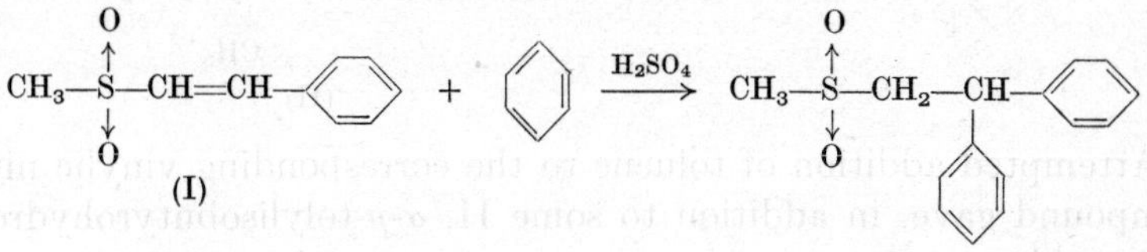

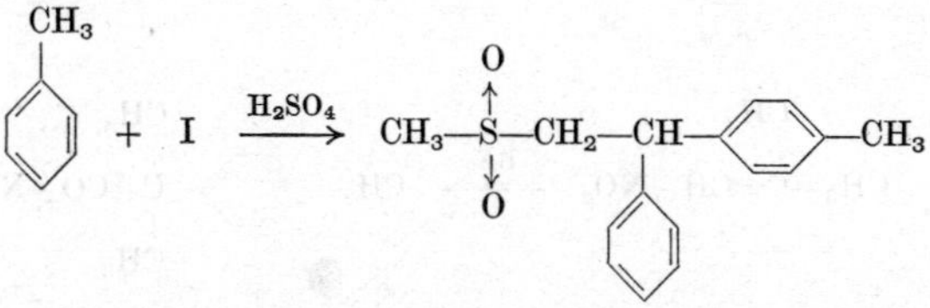

$$CH_3{-}\overset{\uparrow}{\underset{\downarrow}{\overset{O}{\underset{O}{S}}}}{-}CH{=}CH{-}\langle\text{Ph}\rangle + \langle\text{Ph}\rangle \xrightarrow{H_2SO_4} CH_3{-}\overset{\uparrow}{\underset{\downarrow}{\overset{O}{\underset{O}{S}}}}{-}CH_2{-}CH{-}\langle\text{Ph}\rangle$$

(I)

$$\langle\text{CH}_3\text{-Ph}\rangle + I \xrightarrow{H_2SO_4} CH_3{-}\overset{\uparrow}{\underset{\downarrow}{\overset{O}{\underset{O}{S}}}}{-}CH_2{-}CH{-}\langle\text{Ph-CH}_3\rangle$$

It is interesting to note that replacement was not reported in this latter reaction and also that aluminum chloride was not an effective catalyst. Methyl vinyl sulfone did not alkylate benzene or its homologs.

Archer, Malkemus, and Suter (8b) found that alkylbenzenes could be alkylated with sodium 2-methyl-2-propenesulfonate in the presence of sulfuric acid at 0°. Yields were much improved by using boron fluoride–sulfuric acid as catalyst and ethylene chloride as solvent.

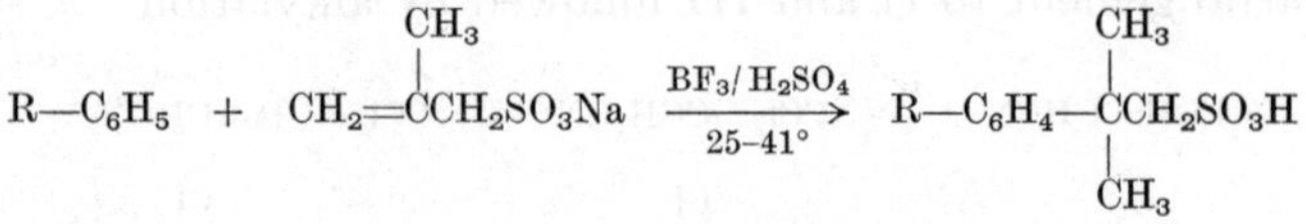

$$R-C_6H_5 \ + \ CH_2{=}\overset{\overset{\displaystyle CH_3}{|}}{C}CH_2SO_3Na \ \xrightarrow[25-41°]{BF_3/H_2SO_4} \ R-C_6H_4-\overset{\overset{\displaystyle CH_3}{|}}{\underset{\underset{\displaystyle CH_3}{|}}{C}}CH_2SO_3H$$

Angelicalactone yields 4,4-diphenylpentanoic acid upon prolonged treatment with benzene and aluminum chloride (58).

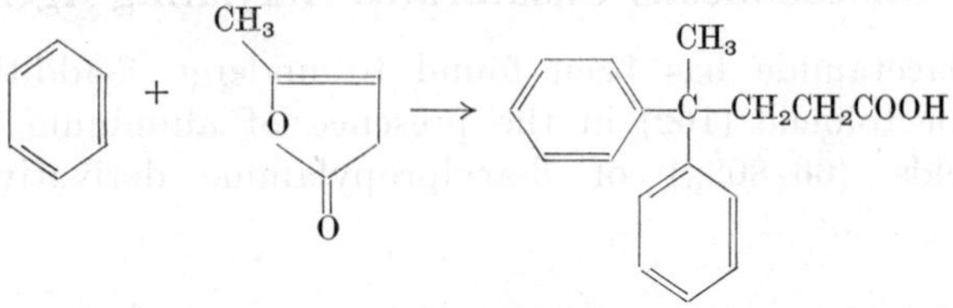

Benzene and toluene undergo addition to the double bond of the allylic nitro compound, 1-nitro-2-methyl-2-propene. Aluminum chloride was used at 30–40° to effect the condensation with benzene whereas toluene could be added at 70–80° in the presence of boron trifluoride (108c).

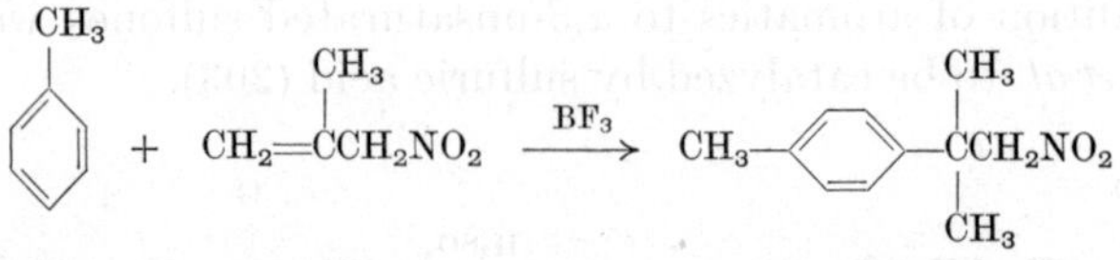

(II)

Attempted addition of toluene to the corresponding vinylic nitro compound gave, in addition to some II, α-p-tolylisobutyrohydroxamic acid.

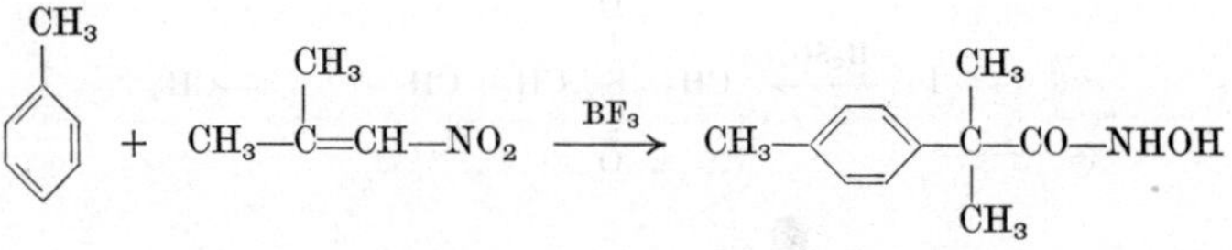

XII. Appendix

TABLE I.   Benzene with dienes

Benzene (Moles)	Diene (Moles)	Catalyst (Moles)	Temp. (°C)	Time (hrs.)	Products (% Yield)	Ref.
—	Butadiene	$AlCl_3$	—	—	Resin and low mol. wt. condensation product	124a
8	1,3-Butadiene (1)	$ZnCl_2$–Al_2O_3(25/75)	225 40 atm.	2 L.H.S.V.	Phenylbutenes (50%)ᵃ	164
4	Butadiene (150 g.)	BF_3–H_2O(1/1.5) 50 cc.	29–35	10	Phenylbutenes (85%)	30
2.8	Butadiene (1.55)	BF_3–CH_3OH (20 g.)	31–33	c	Phenylbutenes (190 g.)	172(11a)
8.5	Butadiene (1)	BF_3–HOAc	30–40	—	Phenylbutene (63%)ᵃ	11a
4	Butadiene (2)	BF_3–H_3PO_4 (50 cc.)	30	—	Phenylbutenes (80%)ᵃ	11(12a)
156 g.	Butadiene (20 g.)	H_2SO_4 (50.2 g.)	0–5	1.5	1,2-Diphenylbutane (14%)	87a
39.8	Butadiene (13.8)	Mixed alkanesulfonic acid (95%) (396 g.)	30	b	1-Phenyl-2-butene (23%), dibutenylbenzene (17%), tributenylbenzene (40%)	160
—	1,3-Butadiene	95% H_3PO_4	—	—	Butenylbenzenes (four isomers, mostly 1,4-addition) (60%)	125
4.5	Butadiene (1)	Silicophosphoric acid (50 g.)	216 27 atm.	4.8 L.H.S.V.	Phenylbutenes (50%)ᵃ, 1,4-dibutenylbenzene (some)	87b(88)
9.25	Butadiene (2.5)	HF (15.5)	5–20	3.25	1,4-dibutenylbenzene (59%)	87a
10	4-Vinyl-1-cyclohexene(1)	BF_3–H_2O(1/1) (5%)	16–23	1.7	1,2,3,4,4a,9,10,10a-Octahydrophenanthrene (about 36 g.)	187
10	4-Vinyl-1-cyclohexene(1)	47% BF_3–HF–H_2O (5%)	12–28	2	1,2,3,4,4a,9,10,10a-Octahydrophenanthrene (38.5 g.)	187
10	4-Vinyl-1-cyclohexene(1)	Superfiltrol	149–163 850 psig.	0.5 S.V.	1,2,3,4,4a,9,10,10a-Octahydrophenanthrene (about 72 g.)	187
150 ml.	Piperylene (49.2 g.)	BF_3–CH_3OH (10 ml.)	31–33	—	p-Tolylpentene (60%)ᵃ	11a

ᵃ Of alkylenate.   ᵇ Butadiene rate = 5160 ml./hr.   ᶜ Butadiene rate = 86 ml./min.

TABLE II. Higher aromatic hydrocarbons with dienes

Aromatic (Moles)	Diene (Moles)	Catalyst (Moles)	Temp. (°C)	Time (hrs.)	Products (% Yield)	Ref.
Toluene (1147 g.)	Butadiene (216 g.)	SiCl$_4$ (46.4 g.) SiO$_2$-Al$_2$O$_3$ (27 g.)	115	4.8	Alkylate (498 g.), monoalkenylated toluene (166 g.)	68
Toluene (100 cc.)	Butadiene (35.5 g.)	95% Alkane-SO$_3$H (25 cc.)	90–140	0.5[b]	Monobutenyltoluene and ditolylbutanes (92 cc.)	160
Toluene	1,3-Butadiene	95% H$_3$PO$_4$	—	—	o- and p-Butenyltoluene (mostly 1,4 addition)	125
Toluene	Piperylene	BF$_3$–H$_2$O	90–95	10	1-(p-Tolyl)-2-pentene (60%)[a]	10
Toluene (3)	Piperylene (1)	BF$_3$–H$_3$PO$_4$ (100 ml.)	30	—	1-(p-Tolyl)-2-pentene (60%)[a]	12a
Toluene	Piperylene	BF$_3$–CH$_3$COOH	25	—	1-(p-Tolyl)-2-pentene (60%)[a]	11a
p-Xylene (88)	Butadiene (16.1)	95% Alkane-SO$_3$H	< 30	—	1-(2,5-Dimethylphenyl)-2-butene (54%)	160
Xylene	Butadiene	95% H$_3$PO$_4$ (396 g.)	—	—	Butenylxylenes (mostly 1,4-addition)	125
Cumene (10)	4-Vinyl-1-cyclohexene (1)	HF-BF$_3$–H$_2$O (5%)	16–18	1.1	Isopropyloctahydrophenanthrene	187
1-Methylnaphthalene (861 g.)	Butadiene (170 g.)	EtSO$_3$H (55.5 g.)	20–28	3	Butenylmethylnaphthalenes (mono- 30%, di- 16%), high boilers (14%)	160
2-Methylnaphthalene (6.1)	Butadiene (2.9)	EtSO$_3$H	—	—	Butenyl-2-methylnaphthalene (31%)	160
Naphthalene (30 g.)	Butadiene (5 psig.)	Al(iso-C$_4$H$_9$)$_3$ (1 g.) SiCl$_4$ (6.7 g.)	106	0.5	Butenylnaphthalene and polymer	69

[a] Of alkenylate.   [b] Additional stirring.

TABLE III. Phenol with dienes

Phenol (Moles)	Diene (Moles)	Catalyst (Moles)	Temp. (°C)	Time (hrs.)	Products (% Yield)	Ref.
1	Butadiene (8)	CH_3SO_3H (10 g.) or $AlCl_3$ (20 g.)	10–22	20	Butenyl ether of butenylphenol (112 g., 97 g.),[f] bis(butenyloxyphenol)butane and its butenyl ether (36 g., 32 g.)[a,f]	36
—	1,3-Butadiene	H_3PO_4 (at 140°), BF_3, BF_3–H_3PO_4, $AlCl_3$ or H_2SO_4	—	—	Largely higher phenols, ethers, and resins	16
—	1,3-Butadiene	$ZnCl_2$ or 85% H_3PO_4	10–40	—	Inactive	16
—	1,3-Butadiene	Polyphosphoric–H_3PO_4, (2/1) $TiCl_4$, Arene–SO_3H, $AlCl_3$–ROH or $AlCl_3$–ether	—	—	Butenylphenol (fair yield)	16
1	Butadiene (4)	BF_3–Et_2O (115 g.)	10–22	20	Butenyl ether of butenylphenol (115 g.), bis(butenyloxyphenol)butane and its butenyl ether (104 g.)	36
10 (2000 cc. Toluene)	1,3-Butadiene (5)	BF_3–85% H_3PO_4 (100 g.)	r.t.	16	Crotylphenol (89%, o-/p- = 30/48) Ethers (3–6%)[c]	16
1	1,3-Butadiene (1)	85% H_3PO_4 (100 g.) 68% H_2SO_4[d]	15	—	Crotylphenol (70%, o-/p- = 60/30)	16
9.5	Butadiene (4.1)	$EtSO_3H$ (20 g.)	32	—	o- (5%), p- (2-Butenyl)phenol (21%), non-phenolics[g]	8a
9.5	Butadiene (2.64)	95% Alkane-SO_3H (102 g.)	20–25	2.25	Butenylphenol (50%) (o-/p- = 16%/53%[b]; chromanes (15%)	160
1 (1000 cc. Toluene)	1,3-Butadiene (1)	85% H_3PO_4 (100 g.) H_2SO_4 (15 g.)	15–25	16	Crotylphenol (78%, o-/p- = approx. 30/48)	16 (34)
155 pts.	1,3-Butadiene (39 pts.)	P_2O_5-kieselguhr (50 pts.)	200 100 psig.	flow 4 hrs.	Butenylphenol (36%)[e], higher (64%)[e]	160
236 g.	Butadiene (68 g.)	Boric acid–oxalic acid (2 g./9 g.)	150	—	Resin (185 g.)	210a

Table continued

TABLE III (*continued*)

Phenol (Moles)	Diene (Moles)	Catalyst (Moles)	Temp. (°C)	Time (hrs.)	Products (% Yield)	Ref.
50 pts.	Butadiene (54 pts.)	Nickel molybdite (5 pts.)	150	5	Alkylated phenol (unsaturated side chain) (63 pts.)	61
2 (3.3 Benzene)	Piperylene (1)	100% H_3PO_4 (0.25)	20–25 35–40 70–75	16 21 15.5	Liquid[a] (61%), resin (14%) Liquid[a] (78%), resin (20%) Liquid[a,h], resin (36%)	213 213 213
—	Isoprene (17 g.)	$SnCl_4$–EtOH(1/5) (47 g.)	12	2.7	Pentenylphenols (25%), chromans, and coumarans (20%)	156
1	Isoprene (8)	BF_3–Et_2O (5 g.)	15–20	20	3-Methylcrotylphenol (o- 23 g., p- 40 g.), γ-hydroxyisoamylphenol (o- 7 g., p- 10 g.), 2,2-dimethylchroman (10 g.)	36
1.3	Isoprene (1.3)	71% H_3PO_4 (130 g.) (230 g. toluene)	20	16	"Isoprenephenol"	17
93 g.	Isoprene (70 g.)	H_2SO_4–HOAc (2g/10 cc.)	—	—	"Isoprenephenol"	110
47 g.	Isoprene (17 g.)	85% H_3PO_4 (37 g.) (Et_2O 25 g.)	28	3	Pentenylphenols (18%), chromans, and coumarans (13%)	157
47 g.	Isoprene (17 g.)	85% H_3PO_4 (36.8 g.) (Et_2O 25 g.)	25	2	Pentenylphenols (35%)	157
940 g.	Cyclopentadiene (165 g.)	85% H_3PO_4 (6 g.) (toluene 250 cc.)	30 r.t.	3 18	2- and 4-(Δ-2-Cyclopentenyl)phenols (75 g.); dicyclopentenyl- (80 g.), tricyclopentenyl-phenol and higher (67 g.)	158
10 (1500 cc. Toluene)	Cyclopentadiene (5)	85% H_3PO_4	25	18	2-(45 g.), 4-(67%)-Cyclopentenylphenol	14
94 (100 cc. Xylene)	Cyclopentadiene (68 g.)	Acid activated montmorillonite (5 g.)	145	2	Cyclopentenylphenol (90 g., o-/p- = 75–80/25–20)	76
72.8 g.	Cyclohexadiene (62 g.) (90 cc. toluene)	70% H_3PO_4–H_2SO_4 (4/1)	20–30 r.t.	— 8	o- (39%), p- (28%), di- (8%)-(2-Cyclohexenyl)phenol; 2,3-cyclohexano-2,3-dihydrobenzofuran (5%)	217

40	2,5-Dimethyl-1,5-hexadiene (44 g.)	$AlCl_3$ (4 g.) (20 g. pet. ether)	0 / 25 / 50	— / 16 / 1	5,5,8,8-Tetramethyl-5,6,7,8-tetrahydro-2-naphthol	26
1 (150 g. HOAc)	2,5-Dimethyl-1,5-hexadiene (55 g.)	BF_3 (28.5%)–HOAc (35 g.)	70	7	1,4-Bis-(p-hydroxyphenyl)-1,1,4,4-tetramethylbutane (37 g.), 1-(p-hydroxyphenyl)-1,1,4,4-tetramethyl-2-butene (25 g.) and its 1,1,4,4-tetramethylbuten-2-yl ether (20 g.)	92
94 g.	Dicyclopentadiene (132 g.)	H_2SO_4 (18 g.)	28–32	2	Phenoxydihydro-exo-dicyclopentadiene (98 g.)	27
24	Dicyclopentadiene (2.5)	85% H_3PO_4 (5 g.)	reflux	22	2-(260 g.),2,4-Di-(2-cyclopentenyl)phenol (some), phenoxydihydro-exo-dicyclopenta-diene (227 g.), 2,3-cyclopentano-2,3-dihydrobenzofuran (20 g.)	14
2243 g.	Dicyclopentadiene (660 g.)	85% H_3PO_4 (5 g.)	150–170	22	2-(Δ-2-Cyclopentenyl)phenol (330 g.)	158
30 g.	Limonene (0.15)	HCl	80	5	Addition product (86%)	170

a Principally 4-(p-hydroxyphenyl)- and some 4-(o-hydroxyphenyl)-2-pentene.
b Author records these as "ortho (?)- and para (?)-butenylphenols."
c Probably 3-ethylcoumaran and 2-methylchroman.
d Conc. H_2SO_4 yields largely higher boiling phenols and ethers.

e Based on diene.
f For respective catalysts.
g Chroman and coumaran.
h Non-phenolics comprise 11% of this fraction.

TABLE IV. Higher phenols and derivatives with dienes

Aromatic (Moles)	Diene (Moles)	Catalyst (Moles)	Temp. (°C)	Time (hrs.)	Products (% Yield)	Ref.
m-Cresol (5.4 kg.)	Butadiene (21.4 kg.)	BF_3–Et_2O (0.5 kg.)	10	2	Product (13.5 kg.); contains 6–10 double bonds/kg.	36
m-Cresol (144 g.)	Piperylene (45.2 g.)	$ZnCl_2$ (20%)–Al_2O_3 (10%)	18–20 / 150 2–3 atm.	20 / 6	4-(4'-Methyl-2'-hydroxyphenyl)-2-pentene (40%), 4-(2'-methyl-4'-hydroxyphenyl)-2-pentene (22%), chroman and coumaran (7%)	218
p-Cresol (54 g.)	Isoprene (17 g.)	85% H_3PO_4 (34 g.)	17	3	Pentenylphenols (37%), chromans, and coumarans (14%)	157
o-Cresol (100 cc. xylene)	Cyclopentadiene (68 g.)	Acid activated montmorillonite (5 g.)	145	2	2-Cyclopentenyl-6-methylphenol (47–55%), 4-Cyclopentenyl-2-methylphenol (26–18%)	76
p-Cresol	Cyclopentadiene	BF_3–FeF_2	25–40 r.t.	2 / 18	2-Cyclopentenyl-p-cresol	158
p-Cresol 2,3,5-Trimethylphenol (5 g.)	Cyclopentadiene Isoprene (2.5 g.)	H_3PO_4 (Toluene) $HgCl_2$ (0.37 g.)	— / 100	— / 6	o-2-Cyclopentenyl-p-cresol 2,2,5,7,8-Pentamethylchroman (2 g.)	14 195
2,3,5-Trimethylphenol (30 g.)	Pentadiene (18 g.)	HCl–HOAc (32 g.)	240 / 0 r.t. w.b.	39 / 12 1	4- or 5- (2'-Methylcrotenyl)-2,3,5-trimethylphenol (15.3 g.) 2,2,5,7,8-pentamethyl-chroman (5.13 g.)	195
p-Cresol (100 cc. xylene)	Cyclopentadiene (68 g.)	Acid activated montmorillonite (5 g.)	145	2	4-Methyl-2-cyclopentenylphenol (82%), some 2,6-dicyclopentenyl-4-methylphenol, some resin	76

Aromatic	Diene	Catalyst	Temp.	Time	Product	Reference
4-Methoxyphenol (18 g.)	Isoprene (11 g.)	HCl–HOAc (25 cc.)	0 / w.b.	12 / 0.5	2,2-Dimethyl-6-methoxy-chroman and 1-o-hydroxy-methoxyphenyl)-3-chloro-butane	195
Guaiacol	Cyclopentadiene	BF₃–FeF₂	25-40 / r.t.	2 / 18	Cyclopentylguaiacol	158
4-Methoxyphenol (12.4 g.)	Dimethylbutadiene (8.2 g.)	HCl–HOAc (10 g.)	0 / w.b.	18 / —	2,2,3-Trimethyl-6-methoxy-chroman (4 g.)	195 (193)
4-Methoxyphenol (12.4 g.)	Dimethylbuta-diene (8.2 g.)	HgCl₂ (1 g.)	—	240	2,2,3-Trimethyl-6-methoxy-chroman	193
2,3,5-Trimethylphenol (34 g.)	Isoprene (17 g.)	ZnCl₂ (4 g.)–HOAc (30 cc.)	r.t.	12	2,2,5,7,8-Pentamethylchroman (22 g.)	195
2-Naphthol (82.5 g.) (165 g. pet. ether)	Butadiene (324 g.)	BF₃–Et₂O (15 g.)	reflux / 10-22	7 / 20	Butenyl ethers of 2-naphthol and of butenyl-2-naphthol	36

TABLE V. Anisole with diones

Anisole (Moles)	Diene (Moles)	Catalyst (Moles)	Temp. (°C)	Time (hrs.)	Products (% Yield)	Ref.
4	Piperylene (1)	$AlCl_3$ (0.07)	10–20	2.5	4-(p-Methoxyphenyl)-2-pentene (65%), high boilers (26%)	212(214)
4	Piperylene (1)	$AlCl_2 \cdot H_2PO_4$ (0.1)	10–20	7	4-(p-Methoxyphenyl)-2-pentene (68%), high boilers (26%)	212(214)
4	Piperylene (1)	BF_3 (0.1)	10–20	1.5	4-(p-Methoxyphenyl)-2-pentene (65%), higher boilers (27%)	212(211, 214)
4	Piperylene (1)	BF_3–Et_2O (0.1)	10–20	50	Pentenylanisole (28%), some 2,3-bis-(p-methoxyphenyl)pentane	212(214)
10	Piperylene (1)	BF_3–ether (0.25)	100	10.5	Alkenylanisole (62%)	214
4	Piperylene (1)	BF_3–H_3PO_4 (0.1)	10–20	8	4-(p-Methoxyphenyl)-2-pentene (62%), high boilers (23%)	212(214)
5	Piperylene (1)	H_2SO_4 (0.25)	10–20	9	4-(p-Methoxyphenyl)-2-pentene (71%), high boilers (22%)	212(214)
—	1,3-Butadiene	H_2SO_4 or 2/1 Poly-phosphoric/85% H_3PO_4	—	—	o- and p-Butenylanisole	16
4–5	Piperylene (1)	100% H_3PO_4 (0.25)	10–20	9[a]	4-(p-Methoxyphenyl)-2-pentene (89%), high boilers (14%)	212(214)
4	Piperylene (1)	100% H_3PO_4 (0.25)	100	13.5	Alkenylanisole (92%)	214

[a] 3 hours gives 38%, 3.5 hours at 50° gives 81% mono-.

TABLE VI. Polyhydric phenols with dienes

Aromatic (Moles)	Diene (Moles)	Catalyst (Moles)	Temp. (°C)	Time (hrs.)	Products (% Yield)	Ref.
Resorcinol (82.5 g.)	Butadiene (325 g.)	BF_3–Et_2O (15 g.)	r.t.	2	Butenyl ethers of resorcinol and of butenylresorcinol	36
Catechol (110 g.)	2,5-Dimethyl-1,5-hexadiene (55 g.)	BF_3 (28.5%)–HOAc	70	7	1-(3',4'-Dihydroxyphenyl)-1,1,4,4-tetramethyl-2-butene (90 g.)	92
2,5-Dimethylhydroquinone (13.8 g.) (70 cc. HOAc)	Isoprene (6.8)	HCl	0, r.t.	168, 24	Dark viscous oil	195
Trimethylhydroquinone (5 g.)	Butadiene (8 cc.)	$ZnCl_2$ (1 g.)–H_2SO_4 (2 drops)–HOAc (25 cc.)	r.t.	168	1-(2,5-Dihydroxy-3,4,6-trimethylphenyl)-2-butene (3.3 g.)	190
Trimethylhydroquinone (2.74 g.)	Pentadiene (1.23 g.)	$ZnCl_2$ (0.3 g.)–HOAc (30 ml.)–H_2SO_4 (1 drop)	reflux	1	2-Ethyl-5,7,8-trimethyl-6-hydroxychroman	196(193)
Trimethylhydroquinone (10 g.)	Isoprene (10 g.)	$ZnCl_2$ (1 g.)–HOAc (100 cc.)–H_2SO_4 (1 drop)	reflux	1	2,2,5,7,8-Pentamethyl-6-hydroxychroman (7 g.)	193
Trimethylhydroquinone (1.3 g.)	Phytadiene (2.5 g.)	HCOOH (5 g.)–HOAc (2 g.)	reflux	3	α-Tocopherol (1.5–2 g.)	195(193)
2-Methyl-1,4-naphthohydroquinone (2 g.)	Isoprene (2 g.)	Oxalic acid (2 g.) (20 cc. dioxane)	180	15	2-Methyl-3-(γ,γ-dimethylallyl)naphthohydroquinone (0.3 g.)	62
2-Methyl-1,4-naphthohydroquinone (3 g.)	2,3-Dimethyl-1,3-butadiene (10 cc.)	Oxalic acid (3 g.) (30 cc. dioxane)	reflux	24	2-Methyl-3-(β,γ,γ-trimethylallyl)naphthohydroquinone (0.11 g.[a])	62
Bis-(p-hydroxyphenyl)-dimethylmethane (115 g.)	Butadiene (324 g.)	BF_3–Et_2O	18–20	20	Butenyl ethers	36

[a] After oxidation to quinone.

TABLE VII. Aromatic amines with dienes

Aromatic Amine (Moles)	Diene (Moles)	Catalyst (Moles)	Temp. (°C)	Time (hrs.)	Products (% Yield)	Ref.
Aniline (200 pts.)	Dicyclopentadiene (100 pts.)	Act. Fuller's earth (5 g.)	200	1	Cyclopentenylaniline: 2- (14.5 pts.); 2,6-di- (35 pts.)	173
o-Toluidine (250 pts.)	Dicyclopentadiene (100 pts.)	Act. Fuller's earth (5 g.)	reflux	1	Cyclopentenylaniline: 2-methyl-6- (110 pts.), 2-methyl-4,6-di- (42 pts.)	173
m-Toluidine (250 pts.)	Dicyclopentadiene (100 pts.)	Act. Fuller's earth (5 g.)	reflux	1	Cyclopentenylaniline: 3-methyl-6- (86 pts.), 3-methyl-4,6-di- (42 pts.)	173
N-Methylaniline (250 pts.)	Dicyclopentadiene (250 pts.)	Act. Fuller's earth	200	1	Cyclopentenylaniline: N-methyl-2- (64 pts.), N-methyl-4- (48 pts.), N-methyl-di- (39 pts.)	173
Diphenylamine (170 pts.)	Dicyclopentadiene (100 pts.)	Act. Fuller's earth (5 g.)	reflux	1	Cyclopentenyldiphenylamine (76 pts.)	173
2-Chloroaniline (240 pts.)	Dicyclopentadiene (100 pts.)	Act. Fuller's earth (5 g.)	reflux	1	Cyclopentenylaniline: 2-chloro-4- (83 pts.), 2-chloro-4,6-di- (59 pts.)	173

TABLE VIII.   Furan and thiophene with dienes

Aromatic (Moles)	Diene (Moles)	Catalyst (Moles)	Temp. (°C)	Time (hrs.)	Products (% Yield)	Ref.
Furan (1.47)	Isoprene (1.4)	EtSO$_3$H (0.173) (0.25 dioxane)	1	3	Pentenylfuran (54%)	74
Furan (17 g.)	2-Methylpentadiene (9.4 g.)	BF$_3$–H$_2$O (5 cc.)	20–30	1.3	Mono- (46%), di-(2%) iso-hexenylfuran^c	155
Thiophene (420 g.)	Butadiene (216 g.)	76% H$_2$SO$_4$ (210 g.)	50–60	1.5	Butenylthiophene (37%)	108(202)
Thiophene (0.9)	Butadiene (0.3)	85% H$_3$PO$_4$ (15 cc.)	100–120	4	Butenylthiophene (28 g.)^a, dithienylbutane (3 g.)	154
Thiophene (76 g.)	Isoprene (17 g.)	SnCl$_4$ (15 g.)	50	2	2-(1′,1′-Dimethylpropenyl)thiophene^b (71%), dipentenylthiophene (11%)	152
Thiophene (504 g.)	Isoprene (272)	85% H$_3$PO$_4$ (200 cc.)	27–37	6	2-(3-Methyl-2-butenyl)thiophene (345 g.)	154
Thiophene (76 g.)	2-Methyl-1,3-penta-diene (20.5 g.)	SnCl$_4$ (15 g.)	50	2	2-(1′,1′-Dimethyl-2′-butenyl)-thiophene (73%), dihexenyl-thiophene (20%)^c	152

^{a} Authors designated this as a mixture of 2-(3-butenyl)- and 2-(2-butenyl)thiophene, but Bader's footnote 15 states correct structures are probably 2-cis- and 2-trans-crotylthiophenes (16).

^{b} No doubt this is the 2-(3-methyl-2-butenyl) derivative (154).

^{c} Probably (1,3-dimethyl-2-butenyl) derivative (see p. 298).

TABLE IX. Benzene with unsaturated halides[a]

Benzene (Moles)	Unsaturated halide (Moles)	Catalyst (Moles)	Temp. (°C)	Time (hrs.)	Products (% Yield)	Ref.
400–500 g.	Vinyl bromide (50 g.)	AlCl₃ (30 g.)	w.b.	—	Ethylbenzene (13 g.), 1,1-diphenylethane (46 g.), styrene (trace)	6
400–500 g.	Vinyl bromide (50 g.)	AlCl₃ (30 g.)	w.b.	—	Dimethyldihydroanthracene[f] (46 g.), styrene (trace), ethylbenzene (small amt.)	6
—	Vinyl bromide	AlCl₃	gentle warming	—	Ethylbenzene, 1,1-diphenylethane, dimethyldihydroanthracene[f]	3
230 g.	Vinyl bromide (500 g.)	AlCl₃ (20 g.)[p]	p	—	Mono- and di-(β-bromoethyl)benzene	73
300 cc.	Vinyl chloride (90 g.)	AlCl₃ (2 g., 50 g.)[a]	0–5	2	Ethylbenzene (4.3 g.), 1,1-diphenylethane (10.5 g.), resin (50.4 g.)	121
300 cc.	Vinyl chloride (90 g.)	AlCl₃ (50 g.)[b]	60–70	2	Ethylbenzene (4 g.), 1,1-diphenylethane (13 g.), resin (33 g.), 9,10-dimethyl-dihydroanthracene[f] (17 g.)	121
—	Vinyl chloride	Al (6 g.)–HgCl₂ (80 g.)	80	h	1,1-Diphenylethane (22 g.),[g] 9,10-dimethyl-9,10-dihydroanthracene[f]	25
150 g.	1,1-Dibromoethylene (28 g.)	AlCl₃ (40–50 g.)	reflux	—	as-Diphenylethylene	49
—	Acetylene dibromide	AlCl₃	w.b.	—	Anthracene, bromobenzene, dibenzyl	49
—	1,2-Dibromoethylene	AlBr₃		—	Dibenzyl	4
400 g.	Tribromoethylene (50 g.)	AlCl₃ (50 g.)	warm	—	1,2-Diphenylethane, styrene, triphenylmethane, bromobenzene (significant amount	6

400 g.	Tribromoethylene (40 g.)	AlCl$_3$ (25–30 g.)	warm	—	as-Diphenylethylene, toluene	6
200 cc.	as-Dichloroethylene (24.2 g.)	AlCl$_3$ (33 g.)	n	—	1,1-Diphenylethylene (36%), 1,1,3-triphenyl-3-methyl-hydrindene (45%)	104 (105)
800 g.	Dichloroethylene (43 g.)[c]	Al (12 g.)–HgCl$_2$ (80 g.)	r.t.[d]	3	Dibenzyl (7 g.), triphenyl-ethane (12 g.), tetraphenyl-ethane (6 g.)	25
400 g.	Dichloroethylene (88 g.)	Al (6 g.)–HgCl$_2$ (90 g.)	80	3	Dibenzyl (64 g.), triphenyl-ethane (74 g.)	25
400 ml.	Trichloroethylene (30 g.)	AlCl$_3$ (30 g.)	reflux	3–4	C$_{40}$H$_{32}$ (40–50 g.)	105
202 g.	Trichloroethylene (16 g.)	AlCl$_3$ (16 g.)	30	4	1,1,2,2-Tetraphenylethane (70%)	210b
400 g.	Trichloroethylene (80 g.)	Al (6 g.)–HgCl$_2$ (90 g.)	80	3	1,1-Diphenylethane (12%), dibenzyl (10%), tetra-phenylethane (8%)	25
1200 g.	Tetrachloroethylene (150 g.)	AlCl$_3$ (150 g.)	70	—	Anthracene (sole product—large quantity)	127 (24)
—	Tetrachloroethylene (50 g.)	Al (6 g.)–HgCl$_2$ (90 g.)	80	3	Very little reaction, tetra-phenylethane (1.5 g.)	25
6	Tetrachloroethylene	Al (10%)	0	3	Dibenzyl (4–5 g.)[t]	54
90	Allyl bromide (100 g.)	Zn	w.b.	—	No reaction	171 (181)
—	Allyl bromide	H$_2$SO$_4$ (SO$_3$/0.8, 1.0, 1.27, 1.36 H$_2$O)	30	—	1,2-Diphenylpropane, phenyl-propane (5 g.); 1-Bromo-2-phenylpropane (45, 59, 58, 36%)[t]	207 (206)
78 g.	Allyl bromide (30 g.)	93.7% H$_2$SO$_4$ (0.5)	30	2	1-Bromo-2-phenylpropane (37%)	122(122a)
2	Allyl chloride (0.7)	AlCl$_3$ (0.15)	—	—	n-Propylbenzene (50%)	227
—	Allyl chloride	AlCl$_3$	—	—	Isopropylbenzene, 1,2-di-phenylpropane	228

Table continued

TABLE IX (continued)

Benzene (Moles)	Unsaturated halide (Moles)	Catalyst (Moles)	Temp. (°C)	Time (hrs.)	Products (% Yield)	Ref.
3	Allyl chloride[k] (1)	$AlCl_3$ (0.5)	50	2	Mono- and diallylbenzene and hydrindene mixture (6%), 1-chloro[k]-3-phenylpropane (4%), 1,2-diphenylpropane (10%), 9-methyl-9,10-dihydroanthracene (27%)[l]	116
7	Allyl chloride (1)	$AlCl_3$ (0.2)	−14 to 45	—	1,2-Diphenylpropane (good yield)	137 (103,183)
312 cc.	Allyl chloride (76.5 g.)	$AlCl_3$ (66 g.)–H_2O (4.5 g.)	50	4	Propylbenzene (18.5 g.), 9,10-diethylanthracene (10 g.)	137
437 cc.	Allyl chloride (77 g.)	$AlCl_3$ (77 g.) (260 cc. $C_3H_7NO_2$)	−5 to 0	0.5	2-Chloro-1-phenylpropane	224
—	Allyl chloride	Al (2%)	r.t.	23	Propylbenzene (1.9 g.) higher (14.8 g.)[o]	54
275 cc.	Allyl chloride (38.2 g.)	$FeCl_3$ (0.1)	−10 to −20	1	(2-Chloropropyl)benzene (26g.), 1,2-diphenylpropane, propenylbenzene	137
—	Allyl chloride	$ZnCl_2$	reflux	—	(2-Chloropropyl)benzene, propylbenzene	137
—	Allyl chloride	H_2SO_4 ± 10% Oleum	—	—	(2-Chloroisopropyl)benzene (20%), bis-(2-chloroisopropyl)benzene[m]	206 (204)
2.1	1,3-Dichloropropene (0.45)	$AlCl_3$ (5 g.)[u] CH_3NO_2 (5–6 g.)	[e]	[f]	(3-Chloroallyl)benzene (47%)	168a
100 cc.	2-Methylallyl bromide (13.5 g.)	$AlCl_3$ (1.67 g.)	30	4	2-Methyl-1,2-diphenylpropane,[r] t-butylbenzene (0.6 g.)	209
3	2-Methylallyl bromide (1)	100% H_2SO_4 (0.2)	20	13	$PhC(CH_3)_2CH_2Br$ (35%)	70

Amount	Reactant	Catalyst	Temp.	Time	Products	Ref.
3.4	1-Bromo-2-methylpropene (1)	H_2SO_4 (100%) (0.25)	20	13	(2-Bromo-1,1-dimethylethyl)benzene (35%)	70
100 ml.	Isocrotyl bromide (13.5 g.)	$AlCl_3$ (3.35 g.)	30	4	2-Methyl-2,3-diphenylpropane (8.8 g.), 2,3-diphenylbutane (5.6 g.), t-butylbenzene (1.2 g.)	209
100 ml.	Crotyl chloride (9 g.)	$AlCl_3$ (5 g.)	45	4	s-Butylbenzene (2 g.), 1,2-diphenylbutane (12 g.)	209
100 g.	2-Methyl-3-chloro-1-propene (32 g.)	Al (2%)	r.t.	23	t-Butylbenzene (5–6 g.), 2,3-diphenylbutane (1 g.), 2,3-diphenyl-2-methylpropane (9 g.)	54
10.2	2-Methallyl chloride (3.3)	H_2SO_4 (400 g.)[u]	0–5	2.5	1,1-Dimethyl-2-phenylethyl chloride (67%), 1,4-bis-(1,1-dimethyl-2-chloroethyl)benzene (3%)	166 (70,148, 198,225)
60 g.	1,3-Dichloro-2-butene (12.5 g.)	Al (0.2 g.)	76–83	4	1-Phenyl-3-chloro-2-butene (45%)	12b
80 g.	1,3-Dichloro-2-methylpropene (55 g.)	$AlCl_3$ (5 g.)–CH_3NO_2 (6, g.)	0	1	1,3-Dichloro-2-phenyl-2-methylpropane (51%)	168a
3.8	3-Chloro-2-chloromethylpropene (1)	100% H_2SO_4 (0.15)[u]	30	13	1,3-Dichloro-2-phenyl-2-methylpropane (3–6%)	70
2.1	1,3-Dichloro-2-methylpropene (0.44)	$AlCl_3$ (5 g.) CH_3NO_2 (5–6 g.)	e	f	1,3-Dichloro-2-phenyl-2-methylpropane (51%), high boilers (13 g.)	168a
2.1	1,3-Dichloro-2-methylpropene (0.44)	$AlCl_3$ (5 g.)	e	f	(3-Chloro-2-methylallyl)benzene (23%), high boilers	168a
100 g.	2-Chloro-2-methyl-5-hexene (0.075 m)	$AlCl_3$ (2 g.)	20–30	0.25	1,1-Dimethyl-6,7-benzosuberan[q] (33%)	40
1.3	1-Chloro-2,4,4-trimethyl-1-pentene (0.4)	H_2SO_4 (30 g.)	e		1-Chloro-2-phenyl-2-methylpropane (10%) and t-butylbenzene	168a

Table continued

TABLE IX (*continued*)

Benzene (Moles)	Unsaturated halide (Moles)	Catalyst (Moles)	Temp. (°C)	Time (hrs.)	Products (% Yield)	Ref.
1.5	3-Chloronortricyclene (0.2)	H_2SO_4 (30 g.)	e	f	(Chlorobicycloheptyl)benzene (67%)	168a
—	3-Chloro-2,6-dimethyl-5-heptene	$AlCl_3$	—	—	1,1,5,5-Tetramethyl-6,7-benzosuberan[q] (28%) and 1,1,5,5,7,7,11,11-octamethyl-dicyclohepta[a,d]benzene[q]	40
—	3-Chloro-2,2,3-trimethyl-6-heptene	$AlCl_3$	—	—	1-Methyl-1-t-butyl-6,7-benzosuberan[q]	40
300 ml.	1-Chloro-2,2-diphenyl-ethylene (25 g.)	$AlCl_3$ (15.5 g.)	warm	4	$C_{40}H_{32}$	105
500 g.	Tolane dibromide (5 g.)	$AlCl_3$ (5 g.) CS_2	r.t. w.b.	0.5 0.5	Tetraphenylethane, *no bromo*-benzene, no anthracene	49
5.62	Isopropenylhexachloro-norbornene (0.2)	$AlCl_3$ (3.6 g.)	reflux	13	2-Phenyl-2-(1,4,5,6,7,7-hexa-chloro-5-norbornenyl)pro-pane (74%)	90

a Trace of I_2 accelerates reaction and greatly increases 9,10-di-methyldihydroanthracene.[j]

b Addition of 1 g. of Hg increases ethylbenzene to 15 g. but decreases resins and eliminates 9,10-dimethyldihydroanthracene.[j]

c *cis* or *trans*.

d No reaction at 0°.

e Ice bath.

f Add unsat. halide in 1–3 hrs.; stir 1 to 2 hrs. more.

g Yield is 60% when run at 0°, 3 hours.

h For a moment.

i At 0°.

j Probably 9,10-dimethylanthracene (see ref. 176a,176c).

k Or bromide.

l For each catalyst composition.

m "Notable amount."

n Reaction proceeds spontaneously.

o Containing some diphenylpropane.

p Add catalyst gradually; avoid overheating.

q These structures questionable. See Chapter XXII.

r Contains 5.6 g. *meso*-2,3-diphenylbutane.

s H_2SO_4 effected little reaction of benzene with 2-chloropropene, 1,3- and 2,3-dichloropropene, 1,3-dichloro-2-methylpropene or 1-chlorocyclohexene (168a).

TABLE X. Alkylbenzenes with unsaturated halides

Aromatic (Moles)	Unsaturated halide (Moles)	Catalyst (Moles)	Temp. (°C)	Time (hrs.)	Products (% Yield)	Ref.
Toluene (3.3)	Vinyl chloride (1)	AlCl$_3$ (0.13)	60	1.5	1,1-Ditolylethane (68%)	210
Toluene (2.5)	Vinyl chloride (1)	AlCl$_3$ (0.5)	65	2	1,1-Ditolylethane (15%), 4-ethyltoluene (10%), 2,6,9,10-tetramethylanthracene (15%)	210
Toluene (2.5)	Vinyl chloride (1)	AlCl$_3$ (1)	70	1.5	1,1-Ditolylethane (10%), 4-ethyltoluene (45%), 1,1-ditolylethylene (23%)	210
Toluene (2)	Allyl chloride (1)	BF$_3$–2H$_2$O (0.58 g.) BF$_3$ (0.58 g.)	reflux	8	1,2-Di-p-tolylpropane	77
Toluene	Allyl chloride	H$_2$SO$_4$	w.b.	—	2-(p-Tolyl)chloropropane	206
Toluene (90 g.)	Allyl bromide (100 g.)	ZnCl$_2$ (15 g.)	25	—	o-Propyltoluene and 1,2-ditolylpropane	171
Toluene (1.5)	Allyl bromide (1)	H$_2$SO$_4$ (2)	25	—	4-Methyl-1-(2-bromoisopropyl)benzene (17%)	126
Toluene (3)	2-Methylallyl chloride (1)	100% H$_2$SO$_4$ (0.15)	10	13	1,1-Dimethyl-1-tolylethyl chloride (75%) (mainly para-, some meta-)	70
Toluene (125 ml.)	2-Methyl-1-chloropropene (0.25)	H$_2$SO$_4$ (50 ml.)	—	1.5	2-Methyl-2-(p-tolyl)propyl chloride (76%)	8b
Toluene (95 ml.)	1,3-Dichloro-2-butene (34 g.)	Al (0.5)	reflux	6.5	1-p-Tolyl-3-chloro-2-butene (33%)	12b(88a)
Toluene	Isopropenylhexachloronorbornene	AlCl$_3$	—	—	2-Tolyl-2-(1,4,5,6,7,7-hexachloro-5-norbornenyl)propane	90
Ethylbenzene (1.5)	Allyl bromide (1)	H$_2$SO$_4$ (2)	25	—	4-Ethyl-1-(2-bromoisopropyl)benzene (17%)	126
Ethylbenzene (1.5)	Allyl chloride (1)	H$_2$SO$_4$ (2)	25	—	4-Ethyl-1-(2-chloroisopropyl)benzene (5%)	126
Ethylbenzene (3)	2-Methylallyl chloride (1)	100% H$_2$SO$_4$ (0.15)	10	13	1,1-Dimethyl-1-(ethylphenyl)ethyl chloride (73%) (mostly para-, some meta-)	70

Table continued

13*

TABLE X (continued)

Aromatic (Moles)	Unsaturated halide (Moles)	Catalyst (Moles)	Temp. (°C)	Time (hrs.)	Products (% Yield)	Ref.
o-Xylene	Isopropenylhexachloronorbornene	AlCl₃	—	—	2-(3',4'-Dimethylphenyl)-2-(1,4,5,6,7,7-hexachloro-5-norbornenyl)propane (74%)	90
m-Xylene[b]	Isopropenylhexachloronorbornene	AlCl₃	—	—	2-(3',5'-Dimethylphenyl)-2-(1,4,5,6,7,7-hexachloro-5-norbornenyl)propane 80%)	90
t-Butylbenzene (1.5)	1-Bromo-2-methylpropene (1)	100% H₂SO₄ (0.15)	20	13	1,1-Dimethyl-1-(4'-t-butylphenyl)ethyl bromide (23%)	70
Cumene (3)	2-Methylallyl chloride (1)	100% H₂SO₄ (0.15)	10	13	1,1-Dimethyl-1-cumylethyl chloride (70%) (mostly para-, some meta-)	70
Cumene and benzene	2-Methylallyl chloride (1)	H₂SO₄	—	—	Equally alkylated	70
t-Butylbenzene (3)	2-Methylallyl chloride (1)	100% H₂SO₄ (0.15, 0.5)	20, 0	13	1,1-Dimethyl-1-(t-butylphenyl)ethyl chloride (64, 98%)[a] (mostly para-, some meta-)	70
Neopentylbenzene (3)	2-Methylallyl chloride (1)	H₂SO₄ (0.5)	20	13	1,1-Dimethyl-1-(4'-neopentylphenyl)ethyl chloride (54%)	70
Cumene (60 cc.)	1,3-Dichloro-2-butene (12.5 g.)	AlCl₃ (0.3 g.)	150	4.5	1-Cumyl-3-chloro-2-butene (44%)	12b(88a)

[a] Resp. for each set of conditions. [b] Alkylation unsuccessful with para-.

TABLE XI. Halogenated benzenes with unsaturated halides

Aromatic (Moles)	Unsaturated halide (Moles)	Catalyst (Moles)	Temp. (°C)	Time (hrs.)	Products (% Yield)	Ref.
Bromobenzene	Allyl chloride	H₂SO₄	—	—	2-(p-Bromophenyl)-1-chloropropane[a]	205
Chlorobenzene	Allyl chloride	H₂SO₄	—	—	2-(p-Chlorophenyl)-1-chloropropane[a]	205

[a] Not obtainable with AlCl₃ catalyst.

TABLE XII.   Polycyclic hydrocarbons with unsaturated halides

Aromatic (Moles)	Unsaturated halide (Moles)	Catalyst (Moles)	Temp. (°C)	Time (hrs.)	Products (% Yield)	Ref.
Naphthalene (12.8 g.)	1,3-Dichloro-2-butene (12.5 g.)	Al (0.1)	120	—	1-Naphthyl-3-chloro-2-butene (43.6%)	12b(88a)
Biphenyl	Dichloroethylene	a	85–100	—	p,p′-Diphenylbibenzyl	176b

a Friedel-Crafts.

TABLE XIII.   Phenolics and derivatives with unsaturated halides

Aromatic (Moles)	Unsaturated halide (Moles)	Catalyst (Moles)	Temp. (°C)	Time (hrs.)	Products (% Yield)	Ref.
Phenol (50)	Vinyl chloride (60)	$AlCl_3$ (10)	100	—	Vinylphenol	174
Phenol (1.0)	Allyl chloride (1.0)	H_2SO_4 (1.0)	r.t.	6 mo.	2-Hydroxy-1-isopropenylbenzene	197
Phenol[a]	Isopropenylhexa-chloronorbornene	$AlCl_3$	reflux	11	2-(Hydroxyphenyl)-2-(1,4,5,6,7,7-hexachloro-5-norbornenyl)propane (69%)	90
Anisole (2)	Vinyl bromide (1)	$AlCl_3$ (0.125–1.0)	0	3	1,1-Dianisylethane (0–21%), 4-ethylanisole (0–14%)	210
			20	17		
Anisole (5)	Vinyl chloride (1)	$AlCl_3$ (0.5)	0	3	1,1-Dianisylethylene (42%), 4-ethylanisole (18%)	210
o-Cresol (1)	Allyl chloride (1)	H_2SO_4 (1)	r.t.	6 mo.	2-Hydroxy-1-methyl-5-isopropenylbenzene	197
m-Cresol (1)	Allyl chloride (1)	H_2SO_4–HOAc (1)/(200 g.)	reflux	8 hr.	2-meta-Cresoxy-1-propene and 3-hydroxy-1-methyl-4-isopropenylbenzene (equal parts) conv. = 30%	197
p-Cresol (1)	Allyl chloride (1)	H_2SO_4 (1)	r.t.	6 mo.	4-Hydroxy-1-methyl-3-isopropenylbenzene	197
Anisole	Allyl chloride	$CuSO_4$–Zn	87–120	1–2	p-Allylanisole (14%), p-(β-chloropropyl)anisole (28%), 1,2-dianisylpropane (20%)	124b

Table continued

TABLE XIII (*continued*)

Aromatic (Moles)	Unsaturated halide (Moles)	Catalyst (Moles)	Temp. (°C)	Time (hrs.)	Products (% Yield)	Ref.
Guaiacol	Allyl chloride	Cu	87–115	6–9	2-Methoxy-4-allylphenol (28%), 2-methoxy-5-allylphenol (some), 2-methoxy-4-(β-chloropropyl)phenol (18%), guaiacol allyl ether, allyl 2-methoxy-4-allylphenyl ether	124b
o-Cresol[a,b]	Isopropenylhexachloronorbornene	AlCl$_3$	reflux	11	2-(4'-Methyl-3'-hydroxyphenyl)-2-(1,4,5,6,7,7-hexachloro-5-norbornenyl)propane (35%)	90
m-Xylohydroquinone (5 g.)	Allyl bromide (10 cc.)	None	150 (s.t.)	3	2,4,6-Trimethyl-7-allyl-5-hydroxycoumaran	196
Trimethylhydroquinone (1 g.)	Allyl bromide (10 cc.)	None	155	4.5	2,4,6,7-Tetramethyl-5-hydroxycoumaran	194
Trimethylhydroquinone (1 g.)	Allyl chloride (5 cc.)	None	150 (s.t.)	3	2,4,6,7-Tetramethyl-5-hydroxycoumaran (0.6)	196
Trimethylhydroquinone (4 g.)	Crotyl bromide (4.3 g.)	ZnCl$_2$ (3.2 g.) 80 cc. pet. ether	reflux	5	2,5,7,8-Tetramethyl-6-oxychroman	94
Trimethylhydroquinone (1 g.)	Dimethylallyl bromide (3 cc.)	None	140	4	2,4,6,7-Tetramethyl-5-hydroxycoumaran	194
Trimethylhydroquinone (1 g.)	Crotyl chloride (4 cc.)	None	150 (s.t.)	4	2,3,4,6,7-Pentamethyl-5-hydroxycoumaran (0.4)	196
Trimethylhydroquinone (1.7 g.)	Phytol bromide (4.8 g.)	ZnCl$_2$ (1 g.)	60–70	1.5	α-Tocopherol	95

[a] o-Dichlorobenzene solution.   [b] m- and p-Cresol failed to alkylate.

TABLE XIV.   Thiophenes with unsaturated halides

Aromatic (Moles)	Unsaturated halide (Moles)	Catalyst (Moles)	Temp. (°C)	Time (hrs.)	Products (% Yield)	Ref.
Thiophene (75.6 g.)	Allyl bromide (25 g.)	BF_3–Et_2O (20 g.)	80	—	Mono- (16.5 g.), di-(3 g.) 2-(β-bromoisopropyl)thiophene	166a
Thiophene (75.6 g.)	Methallyl chloride (39.3 g.)	$SnCl_4$ (15 g.)	–4	—	Mono- (2.7 g.), di- (2.2 g.)-(chloro-t-butyl)thiophene	166a
Thiophene (75.6 g.)	Methallyl chloride (39.3 g.)	BF_3–$2H_2O$ (15 g.)	58	1–4	Mono-(chloro-t-butyl)thiophene	166a
Thiophene	Methallyl chloride	BF_3–Et_2O	80	—	Chloro-t-butylthiophene mono-(47%)[b], di-2,5-(9%)	153 (166a)
Thiophene (100 g.)	Methallyl chloride (50 g.)	80% H_2SO_4 (100 g.)	32	1.66	Chlorobutylthiophene (7%)	108 (202)
Thiophene	Methallyl chloride	Ethane–SO_3H	73	—	2-(Chloro-t-butyl)thiophene (50%)[a]	153
Thiophene (75.6 g.)	Methallyl chloride (36.2 g.)	85% H_3PO_4 (15 g.)	125	—	Mono- (1 g.), di- (4 g.) (chloro-t-butyl)thiophene	166a
Thiophene (75 g.)	1,3-Dichloro-2-methyl-1-propene (25 g.)	BF_3–Et_2O (15 g.)	80	—	1,3-Dichloro-2-methyl-2-thienylpropane (22 g.)	166a
2-Bromothiophene	Methallyl chloride	BF_3–Et_2O	66	—	2-Bromo-5-(chloro-t-butyl)-thiophene (60%)	153
Methylthiophene (81.5 g.)	Methallyl chloride (22.5 g.)	BF_3–Et_2O (15 g.)	66	—	2-(Chloro-t-butyl)thiophene (33.7 g.)	166a

[a] Based on methallyl chloride converted.   [b] 70% 2- and 30% 3-isomer.

TABLE XV. Benzene and homologs with unsaturated alcohols and ethers

Aromatic (Moles)	Unsaturated alcohol or ether (Moles)	Catalyst (Moles)	Temp. (°C)	Time (hrs.)	Products (% Yield)	Ref.
Benzene (5)	Allyl alcohol (1)	AlCl$_3$ (0.5)	r.t.	20–24	Allylbenzene (16%), 1,2-diphenylpropane	84
Benzene (350 cc.)	Allyl alcohol (58 g.)	AlCl$_3$ (67 g.)-nitropropane (255 cc.)	reflux	—	2-Chloro-1-phenylpropane (good yield)	224
Benzene (1)	Allyl alcohol (1)	BF$_3$ (20 g.)	r.t.	20	Allylbenzene (8.7 g.), high boilers (31 g.)	118
Benzene	Allyl alcohol	H$_2$SO$_4$	—	35	1,2-Diphenylpropane (32%)	185
Benzene (1.69)	Allyl alcohol (0.78)	HF (10)	0–7	22	1,2-Diphenylpropane (53%)	32
Benzene	Allyl alcohol	HF	—	—	Allylbenzene (11–20%), 1,2-diphenylpropane (8–12%)	185
Benzene	Ethyl vinyl ether	AlCl$_3$ or BF$_3$	—	—	Ethyl phenylethyl ether	81
Benzene (100 cc.)	Butyl vinyl ether (10 g.)	AlCl$_3$ (14 g.)	13–r.t.	84	Butylphenol (33%), BuOCHPhMe (20%)	208
Toluene (369 pts.)	Allyl alcohol (116 pts.)	IR-20[a] (40 pts.)	reflux	3	Allyltoluene	62a
Toluene (292 pts.)	Diallylether (40 pts.)	IR-20[a]	reflux	4	Allyltoluene (2.8 pts.)	62a
m-Xylene (53 pts.)	Allyl alcohol	IR-20[a]-Dowex-50[a] (60 pts.)	reflux	—	Allylxylene (31%)	62a
Pseudocumene (1000 ml.)	Allyl alcohol (100 cc.)	H$_2$SO$_4$ (100 cc.) + fuming H$_2$SO$_4$ (50 cc.)	—	—	2,2-Dipseudocumylpropane and a polymer (mol. wt. 763)	107

[a] Polystyrene sulfonic acid.

TABLE XVI. Polycyclic hydrocarbons with unsaturated alcohols and ethers

Aromatic (Moles)	Unsaturate (Moles)	Catalyst (Moles)	Temp. (°C)	Time (hrs.)	Products (Yield)	Ref.
Naphthalene	Methyl vinyl ether	$AlCl_3$ or BF_3	—	—	γ-Oxybutylnaphthalene	81

TABLE XVII. Phenolics and derivatives with unsaturated alcohols and ethers

Aromatic (Moles)	Unsaturate (Moles)	Catalyst (Moles)	Temp. (°C)	Time (hrs.)	Products (% Yield)	Ref.
Phenol (1.0)	Allyl alcohol (1.0)	H_2SO_4–HOAc 10 cc./250 cc.	reflux	5	2-Methylcoumaran (50–65%) small amount 2-isopropenyl-phenol	145
Phenol	Allyl alcohol	Dowex-50[d]	reflux	—	o-Allylphenol (30%)	62a
Phenol (excess)	Butoxyethylene	H_3PO_4	50	3	1-Phenoxy-1-butoxyethane	112
Phenol (300 pts.)	Methallyl methyl ether (210 pts.)	Al (4.59 pts.) as Al phenoxide	100–125	1.5	2-(1,1-Dimethyl-2-methoxyethyl)-phenol (good yield)	57
Phenol	Cinnamyl alcohol	—	—	—	2-Benzylcoumaran, 3-phenyl-2-(2-hydroxyphenyl)propene (small amount)	145
Phenol (1)	Oleyl alcohol (1)	$CuCl_2$ (0.2)	70	few	Hydroxyphenyl octadecyl alcohol	141
p-Chlorophenol (1)	Oleyl alcohol (1)	H_2SO_4 (2)	—	—	Sulfuric acid ester of hydroxy-p-chlorophenyloctadecyl alcohol	141
Anisole (10 g.)	Ethoxyethylene (10 g.)	HCl	0	0.75	α-Chloroethylanisole (2.4 g.), unsym-di-(methoxyphenyl)ethane (3 g.)	208
Anisole (16.99)	4-Hydroxy-2-hexene (6 g.)	H_2SO_4 (3 g.)	13–18 r.t.	6.5 15	4-(p-Methoxyphenyl)-2-hexene (77%)	201

Table continued

TABLE XVII (*continued*)

Aromatic (Moles)	Unsaturate (Moles)	Catalyst (Moles)	Temp. (°C)	Time (hrs.)	Products (% Yield)	Ref.
Anisole (6 g.)	4-(*p*-Methoxyphenyl)-2-hexene	H_2SO_4 (3 g.)	10	7	2,3-Di-(*p*-methoxyphenyl)hexane (2.6 g.)	201
o-Cresol (1)	Allyl alcohol (1)	H_2SO_4 (10 cc.) (250 ml. HOAc)	r.t.	16.5	2,6-Dimethylcoumaran (50–65%), 6-methyl-2-isopropenylphenol (small amount)	145
			reflux	5		
o-Cresol	Allyl alcohol	H_3PO_4 (200%) KU-1[d] (10%) $ZnCl_2$–Al_2O_3 (10%)	75 120 150	9 10 10	2-Methyl-6-allylphenol (10, 3, 23%)[c], 2-methyl-4-allylphenol (22, –, 18%)[c], allyl *o*-tolyl ether (–, 6%, 3%)[c] and cyclic compounds	178
m-Cresol (1)	Allyl alcohol (1)	H_3PO_4 (0.1)	r.t.	few days	2-Isopropenyl-5-methylphenol	144
m-Cresol (1)	Allyl alcohol (1)	$ZnCl_2$–Al_2O_3 (10%)	150	8	*o*- (20%), *p*- (26%)-Allyl-*m*-cresol[b]	177
m-Cresol (1)	Allyl alcohol (1)	H_2SO_4 (10 cc.) (250 ml. HOAc)	reflux	5	2,5-Dimethylcoumaran (50–65%), 5-methyl-2-isopropenylphenol (small amount)	145
m-Cresol (1)	Allyl alcohol (1)	KU-1[d] (20%)	95	12	*o*- (23%), *p*- (20%)-Allyl-*m*-cresol[b]	177
m-Cresol (1)	Allyl alcohol (1)	H_3PO_4 (200%)	75	8	*o*- (38%), *p*- (27%)-Allyl-*m*-cresol[b]	177
p-Cresol (1)	Allyl alcohol (1)	H_2SO_4 (10 cc.) (250 ml. HOAc)	reflux	5	2,4-Dimethylcoumaran (50–65%), 4-methyl-2-isopropenylphenol (small amount)	145
p-Cresol	Allyl alcohol	H_3PO_4 (200%) KU-1[d] (10%) $ZnCl_2$–Al_2O_3 (10%)	95–100 120 180–190	10 10 10	4-Methyl-2-allylphenol (2, 1, 19%)[c] 2-(3-methyl-6-hydroxyphenyl)-1-propanol (7, 5, 0%)[c] allyl-*p*-tolylether (0.3, 0.5, 0.4%)[c] and cyclic compounds	178
m-Cresol (1)	3-Buten-1-ol (1)	KU-1[d] (10%)	120[d]	12	3-Methyl-6-(3-buten-2-yl)phenol (2%)[b]	179

Aromatic	Reagent	Catalyst	Temp	Time	Product	Ref
m-Cresol (1)	3-Buten-1-ol (1)	H₃PO₄ (200%)	110	10	3-Methyl-6-(3-buten-2-yl)phenol (7%)[b]; 3-Methyl-4-(3-buten-2-yl)phenol (19%)[b]	179
p-Cresol (2)	3-Buten-1-ol (1)	KU-1[d] (10%)	120	10	All cyclics	179
p-Cresol (2)	3-Buten-1-ol (1)	H₃PO₄ (200%)	135-140	10	4-Methyl-2-(3-buten-2-yl)phenol (2%)[b]	179
m-Cresol (1)	4-Penten-1-ol (1)	H₃PO₄ (200%)	100, 135	8	3-Methyl-4-(4-penten-2-yl)phenol (17, 38%)[a], 3-methyl-6-(4-penten-2-yl)phenol (5, –%)[a,b]	180
p-Cresol (1)	4-Penten-1-ol (1)	H₃PO₄ (200%)	135-140	8	4-Methyl-2-(4-penten-2-yl)phenol[b]	180
m-Cresol (1)	Allyl ethyl ether (1)	H₂SO₄ (1.0)	r.t.	10	2-Isopropenyl-5-methylphenol	144
m-Cresol (1)	Allyl ether (1)	H₂SO₄ (1.0)	r.t.	168	2-Isopropenyl-5-methylphenol	144
o-Cresol (excess)	Butoxyethylene	H₃PO₄ (trace)	100	3	1-(o-Tolyloxy)-1-butoxyethane	112
m-Cresol (excess)	Butoxyethylene	H₃PO₄ (trace)	50	3	1-(m-Tolyloxy)-1-butoxyethane	112
p-Cresol (excess)	Butoxyethylene	H₃PO₄ (trace)	50	3	1-(p-Tolyloxy)-1-butoxyethane	112
o-Cresol (1)	Cinnamyl alcohol (1)	H₂SO₄ (10 cc.) (250 ml. HOAc)	reflux	5	2-Benzyl-6-methylcoumaran, 3-phenyl-2-(2'-hydroxy-3'-methylphenyl)-1-propene (small amount)	145
m-Cresol (1)	Cinnamyl alcohol (1)	H₂SO₄ (10 cc.) (250 ml. HOAc)	reflux	5	2-Benzyl-5-methylcoumaran, 3-phenyl-2-(2'-hydroxy-4'-methyl-phenyl)-1-propene (small amt.)	145
p-Cresol (1)	Cinnamyl alcohol (1)	H₂SO₄ (10 cc.) (250 ml. HOAc)	reflux	5	2-Benzyl-4-methylcoumaran, 3-phenyl-2-(2'-hydroxy-5'-methyl-phenyl)-1-propene (small amount.)	145
m-Cresol (1)	Oleyl alcohol (1)	H₂SO₄ (2)	60-70	2	Sulfuric acid ester of hydroxy-tolyl octadecyl alcohol	141
Phenetole	Allyl alcohol	Dowex-5[d]	reflux	—	Allylphenetole (30%)	62a
3-Methylanisole (0.33)	Allyl alcohol (0.33)	H₃PO₄ (1)	75	2	3-Methyl-6-allylanisole (6 g.)	177
Guaiacol (1)	Oleyl alcohol (1)	H₂SO₄ (2)	r.t.	168	Sulfuric acid ester of guaiacol substituted stearyl alcohol	141
1-Naphthol (1) (HOAc)	Oleyl alcohol (1)	H₂SO₄ (1.5)	50	several	Condensation product	141

Table continued

TABLE XVII (*continued*)

Aromatic (Moles)	Unsaturate (Moles)	Catalyst (Moles)	Temp. (°C)	Time (hrs.)	Products (% Yield)	Ref.
2-Naphthol (44 g.)	2-Methyl-3-buten-2-ol (70 g.)	H_3PO_4	40-45	40	2-Methyl-4-(4-hydroxynaphthyl)-2-butene (20 g.)	93
p-t-Octyl phenol (1)	Oleyl alcohol (1)	H_2SO_4 (1)	70	several	Hydroxy-t-octylphenyloctadecyl monosulfate	141
o-Methylanisole	4-Hydroxy-2-hexene	H_2SO_4 (2 g.)	20-30	22.5	4-(3'-Methyl-4'-methoxyphenyl)hexene (75%)	210
o-Methylanisole (9 g.)	4-(3'-methyl-4'-methoxyphenyl)hexene (9 g.)	H_2SO_4	-3, r.t.	7, 15.5	2,3-Di-(3'-methyl-4'-methoxyphenyl)hexane (26%)	201
Resorcinol (1) (HOAc)	Oleyl alcohol (1)	H_2SO_4 (2)	50	2	—	141
m-Xylohydroquinone (5 g.)	Allyl alcohol (5 cc.)	$ZnCl_2$ (1.5 g.) (10 cc. benzene)	150, 200 (s.t.)	1, 1	2,4,6-Trimethyl-7-allyl-5-hydroxycoumaran	196
Trimethylhydroquinone (1 g.)	Allyl alcohol (1 cc.)	$ZnCl_2$ (0.3 g.) (5 cc. benzene)	200 (s.t.)	3.5	2,4,6-Tetramethyl-5-hydroxycoumarone (0.2 g.)	196(193)
Trimethylhydroquinone (1 g.)	3-Buten-2-ol (1 cc.)	$ZnCl_2$ (0.3 g.) (5 cc. benzene)	200 (s.t.)	3	2,3,4,6-Pentamethyl-5-hydroxycoumarone (0.07 g.)	196(193)
Trimethylhydroquinone (2 g.)	4-Penten-3-ol (2 cc.)	$ZnCl_2$ (0.6 g.) (5 cc. benzene)	150	1	2,4,6-Tetramethyl-3-ethyl-5-hydroxycoumaran	196
2,3,6-Trimethylhydroquinone (0.7 g.)	Phytol (1.0 g.)	$ZnCl_2$ (0.3 g.)	150-200, 180-190	0.25	Racemic α-tocopherol (0.2 g.)	51
m-Xyloquinol (0.46 g.) (in 7 cc. decalin)	Phytol (1 g.)	$ZnCl_2$ (1.0 g.)	reflux	9	Racemic α-tocopherol (0.45 g.)	51

a For respective temperature.
b Plus cyclic compounds.
c For each catalyst, respectively.
d Cationic sulfonic acid type exchange resin.

TABLE XVIII. Benzene with unsaturated acids

Benzene (Moles)	Unsaturated acid (Moles)	Catalyst (Moles)	Temp. (°C)	Time (hrs.)	Products (% Yield)	Ref.
	Acrylic acid	AlCl₃ or BF₃	—	—	β-Phenylpropionic acid	81
50 g.	Crotonic acid (10 g.)	AlCl₃ (13 g.)	30–40	672	β-Phenylbutyric acid	59
400 cc.	Crotonic acid (86 g.)	AlCl₃ (280 g.)–HCl	r.t.	96	2-Phenylbutyric acid (85%)	13 (58,59)
250 cc.	Methacrylic acid (34 g.)	AlCl₃ (160 g.)–HCl	r.t.	0.5	α-Phenylisobutyric acid (30 g.)	159
380 ml.	2-Pentenoic acid (40 g.)	AlCl₃ (80 g.)	w.b.; reflux	4; 16	4-Phenylvaleric acid (70%)	136 (58)
50 g.	Δ¹-Isopentenoic acid (5 g.)	AlCl₃ (6 g.)	30–40	672	Phenylisopropylacetic acid[a]	59
15 g.	Tiglic acid (2 g.)	AlCl₃ (3 g.)	30–40	672	α,β-Dimethyl-β-phenylpropionic acid	59
200 cc.	Pyromucic acid (8 g.) (2-furoic acid)	AlCl₃ (19 g.)	cool; heat	2; 6	β-Phenyl-α,β-dihydropyromucic acid (5 g.)	97
300 cc.	β,β-Dimethylacrylic acid (25 g.)	AlCl₃ (34 g.)	r.t.	504	β-Phenylisovaleric acid (25 g.), some 2-phenyl-2,4,4-trimethylpentane-3,5-dicarboxylic acid	20 (53)
150 ml.	2-Hexenoic acid (23 g.)	AlCl₃ (30 g.)	0; 50	6	5-Phenylcaproic acid	135
	β,γ-Hydrosorbinic acid	AlCl₃			Phenylhexyl acid	58
700 cc.	1-Cyclopentene-1-carboxylic acid (35 g.)	AlCl₃ (135 g.)	cold	0.5	3-Phenylcyclopentanecarboxylic acid (85%)	18 (133)
250 g.	Sorbic acid (32 g.)	AlCl₃ (72 g.)	50; 35; 55	1; 3.5; 2	5-Phenylcaproic acid	135
	Allylmalonic acid	AlCl₃	—	—	No aromatic acid, only lactones	58
75 ml.	3-Methyl-2-hexenoic acid (20 g.)	AlCl₃ (30 g.)	0	6	3-Methyl-5-phenylcaproic acid (21 g.) (exclusively)	135
100 ml.	Cyclohexene-1-carboxylic acid (6.5 g.)	AlCl₃ (13 g.)	45–50	—	1-Phenylcyclohexane-4-carboxylic acid	133
	Cyclohexylideneacetic acid	AlCl₃	35–40; 50	5	4-Phenylcyclohexaneacetic acid	134

Table continued

TABLE XVIII (continued)

Benzene (Moles)	Unsaturated acid (Moles)	Catalyst (Moles)	Temp. (°C)	Time (hrs.)	Products (% Yield)	Ref.
50 cc.	Δ¹-Cyclohexenylacetic acid (10 g.)	AlCl₃	0	0.5	4-Phenylcyclohexylacetic acid (7%)	46 (45,134)
—	Δ¹-Cyclohexenylacetic acid	AlCl₃	25	7	2-Phenylcyclohexylacetic acid[b]	67a
180 cc.	2-Nonenoic acid (26 g.)	AlCl₃ (33.5 g.)	reflux	16	Phenylnonanoic acid (44%; mostly 8-phenyl)	136
40 cc.	Coumarilic acid (5 g.) (2-benzofurancarboxylic acid)	AlCl₃ (8.2 g.)	60–70	6	α-Phenyl-α,β,-dihydrocoumarilic acid (2.9 g.)	97
150 ml.	β-Cyclohexylacrylic acid (20 g.)	AlCl₃ (19 g.)	50	5	4-Phenylcyclohexanepropionic acid	134
220 cc.	Cinnamic acid (15 g.)	AlCl₃ (25 g.)	<10	1	β,β-Diphenylpropionic acid (87%)	52 (59,229)
3.3 cc.	α-Phenylacrylic acid (0.5 g.)	AlCl₃ (0.5 g.)	—	504	Crude product (0.21 g.) yielded α,α-Diphenylpropionic acid	53 (59)
—	o-Chlorocinnamic acid (0.2 g.)	AlCl₃	0	1	β-o-Chlorophenyl-β-phenylpropionic acid (0.05 g.)	53
90 cc.	o-Chlorocinnamic acid (4.5 g.)	AlCl₃ (6 g.)	35–40	1	cis-o-Chlorocinnamic acid	53
75 cc.	p-Chlorocinnamic acid (20 g.)	AlCl₃ (24 g.)	<10	1	β,β-Diphenylpropionic acid	66a
75 cc.	o-Chlorocinnamic acid	AlCl₃ (24 g.)	0; 35–40	1	β,β-Diphenylpropionic acid	66a
50 g.	Cinnamic acid (25 g.)	H₂SO₄ (125 g.)	50	1–2	2,2-Diphenylpropionic acid (3–4 g.)[c]	115
80 g.	Allocinnamic acid (4 g.)	H₂SO₄ (4 g.)	w.b.	4	2,2-Diphenylpropionic acid (4 g.)	114
—	Cinnamic acid	HF	—	—	2,2-Diphenylpropionic acid	185
100 cc.	p-Methylcinnamic acid (4 g.)	AlCl₃ (6 g.)	r.t.[a]	48–72	β,β-Diphenylpropionic acid (4.2 g.)	53
25 g.	β-Campholenic acid (4 g.)	AlCl₃ (8 g.)	r.t.; 40–50	96; 494	Phenyldihydrocampholenic acid	58

	Acid	Catalyst	Temp.	Time (hr.)	Product	Ref.
100 cc.	β-Methyl-β-phenylacrylic acid (4 g.)	$AlCl_3$ (6 g.)	r.t.	48–72	β-Phenyl-n-butyric acid (1.7 g.)	53
60 g.	α-Methylcinnamic acid (10 g.)	$AlCl_3$	—	336	α-Methyl-β,β-diphenylpropionic acid	59
—	Phenylisocrotonic acid	$AlCl_3$	—	—	γ,γ-Diphenylbutyric acid	58
30 g.	2-Phenyl-2-butenoic acid (3 g.)	$AlCl_3$ (3 g.)	30–40	672	No reaction	59
40 cc.	p-Methoxycinnamic acid (1.2 g.)	$AlCl_3$ (4.3 g.)	r.t.	48–72	β-(4-Hydroxy-3-methylphenyl)-β-phenylpropionic acid (0.5 g. crude)	53
75 cc.	β-Benzoylacrylic acid (2 g.)	$AlCl_3$ (20 g.)	w.b.	12	2-Phenyl-3-benzoylpropionic acid (0.4 g.)	161
30 g.	α-Ethylcinnamic acid (4 g.)	$AlCl_3$	—	336	α-Ethyl-β,β-diphenylpropionic acid	59
—	Isolauronolic acid (15 g.)	$AlCl_3$	—	—	Phenyldihydroisolauronolic acid	58
—	β,γ-Hydropiperinic acid	$AlCl_3$	—	—	No satisfactory results	58
200 cc.	α-Phenylcinnamic acid (7 g.)	$AlCl_3$ (6 g.)	—	336	α,β,β-Triphenylpropionic acid	59
10 cc.	β,β-Diphenylacrylic acid (0.9 g.)	$AlCl_3$ (1 g.)	r.t.	48–92	β,β-Diphenylpropionic acid (0.5 g.)	53
100 g.	Linoleic (20 g.)	$AlCl_3$ (14 g.)	w.b.	few	Acid, mol. wt. 396; acid # 168	124
400 g.	Oleic acid (200 g.)	$AlCl_3$ (100 g.)	80	—	9- and 10-Phenylstearic acid (35%)	138 (75,169)
—	Erucic acid	$AlCl_3$	—	—	Phenylbehenic acid	30 (124)
35 cc.	Oleic or elaidic acid (20.7 g.)	$AlCl_3$ (11.5 g.)	reflux	16	Phenylstearic acid (5 g.; 50% 17-phenyl)	136 (117, 124,138, 200)

a Same results if kept 1 hour at < 10°.

b See entry next above.

c Also phenylenediphenylpropionic acid and 3-phenyl-1-indanone (53).

d This is no doubt β-phenylisovaleric acid (53).

TABLE XIX. Alkylbenzenes with unsaturated acids

Aromatic (Moles)	Unsaturated acid (Moles)	Catalyst (Moles)	Temp. (°C)	Time (hrs.)	Products (% Yield)	Ref.
Toluene	Crotonic acid	AlCl₃	30–40	672	No addition product	59
Toluene (200 cc.)	Methacrylic acid (20 g.)	AlCl₃ (70 g.)	5–10	7	α-Tolylisobutyric acid (o- and p-isomers 75%)	44
Toluene (50 g.)	Δ¹-Isopentenic acid (5 g.)	AlCl₃ (6 g.)	30–40	672	Tolylisopentanoic acid (nearly quantitative)	59
Toluene	Angelica acid	AlCl₃	—	—	4-Tolyl-3-pentenoic acid	58
Toluene (191 g.)	2,3,3-Trimethylacrylic acid (0.45)	AlCl₃ (0.8)—HCl (13 g.)	10	7.5	2,3-Dimethyl-3-p-tolylbutyric acid (35 g.)	222
Toluene (30 cc.)	Coumarilic acid (4 g.)	AlCl₃ (6 g.)	heat	1	α-p-Tolyl-α,β-dihydrocoumarilic acid	97
Toluene (300 cc.)	β-Benzoylacrylic acid	AlCl₃ (50 g.)	100	10	2-Tolyl-3-benzoylpropionic acid (5 g.)	161
Toluene (200 cc.)	β-Toluylacrylic acid (15 g.)	AlCl₃ (50 g.)	w.b.	10	2-Tolyl-3-toluylpropionic acid (20%)	161
Toluene (excess)	Oleic acid (0.71)	AlCl₃ (0.75)	80	6	Tolylstearic acid (38%)	200(161a)
m-Xylene (80.5 g.)	Dimethylacrylic acid (19.5 g.)	AlCl₃ (29.3 g.)	5 r.t.	0.25 5.5	β-(3,5-Dimethylphenyl)isovaleric acid (97%)	192 (42)
p-Xylene (8.0 g.)	Dimethylacrylic acid (5.0 g.)	AlCl₃	0	1.5	β-(2,5-Dimethylphenyl)isovaleric acid (4.2 g.)ᵃ	191
Ethylbenzene (100 ml.)	Cinnamic acid (20 g.)	AlCl₃ (40 g.) (80 ml. C₆H₅NO₂)	10–15 r.t.	24	β-Phenyl-β-(4-ethylphenyl)propionic acid (82%)	149
m-Xylene (100 g.)	Cinnamic acid (4 g.)	H₂SO₄ (5 g.)	w.b.	4	β-Xylyl-β-phenylpropionic acid	114
Xylene (excess)	Oleic acid (0.70 g.)	AlCl₃ (0.75)	80	6	Xylylstearic acid (47%)	200 (43)
Pseudocumene (0.36)	Dimethylacrylic acid (0.1)	AlCl₃ (0.2)	–10	2.0	β-(3,4,5-Trimethylphenyl)isovaleric acid (20.8 g.)	191
Hemimellitene (6 g.)	Dimethylacrylic acid (2.5 g.)	AlCl₃	–10	2	β-(3,4,5-Trimethylphenyl)isovaleric acid (6.65 g.)	191
Mesitylene (31.5 g.)	Dimethylacrylic acid	AlCl₃	0	—	"Dimethylphenylisovaleric acid" (3.0 g.)	191

Durene (0.3)	Senecioic acid (0.1) (dimethylacrylic)	AlCl$_3$ (0.23) CS$_2$	r.t. 30–35	5.5 4.5	β-(3,4,5)-Trimethylphenylisovaleric acid (15%), pentamethylbenzene, isovaleric acid	188
Isodurene (0.41)	Senecioic acid (0.2)	AlCl$_3$ (0.4)	r.t. 45	4.5 0.75	β-(3,4,5)-Trimethylphenylisovaleric acid (53%), pentamethylbenzene (51%) isovaleric acid, durene	188
Prehnitene (28 g.)	Senecioic acid (0.1)	AlCl$_3$ (16 g.)	r.t. 45	4.5 0.75	β-(3,4,5)-Trimethylphenylisovaleric acid (51%), pentamethylbenzene (small amount)	188
Pentamethyl-benzene (44.4 g.)	Senecioic acid (0.1)	AlCl$_3$ (0.23) CS$_2$ (100 cc.)	r.t. 30–35	5.5 4.5	Acidic gum (20%), isovaleric acid, hexamethylbenzene	188

a Structure is doubtful.

TABLE XX. Halogenated benzenes with unsaturated acids

Aromatic (Moles)	Unsaturated acid (Moles)	Catalyst (Moles)	Temp. (°C)	Time (hrs.)	Products (% Yield)	Ref.
Bromobenzene (80 cc.)	Cinnamic acid (5 g.)	AlCl$_3$ (8.25 g.)	30–45 r.t.	1 48–72	β-p-Bromophenyl-β-phenylpropionic acid (2.15 g.)	52
Bromobenzene (5 g.)	p-Bromocinnamic acid (45 g.)	AlCl$_3$ (15 g.)	r.t.	3	β,β-Di-(p-bromophenyl)propionic acid (5 g.)	149
Chlorobenzene (130 cc.)	Cinnamic acid (10 g.)	AlCl$_3$ (16.5 g.)	30–45	1	β-p-Chlorophenyl-β-phenylpropionic acid	52
Chlorobenzene	Cinnamic acid	AlCl$_3$	30–45	1	β,β-Di-(p-chlorophenyl)propionic acid (4.3 g.)	52
Chlorobenzene	p-Chlorocinnamic acid	AlCl$_3$	ice bath 35–40	1	β,β-Di-(p-chlorophenyl)propionic acid	52
Chlorobenzene	o-Chlorocinnamic acid	AlCl$_3$	ice bath 35–40	1	β,β-Di-(p-chlorophenyl)propionic acid	52
Fluorobenzene (25 cc.)	Cinnamic acid (2 g.)	AlCl$_3$ (3.3 g.)	30–45 r.t.	1 48–72	β-p-Fluorophenyl-β-phenylpropionic acid (1 g.)	52
Bromobenzene (excess)	Oleic acid (0.709)	AlCl$_3$ (0.75)	80	6	Bromophenylstearic acid (22%)	200
Chlorobenzene (excess)	Oleic acid (0.709)	AlCl$_3$ (0.75)	80	6	Chlorophenylstearic acid (25%)	200

TABLE XXI. Polycyclic hydrocarbons with unsaturated acids

Aromatic (Moles)	Unsaturated acid (Moles)	Catalyst (Moles)	Temp. (°C)	Time (hrs.)	Products (% Yield)	Ref.
Tetralin (37.5 g.)	β,β-Dimethylacrylic acid (7.5 g.)	$AlCl_3$ (13.3 g.)	-10	1.25	β-(6-Tetralyl)isovaleric acid (68%)	189
Naphthalene (20 g.)	Oleic acid (30 g.)	$AlCl_3$ (20 g.) 50 ml. (CS_2)	r.t. r.t.	2 2	9- or 10-(1-Naphthyl)stearic acid	165
Naphthalene (0.5)	Oleic acid (0.5)	HF (25)	60	1	Naphthylstearic acid (61%)	32
Naphthalene (1.3–2)	Oleic acid (1)	Acid activated clay (50 wt. %)	0–5 210	20 2–3	Naphthylstearic acid	108b

TABLE XXII. Phenolics and derivatives with unsaturated acids

Aromatic (Moles)	Unsaturated acid (Moles)	Catalyst (Moles)	Temp. (°C)	Time (hrs.)	Products (% Yield)	Ref.
Phenol (5 g.)	Cinnamic acid (5 g.)	$HOAc$–H_2SO_4 (7 cc./7 cc.)	w.b.	few	3,4-Dihydro-4-phenylcoumarin (only product)	113
Phenol (0.76)ᵃ (100 ml. tetralin)	Cinnamic acidᵃ (0.38)	H_2SO_4 (15 g.)	reflux	2	3,4-Dihydro-4-phenyl-coumarin (25 g.), β-phenyl-β-(4-hydroxyphenyl)pro-pionic acid (26 g.)	30a
Phenol (10 g.)	Allocinnamic acid (10 g.)	$HOAc$–H_2SO_4 (10 g./10 cc.)	0–r.t.	3.5	1-Hydroxyphenyl-1-phenyl-propionic acid, phenyl-hydrocoumarin (4.5 g.)	113
Phenol (10 pts.)	Oleic acid (10 pts.)	70% $HClO_4$ (1 pt.)	to 90 90–100	3 5	Oxyphenylstearic acid, oxy-phenylenedistearic acid	50

Aromatic	Unsaturated acid	Catalyst	Temp. (°C)	Time (hr)	Product	Ref.
Phenol (300 g.)	Oleic acid (850 g.)	BF$_3$ (46 g.)	r.t.	24	Oil (692 g.), acid no. 166, neutralization no. 84.6	170a
Phenol	Oleic acid	AlCl$_3$ [b]	—	—	Hydroxyphenyl derivative of stearic acid	67a
Phenol (1)	Elaeostearic acid (1)	HCl–Acetic	100	1	Hydroxyphenyl derivative	142
Phenol (0.11)	Chaulmoogric acid (0.1)	H$_2$SO$_4$–40 HOAc (5.6 cc. each)	0–5 r.t.	336	Hydroxyphenyldihydrochaulmoogric acid	146 (142)
Phenol	Linoleic acid	AlCl$_3$–CS$_2$ or BF$_3$	35	—	p-Hydroxyphenyl derivative of oleic acid [a]	89
Anisole (35 cc.)	Cinnamic acid (2.5 g.)	AlCl$_3$ (4.2 g.)	10 r.t.	1 48–72	β-p-Methoxyphenyl-β-phenyl-propionic acid	52
Anisole (excess)	Oleic acid (0.709)	AlCl$_3$ (0.75)	80	6	Methoxyphenylstearic acid	200
o-Cresol (108 pts.)	Undecylenic acid (92 pts.)	70% HClO$_4$ (2 pts.)	90–100	2	(3-Methyl-4-hydroxyphenyl)-undecanic acid (much) (35%)	50
o-Cresol	Chaulmoogric acid	H$_2$SO$_4$–HOAc	0–5 r.t.	1 336	Hydroxy-o-tolyldihydrochaul-moogric acid	146
m-Cresol (1)	Oleic acid (1)	H$_2$SO$_4$–HOAc	—	—	10-(2-Hydroxy-4-methyl-phenyl)stearic acid	143 (142)
m-Cresol	Chaulmoogric acid	H$_2$SO$_4$–HOAc	0–5 r.t.	1 336	Hydroxy-m-tolyl-dihydro-chaulmoogric acid	146
m-Cresol	Oleic acid	H$_2$SO$_4$	—	—	2-(Hydroxy-4-methylphenyl)-stearic acid	182
p-Cresol	Chaulmoogric acid	H$_2$SO$_4$–HOAc	0–5 r.t.	1 336	Hydroxy-p-tolyldihydro-chaulmoogric acid	146
Cresols (200 g.) Thymol [d] (solvent) [c]	Oleic acid (300 g.) Cinnamic acid [d]	BF$_3$ (25 g.) H$_2$SO$_4$ [c]	— reflux [c]	12 2 [c]	Viscous oil (365 g.) β-Phenyl-β-(4-hydroxy-2-methyl-5-isopropylphenyl)-propionic acid and a dihydrocoumarin	23 30a
2-Naphthol (114 pts.) (200 pts. nitro-benzene)	Crotonic acid (43 pts.)	70% HClO$_4$ (15 pts.)	90–100	5	β-(β-Hydroxynaphthyl)buta-noic acid	50

Table continued

TABLE XXII (continued)

Aromatic (Moles)	Unsaturated acid (Moles)	Catalyst (Moles)	Temp. (°C)	Time (hrs.)	Products (% Yield)	Ref.
1-Naphthol (144 pts.; 500 pts. benzene)	Maleic acid (49 pts.)	70% $HClO_4$ (5 pts.)	35–45 45–50	— 5	(1-Hydroxynaphthyl)succinic acid	50
Diphenyl ether (excess)	Oleic acid (0.709)	$AlCl_3$ (0.75)	80	6	Phenoxyphenylstearic acid (29%)	200
Resorcinol (35 g.)	Linoleic acid (35 g.)	$AlCl_3$ (19 g.)–CS_2 (300 cc.) or BF_3	35	10	m-Hydroxyphenoxy derivatives of oleic acid	89
Resorcinol (2 g.)	Maleic anhydride (2 g.)	$AlCl_3$ (5 g.) (200 cc. CS_2)	reflux	0.5	No alkylation	161

 a H_2SO_4–HOAc gives similar product but yield is lower.   b BF_3 or H_2SO_4 unsuccessful.   c Probable materials and conditions. d See ref. 30a for preparation of a variety of 3,4-dihydro-4-arylcoumarins via condensation of various phenols with cinnamic acid and substituted cinnamic acids.

TABLE XXIII. Benzene with unsaturated esters

Benzene (Moles)	Unsaturated ester (Moles)	Catalyst (Moles)	Temp. (°C)	Time (hrs.)	Products (% Yield)	Ref.
1	Vinyl acetate (43 g.)	AlCl$_3$ (200 g.)	60–70	few	Small amts. of *unsym*-diphenylethane and 9,10-dimethyl-9,10-dihydro-anthracene,[b] etc.	106
—	Vinyl acetate	AlCl$_3$ or BF$_3$	—	—	Phenylethyl acetate	81
1	Ethyl 4-pentenoate (1)	AlCl$_3$ (2)	0–5	3.75	Ethyl 4-phenylvalerate (93%)	131 (39)
6	Ethyl 2-methyl-4-pentenoate (1)	AlCl$_3$ (1.3)	35	2	Ethyl 4-phenyl-2-methylpentanoate (80–90%)	39
6	Ethyl 2-ethyl 4-pentenoate (1)	AlCl$_3$ (1.3)	35	2	Ethyl 4-phenyl-2-ethylpentanoate (80–90%)	39
50 g.	Ethyl Δ²-cyclopentenyl-acetate	AlCl$_3$ (20 g.)	r.t.	0.25	Ethyl 2-phenylcyclopentylacetate (15 g.)	29a
15 cc.	Coumarine (3 g.)	AlCl$_3$ (5.5 g.)	heat	10	β-Phenyl-α,β-dihydrocoumarine	97
2340 pts.	Allyl orthoborate (303 pts.)	FeCl$_3$ (162 pts.)	25–35 70	0.66 1	Allylbenzene (209 pts.)	199
30 ml.	Ethyl (2-methylcyclohexenyl) and (2-methyl-cyclohexylidene)-acetates (15 g.)	AlCl$_3$ (21.8 g.)	0	3	Ethyl 2-methyl-4-phenylcyclohexylacetate	35
Excess	Angelicalactone (10 g.)	AlCl$_3$ (15 g.)	—	few weeks	4,4-Diphenylpentanoic acid	58
40 g.	Ethyl undecylenate (55 g.)	AlCl$_3$ (40 g.)	heat	3.0	Phenylenediundecanoic diethyl ester	63
—	4-Carbomethoxystilbene	AlCl$_3$–HCl	r.t.	5	1,1-Diphenyl-2-*p*-carbomethoxyphenyl-ethane (63%)	66a
—	4-Bromo-4'-carbomethoxystilbene	AlCl$_3$–HCl	r.t.	5	1,1-Diphenyl-2-*p*-carbomethoxyphenyl-ethane (75%)	66a
100 g.	4-Chloro-4'-carbomethoxystilbene (2.5 g.)	AlCl$_3$ (4 g.)–HCl	r.t.	5	1,1-Diphenyl-2-*p*-carbomethoxyphenyl-ethane (76%)	66a
—	Methyl oleate	AlCl$_3$	a	a	Phenylenedistearic acid, some tri-substituted benzene	29
200 g.	Oleyl acetate (80 g.)	AlCl$_3$ (34.5 g.)	35–65	10	9- and 10-Phenylstearyl acetate (50%)	186

a Method of ref. 63.   b See ref. 185a.

TABLE XXIV. Alkylbenzenes with unsaturated esters

Aromatics (Moles)	Unsaturated ester (Moles)	Catalyst (Moles)	Temp. (°C)	Time (hrs.)	Products (% Yield)	Ref.
Toluene (80 cc.)	Ethyl 4-pentenoate (1)	AlCl₃ (2)	0–5	3.75	Ethyl 4-(m-tolyl)valerate (81%)	131 (22)
Toluene (6)	Ethyl 4-pentenoate (1)	AlCl₃ (1.3)	35	2	Ethyl 4-tolylpentenoate (80–92%)	39
Toluene (6)	Ethyl 2-methyl-4-pentenoate (1)	AlCl₃ (1.3)	35	2	Ethyl 4-tolyl-2-methylpentanoate (80–92%)	39
Toluene (6)	Ethyl 2-ethyl-4-pentenoate (1)	AlCl₃ (1.3)	35	2	Ethyl 4-tolyl-2-ethylpentanoate (80–92%)	39
Toluene (50 g.)	Ethyl Δ²-cyclopentenylacetate (20 g.)	AlCl₃ (20 g.)	r.t.	0.25	Ethyl 2-(o- and p-tolyl)cyclopentylacetate; m-tolylene-2,2-biscyclopentylacetate	29a
Toluene (20 g.)	Ethyl undecylate (22 g.)	AlCl₃ (14 g.)	0	2	Ethyl 10- (12 g.) and 11- (12 g.)-p-tolylhendecanoate	30
Toluene (excess)	Ethyl oleate (0.5)	AlCl₃ (0.535)	80	6	Ethyl tolylstearate (37%)	200
o-Xylene	Ethyl 4-pentenoate	AlCl₃	0–5		Ethyl 4-(3′,4′-dimethylphenyl)pentanoate (81%)	216
m-Xylene (120 cc.)	Ethyl 4-pentanoate (20 g.)	AlCl₃ (41.6 g.)	0–5	3.75	Ethyl 4-(2′,4′-dimethylphenyl)pentanoate (81%)	131
p-Xylene (6)	Ethyl 4-pentenoate (1)	AlCl₃ (1.3)	35	2	Ethyl 4-xylylpentanoate (80–92%)	39
p-Xylene (6)	Ethyl 2-methyl-4-pentenoate (1)	AlCl₃ (1.3)	35	2	Ethyl 4-xylyl-2-methylpentanoate (80–92%)	39
p-Xylene (6)	Ethyl 2-ethyl-4-pentenoate (1)	AlCl₃ (1.3)	35	2	Ethyl 4-xylyl-2-ethylpentanoate (80–92%)	39
o-Xylene	Ethyl Δ²-cyclopentenylacetate	AlCl₃	—	—	Ethyl o-xylyl-2-cyclopentylacetate	31
m-Xylene	Ethyl Δ²-cyclopentenylacetate	AlCl₃	—	—	Ethyl m-xylyl-2-cyclopentylacetate	31

p-Xylene	Ethyl Δ²-cyclopentenylacetate	AlCl₃	—	—	Ethyl p-xylyl-2-cyclopentylacetate	31
Cumene (75 cc.)	Ethyl 4-pentenoate (25 g.)	AlCl₃ (52 g.)	0–5	3+	Ethyl 4-(p-cumyl)valerate (66%)	130 (120)
p-Cymene (100 cc.)	Ethyl 4-pentenoate (15 g.)	AlCl₃ (30 g.)	0–5	3+	Ethyl 4-(2'-methyl-5'-isopropylphenyl)-valerate (58%)	130
Cumene (3600 pts.)	Allylorthoborate (303 pts.)	FeCl₃ (162 pts.)	25–35 / 70	0.66 / 1	p-Allylcumene (325 pts.)	199
Mesitylene	Ethyl Δ²-cyclopentenylacetate	AlCl₃	—	—	Ethyl 2-mesityl-2-cyclopentylacetate	31

TABLE XXV. Halogenated benzenes with unsaturated esters

Aromatic (Moles)	Unsaturated ester (Moles)	Catalyst (Moles)	Temp. (°C)	Time (hrs.)	Products (% Yield)	Ref.
Bromobenzene (6)	Ethyl 4-pentenoate (1)	AlCl$_3$ (1.3)	35	2	Ethyl 4-(bromophenyl)-pentanoate (63–86%)	39
Chlorobenzene (6)	Ethyl 4-pentenoate (1)	AlCl$_3$ (1.3)	35	2	Ethyl 4-(chlorophenyl)-pentanoate (63–86%)	39
Fluorobenzene (6)	Ethyl 4-pentenoate (1)	AlCl$_3$ (1.3)	35	2	Ethyl 4-(fluorophenyl)-pentanoate (63–86%)	39
Bromobenzene (6)	Ethyl 2-methyl-4-pentenoate (1)	AlCl$_3$ (1.3)	35	2	Ethyl 4-(bromophenyl)-2-methyl-pentanoate (63–86%)	39
Chlorobenzene (6)	Ethyl 2-methyl-4-pentenoate (1)	AlCl$_3$ (1.3)	35	2	Ethyl 4-(chlorophenyl)-2-methyl-pentanoate (63–86%)	39
Fluorobenzene (6)	Ethyl 2-methyl-4-pentenoate (1)	AlCl$_3$ (1.3)	35	2	Ethyl 4-(fluorophenyl)-2-methyl-pentanoate (63–86%)	39
Bromobenzene (6)	Ethyl 2-ethyl-4-pentenoate (1)	AlCl$_3$ (1.3)	35	2	Ethyl 4-(bromophenyl)-2-ethyl-pentanoate (63–86%)	39
Bromobenzene	Ethyl Δ^2-cyclopentenyl-acetate	AlCl$_3$	—	—	No reaction	31
Chlorobenzene (6)	Ethyl 2-ethyl-4-pentenoate (1)	AlCl$_3$ (1.3)	35	2	Ethyl 4-(chlorophenyl)-2-ethyl-pentanoate (63–86%)	39
Fluorobenzene (6)	Ethyl 2-ethyl-4-pentenoate (1)	AlCl$_3$ (1.3)	35	2	Ethyl 4-(fluorophenyl)-2-ethyl-pentanoate (63–86%)	39
Bromobenzene (12 g.)	Ethyl undecylenate (22 g.)	AlCl$_3$ (14 g.)	—	—	Ethyl p-bromophenylhendecanoate (5 g.)	30
Chlorobenzene (12 g.) (20 g. CS$_2$)	Ethyl undecylenate (22 g.)	AlCl$_3$ (14 g.)	—	—	Ethyl p-chlorophenylhendecanoate (5 g.)	30

TABLE XXVI. Polycyclic hydrocarbons with unsaturated esters

Aromatic (Moles)	Unsaturated ester (Moles)	Catalyst (Moles)	Temp. (°C)	Time (hrs.)	Products (% Yield)	Ref.
Naphthalene (150 g.)	Ethyl 4-pentenoate (52 g.)	$AlCl_3$ (88 g.)	5–25	2	Ethyl 4-(α- and β-naphthyl)valerate	38
Naphthalene (15 g.) (60 ml. CS_2)	Ethyl 4-pentenoate (15 g.)	$AlCl_3$ (30 g.)	0–15	1.5[a]	Ethyl 4-(β-naphthyl)valerate	128
Naphthalene	Ethyl undecylenate (22 g.)	$AlCl_3$	—	—	Ethyl naphthylhendecanoate (9 g.)	30
Naphthalene	Ethyl hydnocarpate	$AlCl_3$	—	—	Ethyl naphthyldihydrohydnocarpate (5–6 g.)	30
Tetralin	Ethyl undecylenate (22 g.)	$AlCl_3$	—	—	Ethyl 1,2,3,4-tetrahydronaphthylhendecanate (12 g.) and some bis-aryl derivatives	30
Tetralin (125 cc.)	Ethyl 3-pentenoate (20 g.)	$AlCl_3$ (40 g.)	0–5	—	Ethyl γ-[6-(1,2,3,4-tetrahydronaphthyl)]valerate (25 g.)	214a
Biphenyl	Ethyl undecylenate (22 g.)	$AlCl_3$	—	—	Ethyl biphenylhendecanoate (14 g.)	30
Acenaphthene	Ethyl Δ^2-cyclopentenyl-acetate	$AlCl_3$	—	—	Ethyl 2-(5-acenaphthyl)-2-cyclopentyl-acetate	31
Fluorene	Ethyl undecylenate (22 g.)	$AlCl_3$	—	—	Ethyl 2-fluorenylhendecanoate	30
Fluorene	Methyl oleate	$AlCl_3$	—	—	Methyl 2-fluorenylstearate	30
Polystyrene (o-ClC_6H_4Cl)	Methyl oleate, butyl oleate, or 2-ethylhexyl oleate	($C_6H_5NO_2$)	50–60	8	Clear, tough solid	28

[a] Additional stirring at r.t.

TABLE XXVII. Phenolics and derivatives with unsaturated esters

Aromatic (Moles)	Unsaturated ester (Moles)	Catalyst (Moles)	Temp. (°C)	Time (hrs.)	Products (% Yield)	Ref.
Phenol (1.0)	Vinyl acetate (1.0)	H_2SO_4 (0.1)	r.t.	few days	2-Vinylphenol[a]	144 (15,86)
Phenol (850 pts.)	Methyl oleate (666 pts.)	BF_3–H_2O (1:3 mole)$_3$	110	5	Methyl (9)10-phenylolooctadecan-oic-1-acid ester	55
Phenol (31.3 pts.)	Ethyl oleate (103 pts.)	BF_3 (17 pts.)	70	—	Ethyl (9)10-phenylolooctadecan-oic-1-acid ester (27%)	55
Phenol	Ethyl linoleate	$AlCl_3$–CS_2 or BF_3	35	—	p-Hydroxyphenyl derivative of oleic acid	89
Phenol (139 pts.)	β-Hydroxyethyl-oleate (121 pts.)	BF_3–H_2O (1:3 moles) (12 pts.)	100–160	10–5	β-Hydroxyethyl ester of (9)10-phenylol octadecanoic-1-acid (85%)	55
Anisole (6)	Ethyl 4-pentenoate (1)	$AlCl_3$ (1.3)	35	2	Ethyl 4-(methoxyphenyl)-pentanoate (21%)	39
Anisole	Cyclopentene carboxylic acid methyl ester	$AlCl_3$	20	0.5	2-(4-Hydroxyphenyl)cyclo-pentane carboxylic acid methyl ester	131a
Anisole (6)	Ethyl 2-methyl-4-pentenoate (1)	$AlCl_3$ (1.3)	35	2	Ethyl 4-(methoxyphenyl)-2-methylpentanoate (21%)	39
Anisole	Cyclopentene-1,2-acetic acid methyl ester	$AlCl_3$	20	0.5	2-(4-Hydroxyphenyl)cyclo-pentyl acetic acid methyl ester	131a
Anisole (6)	Ethyl 2-ethyl-4-pentenoate (1)	$AlCl_3$ (1.3)	35	2	Ethyl 4-(methoxyphenyl)-2-ethylpentanoate (21%)	39
Anisole (1.926)	Methyl 1-cyclo-hexeneacetate (0.963)	$AlCl_3$ (1.926) (200 cc. pet. ether)	20	0.5	Methyl 2-(p-methoxyphenyl)-cyclohexane acetate	131a
Anisole	Ethyl Δ2-cyclopen-tenylacetate	$AlCl_3$	—	—	No reaction	31

Aromatic	Reagent	Catalyst	Temp.	Time	Product	Ref.
Anisole	Ethyl α-ethyl cyclohexene-Δ-1,2-acetate[c]	AlCl$_3$	20	0.5	α-Ethyl-2-(4-hydroxyphenyl)-cyclohexane acetic acid ethyl ester	131a
Anisole (55 g.)	Ethyl allylmalonate (20 g.)	AlCl$_3$ (85 g.) (100 g. pet. ether)	—	12	Ethyl p-methoxyphenylpropyl malonate (31–34%)	63 (39)[b]
Anisole	Methyl Δ-1,2-octahydro-1-naphthoate	AlCl$_3$	20	0.5	2-(4-Hydroxyphenyl)deca-hydronaphthoic acid methyl ester	131a
Anisole (1.926)	Hydnocarpic acid methyl ester (0.963)	AlCl$_3$ (1.926)	20	0.5	Methoxyphenyldihydrohydno-carpic acid methyl ester	131a
Anisole (1.926)	Chaulmoogric acid methyl ester (0.963)	AlCl$_3$ (1.926)	20	0.5	Methoxyphenyl dihydrochaul-moogric acid methyl ester	131a
Anisole (200 g.)	Linseed oil (300 g.)	BF$_3$ (18 g.)	—	30	Oil (350 g.)	23
m-Cresol (1)	Allyl acetate (1)	H$_2$SO$_4$ (0.1)	r.t.	few days	2-Isopropenyl-5-methylphenol	144
p-Cresol (130 pts.)	Methyl oleate (99 pts.)	BF$_3$ (2.4 pts.)–CH$_3$OH (12 pts.)	110	5	Methyl (9)10-(5-methyl-2-hy-droxyphenyl)octadecanoate	55
Cresols (150 g.)	Olive oil (300 g.)	BF$_3$ (15.5 g.)	45	few	Viscous oil (370 g.)	23
Cresols (150 g.)	Linseed oil (300 g.)	BF$_3$ (18.5 g.)	45	6–7	Viscous oil (405 g.)	23
o-Cresol methyl ether (75 ml.)	Ethyl 4-pentenoate (20 g.)	AlCl$_3$ (40 g.)	0–5	3+	Ethyl γ-(3-methyl-4-methoxy phenyl)valerate (43%)	215
p-Cresol methyl ether (100 g.)	Ethyl 4-pentenoate (20 g.)	AlCl$_3$ (40 g.)	0–5	3+	Ethyl γ-(2-methoxy-5-methyl phenyl)valerate	215
Veratrole	Ethyl Δ2-cyclo-pentenylacetate (20 g.)	AlCl$_3$	—	—	No reaction	31
1,2-Dimethoxy-benzene	Ethyl ω-undecylenate (22 g.)	AlCl$_3$	—	—	Ethyl 3',4'-dimethoxyphenyl-1-undecylate	30
2-Naphthol (173 pts.)	Methyl oleate (99 pts.)	BF$_3$ (2.4 pts.)–CH$_3$OH (12 pts.)	110	5	Methyl (9)10-(7-hydroxy-1-naphthyl)octadecanoate	55
Diphenyl ether (1)	Ethyl undecylenate (1)	AlCl$_3$ (1)	60–70	5	Mono- and bis-(9-carbethoxy-1-methylnonyl)-diphenyl ether	226
Diphenyl ether (excess)	Methyl oleate (0.5)	AlCl$_3$ (0.535)	80	6	Methyl phenoxyphenyl-stearate (44%)	200

14+F.C. II

^{a} In repeating this work Bader (15) found only polymer. ^{b} 3 hours at 50°.

^{c} Similar results with ethyl α-methyl cyclohexene-Δ-1,2-acetate.

TABLE XXVIII.   Miscellaneous aromatics with unsaturated esters

Aromatic (Moles)	Unsaturated ester (Moles)	Catalyst (Moles)	Temp. (°C)	Time (hrs.)	Products (% Yield)	Ref.
Phenylacetic acid (136 g.)	Ethyl undecylenate (10 g.)	$AlCl_3$ (200 g.) (500 g. CS_2)	reflux	several	ω-(4-carboxymethylphenyl)-α-carboethoxydecane	63
Phenylpropionic acid (148 g.)	Ethyl undecylenate (10 g.)	$AlCl_3$ (200 g.) (500 cc. CS_2)	reflux	several	ω-(4-carboxyethylphenyl)-α-carboethoxydecane	63
2,5-Thioxene (8.5 g.)	Ethyl undecylenate (22 g.)	$AlCl_3$	—	—	Ethyl (2',5'-dimethyl-3'-thienyl)-hendecanoate (4 g.)	30
Thiophene (8.5 g.)	Ethyl undecylenate (22 g.)	$AlCl_3$ (14 g.)—CS_2	—	—	Ethyl 10- and 11-α-thienyl-hendecanoate (2 g.)	30
Thiophene (8.5 g.)	Ethyl hydnocarpate (28 g.)	$AlCl_3$ (14 g.)—CS_2 (20 g.)	—	—	Ethyl (2-thienyl)dihydrohydnocarpate (2 g.)	30
Thiophene (8 g.)	Ethyl Δ²-cyclopentenyl acetate (20 g.)	$AlCl_3$ (20 g.) (150 ml. CS_2)	r.t.	few minutes	Ethyl 2-(2'-thiophenyl)cyclopentane acetate (5 g.)	29a

TABLE XXIX.   Benzene with unsaturated ketones

Benzene (Moles)	Unsaturated ketones (Moles)	Catalyst (Moles)	Temp. (°C)	Time (hrs.)	Products (% Yield)	Ref.
	Ketene	AlCl$_3$			Oil (20%)^f	82
200 cc.	3-Buten-2-one (33 g.)	AlCl$_3$ (90 g.)	10–20	3	4-Phenyl-2-butanone (90%)	41 (7)
39 g.	Acetyl ketene (8.4 g.)	AlCl$_3$ (29 g.)	−5	2	Benzoylacetone (11%)	83
	3-Penten-2-one	AlCl$_3$			4-Phenyl-2-pentanone (25%)	41
200 cc.	3-Penten-2-one (42 g.)	AlCl$_3$ (100 g.)–HCl (16 g.)			4-Phenyl-2-pentanone (74%)	41
200 cc.	3-Methyl-3-buten-2-one (42 g.)	AlCl$_3$ (90 g.)	10–20	3	3-Methyl-4-phenyl-2-butanone (65%)	41
150 ml.	3-Hexen-2-one (37 g.)	AlCl$_3$ (68 g.)	r.t. 40	— 7	5-Phenyl-2-hexanone	133
123 cc.	5-Hexen-2-one (33 g.)	AlCl$_3$ (70 g.)	12–20		5-Phenyl-2-hexanone (82%)	43 (21)
200 cc.	Mesityl oxide (49 g.)	AlCl$_3$ (100 g.)	0–10 10–20 25–30		4-Methyl-4-phenyl-2-pentanone (25%, 31%, 25%)^d	41
200 cc.	Mesityl oxide (49 g.)	AlCl$_3$ (100 g.)–HCl (18 g.)			4-Methyl-4-phenyl-2-pentanone (62%)	41
200 cc.	3-Methyl-3-penten-2-one (50 g.)	AlCl$_3$ (200 g.)–HCl (20 g.)			3-Methyl-4-phenyl-2-pentanone (58%)	41
200 cc.	Mesityl oxide (50 g.)	AlCl$_3$ (90 g.)	r.t.	4	4-Methyl-4-phenyl-2-pentanone (81%)	79 (99)
79 g.	Mesityl oxide (30 g.)	ZnCl$_2$ (25%)–Al$_2$O$_3$ (15 g.)	250 100 atm.	4	t-Butylbenzene (26%), poly-alkylated benzene (40%), acetic acid	167
156 g.	Mesityl oxide (49 g.)	HF (200 g.)	60	4	t-Butylbenzene (38%)	151
40 cc.	2-Cyclohexen-1-one (9 g.)	AlCl$_3$ (20 g.)			Phenylcyclohexanone (5%)^c	41
250 ml.	3-Hepten-2-one (86 g.)	AlCl$_3$ (135 g.)	35	7	6-Phenyl-2-heptanone	133

Table continued

TABLE XXIX (*continued*)

Benzene (Moles)	Unsaturated ketones (Moles)	Catalyst (Moles)	Temp. (°C)	Time (hrs.)	Products (% Yield)	Ref.
60 cc.	2-Allylcyclohexanone (8 g.)	AlCl$_3$ (12 g.)	0–15	1.5[b]	2-(β-Methyl-β-phenylethyl)cyclohexanone (6.5 g.)	128
200 cc.	Phorone (69 g.)[g]	AlCl$_3$ (100 g.)–HCl (33 g.)	5–10	—	2,6-Dimethyl-2,6-diphenyl-4-heptanone (65%)	42
Excess	Benzalacetone	AlCl$_3$	<20	—	4,4-Diphenyl-2-butanone (70%)	51
—	Vinyl *p*-anisyl ketone	AlCl$_3$ (150 g.)–CS$_2$ (400 g.)	60–70	2–3	1-Phenyl-3-(*p*-methoxyphenyl)-1-propanone (40%)[h]	19
Excess	Benzalacetone	AlCl$_3$–HCl	—	—	Benzohydrylacetone (59%)	229
200 cc.	*o*-Chlorobenzalacetophenone (20 g.)	AlCl$_3$ (25 g.)–HCl	r.t.	15	β,β-Diphenylpropiophenone[e]	56
200 cc.	*m*-Chlorobenzalacetophenone (20 g.)	AlCl$_3$ (25 g.)–HCl	r.t.	15	β,β-Diphenylpropiophenone[e]	56
200 cc.	*p*-Chlorobenzalacetophenone (20 g.)	AlCl$_3$ (25 g.)–HCl	r.t.	15	β,β-Diphenylpropiophenone[e]	56 (229)
Excess	*p*-Methylbenzalacetone	AlCl$_3$–HCl	—	—	Benzohydrylacetone (68%)	229
—	Cyclohexenylcyclohexanone	AlCl$_3$	—	—	2-(4'-Phenylcyclohexyl)cyclohexanone[a]	66b
150 ml.	2-Allyl-1-tetralone	AlCl$_3$	<10 10–20	1 3	2-(β-Methyl-β-phenylethyl)-1-tetralone (82%)	129
200 cc.	Benzalpinacolone (10 g.)	AlCl$_3$ (17.5 g.)–HCl	r.t.	20	α-(Benzohydryl)pinacolone	223
200 cc.	*o*-Chlorobenzalpinacolone (10 g.)	AlCl$_3$ (17.5 g.)–HCl	r.t.	20	α-(Benzohydryl)pinacolone	223
200 cc.	*p*-Chlorobenzalpinacolone (10 g.)	AlCl$_3$ (17.5 g.)–HCl	r.t.	20	α-(Benzohydryl)pinacolone	223
100 cc.	1,1-Diphenyl-2-trimethylacetylethylene (5 g.)	AlCl$_3$–HCl (10 g.)	—	—	α-(Benzohydryl)pinacolone (3.6 g.)	2

2700 cc.	Benzalacetophenone (0.58)	AlCl$_3$ (1.2)	10–20 r.t.	0.5 1	β,β-Diphenylpropiophenone (76–85%)	176 (51,100, 102,219)
200 cc.	p-Bromobenzalaceto-phenone (20 g.)	AlCl$_3$–HCl (25 g.)	r.t.	15	β,β-Diphenylpropiophenone	56
200 cc.	m-Bromobenzalaceto-phenone (20 g.)	AlCl$_3$–HCl (25 g.)	r.t.	15	β,β-Diphenylpropiophenone	56
—	m-Chlorobenzalaceto-phenone	AlCl$_3$–HCl	<20	21	β-m-Chlorophenyl-β-phenylpropio-phenone (1.2 g.)	51
200 cc.	p-Methylbenzalaceto-phenone (20 g.)	AlCl$_3$–HCl (25 g.)	r.t.	15	β,β-Diphenylpropiophenone	56
—	β-Phenylcrotono-phenone	AlCl$_3$	<20	22	β-Phenylbutyrophenone, β,β-diphenylbutyrophenone	51
25 cc.	Anisalacetophenone (5 g.)	AlCl$_3$ (15 g.)	r.t.	24	No reaction	219
25 cc.	Benzalmenthone (5 g.)	AlCl$_3$ (15 g.)	r.t.	5	Diphenylmethylmenthone	219
—	Cinamylideneaceto-phenone	AlCl$_3$	<20	6	β,δ,δ-Triphenylvalerophenone	51
200 cc.	Benzalquinaldine (10 g.)	AlCl$_3$ (20 g.)–HCl	0	3	α-Benzohydrylquinaldine	80
—	m-Bromobenzal-quinaldine	AlCl$_3$–HCl	—	—	α-Benzohydrylquinaldine	66a
—	p-Bromobenzal-quinaldine	AlCl$_3$–HCl	—	—	α-Benzohydrylquinaldine	66a
100 cc.	p-Chlorobenzalquinal-dine (10 g.)	AlCl$_3$ (20 g.)	r.t.	12	α-Benzohydrylquinaldine	80
40 cc.	Benzallepidine (2 g.)	AlCl$_3$ (4 g.)	—	3	α-Benzohydryllepidine	64
—	p-Chlorobenzallepi-dine	AlCl$_3$	—	—	α-Benzohydryllepidine	64
—	β-Naphthylacrylo-phenone	AlCl$_3$ (3)	<20	30	β,β-Diphenylpropiophenone (60%)	51
20 cc.	1,1-Diphenyl-2-benzoylethylene (0.75 g.)	AlCl$_3$–HCl (1.5 g.)	25	12	α-Benzohydrylacetophenone	2

Table continued

TABLE XXIX (*continued*)

Benzene (Moles)	Unsaturated ketones (Moles)	Catalyst (Moles)	Temp. (°C)	Time (hrs.)	Products (% Yield)	Ref.
20 cc.	1,1-Di-(p-chlorophenyl)-2-benzoylethylene (0.75 g.)	AlCl$_3$–HCl (1.5 g.)	25	12	α-Benzohydrylacetophenone	2
50 cc.	β-Phenylbenzalquinaldine (5.5 g.)	AlCl$_3$ (15 g.)	r.t.	20	α-Benzohydrylquinaldine (92%)	64
200 cc.	Diphenylindone (20 g.)	AlCl$_3$ (30 g.)	reflux	10	2,3,3-Triphenylhydrindone (21.8 g.)	98

[a] *Para*-structure not certain; dehydrogenation yields 30% *meta*- and *para*-terphenyl.
[b] Additional stirring at r.t.
[c] 45% when hydrochloride is formed first.
[d] At each temperature.
[e] Excellent yield.
[f] Contains much acetophenone and high boilers.
[g] Pretreated with HCl to form the dihydrochloride.
[h] Probably 3-phenyl-1-.

TABLE XXX. Alkylbenzenes with unsaturated ketones

Aromatic (Moles)	Unsaturated ketone (Moles)	Catalyst (Moles)	Temp. (°C)	Time (hrs.)	Products (% Yield)	Ref.
Toluene (5)	Methyl vinyl ketone (1)	AlCl$_3$ (1.3)	20	3	Benzylacetone (59%)	7
Toluene (310 cc.)	3-Penten-2-one (52 g.)	AlCl$_3$ (140 g.)	10–20	3	4-p-Tolyl-2-pentanone (8%) (60%)a	41
Toluene (350 cc.)	3-Methyl-3-buten-2-one (58 g.)	AlCl$_3$ (140 g.)	10–20	3	4-Methyl-4-p-tolyl-2-butanone (82%)	41
Toluene (140 g.)	5-Hexen-2-one (33 g.)	AlCl$_3$ (70 g.)	15–10	—	5-p-Tolyl-2-hexanone (68%)	43
Toluene (2)	Mesityl oxide (1)	AlCl$_3$ (1.2)–HCl (200 g. CS$_2$)	0	4.5	4-Methyl-4-p-tolyl-2-pentanone (40%)	87

Toluene (500 cc.)	Mesityl oxide (100 g.)	AlCl₃ (200 g.)	10–20	3	4-Methyl-4-p-tolyl-2-pentanone (24%) (55%)ᵃ	41
Toluene (184 g.)	Mesityl oxide (49 g.)	HF (170 g.)	65	2	4-t-Butyltoluene (40%), methyl p-tolyl ketone (10–20%)	151
Toluene	3-Methylcyclohexen-2-one	AlCl₃	3.5–4 atm.	—	3-Methyl-3-p-tolylcyclohexanone	147
Toluene (150 ml.)	2-Allyl-1-tetralone (9 g.)	AlCl₃ (15 g.)	10–20	4	2-(β-Methyl-β-p-tolylethyl)-1-tetralone	129
Toluene (600 cc.)	p-Methylbenzalacetone (75 g.)	AlCl₃ (100 g.)	cold r.t.	3	p,p′-Dimethylbenzohydrylacetone (50%)	229
o-Xylene	5-Hexen-2-one	AlCl₃	0–5	35	4-(3′,4′-Dimethylphenyl)-2-pentanone (52%)	216
m-Xylene (300 cc.)	3-Methyl-3-buten-2-one (42 g.)	AlCl₃ (100 g.)	—	—	4-(2′,4′-Dimethylphenyl)-3-methyl-2-butanone (68%)	42
p-Xylene (300 cc.)	3-Methyl-3-buten-2-one (42 g.)	AlCl₃ (100 g.)	—	—	3-Methyl-4-(2′,5′-dimethylphenyl)-2-butanone (51%)	42
m-Xylene (600 cc.)	5-Hexen-2-one (98 g.)	AlCl₃ (200 g.)	9–15	—	Mixture (85%) containing 91% of 5-(2′,4′-dimethylphenyl)-2-hexanone	43
p-Xylene (200 cc.)	5-Hexen-2-one (33 g.)	AlCl₃ (70 g.)	13–18	—	5-(2′,5′-Dimethylphenyl)-2-hexanone (74%)	43
m-Xylene (400 g.)	Mesityl oxide (100 g.)	AlCl₃ (100 g.)—HCl (38 g.)ᵇ	—	—	1,1,3,4,6-Pentamethylindene (48 g.); 4-Methyl-4-(3,5-dimethylphenyl)-2-pentanoneᵃ	42
p-Xylene (300 cc.)	Mesityl oxide (50 g.)	AlCl₃ (100 g.)	—	—	1,1,3,4,7-Pentamethylindene	42
Cumene (80 cc.)	5-Hexen-2-one (20 g.)	AlCl₃ (42 g.)	0–5	3	5-p-Cumylhexan-2-one (40%)	130
p-Cymene (60 cc.)	5-Hexen-2-one (16 g.)	AlCl₃ (32 g.)	0–5	3+	5-(2′-Methyl-5′-isopropylphenyl)-2-hexanone (43%)	130
Pseudocumene (0.1)	Mesityl oxide (0.08)	AlCl₃	0 r.t.	3	1,1,3,4,5,7-Hexamethylindene (4 g.)	191

ᵃ With the hydrochloride of the unsaturated ketone.   ᵇ Author pretreats mesityl oxide with HCl to obtain chloroketone.

TABLE XXXI. Halogenated benzenes with unsaturated ketones

Aromatic (Moles)	Unsaturated ketone (Moles)	Catalyst (Moles)	Temp. (°C)	Time (hrs.)	Products (% Yield)	Ref.
Bromobenzene	Mesityl oxide	$AlCl_3$–CS_2	—	4	4-p-Bromophenyl-4-methyl-2-pentanone[a] (41%)	47
Chlorobenzene	Mesityl oxide	$AlCl_3$–CS_2	—	4	4-p-Chlorophenyl-4-methyl-2-pentanone[a] (95%)	47
Fluorobenzene	Mesityl oxide	$AlCl_3$–CS_2	—	4	4-p-Fluorophenyl-4-methyl-2-pentanone[a] (70%)	47
Chlorobenzene (500 cc.)	Benzalacetone (75 g.)	$AlCl_3$	r.t.	5	p-Chlorobenzohydrylacetone (84.7 g.)	229
Chlorobenzene (350 cc.)	p-Chlorobenzalacetone (27 g.)	$AlCl_3$ (120 g.)	r.t.	24	p,p'-Dichlorobenzohydrylacetone (37 g.)	229
Bromobenzene	Benzalacetophenone	$AlCl_3$	<20	7	β-p-Bromophenyl-β-phenylpropiophenone (50%)	51
Chlorobenzene	Benzalacetophenone	$AlCl_3$	<20	5	β-p-Chlorophenyl-β-phenylpropiophenone (32%)	51
Chlorobenzene	Benzalacetophenone	$AlCl_3$	<20	17	β,β-Di-p-chlorophenylpropiophenone (59%)	51
Chlorobenzene	m-Bromobenzalacetophenone	$AlCl_3$–HCl	r.t.	15	β,β-Di-(p-chlorophenyl)propiophenone	56
Chlorobenzene	p-Chlorobenzalacetophenone	$AlCl_3$–HCl	r.t.	15	β,β-Di-(p-chlorophenyl)propiophenone	56
Chlorobenzene	o-Chlorobenzalacetophenone	$AlCl_3$–HCl	r.t.	15	β,β-Di-(p-chlorophenyl)propiophenone	56
Chlorobenzene (200 cc.)	Benzalpinacolone (10 g.)	$AlCl_3$ (17.5 g.)–HCl	r.t.	20	α-(p,p'-Dichlorobenzohydryl)pinacolone	223
Chlorobenzene (200 cc.)	o-Chlorobenzalpinacolone (10 g.)	$AlCl_3$ (17.5 g.)–HCl	r.t.	20	α-(p,p'-Dichlorobenzohydryl)pinacolone	223
Chlorobenzene (200 cc.)	p-Chlorobenzalpinacolone (10 g.)	$AlCl_3$ (17.5 g.)–HCl	r.t.	20	α-(p,p'-Dichlorobenzohydryl)pinacolone	223

[a] Reaction run according to method of Hoffman (79).

TABLE XXXII.   Polycyclic hydrocarbons with unsaturated ketones

Aromatic (Moles)	Unsaturated ketone (Moles)	Catalyst (Moles)	Temp. (°C)	Time (hrs.)	Products (% Yield)	Ref.
Naphthalene	Ketene	AlCl₃	ice	—	α- and β-Naphthylmethylketones (21–37%)	82
Naphthalene (150 g.)	5-Hexen-2-one (40 g.) (600 g. Cl₂CHCH₃)	AlCl₃ (88 g.)	3–5	1	5-(1-Naphthyl)-2-hexanone and 5-(2-naphthyl)-2-hexanone (85%)	38
Naphthalene (26 g.) (50 ml. CS₂)	5-Hexen-2-one (20 ml.)	AlCl₃ (36 g.)	0–15	1.5	2-(β-Naphthyl)-5-hexanone (40%)	128
Tetralin (75 cc.)	4-Hexen-2-one (10 g.)	AlCl₃ (20 g.)	—	—	5-[6-(1,2,3,4-Tetrahydronaphthyl)]-2-hexanone (16.9 g.)	214a
Tetralin	2-Allylcyclohexanone	AlCl₃	—	—	2-{2-Methyl-2-[6-(1,2,3,4-tetrahydro-naphthyl)]ethyl}cyclohexanone (55%)	214a

14*

TABLE XXXIII. Phenolics and derivatives with unsaturated ketones

Aromatic (Moles)	Unsaturated ketone (Moles)	Catalyst (Moles)	Temp. (°C)	Time (hrs.)	Products (% Yield)	Ref.
Phenol (0.11)	Methyl vinyl ketone (0.1)	H_2SO_4 (0.1–0.3) CH_3OH (30 cc.)	reflux	1	p-Hydroxybenzylacetone	7
Phenol (1.0)	Mesityl oxide (1.0)	H_2SO_4	15–20	168	2,2,4-Trimethyl-2-chromanol	140 (191)
Phenol (53 g.)	Anisalacetone (50 g.)	H_2SO_4 (2 ml.)[a]	reflux	12	(4-Hydroxy-4'-methoxybenzhydryl)acetone (20 g.)	30a
4-Bromophenol (9.9 g.)	Mesityl oxide (9.9 g.)	H_2SO_4 (10 cc.)	r.t.	144	Product not identified	191
4-Chlorophenol (2.97 g.)	Mesityl oxide (2.97 g.)	$AlCl_3$ (4 g.)	100	3	Product not identified	191
o-Nitrophenol	Mesityl oxide	H_2SO_4	—	—	2,4,4,8-Tetramethyl-2-chromanol	140
m-Nitrophenol	Mesityl oxide	H_2SO_4	—	—	7-Nitro-2,2,4-trimethyl-2-chromanol	140
p-Nitrophenol	Mesityl oxide	H_2SO_4	—	—	6-Nitro-2,2,4-trimethyl-2-chromanol	140
Anisole	Ketene	$AlCl_3$	—	—	Mixture of ketones (45%) chiefly o- and p-methoxyacetophenone and high boilers	82
Anisole (5)	Methyl vinyl ketone (1)	$AlCl_3$ (1.3)	<20	3	p-Methoxybenzylacetone (65%)	7
Anisole (54 g.)	3-Methyl-3-buten-2-one (21 g.)	$AlCl_3$ (50 g.) (CS_2 120 cc.)	10	—	3-Methyl-4-(p-methoxyphenyl)-2-butanone (81%)	41
4-Chloroanisole (4.26)	Mesityl oxide (2.97 g.)	$AlCl_3$ (4 g.) (Nitrobenzene 15 cc.)	100	2.5	No reaction	191
o-Cresol (2)	Phorone (1)	H_2SO_4 (1)	cold	168	2,6-Dimethyl-2,6-di-(3'-methyl-2'-oxyphenyl)-4-heptanone (>35%)	142a
m-Cresol (2)	Phorone (1)	H_2SO_4 (3)	r.t. 100	48 1	Phorone di-m-cresyl ether (80%)	139

m-Cresol (1)	Phorone (1)	H_2SO_4 (1)	cold	168	Internal ether of 2,6-dimethyl-2,6-di-(2'-oxy-4'-methylphenyl)-4-heptanone	142a
p-Cresol (1)	Phorone (1)	H_2SO_4 (1)	cold	168	Internal ether of 2,6-dimethyl-2,6-di-(2'-oxy-5'-methylphenyl)-4-heptanone	142a
o-Cresol (43 g.) (toluene)	Benzalacetone (41 g.)	H_2SO_4 (2 ml.)[a]	reflux	12	(3-Methyl-4-hydroxybenzhydryl)-acetone (25 g.)	30a
o-Cresol (43 g.)	Anisalacetone (50 g.)	H_2SO_4 (2 ml.)[a]	reflux	—	(3-Methyl-4-hydroxy-4'-methoxy-benzhydryl)acetone (44 g.)	30a
p-Cresol (108 pts.)	Cyclohexylidene-cyclohexanone (89 pts.)	70% $HClO_4$ (2 pts.)	35–80 / 80–85	2 / 6	Viscous yellow liquid + resin	50
o-Cresol methyl ether (75 g.)	Allylacetone (12.5 g.)	$AlCl_3$ (25 g.)	0–5	3+	1,4,7-Trimethyl-6-methoxy-1,2-dihydronaphthalene (40%)	215
p-Cresol methyl ether	Allylacetone (10 g.)	$AlCl_3$ (40 g.)	0–5	3+	1,4,5-Trimethyl-8-methoxy-1,2-dihydronaphthalene (41%)	215
Hydroquinone dimethyl ether (6.9 g.)	Mesityl oxide (4.95 g.)	$AlCl_3$ (CS_2)	reflux	1	Product not identified	191
Pseudo-6-cumenol 2,6-Di-t-butyl-phenol	Mesityl oxide (9.9 g.) 2,6,3',5'-Tetra-t-butyl-4'-hydroxy-phenyl-4-methylene-2,5-cyclohexadien-1-one	H_2SO_4 (10 cc.) H_2SO_4–HOAc	r.t. / —	144 / —	Product not identified Tri-(3'5'-di-t-butyl-4-hydroxy-phenol) methane and its corresponding quinone methide	191 230
o-(2-Phenylethyl)phenol (800 g.)	1-Δ^1-Cyclohexenyl-cyclohexanone-2 (260 g.)	Bleaching clay (100 g.)	175–180 7–8 atm.	10–12	2- and 4-Cyclohexylphenol (277 g.)	199a

[a] Plus 20 g. benzoyl peroxide.

TABLE XXXIV. Miscellaneous aromatics with unsaturated ketones and aldehydes

Aromatic (Moles)	Unsaturated ketone or aldehyde (Moles)	Catalyst (Moles)	Temp. (°C)	Time (hrs.)	Products (% Yield)	Ref.
Aniline (0.625)	Methyl vinyl ketone (0.5)	$FeCl_3 \cdot 6H_2O$ (1) $ZnCl_2$ (10 pts.)[c]	55–75 reflux	1–1.5 1.5–2	Lepidine (73%)	33
Aniline (0.313)	3-Penten-2-one (0.25)	$FeCl_3 \cdot 6H_2O$ (0.5) $ZnCl_2$ (5 pts.)[c]	55–75 reflux	1–1.5 1.5–2	2,4-Dimethylquinoline (62%)	33
p-Toluidine hydrochloride (0.313)	Methyl vinyl ketone (0.25)	$FeCl_3 \cdot 6H_2O$ (0.5) $ZnCl_2$ (10 pts.)[c]	55–75 reflux	1.0–1.5 1.5–2	4,6-Dimethylquinoline (65%)	33
p-Anisidine hydrochloride (0.625)	Methyl vinyl ketone (0.5)	$FeCl_3 \cdot 6H_2O$ (1) $ZnCl_2$ (10 pts.)[c]	55–75 reflux	1–1.5 1.5–2	6-Methoxylepidine (52%)	33
Furan (146 g.)	Acrolein (120 g.) (0.5 g. hydroquinone)	0.5 ml. aq. SO_2	100	1	β-(α-Furyl)propionaldehyde (17 g.) β,β-(α,α-Furyl)dipropionaldehyde (30.4 g.)	175
Furan (1)	Acrolein (0.5)	HOAc (5 cc.)–H_2O (50 g.)[b]	130	2	2-Furanpropionaldehyde (14%)	221
Furan (1.5)	Methyl vinyl ketone (0.65)	SO_2 (1 g.)–H_2O (3 g.)[b]	90	2	2-(27 g.), 2,5-Bis(35 g.)-(3-oxobutyl)furan	221
Furan (20 g.)	Methyl vinyl ketone (20 g.)[b]	2 Drops sat. aq. SO_2	130	2	2,5-Bis-(γ-ketobutyl)furan (33%)	1
Furan	Vinyl β,β-dimethyl-vinyl ketone	Aq. SO_2 (2 drops) 1% pyrogallol	35	5	2,5-Bis-(5-methyl-3-oxo-4-hexenyl)furan (10 g.)	132
2-Methylfuran (10 g.)	Crotonaldehyde (8.6 g.)	4 Drops p-Tol.·SO_2CH_3	—	—	β-(5-Methylfuryl-(2)butyraldehyde (24%)	1
2-Methylfuran (10 g.)	Methyl vinyl ketone (8.6 g.)[b]	2 Drops 50% H_2SO_4, 12 N. HCl, or CH_3OH sat. with HCl	—	—	5-Methylfurfurylacetone (52–62%)	1
2-Methylfuran (0.2)	Methyl vinyl ketone[d] (0.2)	H_2SO_4[b]	20–25	1.5	1-(5-Methyl-2-furyl)-3-butanone (50%)[d]	232

Aromatic	Reagent	Catalyst	Temp.	Time	Product	Ref.
2-Methylfuran (10 g.)	Methyl vinyl ketone (8.6 g.)[b]	2 Drops p-Tol.-SO₂Cl, C₆H₅SO₂Cl or Et₂SO₄	—	—	5-Methylfurfurylacetone (54%)	1
2-Methylfuran (10 g.)	Methyl vinyl ketone (8.6 g.)[b]	5 Drops p-Tol.-SO₂CH₃	—	—	5-Methylfurfurylacetone (59%)	1
2-Methylfuran (20 g.)	Methyl vinyl ketone (17.1 g.)[b]	2 Drops sat. aq. SO₂	0–r.t.	1	5-Methylfurfurylacetone (65%)	1
2-Methylfuran (0.27)	Mesityl oxide (0.27)	BF₃ (60%)–Et₂O (8 cc.) Hydroquinone (0.05 g.)	50	3	1,1-Dimethyl-1-(5-methyl-2-furyl)-3-butanone (47%)	231
2-Methylfuran (0.27)	4-Methyl-3-penten-2-one (0.26)	H₂SO₄ (0.2) Hydroquinone (0.05 g.)	w.b.	8	1,1-Dimethyl-1-(5-methyl-2-furyl)-3-butanone (50%)	231
2-Methylfuran (55 g.)	3-Penten-2-one (56 g.)	Conc. HCl (1 cc.)	—	—	4-(5-Methyl-2-furyl)-2-pentanone (52 g.)	109
2-Methylfuran (55 g.)	Mesityl oxide (65 g.)	Conc. HCl	—	—	4-Methyl-4-(5-methyl-2-furyl)-2-pentanone (70 g.)	109
2-Methylfuran (55 g.)	3-Methyl-3-buten-2-one (56 g.)	HCl (1 cc.)[a]	25	2	3-Methyl-4-(5-methyl-2-furyl)-2-butanone (70 g.)	109
2-Methylfuran (42 g.)	Vinyl β,β-dimethyl-vinyl ketone (53 g.)	Aq. SO₂ (2 drops) 1% pyrogallol	40–50	5	2-(5-Methyl-3-oxo-4-hexenyl)-furan	132
2-Methylfuran (9.2 g.)	Phenyl vinyl ketone (15 g.)[b]	2 Drops sat. aq. SO₂	35	—	5-Methylfurfurylacetophenone (25%)	1
2-Ethylfuran (0.16)	Mesityl oxide (0.15)	H₂SO₄ (0.1) Hydroquinone (0.05 g.)	w.b.	8	1,1-Dimethyl-1-(5-ethyl-2-furyl)-3-butanone (50%)	231
Thiophene (1)	Methyl vinyl ketone (0.6)	SO₂ (1 g.)–H₂O (20 g.)[b]	130	2	2-(3-Oxobutyl)thiophene (5 cc. crude)	221

[a] Can use H₂SO₄, H₃PO₄, C₆H₅SO₃H, p-Tol.-SO₃H.   [b] Hydroquinone.   [c] 365 parts EtOH.

[d] Method affords 40–60% yields of similar condensation products from vinyl isobutyl ketone, ethylideneacetone, propylideneacetone, butylideneacetone, isobutylideneacetone, enanthylideneacetone, 3-methyl-3-buten-2-one, 3-methyl-2-penten-4-one, mesityl oxide, 3-methyl-3-hepten-5-one, and 2,3-dimethyl-2-penten-4-one.

TABLE XXXV.　Aromatic hydrocarbons* with unsaturated nitriles

Aromatic (Moles)	Unsaturated nitrile (Moles)	Catalyst (Moles)	Temp. (°C)	Time (hrs.)	Products (% Yield)	Ref.
Benzene (29 g.)	Acrylonitrile (6.8 g.)	$AlCl_3$ (47.7 g.)	150–160	10	Hydrocinnamonitrile (27%)	72
Benzene (29.9 g.)	Acrylonitrile (6.8 g.) (saturated with HCl)	$AlCl_3$ (60 g.)	84–98	30	Hydrocinnamonitrile (66%)	72
Chlorobenzene (29 g.)	Acrylonitrile (6.8 g.)	$AlCl_3$ (56.3 g.)	140–165	30	o-Chlorohydrocinnamonitrile (12%)	72
Benzene (excess)	3-Butenenitrile (14 g.)	$AlCl_3$ (20 g.)	—	—	3- and 4-Phenylbutyronitrile	58
Benzene (100 ml.)	3-Butenenitrile (16.8 g.)	$AlCl_3$ (49.9 g.)	75	2.5	3-Phenylbutyronitrile	207a
Benzene (10)	4,4,4-Trichlorocrotonitrile (1)	$AlCl_3$ (1.2)	70	2	4,4-Dichloro-2-phenyl-3-butenenitrile (62%)	71(72)
Benzene (10)	4,4,4-Trichlorocrotonitrile (1)	$AlCl_3$ (<1)	70	2	4,4-Dichloro-2-phenyl-3-butenenitrile (lower yield); 3-phenyl derivative (9–11%)	71
Benzene (5)	1-Cyanocyclohexene (1) (saturated with HCl)	$AlCl_3$ (1.5)	0–5 reflux	1.75 1	1-Phenyl-4-cyanocyclohexane (76%)	37
Benzene (35 g.)	Cinnamonitrile (6.4 g.)	$AlCl_3$ (10 g.)	80	5	3,3-Diphenylpropionitrile (93%)	72
Benzene (468 g.)	Oleonitrile (263 g.)	$AlCl_3$ (148 g.)	70–85	2.5	Phenylstearonitrile (176 g.)	161b
Toluene (5)	1-Cyanocyclohexene (1)	$AlCl_3$ (1.5)	0–5 reflux	1.75 1	4-p-Tolyl-1-cyanocyclohexane (75%)	37
Toluene (134.4 g.)	Undecylenonitrile (48.3 g.)	$AlCl_3$ (49.9 g.)	r.t.–70	1.5	Tolylundecanonitrile	161b
Toluene (230 g.)	Oleonitrile (131.5 g.)	$AlCl_3$ (74 g.)	70	1.5	Tolylstearonitrile (125 g.)	161b
Toluene (62 g.)	Δ^{13}-Docosenonitrile (32.4 g.)	$AlCl_3$ (14 g.)	60–70	1.1	Tolylbehenonitrile (25.8 g.)	161b
o-Xylene (11.3 g.)	Acrylonitrile (6.4 g.)	$AlCl_3$ (48.2 g.)	130	9	p-Methylhydrocinnamonitrile and isomers	72
p-Xylene (5)	1-Cyanocyclohexene (1)	$AlCl_3$ (1.5)	0–5 reflux	1.75 1	4-p-Xylyl-1-cyanocyclohexane (64%)	37
m-Xylene (530 g.) (300 ml. CS_2)	Oleonitrile (263 g.)	$AlCl_3$ (148 g.)	55–65	4.6	Xylylstearonitrile (257 g.)	161b
Mesitylene (22.8 g.)	Acrylonitrile (6.8 g.)	$AlCl_3$ (52.5 g.)	130	9.5	Methylhydrocinnamonitrile (47%)	72

Mesitylene (600 g.) (300 ml. CS$_2$)	Oleonitrile (263 g.)	AlCl$_3$ (148 g.)	50–60	4.6	Mesitylstearonitrile (284 g.)	161b
Cumene (480 g.) (200 ml. CS$_2$)	Oleonitrile (263 g.)	AlCl$_3$ (146 g.)	r.t. 60–65	15 1	Cumylstearonitrile (219.5 g.)	161b
Naphthalene (769 g.) (500 ml. CS$_2$)	Oleonitrile (263 g.)	AlCl$_3$ (148 g.)	65	4.6	Naphthylstearonitrile (51%)	161b
α- and β-Methylnaphthalene (710 g.)	Oleonitrile (263 g.)	AlCl$_3$ (148 g.)	30–50 50	0.5 1	Methylnaphthylstearonitrile (166 g.)	161b
Biphenyl (3)	Acrylonitrile (1)	AlCl$_3$ (3.5)	164–170	8	p-Cyanoethylphenylbenzene	123
Biphenyl (924 g.) (500 ml. CS$_2$)	Oleonitrile (263 g.)	AlCl$_3$ (148 g.)	r.t. 65	1.1 3	Biphenylstearonitrile (51%)	161b

* And chlorobenzene.

TABLE XXXVI.   Benzene and bromobenzene with miscellaneous unsaturated compounds

Benzene (Moles)	Unsaturated compound (Moles)	Catalyst (Moles)	Temp. (°C)	Time (hrs.)	Products (% Yield)	Ref.
1,300 g.	Acrylyl chloride (170 g.)	AlCl$_3$ (350 g.)	65–70	2	1,3-Diphenyl-1-propanone	19
50 g.	Crotonyl chloride (50 g.)	AlCl$_3$ (150 ml. CS$_2$)	0.25	—	1-Phenyl-2-buten-1-one	101
Excess	Cinnamyl chloride[a]	AlCl$_3$ (10 g.)	—	—	β,β-Diphenylpropionic acid (5 g.) β,β-Diphenylpropiophenone (11.5 g.)	119
2	Cinnamyl chloride (1)	AlCl$_3$ (CS$_2$)	r.t.[c]	—	β,β-Diphenylpropiophenone (93%) some 3-phenyl-1-indanone	102

Table continued

TABLE XXXVI (continued)

Benzene (Moles)	Unsaturated compound (Moles)	Catalyst (Moles)	Temp. (°C)	Time (hrs.)	Products (% Yield)	Ref.
—	N-Allylacetamide	AlCl₃	—	—	N-2-Phenylpropylacetamide (66%)	162
300 cc.	Allylsuccinic anhydride (0.36)	AlCl₃ (0.83)	r.t.	36	Crude acid (55 g.); methyl 3-phenylcyclohexanone-5-carboxylate (18%)ᵇ and methyl-α-phenacyl-γ-valerate (14%)ᵇ	150
100 cc.	Methyl ω-styryl sulfone (0.025)	H₂SO₄ (0.1)	0	2	β,β-Diphenylethyl methyl sulfone (76%)ᵇ	203
ᵈ	Cinnamyl chloride	AlCl₃ (CS₂)	r.t. / 0	4 / —	Benzal-p-bromoacetophenone, 5-bromo-3-phenyl-1-indanone	102
50 cc.	2-Methyl-1-nitro-2-propene (10 g.)	AlCl₃ (16 g.)	30–40	1.25	2-Methyl-1-nitro-2-phenylpropane (56%)	108c
20 cc.	Maleic anhydride (10 g.)	AlCl₃ (75 g.)	reflux	12	2-Phenyl-3-benzoylpropionic acid (4 g.)	161
75 cc.	β-Benzoylacrylic acid (2 g.)	AlCl₃	w.b.	12.5	2-Phenyl-3-benzoylpropionic acid (0.4 g.)	161

ᵃ From 10 g. of acid.   ᵇ After esterification.   ᶜ No reaction at −20° until placed in sunlight.   ᵈ Bromobenzene.

TABLE XXXVII. Alkylbenzenes* with miscellaneous unsaturated compounds

Aromatic (Moles)	Unsaturated compound (Moles)	Catalyst (Moles)	Temp. (°C)	Time (hrs.)	Products (% Yield)	Ref.
Toluene	N-Allylacetamide	AlCl₃	—	—	N-2-p-Tolylpropylacetamide (80%)	162
Toluene (300 cc.)	Maleic anhydride (0.1)	AlCl₃ (0.6)	w.b.	12	2-Tolyl-3-toluylpropionic acid (20%)	161

Aromatic	Reactant	Catalyst	Temp.	Time	Product	Ref.
Toluene (92 pts.)	Sodium 2-methyl-2-propenesulfonate (20 pts.)	H_2SO_4 (72 pts.)[c]	0	5	2-p-Tolyl-2-methylpropane-sulfonic acid (50 pts.)	159a(8b)
Toluene (200 cc.)	β-Toluylacrylic acid (15 g.)	$AlCl_3$ (50 g.)	w.b.	10.5	2-Tolyl-3-toluylpropionic acid (20%)	161
Toluene (300 cc.)	β-Benzoylacrylic acid (15 g.)	$AlCl_3$ (50 g.)	100	10	2-Tolyl-3-benzoylpropionic acid (5 g.)	161
Toluene (100 cc.)	Methyl ω-styryl-sulfone (0.025)	H_2SO_4 (0.1)	0, r.t.	2, 9	β-Phenyl-β-p-tolylethylmethyl sulfone (37%)	203
Toluene (100 cc.)	ω-Styryl-p-tolyl sulfone (0.039)	H_2SO_4 (0.1)	0, r.t.	1, 6	β-Phenyl-β-p-tolylethyl-p-tolyl sulfone	203
Toluene (100 cc.)	2-Methyl-1-nitro-2-propene (10 g.)	$AlCl_3$ (16 g.)	30–40	1.25	2-Methyl-1-nitro-2-tolyl-propane (5 g.)	108b
Toluene (100 cc.)	2-Methyl-3-nitro-2 propene (20 g.)	BF_3 (to sat'n.)	50	—	α-(p-Tolyl)-isobutyrohydroxa-mic acid (22%), 2-methyl-1-nitro-2-tolylpropane	108b
m-Xylene (175 cc.)	3-Methyl-2-butenoyl chloride (118 g.)	$AlCl_3$ (200 g.) (300 cc. CS_2)	0–10	2	1,1,4,6-Tetramethylindanone (58%)	42
Pseudocumene (0.1)	Dimethylacrylic acid chloride	$AlCl_3$–CCl_4	–10	2	Isopropylidene-2,4,5-trimethyl-acetophenone[a] (8.5 g.)	191
Ethylbenzene[d] (85 ml.)	Sod. 2-methyl-2-propenesulfonate[e]	BF_3–H_2SO_4 (5 ml.) ($ClCH_2CH_2Cl$)	25–41	0.5, 2	2-(Ethylphenyl)-2-methyl-propanesulfonic acid (77%)	8b
n-Decylbenzene[d] (45 ml.)	Sod. 2-methyl-2-propenesulfonate[e]	BF_3–H_2SO_4 (5 ml.) (100 ml. $ClCH_2CH_2Cl$)	—	3b	2-Dodecylphenyl-2-methyl-propanesulfonic acid (38%)	8b
Nonylnaphthalene (23 pts.)	Sod. 2-methyl-2-pro-penesulfonate (54 pts.)	BF_3 (136 g. $ClCH_2CH_2Cl$)	50–60	5	2-Nonylnaphthyl-2-methyl-propanesulfonic acid (good detergent)	159a

* And nonylnaphthalene.   [a] Alkylation did not occur.   [b] One half-hour with H_2SO_4 alone; add BF_3 for ½ hour; stir 2 hours more.
[c] BF_3 is good catalyst for this reaction.
[d] Similarly with other alkylbenzenes: toluene afforded 73%, n-butyl 55%, t-butyl 47%, t-amyl 85%, n-hexyl 52%, n-octyl 48%, n-undecyl 44%, and n-tridecyl 48% of the corresponding 2-(alkylphenyl)-2-methylpropanesulfonic acids. n-Propyl- and isopropyl-benzenes yielded 61% and 30%, respectively, no solvent being used.   [e] 10 g.

TABLE XXXVIII.   Phenolics, phenol ethers, and thiophene with miscellaneous unsaturates

Aromatic (Moles)	Unsaturated compound (Moles)	Catalyst (Moles)	Temp. (°C)	Time (hrs.)	Product (% Yield)	Ref.
Phenol (1)	Acrylonitrile (1)	AlCl$_3$ (0.5)–HCl	27	1	o-Hydroxyphenylpropionitrile (12%)	91
Phenol (6)	Acrylonitrile (6)	AlCl$_3$ (3.5)–HCl	15–27	2.5	p-Hydroxyphenylpropionitrile (242 g.)	91
Anisole (650 g.) (300 g. n-heptane)	Propenoyl chloride	AlCl$_3$ (210 g.) BF$_3$	55–70	2	1,3-Bis-(p-methoxyphenyl)-1-propanone	19
Laurylphenol (33.4 g.)	Sod. 2-methyl-2-propenesulfonate (9.5 pts.)	(ClCH$_2$CH$_2$Cl)	25	7	Alkylate is good detergent	159a
Anisole (26 g.) (50 ml. benzene)	1-Chloro-1-buten-3-one (28.5 g.)	SnCl$_4$[a] (59 g.)	0	1	1-(p-Methoxyphenyl)-1-buten-3-one (54%)	124c
Anisole	1-Chloro-1-hexen-3-one	SnCl$_4$	warm	0.5	1-(p-Methoxyphenyl)-1-hexen-3-one (57%)	124c
Anisole	1-Chloro-1-octen-3-one	SnCl$_4$	—	—	1-(p-Methoxyphenyl)-1-octen-3-one (62%)	124c
Phenetole	1-Chloro-1-buten-3-one	SnCl$_4$	—	—	1-(p-Ethoxyphenyl)-1-buten-3-one (55.6%)	124c
p-Cresol methyl ether	1-Chloro-1-buten-3-one	SnCl$_4$	—	—	1-(2-Methoxy-5-methylphenyl)-1-buten-3-one (41.5%)	124c
1,3-Dimethoxy-benzene	1-Chloro-1-buten-3-one	SnCl$_4$	—	—	1-(2,4-Dimethoxyphenyl)-1-buten-3-one (14%)	124c
1,4-Dimethoxy-benzene	1-Chloro-1-buten-3-one	SnCl$_4$	—	—	1-(2,5-Dimethoxyphenyl)-1-buten-3-one (12.5%)	124c
1,3-Dimethoxy-benzene[b] (71.5 g.)	Maleic anhydride (53.6 g.) (150 g. CS$_2$)	AlCl$_3$	0	—	(2,4-Dimethoxyphenyl) succinic anhydride (40%)[b]	161a
Thiophene	1-Chloro-1-buten-3-one	SnCl$_4$	—	—	1-(2-Thienyl)-1-buten-3-one (39%)	124c

[a] Added over one hour.
[b] 1,2- and 1,4-dimethoxybenzene and the methylanisoles yield β-aroyl-α-arylpropionic acids on reaction with maleic anhydride (62b).

References

1. Alder, K., and S. Schmidt, *Ber.*, **76**, 183 (1943).
2. Alexander, L. L., A. L. Jacoby, and R. C. Fuson, *J. Am. Chem. Soc.*, **57**, 2208 (1935).
3. Angelbis, A., and R. Anschütz, *Ber.*, **17**, 167 (1884).
4. Anschütz, R., *Ber.*, **16**, 622 (1883).
5. Anschütz, R., *Ann.*, **235**, 150 (1886).
6. Anschütz, R., *Ann.*, **235**, 299 (1886).
7. Arai, Hidea, and Niro Murata, *Kogyo Kagaku Zasshi*, **61**, 563 (1958); *C.A.*, **55**, 10371b (1961).
8a. Arbuzov, B. A., and L. A. Shapshinskaya, *Dokl. Akad. Nauk S.S.S.R.*, **110**, 991 (1956).
8b. Archer, S., J. D. Malkemus, and C. M. Suter, *J. Am. Chem. Soc.*, **67**, 43 (1945).
9. Arbuzov, B. A., and E. V. Kuznetsov, *Compt. rend. acad. sci. U.R.S.S.*, **39**, 311 (1943).
9a. Axe, W. N., U.S. Pat. 2,403,963 (July 16, 1946).
10. Axe, W. N., U.S. Pat. 2,404,120 (July 16, 1946).
11. Axe, W. N., U. S. Pat. 2,412,595 (Dec. 17, 1946).
11a. Axe, W. N., U.S. Pat. 2,430,660 (Nov. 11, 1947).
12a. Axe, W. N., U.S. Pat. 2,471,922 (May 31, 1949).
12b. Azatyan, V. D., *Dokl. Akad. Nauk S.S.S.R.*, **59**, 901 (1948).
13. Baddeley, G., and W. Pickles, *J. Chem. Soc.*, 2855 (1957).
14. Bader, A. R., *J. Am. Chem. Soc.*, **75**, 5967 (1953).
15. Bader, A. R., *J. Am. Chem. Soc.*, **77**, 4155 (1955).
16. Bader, A. R., *J. Am. Chem. Soc.*, **79**, 6164 (1957).
17. Bader, A. R., and W. C. Bean, *J. Am. Chem. Soc.*, **80**, 3073 (1958).
18. Baker, W., and W. G. Leeds, *J. Chem. Soc.*, 974 (1948).
18a. Barnett, E. de B., and M. A. Matthews, *Ber.*, **59**, 1429 (1926).
19. Becke, F., and H. Bittermann, *Ber.*, **93**, 2344 (1960).
20. Bergmann, E., H. Taubadel, and H. Weiss, *Ber.*, **64**, 1499 (1931).
21. Bhattacharyya, N. K., and S. M. Mukherji, *Sci. Cult.* (*Calcutta*), **16**, 374 (1951).
22. Bhattacharyya, N. K., S. Singh, O. P. Vig, and S. M. Mukherji, *Sci. Cult.* (*Calcutta*), **18**, 341 (1953).
23. Binapfl, J., and J. Kuchenbuch, U.S. Pat. 2,031,586 (Feb. 25, 1936).
24. Boeseken, J., *Rec. Trav. Chim.*, **30**, 389 (1911).
25. Boeseken, J., and M. C. Bastet, *Rec. Trav. Chim.*, **32**, 184 (1914).
26. Bruson, H. A., and J. W. Kroeger, *J. Am. Chem. Soc.*, **62**, 36 (1940).
27. Bruson, H. A., and T. W. Riener, *J. Am. Chem. Soc.*, **68**, 8 (1946).
28. Butler, J. M., U.S. Pat. 2,572,557 (Oct. 23, 1951).
29. Buu-Hoi, N. P., and P. Cagniant, *Bull. Soc. Chim. France*, **10**, 477 (1943).
29a. Buu-Hoi, N. P., and P. Cagniant, *Compt. rend.*, **220**, 744 (1945).
30. Buu-Hoi, N. P., and Dat Xuong, *Bull. Soc. Chim. France*, 751 (1948).
30a. Buu-Hoi, N. P., H. LeBihan, F. Binon, and P. Maleyran, *J. Org. Chem.*, **17**, 1122 (1952).
31. Cagniant, P., *Compt. rend.*, **228**, 98 (1949).
32. Calcott, W. S., J. M. Tinker, and V. Weinmayr, *J. Am. Chem. Soc.*, **61**, 1010 (1939).

33. Campbell, K. N., U.S. Pat. 2,451,610 (Oct. 19, 1948).
34. Christenson, R. M., and R. A. Freeman, U.S. Pat. 2,831,821 (April 12, 1958).
35. Chuang, Chang-Kong, Jen-Hung Chu, and Yee-Sheng Koo, *Ber.*, **73**, 1347 (1940).
36. CIBA, French Pat. 1,262,181 (April 17, 1961).
36a. Claisen, L., *Ber.*, **54B**, 200 (1921).
37. Colonge, J., and H. Daunis, *Bull. Soc. Chim. France*, 2238 (1961).
38. Colonge, J., and R. Domenech, *Bull. Soc. Chim. France*, 1000 (1952).
39. Colonge, J., and E. Grimaud, *Compt. rend.*, **231**, 580 (1950); *Bull. Soc. Chim. France*, 439 (1951).
40. Colonge, J., and A. Lagier, *Bull. Soc. Chim. France*, 27 (1949).
41. Colonge, J., and L. Pichat, *Bull. Soc. Chim. France*, 177 (1949).
42. Colonge, J., and L. Pichat, *Bull. Soc. Chim. France*, 421 (1949).
43. Colonge, J., and L. Pichat, *Bull. Soc. Chim. France*, 853 (1949).
44. Colonge, J., and G. Weinstein, *Bull. Soc. Chim. France*, 820 (1951).
45. Cook, J. W., *Chem. and Ind.*, **56**, 290 (1937).
46. Cook, J. W., and F. Goulden, *J. Chem. Soc.*, 1559 (1937).
47. Corse, J., and E. Rohrmann, *J. Am. Chem. Soc.*, **70**, 370 (1948).
48. Davidson, J. M., and A. Lowy, *J. Am. Chem. Soc.*, **51**, 2978 (1929).
49. Demole, E., *Ber.*, **12**, 2245 (1879).
50. Deutsche Hydrierwerke A-G., Brit. Pat. 469,548 (July 23, 1937).
51. Dippy, J. F. J., and A. L. L. Palluel, *J. Chem. Soc.*, 1415 (1951).
52. Dippy, J. F. J., and J. T. Young, *J. Chem. Soc.*, 1817 (1952).
53. Dippy, J. F. J., and J. T. Young, *J. Chem. Soc.*, 3919 (1955).
54. Dolgov, B. N., and N. A. Larin, *J. Gen. Chem. U.S.S.R.*, **20**, 475 (1950).
55. duPont, E. I. de Nemours & Co., Brit. Pat. 573,909 (Dec. 12, 1945).
56. Eaton, J. T., D. B. Black, and R. C. Fuson, *J. Am. Chem. Soc.*, **56**, 687 (1934).
57. Ecke, G. G., and A. J. Kolka, U.S. Pat. 2,831,898 (April 22, 1958).
58. Eykman, J. F., *Chem. Weekblad*, **4**, 727 (1907); *Chem. Zentr.*, II, 2046 (1907).
59. Eykman, J. F., *Chem. Weekblad*, **5**, 655 (1908); *Chem. Zentr.*, II, 1100 (1908).
60. Farbenfabriken Bayer A.G., Brit. Pat. 807,668 (Jan. 21, 1959).
61. Fawcett, F. S., and B. W. Hawk, U.S. Pat. 2,572,019 (Oct. 23, 1951).
62. Fieser, L. F., W. P. Campbell, E. M. Fry, and M. D. Gates, *J. Am. Chem. Soc.*, **61**, 3216 (1939).
62a. Fischer, R. F., U.S. Pat. 2,915,563 (Dec. 1, 1959).
62b. Flett, L. H., and W. H. Gardner, *Maleic Anhydride Derivatives*, John Wiley and Sons, New York, p. 92, 1952.
63. Fourneau, E., and P. M. Baranger, *Bull. Soc. Chim. France*, (4), **49**, 1161 (1931).
64. Fuson, R. C., L. L. Alexander, E. Ellingboe, and A. Hoffman, *J. Am. Chem. Soc.*, **58**, 1979 (1936).
65. Fuson, R. C., and H. G. Cooke, *J. Am. Chem. Soc.*, **73**, 3515 (1951).
66a. Fuson, R. C., A. P. Kozacik, and J. T. Eaton, *J. Am. Chem. Soc.*, **55**, 3799 (1933).
66b. Ganguly, B. K., and S. M. Mukherji, *Nature*, **168**, 1003 (1951).
67. Ghosh, R., *Sci. Cult. (Calcutta)*, **3**, 55 (1937).

67a. Gisser, H., J. Messina, and J. Snead, Delaware Valley Regional Am. Chem. Soc. Meeting, Feb. 16, 1956.

68. Gordon, L. B., and T. P. Motte, U.S. Pat. 2,927,085 (Mar. 1, 1960).

69. Gordon, L. B., and T. P. Motte, U.S. Pat. 2,927,086 (Mar. 1, 1960).

70. Gramenitskaia, V. N., G. I. Nikishin, and A. D. Petrov, *Proc. Acad. Sci. U.S.S.R.*, **118**, 65 (1958).

71. Grebenyuk, A. D., and I. P. Tsukervanik, *Zh. Obshch. Khim.*, **28**, 2380 (1958).

72. Grebenyuk, A. D., and I. P. Tsukervanik, *J. Gen. Chem. U.S.S.R.*, **25**, 269 (1955).

73. Hanriot and Guilbert, *Compt. rend.*, **98**, 525 (1884).

74. Harban, A. A., and C. E. Johnson, U.S. Pat. 2,641,600 (June 9, 1953).

75. Harmon, J., and C. S. Marvel, *J. Am. Chem. Soc.*, **54**, 2515 (1932).

76. Hausweiler, A., K. Schwarzer, and R. Stroh, Germ. Pat. 1,092,010 (Nov. 3, 1960).

77. Hennion, G. F., and R. A. Kurtz, *J. Am. Chem. Soc.*, **65**, 1001 (1943).

78. Hickinbottom, W. J., *J. Chem. Soc.*, 404 (1937).

79. Hoffman, A., *J. Am. Chem. Soc.*, **51**, 2542 (1929).

80. Hoffmann, A., M. W. Farlow, and R. C. Fuson, *J. Am. Chem. Soc.*, **55**, 2000 (1933).

81. Hopff, H., Germ. Pat. 666,466 (Oct. 20, 1938).

82. Hurd, C. D., *J. Am. Chem. Soc.*, **47**, 2777 (1925).

83. Hurd, C. D., and C. D. Kelso, *J. Am. Chem. Soc.*, **62**, 1548 (1940).

84. Huston, R. C., and D. D. Sager, *J. Am. Chem. Soc.*, **48**, 1955 (1926).

85. I. G. Farben, A.-G., French Pat. 628,440 (Oct. 10, 1927).

86. I. G. Farben, A.-G., French Pat. 675,668 (May 24, 1929).

87. Ipatieff, V. N., H. Pines, and R. C. Olberg, *J. Am. Chem. Soc.*, **70**, 2123 (1948).

87a. Ipatieff, V. N., H. Pines, and R. E. Schaad, *J. Am. Chem. Soc.*, **66**, 816 (1944).

88. Ipatieff, V. N., R. E. Schaad, H. Pines, and G. S. Monroe, *J. Am. Chem. Soc.*, **67**, 1060 (1945); U.S. Pat. 2,382,260 (1945).

88a. Isagulyants, V. I., and N. G. Mushcheghian, *Compt. rend. acad. sci. U.R.S.S.*, **56**, 165 (1947).

89. Jacini, G., *Chim. Ind. (Paris)*, **30**, 236 (1948).

90. Jason, E. F., and E. K. Fields, *J. Org. Chem.*, **26**, 937 (1961).

91. Johnston, H. W., U.S. Pat. 2,789,995 (Apr. 23, 1957).

92. Jones, D. G., and P. E. Schick, Brit. Pat. 706,425 (1954).

93. Kakhniashvili, A. L., and G. Glonti, *Tr. Tbilissk. Gos. Univ.*, **74**, 369 (1959); *C.A.*, **55**, 27222d (1961).

94. Karrer, P., R. Escher, H. Fritzsche, H. Keller, B. H. Ringier, and H. Salomon, *Helv. Chim. Acta*, **21**, 939 (1938).

95. Karrer, P., H. Fritzsche, B. H. Ringer, and H. Salomon, *Helv. Chim. Acta*, **21**, 520 (1938).

96. Kimura, W., T. Omura, and H. Taniguchi, *Ber.*, **71**, 2686 (1938).

97. King, E. J., *J. Am. Chem. Soc.*, **49**, 562 (1927).

98. Koelsch, C. F., *J. Org. Chem.*, **3**, 456 (1938).

99. Koelsch, C. F., and C. D. LeClaire, *J. Org. Chem.*, **6**, 516 (1941).

100. Kohler, E. P., *Am. Chem. J.*, **31**, 642 (1904).

101. Kohler, E. P., *Am. Chem. J.*, **42**, 375 (1909).

102. Kohler, E. P., G. L. Heritage, and M. C. Burnley, *Am. Chem. J.*, **44**, 60 (1910).
103. Konowalow, M., and S. Dobrowolski, *J. Russ. Phys. Chem. Soc.*, **37**, 547 (1905); *Chem. Zentr.*, II, 825 (1905).
104. Korshak, V. V., and K. K. Samplavskaya, *Zh. Obshch. Khim.*, **18**, 1470 (1948).
105. Korshak, V. V., K. K. Samplavskaya, and M. A. Andreeva, *J. Gen. Chem. U.S.S.R.*, **19**, 655 (1949).
106. Korshak, V. V., K. K. Samplavskaya, and A. I. Gershanovich, *J. Gen. Chem. U.S.S.R.*, **16**, 1065 (1946).
107. Kraemer, G., and A. Spilker, *Ber.*, **24**, 2788 (1891).
108. Kreuz, K. L., and R. T. Sanderson, U.S. Pat. 2,529,298 (Nov. 7, 1950).
108a. Kundiger, D. C., and H. Pledger, *J. Am. Chem. Soc.*, **78**, 6098, 6101 (1956).
108b. Kuwata, T., A. Misono, K. Higuchi, M. Takeda, and M. Hiraoka, *J. Chem. Soc. Japan, Ind. Chem. Sect.*, **54**, 101 (1951).
108c. Lambert, A., J. D. Rose, and B. C. L. Weedon, *J. Chem. Soc.*, 42 (1949).
109. Lambiotte & Co., French Pat. 972,652 (Feb. 1, 1951).
110. Lee, W. M., and Lee H. Clark, U.S. Pat. 2,050,188 (Aug. 4, 1936).
111. Lefebvre, H., and E. Levas, *Compt. rend.*, **220**, 826 (1945).
112. Levas, E., *Compt. rend.*, **228**, 100 (1949).
113. Liebermann, C., and A. Hartmann, *Ber.*, **24**, 2582 (1891).
114. Liebermann, C., and A. Hartmann, *Ber.*, **25**, 957 (1892).
115. Liebermann, C., and A. Hartmann, *Ber.*, **25**, 2124 (1892).
116. Losev, I. P., O. V. Smirnova, and T. A. Pfeifer, *J. Gen. Chem. U.S.S.R.*, **21**, 737 (1951).
117. McKee, R. H., and H. B. Faber, U.S. Pat. 1,972,568 (Sept. 4, 1934).
118. McKenna, J. F., and F. J. Sowa, *J. Am. Chem. Soc.*, **59**, 470 (1937).
119. McKenzie, A., and F. Barrow, *J. Chem. Soc.*, **119**, 69 (1921).
120. Maheshwary, N. K., O. P. Vig, and S. M. Mukherji, *Current Sci. (India)*, **22**, 147 (1953).
121. Malinovskii, M. S., *Zh. Obshch. Khim.*, **17**, 2235 (1947).
122. Mamedaliev, Yu G., R. A. Babakhanov, and A. R. Musseva, *Azerb. Khim. Zh.* No. 2, 3 (1961); *C.A.*, **56**, 2357h (1962).
122a. Mamedaliev, Yu G., R. A. Babakhanov, et al., *Dokl. Akad. Nauk Azerb. S.S.R.*, **18**, 23 (1962).
123. Mandrosora, F. M., and G. I. Kudoyavtsev, *Zh. Obshch. Khim.*, **31**, 2246 (1961).
124. Marcusson, J., *Z. angew. Chem.*, **33**, 234 (1920).
124a. Masuo, F., and S. Hattorii, *J. Soc. Chem. Ind. Japan*, **48**, 55 (1945).
124b. Mel'kanovitskaya, S. G., and I. P. Tsukervanik, *Dokl. Akad. Nauk Uz. S.S.R.*, No. 11, 40 (1959).
124c. Mesmeyanov, A. N., N. K. Kochetkov, and L. A. Matov, *Dokl. Akad. Nauk S.S.R.*, **92**, 85 (1953).
125. Moeller, K. E., *Brennstoff-Chem.*, **42**, 361 (1961).
126. Monteils, Y., *Bull. Soc. Chim. France*, 637 (1951).
127. Mouneyrat, A., *Bull. Soc. Chim. France*, (3), **19**, 557 (1898).
128. Mukherji, S. M., and N. K. Bhattacharyya, *J. Org. Chem.*, **17**, 1202 (1952).
129. Mukherji, S. M., V. S. Gaind, and P. N. Rao, *J. Org. Chem.*, **19**, 328 (1954).

130. Mukherji, S. M., O. P. Vig, N. K. Maheswary, and S. S. Sandhu, *J. Indian Chem. Soc.*, **34**, 1 (1957).

131. Mukherji, S. M., O. P. Vig, S. Singh, and N. K. Bhattacharyya, *J. Org. Chem.*, **18**, 1499 (1953).

131a. Natelson, S., B. Kramer, and R. Tekel, U.S. Pat. 2,496,064 (Jan. 13, 1950).

132. Nazerov, I. N., and T. D. Nagibina, *Bull. Acad. Sci. U.R.S.S., Div. Chem. Sci.*, 641 (1947).

133. Nenitzescu, C. D., and I. Gavat, *Ann.*, **519**, 260 (1935).

134. Nenitzescu, C. D., and I. Gavat, *Ber.*, **70**, 1883 (1937).

135. Nenitzescu, C. D., I. G. Gavat, and D. Cocora, *Ber.*, **73**, 233 (1940).

136. Nenitzescu, C. D., and Mme. A. L. Glatz, *Bull. Soc. Chim. France*, 218 (1961).

137. Nenitzescu, C. D., and A. Isacescu, *Ber.*, **66**, 1100 (1933).

138. Nicolet, B. H., and C. M. de Milt, *J. Am. Chem. Soc.*, **49**, 1103 (1927).

138a. Niederhauser, W. D., U.S. Pat. 2,476,264 (July 12, 1949).

139. Niederl, J. B., *J. Am. Chem. Soc.*, **50**, 2230 (1928).

140. Niederl, J. B., *J. Am. Chem. Soc.*, **51**, 2426 (1929).

141. Niederl, J. B., U.S. Pat. 2,029,539 (Feb. 4, 1936).

142. Niederl, J. B., U.S. Pat. 2,082,459 (June 1, 1937).

142a. Niederl, J. B., and R. Casty, *Monatsh.*, **51**, 86, 1038 (1929).

143. Niederl, J. B., and C. Liotta, *J. Am. Chem. Soc.*, **55**, 3025 (1933).

144. Niederl, J. B., R. A. Smith, and M. E. McGreal, *J. Am. Chem. Soc.*, **53**, 3390 (1931).

145. Niederl, J. B., and E. A. Storch, *J. Am. Chem. Soc.*, **55**, 4549 (1933).

146. Niederl, J. B., and B. Whitman, *J. Am. Chem. Soc.*, **56**, 1966 (1934).

147. Parker, W., R. Ramage, and R. A. Raphael, *Proc. Chem. Soc.*, 74 (1961).

148. Petrov, A. D., O. M. Nefedov, and Yu. N. Ogibin, *Izv. Akad. Nauk S.S.S.R., Otd. Khim. Nauk*, 1004 (1957).

149. Pfeiffer, P., E. Schmitz, H. Stocker, H. Kramer, and G. Reuter, *Ann.*, **581**, 149 (1953).

150. Phillips, D. D., and T. B. Hill, *J. Am. Chem. Soc.*, **80**, 3663 (1958).

151. Pines, H., and V. N. Ipatieff, U.S. Pat. 2,410,554 (Nov. 5, 1946).

152. Pines, H., and B. Kvetinskas, U.S. Pat. 2,616,897 (Nov. 4, 1952).

153. Pines, H., B. Kvetinskas, and J. A. Vesely, *J. Am. Chem. Soc.*, **72**, 1568 (1950).

154. Pines, H., B. Kvetinskas, J. A. Vesely, and E. Baclowski, *J. Am. Chem. Soc.*, **73**, 5173 (1951).

155. Pines, H., and J. A. Vesely, U.S. Pat. 2,532,515 (Dec. 5, 1950).

156. Pines, H., and J. A. Vesely, U.S. Pat. 2,553,470 (May 15, 1951).

157. Pines, H., and J. A. Vesely, U.S. Pat. 2,578,206 (Nov. 11, 1951).

158. Pittsburg Plate Glass Co., Brit. Pat. 741,446 (Dec. 7, 1955).

159. Prijs, B., *Helv. Chim. Acta*, **35**, 780 (1952).

159a. Proctor and Gamble, Brit. Pat. 568,725 (April 18, 1945).

160. Proell, W., *J. Org. Chem.*, **16**, 178 (1951); U.S. Pat. 2,564,077 (Aug. 14, 1951).

161. Pummerer, R., and E. Buchta, *Ber.*, **69**, 1005 (1936).

161a. Rice, G. P., *J. Am. Chem. Soc.*, **53**, 3153 (1931).

161b. Rohm and Haas Co., Brit. Pat. 642,930 (Sept. 13, 1956); see ref. 138a.

162. Saha, N. N., P. K. Dutta, and S. M. Mukherji, *Sci. Cult. (Calcutta)*, **18**, 152 (1952).

163. Schaad, R. E., U.S. Pat. 2,283,465 (May 19, 1942).

164. Schaad, R. E., U.S. Pat. 2,382,260 (Aug. 14, 1945).

165. Schlutius, E., *J. Prakt. Chem.*, **142**, 49 (1935).

166. Schmerling, L., U.S. Pat. 2,485,017 (Oct. 18, 1949).

166a. Schmerling, L., U.S. Pat. 2,563,073 (Aug. 7, 1951).

167. Schmerling, L., and V. N. Ipatieff, *J. Am. Chem. Soc.*, **67**, 1862 (1945).

168. Schmerling, L., and V. N. Ipatieff, U.S. Pat. 2,410,553 (Nov. 5, 1946).

168a. Schmerling, L., J. P. West, and R. W. Welch, *J. Am. Chem. Soc.*, **80**, 576 (1958).

169. Schmidt, E. G., *J. Am. Chem. Soc.*, **52**, 1172 (1930).

170. Schrauth, W., and K. Quasebarth, *Ber.*, **57**, 854 (1924).

170a. Schroetter, M. M., Germ. Pat. 947,187 (Aug. 9, 1956).

171. Schukowsky, S., *Bull. Soc. Chim. France*, (3), **16**, 126 (1896).

172. Schulze, W. A., and W. M. Axe, U.S. Pat. 2,425,839 (Aug. 19, 1947).

173. Schwarzer, K., A. Hausweiler, and R. Stroh, Germ. Pat. 1,079,628 (April 14, 1960).

174. Seymur, G. W., U.S. Pat. 2,006,517 (July 2, 1935).

175. Sherlin, S. M., A. Ya. Berlin, T. A. Serebrennikova, and F. E. Rabinovich, *Zh. Obshch. Khim.*, **8**, 7 (1938).

176. Shildneck, P. R., *Org. Syn.*, Vol. 17, John Wiley & Sons, New York, p. 51, 1937.

176a. Shishido, K., *J. Soc. Chem. Japan, Suppl. Bind.*, **45**, 169B (1942); *C.A.*, **44**, 8340 (1950).

176b. Shishido, K., and I. Irie, *J. Soc. Chem. Ind. Japan*, **48**, 10 (1945); *C.A.*, **42**, 6343 (1948).

176c. Shishido, K., and T. Isida, *J. Am. Chem. Soc.*, **70**, 1289 (1948).

176d. Shishido, K., and H. Nozaki, *J. Am. Chem. Soc.*, **70**, 1609 (1948).

177. Shuikin, N. I., E. A. Viktorova, and I. E. Pokrovskaya, *Izv. Akad. Nauk S.S.S.R.*, *Otd. Khim. Nauk*, 1094 (1961).

178. Shuikin, N. I., E. A. Viktorova, I. E. Pokrovskaya, and T. G. Malysheva, *Izv. Akad. Nauk S.S.S.R.*, *Otd. Khim. Nauk*, 1660 (1961).

179. Shuikin, N. I., E. A. Viktorova, I. E. Pokrovskaya, and T. G. Malysheva, *Izv. Akad. Nauk S.S.S.R.*, *Otd. Khim. Nauk*, 1847 (1961).

180. Shuikin, N. I., E. A. Viktorova, I. E. Pokrovskaya, and T. G. Malysheva, *Izv. Akad. Nauk S.S.S.R.*, *Otd. Khim. Nauk*, 1851 (1961).

181. Shukow, A., and P. J. Schestakow, *J. Russ. Phys. Chem. Soc.*, **35**, 1 (1903); *Chem. Zentr.*, (I), 825 (1903).

182. Shukowki, N. I., *J. Russ. Phys. Chem. Soc.*, **27**, 297 (1895).

183. Silva, R. D., *Compt. rend.*, **89**, 606 (1879).

184. Silva, R. D., *Bull. Soc. Chim. France*, (2), **43**, 317 (1885).

185. Simons, J. H., and S. Archer, *J. Am. Chem. Soc.*, **61**, 1521 (1939).

185a. Sisido, K., and T. Isida, *J. Am. Chem. Soc.*, **70**, 1289 (1948).

186. Sisley, J. P., *Chim. Ind. (Paris)*, *Special No.* 763 (April, 1934); *C.A.*, **28**, 5813 (1934).

187. Smith, F. M., U.S. Pat. 2,623,912 (Dec. 30, 1952).

188. Smith, L. I., *J. Am. Chem. Soc.*, **73**, 3843 (1951).

189. Smith, L. I., and Chien-Pen Lo, *J. Am. Chem. Soc.*, **70**, 2215 (1948).

190. Smith, L. I., and J. A. King, *J. Am. Chem. Soc.*, **63**, 1887 (1941).
191. Smith, L. I., and W. W. Prichard, *J. Am. Chem. Soc.*, **62**, 771 (1940).
192. Smith, L. I., and L. J. Spillane, *J. Am. Chem. Soc.*, **65**, 202 (1943).
193. Smith, L. I., and H. E. Ungnade, U.S. Pat. 2,421,811 (June 10, 1947).
194. Smith, L. I., H. E. Ungnade, H. H. Hoehn, and S. Wawzonek, *J. Org. Chem.*, **4**, 305 (1939).
195. Smith, L. I., H. E. Ungnade, H. H. Hoehn, and S. Wawzonek, *J. Org. Chem.*, **4**, 311 (1939).
196. Smith, L. I., H. E. Ungnade, J. R. Stevens, and C. C. Christman, *J. Am. Chem. Soc.*, **61**, 2615 (1939).
197. Smith, R. A., and J. B. Niederl, *J. Am. Chem. Soc.*, **55**, 4151 (1933).
198. Smith, W. T., Jr., and J. T. Sellas, *Org. Syn.*, Vol. 32, John Wiley & Sons, New York, p. 90, 1952.
199. Société des usines chimiques Rhône-Poulenc, Brit. Pat. 787,615 (Dec. 11, 1957).
199a. Steindorff, A., C. Platz, and J. Rosenbach, Germ. Pat. 738,198 (Aug. 31, 1943).
200. Stirton, A. J., and R. F. Peterson, *Ind. Eng. Chem.*, **31**, 856 (1939).
201. Tanabi, S., and S. Onishi, *J. Pharm. Soc. Japan*, **73**, 38 (1953); *C.A.*, **47**, 10509h (1953).
202. Texaco Development Co., Brit. Pat. 625,173 (January 23, 1949).
203. Truce, W. E., J. A. Simms, and H. E. Hill, *J. Am. Chem. Soc.*, **75**, 5411 (1953).
204. Truffault, R., *Compt. rend.*, **202**, 1286 (1936).
205. Truffault, R., *Compt. rend.*, **207**, 676 (1938).
206. Truffault, R., and Y. Monteils, *Bull. Soc. Chim. France*, (5), **6**, 726 (1939).
207. Truffault, R., and Y. Monteils, *Bull. Soc. Chim. France*, 230 (1951).
207a. Tsukervanik, I. P., and A. D. Grebenyuk, *Dokl. Akad. Nauk S.S.S.R.*, **76**, 223 (1951).
208. Tsukervanik, I. P., and N. G. Simkhaev, *J. Gen. Chem. U.S.S.R.*, **20**, 329 (1950).
209. Tsukervanik, I. P., and K. Y. Yuldashev, *Uzbeksk. Khim. Zh.*, No. 6, 58 (1960).
210. Tsukervanik, I. P., and K. Y. Yuldashev, *Zh. Obshch. Khim.*, **31**, 858 (1961).
210a. Turkington, V. H., L. R. Whiting, and L. P. Rankin, U.S. Pat. 2,353,282 (July 11, 1944).
210b. Vasil'eva, N. V., and I. P. Tsukervanik, *J. Gen. Chem. U.S.S.R.*, **27**, 1767 (1957).
211. Vdovtsova, E. A., *Zh. Obshsch. Khim.*, **31**, 95 (1961).
212. Vdovtsova, E. A., *Zh. Obshch. Khim.*, **31**, 102 (1961).
213. Vdovtsova, E. A., and A. M. Romanikhin, *Zh. Obshch. Khim.*, **31**, 479 (1961).
214. Vdovtsova, E. A., and S. V. Zavgorodnii, *Dokl. Akad. Nauk S.S.S.R.*, **113**, 590 (1957).
214a. Vig, O. P., S. V. Kessar, V. P. Kubba, and S. M. Mukherji, *J. Indian Chem. Soc.*, **32**, 697 (1955).
215. Vig, O. P., S. S. Sandhu, and S. M. Mukherji, *J. Indian Chem. Soc.*, **34**, 81 (1957).

216. Vig, O. P., and S. S. Sandhu, *Sci. Cult. (Calcutta)*, **19**, 311 (1953).

216a. Viktorova, E. A., N. I. Shuikin, and B. G. Bubnova, *Izv. Akad. Nauk S.S.S.R.*, *Otd. Khim. Nauk*, 1657 (1961).

217. Viktorova, E. A., N. I. Shuikin, and E. I. Polyanskaya, *Izv. Akad. Nauk S.S.S.R.*, *Otd. Khim. Nauk*, 2048 (1960).

218. Viktorova, E. A., N. I. Shuikin, and G. V. Popova, *Vestn. Mosk. Univ. Ser. II: Khim.*, **15**, No. 6, 62 (1960).

219. Vorlander, D., and A. Friedberg, *Ber.*, **56**, 1144 (1923).

220. Wagner, C. R., U.S. Pat. 2,393,132 (Jan. 15, 1946).

221. Webb, I. D., and G. T. Borcherdt, *J. Am. Chem. Soc.*, **73**, 752 (1951).

222a. Weber, S. H., D. B. Spoelstra, and E. H. Polak, *Rec. Trav. Chim.*, **74**, 1179 (1955).

222b. Wislicenus, W., and K. Eble, *Ber.*, **50**, 250 (1917).

223. Weinstock, H. H., and R. C. Fuson, *J. Am. Chem. Soc.*, **56**, 1241 (1934).

224. Weston, A. W., U.S. Pat. 2,654,791 (Oct. 6, 1953).

225. Whitmore, F. C., C. A. Weisgarber, and A. C. Shabica, Jr., *J. Am. Chem. Soc.*, **65**, 1469 (1943).

226. Wilgus, D. R., U.S. Pat. 2,995,587 (Aug. 8, 1961).

227. Wispek, P., and R. Zuber, *Ann.*, **218**, 379 (1883).

228. Wispek, P., and R. Zuber, *Bull. Soc. Chim. France*, (2), **43**, 588 (1885).

229. Woodward, C. F., G. T. Borcherdt, and R. C. Fuson, *J. Am. Chem. Soc.*, **56**, 2103 (1934).

230. Yang, N. C., and A. J. Castro, *J. Am. Chem. Soc.*, **82**, 6208 (1960).

231. Yur'ev, Yu. K., N. S. Zefirov, A. A. Shteĭnman, and V. M. Gurevich, *J. Gen. Chem. U.S.S.R.*, **30**, 434 (1960).

232. Yur'ev, Yu. K., N.S. Zefirov, A. A. Shteĭnman, and V. I. Ryboedov, *Zh. Obshch. Khim.*, **30**, 3214 (1960).

CHAPTER XVI

Alkylation of Aromatics with Alkynes

V. Franzen

Max Planck Institut für Medizinische Forschung, Heidelberg,
Germany

I. Alkylation with Acetylene

The reaction of acetylene with benzene in the presence of aluminum chloride was first investigated by Varet and Vienne (20). Their experimental results, however, could not be duplicated by Cook and Chambers (4), who found that two benzene molecules add to one of acetylene to form 1,1-diphenylethane. In a side reaction, 9,10-dihydro-9,10-dimethylanthracene is formed according to the equation

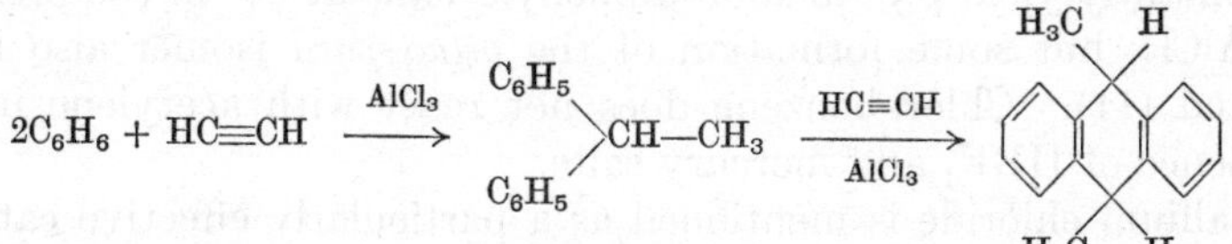

The main product of the reaction is a mixture of polymeric substances of unknown structure. The yield of 1,1-diphenylethane depends to a great extent on the activity of $AlCl_3$. Thus, aged $AlCl_3$ gives better yields, whereas freshly prepared $AlCl_3$ produces more 9,10-dihydro-9,10-dimethylanthracene. Styrene is produced in very minute quantities, if at all.

Toluene reacts with acetylene in the presence of $AlCl_3$ to form 1,1-p,p'-ditolylethane and various methylanthracenes as by-products. In an analogous reaction, unsymmetrical p,p-dichlorodiphenylethane and unsymmetrical p,p'-tetramethyldiaminodiphenylethane are formed from chlorobenzene and dimethylaniline, respectively.

Boeseken and Adler (2) investigated the polymeric substances formed from the reaction of benzene and acetylene in the presence of $AlCl_3$ and reported that the polymer seems to contain the two reactants in a $1:1$ ratio, but is probably not a pure hydrocarbon.

At low temperatures, acetylene and $AlCl_3$ form a complex which is said to possess the structure $(AlCl_3)_2 \cdot (C_2H_2)_{12}$ (1) whereas at high temperatures $AlCl_3$ is reported to have a strongly polymerizing effect on acetylene (6).

Nozu and Han-Ying Li (7) have studied the reaction of acetylene with benzene in the presence of $AlCl_3$ as a function of temperature. They have found that the reaction is almost the same at $2°$ as at $85°$, and have identified 1,4-diethylbenzene, butenylbenzene, as well as o-di-(1-phenylethyl)benzene as side products.

Usually no more than traces of styrene are found in the reaction of benzene with acetylene, although it is reported that $AlCl_3$ containing $2-5\%$ ferric chloride improves the styrene yield (10). 1,2-Diphenylethane is said to be formed also. This, however, does not seem probable. Under the reaction conditions styrene is easily polymerized. At lower temperatures and with anhydrous HF as catalyst, xylene is reported to give reasonable yields of dimethylstyrene (5).

Whether the alkylation of substituted aromatic compounds exclusively produces p,p'-disubstituted diarylethanes cannot be stated with certainty. Thus, chlorobenzene and acetylene predominantly yield p,p'-dichlorodiphenylethane at $80°$ in the presence of $AlCl_3$, but some formation of the *ortho–para* isomer also is reported (11). Chlorobenzene does not react with acetylene in the presence of HBF_4 and mercury salts.

Gallium chloride is mentioned as a particularly effective catalyst (12) in the presence of which benzene reacts with acetylene at $50-60°$ to form alkylbenzene. Thus, the alkylation reaction also involves a hydrogenation.

No reaction between phenol and acetylene takes place in the presence of $AlCl_3$, probably owing to the formation of an addition compound of $AlCl_3$ and phenol. Reichert and Nieuwland (8) have developed a method of alkylating various phenols involving an acid or a Lewis acid as catalyst, other than $AlCl_3$. This method can also be used for the alkylation of aromatic hydrocarbons in good yields.

Benzene reacts with acetylene in the presence of phosphoric acid which has been saturated with boron trifluoride with formation of 1,1-diphenylethane, in a yield of 65% of theory. In addition, some polymeric substances are formed, the amount of which increases with increasing reaction time (14). The aforementioned alkylation reaction proceeds particularly well if a little mercuric oxide is added to the catalyst and the temperature is maintained at 30–40° (13).

Naphthalene reacts with acetylene in the presence of the same catalyst to produce 1,1-di-(2-naphthyl)ethane in 40% yield (19), whereas in the presence of concentrated sulfuric acid and HgO no reaction occurs. This last type of catalyst is not very efficient. Polynuclear hydrocarbons such as diphenyl, diphenylmethane, or dibenzyl do not react with acetylene, but benzene derivatives with saturated side chains yield, with concentrated sulfuric acid and HgO as catalyst, substituted diphenylethylidene hydrocarbons (9).

The alkylation of aromatic compounds with acetylene in the presence of mercuric oxide and acids probably does not have a true Friedel-Crafts alkylation mechanism. It is possible that, under the influence of the mercury catalyst, acetylene is first hydrated with formation of acetaldehyde since the acids used in the reaction are not anhydrous. The subsequent reaction step involves a condensation of acetaldehyde with aromatic compounds. This assumption is confirmed by the fact that in the presence of anhydrous alcohols as solvents, the yield of alkylated product is very insignificant (16).

Phenols can be alkylated by acetylene particularly well in the presence of an acid and mercuric salt as catalysts. Depending on the reaction conditions phenol produces 1,1-di-(p'-hydroxyphenyl)-ethane (maximum yield 16%) or polymers of the Novolack type. The alkylation of cresol proceeds with much better yield, which depends on the catalyst:cresol ratio (15). Under the most favorable conditions the yields of 1,1-diarylethane amount to 98% in the case of p-cresol, 94% for m-cresol, and 89% for o-cresol. No vinyl compounds or polymers are formed. In the presence of alcohol only polymers are produced (17). 2-Hydroxynaphthalene gives 9-methyl-1,2,7,8-dibenzoxanthene in a yield of 68% (18).

II. Alkylation with Haloalkynes

3-Chloropropyne reacts with benzene in the presence of $AlCl_3$ to form small quantities of 1,1,2-triphenylpropane (3):

$$3C_6H_6 + ClCH_2-C\equiv CH \xrightarrow{AlCl_3} \begin{array}{c} C_6H_5 \\ \diagdown \\ CH-\overset{\displaystyle C_6H_5}{\underset{\displaystyle H}{C}}-CH_3 + HCl \\ \diagup \\ C_6H_5 \end{array}$$

The predominant reaction product is again polymeric. The formation of 1,1,2-triphenylpropane is explained by isomerization of

3-chloropropyne to 1-chloropropadiene, which then reacts with benzene.

6-Chlorohexyne-1 and 5-chloro-4-ethylpentyne-1 do not form any well-defined reaction products with benzene in the presence of $AlCl_3$.

The low yields observed with acetylenes in Friedel-Crafts reaction are caused by a strong polymerizing effect of $AlCl_3$ on the acetylene compounds involved. Butylacetylene, for example, does not react with $AlCl_3$ at $-10°$, but a sudden reaction occurs at $0°$ with formation of polymers. However, acetylene compounds can react with alkyl halides if an addition compound of $AlCl_3$ and alkyl halide is first formed and is then allowed to react with the alkyne component (9a).

References

1. Baud, E., *Ann. Chim. Phys.*, **1**, 36 (1904).
2. Boeseken, J., and A. A. Adler, *Rec. Trav. Chim.*, **48**, 474 (1929).
3. Cologne, J., and Y. Infarnet, *Bull. Soc. Chim. France*, 1916 (1960).
4. Cook, O. W., and V. J. Chambers, *J. Am. Chem. Soc.*, **43**, 334 (1923).
5. Dominion Tar and Chemical Co. Ltd., Brit. Pat. 616,751; through *C.A.*, **43**, 5636 (1949).
6. Hunter, H. W., and R. V. Yohe, *J. Am. Chem. Soc.*, **55**, 1248 (1933).
7. Nozu, R., and Han-Yin Li, *J. Chem. Soc. Japan*, **60**, 895 (1939); through *C.A.*, **36**, 2843 (1942); *J. Chem. Soc. Japan*, **61**, 11 (1940); through *C.A.*, **36**, 2844 (1942).
8. Reichert, J. S., and J. A. Nieuwland, *J. Am. Chem. Soc.*, **45**, 3090 (1923); *Org. Syn.*, Vol. I, John Wiley and Sons Inc., New York, p. 229, 1932.
9. Reilly, J. A., and J. A. Nieuwland, *J. Am. Chem. Soc.*, **50**, 2564 (1928).
9a. Schlubach, H. H., and V. Franzen, *Ann.*, **583**, 93 (1953).
10. Tsukervanik, I. P., *Dokl. Akad. Nauk S.S.S.R.*, **74**, 959 (1950); through *C.A.*, **45**, 4666 (1951).
11. Tsukervanik, I. P., and T. G. Gar'kovets, *Zh. Obsch. Khim.*, **25**, 919 (1955); through *C.A.*, **50**, 3347 (1956).
12. Ulich, H., *Brennstoff-Chem.*, **39**, 532 (1943).
13. Vaiser, V. L., *Dokl. Akad. Nauk S.S.S.R.*, **70**, 621 (1950); through *C.A.*, **44**, 4888 (1950).
14. Vaiser, V. L., *Dokl. Akad. Nauk S.S.S.R.*, **91**, 535 (1953); through *C.A.*, **48**, 10626 (1954).
15. Vaiser, V. L., *et al.*, *Dokl. Akad. Nauk S.S.S.R.*, **74**, 57 (1950); **97**, 671 (1954); **103**, 839 (1945); through *C.A.*, **45**, 3827 (1951); **49**, 10242 (1955); **50**, 9353 (1956).
16. Vaiser, V. L., and V. D. Ryabov, *Dokl. Akad. Nauk S.S.S.R.*, **100**, 271 (1955); through *C.A.*, **50**, 1649 (1956).
17. Vaiser, V. L., and A. M. Polikarpova, *Dokl. Akad. Nauk S.S.S.R.*, **108**, 469 (1956); through *C.A.*, **51**, 1109 (1957).
18. Vaiser, V. L., *Dokl. Akad. Nauk S.S.S.R.*, **115**, 91 (1957); through *C.A.*, **52**, 5356 (1958).
19. Vaiser, V. L., and V. D. Ryabov, *Dokl. Akad. Nauk S.S.S.R.*, **121**, 648 (1958); through *C.A.*, **53**, 1244 (1959).
20. Varet, R., and G. Vienne, *Compt. rend.*, **164**, 1375 (1886).

CHAPTER XVII

Alkylation of Aromatics with Haloalkanes

FRANZ A. DRAHOWZAL

Technical University, Vienna, Austria

I. Introduction

The alkylation of aromatic compounds with alkyl halides has been intensively studied ever since the original work of Friedel and Crafts but to date no general agreement has yet been reached on the mechanism of the reaction. Although it is easy to produce alkylbenzenes by alkylation with alkyl halides the accompanying phenomena are diverse and abundant. The alkylation of aromatics may also be effected by many other reagents but the alkyl halide method is the most convenient and consequently a vast amount of information has accumulated on the topic. The present treatment will attempt to show the many facets of the nature of the reaction and more stress will be attached to the course and mechanism rather than to the preparative aspects.

In order to present as complete an account as possible it has been necessary to include in this chapter brief mention of some points which are covered more extensively elsewhere in this monograph. Some overlapping will also be found on the question of isomerization since this is often a consequence of the alkylation conditions. No attempt has been made to include a complete list of references to alkylation of aromatic substrates by alkyl halides. Such data are adequately recorded elsewhere (67a,138a).

II. Catalysts and Solvents

1. Aluminum Halides

In discussing Friedel-Crafts alkylations it is often difficult to distinguish between solvent and catalytic effects and thus the two are best considered together.

Anhydrous aluminum chloride is the catalyst most frequently used for Friedel-Crafts reactions in spite of the many difficulties which

arise from its use.   The choice of solvent has not been so general.
Carbon disulfide and nitrobenzene have often been used in other
Friedel-Crafts reactions, but not in alkylations.   Here the alkyl
halides, excess aromatic substrate, and the aralkyl product are often
solvent enough.   The course of the reaction may be influenced by
changing the ratio of these components and also by the inclusion of
an inert solvent.   For example, when aluminum chloride is the catalyst in nitromethane solvent the formation of tertiary alkyl compounds is favored (155).   Thus 2-phenyl-3,3-dimethylbutane results
from the alkylation of benzene with 1-chloro-3,3-dimethylbutane
(52), or 2-chloro-2,3-dimethylbutane.   The catalyst used has little
effect, whether it is aluminum chloride at 0° or aluminum bromide or
zirconium chloride at 85°.   However, if the reaction is carried out
in nitromethane the product is invariably a tertiary compound,
2-phenyl-2,3-dimethylbutane.

$$PhH + (CH_3)_2CHCCl(CH_3)_2 \longrightarrow (CH_3)_3CCHCH_3$$
$$\underset{Ph}{|}$$
$$PhH + (CH_3)_3CCH_2CH_2Cl \longrightarrow (CH_3)_2CHC(CH_3)_2$$
$$\underset{Ph}{|}$$

    The difficulty of establishing fixed rules for reactions with alumin-
um chloride was shown when Friedman (53) was unable to synthesize
t-amyl-p-xylene from t-amyl chloride and p-xylene.   Although
aluminum chloride and nitromethane were present the product was
always s-amyl-p-xylene.   It has also been shown (155) that in the
aluminum chloride–nitromethane system secondary alkyl chlorides
are more reactive than the primary isomers.   Thus isopropyl
chloride and benzene yield 45% isopropylbenzene and 30% diisopropylbenzene at room temperature in the presence of aluminum
chloride and either nitromethane or nitropropane.   With n-propyl
chloride only 4% propylbenzene is obtained.   The propylbenzene
so formed is mainly isopropylbenzene and the yield does not vary
with temperatures up to 70°.
    A more gentle catalyst for the alkylation is $AlCl_2 \cdot HSO_4$ (176,177).
Neither an intermolecular hydrogen transfer nor an isomerization
of the n-propyl group occurs with this catalyst.
    Nenitzescu (115,117) has determined that rearrangement of the
alkylbenzenes is accelerated by traces of water.   However, such
rearrangements also occur in the opposite direction to those previously
mentioned; thus tertiary alkylbenzenes tend to form secondary
alkylbenzenes which in turn yield primary alkylbenzenes.   For

example, a secondary butyl group will be transformed to an isobutyl group under these conditions. The question arises as to whether alkylation and rearrangement proceed simultaneously.

Others workers have shown (82,83) that non-monomolecular aluminum halides may participate in the reaction; aluminum chloride is present initially as the dimer Al_2Cl_6.

The activity of aluminum chloride can also be moderated by the addition of sodium chloride (15). This variation in activity can be utilized in the presence of nitromethane even though sodium chloride is insoluble in nitromethane (155). Owing to this insolubility a solution of aluminum chloride in nitromethane must first be made and then a nearly molar amount of sodium chloride added. Upon the addition of the aromatic hydrocarbon to be alkylated the catalyst forms a deep red, second liquid phase. After the reaction is completed this phase of catalyst may be separated and used for further experiments since no intermixing takes place during the alkylation. Without sodium chloride aluminum chloride in nitromethane gives homogeneous solutions and no second phase is formed by addition of aromatic compounds.

The alkylation in the presence of amine complexes shows some peculiarities. There are all the advantages of a liquid catalyst and by changing the quantitative proportion of the starting components the reaction may be carried out in a single homogeneous liquid phase or with a separated liquid catalyst phase of higher density. A little amine is all that is necessary to achieve a homogeneous solution, contrary to carbon disulfide, which usually gives homogeneous solutions only in high dilution. In preparative laboratory experiments the amine–aluminum chloride complexes are advantageous for the synthesis of long-chain alkylbenzenes from long-chain alkyl halides. The alkylation is not disturbed by simultaneous formation of alkenes or alkanes, as often happens in conventional alkylations.

The previously mentioned restricted activity of aluminum catalysts was also observed with these amine complexes when the alkylation was carried out in a nitrogen atmosphere (free from oxygen) and all components were carefully dried. When some alkylation had occurred the reaction stopped suddenly without a slow decline of the reaction rate. This stop was accompanied by a rapid increase in the heat of reaction. Therefore, a separate terminating reaction seems to be a possibility but its nature has not been discovered.

Compared with the amine, greater than molar amounts of aluminum chloride are necessary. The excess of aluminum chloride and the structure of the amine are important factors in the alkyla-

15+F.C. II

tion. For all these observations a dimolar aluminum compound containing the tertiary amine is necessary.

$$\left[\begin{array}{c} R_3N \rightarrow Al \diagup^{Cl} \diagdown_{Cl} \end{array}\right]^{+} \left[\begin{array}{c} Cl \diagdown \diagup Cl \\ Al \\ Cl \diagup \diagdown Cl \end{array}\right]^{-}$$

When primary alkyl halides are inserted in the above cationic part we obtain a formulation similar to that proposed by H. C. Brown *et al.* (24). This may be considered especially for long-chain alkyl halides which give very good results in the presence of such amine complexes.

$$\left[\begin{array}{c} Cl \quad \delta- \quad\quad \delta+ \; \delta- \quad\quad \delta+ \\ R_3N \rightarrow Al\cdots Cl \text{---} R \cdots Cl\text{---}R \\ Cl \end{array}\right]^{+} \left[\begin{array}{c} Cl \diagdown \diagup Cl \\ Al \\ Cl \diagup \diagdown Cl \end{array}\right]^{-}$$

A kinetic reaction termination step, as proposed by Nenitzescu (117), may be the real reason then for the influence of the nature of the amine and of the aluminum chloride excess on the ratio obtained between mono- and dialkylbenzenes.

In complexes prepared with pyridine or dimethylaniline no alkylations of the amine compound are observed. The latter forms very small amounts of Crystal Violet (hexamethylpararosaniline) on addition of the aluminum chloride.

The sudden color change showing the starting activity of the complex, is very useful in calculating the desired excess of aluminum chloride, especially if the purity of the aluminum chloride is considerably less than 100%. Only a few simultaneous side reactions disturb the alkylation, the formation of tar and resin products being especially diminished. Work in this field, however, is just beginning and no conclusion can be drawn from these preliminary results.

Alkylation of the aromatic ring of primary aromatic amines is possible if the amino group has first been acetylated. Thus acetanilide forms *p-t*-butylacetanilide by reaction with isobutyl bromide in the presence of aluminum chloride (76,78). For Friedel-Crafts acylation previous acetylation of the amino group is also a condition.

Although extensive work has been done to establish the mechanism of alkylation of aromatics with alkyl halides, much less has been done to investigate the influence of the amount, different mixtures and impurities of the catalyst on the reaction. There are numerous patents for producing maximum activity of the catalyst, especially starting from aluminum chloride, but the resulting activity of such catalysts is not well defined. The alkylations are very sensitive to differences in the catalyst and this may be the real reason for divergences among the published results (146,148).

The more soluble aluminum bromide is often preferred for basic research whereas aluminum chloride is the favorite catalyst for alkylations of aromatics with alkyl halides on an industrial scale. The desire for a homogeneous reaction phase is the main reason for the above mentioned multiplicity of procedures in the preparation of highly active catalysts which are based upon aluminum chloride (157). The homogeneous phase results in a much more steady reaction (55,56,151,152,153).

Aluminum bromide was preferred by Sharman (161a) when he tested the influence of different conditions on the alkylation of aromatics with n-octyl and n-dodecyl bromide. Using primary bromides the formation of primary alkylarenes increases with decreasing temperature and increasing nucleophilicity of the benzene ring. Also the catalysts have different tendencies to form primary alkylbenzenes: $GaBr_3$ < $AlCl_3$ < $AlBr_3$. There is a trend to attain an equilibrium between all possible secondary positions of the chain, yet once formed primary alkylbenzene never rearranges to a secondary isomer.

Primary alkylbenzenes never result from any secondary alkyl bromide for neither π- nor σ-complexes of the secondary compounds rearrange in this direction. The inverse reaction is always in concurrence during the alkylation with primary bromides. Secondary alkyl groups are also easily transferred to another aromatic and only some primary dodecylethylbenzene remained unchanged if a product from the dodecylation of ethylbenzene was treated with benzene, aluminum bromide, and hydrogen bromide.

2. Gallium Halides

In recent years interest in gallium chloride for basic research and kinetic tests has increased in view of its solubility (185,186).

Gallium chloride forms addition compounds with alkyl halides, even with methyl chloride (23), bromide, and iodide (18). The complex compounds of gallium chloride with aromatics in the presence of hydrogen halides are similar to those formed with aluminum halides (23).

H. C. Brown has shown (21a,25,35,171,172) that improved results may be obtained by using gallium bromide. The relative reaction rates of the alkylation of benzene and toluene have been estimated with methyl, n-propyl, isopropyl, and t-butyl bromide. These kinetic studies confirm the assumption of two different mechanisms of alkylation; the much faster ionic mechanism, in the cases of isopropyl and t-butyl bromides, which is replaced by a nucleophilic displacement mechanism for unbranched primary alkyl halides like methyl, ethyl, or n-propyl bromides.

Analyses have shown that large amounts of isopropylbenzene are formed by alkylation of benzene with n-propyl bromide (72%). H. C. Brown has postulated that prior to the alkylation the n-propyl bromide isomerizes to the iso compound and the latter then reacts much faster with the aromatic nuclei. This seems to be a very good explanation for the astonishing higher relative alkylation rate of the n-propyl bromide compared to ethyl bromide, which would otherwise be the inverse due to the decreasing reactivity expected with increasing length of the carbon chain. By a kinetic study it is shown that the rate of the alkylation of benzene or toluene in a non-ionic displacement reaction declines from ethyl bromide to n-propyl bromide (172).

3. Boron Trifluoride

It has often been shown that the activity of a Friedel-Crafts catalyst may be improved by the presence of oxygen-containing compounds (88). One of the most widely used is the boron trifluoride–etherate but in the case of alkylation with alkyl halides its use has been very limited. Korshak and Lebedev (83) have postulated that the activity of this catalyst is due to the formation of a dipole between the positive oxygen and the negative boron. But, as discussed in Chapters IV and VI, it is more plausible to consider the oxygenated compounds as co-catalysts, providing a strong proton acid catalyst. In the presence of large quantities of boron trifluoride p-cresol may be alkylated with t-butyl chloride to give, besides alkylation, a 15–20% yield of isomerization product. Exchange of the methyl group with an isobutyl group can also be observed (101).

Boron trifluoride is insoluble in water-free solutions of alkyl halides in benzene and therefore the alkylation cannot proceed, but after addition of water, alcohol, sulfuric acid, or any other suitable polar compound the alkylation takes place without further difficulty if tertiary or secondary alkyl halides are used. With primary alkyl halides alkylation is only successful in special cases, e.g., with benzyl or allyl halides (62).

4. Titanium Tetrachloride

Concerning the catalytic effect of titanium tetrachloride very few systematic experiments have been reported. Cullinane and Leyson

(41) observed that alkyl groups enter predominantly in the *para*-position of aromatic rings. They further determined that with *t*-butyl chloride a *t*-butyl group enters the aromatic ring unchanged; however, *t*-amyl chloride (Me_2EtCCl) gives varying amounts of the 2,2-dimethylpropyl (neopentyl, Me_3CCH_2) product; this corresponds to the rearrangements of alkylbenzenes in the direction of primary alkyl products as reported by Nenitzescu (115,117) (see Section V-5). More recent studies (132) show that toluene may be alkylated in positions other than *para* and that isobutyl chloride alkylates toluene slower and in smaller yields than *t*-butyl chloride. With the latter *t*-butyltoluenes are obtained in 70% yield with a reaction time of 30 minutes at 100°.

5. Antimony Pentachloride

That antimony pentachloride is a generally less active catalyst for alkylation than aluminum chloride was impressively shown, in the case of benzene, by Perova (134) (see Table I).

TABLE I. The comparison of the activity of antimony pentachloride and aluminum chloride in alkylation of benzene (134)

Alkyl halide	Metal halide	Products and yield			
$PhCH_2Cl$	$SbCl_5$	$PhCH_2Ph$	35%		
$PhCH_2Cl$	$AlCl_3$	$PhCH_2Ph$	46.8%		
BuBr	$SbCl_5$	MeEtCHPh	6%	BuPh	—
BuBr	$AlCl_3$	MeEtCHPh	38.8%	BuPh	13%
BuCl	$SbCl_5$	MeEtCHPh	3%	BuPh	—
BuCl	$AlCl_3$	MeEtCHPh	28.3%	BuPh	25.4%

2 moles benzene, 0.5 mol. alkyl halide, and 0.125 mol. catalyst at 70° for 4 hours

6. Zinc Chloride

Zinc chloride seems one of the weakest catalysts for Friedel-Crafts reactions, therefore the amounts of higher alkylated products are always small and usually alkylation requires higher temperatures in addition to long reaction times. Kuchkarov and Tsukervanik (89) have used zinc chloride in the presence of hydrogen chloride. For the alkylation of benzene, in view of the higher temperature (170–240°), pressure was necessary to maintain the reaction in a liquid phase; nevertheless the reaction time was very long (7–12 hours). Under such conditions *n*-butyl chloride yields secondary butylbenzene and isoamyl chloride forms *t*-amylbenzene. It seems that in the presence of zinc chloride rearrangements are not directed

to the formation of primary alkylbenzenes otherwise these latter
reactions would have formed isobutylbenzene and neopentylbenzene
respectively. Use of a combination of zinc chloride and hydrogen
chloride raises the question as to which is the more important
component. In addition it must be remembered that hydrogen
chloride itself is a catalyst of limited use for such alkylations with
alkyl halides.

7. Ferric Chloride

Ferric chloride has been proved very useful for the preparation of
alkylbenzenes with tertiary alkyl groups. Inatome *et al.* (67) have
synthesized *t*-amylbenzene from benzene, *t*-amyl chloride, and dry
ferric chloride with a 60% yield calculated on *t*-amyl chloride. By
combination of ferric chloride with nitromethane the purity of the
t-amylbenzene formed was diminished, contrary to alkylations in the
presence of aluminum chloride. Further synthesis of *t*-alkylbenzenes
from *t*-alkyl chlorides with ferric chloride is the alkylation of
benzene with 2-chloro-2-methylpentane and with 3-chloro-3-ethyl-
pentane. This latter *t*-alkyl chloride also forms a tertiary hydrocarbon but instead of the 3-phenyl-3-ethylpentane expected 3-
phenyl-3-methylhexane was isolated (110):

$$\text{Et}_3\text{CCl} + \text{PhH} \rightarrow \underset{\underset{\text{Ph}}{|}}{\overset{\overset{\text{Me}}{|}}{\text{Et}\text{C}\text{Pr}}}$$

According to Ibuki (64) the optimum temperature for isomerization with ferric chloride is between $-5°$ and $0°$. The isomerized
alkyl chloride then alkylates the aromatic nucleus.

Ferric chloride (99) and ferrous fluoride (188) combine with
hydrogen fluoride and boron trifluoride. These complexes are
useful catalysts for the alkylation of aromatics with alkyl halides
and olefins. For reaction temperatures above 50° alkylation under
pressure is recommended in view of the tendency of these complexes
to decompose at higher temperatures. Ferrous fluoride may be
replaced by other divalent fluorides of the iron group such as CoF_2
or NiF_2.

8. Proton Acids

Proton acids, such as sulfuric acid, hydrogen fluoride, and hydrogen chloride, also catalyze the alkylation of aromatic substrates
with alkyl halides. Generally such materials are much less frequently used than Lewis acid catalysts.

9. Acidic Oxides: Alumina

Alumina, after treatment with dry hydrogen chloride, is reported to be a suitable catalyst for the alkylation of aromatics with alkyl halides (*e.g.*, propyl chloride, isobutyl chloride) (139,140). The corresponding mono- and dialkylbenzenes are the resulting products. For compounds with oxygen attached to the aromatic ring, such as 1- or 2-naphthols or phenoxybenzenes, the yield may be improved if the alumina is activated with sulfuric or phosphoric acid and zinc chloride added to the mixture of reactants. The chlorides of beryllium, magnesium, cobalt, or mercury often give much better yields than zinc chloride. The metal chlorides seem to be the important component of the catalyst.

10. Aqueous Metal Halides

In the original experiments of Jenny (71) benzene was alkylated with reactive alkyl chlorides (ethyl, isopropyl, cyclohexyl, or benzyl chloride) in the presence of aqueous hydrochloric acid solutions of zinc chloride or ferric chloride. By this method, if the optimum concentration of either zinc chloride or ferric chloride is chosen, good yields are possible; *e.g.*, a mixture of 2 moles benzene and 1 mole isopropyl chloride gives cumene in 66% yield calculated on isopropyl chloride, if treated for 4 hours at 25° with an aqueous solution containing 75% ferric chloride and saturated with hydrogen chloride.

11. Metal Catalysts (*in situ* formation of metal halides)

A. *Aluminum*

The use of activated aluminum metal has greatly increased in recent alkylations of aromatics with alkyl halides. Radzivanovskii (142) was the first to successfully use activated aluminum metal in place of aluminum chloride. After the observation that benzylation of benzene is possible without any catalyst if the temperature is high enough in the mixture of benzyl chloride and excess benzene, aluminum shavings were tested for their catalytic efficiency. Small quantities of aluminum shavings placed in an excess of aromatic hydrocarbon have been activated with gaseous hydrogen chloride or mercuric chloride. Alkylation of the aromatic hydrocarbon starts immediately when the mixture is charged with the corresponding alkyl halide (ethyl bromide, benzyl chloride, etc.). It has also been reported that polyalkylbenzenes suffer some dealkylation by such activated aluminum shavings. Some of the later patents (154) suggest that hydrogen chloride or mercuric chloride activate the aluminum shavings by formation of traces of aluminum chloride which would be necessary to initiate the reaction. But these patents do not always need mercuric chloride or separate hydrogen chloride; small amounts of aluminum chloride are added and the reaction begins with formation of hydrogen halide, which then continuously activates the aluminum shavings. During the alkylation aluminum chloride and aluminum metal catalysts always lose their activity. This may be compensated for very easily by the addition of further aluminum shavings without interruption of the reaction (175,198,199).

Dolgov (45–47) also recommends this simplified reactivation. In addition simple methods of alkylation of aromatics with alkyl halides have been developed and the efficiency of aluminum chloride has been compared with that of aluminum shavings after activation with hydrogen chloride (104).

Azatyan (4,5) has succeeded in the most diverse alkylations of aromatics with alkyl halides in the presence of freshly cut aluminum shavings without any further activation. Though remarkably small amounts of aluminum were used, the alkylbenzenes were formed with a yield of about 80%. More recently Turova-Pollak et al. (182, 184) have continued the alkylation by this method and yields up to 96% are now possible. If alkyl bromides (ethyl bromide, propyl bromide, butyl bromide) are used, the formation of a complex compound is the first step. These red-colored complexes establish a separate liquid phase which can be used as catalyst for subsequent charges of aromatic, but its activity declines in complete accordance with the behavior of all other Friedel-Crafts catalysts with aluminum as base. In a charge of 8 moles benzene, 1 mole ethyl bromide, and 0.01 gram-atom aluminum metal, 96% of the ethyl bromide forms ethylbenzene. In charges with cyclohexyl chloride or cyclopentyl chloride no complex is formed but the unconsumed aluminum shavings themselves may be used for subsequent charges. Such twice-used shavings favor monoalkylation and their use enhances the reaction rate. In the presence of aluminum shavings a lower temperature also favors monoalkylation.

The activation of aluminum by traces of halogen is described by Prey et al. (136,137), and recalls the Grignard reaction. But there may be more than a formal similarity because aluminum metal reacts with alkyl halides with formation of aluminum alkyl halides (Ziegler compounds $Al_2R_3X_3$) if the work is carried out in an inert gas atmosphere. The compounds $Al_2R_3X_3$ often have been proved to be extremely active catalysts for the alkylation of aromatics with alkyl halides (59,103,105).

B. Zinc

The first successful alkylation of aromatics with alkyl halides was described by Zincke (200).   The first reactions were carried out with benzyl chloride in the presence of zinc metal.   Other workers were also active in the field (141).   Early publications report that benzene, toluene, and ethylbenzene react with α-phenylethyl bromide upon the addition of zinc metal.   The Zincke method has never been totally superseded and today zinc metal is still used for alkylation with alkyl halides.

C. Copper

Zinc and aluminum are not the only metals applicable to Friedel-Crafts catalyses.   Metallic copper is also suitable (161) and has been used in a series of experiments concerning the benzylation of aromatics.   This catalyst seems preferable for benzylation of phenol and its ethers.

Tsukervanik (107,108,178,180) studied the catalytic effect of metallic copper on alkylations.   Besides benzyl chloride and diphenylchloromethane (Ph_2CHCl) reactions with aliphatic alkyl halides such as n-butyl chloride were attempted with substituted and unsubstituted aromatics.   The added copper was partly changed during the reaction into cuprous chloride, but cuprous chloride itself does not catalyze such alkylations.   According to these reports there is neither an ionic nor a radical mechanism.   A complex compound must be considered, which is subsequently decomposed without formation of free radicals.

D. Other Metals

Tsukervanik and Rozhkova (179) found that powdered titanium, chromium, molybdenum, and tungsten could be used between 95° and 200° provided that the metals were finely divided.   Azatyan (6) has shown the catalytic efficiency of chromium, selenium, tin, and lead.   When these metals are used as powders they catalyze alkylations of aromatics with different alkyl halides without any previous activation.

15*

III. Haloalkanes

1. Fluorides, Chlorides, Bromides, and Iodides

Friedel and Crafts discovered the catalytic action of aluminum chloride in organic substitution reactions in 1877 in the case of an alkylation reaction with an alkyl halide.

Owing to their availability and low cost alkyl chlorides and bromides are most frequently used as alkylating agents. Alkyl iodides are less suitable owing to the fact that the alkylation reactions are generally accompanied by side reactions and decomposition.

Alkyl fluorides are the most reactive alkyl halides in alkylation reactions. Besides aluminum chloride and related catalysts, boron trifluoride was found to be a very suitable catalyst for alkylations with an alkyl fluoride (130). Boron trichloride, boron tribromide, and boron triiodide also catalyze alkylations with alkyl fluorides; however, they are inactive in related alkylations with alkyl chlorides or bromides.

Investigation of the reaction of toluene with cyclohexyl halides showed that BF_3 does not activate the cyclohexylation of toluene with cyclohexyl bromide or chloride, but is a very reactive catalyst for the cyclohexylation of toluene with cyclohexyl fluoride.

2. Relative Reactivity

Alkylation generally occurs most readily with tertiary halides and benzyl halides, less readily with secondary and least readily with primary halides. In the series of primary halides methyl halides are the least reactive. However, no strict order of relative reactivity can be derived from the available data.

It is generally necessary to use increasingly vigorous catalysts to introduce the alkyl groups in the above sequence. For example, reactive halides like benzyl chloride will react with benzene in the presence of a weak catalyst such as zinc chloride, whereas a more inert halide like methyl chloride requires a considerably more powerful catalyst such as aluminum chloride.

The relative reactivity of the alkyl halides is also governed by the halogen atom. For aluminum chloride catalyzed alkylations with either n-butyl or t-butyl halides, the order of activity is fluorine > chlorine > bromine > iodine (30,170).

3. Cyclialkylation with Haloaralkanes

With alkyl halides which bear an aromatic ring in the chain an intramolecular ring closure may be induced (11). Alkylation of the aromatic ring of the alkyl halide may also occur through an inter-molecular reaction. In addition, alkylation of any aromatic hydro-carbon present is to be expected (169). The reaction of β-phenylethyl chloride is a typical example of this internal alkylation occurring simultaneously to alkylation of another ring. High molecular weight compounds may be obtained by such reactions.

$$PhCH_2CH_2Cl + C_6H_6 \rightarrow PhCH_2CH_2Ph + HCl$$

$$2PhCH_2CH_2Cl + C_6H_6 \rightarrow PhCH_2CH_2C_6H_4CH_2CH_2Ph + 2HCl$$

$$3PhCH_2CH_2Cl + C_6H_6 \rightarrow PhCH_2CH_2C_6H_4CH_2CH_2C_6H_4CH_2CH_2Ph + 3HCl$$

The scope of the reaction includes intramolecular ring closures of halogen alkylbenzenes having the halogen in the side chain. Five-, six-, and seven-membered saturated rings have been prepared by this process.

The carbonyl group does not interfere with the reaction; p-chlorobutylacetophenone reacts with formation of the corresponding acetoindane and with halogen alkyl phenyl ketones the expected cyclic ketones are obtained (11):

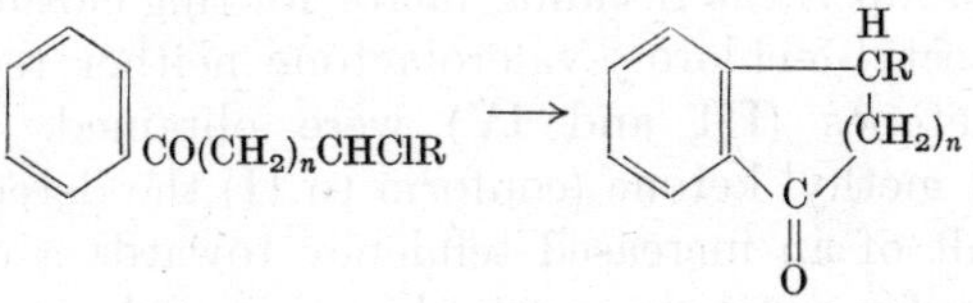

Sometimes rearrangement of the side chain occurs before the ring closure:

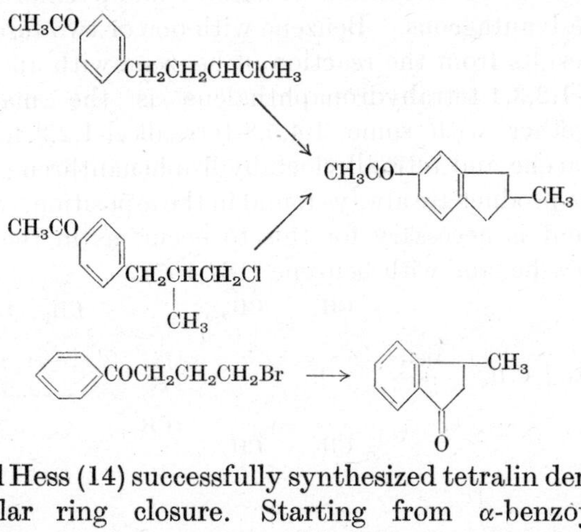

Beyer and Hess (14) successfully synthesized tetralin derivatives by intramolecular ring closure. Starting from α-benzoyl-δ-chloro-γ-valerolactone in the reaction with benzene, aluminum chloride catalyzes the formation of the tetralin ring. In the products III and

IV it seems that an intramolecular ring closure occurs with attachment to the aromatic ring. The formation of γ,δ-diphenyl-n-butyl phenyl ketone (3,4-diphenyl-n-butyl phenyl ketone) (II) shows that in the Friedel-Crafts reaction the chlorine atom is not the only reacting functional group of the α-benzoyl-δ-chloro-γ-valerolactone.

$$ClCH_2CHCH_2CHCOPh \longrightarrow$$
$$\underset{O\text{——}CO}{|}$$

(I)

$$PhCH_2\underset{\underset{Ph}{|}}{CH}CH_2CH_2COPh \quad (II)$$

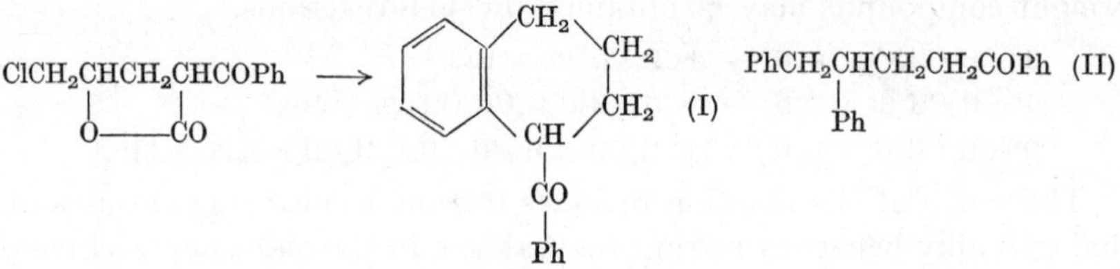

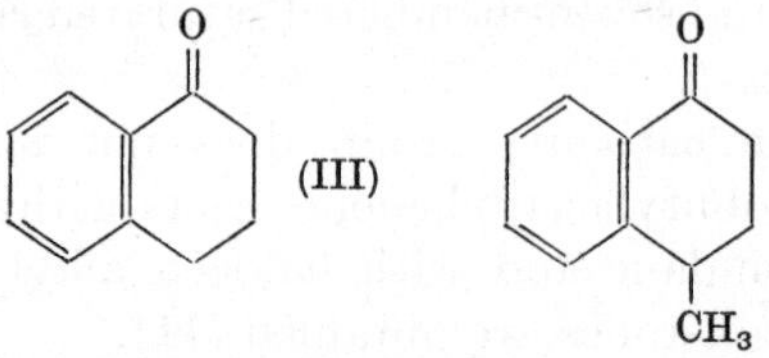

(III)

(IV)

The benzoyl group is the deciding factor for ring closure. With the analogous α-acetyl-δ-chloro-γ-valerolactone neither tetralin (I) nor any cyclic ketones (III and IV) were obtained. Besides 3,4-diphenylbutyl methyl ketone (conform to II) the detected products seem the result of an increased tendency towards a cleavage with hydrogen transfer (acetone, acetophenone, α-phenylethyl methyl ketone) (14a).

For ring closures aluminum chloride–sodium chloride mixtures often seem advantageous. Benzene with one or two fused saturated rings also results from the reaction of benzene with alkyl dihalides. 1,4-Dialkyl-1,2,3,4-tetrahydronaphthalene is the main product formed together with some 1,4,5,8-tetraalkyl-1,2,3,4,5,6,7,8-octahydroanthracene and tetraalkyloctahydrophenanthrene. The alkyl groups of the product are always found in the α-position. Sometimes a rearrangement is necessary for this to occur, as in the reaction of 3,4-dichloro-n-hexane with benzene (164,167):

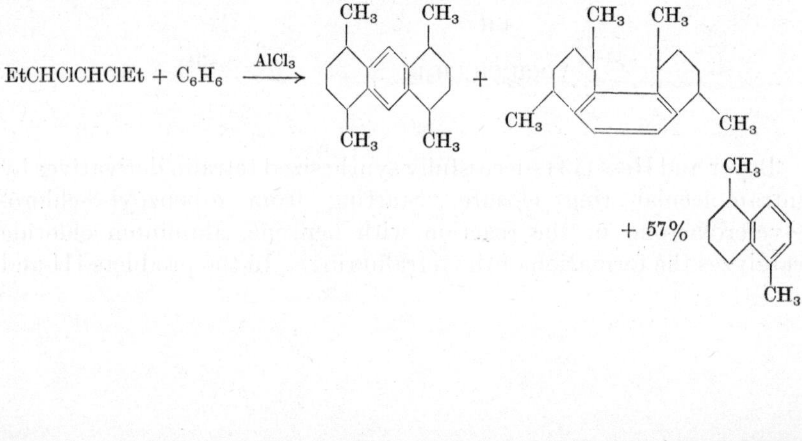

$$EtCHClCHClEt + C_6H_6 \xrightarrow{AlCl_3}$$

$+$

$+ 57\%$

IV. Aromatic Substrates

1. Mono- and Polynuclear Hydrocarbons

The Friedel-Crafts alkylation is a typical reaction of the aromatic ring, but at present few systematic alkylations of polynuclear compounds or their derivatives have been reported. Mainly benzene and its homologs, toluene and xylene, and derivatives of these mononuclear compounds have been tested. Lebedev and Baltadzhi (96) investigated the influence of the structure of the alkyl chloride used on the alkylation of benzene and toluene; the reaction was catalyzed by a solution of aluminum chloride in nitrobenzene. The results indicate a first-order reaction in aromatics, the ring being polarized at the moment of reaction. The tendency towards polarization of the aromatic ring is thought to be dependent on the alkyl chloride used and therefore the structure of the alkyl chloride has a dominant influence on the reaction.

Alkylations of benzene have been carried out much more frequently than those of naphthalene and alkylations of polynuclear aromatics are very rare. With these compounds dehydrogenating condensation is the main reaction in the presence of aluminum chloride. For the benzylation of anthracene, phenanthrene, and fluorene (anthracene and phenanthrene in positions 9 and 10) metallic zinc has been used as a catalyst and though an organometallic intermediate zinc compound is possible its presence has not been unequivocally demonstrated (44,58,100).

Acenaphthene may be benzylated in the presence of metallic titanium or zinc chloride (50,51,161). t-Butyl chloride alkylates acenaphthene in a reaction catalyzed by ferric chloride only after high dilution with carbon disulfide. The composition of the mixture of t-butylacenaphthenes formed varies according to the temperature of the reaction. In boiling carbon disulfide 45% 1-t-butylacenaphthene and 55% 3-t-butylacenaphthene result but at temperatures of 10–15° 83% 1-t-butylacenaphthene and 17% 3-t-butylacenaphthene are obtained (65). In addition to monobutylation some 1,6-di-t-butylacenaphthene may be isolated; it is possible that in boiling carbon disulfide 1-t-butylacenaphthene is further alkylated to the 1,6-compound.

Biphenyl is benzylated at its boiling point by benzyl chloride in the absence of any catalyst and a low yield of p-benzylbiphenyl results (125). In the presence of metallic titanium at 90° the yield is increased to 23% and with metallic zinc at 100° a 50% yield of p-benzylbiphenyl is possible. For methylation and ethylation of biphenyl, aluminum chloride is also useful, but in accordance with the higher reactivity of aluminum chloride with polynuclear compounds p- and m-terphenyl are formed simultaneously (1,2).

Ogata and Oda (125) have investigated the sequence of reactivity of different aromatics in the Friedel-Crafts reaction. They found naphthalene to be one of the most reactive aromatics and terphenyl the least reactive. By the alkylation of naphthalene 1- and 2-alkylnaphthalenes may both be obtained and conditions for making the substitution more selective have been reported (36,79). In the presence of pure aluminum chloride the corresponding 2-alkylnaphthalenes result whereas 1-alkylnaphthalenes are formed if nitrobenzene is added or if aluminum chloride is replaced by other catalysts (sulfuric acid, phosphoric acid, ferric chloride, or zinc chloride). More exact experiments with benzyl chloride (79) have shown that some 2-alkylnaphthalene is always formed but the amount is greatly diminished if only a small amount of aluminum chloride is used. Brown and Nelson (21) have also shown that variations in the catalytic conditions make a considerable difference to the ratio of the 1- and 2-alkylnaphthalenes formed. However, the total yield is always constant and is independent of the reaction time and temperature. It is possible to control the direction of substitution by variations of reaction temperatures and times (150,190). Thus ten minutes at a reaction temperature of 80° produces substitution in the 1-position, whilst heating for one hour at 150° yields 2-alkylnaphthalenes even though aluminum chloride is present in the same amount in both cases. The formation of 1-alkylnaphthalenes is favored by mild conditions and may occur in the absence of any catalyst (116) or in the presence of less active catalysts such as metallic titanium (161).

If only a small amount of aluminum chloride is present then it is largely complexed by the naphthalene and benzyl chloride. Similarly the activity of aluminum chloride is diminished when nitrobenzene is present as a solvent. Increasing amounts of aluminum chloride and longer reaction times favor rearrangement to 2-alkylnaphthalene; similarly 1-chloronaphthalene may be rearranged to the corresponding 2-chloronaphthalene by aluminum chloride (69).

In the methylation of naphthalene the halogen of the methyl halide used also has some influence. In reactions carried out under comparable conditions Tcheou and Yung (174) obtained 2-methylnaphthalene in 11% yield starting from methyl chloride and naphthalene but with methyl bromide or iodide a mixture of 4–5% 1- and 4–5% 2-methylnaphthalene was formed. Benzylation of azulene in the α-position has been observed (3). The reaction took place in chloroform solution and tin tetrachloride was the catalyst used. Results show that the main product contains an alkyl group in the α-position of the five-membered ring of azulene. Usually the products obtained are very impure and the yields are low.

2. Heterocyclic Compounds

Successful alkylations of heterocyclic compounds are very rare. Furfural and esters of 2-furoic acid react with alkyl chlorides in the presence of an excess of aluminum chloride. Furan compounds with a bromine atom in the 5-position require large amounts of aluminum chloride. The 5-position is the preferred point of alkylation but when this position is occupied 4-alkyl compounds are formed. An exception is found in the isopropylation of furfural. 4-Isopropylfurfural is produced even when the 5-position is vacant. Furfural itself generally gives only 10–12% yield whereas the alkylation of furoates proceeds much more favorably. Reichstein (144) has reported an 82% yield of methyl 5-t-amyl-2-furoate when the temperature of the reaction mass is raised slowly during 24 hours from 0° to 25°. If the temperature is kept constant at 25° the yield is only 57%. This shows the sensitivity of the reaction to different experimental factors.

Thiophene is very resistant to alkylation unless an α-substituent is already present (109). Thus 2-methylthiophene may be ethylated, isopropylated, and isobutylated by the corresponding alkyl halides to give mainly the 2-methyl-3-alkylthiophenes. Alkylation of 2-acetothiophene with isopropyl chloride gives 4-isopropyl-2-aceto-thiophene. For all alkylations of thiophene compounds larger amounts of aluminum chloride seem preferable.

A true Friedel-Crafts alkylation of a pyridine or quinoline derivative has never been described. 2-Chloroquinoline and 4,7-dichloroquinolines both react as alkyl halides with resorcinol if aluminum chloride is present in nitrobenzene solution. The resorcinol is "quinolinated" in the 4-position; e.g.,

3. Effect of Substituents

Tetrahydronaphthalene (tetralin) has only one aromatic ring and may be considered as a substituted benzene. Very little experimental work has been done on its alkylation. In the older literature

(12,16) no alkylations in the α-position have been reported; β-alkyl derivatives were always obtained. Polymeric compounds are obtained from the reaction of tetrahydronaphthalene with 1,2-dichloroethane in the presence of aluminum chloride (77). Polymers of maximum molecular weight result if molar amounts of tetrahydronaphthalene and 1,2-dichloroethane are used. With an excess of 1,2-dichloroethane the yield of polymer decreases but with increasing amounts of tetrahydronaphthalene the polymer yield becomes more and more constant and independent of all other factors. The compound of smallest molecular weight to be separated from such a reaction is 1,2-bis-(2-tetrahydronaphthyl)ethane. Substitution has occurred in the β-position of the tetrahydronaphthalene:

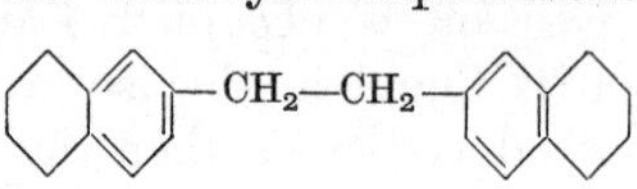

Alkylation of benzene with polyhaloalkanes usually yields a tetrahydronaphthalene. Depending on reaction conditions the saturated ring may also be alkylated. Alkylation of the aromatic ring is rare in tetrahydronaphthalene because of the greatly diminished reactivity. Therefore after the formation of the tetrahydronaphthalene system generally no further alkylation is possible.

In benzene rings the tendency for hydrogen atoms to be replaced by alkyl groups, under Friedel-Crafts alkylation conditions, is greatly influenced by any other ring substituents. Kharasch and Flenner (73) have found that with increasing electronegativity there is a declining activity of the aromatic ring and the following general sequence results:

$$-OH > -OCH_3 > -N(CH_3)_2 > -CH_3 > -H > \begin{matrix} -Cl \\ -Br \\ -I \end{matrix}$$

$$> -COCH_3 > -COOR > -NO_2 > -CN$$

However, in the case of substitutions requiring the presence of Lewis acids the order may be altered owing to complex formation by some groups. Thus the presence of the dimethylamino group makes alkylation difficult because the unshared electron pair of the nitrogen is donated to the incomplete shell of aluminum (chloride) and the anilinium compound so formed is similar to nitrobenzene in its resistance to alkylation. The Lewis acid also causes a change in the reactivity of phenols and phenol ethers, but complex formation is not sufficient in these compounds to prevent alkylation.

In phenols and their ethers and in aromatic amines substitution in the *para*-position is preferred. In *m*-cresol the reactivity of the position *para* to the methyl group is greatly increased; in addition, transformation of the hydroxyl group to an ether is helpful. This may be illustrated by the comparison of the benzylation of *m*-cresol methyl ether with that of the free *m*-cresol. Both have been benzylated with benzyl chloride in chloroform solution under the catalytic action of zinc chloride (111).

TABLE II. Benzylation of *m*-CH$_3$C$_6$H$_4$OR

Benzylating agent	R	Products
Benzyl chloride (111)	CH$_3$	18% 5-Methyl-2-benzylphenol methyl ether 32% 3-Methyl-4-benzylphenol methyl ether Some 5-Methyl-2,4-dibenzylphenol methyl ether
Benzyl chloride (111)	H	9% 5-Methyl-2-benzylphenol 41% 3-Methyl-4-benzylphenol 25% 5-Methyl-2,4-dibenzylphenol
Benzyl alcohol (AlCl$_3$) (63)	H	21% 5-Methyl-2-benzylphenol 18% 3-Methyl-4-benzylphenol 35% 5-Methyl-2,4-dibenzylphenol

In the alkylation of the aromatic ring of phenols or phenol ethers, zinc chloride, metallic zinc or other metals are often used in place of aluminum chloride (13).   These are not only mild catalysts but have less tendency to form complex compounds with the oxygen of the phenol.   Metallic aluminum also seems preferable to aluminum chloride (5).   If metallic aluminum is activated with iodine it reacts with the phenol with formation of aluminum phenolate (phenoxide). This is very suitable for reactions with alkyl halides which alkylate the aromatic ring of the phenolate (61).   In the older literature the reaction has been reported with strong phenolates such as sodium *o*-cresolate, which with benzyl bromide gives *o*-cresyl benzyl ether, 6-benzyl-6-methylcyclohexadienone, and 2-methyl-6-benzylphenol (43).   The Friedel-Crafts alkylation, in this case, seems to be no more than a side reaction.

Halogenated aromatics are alkylated only with difficulty.   The Friedel-Crafts alkylation of trichlorobenzenes with carbon tetrachloride yields hexachlorodiphenyl ketones.   The unsymmetrical

1,2,4-trichlorobenzene gives a five times greater yield of the 2,4,5:2′, 4′,5′ compound than the symmetrical 1,3,5-trichlorobenzene gives of 2,4,6:2′,4′,6′-hexachlorodiphenyl ketone (193). An acetyl group also reduces the activity of the aromatic ring in nucleophilic reactions (11).

V. Mechanism

1. General Considerations

In the older literature the view is often expressed that olefins first produce alkyl halides when they are used for the alkylation of aromatics. The reverse formation of an olefin from an alkyl halide has rarely been considered. The activity of benzyl halides in alkylations is good evidence that the latter reaction does not occur. In laboratory work alkylation with alkyl halides is generally preferred to that with olefins, because the danger of polymerization as a concomitant reaction is much less.

On the assumption that the reaction actually occurs on the halogen-bearing carbon atom, in all investigations concerning the reaction mechanism of alkylation the alkyl halides are the most suitable reagents. Their chemistry is much better known than that of sulfonic acid esters or inorganic esters.

The alkylation of aromatics with alkyl halides proceeds according to the following general equation:

$$ArH + RX \rightarrow ArR + HX$$

Therefore for every entering alkyl group one equivalent of hydrogen halide is formed. The hydrogen halide produced appears to favor the alkylation reaction. Thus in alkylation with olefins, some alkyl halide is often added in order to aid the reaction. The assumption of intermediate formation of alkyl halide from olefin is, however, not sufficient to explain the effect of hydrogen halide, since this is also observed in alkylations in the absence of olefins. A more reasonable assumption is that hydrogen halide favors the formation of soluble complexes of the type "$ArHAlCl_4$", which can dissolve further aluminum chloride. Thus formation of a homogeneous solution containing a large amount of aluminum chloride seems to be the real reason for the stimulating effect of hydrogen halide on the alkylation.

Alkyl halides are used in many syntheses in organic chemistry and generally no change in the structure of the chain of an alkyl group occurs (Grignard synthesis, etc.). However, in alkylations of aromatics with alkyl halides, especially those between propyl and hexyl, various forms of isomerization can be observed in the alkyl groups introduced.

A special feature of the Friedel-Crafts alkylation with alkyl halides is the inversion of the reactivity of the different halogens. Alkyl fluorides are the most reactive compounds and the slowest to react are the alkyl iodides (30,170). In addition, the halogen of the metal halide catalysts also has an effect on the reaction especially if the metal halide has a different halogen than the alkyl halide. In such cases the hydrogen halide formed in the alkylation is a mixture dependent on the proportion of the halogen of alkyl halide to that of aluminum halide; thus if the reaction starts with 1 mole of alkyl halide, RX, in the presence of 1 mole aluminum halide, AlY_3, we get hydrogen halide which, for every mole of HX (formerly the RX), contains 3 moles of HY originating from the aluminum halide (80,81):

$$RX + C_6H_6 + AlY_3 \rightarrow RC_6H_5 + \tfrac{1}{4}HX + \tfrac{3}{4}HY$$

Similarly when an alkyl bromide, labeled with bromine-82, is used in the presence of normal aluminum bromide ($AlBr_3{}^{80}$) a mixture of normal hydrogen bromide (HBr^{80}) and labeled hydrogen bromide (HBr^{82}) is formed.

The last observation is strong support for the suggestion of an ionic mechanism for the alkylation. The first step of such a reaction would be the formation of an alkyl carbonium ion:

$$RX + MY_3 \rightarrow R^+[MY_3X]^-$$

$$R^+ + ArH \rightarrow \left[Ar \begin{matrix} H \\ \diagup \\ \diagdown \\ R \end{matrix} \right]^+ \rightarrow RAr + H^+$$

$$H^+ + [MY_3X]^- \rightarrow MY_3 + HX$$

It is also in accordance with this theory that a diminished tendency to ionization is indicative of a lower reactivity of alkyl halides in the Friedel-Crafts alkylation. Yet the results of more recent experiments suggest that it is doubtful that the whole topic of the alkylation of aromatics by alkyl halides under the influence of Lewis acids can be explained by a single mechanism. The above equations possibly express the mechanism of alkylation under limiting conditions.

Recently Adams and Nicksic (2a) reported an increasing electron paramagnetic resonance absorption during the Friedel-Crafts alkylation of benzene in the presence of aluminum chloride. They think the observed free radicals are aromatic and free of oxygen or chlorine. The question arises, however, of the importance of such radicals in alkylation, as they may result also from side reactions.

2. Carbonium-ion Mechanism or Nucleophilic Displacement of the Alkyl Halide–Catalyst Complex

Tertiary alkyl halides have the highest tendency to ionization. Secondary halides are intermediate and primary normal alkyl halides are least prone to such transformations. To the same extent that the tendency to ionization declines the ionic mechanism may change more and more to a reaction of a nucleophilic substitution type; the tendency of the Lewis acid to complete its valence shell becomes more important as the driving force of the reaction. The halogen atom is transferred from the alkyl halide to the Lewis acid and the alkyl group is simultaneously added to the aromatic in a nucleophilic displacement reaction. A σ-complex is thus intermediately obtained.

For the formation of such a σ-complex a polarization and then a separation of the charges of the bond between the carbon and halogen atoms are necessary. It is to be expected that the separation will be facilitated if the halogen–carbon bond is susceptible to the polarization. By this hypothesis of alkylations proceeding through an intermediate of this type alkyl fluorides should be the most reactive halides. The advantage of alkyl fluorides over all other alkyl halides in Friedel-Crafts alkylation has been demonstrated (126,127,130,131) in experiments on the alkylation of aromatics by the boron trifluoride catalyzed reaction of alkyl fluorides. Boron trifluoride has a diminished catalytic activity in alkylation compared with that of aluminum chloride if other alkyl halides are used but affords high yields of alkylate with alkyl fluorides. The most interesting aspect of the reaction is the complex compound formed between the aromatic hydrocarbon, alkyl fluoride, and boron trifluoride at low temperatures. Olah and Kuhn (126,127) have made a detailed examination of these compounds which seem to be a significant step in the mechanism of Friedel-Crafts alkylations. Starting with aromatic hydrocarbons, alkyl fluorides, and boron trifluoride (Lewis acid) such σ-complexes may often be isolated. The intensive color, increased conductivity and homogeneity of the substance, together with spectroscopic data, is evidence for the formation of such a previously unknown σ-complex. But the most significant observation is that after formation of the σ-complex at low temperature it decomposes at higher temperatures with the formation of hydrogen fluoride, boron trifluoride, and alkylbenzene. Therefore the alkylation may be separated into two different steps. The existence of these σ-complexes was previously proposed by H. C. Brown (24a) who considered them to be unstable intermediates.

In view of the fact that alkyl fluorides are often not readily available the preparative procedure has been modified (127). The alkyl halide (chloride or bromide) is added with stirring to a solution of silver tetrafluoroborate in an excess of the chosen aromatic hydrocarbon (benzene, toluene, xylenes, etc.):

$$ArH + AgBF_4 + RX \rightarrow ArHR^+BF_4^- + AgX$$

The soluble σ-complex may be separated from the precipitated silver halide. Under these extreme conditions the σ-complex is a stable intermediate in the reaction and it is easy to imagine that this σ-complex tends to become more and more an unstable transition state as the starting materials and conditions of the reaction are changed. The decomposition of σ-complexes which contain different halogens originating from the alkyl halide and Lewis acid might also give a mixture of hydrogen halides according to the proportion of the different halogens together in the complex.

A further conformation for such a mechanism is seen in the results of the kinetic tests of H. C. Brown (20). In the alkylation of an aromatic ring with 3,4-dichlorobenzyl chloride under the influence of aluminum chloride, the results were found to depend on the proportions of all three components. The dielectric constant of the solvent used had only a small influence but the structure of the aromatic itself (basicity) was very important. Referred to benzene ($= 1.00$) the following sequence of alkylation rates was found:

ArH:	C_6H_5Cl	C_6H_6	$C_6H_5CH_3$	$m\text{-}C_6H_4(CH_3)_2$
k:	0.47	1.00	1.64	2.08

Most of the reported alkylations of aromatics have been carried out with aluminum chloride, which is particularly unsuitable for standard experiments. Under extreme conditions the σ-complex is indeed a stable intermediate of the Friedel-Crafts alkylation (and also acylation) of aromatics; often it is assumed that this stable intermediate can undergo isomerization before proton elimination. It must also be remembered that with increasing reactivity of the alkylating agent alkylation may proceed by another reaction mechanism. Kinetic measurements show the influence of the solvent on the alkylation rate (94,95). In carbon tetrachloride and nitrobenzene solution benzene was alkylated with twenty different alkyl halides in the presence of aluminum chloride. The alkylations fit a first-order equation ($k_1 = -dx/dt$ RCl min.$^{-1}$) (92,93,94,95). The facility of alkylation of an aromatic compound increases with the number of side chains, but the side chain itself loses its activating influence as its length and degree of branching increase (70). The following sequence of declining influence of side chains has been determined:

$$\text{Me} > \text{Et} > \text{Me}_2\text{CH} > \overset{\displaystyle \text{Et}}{\underset{\displaystyle \text{Me}}{\diagup\!\!\!\diagdown}}\text{CH} > \text{Me}_3\text{C}$$

The difficulties resulting from the use of aluminum chloride may be avoided with strong proton acids as catalysts (118). Benzenesulfonic acid is particularly recommended. From the alkylation of excess aromatic hydrocarbons with differently substituted benzyl chlorides, the influence of substituents on the reaction rate is in accordance with that of other substitution reactions. Benzyl chlorides, especially nitrobenzyl chloride and chlorobenzyl chloride, cause inverse displacements of the alkylation rate through substitution by a bimolecular displacement mechanism. The reaction *via* formation of a carbonium ion fits first-order kinetics (S_N1) and therefore the former mechanism is preferred.

3. The Preferred *meta*-Position

Special consideration must be given to the preference of alkyl groups to enter the *meta*-position under the conditions of Friedel-Crafts alkylation. Starting from alkylbenzene a second alkyl group enters to a substantial degree *meta* to the first group and the dialkylbenzenes formed thus contain high proportions of *meta*-

dialkylbenzenes. In the older literature this is usually thought of as the result of a preceding 1,2,4-trialkylation followed by a dealkylation

$$\text{C}_6\text{H}_6 + 3\text{RX} \longrightarrow \text{(1,2,4-trialkylbenzene)} \longrightarrow \text{(dialkylbenzene)} + \text{RX}.$$

Pajeau and Fierens (133) (see also Chiurdoglu and Fierens (34)) propose a carbonium ion transition state and they assume that the alkylation is followed by slow isomerization with formation of the thermodynamically most stable isomers. This would be *meta*-dialkylbenzene and 1,3,5-trialkylbenzene in the case of trialkylation. Contrary to this hypothesis, Nenitzescu (115,117) has shown that alkylation of aromatics and dealkylation or rearrangement of alkylbenzenes often require different conditions. Today the small amount of alkylation in the *ortho*-position is considered a result of steric hindrance. H. C. Brown (19,21,25) has shown that the increased *meta*-substitution is afforded by an alkylation under non-selective conditions. In other substitutions in aromatic compounds a primary substituent also loses a lot of its directing power to the *ortho*- and *para*-positions in a reaction under non-selective conditions (see chapter XI).

The conditions for selective alkylation might be more favorable if alkyl halides were chosen with increasing capacity for forming stable carbonium ions or σ-complexes respectively. Such a change of alkylating agent always gives higher ratios of alkylation in the *ortho*- and *para*-positions. Again, for steric reasons the *para*-isomer predominates. Thus the alkylation of isopropylbenzene with *t*-butyl chloride yields less *m*-isopropyl-*t*-butylbenzene than isopropyl chloride does with its less stable but more reactive carbonium ion in the alkylation of *t*-butylbenzene (21). In agreement with this Norris and Rubinstein (124) have shown that methylation at lower temperature gives more *ortho*- and *para*-isomers than are obtained at higher temperatures.

Nevertheless, rearrangements of alkyl groups of alkylbenzenes have been reported. Baddeley and Kenner (10) transformed *p*-di-*n*-propylbenzene to *m*-di-*n*-propylbenzene in two hours by the action of aluminum chloride at 100°. No isomerization of the rearranged propyl groups was observed. In the rearrangement of 1,3-dimethyl-4-butylbenzene to 1,3-dimethyl-5-butylbenzene Nightingale and Smith (122) used aluminum chloride and found an isomerization of the butyl group.

Often the ratio between aromatic and aluminum chloride is thought to affect the polyalkylation in such a way that increasing amounts of aluminum chloride enhance polyalkylation (16,123,192). These findings thus seem to be a verification of an alkylation mechanism which includes an aluminum halide complex. In addition the reaction time becomes important in long reactions. Here the number of methyl groups entering the aromatic ring becomes more and more dependent on the reaction time (37,38).

The methods of organic analysis have been much improved in recent years and by gas-chromatographic analysis mixtures of hydrocarbons can be identified exactly. This was once one of the hardest tasks. Therefore it is no longer necessary to minimize the number of components formed by an alkylation which is being studied. Recently Olah (128,129) used this method extensively in a series of experiments. The relative reaction rate of benzylation of different aromatics was determined directly in a mixture of aromatics and control tests were made with different quantitative proportions of components. These results indicated a reaction of the first order in aromatics. Homogeneous solutions were obtained by using aluminum chloride together with nitromethane. Competitive benzylation of alkylbenzenes and benzene was investigated with the same aluminum chloride–nitromethane catalyst. The absolute activity of the catalyst had little influence on the relative rate of alkylation. Remarkably, only small quantities of *meta*-substituted diphenylmethanes were obtained both from alkylbenzenes and halobenzenes. The old rule of preferential substitution in the *meta*-position in all Friedel-Crafts alkylations is thus broken. Further, alkylation under such conditions is not accompanied by isomerization. In view of these observations it is probable that the products result from a kinetically controlled reaction, with no appreciable thermodynamically controlled isomerization of the alkylates. It is suggested that the reaction proceeds *via* a π-complex type transition state as the substrate rate-determining step, followed by a σ-complex type of activated state determining isomer distribution.

In addition to aluminum chloride–nitromethane, ferric chloride–nitromethane, and silver perchlorate in nitromethane are suitable catalysts for alkylation of toluene with isopropyl bromide or *t*-butyl bromide under predominantly kinetically controlled conditions. With *t*-butyl bromide no *ortho*-substitution occurs. Toluene is alkylated faster than benzene but the advantage of the former depends greatly on the catalyst used.

4. Complexes

Turova-Pollak (183) has reported that complexes are formed from aluminum shavings, aromatic hydrocarbons, and alkyl bromides but no structure or other details of constitution are given for these highly interesting compounds. Ray (143) has postulated that the effect of mercuric chloride on the activation of aluminum shavings may be the result of the formation of a complex between the aromatic compound, aluminum chloride, and mercuric chloride. He has proposed the following reaction:

$$C_6H_6 + Al + 2HgCl_2 \rightarrow C_6H_6AlCl_3HgCl + Hg$$

Today it is generally agreed that many Friedel-Crafts alkylating catalysts, especially those made from aluminum halides or aluminum metal, operate through formation of complex compounds. The aromatic hydrocarbon and also the alkyl halide may be included in such complexes but it seems that its structure is not so simple as was once thought (see refs. 114 and 138).

The simple formulation of Meerwein (106), $[R^+][AlX_4]^-$, is not always in accordance with the results of electrolysis. Aluminum metal separates on the cathode from solutions of aluminum halides in alkyl halides. Lebedev (82,91) has proposed the following complex compound: $[AlCl_2 nRX]^+ [AlCl_4]^-$. The number "$n$" refers to the number of moles of alkyl halide introduced and these depend on the concentration of the solution.

Hydrogen halide is formed by the alkylation reaction RX + ArH→ArR + HX. The hydrogen halide remains partially in the catalyst. Not all of it is freed. This has been estimated in various experiments with aluminum chloride or aluminum bromide. But, as previously mentioned (Section V-1), an exchange takes place between the catalyst and the halogen of the hydrogen halide, if the catalyst and the alkyl halide have different halogens. Alkyl fluorides, chlorides, bromides, and iodides have been tried; all the hydrogen halides expected were found in addition to hydrogen fluoride.

Ethyl bromide in which aluminum bromide is dissolved has an essentially different ultraviolet spectrum from the pure compound. The rapid rise in absorption of solutions of low concentration is especially impressive. Yet the conductivity of such solutions increases only insignificantly. This means that such a solution would not contain higher concentrations of any ionic complexes such as $[AlBr_2EtBr]^+[AlBr_4]^-$ or $[Et]^+[AlBr_4]^-$ (26).

Various complexes are described as resulting from the association of aromatics with aluminum halide (26), but those which contain hydrogen halide are of greater interest (22,84). Complexes of this type were the first isolated σ-complexes. In this case boron trifluoride was used instead of aluminum chloride and the hydrogen halide introduced was hydrogen fluoride. Such complexes may be cleaved to the starting components but if deuterium fluoride is used cleavage follows a different course and deuterated aromatics are also obtained. If hydrogen fluoride is replaced by alkyl fluorides at low temperatures σ-complexes are again formed and give the corresponding alkylbenzenes on subsequent cleavage. Therefore the alkylation reaction may be said to occur in two steps.

Long-chain alkylbenzenes obtained from Friedel-Crafts alkylation may be isolated and purified as complex compounds such as alkylbenzenes give with hydrogen halide (HCl or HBr), aluminum bromide, or aluminum chloride (31).

The course of some alkylations is influenced by various solvents (36). The effect of the solvent may be ascribed to the formation of aluminum halide complexes which include the solvent (118). So far it has been impossible to establish any direct relationship between the stability of such aluminum halide–solvent complexes and the observed course of alkylation. It is to be assumed that a tendency for the solvent to form a complex with aluminum halide diminishes the catalytic activity of the latter in the alkylation, but the solution attains a more polar character and its dissolving power increases. As these considerations suggest, no catalytic activity was found when aluminum chloride was complexed with equivalent amounts of different tertiary amines. But in such complexes the activity increases rapidly if larger than equivalent amounts of aluminum chloride are used (49). Usually the most efficient combinations have 10–20% excess of aluminum chloride. In alkylations in the presence of such amine–aluminum halide complexes the ratio between mono- and dialkylbenzenes depends not only on the excess of aluminum chloride over the amine but also on the structure of the amine used (48).

5. Rearrangements accompanying Alkylation

In the course of a Friedel-Crafts alkylation with an alkyl halide the structure of the entering alkyl group may be rearranged or it may enter unchanged. The rearrangement may occur before the alkylation, simultaneously with the Friedel-Crafts reaction, or it may be a subsequent reaction of the highly reactive alkylbenzene formed. There are many factors which decide to what extent rearrangement of the alkyl group occurs.

Rearrangements of aliphatic alkyl halides have been shown to be possible under the catalytic influence of aluminum chloride or activated aluminum. Usually this isomerization occurs in a particular direction. n-Propyl chloride may be rearranged to isopropyl chloride by aluminum chloride but remains unchanged by aluminum chloride sulfate $AlCl_2HSO_4$ (177). Deuterium chloride present does not introduce any deuterium into the isopropyl chloride.

Attempts to effect the inverse rearrangement of isopropyl chloride to n-propyl chloride failed.

1-C^{14}-Ethyl chloride is partially rearranged by aluminum chloride and a mixture of 1-C^{14}- and 2-C^{14}-ethyl chloride results. But the alkylation of benzene proceeds much faster; only 1-C^{14}-ethylbenzene results (147) from the alkylation of benzene with 1-C^{14}-ethyl chloride. Similar results (98) were obtained with 2-C^{14}-ethyl chloride, but with 2-C^{14}-ethyl iodide isomerization was observed. For equilibrium (50% 1-C^{14} and 50% 2-C^{14} compound) 42 hours were calculated as being necessary, indicating that isomerization was much slower than alkylation. Similar rearrangements have been observed with the C^{14}-atom in t-butyl and t-amyl chloride (145). Anisole may be alkylated with 2-phenyl-1-C^{14}-ethyl chloride (97) to give a 20% total yield of a mixture of 2-phenyl-1-C^{14}- and 2-phenyl-2-C^{14}-anisylethane in the presence of aluminum chloride.

McMahon and Bunce (105a) have alkylated toluene in the presence of aluminum chloride with 2-phenylethyl-1-C^{14} chloride. Fifty-two per cent of the β-tolylethylbenzene obtained had the C^{14}-isotope rearranged in the α-position; a non-aromatic symmetrical intermediate is proposed, similar to Olah's σ-complexes.

$$\left[\begin{array}{c} CH_2-C^{14}H_2 \\ \end{array} \right]^{+} \quad AlCl_4^{-}$$

The following nucleophilic attack of toluene forms p-methylbibenzyls with the C^{14} in the α- or β-position. The constantly preferred formation of the rearranged compound results from an intramolecular isotope effect which disturbs the complete symmetry. The diminished rearrangement with 2-p-nitrophenylethyl-1-C^{14} chloride (only 8.6%) indicates the deviation to another mechanism. The chlorine has nearly lost its nucleophilicity in $AlCl_4^-$ and this may explain the failure of rearrangement in any regenerated 2-phenylethyl chloride from interrupted alkylations.

Experiments with unsymmetrical alkyl halides which have the halogen on an optically active carbon atom also belong in this group of reactions. It has been observed that the alkylation is preceded by a partial racemization (60). (For a detailed discussion of this topic, see Chapter XIII.)

Attempts are continuously being made to improve the rules of the isomerization which attends the alkylation, but there are always some exceptional cases.

The comprehensive report of Gilman and Meals (54a) deals with the problem of the isomerization of the entering alkyl groups. According to this review the products of alkylation of benzene with primary alkyl halides are primary and secondary alkylbenzenes and the amounts of the secondary products are increased by higher reaction temperatures. Secondary alkyl halides yield secondary alkylbenzenes and tertiary alkyl halides form tertiary alkylbenzenes. Tertiary alkylbenzenes are also the predominant products in alkylations with isoalkyl halides. By alkylation of benzene with primary alkyl halides the phenyl group will be found attached to various carbon atoms of the chain, e.g., from n-hexyl chloride 1-, 2-, and 3-phenylhexanes will be formed:

$$
CH_3(CH_2)_4CH_2Cl + C_6H_6 \longrightarrow
\begin{cases}
CH_3(CH_2)_4CH_2Ph \\
CH_3(CH_2)_3CHCH_3 \\
\quad\quad\quad\quad | \\
\quad\quad\quad\quad Ph \\
CH_3(CH_2)_2CHCH_2CH_3 \\
\quad\quad\quad\quad | \\
\quad\quad\quad\quad Ph
\end{cases}
$$

It is suggested that these various forms of secondary phenylalkanes result from the elimination of hydrogen halide prior to reaction with the phenyl ring.

Primary alkyl chlorides produce primary and secondary alkylbenzenes and also tertiary alkylbenzenes if a tertiary hydrogen atom is available in the chain (29,158). s-Butyl chloride and isoamyl bromide form some of the expected tertiary alkylbenzenes. The yields of t-amylbenzene from isoamyl bromide are diminished to 15%

if the aluminum chloride catalyzed alkylation is carried out at 0°. Under these conditions t-amyl chloride yields mainly 2-methyl-3-phenylbutane (135). Many rearrangements in the structure of the side chains are often assumed to be typical attendant phenomena of Friedel-Crafts alkylation.

Schmerling and West (158) investigated alkylations with 2-chloro-2,3-dimethylbutane and determined the influence of different catalysts ($AlCl_3$, $AlCl_3$–CH_3NO_2, $FeCl_3$, $ZrCl_4$) and various reaction conditions on rearrangements in the structure of the aliphatic chain. In the presence of aluminum chloride or zirconium chloride respectively they obtained mainly 2,2-dimethyl-3-phenylbutane, whilst the mild catalysts such as aluminum chloride–nitromethane or ferric chloride gave pure 2,3-dimethyl-3-phenylbutane without any rearrangement. With 1-chloro-3,3-dimethylbutane it was demonstrated that the difference in the course of alkylation depends on the catalyst used. The products were not so pure and not obtained in such good yields as before. Primary alkylbenzenes were never obtained, even starting from a primary alkyl halide, but the most interesting result is that aluminum chloride or zirconium chloride again caused formation of the secondary 2,2-dimethyl-3-phenylbutane whereas ferric chloride produced 2,3-dimethyl-3-phenylbutane with its tertiary phenyl group.

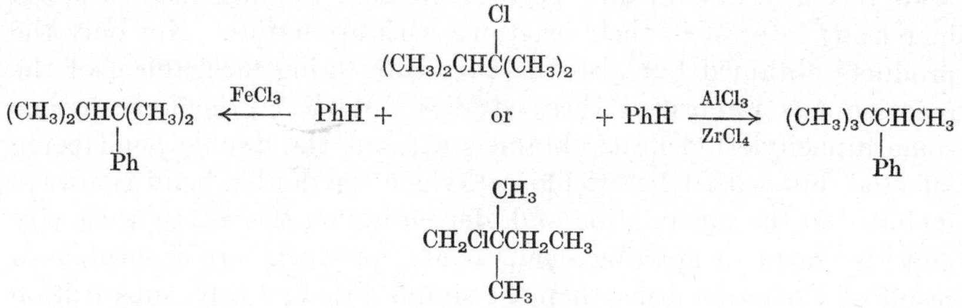

Therefore it seems that the nature of the catalyst is decisive in the formation of secondary or tertiary alkylbenzenes.

In accordance with this hypothesis of isomerization of previously formed hexylbenzenes or dihexylbenzenes aluminum chloride produces secondary hexylbenzenes and ferric chloride yields tertiary hexylbenzenes.

It has also been observed (9,11) that t-alkyl halides alkylate benzene with formation of secondary alkylbenzenes, although a mixture of primary and secondary alkylbenzenes may be obtained starting from primary alkyl halides. It is thought that alkyl cations have diminishing reactivity as electrophilic reagents in the sequence primary > secondary > tertiary alkyl cation and therefore the ability to alkylate declines. But in the same sequence these groups acquire an increasing tendency for dealkylation. According to Nenitzescu (115) t-alkyl groups are the most easily rearranged alkyl groups, e.g., t-amylbenzene rearranges to neopentylbenzene. Nevertheless it seems difficult at present to distinguish between rearrangement and alkylation.

The influence of different substituents on aromatic rings on the Friedel-Crafts alkylation of these rings has been studied extensively. Concerning the influence of structure and substituents of the alkyl halides on the course of alkylation there are many divergent reports. It is generally assumed that alkyl halides stimulate Friedel-Crafts alkylation with increasing tendency for formation of carbonium ions. After reaching a maximum the ability for electrophilic reaction again decreases. Thus triphenylmethyl chloride has lost its reactivity to such an extent that it does not react with benzene to form tetraphenylmethane, or if it does, the dearylation of tetraphenylmethane is so fast that the latter product cannot be observed.

VI. Alkylations with Substituted, Polyfunctional Haloalkanes

In recent years di- and polyhalogenated alkanes have aroused increasing interest in their reactions with aromatics. Not only the products obtained but also the very interesting mechanism of the reaction has intensified these studies. With 1,1-dichloroethylene some diphenylethylene is obtained without the double bond being affected, but with 1,1,2-trichloroethylene the double bond is always included in the phenylation and, depending on the reaction velocity and the ratio of starting components, products are formed as a result of a reaction other than the simple Friedel-Crafts substitution (87,189):

$$CHCl{=}CCl_2 + 4C_6H_6 \xrightarrow{\text{AlCl}_3} Ph_2CHCHPh_2$$

$$Ph_2CHCHPh_2 + CHCl{=}CCl_2 + C_6H_6 \xrightarrow[\text{AlCl}_3]{} Ph_2CHCH(C_6H_4)_2CHCHPh_2$$
$$+ Ph_3CCH_2C_6H_4CH_2CPh_3$$

$$Ph_2CHCHPh_2 + AlCl_3 \dashrightarrow Ph_2CH_2 + PhCH_2CHPh_2 + PhCH_2CH_2Ph.$$

With 1,1-dichloroethylene the double bond is partially included in the reaction with benzene, but no simple phenylation occurs.

As a result of partial dimerization some 1,1,3-triphenyl-3-methyl-indane is formed (85):

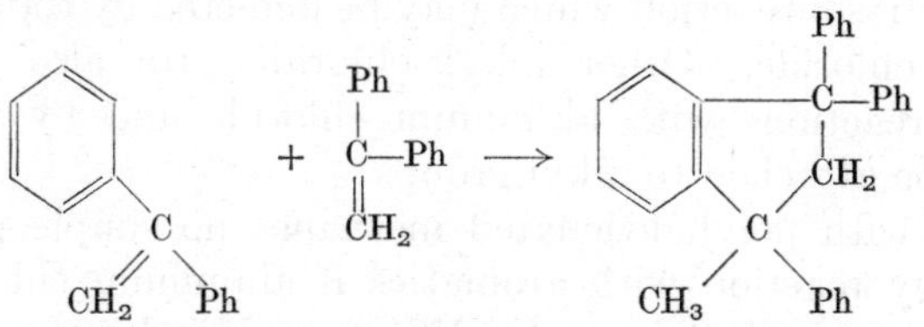

Ph
|
+   C—Ph   ⟶
‖
CH$_2$

(Ph, C, CH$_2$, Ph, CH$_3$, C, CH$_2$, Ph, CH$_3$, Ph structures)

It seems that before the formation of such an indane ring is possible one carbon atom of the ethylene must be completely free of phenyl substituents.

The differences in Friedel-Crafts alkylations with halides compared with those with alkenes are best shown by the experiments of Colonge (39,40,41). In unsaturated alkyl halides where the double bond is isolated from the halogen only the halogen reacts in the presence of moist aluminum chloride and the corresponding aralkene results. Yet, if the more active, dry aluminum chloride is used, the double bond takes part in the Friedel-Crafts alkylation and intramolecular ring closures are possible. Special attention may be given to the formation of 6,7-benzosuberanes from γ-chloroalkenes by this reaction.

1. Di- and Polyhaloalkanes

Exact knowledge of the reactivity of chloroform and carbon tetrachloride is very important as these are often used as solvents and diluents in reactions with Lewis acids. Polyhalides, like chloroform, dichloromethane, or ethylene chloride (1,2-dichloroethane) are the proposed solvents for the synthesis of α-naphthyl ketones from naphthalene and acid chlorides (7).

Willard (112,113,191) prefers chloroform and carbon tetrachloride for studying the exchange of chlorine atoms between aluminum chloride and alkyl chlorides, as these polyhalides react rapidly even at low temperatures. The absence of moisture on the surface of the aluminum chloride is vital for a satisfactory exchange reaction. With perfectly dry aluminum chloride and careful exclusion of moisture during the experiment exchange may be observed down to the freezing point of carbon tetrachloride (−21°) and chloroform (−63°). Moisture is a big hindrance; at low temperatures the reaction is completely quenched and at higher temperatures the rate of reaction is only very small. The exchange fails when gaseous aluminum chloride and carbon tetrachloride are used. This seems to be an indication of a surface reaction, since at the surface of solid, dry aluminum chloride a mixture of gaseous carbon tetrachloride and benzene starts a reaction which may be detected by the formation of hydrogen chloride. Other alkyl chlorides are also suitable for exchange reactions with aluminum chloride and by this method Cl^{36} may be attached to alkyl groups.

Usually with polyhalogenated methanes no simple products are obtained by reaction with aromatics if aluminum chloride or aluminum metal catalyst is used. When triphenylmethane dyes were popular great attention was given to the reactivity of carbon tetrachloride and chloroform with aromatics. Summarizing the large amount of experimental data available the conclusion seems permissible that with carbon tetrachloride triarylmethanes are the highest arylation step which may be reached. Mainly diarylmethanes are obtained with chloroform. Variations in the catalyst seem to affect only the yields of diarylmethane (47). Yields are increased with higher amounts of catalyst and addition of cuprous chloride also improves the reaction in this direction.

The formation of hexachlorodiphenyl ketone from trichlorobenzene and carbon tetrachloride with simultaneous hydrolysis of two chlorine atoms of the latter has already been discussed (193).

With 1,2-dibromo-1,2,3,4-tetrahydronaphthalene only the bromine atom in the β-position enters a Friedel-Crafts reaction with benzene. The α-bromine atom is simultaneously split off with the formation of hydrogen bromide; the remaining 3-phenyl-1,2-dihydronaphthalene undergoes disproportionation by the aluminum chloride present and a mixture of 2-phenyl-1,2,3,4-tetrahydronaphthalene and 2-phenylnaphthalene results (165).

With di- or polyhalogenated aliphatic hydrocarbons, even though the carbon chain may be saturated or a double bond included, the products of a Friedel-Crafts reaction are usually not those of a simple exchange between a halogen and the aromatic ring. Even with alkyl monohalides polyalkylbenzenes are obtained in addition to simple monoalkylbenzenes. The mathematical possibility of variations is greatly increased with each further reactive halogen atom entering the chain. Therefore the formation of polymers is possible with dihalides. Studies on the influence of the conditions on the course of the reaction and on the structures of these polymeric compounds arising from 1,2-dichloroethane have aroused a great deal of interest. The catalytic effect of aluminum chloride, aluminum metal, and alkylaluminum halides has been proved. As might be expected, the formation of 1,2-diarylethanes is favored by an excess of aromatic compounds (195,196) and the yield of the simultaneously formed polymers is increased by a higher ratio of 1,2-dichloroethane. The application of alkylaluminum halides only improved the yields of polymer. For such reactions Nicolescu and Iovu (121) have prepared *in situ* the organoaluminum compound from activated aluminum powder and 1,2-dichloroethane; 1,2-dibromoethane is useful for initiating the reaction with the metal. The polymer formed attained the highest molecular weight (about 15,000) if 1.1 moles of benzene were used for 1 mole of 1,2-dichloroethane. The molecular weight of the polymer did not increase with greater excess of 1,2-dichloroethane, instead the solubility of the polymer declined. Kolesnikov (77) had used aluminum chloride for the preparation of polymers from 1,2-dichloroethane and tetrahydronaphthalene. These polymers also had the highest molecular weights in the runs with 1.1 moles tetrahydronaphthalene for every mole of 1,2-dichloroethane. The product of lowest molecular weight is mainly 1,2-di-(2-tetrahydronaphthyl)ethane.

Chlorobenzene reacts with excess 1,2-dichloroethane in the presence of large amounts of aluminum chloride (162). In elucidation of the chemical structure of the polymer formed the yellow elastic polymer was oxidized by chromic acid and 4-chloroisophthalic acid was produced. Since 4-chloro-1,3-xylene could be oxidized to the same 4-chloroisophthalic acid by potassium permanganate, the following structural formula is possible for the polymer:

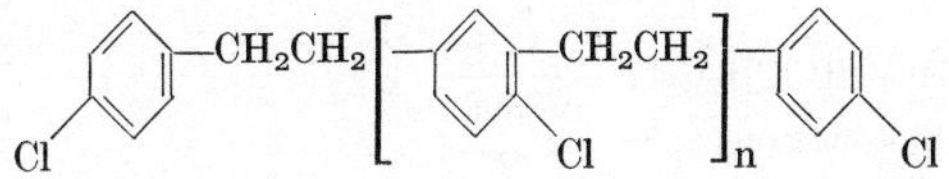

A further confirmation of this structure is that after a short reaction time larger amounts of 4,4'-dichlorobibenzyl are isolated:

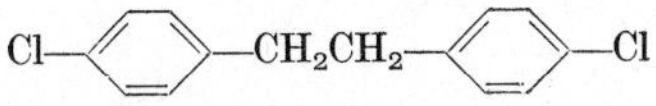

Together with 1,2-diphenylethane, prepared from 1,2-dichloro-ethane and benzene under the influence of aluminum metal, Dolgov and Larin (46) detected small amounts of 1,1-diphenylethane. The latter was synthesized from 1,1-dichloroethane by Schmerling (157). 4,4'-Diphenylbibenzyl may be obtained from biphenyl in a reaction with 1,2-dichloroethane (163). A ring closure with formation of phenanthrene compounds was not observed as dichloroethane does not form the necessary o–o' bridge.

With higher alkyl dihalides distinct ring closures sometimes occur during Friedel-Crafts reactions with benzene. Tetrahydronaphthalenes and octahydroanthracenes are the products instead of diphenylated hydrocarbons. 1,4-Dichlorobutane has a particularly strong tendency to form such ring systems and instead of 1,4-diphenylbutane various partially hydrogenated aromatics are obtained from benzene in the presence of aluminum chloride. The hydrogenated rings may be dehydrogenated to the corresponding aromatics on heating with sulfur at 180–300°. This process is also helpful for identification purposes (160,164,197). If a solution of 1,4-dichlorobutane in benzene is kept at room temperature and aluminum chloride is added, dodecahydrotriphenylene is formed.

At 75–80° triphenylene is produced. During reactions catalyzed by aluminum chloride dehydrogenation is often stimulated at higher temperatures and there may be a similarity to the alkylation of aromatics by hydrocarbons containing a tertiary hydrogen atom. In both types of reaction hydride transfer caused by aluminum chloride seems to be the essential step. The 1,4-position between the halogens is not an essential supposition for the formation of tetrahydronaphthalenes or polyhydroanthracenes; other dihalides have also been successfully used with benzene and aluminum chloride, as illustrated by the following examples (167):

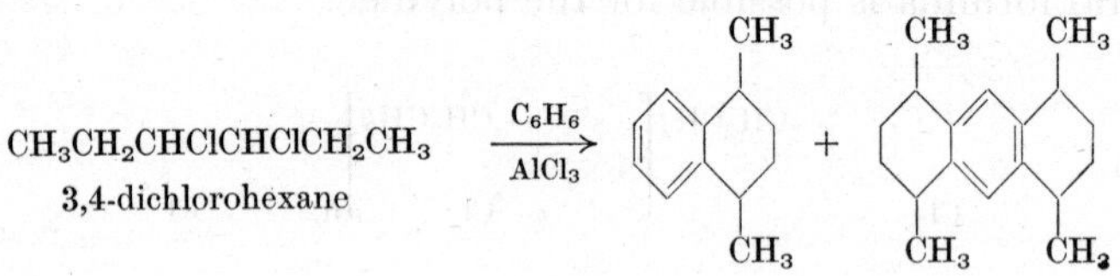

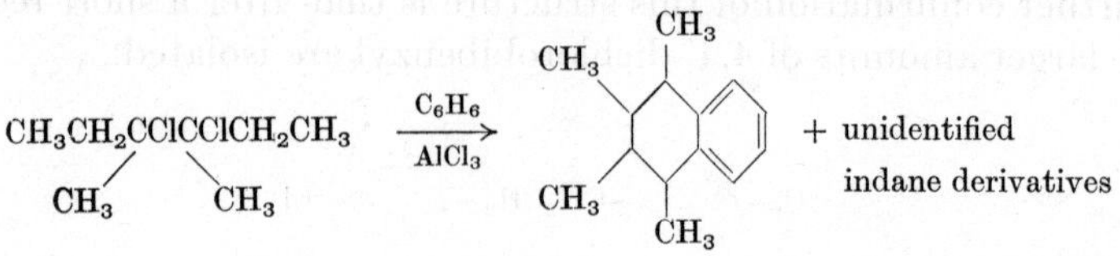

$$CH_3CH_2CHClCHClCH_2CH_3 \xrightarrow[AlCl_3]{C_6H_6}$$
3,4-dichlorohexane

$$CH_3CH_2CClCClCH_2CH_3 \xrightarrow[AlCl_3]{C_6H_6}$$
(with CH_3 groups) + unidentified indane derivatives

$$C_{14}H_{29}CHBrCH_2Br \xrightarrow[\text{AlCl}_3]{C_6H_6}$$

Preferential formation of indane derivatives has been reported (166) if 2,3-dimethyl-2,3-dichlorobutane is used; 1,1,2-trimethylindane was obtained as the main product together with a small amount of hexylbenzene.

$$(CH_3)_2CClCCl(CH_3)_2 + C_6H_6 \xrightarrow{\text{AlCl}_3} \quad + \; C_6H_5C_6H_{13}$$

The reaction between 1,1-dichloroethylene and benzene to yield 1,1,3-triphenyl-3-methylindane has been discussed before (85).

Dolgov and Larin (46) found that aluminum metal catalyzes the reaction of alkyl polyhalides with aromatics in the same way as aluminum chloride except that both cleavage and rearrangement are more favored with the metal powder. These side reactions decline with increasing numbers of halogen atoms and halogens attached to a double bond are usually quite unreactive.

In non-symmetrical di- or polyhalides one of the halogens usually has a preferred reactivity and at first only this halogen is replaced by an aromatic ring. This exchange produces an alkyl halide with an attached aromatic ring in the chain which often greatly influences the reactivity of the remaining second halogen by "anchimeric assistance" (194). According to Schmerling (157,159) the second halogen atom leaves the alkyl halide, in the presence of aluminum chloride, in the form of an $AlCl_4^-$ anion. The presence of a second aromatic ring favors this reaction by anchimeric assistance assuming there is an acceptable conformation of groups. There is also a tendency to replace the lost chlorine anion by a hydride ion; if a saturated hydrocarbon with a tertiary hydrogen atom is present this hydride ion produces a carbonium ion from the saturated hydrocarbon which is suitable for alkylating aromatic rings and the corresponding alkylbenzenes are also obtained. Thus the dihalide is converted to an alkylbenzene with only one aromatic ring, though the chain is free of halogen. Simultaneously the saturated tertiary hydrocarbon alkylates another aromatic ring. The tertiary hydrocarbon may be an open-chain or a cyclic hydrocarbon. If the remaining halogen does not receive any assistance from the first aromatic ring then a large amount of monoarylated alkyl monohalides may be obtained.

Infra-red analysis of the products from 1,1-dichloro-3-methylbutane, benzene, and aluminum chloride shows that the hydride ion may be formed by a tertiary hydrogen atom of the alkyl halide itself and no further hydrocarbon with a tertiary hydrogen is necessary for hydrogen transfer. In this case some ring closure is also observed, with formation of an indane ring (157):

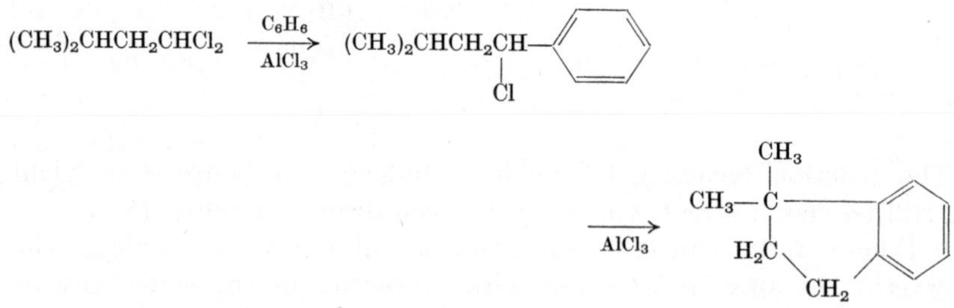

$$(CH_3)_2CHCH_2CHCl_2 \xrightarrow[\text{AlCl}_3]{\text{C}_6\text{H}_6} (CH_3)_2CHCH_2CH\underset{\overset{|}{Cl}}{-}\text{(phenyl)}$$

$$\xrightarrow[\text{AlCl}_3]{} \text{(indane structure with } CH_3-C-CH_3, H_2C, CH_2\text{)}$$

Summarizing, it may be assumed that this impeded replacement of both halogens by the aryl group is a result of the preferred formation of saturated halogen-free monoalkylbenzenes. This, in turn, is a characteristic of a hydrogen transfer of a tertiary hydrogen. A similar hydrogen transfer from a suitable alkyl dihalide occurs in the alkylation of benzene with cyclohexyl-2,2-dibromoethane. A 37% yield of 1-phenyl-2-cyclohexylethane is obtained by such a hydrogen transfer. A carbonium ion is produced from the dihalide but no corresponding products of an arylation in this position have been reported apart from the ring closure previously mentioned. The problem is complicated by the large number of compounds formed.

2. Haloalkenes

In 1,1,3-trichloro-2-methyl-1-propene there is one allyl chlorine atom, which reacts readily with phenols. Friedel-Crafts alkylation of phenol itself occurs on warming. In the presence of aluminum

TABLE III. Alkylation of aromatics with di- and polyhalides

Alkyl halide	Aromatic compound	Catalyst	Product	Ref.
$CHCl_3$	$1,2,4\text{-}Cl_3C_6H_3$	$AlCl_3$	$(2,4,5\text{-}Cl_3C_6H_2)_3CH$	193
CCl_4	$1,2,4\text{-}Cl_3C_6H_3$	$AlCl_3$	$(2,4,5\text{-}Cl_3C_6H_2)_2CO$	193
CCl_4	$1,2,5\text{-}Cl_3C_6H_3$	$AlCl_3$	$(2,4,6\text{-}Cl_3C_6H_2)_2CO$	193
$CHCl_3$	C_6H_6	$Al + CuCl$	$Ph_2CH_2,\ Ph_3CH$	47
$ClCH_2CH_2CH_2CH_2Cl$	C_6H_6		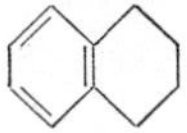 [structure]	197
$ClCH_2CH_2CH_2CH_2Cl$	C_6H_6	$AlCl_3$	[structure]	160
$ClCH_2CH_2CH_2CH_2Cl$	C_6H_6	$AlCl_3$	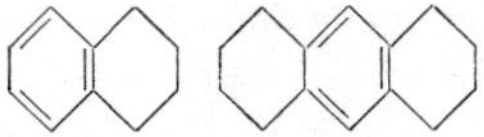 [structure] etc.	164
$C_2H_5CHClCHClC_2H_5$	C_6H_6	$AlCl_3$	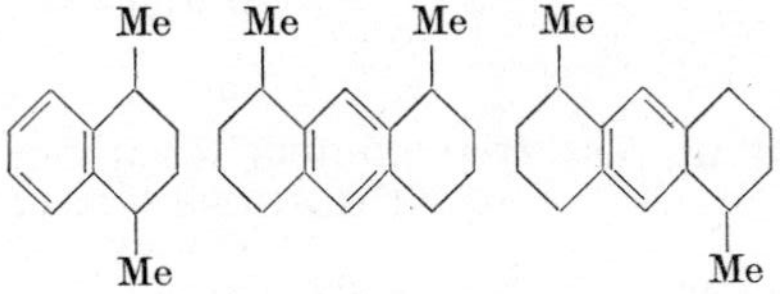 [structures with Me]	167
$Me_2CClCH_2CH_2CClMe_2$	C_6H_6	$AlCl_3$	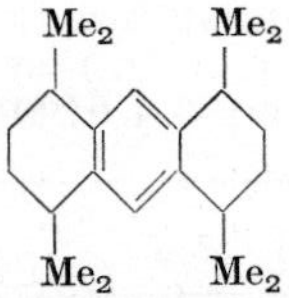 [structure with Me_2]	149
Me_3CCl	 $Me_3C\text{-}C_6H_4\text{-}CMe_3$	$AlCl_3$	(1,1-4,5,5-8,8-Octamethyl- 1,2,3,4,5,6,7,8-octahydroanthracene	149
Me_3CCl	etc.	$AlCl_3$	$+\ Me_3CH$ (by $1,3,5\text{-}t\text{-}Bu_3C_6H_3$)	149

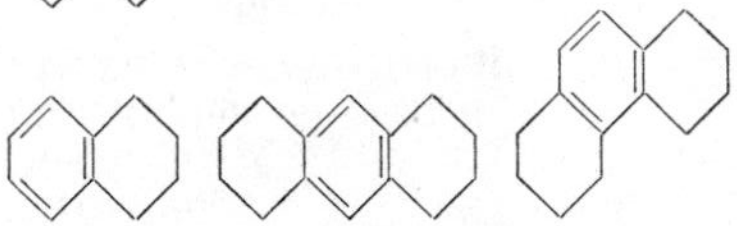

Table continued

TABLE III (continued)

Alkyl halide	Aromatic compound	Catalyst	Product	Ref.
$Cl_2CHCHCl_2$	C_6H_6	$AlCl_3$	$Ph_2 \cdot CH_2$, Anthracene	86
Cl_3CCCl_3	C_6H_6	$AlCl_3$	Ph_2CH_2, Ph_3CH, Anthracene, p-xylene	86
$ClCH_2Cl$	C_6H_6 8 moles	Al	25–30% $PhCH_2CH_2Ph$, traces of Ph_2CHCH_3	46
$Cl_2CHCHCl_2$	C_6H_6 1 mole	Al	6.5% $PhCH_2CH_2Ph$ and a lot of tar; 20°: Anthracene	46
Me_2CBrCH_2Br	C_6H_6	Al	70–75°: $PhCH_2CH_2Ph$; Me_2CPhCH_2Ph,BuPh (with 89% t-BuPh), [structure with Ph groups]; traces $(MeCH)_n$	46
$BrCH_2CMeBrCH_2Cl$	C_6H_6	Al	60°: increasing amounts of $(MeCHPh)_2$; $(MeCHPh)_2$	46
$MeCBr(CH_2Br)_2$	C_6H_6	Al	$(MeCHPh)_2$	46
$CHBr(CH_2Br)_2$	C_6H_6	Al	$Ph_2C_3H_6$ but no $Ph_3C_3H_5$	46
$MeCHClCH_2CH_2Cl$	C_6H_6	$AlCl_3$	s-BuPh, meso-$(MeCHPh)_2$ + dl	166
$Me_2CClCClMe_2$	C_6H_6	$AlCl_3$	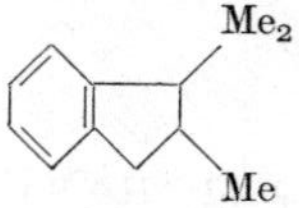 [indane structure, Me_2, Me] + Hexylbenzene	166
$(C_2H_5CClMe)_2$	C_6H_6	$AlCl_3$	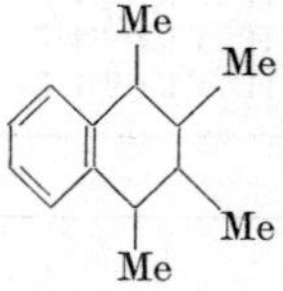 [indane structure, Me, Me, Me] + Unidentified Indane	166

$CH_2BrCHBrC_{14}H_{29}$	C_6H_6		0–5°: Dodecyltetrahydronaphthalene, + 1,5- or 1,8-didodecyloctahydroanthracene hot: $C_{16}H_{33}Ph$, $C_{16}H_{34}$	168
$CH_2BrCHBrCHBrCH_2Br$	C_6H_6	$AlCl_3$	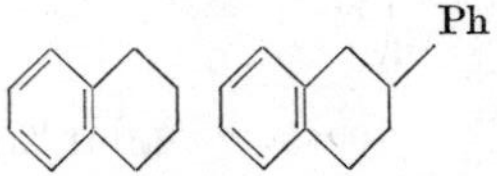 (Ph-substituted dihydronaphthalene, Ph-Ph)	159
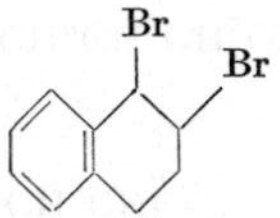 (dibromo-tetrahydronaphthalene, Br Br)	C_6H_6	$AlCl_3$	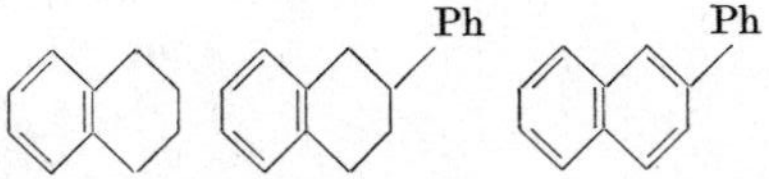 (Ph, Ph substituted dihydronaphthalenes)	165
$MeCHClCHMeCH_2Cl$	C_6H_6	$AlCl_3 \cdot MeNO_2$	PhC—$Me_2CH_2CH_2Cl$, $ClCH_2CH_2$—CMe_2——CMe_2—CH_2—CH_2Cl 	156
$MeCHClCHMeCH_2Cl$	Ph—CMe_2—Et		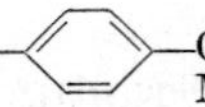 EtC—$CHCH_2CH_2Cl$, Me_2 / Me	

TABLE IV. Alkylation of benzene with polyhaloalkanes in the presence of cycloalkanes. (Effect of hydride transfer)

Alkyl polyhalide	Saturated hydrocarbon (when present)	Catalyst	Products	Ref.
$Cl_2CHCH_2CMe_3$		$AlCl_3$	$Ph_2CHCH_2CMe_3$ 26–28%, $PhCH_2CH_2CMe_3$ 19–20%	157a
$Cl_2CHCH_2CMe_3$	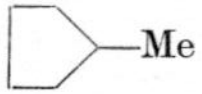 (methylcyclopentane)	$AlCl_3$	$Ph_2CHCH_2CMe_3$ 6%, $PhCH_2CH_2CMe_3$ 60%	157a
$ClCH_2CH_2CClMe_2$		$FeCl_3$	$ClCH_2CH_2CPhMe_2$ 19%	159a
$ClCH_2CH_2CClMe_2$		$AlCl_3$	$ClCH_2CH_2CPhMe_2$ 28%, $MeCHPhCPhMe_2$ 29%	159a
$ClCH_2CH_2CClMe_2$		$AlCl_3MeNO_2$	$ClCH_2CH_2CPhMe_2$ 55%, $C_6H_4(CMe_2CH_2CH_2Cl)_2$ 22%	159a
$ClCH_3CClMe_2$		$AlCl_3$	$PhCH_2CPhMe_2$	159a
$ClCH_2CClMe_2$	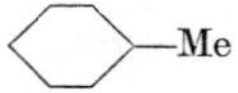 (methylcyclohexane)	$AlCl_3$	$PhCH_2CHMe_2$, $MeC_6H_{10}Ph$, Me_2CHCH_2–[$C_6H_{10}Me$ para-substituted ring] 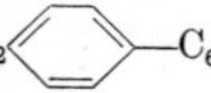	159a
CH_3CHCl_2	(methylcyclohexane)	$AlCl_3$	Ph_2CHCH_3 33%, PhEt 2%	157
CH_3CHCl_2	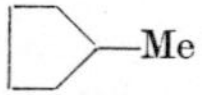 (methylcyclopentane)	$AlCl_3$	3–4°: 42% PhEt, 38%; 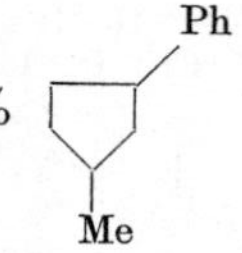 40°: 60% PhEt, 60% [Ph-, Me-cyclopentane]	157
$CH_3CH_2CH_2CHCl_2$		$AlCl_3$	36% Ph_2CHPr, 3% BuPh	157
$CH_3CH_2CH_2CHCl_2$	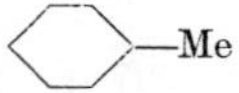 (methylcyclohexane)	$AlCl_3$	$PhC_6H_{10}Me$, 63–64% BuPh	157
$Cl_2CHCH_2CHMe_2$		$AlCl_3$	$PhCH_2CH_2CHMe_2$ 21.6%, 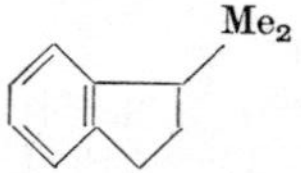 [indane–Me_2 structure], $Me_2CHCHPhMe$	157

Haloalkane	Aromatic	Catalyst	Products	Ref.
$Cl_2CHCH_2CHMe_2$	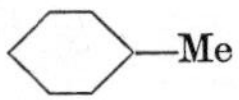 $\bigcirc$–Me	$AlCl_3$	$PhCH_2CH_2CHMe_2$ 43%, Ph$\bigcirc$Me, 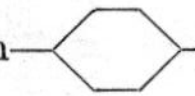	157
Br_2CHCH_2–$\bigcirc$ 	$\bigcirc$	$AlCl_3$	$PhCH_2CH_2$– 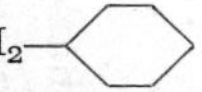	157
$ClCH_2CHClCH_2CH_3$		$AlCl_3$	$ClCH_2CHPhEt$ 37%, $PhCH_2CHPhEt$ 7%, 1–2% $(MeCHPh)_2$	157
$ClCH_2CHClCH_2CH_3$	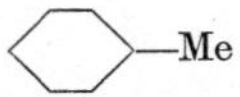 $\bigcirc$–Me	$AlCl_3$	$ClCH_2CHPhEt$ 50%, $PhCH_2CHPhEt$ 6.5%, Me$\diagdown$Et$\diagup$CHPh 7%	157
$(MeCHBr)_2$		$AlCl_3$	meso-$(MeCHPh)_2$, BuPh	157
$(MeCHBr)_2$	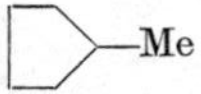 $\bigcirc$–Me	$AlCl_3$	s-BuPh, iso-BuPh, PhC_5H_8Me	157
Cl_2CHCH_2Cl	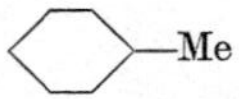 $\bigcirc$–Me	$AlCl_3$	$PhCH_2CH_2Ph$	157

16*

chloride both 1,1,3-trichloro-2-methyl-1-propene and 3,3,3-trichloro-2-methyl-1-propene yield 2-(3,3-dichloro-2-methyl-2-propenyl)-4-methylphenol from p-cresol (90):

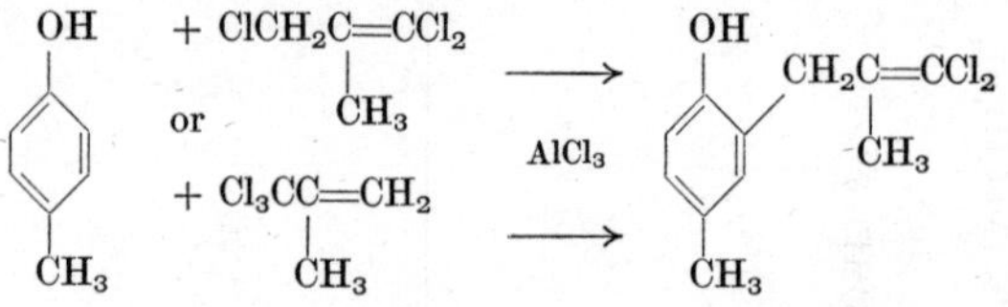

If the reaction of 3,3,3-trichloro-2-methyl-1-propene is compared with that of γ-trichlorocrotonic acid it seems that in trichloro compounds with all chlorine atoms in the allyl position allyl re-arrangements in Friedel-Crafts reactions are favored.

In 1,1-dichloroethylene ($Cl_2C{=}CH_2$) and in 1,1,2-trichloroethylene ($Cl_2C{=}CHCl$) all chlorine atoms react with benzene by Friedel-Crafts alkylation and are not hindered by the double bonds.

3. Alkoxyhaloalkanes (Haloalkyl Ethers)

Alkoxyhaloalhanes, particularly chloromethyl ethers, have often been used in Friedel-Crafts reactions but the results are complicated owing to the different conditions which alkoxy groups and halogens require for reaction with the aromatic ring. Besides the possible variations arising from two different functional groups the formation of anthracene has been reported.

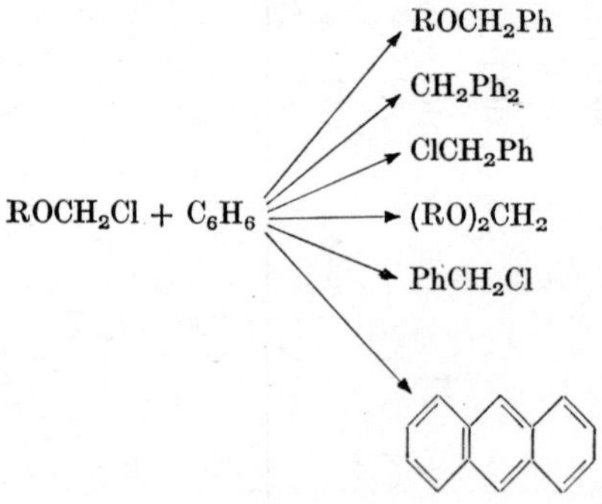

It is possible that the conditions employed determine the course of reaction (102). In carbon disulfide solution of chloromethyl butyl ether the chlorine alone reacts at low temperatures with benzene to form mainly benzyl ether and a little dibutylformal and benzyl chloride:

$$BuOCH_2Cl + C_6H_6 \rightarrow BuOCH_2Ph \ (+ (BuO)_2CH_2 + PhCH_2Cl)$$

TABLE V. Alkylation of aromatics with haloalkenes

Alkyl halide	Aromatic compound	Catalyst	Product	Ref.
$ClCH=CHCl$	C_6H_6	$AlCl_3$	Ph_2CH_2, Ph_3CH, Anthracene	86
$Cl_2C=CCl_2$	C_6H_6	Al	No reaction	46
$CH_2=CMeCH_2Cl$	C_6H_6	Al	Me_2CPhCH_2Ph, $BuPh$ {with 80% t-BuPh}, few $(MeCHPh)_2$	46
$CH_2=CHCH_2Cl$	C_6H_6	Al	$PrPh$, $Ph_2C_3H_6$	46
$CH_2=CCl_2$	C_6H_6	$AlCl_3$	$Ph_2C=CH_2$, 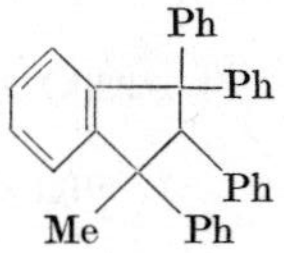 [structure with Ph, Ph, Ph, Me]	85
$ClCH=CCl_2$	9 moles C_6H_6	$AlCl_3$	$Ph_2C=CH_2$	87
$ClCH=CCl_2$	20 moles C_6H_6	$AlCl_3$	Chlorine-free residue, containing Ph_2CH_2, Ph_3CH	189
	20 moles C_6H_6		Cold: $Ph_2CHCHPh_2$ 70%, + Ph_2CHCH_2Ph, $(PhCH_2)_2$, more drastic conditions, more Ph_2CHCH_2Ph, $(PhCH_2)_2$	
$Cl_3CCH=CH_2$	$PhBr$	$AlCl_3$	 $Cl_2C=CHCH_2$-C6H4-Br	119
$Cl_3CCH=CH_2$	$PhCl$	$AlCl_3$	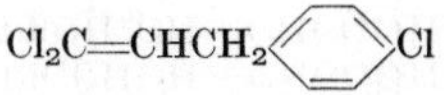 $Cl_2C=CHCH_2$-C6H4-Cl	119
$Cl_3CCH=CH_2$	$PhOH$	$AlCl_3$	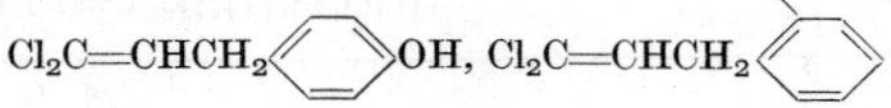 $Cl_2C=CHCH_2$-C6H4-OH, $Cl_2C=CHCH_2$-C6H4-OH	119
$Cl_3CCH=CH_2$	$PhOMe$	$AlCl_3$	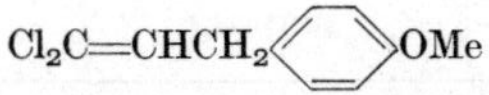 $Cl_2C=CHCH_2$-C6H4-OMe	119

Table continued

TABLE V (continued)

Alkyl halide	Aromatic compound	Catalyst	Product	Ref.
$Cl_3CCH=CHCOOH$	C_6H_6	$AlCl_3$	$Cl_2C=CHCHPhCOOH$	120
$Cl_2CHCH=CHCOOH$	C_6H_6	$AlCl_3$	$Ph_2CHCH=CHCOOH$	120
$ClCH_2CH=CHCOOH$	C_6H_6	$AlCl_3$	$PhCH_2CH=CHCOOH$	120
$MeCCl=CHCH_2Cl$	C_6H_6	Al	$PhCH_2CH=CClMe$	4
$MeCCl=CHCH_2Cl$	MePh	Al	Me⟨ring⟩$CH_2CH=CClMe$ 	4
$MeCCl=CHCH_2Cl$	iso-PrPh	Al	iso-$PrC_6H_4CH_2CH=CClMe$	4
$MeCCl=CHCH_2Cl$	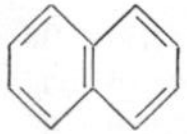 ⟨indane⟩	Al	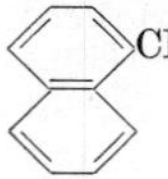 ⟨ring⟩$CH_2CH=CClMe$	4
$MeCCl=CHCH_2Cl$	C_6H_6	$AlCl_3$	$PhCH_2CH=CClMe$	68
$MeCCl=CHCH_2Cl$	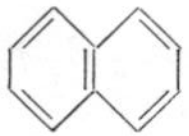 ⟨indane⟩	$AlCl_3$	 ⟨ring⟩$CH_2CH=CClMe$	68
$MeCCl=CHCH_2Cl$	MePh	$AlCl_3$	Me⟨ring⟩$CH_2CH=CClMe$ 	68
$MeCCl=CHCH_2Cl$	iso-PrPh	$AlCl_3$	iso-Pr⟨ring⟩$CH_2CH=CClMe$ 	68
$MeCCl=CHCH_2Cl$	PhOPh	$AlCl_3$	PhO⟨ring⟩$CH_2CH=CClMe$ 	68

$MeCCl=CHCH_2Cl$	MePh	Se,	$ArCH_2CCl=CHMe$ 45–80%	5,6
$MeCCl=CHCH_2Cl$	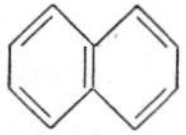 [fused bicyclic arene]	Sn,		5,6
$MeCCl=CHCH_2Cl$	PhOH	Pb,		5,6
$MeCCl=CHCH_2Cl$	PhOEt	Cr,		5,6
$MeCCl=CHCH_2Cl$	PhOMe	Al		5,6
$MeCCl=CHCH_2Cl$	PhBr			5,6
$Cl_2C=CMeCH_2Cl$	PhOH	$AlCl_3$	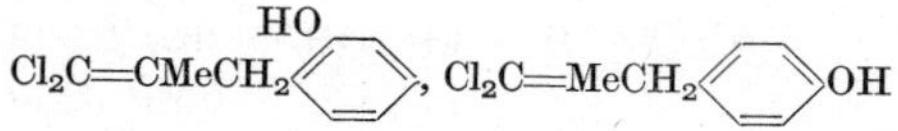 $Cl_2C=CMeCH_2$⟨⟩HO , $Cl_2C=MeCH_2$⟨⟩OH	90
$CH_2=CMeCCl_3$	PhOH		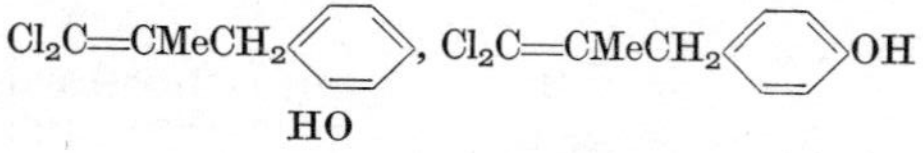 $Cl_2C=CMeCH_2$⟨⟩OH(HO) , $Cl_2C=CMeCH_2$⟨⟩OH	90
$CH_2=CMeCCl_3$	 Me⟨⟩OH		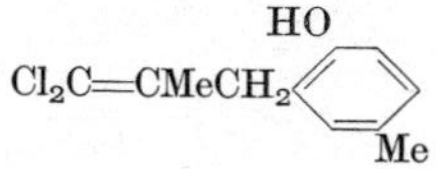 $Cl_2C=CMeCH_2$⟨⟩HO Me	90
$Cl_2C=CMeCH_2Cl$	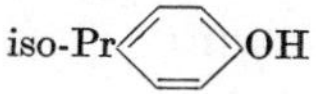 iso-Pr⟨⟩OH		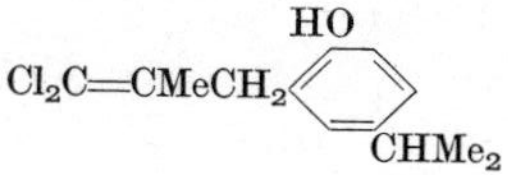 $Cl_2C=CMeCH_2$⟨⟩HO CHMe$_2$	90
$Cl_2C=CMeCH_2Cl$	 t-Bu⟨⟩OH		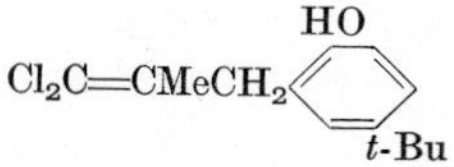 $Cl_2C=CMeCH_2$⟨⟩HO t-Bu	90

Table continued

TABLE V (continued)

Alkyl halide	Aromatic compound	Catalyst	Product	Ref.
Cl₂C=CMeCH₂Cl	Cl⬡OH	AlCl₃	Cl₂C=CMeCH₂⬡(HO)(Cl), CCl₂=CMe-CH₂⬡(HO)(Cl)	90
Cl₂C=CMeCH₂Cl	Me₃C(Cl)⬡OH	FeCl₃	Cl₂C=CMeCH₂⬡(HO)(Cl)(CMe₃)	90
CH₂=CClCH₂Cl	C₆H₆	AlCl₃,MeNO₂	Little reaction	159
CHCl=CHCH₂Cl	C₆H₆	AlCl₃,MeNO₂	PhCH₂CH=CHCl	159
CHCl=CMeCH₂Cl	C₆H₆	AlCl₃,MeNO₂	PhC(CH₂Cl)₂	159
CHCl=CMeCH₂Cl	C₆H₆	AlCl₃	PhCH₂CMe=CHCl, (Ph₂C₄H₈ Ph₃C₄H₇)	159
trans-CHCl=CHCl	C₆H₆	AlCl₃	PhCH₂CH₂Ph	159
CHCl=CCl₂	C₆H₆	AlCl₃	Ph₂CHCHPh₂, Ph₂CHCH₂Ph	159

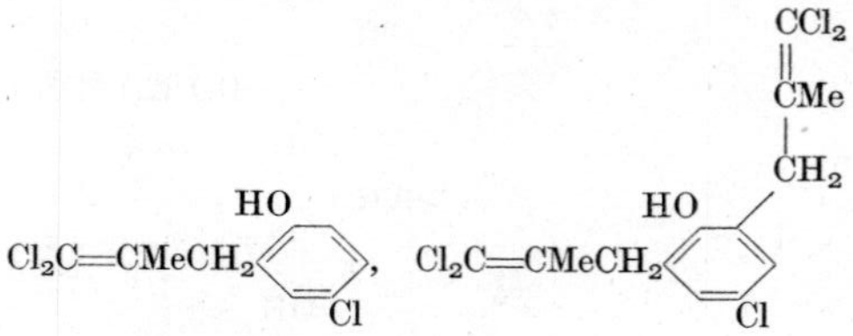

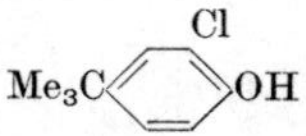

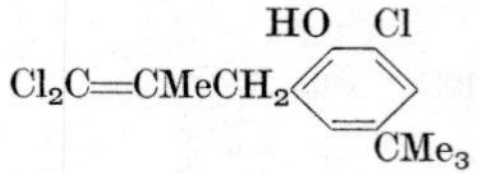

These by-products result from a side reaction and not from disproportionation:

$$2BuOCH_2Cl \rightarrow (BuO)_2CH_2 + CH_2Cl_2$$

$(BuO)_2CH_2$ itself does not react with benzene to $BuOCH_2Ph$ and no
CH_2Cl_2 is produced. Though α-chloroethyl butyl ether can be used
for Friedel-Crafts reactions, β-chloroethyl butyl ether remains mostly
unchanged. The α-position is the deciding factor, as was observed
in the case of the higher reactivity of Grignard reagents with such
compounds.

4. Haloalkyl Sulfides

β-Chloroethyl thioethers ($RSCH_2CH_2Cl$) may react with aromatics
if enough aluminum chloride is present (74). The structure of the alkyl
group, R, has a considerable influence on the reaction and the following
declining sequence in activity has been reported: tolyl > n-butyl >
phenyl. From these β-chloroethyl thioethers products with a
phenyl group in the α-position have never been obtained, but some
traces of ethylene disulfides $RSCH_2CH_2SR$ are always detected. A
mechanism with a sulfonium-ion complex is assumed as an intermediate step:

$$\left[\begin{array}{c} CH_2-CH_2 \\ \diagdown S \diagup \\ R \end{array}\right]^{+} \left[\begin{array}{c} \\ AlCl_4 \\ \\ \end{array}\right]^{-}$$

The large amounts of aluminum chloride required would be accounted
for in the formation of the complex. This would also explain the
reactivity of the β-chlorine compounds compared to β-chloroethyl
ethers and β-chloroethyl sulfones (*e.g.*,

$$CH_3-\langle\ \rangle-SO_2CH_2CH_2Cl)$$

The latter are unable to form such complex compounds.

5. Haloalkyl Amines and Imines

1-Benzenesulfonyl-2-bromomethyl ethylene imine reacts in various
ways with benzene and the amounts of aluminum chloride used
have a decisive influence on the course of the reaction. A large
excess of benzene is always necessary and reaction of the imine starts
only if more than molar amounts of aluminum chloride are used.
With 1.5 moles of aluminum chloride the imine ring is opened and
N-(3-phenylpropyl)benzenesulfonamide is formed. With 2 moles of
aluminum chloride benzenesulfonamide is obtained (54).

$$\text{C}_6\text{H}_6 + \quad \underset{\substack{| \\ \text{SO}_2\text{Ph}}}{\overset{\displaystyle \text{BrCH}_2\text{---CH---CH}_2}{\diagdown \text{N} \diagup}} \begin{array}{l} + \ 1.5\text{AlCl}_3 \rightarrow \text{PhSO}_2\text{NHCH}_2\text{CH}_2\text{CH}_2\text{Ph} \\[2.5em] + \ 2\text{AlCl}_3 \rightarrow \text{PhSO}_2\text{NH}_2 \end{array}$$

The reaction of chloroquinoline with aromatics has already been mentioned.

6. Haloalkyl Halosilanes

Chlorosilanes which are also chlorinated in the carbon chain contain two types of chlorine atoms; those which are bound to the silicon and those bonded to carbon. It is possible to effect a Friedel-Crafts reaction with the carbon-bonded chlorine without any participation of the chlorine atoms attached to the silicon. The reaction may be catalyzed by metallic aluminum or aluminum chloride. From the latter the product formed is purified with phosphorus oxychloride. Many aromatic compounds react successfully with haloalkyl halosilanes. In the absence of aromatic compounds α- and β-chloroethyl ethyldichlorosilane react violently on addition of aluminum chloride to form ethyltrichlorosilane (32,33).

$$\underset{\displaystyle \text{ArCH}_2\text{CH}_2\text{SiCl}_2}{\overset{\displaystyle \text{Et}}{|}} \xleftarrow[\text{AlCl}_3]{\text{ArH}} \underset{\substack{| \\ \text{Et}}}{\overset{\displaystyle \overset{\text{Et}}{|}}{\begin{array}{l} \text{ClCH}_2\text{CH}_2\text{SiCl}_2 \\[1em] \text{CH}_3\text{CHCl---SiCl}_2 \end{array}}} \xrightarrow{\text{AlCl}_3} \text{EtSiCl}_3$$

In Friedel-Crafts reactions with α- or β-chloroethylsilanes the aromatic product is generally a β-substituent.

7. Haloacyl Halides, Halocarboxylic Acids and Esters

With chloroacetyl chloride other haloaliphatic acid chlorides or chloroalkyl aryl ketones are formed by reaction with aromatics. Yet with the corresponding free acids a side-chain chlorine atom reacts and, for example, naphthylstearic acid is formed from naphthalene and chlorostearic acid in the presence of aluminum chloride (173).

Tsukervanik and Terent'eva (181) have shown the influence of ester groups on the halogen in a Friedel-Crafts substitution. The ester group loses its influence with increasing chain length. As the reaction conditions are varied, mono-, different di-, and 1,2,3-triethylbenzenes result from reactions with chloroacetic acid ethyl ester.   Only the ethyl group of the ester is involved.   With β-chloropropionic acid ethyl ester up to 74% β-phenylpropionic acid is obtained in addition to β-chloropropiophenone and ethylbenzene. With γ-chlorobutyric acid ethyl ester the intramolecular ring closure becomes more important and a naphthalenone is produced.

8. Unsaturated Halocarboxylic Acids

The different halogenated crotonic acids yield various products depending on the number of halogen atoms and their positions with respect to the double bond (75,120).

$$CCl_3CH{=}CHCOOH + C_6H_6 \rightarrow CCl_2{=}CHCHPhCOOH$$

$$CHCl_2CH{=}CHCOOH + 2C_6H_6 \rightarrow Ph_2CHCH{=}CHCOOH$$

$$CH_2BrCH{=}CHCOOH + C_6H_6 \rightarrow PhCH_2CH{=}CHCOOH$$

$$CH_3CCl{=}CHCOOH + 2C_6H_6 \rightarrow CH_3CPh_2CH_2COOH$$

Only one chlorine atom reacts in γ-trichlorocrotonic acid, but the double bond changes position and the phenyl group is attached to a carbon atom other than the one from which the chlorine departed. Therefore an inclusion of the double bond in the reaction mechanism seems probable, but rearrangement and alkylation may take place in two steps.   A prior allylic rearrangement

$$(\overset{+}{C}Cl_2CH{=}CHCOOH \rightleftharpoons CCl_2{=}CH\overset{+}{C}HCOOH)$$

would cause the formation of $CCl_2{=}CHCHPhCOOH$.   The chlorine atom and double bond react in β-chlorocrotonic acid and therefore here the saturated β,β-diphenylbutyric acid is obtained.   It is not usual in Friedel-Crafts reactions that a halogen on a carbon double bond react together.   Many aromatics have been alkylated in Friedel-Crafts reactions with 1,3-dichlorobutene-2 and as far as the resulting products have been identified the double bond and the chlorine atom in position 3 (on the double bond) have a mutually disturbing effect.   The primary halogen reacts normally and so various γ-chlorocrotyl derivatives $ArCH_2CH{=}CClCH_3$ may be synthesized (4,5,6,68).   Baddeley (9) suggests that primary alkyl halides react best in Friedel-Crafts alkylation and the γ-chlorocrotyl chlorides may be especially reactive since the chlorine is also in the allyl position.   Azatyan (6) has used γ-chlorocrotyl chloride for experiments on the activity of different metals in Friedel-Crafts catalysis (see Section II-11).   From the γ-chlorocrotylarene obtained the corresponding arylbutadiene is made by elimination of hydrogen chloride with alcoholic base.

From this review on the alkylation of aromatics with alkyl halides one may get an impression of the enormous number of reports published in this field and of the tremendous amount of research already done. Above all it is to be hoped that it will stimulate further research.

Newer analytical methods, particularly infra-red and n.m.r. spectroscopy and gas chromatography are very helpful in solving problems which once were thought to be insoluble and many mistakes in the older literature may be corrected by systematic experimental work.   Further, we should recognize the sensitivity of the reaction to the applied conditions and the purity of the reactants used.   Often surprising results might be caused by slight variations which at first were thought unimportant.   An accurate analysis of the products formed would always extend the knowledge of the course and mechanism of the reaction.   At present, however, exact data on many alkylations are lacking; even physical constants and spectra of pure di- and polyalkylbenzenes are rare.

References

1. Adam, P., *Ann. Chim. Phys.*, (6), **15**, 224 (1888).
2. Adam, P., *Bull. Soc. Chim. France*, (2), **49**, 98 (1888).
2a. Adams, J. Q., and S. W. Nicksic, *J. Am. Chem. Soc.*, **84**, 4355 (1962).
3. Anderson, A. G., Jr., E. J. Cowles, J. J. Tazuma, and J. A. Nelson, *J. Am. Chem. Soc.*, **77**, 6321 (1955).
4. Azatyan, V. D., *Dokl. Akad. Nauk S.S.S.R.*, **59**, 901 (1948); through *C.A.*, **42**, 6758i (1948).
5. Azatyan, V. D., *Dokl. Akad. Nauk Arm. S.S.R.*, **25**, 235 (1957); through *C.A.*, **52**, 12811i (1958).
6. Azatyan, V. D., *Dokl. Akad. Nauk Arm. S.S.R.*, **28**, No. 1, 7 (1959); through *C.A.*, **53**, 19927d (1959).
7. Baddeley, G., Brit. Pat. 591,610 (Aug. 22, 1947); through *C.A.*, **42**, 1320f (1948).
8. Baddeley, G., *J. Chem. Soc.* (Suppl. Issue, No. 1), 229 (1949); through *C.A.*, **43**, 8367c (1949).
9. Baddeley, G., *Quart. Rev.* (*London*), **8**, 355 (1954).
10. Baddeley, G., and J. Kenner, *J. Chem. Soc.*, 303 (1935).
11. Baddeley, G., and R. Williamson, *J. Chem. Soc.*, 4647 (1956).
12. Barbot, A., *Bull. Soc. Chim. France*, (4), **47**, 1314 (1930).
13. Bethell, D., and V. Gold, *J. Chem. Soc.*, 1930 (1958).
14. Beyer, H., and U. Hess, *Ber.*, **94**, 1717 (1961).
14a. Beyer, H., U. Hess, and H. Fröhlich, *Ber.*, **95**, 1989 (1962).
15. Blunk, F. H., and D. R. Carmody, *Ind. Eng. Chem.*, **40**, 2072 (1948).
16. Boedtker, E., and O. M. Halse, *Bull. Soc. Chim. France*, **19**, 444 (1916).
17. Brown, H. C., and B. A. Bolto, *J. Am. Chem. Soc.*, **81**, 3320 (1959).
18. Brown, H. C., L. P. Eddy, and R. Wong, *J. Am. Chem. Soc.*, **75**, 6275 (1953).

19. Brown, H. C., and C. W. Gary, *J. Am. Chem. Soc.*, **77**, 2300 (1955).
20. Brown, H. C., and M. Grayson, *J. Am. Chem. Soc.*, **75**, 6285 (1953).
21. Brown, H. C., and K. Le Roi Nelson, *J. Am. Chem. Soc.*, **75**, 6292 (1953).
21a. Brown, H. C., and A. H. Neyens, *J. Am. Chem. Soc.*, **84**, 1655 (1962).
22. Brown, H. C., and H. W. Pearsall, *J. Am. Chem. Soc.*, **74**, 191 (1952).
23. Brown, H. C., H. W. Pearsall, and L. P. Eddy, *J. Am. Chem. Soc.*, **72**, 5347 (1950).
24. Brown, H. C., H. W. Pearsall, L. P. Eddy, W. J. Wallace, M. Grayson, and K. Le Roi Nelson, *Ind. Eng. Chem.*, **45**, 1462 (1953).
24a. Brown, H. C., and J. D. Brady, *J. Am. Chem. Soc.*, **74**, 3580 (1952).
25. Brown, H. C., and Ch. R. Smoot, *J. Am. Chem. Soc.*, **78**, 2176 (1956).
26. Brown, H. C., and W. J. Wallace, *J. Am. Chem. Soc.*, **75**, 6265 (1953).
27. Brown, H. C., and H. L. Young, *J. Org. Chem.*, **22**, 724 (1957).
28. Buu-Hoï, Ng. Ph., B. Eckert, and R. Royer, *Compt. rend.*, **233**, 627 (1951).
29. Calloway, N. O., *Chem. Rev.*, **17**, 327 (1935); through *Chem. Zentr.*, I, 2060 (1936).
30. Calloway, N. O., *J. Am. Chem. Soc.*, **59**, 1474 (1937).
31. Chem. Werke Huls A.G., Brit. Pat. 786,112 (Nov. 13, 1957); through *C.A.*, **52**, 10170i (1958).
32. Chernyshev, E. A., M. E. Dolgaya, and Yu. P. Egorov, *J. Gen. Chem. U.S.S.R.*, **27**, 267 (1957); through *C.A.*, **52**, 7187b (1958).
33. Chernyshev, E. A., M. E. Dolgaya, and Yu. P. Egorov, *J. Gen. Chem. U.S.S.R.*, **28**, 2829 (1958); through *C.A.*, **53**, 9110c (1959).
34. Chiurdoglu, G., and P. J. C. Fierens, *Bull. Soc. Chim. France*, D27–34 (1950); *C.A.*, **45**, 1528f (1951).
35. Choi, Sang Up, and H. C. Brown, *J. Am. Chem. Soc.*, **81**, 3315 (1959).
36. Chubachi, E., M. Ookawa, and T. Kaneko, *J. Chem. Soc. Japan*, **72**, 326 (1951); through *C.A.*, **46**, 2530e (1952).
37. Clement, H., *Ann. Chim. Phys.*, **13**, 243 (1940).
38. Clement, H., and J. Savard, *Compt. rend.*, **206**, 610 (1938).
39. Colonge, J., and A. Lagier, *Bull. Soc. Chim. France*, 27 (1949); through *C.A.*, **43**, 5736f (1949).
40. Colonge, J., and P. Garnier, *Bull. Soc. Chim. France*, 436 (1948); through *C.A.*, **42**, 6790d (1948).
41. Cullinane, N. M., and D. M. Leyson, *J. Chem. Soc.*, 2942 (1954); *C.A.*, **49**, 12323d (1955).
42. Colonge, J., and A. Lagier, *Compt. rend.*, **225**, 1160 (1947); through *C.A.*, **42**, 4563f (1948).
43. Curtin, D. Y., and M. Wilhelm, *J. Org. Chem.*, **23**, 9 (1958).
44. Dilthey, W., S. Henkels, and M. Leonhard, *J. Prakt. Chem.*, **151**, 114 (1938).
45. Dolgov, B. N., and N. A. Kuchumova, *J. Gen. Chem. U.S.S.R.*, **20**, 445 (1950); through *C.A.*, **45**, 566b (1951); and through *Chem. Zentr.*, 8325 (1953).
46. Dolgov, B. N., and N. A. Larin, *J. Gen. Chem. U.S.S.R.*, **20**, 450 (1950); through *C.A.*, **45**, 566f (1951); and through *Chem. Zentr.*, 8325 (1953).
47. Dolgov, B. N., N. T. Sorokina, and A. S. Cherkasov, *J. Gen. Chem. U.S.S.R.*, **21**, 509 (1951); through *Chem. Zentr.*, 1631 (1952); and through *C.A.*, **45**, 8464e (1951).
48. Drahowzal, F.. *Monatsh.*, **88**, 842 (1957); *C.A.*, **52**, 8987a (1958).

49. Drahowzal, F., and H. Bildstein, Austrian Pat. 190,501 (July 10, 1957); C.A., **51**, 15561i (1957).

50. Dziewonski, K., and E. Dotta, *Bull. Soc. Chim. France*, (3), **31**, 373 (1904).

51. Dziewonski, K., and M. Rychlik, *Ber.*, **58**, 2239 (1925).

52. Friedman, B. S., and F. L. Morritz, *J. Am. Chem. Soc.*, **78**, 2000 (1956).

53. Friedman, B. S., F. L. Morritz, C. J. Morrissey, and R. Koncos, *J. Am. Chem. Soc.*, **80**, 5867 (1958).

54. Gensler, W. J., and J. C. Rockett, *J. Am. Chem. Soc.*, **77**, 3262 (1955).

54a. Gilman, H., and R. N. Meals, *J. Org. Chem.*, **8**, 126 (1943).

55. Gislon, A. (to Compagnie française de raffinage), U.S. Pat. 2,499,488 (March 7, 1950); through C.A., **44**, 4672c (1955).

56. Gislon, A. (to Compagnie française de raffinage), Germ. Pat. 894,392 (Oct. 26, 1953); through C.A., **49**, 1319c (1955).

57. Goebel, C. G., U.S. Pat. 2,678,324 (May 11, 1954); through C.A., **48**, 9752g (1954).

58. Goldschmiedt, G., *Monatsh*, **2**, 433 (1881).

59. Groizeleau, L., *Compt. rend.*, **244**, 1223 (1957); C.A., **51**, 12867g (1957).

60. Hart, H., Wm. L. Spliethoff, and H. S. Eleutrio, *J. Am. Chem. Soc.*, **76**, 4547 (1954).

61. Hathaway, C. T. (General Electric Co.), U.S. Pat. 2,800,512 (July 23, 1957); through C.A., **52**, 10176c (1958).

62. Hennion, G. F., and R. A. Kurtz, *J. Am. Chem. Soc.*, **65**, 1001 (1943); through C.A., **37**, 4707 (1943).

63. Huston, R. C., and A. V. Houk, *J. Am. Chem. Soc.*, **54**, 1506 (1932).

64. Ibuki, E., *J. Chem. Soc. Japan*, **67**, 103 (1946); through C.A., **45**, 566a (1951).

65. Illingworth, E., and A. T. Peters, *J. Chem. Soc.*, 1602 (1951).

66. Illuminati, G., and H. Gilman, *J. Am. Chem. Soc.*, **74**, 2896 (1952).

67. Inatome, M., K. W. Greenlee, J. M. Derfer, and Cecil E. Boord, *J. Am. Chem. Soc.*, **74**, 292 (1952).

67a. *Industrial and Engineering Chemistry*, Annual reviews on Unit Processes.

68. Isagulyants, V. I., and G. T. Esayan, *Izv. Akad. Nauk Arm. S.S.R.*, **3**, No. 6, 547 (1950); through C.A., **47**, 3252d (1953).

69. Jacobs, T. L., S. Winstein, J. W. Ralls, and J. H. Robson, *J. Org. Chem.*, **11**, 21 (1946); through C.A., **40**, 3109 (1946).

70. Jacobsen, O., *Ber.*, **14**, 2624 (1881).

71. Jenny, R., *Compt. rend.*, **246**, 3477 (1958); C.A., **53**, 2122c (1959).

72. Jungk, H., C. R. Smoot, and H. C. Brown, *J. Am. Chem. Soc.*, **78**, 2185 (1956).

73. Kharasch, M. S., and A. L. Flenner, *J. Am. Chem. Soc.*, **54**, 674 (1932).

74. Klamann, D., and H. Bertsch, *Ber.*, **88**, 1226 (1955).

75. Koelsch, C. F., H. Hochmann, and C. D. Le Claire, *J. Am. Chem. Soc.*, **65**, 59 (1943); through C.A., **37**, 1410 (1943).

76. Kolesnikov, G. S., and K. V. Borisova, *J. Gen. Chem. U.S.S.R.*, **17**, 1519 (1947); through C.A., **42**, 2239b (1948).

77. Kolesnikov, G. S., V. V. Khorshak, M. A. Andreeva, and A. T. Kitai-gorodskii, *Izv. Akad. Nauk S.S.S.R., Otd. Khim. Nauk*, 114 (1956); *Bull. Acad. Sci. U.S.S.R., Div. Chem. Sci.*, 107 (1956); through C.A., **50**, 13814b (1956).

78. Kolesnikov, G. S., and T. V. Smirnova, *J. Gen. Chem. U.S.S.R.*, **20**, 1427 (1950); through *C.A.*, **45**, 2431c (1951).
79. Koike, E., and M. Okawa, *Rept. Govt. Chem. Ind. Res. Inst., Tokyo*, **50**, 6 (1955); through *C.A.*, **50**, 11297b (1956).
80. Korshak, V. V., and G. S. Kolesnikov, *J. Gen. Chem. U.S.S.R.*, **14**, 10925 (1944); through *C.A.*, **40**, 4033[6] (1946).
81. Khorshak, V. V., and G. S. Kolesnikov, *J. Gen. Chem. U.S.S.R.*, **17**, 1643 (1947); through *C.A.*, **42**, 2938g (1948).
82. Korshak, V. V., and N. N. Lebedev, *J. Gen. Chem. U.S.S.R.*, **18**, 1766 (1948); through *C.A*, **43**, 2930d (1949).
83. Korshak, V. V., and N. N. Lebedev, *J. Gen. Chem. U.S.S.R.*, **20**, 266 (1950); through *C.A.*, **44**, 6395h (1950).
84. Korshak, V. V., N. N. Lebedev, and S. D. Fedoseev, *J. Gen. Chem. U.S.S.R.*, **17**, 575 (1947); through *C.A.*, **42**, 1217h (1948).
85. Korshak, V. V., and K. K. Samplavskaya, *J. Gen. Chem. U.S.S.R.*, **18**, 1470 (1948); through *C.A.*, **43**, 2193c (1949).
86. Korshak, V. V., and K. K. Samplavskaya, *Sb. Statei Obshch. Khim.*, **2**, 1020 (1953); through *C.A.*, **49**, 8207c (1955).
87. Korshak, V. V., K. K. Samplavskaya, and M. A. Andreeva, *J. Gen. Chem. U.S.S.R.*, **19**, 690 (1949); through *C.A.*, **44**, 3470b (1950).
88. Kraus, C. A., and J. D. Calfee (to Standard Oil Development Co.), U.S. Pat. 2,491,116 (Dec. 13, 1949); through *C.A.*, **44**, 4168f (1950).
89. Kuchkarov, A. B., and I. P. Tsukervanik, *J. Gen. Chem. U.S.S.R.*, **20**, 458 (1950); through *C.A.*, **45**, 567a (1951).
90. Kundiger, D. G., and Huey-Pledger (to Dow Chemical Co.), U.S. Pat. 2,837,576 (June 3, 1958); through *C.A.*, **52**, 16293g (1958).
91. Lebedev, N. N., *Zh. Fiz. Khim.*, **22**, 1505 (1948); through *C.A.*, **43**, 2851f (1949).
92. Lebedev, N. N., *Tr. Mosk. Khim.-Tekhnol. Inst.*, No. 23, 40 (1956); through *C.A.*, **53**, 9106f (1959).
93. Lebedev, N. N., *J. Gen. Chem. U.S.S.R.*, **27**, 2460 (1957); through *C.A.*, **52**, 7176b (1958).
94. Lebedev, N. N., *J. Gen. Chem. U.S.S.R.*, **28**, 1151 (1958); through *C.A.*, **52**, 17922e (1958).
95. Lebedev, N. N., *Z. anorg. allgem. Chem.,* **28**, (90), 1151 (1958); through *Chem. Zentr.*, 11257 (1960).
96. Lebedev, N. N., and I. I. Baltadzhi, *Nauchn. Dokl. Vysshei, Khim. i. Khim. Tekhnol.*, No. 1, 104 (1958); through *C.A.*, **52**, 19987i (1958).
97. Lee, C. C., A. G. Forman, and A. Rosenthal, *Can. J. Chem.*, **35**, 22 (1957); *C.A.*, **51**, 12856i (1957).
98. Lee, C. C., M. C. Hamblin, and Nadine James, *Can. J. Chem.*, **36**, 1597 (1958); *C.A.*, **53**, 11273i (1959).
99. Linn, C. B., U.S. Pat. 2,886,535 (May 12, 1959); through *C.A.*, **53**, 20630c (1959).
100. Lippmann, E., and R. Fritsch, *Monatsh.*, **25**, 793 (1904).
101. Malchick, S. P., and R. B. Hannan, *J. Am. Chem. Soc.*, **81**, 2119 (1959).
102. Mason, C. T., and L. A. Gist, Jr., *J. Am. Chem. Soc.*, **73**, 4644 (1951).
103. Mavity, J. M. (to Universal Oil Products Co.), U.S. Pat. 2,388,428 (Nov. 6, 1945); through *C.A.*, **40**, 1022 (1946).

104. Mazonski, T., and A. Hopfinger, *Przemysl Chem.*, **37**, 590 (1958); through *C.A.*, **53**, 17013i (1959).

105. McCall, M. A., and H. W. Coover (Eastman Kodak Co.), U.S. Pat. 2,824,145 (Feb. 18, 1958); through *C.A.*, **52**, 10170c (1958).

105a. McMahon, M. A., and S. C. Bunce, Abstracts of the American Chemical Society Meeting, Atlantic City, Sept. 1962; *J. Org. Chem.*, in press.

106. Meerwein, H., *Ann.*, **455**, 227 (1927); *Chem. Zentr.*, I, 212 (1927).

107. Mel'kanovitskaya, S. G., and I. P. Tsukervanik, *J. Gen. Chem. U.S.S.R.*, **28**, 11 (1958); through *C.A.*, **52**, 11784h (1958).

108. Mel'kanovitskaya, S. G., and I. P. Tsukervanik, *J. Gen. Chem. U.S.S.R.*, **28**, 2032 (1958); through *C.A.*, **53**, 2168d (1959).

109. Messina, N., and E. V. Brown, *J. Am. Chem. Soc.*, **74**, 920 (1952).

110. Meyerson, S., and P. N. Rylander, Jr. (to Standard Oil Co.), U.S. Pat. 2,880,250 (Mar. 31, 1959); through *C.A.*, **53**, 15007e (1959).

111. Miquel, J. F., N. P. Buu-Hoï, and R. Royer, *J. Chem. Soc.*, 3417 (1955); through *C.A.*, **50**, 7774 (1956).

112. Monte Blau, and J. E. Willard, *J. Am. Chem. Soc.*, **73**, 442 (1951).

113. Monte Blau, and J. E. Willard, *J. Am. Chem. Soc.*, **75**, 3330 (1953).

114. Murakami Masuo, and Yasuhide Yukawa, *J. Chem. Soc. Japan, Pure Chem. Sect.*, **71**, 277 (1950); through *C.A.*, **45**, 6598f (1951).

115. Nenitzescu, C. D., *Experientia*, **XVI/7**, 332 (1960).

116. Nenitzescu, C. D., D. A. Isacescu, and C. N. Ionescu, *Ann.*, **491**, 210 (1931).

117. Nenitzescu, C. D., I. Necsoiu, A. Glatz, and M. Zalman, *Ber.*, **92**, 10 (1959).

118. Nenitzescu, C. D., S. Titeica, and V. Ioan, *Acta Chim. Acad. Sci. Hung.*, **12**, 195 (1957).

119. Nesmeyanov, A. N., R. Kh. Freidlina, and N. A. Semenov, *Izv. Akad. Nauk S.S.S.R., Otd. Khim. Nauk*, 993 (1955); through *C.A.*, **50**, 11278 (1956).

120. Nesmeyanov, A. N., L. T. Zakharkin, and R. Kh. Freidlina, *Dokl. Akad. Nauk S.S.S.R.*, **111**, 114 (1956); through *C.A.*, **51**, 8694b (1957).

121. Nicolescu, I. V., and M. Iovu, *Ind. Plastiques Mod. (Paris)*, **10**, No. 10, 46 (1958); through *C.A.*, **53**, 11273d (1959).

122. Nightingale, D., and L. I. Smith, *J. Am. Chem. Soc.*, **61**, 101 (1939).

123. Norris, J. F., and J. N. Ingraham, *J. Am. Chem. Soc.*, **60**, 1421 (1938).

124. Norris, J. F., and D. Rubinstein, *J. Am. Chem. Soc.*, **61**, 6163 (1939).

125. Ogata, Y., and R. Oda, *Sci. Papers Inst. Phys. Chem. Res. (Tokyo)*, **41**, 182 (1943); through *C.A.*, **41**, 6557d (1947).

126. Olah, G. A., and S. J. Kuhn, *J. Am. Chem. Soc.*, **80**, 6535 (1958).

127. Olah, G. A., and S. J. Kuhn, *J. Am. Chem. Soc.*, **80**, 6541 (1958).

128. Olah, G. A., S. J. Kuhn, and S. H. Flood, *J. Am. Chem. Soc.*, **84**, 1688 (1962).

129. Olah, G. A., S. J. Kuhn, and S. H. Flood, *ibid.*, **84**, 1695 (1962).

130. Olah, G. A., S. J. Kuhn, and J. A. Olah, *J. Chem. Soc.*, 2174 (1957).

131. Olah, G. A., A. E. Pavlath, and J. A. Olah, *J. Am. Chem. Soc.*, **80**, 6540 (1958).

132. Pajeau, R., *Compt. rend.*, 247, 935 (1958).

133. Pajeau, R., and P. Fierens, *Bull. Soc. Chim. France*, 587 (1949); *C.A.*, **44**, 2350c (1950).

134. Perova, A. M., *J. Gen. Chem. U.S.S.R.*, **24**, 491 (1954); through *C.A.*, **49**, 6150h (1955).
135. Pines, H., L. Schmerling, and V. N. Ipatieff, *J. Am. Chem. Soc.*, **62**, 2901 (1940); *Chem. Zentr.*, I, 1622 (1942).
136. Prey, V., and B. Metzner, Austrian Pat. 166,212 (June 26, 1950); *C.A.*, **47**, 235d (1953).
137. Prey, V., B. Metzner, and H. Berbalk, *Monatsh.*, **81**, 760 (1950); *C.A.*, **45**, 3810 (1951).
138. Prins, J., *Chem. Weekblad*, **24**, 615 (1927).
138a. Price, C. C., *Org. Reactions*, Vol. III, John Wiley and Sons, New York, 1946.
139. Radzevenchuk, I. F., *J. Gen. Chem. U.S.S.R.*, **28**, 2423 (1958); through *C.A.*, **53**, 3109i (1959).
140. Radzevenchuk, I. F., U.S.S.R. Pat. 116,610 (Jan. 19, 1959); through *C.A.*, **53**, 19970h (1959).
141. Radzivanovskii, C., *Ber.*, **7**, 141 (1874).
142. Radzivanovskii, C., *Ber.*, **28**, 1135 (1895).
143. Ray, J. N., *J. Chem. Soc.*, **117**, 1335 (1920); *C.A.*, **15**, 1133 (1921).
144. Reichstein, T., H. R. Rosenberg, and R. Eberhardt, *Helv. Chim. Acta*, **18**, 721 (1935).
145. Roberts, J. D., R. E. McMahon, and J. S. Hine, *J. Am. Chem. Soc.*, **72**, 4237 (1950).
146. Roberts, R. M., and Y. W. Han, *Tetrahedron Letters*, **6**, 5 (1959).
147. Roberts, R. M., and S. G. Panoides, *J. Org. Chem.*, **23**, 1080 (1958).
148. Roberts, R. M., and D. Shiengthong, *J. Am. Chem. Soc.*, **82**, 732 (1960).
149. Barclay, L. R. C., and E. E. Betts, *J. Am. Chem. Soc.*, **77**, 5735 (1955).
150. Roux, L., *Ann. Chim. Phys.*, (6), 12, 289 (1887).
151. Ruhrchemie, A. G. (F. Rappen), Germ. Pat. 871,746 (March 26, 1953; Cl. 120,101); through *C.A.*, **52**, 20053e (1958).
152. Ruhrchemie, A. G. (H. Kolling and F. Rappen), Germ. Pat. 897,998 (Nov. 26, 1953); through *C.A.*, **52**, 8533a (1958).
153. Ruhrchemie, A. G. (H. Kolling, and F. Rappen), Germ. Pat. 907,168 (March 22, 1954); through *C.A.*, **52**, 10170g (1958).
154. Ruhrchemie, A. G. (H. Kolling, and F. Rappen), Germ. Pat. 914,129 (June 28, 1954; Cl. 120,101); through *C.A.*, **52**, 12274b (1958).
155. Schmerling, L., *Ind. Eng. Chem.*, **40**, 2072 (1948).
156. Schmerling, L., U.S. Pat. 2,631,172 (March 10, 1953); through *C.A.*, **48**, 435e (1954).
157. Schmerling, L., R. W. Welch, and J. P. Luvisi, *J. Am. Chem. Soc.*, **79**, 2636 (1957).
157a. Schmerling, L., J. P. Luvisi, and R. W. Welch, *J. Am. Chem. Soc.*, **77**, 1774 (1955).
158. Schmerling, L., and J. P. West, *J. Am. Chem. Soc.*, **76**, 1917 (1954).
159. Schmerling, L., J. P. West, and R. W. Welch, *J. Am. Chem. Soc.*, **80**, 576 (1958).
159a. Schmerling, L., R. W. Welch, and J. P. West, *J. Am. Chem. Soc.*, **78**, 5406 (1956).
160. Shadmanov, K. M., *Dokl. Akad. Nauk Uz. S.S.R.*, No. 11, 37 (1957); through *C.A.*, **53**, 5214f (1959).

161. Sharma, V. N., and S. Dutt, *J. Indian Chem. Soc.*, **12**, 774 (1935); through *Chem. Zentr.*, II, 966 (1936); and through C. C. Price, *Org. Reactions*, Vol. III, John Wiley and Sons, New York, 1946.
161a. Sharman, S. H., *J. Am. Chem. Soc.*, **84**, 2945, 2951 (1962).
162. Shishido, K., *J. Soc. Chem. Ind. Japan*, Suppl. binding, **44**, 463 (1941); through *C.A.*, **45**, 1558i (1951).
163. Shishido, K., and I. Irie, *J. Soc. Chem. Ind. Japan*, **48**, 10 (1945); through *C.A.*, **42**, 6343i (1948).
164. Shishido, K., and H. Nozaki, *J. Soc. Chem. Ind. Japan*, **47**, 516 (1944); through *C.A.*, **48**, 2016h (1954).
165. Shishido, K., and H. Nozaki, *J. Soc. Chem. Ind. Japan*, **49**, 141 (1946); through *C.A.*, **42**, 6349d (1948).
166. Shishido, K., and H. Nozaki, *J. Am. Chem. Soc.*, **69**, 961 (1947).
167. Shishido, K., and H. Nozaki, *J. Am. Chem. Soc.*, **70**, 1288 (1948).
168. Shishido, K., and H. Nozaki, *J. Soc. Chem. Ind. Japan*, **48**, 35 (1945); through *C.A.*, **42**, 6521d (1948).
169. Shishido, K., and O. Odajima, *J. Soc. Chem. Ind. Japan*, **45**, 222 (1942); through *C.A.*, **45**, 588h (1951).
170. Smith, L. I., and F. J. Dobrovolny, *J. Am. Chem. Soc.*, **48**, 1413 (1926).
171. Smoot, C. R., and H. C. Brown, *J. Am. Chem. Soc.*, **78**, 6245 (1956).
172. Smoot, C. R., and H. C. Brown, *J. Am. Chem. Soc.*, **78**, 6249 (1956).
173. Stoll, W. G., and C. J. Morel (to Geigy), Brit. Pat. 685,133 (Dec. 31, 1952); through *C.A.*, **48**, 3394c (1954).
174. Tcheou, and Yung, *Contrib. Inst. Chem., Nat. Acad. Peiping*, **2**, No. 8, 127, No. 9, 149 (1936); through *C.A.*, **31**, 6646 (1937).
175. Timbrol Ltd. (C. M. Gibian, and F. Kaufler), Australian Pat. 154,298 (Nov. 24, 1953); through *C.A.*, **52**, 2064d (1958).
176. Topchiev, A. V., and B. A. Krentsel, *World Petrol Congr., Proc., 4th, Rome, 1955*, Sect. IV, 327; through *C.A.*, **53**, 6588d (1959).
177. Topchiev, A. V., B. A. Krentsel, and L. N. Andreev, *Dokl. Akad. Nauk S.S.S.R.*, **92**, 781 (1953); through *C.A.*, **49**, 3039 (1955).
178. Tsukervanik, I. P., and S. G. Mel'kanovitskaya, *J. Gen. Chem. U.S.S.R.*, **28**, 11 (1958); through *C.A.*, **52**, 11784h (1958).
179. Tsukervanik, I. P., and N. K. Rozhkova, *Dokl. Akad. Nauk Uz. S.S.R.*, No. 7, 23 (1958); through *C.A.*, **53**, 21724h (1959).
180. Tsukervanik, I. P., G. S. Semeshko, *J. Gen. Chem. U.S.S.R.*, **27**, 1143 (1957); through *C.A.*, **52**, 3743i (1958).
181. Tsukervanik, I. P., and I. V. Terent'eva, *Dokl. Akad. Nauk S.S.S.R.*, **50**, 257 (1945); through *C.A.*, **43**, 4638e (1949).
182. Turova-Pollak, M. B., and I. R. Davydova, *J. Gen. Chem. U.S.S.R.*, **26**, 2710 (1956); through *C.A.*, **51**, 7317b (1957).
183. Turova-Pollak, M. B., and M. A. Maslova, *J. Gen. Chem. U.S.S.R.*, **26**, 2185 (1956); through *C.A.*, **51**, 4972e (1957).
184. Turova-Pollak, M. B., and M. A. Maslova, *J. Gen. Chem. U.S.S.R.*, **27**, 897 (1957); through *C.A.*, **52**, 3705a (1958).
185. Ulich, H., *Ol und Kohle* (+ *Brennstoff Chemie*), **39**, 523 (1943); *C.A.*, **38**, 958 (1944).
186. Ulich, H., and G. Heyne, *Z. Elektrochem.*, **41**, 508 (1935).
187. Ulich, H., A. Keutmann, and A. Geierhaas, *Z. Elektrochem.*, **49**, 292 (1943); through *C.A.*, **37**, 6650 (1943).

188. Universal Oil Products Co., Brit. Pat. 794,153 (April 30, 1958); through *C.A.*, **53**, 4204f (1959).
189. Vasil'eva, N. V., and I. P. Tsukervanik, *J. Gen. Chem. U.S.S.R.*, **27**, 1767 (1957); through *C.A.*, **52**, 4573h (1958).
190. Vincent, C., and L. Roux, *Bull. Soc. Chim. France*, (2), **40**, 163 (1883).
191. Wallace, C. H., and J. E. Willard, *J. Am. Chem. Soc.*, **72**, 5275 (1950).
192. Wertyporoch, E., and T. Firla, *Ann.*, **500**, 287 (1933).
193. Wilson, St. D., and Shu-chien-shih, *J. Chinese Chem. Soc.*, **16**, 85 (1949); through *C.A.*, **44**, 3920g (1950).
194. Winstein, S., C. R. Lindgren, H. Marshall, and L. L. Ingraham, *J. Am. Chem. Soc.*, **75**, 147 (1953).
195. Yura Shozo, and T. Hashimoto, *J. Soc. Chem. Ind. Japan*, **47**, 814 (1944); through *C.A.*, **42**, 6347i (1948).
196. Yura Shozo, Katsuaki Sato, Teizo Koizumi, and Ryohei Oda, *J. Soc. Chem. Ind. Japan*, **44**, 722 (1941); through *C.A.*, **42**, 2248a (1948).
197. Yura Shozo, and Rychei Oda, *J. Soc. Chem. Ind. Japan*, **46**, 531 (1943); through *C.A.*, **42**, 6348h (1948).
198. Zapp, R., Società in Accomandita, Ital. Pat. 438,469 (Aug. 10, 1948); through *C.A.*, **44**, 5386g (1950).
199. Zapp, R., Società in Accomandita, Ital. Pat. 459,251 (Sept. 1, 1950); through *C.A.*, **46**, 5083f (1952).
200. Zincke, T., *Ann.*, **159**, 374 (1871); *Ann.*, **161**, 93 (1872); *Ber.*, **5**, 799 (1872); *Ber.*, **6**, 119 and 906 (1874).

Reviews:

Gilman, H., and R. N. Meals, *J. Org. Chem.*, **8**, 126–46 (1943) (88 refs.).
Unit Processes Review, *Industrial and Engineering Chemistry*, Chapter entitled "Friedel-Crafts." *Ind. Eng. Chem.*, **40**, 1608 (1948), by P. H. Groggins; **41**, 1880 (1949); **42**, 1690 (1950); **43**, 1970 (1951); **44**, 2012 (1952), by P. H. Groggins and S. B. Detwiler; **46**, 1827 (1954), by H. T. Lacey; **47**, 1926 (1955); **42**, 1670 (1956), by K. LeRoi Nelson. Chapter "Alkylation"; *ibid.*, **49**, 1461 (1957); **50**, 1321 (1958); **51**, 1056 (1959); **52**, 535 (1960), by L. F. Albright, and R. N. Shreve.

Books:

C. A. Thomas, *Anhydrous Aluminum Chloride in Organic Chemistry*, American Chemical Society Monograph Series. Reinhold Publishing Corp., New York, 1941.
C. C. Price, "The Alkylation of Aromatic Compounds by the Friedel-Crafts Method," in *Org. Reactions*, Vol. III, Chapter 1. John Wiley and Sons, New York, 1946.

CHAPTER XVIII

Alkylation of Aromatics with Alcohols and Ethers

ALAN SCHRIESHEIM

Esso Research and Engineering Company, Linden, New Jersey

I. Introduction

Acid-catalyzed alkylation of organic molecules with alcohols and ethers is a relatively old reaction on the chemist's list of synthetic techniques. However, the reaction has not been exploited practically or investigated fundamentally to the same extent as acid-catalyzed alkylations involving either olefins or organic halides. The apparent reason for this situation is the ease of obtaining olefin or halide starting materials and the corresponding importance of commercial and laboratory processes involving them, such as iso-paraffin–olefin alkylation to produce motor fuels.

Since alkylation reactions involving alcohols and ethers represent useful synthetic approaches, most of the reported work descriptive, and lists starting materials, conditions and product distributions. This chapter will attempt to cover the descriptive chemistry and, also, to discuss those aspects of the mechanism that have been elucidated. In order to accomplish this goal, the bulk of the descriptive chemistry is listed in the Appendix to this chapter. No attempt has been made to be comprehensive in each area but many leading references to the literature are given. Also, many patents have been consulted and such "patent art" has been described where applicable.

The scope of the reactions under discussion has been rather arbitrarily decided on by limiting the review to work involving the reactions shown in equations (1) and (2).

$$R\text{—}O\text{—}H + M \xrightarrow{\text{acid}} R\text{—}M + HOA \quad (1)$$

$$R\text{—}O\text{—}R' + M \xrightarrow{\text{acid}} \begin{array}{cc} R\text{—}M + ROA \\ \text{or} \quad \text{or} \\ R'\text{—}M \quad R'OA \end{array} \quad (2)$$

477

where M represents an alkylatable compound as an aromatic, olefin, mercaptan, amine, etc.

R,R′ represents an alkyl or aryl group.

A represents a substituent such as H or an alkyl or a catalyst molecule that becomes attached to the alcohol or ether during the alkylation reaction.

It is evident that the R–M bond in equations (1) and (2) may be between carbon and a wide variety of alkylatable materials. The scope of the present chapter, however, will include only C–C, C–S, and C–N bond formation. The following examples characterize the reactions.

C–C Example

Alkylation of Aromatics or Polycyclics

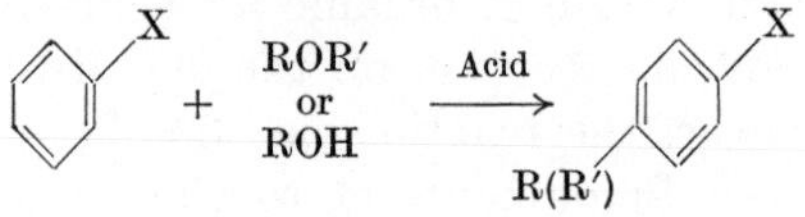

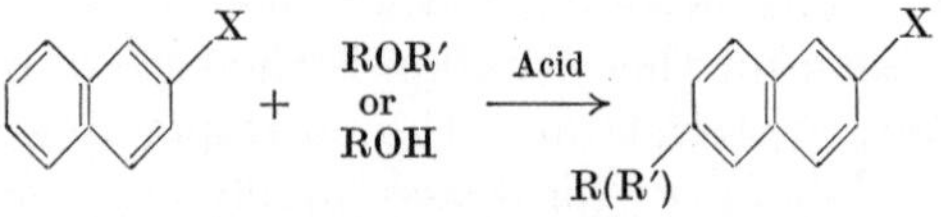

$$\text{C}_6\text{H}_5\text{X} + \begin{matrix} \text{ROR}' \\ \text{or} \\ \text{ROH} \end{matrix} \xrightarrow{\text{Acid}} \text{X--C}_6\text{H}_4\text{--R(R}')$$

$$\text{Naphthyl-X} + \begin{matrix} \text{ROR}' \\ \text{or} \\ \text{ROH} \end{matrix} \xrightarrow{\text{Acid}} \text{X--Naphthyl--R(R}')$$

where X is a substituent such as CH_3, OH, $-\overset{\displaystyle O}{\overset{\|}{C}}-CH_3$.

C–N Example

Alkylation of Amines

$$\text{RNH}_2 + \begin{matrix} \text{R}'\text{OR}'' \\ \text{or} \\ \text{R}'\text{OH} \end{matrix} \xrightarrow{\text{acid}} \text{RNH--R}' \text{ or } \text{RNH--R}''$$

C–S Example

Alkylation of Mercaptans

$$\text{RSH} + \begin{matrix} \text{R}'\text{OR}'' \\ \text{or} \\ \text{R}'\text{OH} \end{matrix} \longrightarrow \text{RSR}' \text{ or } \text{RSR}''$$

With respect to the catalyst, a comprehensive concept of the Friedel-Crafts reaction has been used. Thus, both Lewis acids such as the metallic halides and Brønsted acids such as sulfuric or phosphoric are discussed. Also included are the solid oxide systems such as alumina and silica–alumina.   Recent research clearly shows that such oxides contain active acid sites of both Lewis and Brønsted type, and it is known that they are effective for certain "typically" acid-catalyzed alkylation reactions.

II. Consideration of Reaction Mechanisms

This chapter on alkylation reactions involving alcohols and ethers has been mainly organized around the catalyst systems involved. These systems are the metal halides, proton-donating acids, and inorganic acid oxides.   The rationale for such a scheme is that the chemist is usually faced with the prospect of deciding on a catalytic system to accomplish a reaction under consideration.   By organizing this chapter around broad areas of catalysts, the similarities or differences as well as the general utility of each system become apparent.   In order to compare catalytic systems however, it is necessary to discuss the general mechanism of the alkylation reaction.

Broadly, acid-catalyzed alkylations involving alcohols or ethers as alkylating agents can be interpreted on the basis of intermediate formation of carbonium ionic species.   Classical questions arise concerning the freedom of these positive ionic intermediates.   Thus, they may be free solvated carbonium ions similar in all their physical properties to inorganic ions; they may be, on the other extreme, polarized molecules; or they may be "relatively" free ions held by a combination of electrostatic and covalent forces to the counter or "gegen" ion.

This situation can be summarized by discussing a reaction of ROR′ with an acid catalyst where R can be an alkyl or aryl group and R′ also an alkyl or aryl group, or a hydrogen atom.   Initially, the acid coordinates with the available electron pair on the oxygen atom to yield a species that has a partial positive charge

$$\left[\begin{array}{c} R \\ \overset{\sigma^+}{\diagdown} \overset{\textstyle \cdot\cdot}{\underset{\diagup}{O}} : \text{Catalyst}^{\sigma^-} \\ R' \end{array} \right]$$

The ability to form such an entity will be a complex function of the electron-acceptor properties of the acid, the electron-donor properties of the substituted oxygen molecule, steric requirements of both substances and the environment surrounding the reacting molecules.

The electron-donor properties of the oxygen molecule depend

upon the nature of the substituted groups. As one proceeds from methoxide to *t*-butoxide ion, as an example, the oxygen basicity increases owing to increasing electron release of the substituting groups (1). However, if the groups become extremely bulky, the acid will have difficulty in coordinating due to F-strain (1). Questions concerning catalyst acidity are extremely complex. These questions depend not only on the inherent ability of the catalyst to coordinate with the unshared electron pair, but also on the solubility or miscibility of the catalyst–organic combination, ionic environment, etc. No standard catalyst activity series has been evolved in the ether or alcohol alkylation reaction.

Once the ionic complex is formed, it may undergo alkylation by a variety of mechanisms. Alternatively, an intermediate mechanism may occur in which the complex itself decomposes to yield an organic species that will, in turn, complex with more catalyst to form the reactive entity. The latter situation seems to be the case with $AlCl_3$ and primary alcohols which can yield alkyl halides as intermediates (2).

1. Carbonium-ion Reactions

No matter what the mode of generation, the conception of an ionic species seems best for purposes of interpretation of the experimental data. The ease of formation of the ionic entity will follow the well-established laws of carbonium-ion behavior. Benzyl-type ions are stable and readily formed, followed, in ease of formation, by tertiary, secondary, and primary alkyl ions. Once formed, the ionic entity can undergo the alkylation reaction as described in Section III or it can take part in numerous side reactions. Side reactions involving these ions are well established in fields such as isoparaffin–olefin alkylation, olefin polymerization, and paraffin isomerization. For example, alkyl carbonium ions can undergo proton loss leading to olefin formation:

$$\overset{+}{R}CHCH_2R' \rightleftharpoons RCH{=}CHR' + H^+ \tag{3}$$

The ion can also undergo intermolecular hydride abstraction to yield a paraffin (equation 4) or an intramolecular 1,2-shift involving

$$\overset{+}{R}CHCH_2R' \xrightarrow{\ H^-\ } RCH_2CH_2R' \tag{4}$$

either hydrogen (equation 5) or an alkyl group (equation 6) to generate a new ion. The driving force for the formation of these

$$\overset{+}{R}CHCH_2R' \xrightarrow{\ \sim H^-\ } RCH_2\overset{+}{C}HR' \tag{5}$$

$$\overset{+}{R}CHCHR' \xrightarrow{\ \sim R^-\ } \underset{\underset{R'}{|}}{R\!-\!CHCH_2}{}^+ \tag{6}$$

ions is the difference in ion stability and it is expected that a primary ion will tend to isomerize into a secondary ion which, in turn, will tend to isomerize into a tertiary structure. Hydrogen shifts within a molecule require less energy than skeletal isomerization and it is expected that the former will predominate.

In addition to such simple reactions as proton loss, hydride transfer, or 1,2-shifts, more complex reactions can occur. The olefin resulting from a proton-loss reaction may be alkylated by another ion to form a higher molecular weight intermediate. This intermediate can rearrange and undergo a β-scission reaction leading to a host of smaller fragments (equation 7).

β-Scission

$$\underset{\underset{C}{|}}{C\!-\!C}\overset{\overset{C}{|}}{\underset{}{}}\overset{\curvearrowleft}{}\overset{+}{C}\!-\!\overset{+}{C}\!-\!R \rightarrow \underset{\underset{C}{|}}{C\!-\!\overset{\overset{C}{|}}{C}}{}^+ + C\!=\!C\!-\!R \tag{7}$$

Each of these fragments, in turn, might be an alkylating agent thus leading to complex product mixtures. The original molecule can also undergo β-scission to generate a lower molecular weight ion or olefin which will also be a potential alkylating agent.

2. Aromatic Substitution

The compounds most often alkylated by alcohols and ethers in the presence of acids are the various aromatics. Before describing the aromatic alkylation reaction using alcohols and ethers, it is important to discuss the mechanism of this reaction. The nature of aromatic alkylation has been the subject of much controversy over the years. It is only in the past decade that knowledge obtained on the nature of the complexes of strong acids and aromatic systems has shed light on aromatic alkylation (3). These complexes are reviewed in Chapters VIII and XXIV and only a brief summary of the more salient points will be presented here.

Relative basicities of the alkyl aromatics have been measured in $HF\text{–}BF_3$ media where the reaction is presumed to involve aromatic protonation (4).

$$\text{Arene} + HF + BF_3 \rightleftharpoons \text{Arene } H^+ + BF_4^- \tag{8}$$

It has been found that an increase in the number of methyl substituents leads to an increase in aromatic basicity and that a marked enhancement of base character is developed in alkyl aromatics.

The interpretation which is now commonly accepted for these findings is that the aromatic ring is protonated to form a "σ-complex". In such a σ-complex, the proton has formed a bond directly to a ring carbon atom and is thereby distinguishable from a π-complex in which a weak electrophilic agent combines loosely with the ring electron cloud.

This situation is depicted as follows:

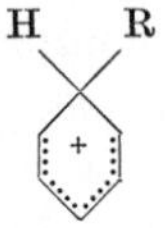

With two or more alkyl groups, additional resonance forms are possible owing to distribution of the positive charge to the alkyl groups. It has been recently possible to isolate such σ-complexes and this is discussed in Chapter VIII of this treatise. The isolation of these complexes and the fundamental measurements described above have been combined with reaction data so that aromatic alkylation and two competing side reactions, isomerization and disproportionation, are now understood in an overall mechanistic sense.

A. Alkylation, Isomerization, and Disproportionation

Acid-catalyzed aromatic alkylation involving alcohols and ethers is a subdivision of the general reaction category entitled electrophilic aromatic substitution. It has been shown that such substitution reactions are not single-stage replacements but go through an intermediate complex formation and that the rates of electrophilic substitution can be correlated with the stabilities of the σ-complexes formed by aromatic hydrocarbons (5). Thus, the transition state in substitution is probably similar to the picture of the stable σ-complex shown above.

These considerations lead to a rationale for the directive effects in electrophilic substitution. They are primarily the result of the entering reagent activity, stability of the σ-complex intermediate, and steric requirements. For example, a substituent on the ring that is electron-donating will enhance the stability of a σ-complex resulting from the addition of a reagent *ortho* or *para* to the substituent group. The opposite will result with an electron-attracting substituent group. Halogens are deactivating groups but have a resonance interaction with the ring so that they orient *ortho* and *para* in the σ-complex.

Steric effects are also important and anomalously low yields of *ortho*-substituted products are often caused by interference of non-bonded atoms (6).

In addition to the directive influence of the substituent group, a large body of confusing data has been cleared up by the suggestion of Brown and Nelson that the activity of the entering reagent is also important (7). A very reactive reagent will not be very selective since the stabilization provided by the σ-complex is outweighed by the entering group activity. This is quantitatively expressed by Brown in terms of the relative rates of substitution in the *meta*- or *para*-positions and called a partial rate factor (7).

The actual alkylation reaction can proceed by one of two mechanisms. In both mechanisms the first step involves a catalyst complex with the alkyl derivative to form a polarized intermediate.

$$RX + \text{Catalyst} \rightleftharpoons R^{\delta+} X \text{ Catalyst}^{\sigma-} \tag{9}$$

X = OH or OR′.

Easily ionized species, such as benzyl derivatives or tertiary alkyl groups, ionize directly to the corresponding carbonium ions (equation 10) and then add to the ring (equation 11). Primary and possibly secondary derivatives, however, probably react by an S_N2 displacement (equation 12).

Ionization

$$R^{\delta+} X \text{ Catalyst}^{\sigma-} \rightarrow R^{+} + X \text{ Catalyst}^{-} \tag{10}$$

$$X \text{ Catalyst}^{-} R^{+} + \bigcirc \rightarrow \bigoplus + X \text{ Catalyst}^{-} \tag{11}$$

Displacement

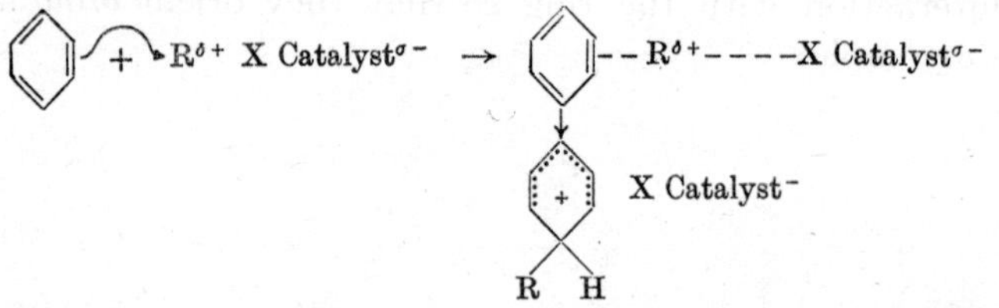

$$\text{⬡} + R^{\delta+} \text{ X Catalyst}^{\sigma-} \rightarrow \text{⬡} - - R^{\delta+} - - - - X \text{ Catalyst}^{\sigma-} \quad (12)$$

X Catalyst⁻ represented below:

R   H

Thus, if the polarization of the RX bond is complete or nearly complete before reaction, the reaction will exhibit low selectivity for the activated *ortho* and *para* ring positions and the selectivity will be independent of the nature of X and the catalyst. Allan and Yats studied a wide variety of catalysts and alkylating agents including olefins, alcohols, and halides, and found that the above generalization described the situation very well (8). Table I shows the *o-*, *m-*, and *p*-isomers at zero time found by Allan and Yats for a variety of catalysts in the methylation, ethylation, isopropylation, and *t*-butylation of toluene.

TABLE I. Alkylation of toluene

	Isomer distribution, %				
	p-	*m-*	*o-*	$\dfrac{2p}{m}$	Relative rates[d]
Methylation[a]	26	14	60	3.7	1.0
Ethylation[b]	34	18	48	3.8	13.7
Isopropylation[c]	36.5	21.5	42	3.4	20,000
t-Butylation	93	7	0	26.6	—

[a] $BF_3 \cdot P_2O_5/CH_3OH$, $AlBr_3/CH_3Br$, $AlCl_3/CH_3Cl$, $AlBr_3/CH_3I$.
[b] $BF_3 \cdot P_2O_5/C_2H_5OH$, $GaBr_3/C_2H_5Br$, $AlBr_3/C_2H_5Br$, $AlCl_3/C_2H_5Cl$, $AlBr_3/C_2H_5I$.
[c] $TiCl_4/iso\text{-}C_3H_7OH$, $AlBr_3/isoC_3H_7I$, $AlCl_3/C_3H_6$, $AlBr_3/C_3H_6$, $TiCl_4/C_3H_6$.
[d] Obtained for $GaBr_3$/alkyl bromide alkylations.

The high ratios of *para*-isomer composition to *meta*-isomer composition for the *t*-butylation of toluene shown above indicate a high selectivity and therefore a low reactivity. It is reasonable to envisage the known rapid rate of *t*-butylation as being due to the relatively large quantities of polarized *t*-alkyl species. These are relatively stable, however, and react with toluene in a more selective fashion than the corresponding reactions involving methylation, ethylation, and isopropylation. It is probable that reactions involving benzyl carbonium ions, which also give large amounts of *para*-derivatives, proceed in a fashion similar to *t*-butylation.

Finally, after the alkylating group has entered the ring, intermolecular migration of the groups or isomerization of the alkyl chain can occur. The former is termed disproportionation and again can proceed by one of two mechanisms. With secondary and tertiary alkyl groups it probably occurs by way of free alkyl carbonium ions (9). Primary alkyl groups transfer without rearrangement, however, and recent theory indicates that this is a step-transition from a σ-complex to a localized π-complex and then reaction of the π-complex with a free aromatic (10,11).

Allan and Yats (8) also showed that isomer distributions reported in the literature could be rationalized by assuming that isomerization of the substituent in question to another position on the ring had occurred. The kinetic equations used to calculate initial position attack are of the form:

$$O_{(t)} = O^* + Ae^{-\alpha t} + Be^{-\beta t} \tag{13}$$

$$P_{(t)} = O^* + Ce^{-\alpha t} + De^{-\beta t} \tag{14}$$

where $O_{(t)}$ is the concentration of *ortho*-isomer at time t, O is the equilibrium concentration of *ortho*-isomer, A and B are determined by the starting isomer distribution and α and β are evaluated from rate constant sets.

Such considerations do not take into account the large *meta*-isomer distributions that can be obtained when an excess of catalyst is used. This latter type of distribution is due to the enhanced stability of the σ-complex of the *meta*-isomer.

B. Conclusions

This discussion sets the stage for a general description of alkylation reactions using alcohols and ethers as alkylating agents. Such reactions using acid catalysts are expected to proceed *via* polarized complexes. These complexes may split into relatively free carbonium ions or they may be partially polarized and a discussion of carbonium-ion character only justified on the basis of overall product distribution. The alkylating agent can isomerize, crack, form olefins, or polymerize depending on well-known factors governing such ionic species. Finally, in aromatic alkylation the product will be a function of the degree of polarity of the bond, steric forces, and other considerations. Isomerization of the product may occur and, indeed, probably will occur if severe reaction conditions are used.

Thus, the alkylation reaction is complex and each case must be evaluated individually. However, with the above foundation this reviewer feels that most of the facts, while not always predictable, are usually interpretable.

III. Alkylation using Alcohols as Alkylating Agents

Alkylation reactions involving alcohols have been carried out since 1897. A wide variety of alcohols were studied experimentally including normal and branched-chain types, aromatic and olefinic alcohols and polycyclics. Almost any material that can be termed an acid has been used to catalyze the reaction. These include many Friedel-Crafts halides, several proton-donating acids, and a variety of oxides. Unfortunately, a single investigator has yet to choose a standard alkylation reaction and compare a variety of catalysts and conditions. Therefore, there is no standard catalyst activity or selectivity series that can be referred to with any degree of confidence.

1. Friedel-Crafts Halides

Two Friedel-Crafts halides, aluminum chloride and boron fluoride, have been extensively used in alkylation reactions involving alcohols as alkylating agents. Other less reactive halides as zinc or iron chloride have been also used, but to a lesser extent. The following section covers the former catalytic systems in some detail and the latter ones in a rather cursory manner. The first system discussed is boron fluoride since it has received the most thorough attention.

A. Alkylation by Alcohols, using Boron Fluoride

Systems composed of BF_3 have been extensively studied as alkylation catalysts (12). It seems reasonable to start a discussion of the BF_3 catalyzed alcohol alkylation reaction by a description of the complexes that may be formed between the halide and the alcohol. Coordination compounds of BF_3 with alcohols are very likely formed as intermediate products in all reactions in which BF_3 is used as a catalyst. Compounds of this type are almost always strong acids and extremely active catalysts for a variety of reactions such as olefin–isoparaffin alkylation, aromatic–olefin alkylation, and diolefin polymerization (12). The addition compounds are usually liquids or difficult to crystallize solid substances which are readily decomposed by water.

The coordination compounds that may be formed with boron trifluoride are mainly of two types, $BF_3 \cdot ROH$ and $BF_3 \cdot 2ROH$ (13)

and these are strong acids but are weaker than the hydrates of boron trifluoride (14). Electrical conductivity studies show that $BF_3 \cdot CH_3OH$ can be regarded as methoxyfluoroboric acid $(CH_3OBF_3)^- H^+$ and that $BF_3 \cdot C_2H_5OH$ can be regarded as $(C_2H_5OBF_3)^- H^+$ (15). In addition, a compound $BF_3 \cdot 2C_2H_5OH$ was detected which was shown to be as strong as sulfuric acid. In relation to these protonic alkoxyfluoroboric acids, alcohols behave as bases and form salts (16) (equation 15).

$$[BF_3OR^-]H^+ + ROH \rightarrow [BF_3OR^-][RH_2O]^+ \qquad (15)$$

The thermal stability of the coordination compounds in the primary alcohol series decreases as their molecular weight increases (17). This series has also been studied using n.m.r. techniques with similar conclusions (18). As the carbon skeleton changes from primary to tertiary, the thermal stability also decreases (17). This would fall in line with ease of carbonium-ion formation followed by proton elimination resulting in olefin production. As an example, the coordination compounds of BF_3 with secondary alcohols are very unstable and on distillation form olefins which polymerize. Primary alcohols on distillation are reported to give alcoholates and this is depicted with ethyl alcohol (19) in equation 16.

$$7BF_3 + 7C_2H_5OH \rightarrow C_2H_5OBF_2 + 3BF_3 \cdot O(C_2H_5)_2 + 2HBF_4 + 2HF + H_3BO_3 \qquad (16)$$

The question of the alkylating species in the alcohol alkylation reaction is important. Possible intermediates together with their precursors are shown in Table II. Row one indicates an oxyfluoro-

TABLE II. Alkylation precursors

Precursors	Intermediates
1. $ROH + BF_3$	$R^+ \ O\overline{H}BF_3$
2. $H^+[BF_3OR^-] + ROH$	$[BF_3OR^-][RH_2O^+]$
3. $[ROBF_3]$	RF

boric acid intermediate. With a primary alcohol, the oxyfluoroboric acid might be largely unionized and have a very low formal charge on the R group. With an iso-alcohol, however, the R group may carry a high formal charge and act as a typical ion. The second row shows a salt as the intermediate and here it is expected that $[RH_2O^+]$ could be the active species. Finally, a breakdown of the alcoholate could lead to alkyl fluorides (row 3) which are known to be effective alkylating agents in the presence of BF_3 (20). The evidence does not clearly allow a differentiation of these three paths. However, as described in the section on general mechanisms, a polarized complex of the type shown in row 1 is most useful to describe the phenomena. (For a more detailed discussion of the alcohol–boron trifluoride complexes see Chapters VI and VIII.)

a. Alkylation of benzene and phenol and their homologs

Early work on the alkylation of benzene was carried out in 1937 by McKenna and Sowa (21) who found a mixture of mono-, di-, and polyalkylbenzenes on heating a mixture of alcohol, benzene, and BF_3 at 60° for six hours. Also, they determined that secondary alkylbenzenes are formed from normal, primary, and secondary alcohols and that tertiary alcohols yield tertiary alkylbenzenes. Such isomerization of alkyl groups is in accord with a polarized alcohol–catalyst complex in which isomerization may occur to yield the more stable ionic entity.

Dialkylbenzenes are also found and these are mainly *para*-isomers with small quantities of the *ortho*-derivatives (22). Welsh and Hennion alkylated toluene and ethylbenzene with different alcohols using BF_3 and P_2O_5 (23). They reported the sole formation of *para*-dialkylbenzenes. A more recent study by Serijan *et al.*, however, on the alkylation of toluene with *t*-butyl alcohol in the presence of BF_3 and $AlCl_3$ gave different results (24). The latter investigators used a distillation column with an efficiency of 100 theoretical plates and found that both *para*- and *meta-t*-butyl toluenes are formed in approximately equal quantities. When $AlCl_3$ is used, the *meta*-isomer is obtained in considerably larger quantities than the *para*-isomer and no *ortho*-isomer is detected at all. Lack of *ortho*-isomer can be attributed to steric effects and production of the *para*- and *meta*-isomer falls in line with the selectivity factors mentioned in Section II-2. The enchanced *meta*-isomer formation from $AlCl_3$ is probably the result of further isomerization of the alkylated product.

Sowa *et al.* (25) also showed that neither methyl nor ethyl alcohol react with phenol in the presence of BF_3 on heating at atmospheric pressure. Both react at 170° in a sealed tube and the main product consists of alkylphenyl ethers and only small amounts of alkylphenols. At 115° normal and isopropyl alcohols are reported by Sowa *et al.* to give an identical product with phenol and BF_3—the isopropyl ether of 2,4-diisopropylphenol.

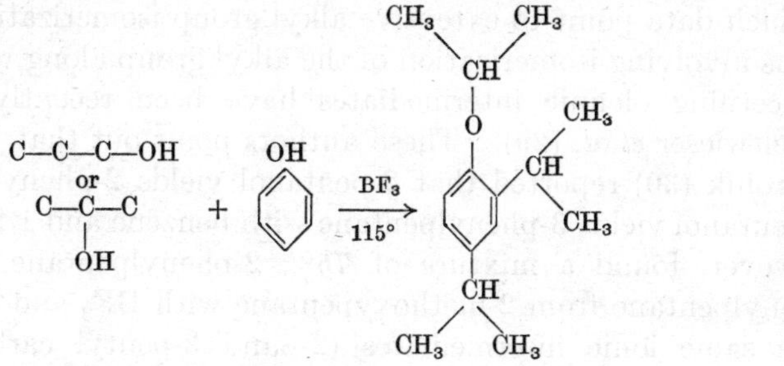

$$
\begin{array}{c}
\text{C—C—C—OH} \\
\text{or} \\
\underset{\underset{\text{OH}}{|}}{\text{C—C—C}}
\end{array}
+
\text{(benzene)}
\xrightarrow[115°]{\text{BF}_3}
\text{(product)}
\qquad (16)
$$

The authors consider that the above reaction takes place *via* intermediate alkene formation as follows:

$$C_nH_{2n+1}OH \rightarrow C_nH_{2n} + H_2O$$

$$C_6H_5OH + C_nH_{2n} \rightarrow C_6H_5OC_nH_{2n+1} \qquad (17)$$

They do not feel that an ether intermediate isomerizes to form the alkylated product. Phenol has also been methylated in the nucleus using a boron fluoride saturated methyl alcohol system (26).

When benzene is alkylated, it is often helpful to add promoters to the BF_3–alcohol mixtures (27,28). These promoters include P_2O_5, H_2SO_4, H_3PO_4, and $C_6H_5 \cdot SO_3H$. It has been stated that the primary reason for the addition of these reagents is their ability to aid in the dehydration of the alcohol. A second and perhaps more important role with most of the additives is the function of proton activity enhancement. This might come about by the addition of the BF_3 molecule to an oxygen atom with a consequent increase in the proton acidity:

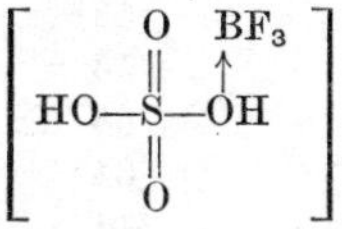

$$
\left[
\begin{array}{c}
\text{O} \quad \text{BF}_3 \\
\parallel \quad \uparrow \\
\text{HO—S—OH} \\
\parallel \\
\text{O}
\end{array}
\right]
\qquad (18)
$$

An example of this enhancement is shown by the addition of 0.5 mole of H_2SO_4 to 0.5 mole of n-butyl alcohol in the presence of 0.5 mole of benzene and 0.5 mole of BF_3. At room temperature, a 37% yield of the isomerized product, s-butylbenzene, is obtained. No reaction occurs without sulfuric acid addition. The addition of H_3PO_4 also yields an effective alkylation catalyst and the alkylation of benzene with propyl and butyl alcohols using $BF_3 \cdot H_3PO_4$ has been accomplished. Conditions were worked out for the pre-domination of the monoalkyl product and this is the isomerized isopropyl or s-butyl derivative.

Such data point to extensive alkyl group isomerization and questions involving isomerization of the alkyl group along with problems concerning olefinic intermediates have been recently studied by Streitwieser *et al.* (29). These authors point out that Hennion and Pieronik (30) reported that 2-pentanol yields 2-phenylpentane and 3-pentanol yields 3-phenylpentane with benzene and BF_3. Burwell, however, found a mixture of 75% 2-phenylpentane and 25% 3-phenylpentane from 2-methoxypentane with BF_3 and benzene (31). The same ionic intermediates (2- and 3-pentyl carbonium ions) would be expected from both alkylating agents. In order to study this dichotomy, a large excess of benzene was used to minimize production of dialkylated products and a few drops of water were added with the primary alcohols (29).

It was conclusively shown that *n*-propyl and *n*-butyl alcohols give isopropyl and *s*-butylbenzenes, respectively. Ethanol does not react. Amyl alcohols react to give mixtures of monoalkylated products. Rate-wise, the secondary alcohols alkylate at a much higher rate than the primary alcohols. Rearrangements, therefore, are general and are sometimes apparently rather deep-seated. This is illustrated by Table III.

TABLE III. Reaction products from benzene, boron fluoride, and the amyl alcohols

	Temp., °C	Product composition,* %			
		2-Phenyl-pentane	3-Phenyl-pentane	*t*-Amyl-benzene	Other
1-Pentanol	60	53	20	25	3
2-Pentanol	60	55	21	13	11
2-Pentanol	0	66	23	9	2
3-Pentanol	0	64	23	10	3
3-Methyl-1-butanol	60	14	2	81	3
2-Methyl-1-butanol	60	20	4	75	2
Neopentyl alcohol	60	≤4	<1	≥96	0
3-Methyl-2-butanol	0	10	<1	88	28

* Results are by mass spectroscopy only. For complete analysis see original paper (29).

Within experimental error, 2-pentanol and 3-pentanol give identical product mixtures. The ratio of 2-phenylpentane to 3-phenylpentane (2.6) may be compared with ratios found in other systems in Table IV.

TABLE IV.   2-Phenylpentane/3-phenylpentane ratios

Alkylating agent	Catalyst	Ratio	Ref.
Ethylcyclopropane	HF ⎫		
Ethylcyclopropane	H_2SO_4 ⎬	1.7	32
Ethylcyclopropane	$AlCl_3$ ⎭		
2-Pentanol	$AlCl_3$	1.5	33
3-Pentanol	$AlCl_3$	3.2	33
2-Methoxypentane	BF_3	3.0	31

All values are close to the equilibrium values of 2.5 found for the acid-catalyzed isomerization of 2- or 3-phenylpentane (34). It is clear that carbonium-ion type intermediates are involved and a rearrangement represented by $C\overset{+}{-}C\overset{}{-}C\overset{}{-}C\overset{}{-}C \rightleftharpoons C\overset{}{-}C\overset{+}{-}C\overset{}{-}C$ must be rapid compared to the alkylation step.

Since *t*-amylbenzene is also found, skeletal isomerization must

$$C\overset{+}{-}C\overset{+}{-}C-C-C \rightleftharpoons \overset{+}{C}-\underset{\underset{H}{|}}{\overset{\overset{C}{|}}{C}}-C-C \rightleftharpoons C-\overset{\overset{C}{|}}{\underset{+}{C}}-C-C \tag{19}$$

occur.   Starting with the *t*-amyl ion precursor, *t*-amyl alcohol, how-ever, only a polymeric olefin was obtained.   Neopentyl alcohol, on the other hand, gives pure *t*-amylbenzene and this difference between amyl alcohols is probably associated with differences in π- or σ-complex stabilities of the aromatic ring system.

Finally, optically active 2-methyl-1-butanol gives only racemic product.   This extensive racemization has been found by other investigators in similar systems.   As discussed by Burwell, such racemization could occur even in a stereoselective process if the ion isomerization was rapid, *i.e.*,

$$\begin{bmatrix} C\overset{+}{-}C-C-C \\ \updownarrow \\ C-C\overset{+}{-}C-C-C \end{bmatrix} \tag{20}$$

compared to the alkylation step.

A second paper by Streitwieser *et al.* demonstrates that benzene is involved in the rate-determining alkylation step (35).   1-Pentanol and BF_3 which do not react in pentane solution react when benzene or hexamethylbenzene is added.   In the former case alkylate is obtained and in the latter case polymeric olefins are produced.   It

17*

was also shown that at 0° some secondary alcohols do not involve
significant reaction *via* an olefinic intermediate. Thus, the alkylation of benzene with 2-butanol-*d* at 0° gave 2-phenylbutane with no
deuterium substitution. If a significant amount of alkylation
proceeded by way of carbonium ions produced *via* butene, partially
deuterated product would be expected because of the following
reactions :

$$C_4H_9OD \cdot BF_3 \longrightarrow C_4H_8 + HOD \cdot BF_3$$

$$C_4H_9{}^+ + BF_3OD{}^- \qquad C_4H_8D{}^+ + BF_3OH{}^- \tag{21}$$

In addition, the reaction of 2-propanol-1-*d* with benzene at 0°
gives 2-phenylpropane-1-*d*, with no observable loss or rearrangement
of deuterium. Finally, no propene could be detected in the exit
gases from an alkylation of benzene with isopropyl alcohol at 0°.
This falls in line with earlier results of Price and Ciskowski (36) who
found that cyclohexanol does not form olefins with BF_3 under
conditions at which alkylation occurs.

At higher temperatures (60°) the alkylation of benzene with 2-
pentanol-*d* gives an alkylation product containing a considerable
amount of deuterium. This does not prove that an olefin is an
intermediate in the alkylation reaction since the following equilibrium can be envisaged:

$$ROH \cdot BF_3 \rightleftharpoons R^+ + BF_3OH \rightleftharpoons Olefin + H_2O \cdot BF_3 \tag{22}$$
$$\text{Product} \qquad \text{Product} \qquad \text{Product}$$

If rapid equilibrium among the three species is established compared to the alkylation rates, then the product could contain
deuterium although the olefin is not directly involved in the alkylation step.

These results can be discussed in terms of the aromatic substitution reaction mechanism outlined in the preceding section. Streitwieser *et al.* have suggested the mechanistic scheme shown in
Chart I.

With tertiary alcohols, which are readily formed, reaction occurs
primarily or entirely by path A. Path A is also important with
secondary alcohols and some primary alcohols at elevated temperatures as shown by the deuterium tracing studies. With some
secondary alcohols at lower temperatures reactions can occur
through formation of complex I. Straight-chain secondary alcohols
in benzene at 0° proceed entirely by path C. Strong evidence for

Chart I

Mechanism of boron fluoride–alcohol alkylation

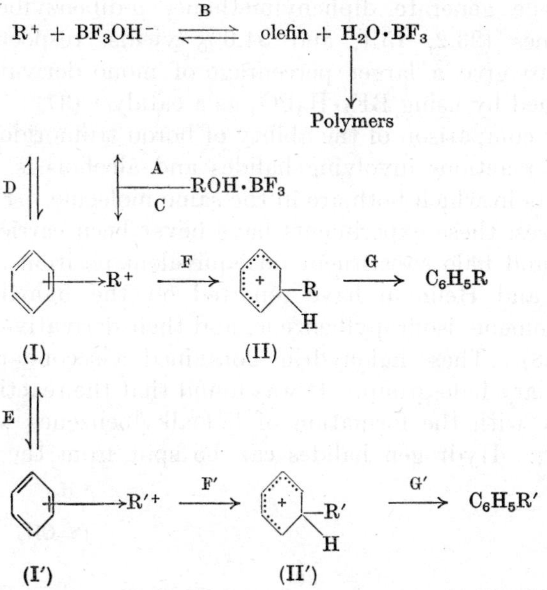

$$R^+ + BF_3OH^- \underset{B}{\overset{}{\rightleftharpoons}} \text{olefin} + H_2O \cdot BF_3$$

$$\downarrow$$

Polymers

$$\underset{C}{\overset{A}{\longleftrightarrow}} ROH \cdot BF_3$$

(I) $\xrightarrow{F}$ (II) $\xrightarrow{G}$ C_6H_5R

(I') $\xrightarrow{F'}$ (II') $\xrightarrow{G'}$ C_6H_5R'

the rate-determining nature of step C is given by the hexaethylbenzene results which also show that such π-complexes are important. The nature of the leaving group and its degree of tightness are left unanswered.

The identity of the product mixture from 2-pentanol and 3-pentanol together with their non-rearrangement in the absence of benzenes necessitates that the isomerization reaction, E, be much faster than the product-determining alkylation reaction, F. This suggests that 1 and 1′ are π-complexes retaining much carbonium-ion character. When the rearranged cation 1′ is of approximately equal or greater stability than 1, the rearrangement E is more rapid than F or F′. Since neopentyl alcohol yields t-amylbenzene while t-amyl alcohol only forms polymer, F and F′ must be faster than D. The differences in product are probably due to unknown differences in the manner in which the two alcohols are complexed to benzene. Primary alcohols are slow owing to the difficulty of forming primary ions. Since propyl alcohol reacts while ethanol does not, the driving force in the former case may be partially due to formation of the isopropyl carbonium ion. While not studied in this work, aromatic alcohols should also work well. As expected, aromatic alcohols are excellent alkylating agents in the alkylation reaction using boron fluoride (21,37). For example, benzyl alcohol and benzene generate diphenylmethane, p-dibenzylbenzene, and polybenzenes (23.2, 15.1, and 34.0% yields, respectively) (21). Reaction to give a larger percentage of mono derivative may be accomplished by using $BF_3 \cdot H_3PO_4$ as a catalyst (37).

A direct comparison of the ability of boron trifluoride to catalyze alkylation reactions involving halides and alcohols is afforded by experiments in which both are in the same molecule. For comparison purposes, these experiments have never been carried out using hydroxyl and halo substituent on equivalent positions. However, Bachman and Hellman have reported on the haloalkylation of benzene, toluene, isopropylbenzene, and their derivatives with halohydrins (38). These halohydrins contained a secondary hydroxyl and a primary halo group. It was found that the reaction proceeds exclusively with the formation of haloalkylbenzenes with a yield of 30–50%. Hydrogen halides can be split from the compounds

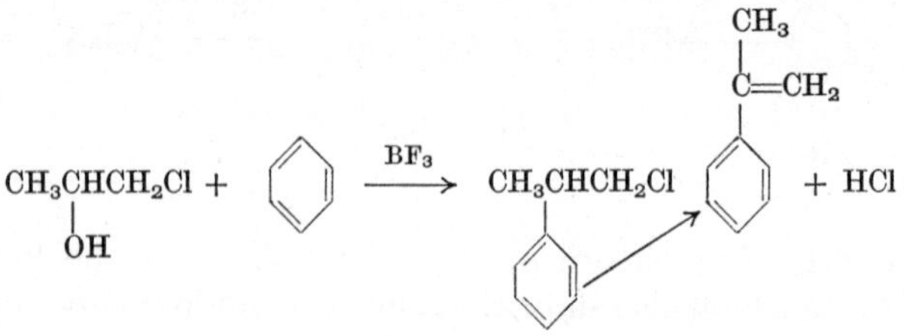

$$CH_3CHCH_2Cl + \underset{OH}{} \bigcirc \xrightarrow{BF_3} CH_3CHCH_2Cl \cdots + HCl \qquad (23)$$

studied and α-methylstyrenes obtained (equation 23). This synthesis has been applied to a variety of aromatics and halohydrins. A further reaction could obviously be carried out with $AlCl_3$ and a suitable compound to give a new Friedel-Crafts reaction as shown in equation 24. This is an intriguing use of a combined

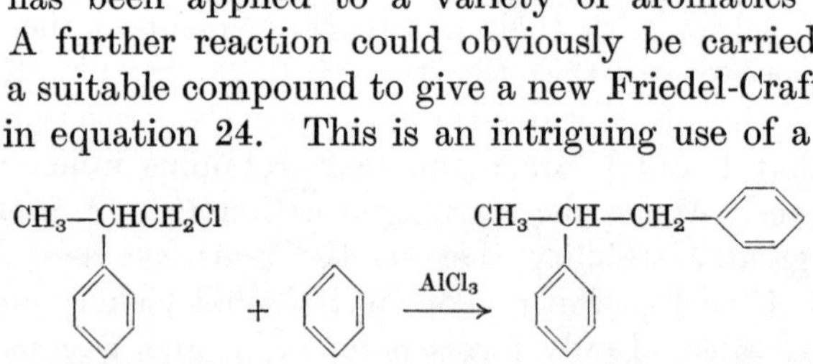

$$CH_3{-}CHCH_2Cl \quad + \quad \bigcirc \xrightarrow{AlCl_3} CH_3{-}CH{-}CH_2{-}\bigcirc \qquad (24)$$

system composed of BF_3 and $AlCl_3$ or other suitable catalyst sequences.

b. Alkylation of naphthalene and other polycyclic aromatics

The alkylation of naphthalene is discussed in greater detail in Section III-3-B. Boron fluoride is used as a catalyst for this alkylation and the substituent usually enters the β-position (36,39,40). For example, β-alkylnaphthalenes are obtained from isopropyl, t-butyl, and cyclohexyl alcohols. Higher alcohols alkylate naphthalene but, here, P_2O_5, H_2SO_4, or $C_6H_5 \cdot SO_3H$ may be needed. Partial rate and selectivity factors point to the α-carbon atom as the most active in nucleophilic substitution (Section III-3-B). The formation of the β-isomer can be due either to steric effects involving bulky catalyst complexes or to initial alkylation at the α-position followed by isomerization to the less active β-position. Price and Ciskowski (36) first pointed out that benzyl derivatives cause alkylation at the α-position and this may be due to the ready ionization of benzyl derivatives to a relatively free benzyl carbonium ion which may not be sterically blocked from alkylating at the α-position.

Isomerization has been noted by Romadin in the alkylation of naphthalene with alcohols in the presence of the molecular addition compounds $2ROH \cdot BF_3$ at 165–170° (41). The alcohols studied were isopropyl, isobutyl, and isoamyl. The mono- and dialkyl naphthalenes were made in 10–48% yield. However, in the cases of isobutyl and isoamyl the products were the tertiary naphthalenes. Again, the attacking agent could be pictured as an alkyl carbonium ion (equation 25).

$$C-\overset{\overset{\displaystyle C}{|}}{C}-C-OH + BF_3 \rightarrow \left[C-\overset{\overset{\displaystyle C}{|}}{C}-C^+ \right] BF_3OH^- \qquad (25)$$

$$\left[C-\overset{\overset{\displaystyle C}{|}}{C}-C^+ \right] BF_3OH^- \rightleftharpoons \left[C-\overset{\overset{\displaystyle C}{|}}{\underset{+}{C}}-C \right] BF_3OH^- \qquad (26)$$

$$\downarrow$$

Product

The postulate of olefin formation has been invoked but there seems to be no proof of this intermediate. Using normal alcohols in the presence of BF_3, Romadin obtained alkylnaphthalenes in 88–98% yields. These were mixtures of 1- and 2-alkylnaphthalenes and no isomerization of the alkyl group occurred so that only the normal product was received.

c. Alkylation of esters

Esters containing an active α-hydrogen atom can be alkylated by alcohols in the presence of boron fluoride catalysts (42,43,44,45).

The reaction was uncovered by Hauser and Breslow and applied to acetoacetic ester and various alcohols. The alcohols studied were isopropyl, t-butyl, cyclohexyl, n-butyl, s-butyl, and isobutyl. Acetoacetic ester and, more recently, malonic ester were also studied. The latter compound was alkylated with ethylene oxide using $AlCl_3$ (46) as described in a later section.

The alkylation of these β-keto esters depends on the activity of both components. Both s- and t-alcohols are capable of alkylating acetoacetic ester in the presence of BF_3, whereas aliphatic primary alcohols are not. Product formation leads to α-derivative as shown in equation 27.

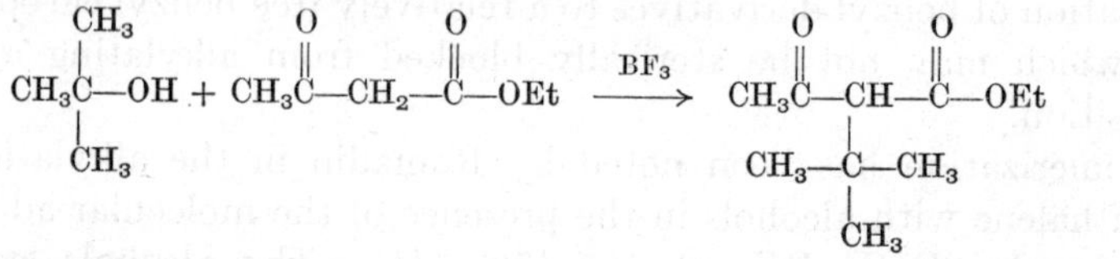

$$
\underset{\underset{CH_3}{|}}{CH_3\overset{CH_3}{\underset{|}{C}}-OH} + CH_3\overset{O}{\overset{\|}{C}}-CH_2-\overset{O}{\overset{\|}{C}}-OEt \quad \xrightarrow{BF_3} \quad CH_3\overset{O}{\overset{\|}{C}}-\underset{\underset{CH_3}{|}}{\underset{CH_3-\overset{|}{C}-CH_3}{CH}}-\overset{O}{\overset{\|}{C}}-OEt \tag{27}
$$

It is usually difficult to introduce such bulky alkyl groups into methylene positions and this represents an elegant technique for accomplishing such introduction. The reaction mechanism is somewhat obscure but it may be considered to involve a nucleophilic attack of the enolate form of the acetoacetic ester on the polarized alcohol complex. A transesterification reaction can occur and in

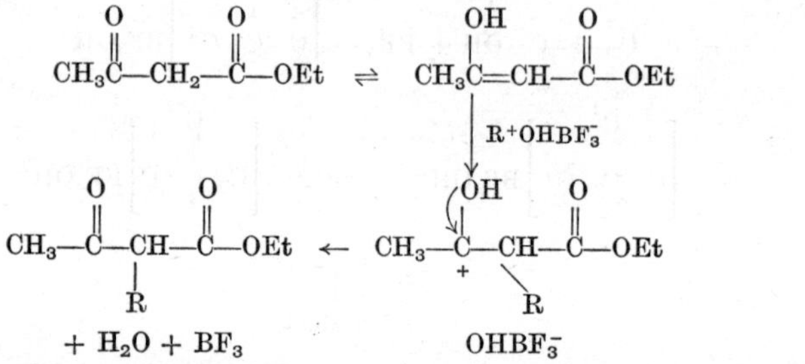

$$
CH_3\overset{O}{\overset{\|}{C}}-CH_2-\overset{O}{\overset{\|}{C}}-OEt \quad \rightleftharpoons \quad CH_3\overset{OH}{\overset{|}{C}}=CH-\overset{O}{\overset{\|}{C}}-OEt \tag{28}
$$

$$
\downarrow R^+OHBF_3^-
$$

$$
CH_3-\overset{O}{\overset{\|}{C}}-\underset{R}{\underset{|}{CH}}-\overset{O}{\overset{\|}{C}}-OEt \quad \leftarrow \quad CH_3-\overset{OH}{\overset{|}{C}}-\underset{R}{\underset{+}{\underset{|}{CH}}}-\overset{O}{\overset{\|}{C}}-OEt \tag{29}
$$

$$
+ H_2O + BF_3 \qquad\qquad OHBF_3^-
$$

the above reaction some t-butyl α-t-butylacetoacetate may form. (An alternate mechanism is suggested in Chapter XLVII.)

d. Miscellaneous

Most amines coordinate with BF_3 forming stable coordination compounds and deactivate the catalyst. A patent claims that a large excess of an alcohol can be used to alkylate aniline at elevated temperatures using BF_3 (47). A patent also claims that fluoroboric acid plus BF_3 ($H_3BO_2F_2 + BF_3$) is a useful catalyst for the alkylation of thiophene with alcohols (48). The example given shows a

3% yield of *t*-butylthiophene (based on *t*-butanol charged) at 65° from *t*-butanol and thiophene.

B. Alkylation by Alcohols using AlCl₃

Aluminum chloride is readily available and convenient to use. It is a standard reagent for the organic chemist and has been extensively used for a wide variety of acid-catalyzed reactions. These reactions include isoparaffin–olefin alkylation, aromatic alkylation with olefins, alcohols, and halides, and olefin and diolefin polymerization, etc. The mode of action of aluminum chloride, however, is notoriously difficult to determine. For example, trace amounts of moisture, oxygen, or organic halides are known to serve as potent cocatalysts. Because of these factors most of the experimental work involving this halide is of the more descriptive kind and is mainly concerned with product distributions from various reactants.

a. Alkylation of benzene and phenol and their homologs

Aluminum chloride has been used extensively; however, even with this much-used catalyst, the reaction mechanism is somewhat obscure. At first, it was believed that only "activated" molecules such as benzyl alcohol could be utilized (49). Primary alcohols were felt to be too unreactive and secondary alcohols were reported to react with difficulty. The alkylation reaction was found to be critically dependent on the reagent proportions involved and the temperature used (50). Thus, at 25–30° with the molar ratios of aromatic, alcohol, and aluminum chloride of 1:1:0.5 little or no reaction occurs with primary alcohols. If the amount of aluminum chloride is increased to two moles/mole of reactant and the temperature is raised, alkylation takes place. The suggestion was made that alcoholates of the primary and secondary alcohols are first formed, and that these react further (2,50,51). This situation is shown below with respect to the alkylation of phenol:

$$ROH + AlCl_3 \rightarrow ROAlCl_2 + HCl \tag{30}$$

$$C_6H_5OH + AlCl_3 \rightarrow C_6H_5OAlCl_2 + HCl \tag{31}$$

$$C_6H_5OAlCl_2 + ROAlCl_2 \xrightarrow{\text{HCl}} C_6H_5OR + AlCl_3 + AlCl_2OH \tag{32}$$

$$C_6H_5OR + ROH + AlCl_3 \rightarrow RC_6H_5OR + AlCl_2(OH) + HCl \tag{33}$$

In steps 30 and 31, metal alcoholates and phenolates are formed with the alcohols and ethers respectively, explaining the need for excess AlCl₃. These then react in step 32 to yield an ether which is alkylated in turn in step 33 by more alcohol. The ether can generate the phenol *via* the following paths, all of which have been demonstrated (52,53,54).

$$RC_6H_4OR + HCl \rightarrow RC_6H_4OH + RCl \tag{34}$$

$$RC_6H_4OR + C_6H_5OH \rightarrow 2RC_6H_4OH \tag{35}$$

$$2RC_6H_4OR \rightarrow RC_6H_4OH + R_2C_6H_3OR \tag{36}$$

The actual alkylation, step 33, may proceed *via* alkyl halide formation, step 37. This reaction has been demonstrated by Norris (2) and is used as a synthetic technique for alkyl halide

$$AlCl_2OR \rightarrow RCl + AlOCl \tag{37}$$

production. The resulting alkyl halide can obviously participate in an alkylation reaction *via* the intermediate complex $R^+AlCl_4^-$. Illari (55) has criticized Norris and Sturgis (2) and Huston and Friedemann (56,57) for their suggestion that halides are intermediates in either aliphatic or aromatic alkylations (equations 38 to 40).

$$C_2H_5OH + AlCl_3 \rightarrow C_2H_5OH{-}AlCl_3 \rightarrow C_2H_5OAlCl_2 + HCl + C_2H_5Cl + AlOHCl_2 \tag{38}$$

$$C_2H_5OH + C_6H_6 + AlCl_3 \rightarrow C_2H_5C_6H_5 + HCl + AlOHCl_2 \tag{39}$$

$$C_6H_5CH_2OH + AlCl_3 \xrightarrow{\text{Above } 40°C} C_6H_5CH_2Cl \tag{40}$$

For example, Illari is not convinced that $C_6H_5CH_2Cl$ is an intermediate in the aromatic alkylation reaction since it is only obtained at temperatures above 40°C. He finds that at low temperatures, polybenzyl alcohol is made from benzyl alcohol and benzene over $AlCl_3$.

The reaction mechanisms depicted in equations 41 to 43 were proposed.

$$ROH \xrightarrow[-HCl]{AlCl_3} ROAlCl_2 \xrightarrow[-Al(OH)Cl_2]{+C_6H_5} RC_6H_5 \tag{41}$$

$$ROH \xrightarrow[-HCl]{+AlCl_3} ROAlCl_2 \xrightarrow{-OAlCl} RCl \xrightarrow[-HCl]{AlCl_3 + C_6H_6} C_6H_5R \tag{42}$$

$$R'CH_2CR''R'''OH \xrightarrow[-HCl]{AlCl_3} R'CH_2CR''R'''OAlCl_2$$

$$R'CH_2 + C_6H_5R''R''' \xleftarrow{AlCl_3 + C_6H_6} R'CH{:}CR''R''' \tag{43}$$

Uncertainties arise, however, in comparing data and in assuming that the conditions which favored retention of the alkyl halide–aluminum chloride complex would necessarily yield the same results as those obtained by previous investigators who worked at conditions that could yield the volatile alkyl halide. This question has not been resolved completely satisfactorily and it is probable that a number of different complexes can be involved in the alkylation step depending on the structure of the alcohol (*i.e.*, primary, secondary, tertiary, or benzyl) and the activity of the substance to be alkylated.

When the alkylating agents are benzyl, secondary, and tertiary alcohols, a complex that is more polar than one involving primary alcohols probably forms, since the former species yields more stable carbonium ions. With such alcohols, alkylation without excess $AlCl_3$ at mild conditions is possible. Even with tertiary alcohols the use of excess $AlCl_3$ is usually advantageous and Huston presented evidence showing that the reaction terminates when $AlCl_3$ becomes hydrated to such an extent that it no longer forms a bond to the alcoholic oxygen (58). Presumably, this hydration occurs through a reaction such as equation 44.

$$ROH + AlCl_3 \rightarrow R^+ OH\bar{A}Cl_3 \rightarrow R^+ + \left[HOA\bar{l}Cl_3 \right] \quad (44)$$

$$HO^- + AlCl_3 \quad Al(OH)Cl_2 + Cl^-$$

R = tertiary alkyl group.

The hydrated aluminum chlorides are apparently not as effective as $AlCl_3$ in maintaining an alkylation reaction.

The question of alkyl group isomerization using $AlCl_3$ has been studied by many investigators. Pines *et al.* investigated isomerization accompanying the alkylation of benzene over $AlCl_3$. These authors used 2- and 3-pentanol and found that 2- and 3-phenylpentanes are produced (33)

$$CH_3CH_2CHCH_2CH_3 + C_6H_6 \xrightarrow[25-35°]{AlCl_3} C_6H_5CHCH_2CH_2CH_3 + C_6H_5CH \quad (45)$$

with CH_3, OH, 76%, CH_2CH_3, CH_2CH_3, 24%

$$CH_3CHCH_2CH_2CH_3 + C_6H_6 \xrightarrow[25-35°]{AlCl_3} C_6H_5CHCH_2CH_2CH_3 + C_6H_5CH \quad (46)$$

with CH_3, OH, 60%, CH_2CH_3, CH_2CH_3, 40%

This reaction is certainly interpretable on the basis of a rapid isomerization of 2- and 3-pentyl carbonium ions as discussed in the section on boron fluoride catalysis. These results differ from the earlier work of Huston and Hsieh who reported only 2-phenylpentane (49).

Ipatieff, Pines, and Schmerling (59) found that neopentyl alcohol on refluxing with benzene over $AlCl_3$ for eight hours gives only a 9% yield of neopentylbenzene. Neopentyl chloride, however, gives a 24% yield of 2-methyl-3-phenylbutane. The alcohol–$AlCl_3$ complex is obviously not polar enough to undergo an isomerization reaction. With a primary alcohol, the reaction path probably involves a bimolecular reaction between benzene and the ionized

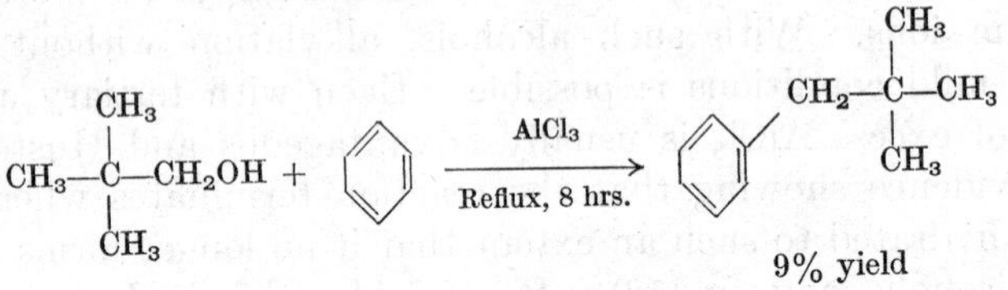

(47)

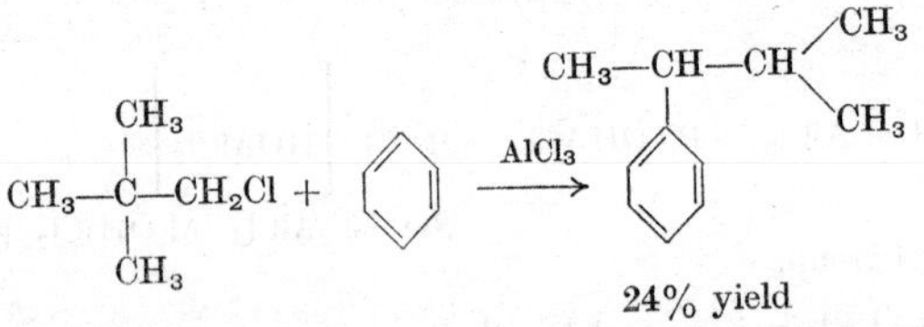

9% yield

(48)

24% yield

alcohol–$AlCl_3$ complex. The neopentyl halide–$AlCl_3$ complex must be considerably more ionic and here alkyl group shift occurs.

It is interesting to compare the effect of boron fluoride and $AlCl_3$ on aromatic alkylation using neopentyl alcohol. As reported in Section III-1-A, boron fluoride forms t-amylbenzene while $AlCl_3$ only forms small quantities of the unrearranged product. This difference in reaction products could arise from a difference in the degree of polarization within the alcohol–catalyst complexes. It is also possible to discuss the difference in terms of π- or σ-complex stabilities and there are not enough data to justify either extreme.

The question of alkyl group degradation and rearrangement was studied and a reactive aromatic such as phenol can undergo alkylation with certain complex tertiary alcohols with little or no side reactions (60,67). Benzene with complex tertiary alcohols, however, forms products that usually arise by degradation of the alkyl group (58,60–69). These results are interpretable by assuming that positive ionic alkyl intermediates are present and that these are derived from the alcohol–catalyst complex. Phenol is relatively active in electrophilic substitution and the alkyl ion reacts as soon as it forms. Benzene, however, is not as reactive and thus the alkyl ion has a longer life and can undergo competing side reactions.

$$\underset{\text{OH}}{\bigcirc} + CH_3-\underset{}{\overset{CH_3}{\underset{|}{CH}}}-\underset{\underset{OH}{|}}{\overset{CH_3}{\underset{|}{C}}}-\overset{CH_3}{\underset{|}{CH}}-CH_3 \xrightarrow{AlCl_3} \quad \begin{array}{l}\text{60\% yield of alkyl phenol} \\ \text{with no evidence of fragmentation}\end{array} \quad (49)$$

$$\underset{}{\bigcirc} + CH_3-\overset{CH_3}{\underset{|}{CH}}-\underset{\underset{OH}{|}}{\overset{CH_3}{\underset{|}{C}}}-\overset{CH_3}{\underset{|}{CH}}-CH_3 \xrightarrow{AlCl_3} \quad \begin{array}{l}\text{10\% of 5-octylbenzene—main} \\ \text{product from rearrangement and} \\ \text{fragmentation}\end{array} \quad (50)$$

In line with this hypothesis it is known that ring deactivation leads to rearranged and cracked products. Acetophenone which is a less active nucleophilic agent than either benzene or phenol leads to rearrangement and extensive demethylation on alkylation with n-propyl alcohol or di-n-propyl ether over $AlCl_3$ (70,71).

As the alcohol becomes larger a wider variety of ionic reactions can occur. For example, the isomerized product is obtained when phenol is alkylated with 2-methylpentan-4-ol to give 2-methyl-2-(p-hydroxyphenyl)pentane (49).

Huston and co-workers suggest a mechanism for this reaction

$$CH_3\underset{\underset{CH_3}{|}}{CH}-CH_2\underset{\underset{OH}{|}}{CH}CH_3 + C_6H_5OH \xrightarrow[AlCl_3]{} HO-\bigcirc-\overset{CH_3}{\underset{\underset{CH_3}{|}}{\underset{|}{C}}}-C_3H_7 \quad (51)$$

involving olefin formation followed by subsequent double bond isomerization (49). It would seem reasonable in the light of current thinking to ascribe these results to a rapid isomerization of the secondary carbonium ion to the energetically favored tertiary ion.

$$\left[CH_3\underset{\underset{CH_3}{|}}{CH}CH_2\underset{\underset{OH}{|}}{CH}CH_3 \right] AlCl_3 \rightarrow \left[CH_3\underset{\underset{CH_3}{|}}{CH}\overset{+}{C}HCH_2CH_3 \right] OHAlCl_3^-$$

$$(52)$$

$$HO-\bigcirc-\overset{CH_3}{\underset{\underset{CH_3}{|}}{\underset{|}{C}}}-CH_2CH_2CH_3 \quad \underset{\underset{OH}{\bigcirc}}{\overset{CH_3}{\swarrow}} \quad \left[CH_3-\overset{+}{\underset{\underset{CH_3}{|}}{C}}-CH_2CH_2CH_3 \right] OHAlCl_3^-$$

As mentioned earlier, scission reactions are also possible and it is known that large carbonium ions can undergo a β-scission reaction leading to smaller, more stable, fragments. Huston has carried out an extensive study using tertiary alcohols and isomerized products as well as those products that may arise by a β-scission reaction result. The alkylation of phenol by 2,2-dimethylbutan-3-ol and by 2,3,3-trimethylbutan-2-ol illustrate these points.

With 2,2-dimethylbutan-3-ol an alkylated product consisting entirely of 2,3-dimethyl-2-(p-hydroxyphenyl)butane is obtained (72). The formation of this compound can be explained by the rearrangement of the less stable $(CH_3)_3\overset{+}{C}CHCH_3$ ion to the more stable ion $CH_3\overset{+}{C}(CH_3)CH(CH_3)_2$. This latter ion then condenses with phenol (or the phenol aluminate).

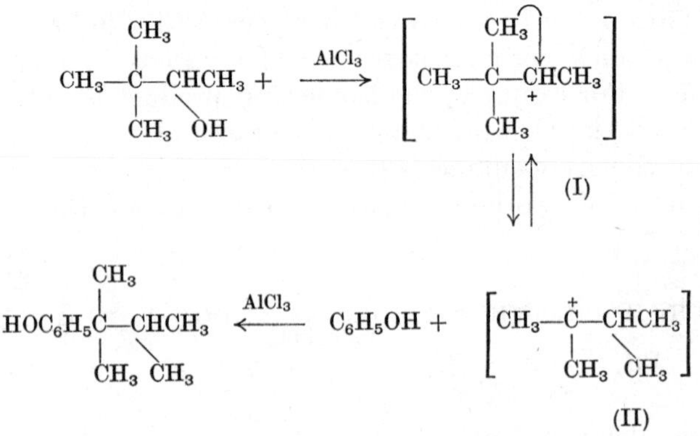

$$
\begin{array}{c}
CH_3 \\
| \\
CH_3-C-CHCH_3 \; + \\
| \quad \backslash \\
CH_3 \quad OH
\end{array}
\xrightarrow{\;AlCl_3\;}
\left[
\begin{array}{c}
CH_3 \\
| \\
CH_3-C-CHCH_3 \\
| \qquad + \\
CH_3
\end{array}
\right]
\qquad (53)
$$

$$\big\updownarrow \quad (I)$$

$$
\begin{array}{c}
CH_3 \\
| \\
HOC_6H_5C-CHCH_3 \\
| \quad \backslash \\
CH_3 \quad CH_3
\end{array}
\xleftarrow{\;AlCl_3\;}
C_6H_5OH \; +
\left[
\begin{array}{c}
CH_3-\overset{+}{C}-CHCH_3 \\
| \quad \backslash \\
CH_3 \quad CH_3
\end{array}
\right]
\qquad (54)
$$

$$(II)$$

It is interesting to note that the equilibrium ratio of 2,2-dimethylbutane to 2,3-dimethylbutane is 3:1 at the alkylation temperature (73). In addition, the rate of acid-catalyzed isomerization of 2,2-dimethylbutane is very much lower than that involving 2,3-dimethylbutane (74). The differences in isomerization rates have been ascribed to a steric factor involving the bulky methyl groups that are next to the developing carbonium ion in the 2,2-structure. These two factors lead one to suspect that part of the reason for the sole production of the 2,3-dimethyl-2-hydroxymethylbutane is a steric effect. Such an effect would operate to favor alkylation involving the 2,3-ion (II) over an alkylation involving a 2,2-dimethylbutyl carbonium ion (I).

Alkylation of benzene with 2,3,3-trimethylbutan-2-ol gives rise to a variety of alkylated benzenes. The well-known β-scission reaction of an alkyl carbonium ion will explain the major reaction products found and the following scheme can be depicted.

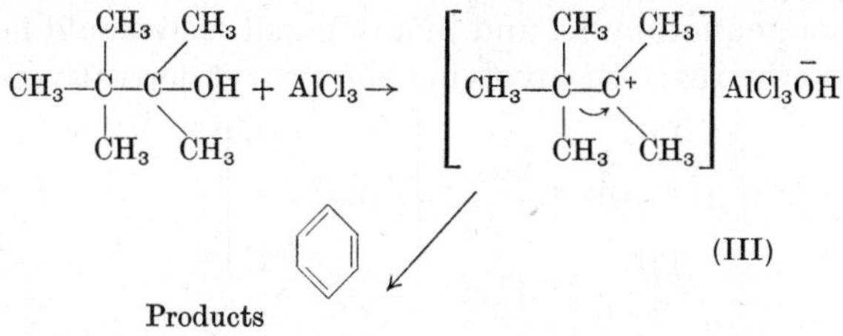

$$\underset{\substack{|\\ CH_3}}{\overset{\substack{CH_3 \ CH_3\\ \diagup}}{CH_3-C-C-OH}} + AlCl_3 \rightarrow \left[\underset{\substack{|\\ CH_3}}{\overset{\substack{CH_3 \ CH_3\\ \diagup}}{CH_3-C-C^+}} \right] AlCl_3\overline{O}H \qquad (55)$$

(III)

Products

Carbonium ion III is bulky and the rate of proton loss to give an olefin is likely to compete with the alkylation rate since the latter involves steric hindrance. In addition, such olefins can be alkylated on terminal methyl groups to give C_{14}^+ ions that are known to rearrange and crack *via* β-scission reactions leading to smaller ionic fragments. Any one of these fragments could alkylate benzene. Thus, the overall reaction of a bulky branched compound such as 2,3,3-trimethylbutan-2-ol is likely to proceed *via* a "synthesis-cracking" mechanism similar to those postulated to occur during paraffin isomerization reactions (74).

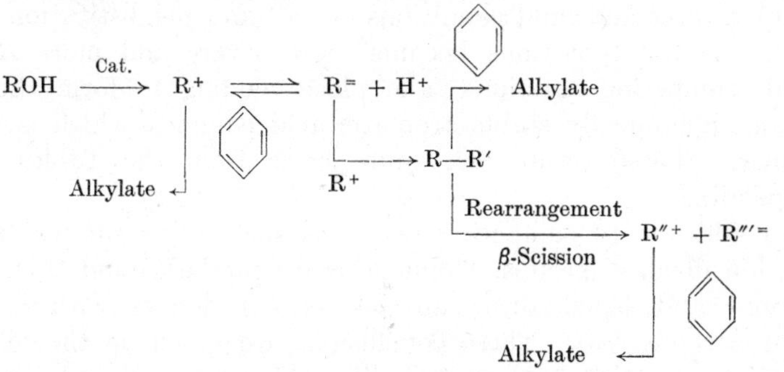

ROH $\xrightarrow{\text{Cat.}}$ R$^+$ $\rightleftharpoons$ R$^=$ + H$^+$ $\longrightarrow$ Alkylate

Alkylate $\longleftarrow$

$\longrightarrow$ R—R$'$

R$^+$

Rearrangement

$\longrightarrow$ R$''^+$ + R$'''^=$

β-Scission

Alkylate $\longleftarrow$

The alkylation of aromatics by aromatic alcohols in the presence of $AlCl_3$ is a relatively easy reaction (75–81). This reaction occurs particularly readily with alcohols containing one or more phenyl groups in the molecule. In addition, an increase in the number of phenyl groups causes the yield of substituted compound to rise (79–81). As an example, in the condensation of phenol with dimethylphenyl, methyldiphenyl, and triphenyl carbinol the yield of *p*-substituted products amounted to 72, 80, and 95%, respectively (80).

Again, these reactions may be interpreted on the basis of ready carbonium-ion formation to yield mono-, di-, and triarylmethyl carbonium ions. Olefins were isolated in the first two cases and Welsh and Drake (80) postulated these as reaction intermediates. However, it is likely that olefins represent a competing proton-loss side reaction, equation 56, and in any event they could not be intermediates in the reaction involving the triaryl derivative.

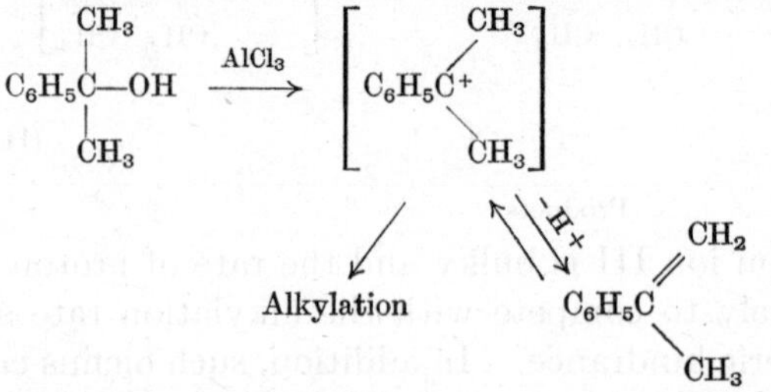

$$
\begin{array}{ccc}
\overset{CH_3}{\underset{CH_3}{C_6H_5C-OH}} & \xrightarrow{AlCl_3} & \left[\overset{CH_3}{\underset{CH_3}{C_6H_5C^+}}\right]
\end{array}
\tag{56}
$$

Alkylation $\overset{-H^+}{\longleftrightarrow}$ $C_6H_5C\overset{CH_2}{\underset{CH_3}{=}}$

The $AlCl_3$ catalyzed alkylation of aromatic hydrocarbons by alcohols is rather confused on the matter of position attack. It is well known that $AlCl_3$ is an excellent isomerization and disproportionation catalyst at mild conditions. As pointed out in Section II-2-A final product can be a function of three factors: (a) position attack, (b) isomerization of the alkyl group around the ring, and (c) disproportionation of the alkyl group. In summary, at low temperatures and mild conditions o-, m-, and p-substitution occurs (82). As the conditions become more severe and more $AlCl_3$ is used, competing reactions take place tending to form the most thermodynamically stable aromatic acid complex which is the m-isomer. These results are quite clear from the Tables in the Appendix.

In addition to competing reactions such as proton-loss and β-scission of alkyl groups, Ungnade and Crandall found that benzyl alcohol and benzhydrol can act as CO donors with aromatic hydrocarbons (83). These conclusions are based on the following reactions to give anthracene, dibenzylanthracene and dimethylanthracene.

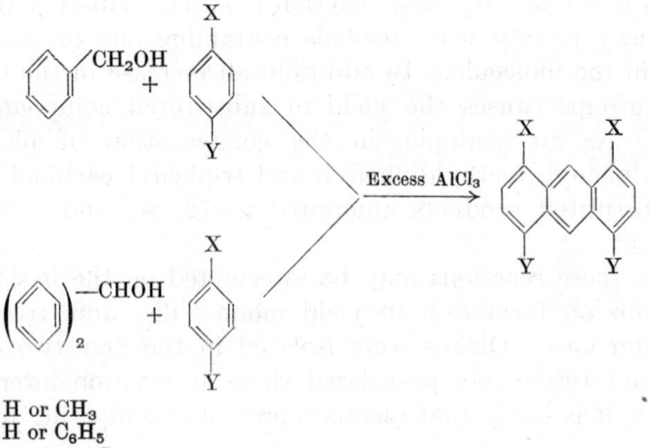

$$
\begin{array}{c}
C_6H_5CH_2OH \\
+ \\
\text{(aryl with X, Y)}
\end{array}
\quad\searrow\quad \xrightarrow{\text{Excess } AlCl_3} \quad \text{(anthracene with X, X, Y, Y)}
\tag{57}
$$

$$
\begin{array}{c}
(C_6H_5)_2CHOH \\
+ \\
\text{(aryl with X, Y)}
\end{array}
\quad\nearrow
$$

where X = H or CH_3
      Y = H or C_6H_5

A further indication of the correctness of this argument is the finding that CO is liberated from both benzhydrol and benzyl alcohol on stirring with $AlCl_3$ at 60°. Thus the aromatic solvent would furnish the outside rings of the substituted anthracenes while the CO from the carbinol would furnish the *meso*-atom. Hey proposed a similar mechanism based on work with benzaldehyde. The scope of this reaction is probably restricted, and triphenyl-carbinol does not form CO on stirring with $AlCl_3$ at 60°.

Alkylation of aromatics and phenols with saturated cyclic alcohols called "cyclialkylation" has also been affected by $AlCl_3$. This reaction is susceptible to competing side reactions such as changes in ring size and one example of the confusion that arises when such competing reactions are possible concerns the early work of Sidorova and Tsukervanik (84). These authors found cycloheptylbenzene in the $AlCl_3$ catalyzed alkylation of benzene with cycloheptanol. Pines *et al.* in a later paper showed that under the same conditions $AlCl_3$ actually gives rise to a product that is mainly the isomeric 4-methyl-cyclohexylbenzene (85). Sulfuric acid, a milder catalyst, at 80°C gave more cycloheptylbenzene but also yielded some isomerized product.

Recently, Sidorova and Tsukervanik (86) reinvestigated the cycloheptanol–benzene alkylation reaction. They used very mild conditions and added the $AlCl_3$ very slowly to a stirred mixture of the alcohol and benzene. This differs from the previous work in which the reactants were contacted at once. Under the new conditions, a 73% yield of cycloheptylbenzene was obtained. Thus mild conditions favor the unrearranged product and this is predictable from our knowledge of the effect of acid catalysts on the promotion of isomerization reactions.

An interesting example of isomerization accompanying alkylation of cyclic materials is found in the alkylation of 1-phenyl-4-methyl-cyclohexanol with benzene using $AlCl_3$ (87). Reduction products are found in addition to the expected alkylated benzene.

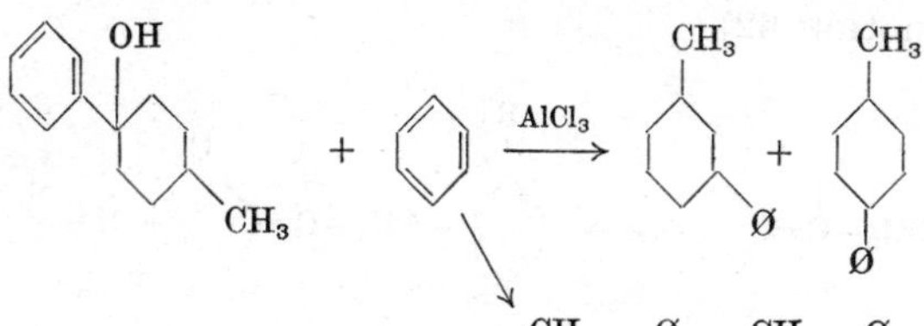

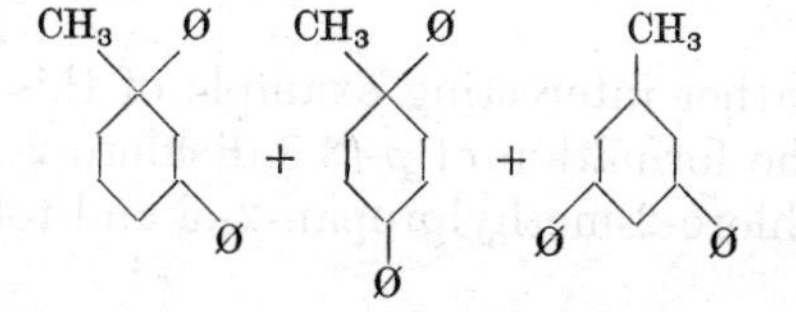

The reduction products undoubtedly arise *via* hydride transfer to carbonium ion I. Hydride ions can be abstracted from either an olefin to give an allylic ion (equation 60) or from a C–H bond. It is usually not possible to pinpoint the source and it is known that acid sludges form and these could be produced from the allylic ions.

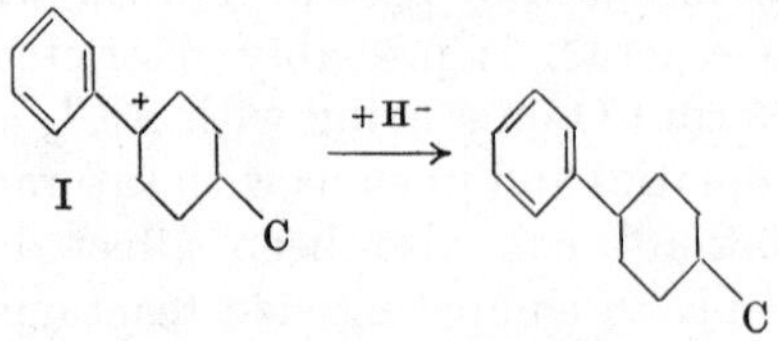

$$(60)$$

$$R^+ + R' \rightleftharpoons R^{=+} + R'{-}H$$

In this case, mild conditions also result in a product that is not isomerized.

Another example of this cyclialkylation reaction is the alkylation of benzene with 1-methylcyclopentan-1-ol over $AlCl_3$. The intermediate expected is the relatively stable methylcyclopentyl carbonium ion and this apparently readily alkylates since a 43% yield of 1-phenyl-1-methylcyclopentane results.

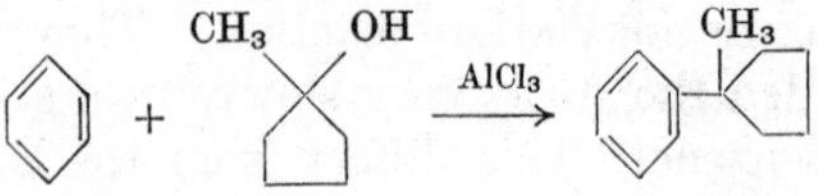

$$(61)$$

b. *Miscellaneous*

There are many other examples of the use of $AlCl_3$ as an alkylation catalyst for alcohols. The following section is a brief description of some of the more useful or important synthetic applications and the more interesting mechanistic work.

In addition to alkylation by a species resembling a primary, secondary or tertiary carbonium ion, alkylation by an allylic ion is also possible (equation 62).

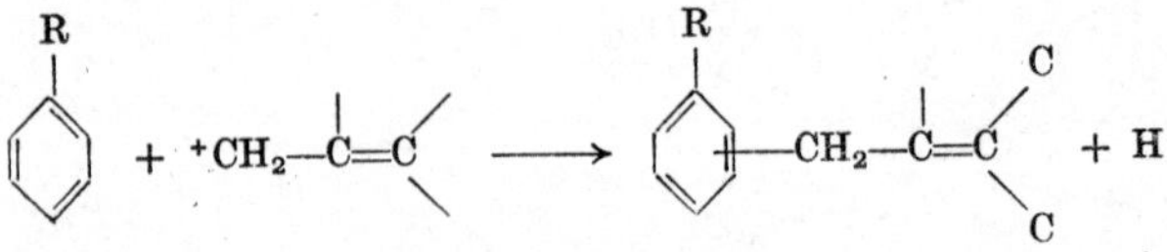

$$(62)$$

A rather interesting example of this type of an alkylation reaction is the formation of *p*-(3,3-dichloro-2-methylallyl)toluene from 1,1,1-trichloro-2-methylpropan-2-ol and toluene (88).

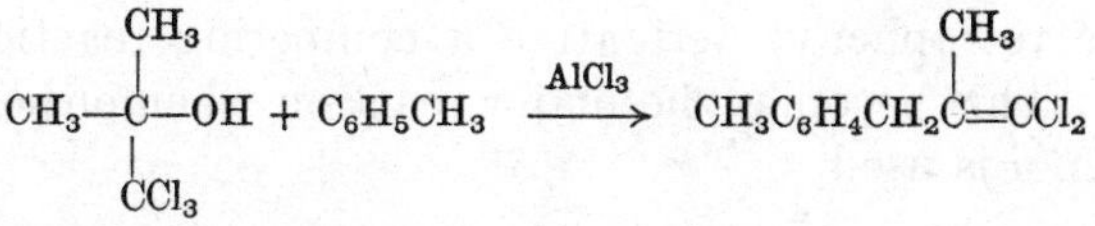

$$\underset{\underset{CCl_3}{|}}{\overset{\overset{CH_3}{|}}{CH_3-C-OH}} + C_6H_5CH_3 \xrightarrow{AlCl_3} \underset{\underset{CCl_2}{}}{\overset{\overset{CH_3}{|}}{CH_3C_6H_4CH_2C=CCl_2}} \qquad (63)$$

The reaction mechanism presumably involves intermediate ionization and allylic rearrangement.

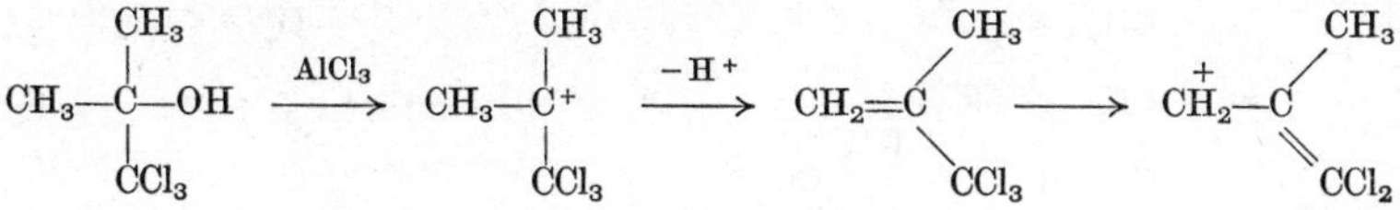

$$\underset{\underset{CCl_3}{|}}{\overset{\overset{CH_3}{|}}{CH_3-C-OH}} \xrightarrow{AlCl_3} \underset{\underset{CCl_3}{|}}{\overset{\overset{CH_3}{|}}{CH_3-C^+}} \xrightarrow{-H^+} \underset{\underset{CCl_3}{}}{\overset{\overset{CH_3}{}}{CH_2=C}} \longrightarrow \underset{\underset{CCl_2}{}}{\overset{\overset{CH_3}{}}{CH_2-C^+}} \qquad (64)$$

A direct comparison of the relative ease of reacting primary and secondary alcohol is afforded by the AlCl$_3$ catalyzed alkylation of benzene with the diol 1,4-dihydroxypentane. At room temperature, no 1-phenylpentane derivatives are produced. As some 1-methyl-tetrahydronaphthalene is also formed, however, it probably arises from cyclization of the 4-phenylpentan-1-ol. The latter reaction is an example of the broad class of reactions first described by Bruson as cyclialkylation (89).

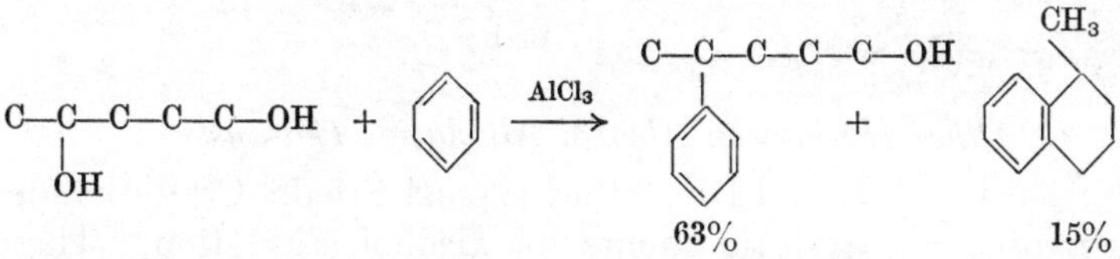

$$\underset{\underset{OH}{|}}{C-C-C-C-C-OH} + \bigcirc \xrightarrow{AlCl_3} \quad \underset{63\%}{\overset{C-C-C-C-C-OH}{\bigcirc}} \quad + \quad \underset{15\%}{\overset{CH_3}{\bigodot}} \qquad (65)$$

This cyclialkylation reaction can be carried out using appropriate diols or ethers. The following examples are illustrative (for a fuller discussion see Chapter XXII):

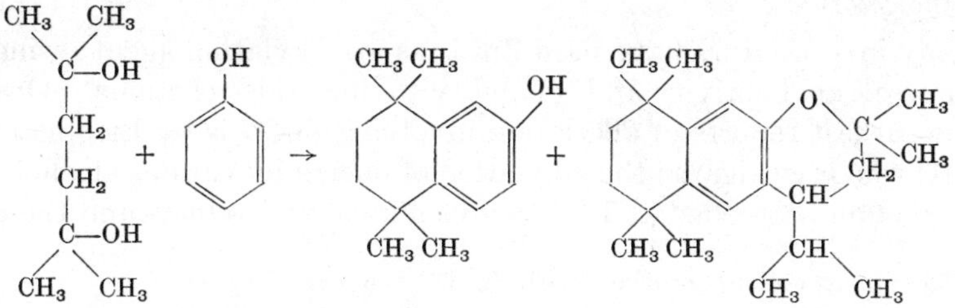

$$(66)$$

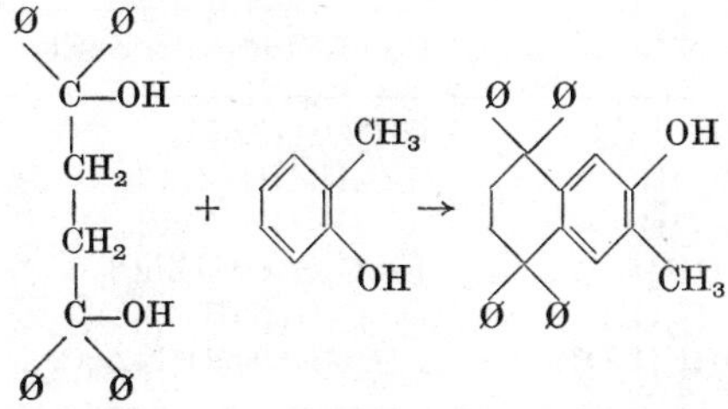

$$(67)$$

With the tetraphenyl derivative a competing reaction is diene formation. This becomes the major reaction when either phenol or o-chlorophenol is used.

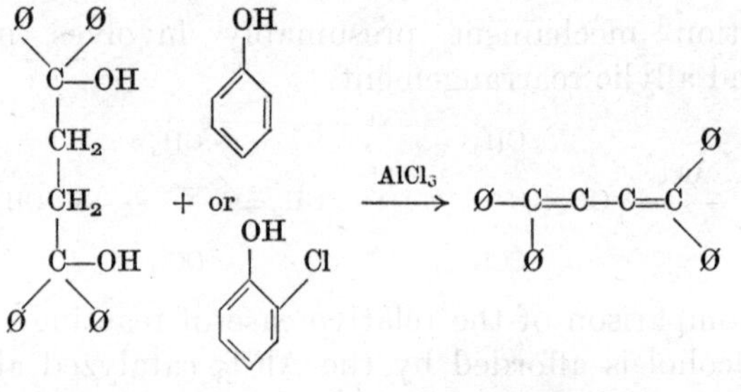

$$\begin{array}{c} \emptyset \quad \emptyset \\ \diagdown / \\ C\!-\!OH \\ | \\ CH_2 \\ | \\ CH_2 \quad + \text{ or } \quad \xrightarrow{\ \ AlCl_3\ \ } \quad \emptyset\!-\!C\!=\!C\!-\!C\!=\!C \\ | \\ C\!-\!OH \\ / \diagdown \\ \emptyset \quad \emptyset \end{array} \qquad (68)$$

In addition to the phenol and benzene alkylation discussed in the preceding section, polycyclics react. Thus, naphthalene yields a polyalkyl derivative on alkylation with cyclohexyl alcohol.

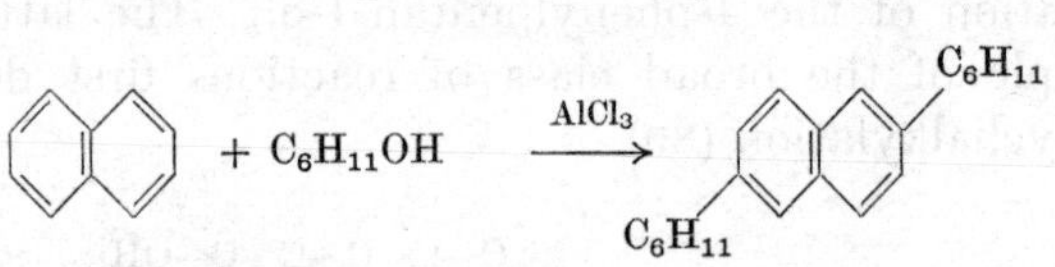

$$\text{(naphthalene)} + C_6H_{11}OH \quad \xrightarrow{\ \ AlCl_3\ \ } \quad \text{(dicyclohexylnaphthalene)} \qquad (69)$$

C. Other Halides as Alcohol Alkylation Catalysts

In addition to $AlCl_3$ and BF_3, other typical Friedel-Crafts halides have been used as catalytic agents for alcohol alkylation. These halides, however, have not been extensively studied and this section outlines some of the more frequently used reagents.

a. Zinc chloride

Many investigators have used $ZnCl_2$ as an alkylating agent owing to its weak acid activity and its ability to limit side reactions. One of the earliest reports of alkylation involving $ZnCl_2$ is by Liebmann (90,91) who investigated the alkylation of phenol by various alcohols. The reaction proceeded at 180° to give alkylated products and these

TABLE V.   Alcohol complexes with $ZnCl_2$

Alcohol	Compound with $ZnCl_2$
CH_3OH	$CH_3OH \cdot ZnCl_2$
$n\text{-}C_3H_7OH$	$n\text{-}C_3H_7OH \cdot ZnCl_2$
$n\text{-}C_4H_9OH$	$n\text{-}C_4H_9OH \cdot ZnCl_2$
$iso\text{-}C_3H_7OH$	$iso\text{-}C_3H_7OH \cdot ZnCl_2$
$iso\text{-}C_5H_{11}OH$	$iso\text{-}C_5H_{11}OH \cdot ZnCl_2$
CH_2OHCH_2OH	$CH_2OHCH_2OH \cdot ZnCl_2$

were later shown to be p-isomers in the case of t-butyl derivatives (92,93). Such product distributions suggest that $ZnCl_2$–ROH systems might be considered carbonium-ion precursors.

A systematic study of $ZnCl_2$ as a catalyst was made by Kuchkarov in 1952 (94). This investigator isolated the following molecular addition compounds of $ZnCl_2$ and alcohols (94,95).

These complexes are considered to be of the type $(ZnCl_2 \cdot (OR))H$, $(ZnCl_2 \cdot (OR_2)_2)H_2$. They are analogous to the acids formed when $ZnCl_2$ is added to water, $i.e.$,

$$ZnCl_2 + H_2O \rightleftharpoons [ZnCl_2 \cdot (OH)_2]H_2 \rightleftharpoons [ZnCl_2(OH)_2]^= + 2H^+ \tag{70}$$

Thus they are similar to the $BF_3 \cdot ROH$ complexes or the $AlCl_3 \cdot ROH$ complexes and one might expect them to behave in a similar fashion but to be less polar. Kuchkarov has found that such complexes are thermally cleaved to olefins, ethers, aldehydes, hydrogen, water, and zinc oxychloride. Examples are shown in Table VI.

TABLE VI.   Cleavage products of $ZnCl_2$–alcoholates

	Temperature	Main organic product
$CH_3OH \cdot ZnCl_2$	180°	CH_3OCH_3
$C_2H_5OH \cdot ZnCl_2$	170–175°	$C_2H_5OH + CH_3CHO + CH_2\text{:}CH_2$
$n\text{-}C_3H_7OH \cdot ZnCl_2$	160–165°	$CH_3CH\text{:}CH_2$
iso-$C_3H_7OH \cdot ZnCl_2$	150–160°	CH_3CHCH_2
$n\text{-}C_4H_9OH \cdot ZnCl_2$	160–165°	$CH_3CH_2CHCH_2$
iso-$C_4H_9OH \cdot ZnCl_2$	140–150°	Oil
$CH_2OHCH_2OH \cdot ZnCl_2$	150–155°	Oil
$(C_6H_{11}OH)_2 \cdot ZnCl_2$	140°	Cyclohexene + Oil

The complexes of n-butyl, n-propyl, and isoamyl alcohols were used to alkylate toluene. This alkylation reaction did not proceed at 165–175° even in the presence of excess $ZnCl_2$. However, above the breakdown temperature of the complexes, $i.e.$, above 200° alkylation took place. The mechanism proposed is one involving olefin formation followed by subsequent alkylation:

$$RCH_2CH_2OH + ZnCl_2 \rightarrow [RCH_2CH_2O \cdot ZnCl_2]H \tag{71}$$

$$[RCH_2CH_2O \cdot ZnCl_2]H \rightarrow RCH{=}CH_2 + [ZnCl_2 \cdot OH]H \tag{72}$$

$$RCH{=}CH_2 + Ar \rightarrow ArCH\begin{smallmatrix}CH_3\\\\R\end{smallmatrix} \tag{73}$$

It should be pointed out that the presence of an olefin is not a sufficient requirement for postulation as an active intermediate. If the complex is ionic, then, at the temperature in question, it could undergo a competing proton loss to form the olefin in addition to toluene alkylation. Indeed, in view of the evidence presented in this chapter an ionic complex that undergoes a competing series of reactions is preferred.

While these "unactivated" alcohols studied by Kuchkarov require high temperatures for reaction, Olah has reported that fluoromethyl alcohol is a relatively active alkylating agent (96). For example, at 40–50° $ZnCl_2$ will produce fluoromethylbenzene from benzene and fluoromethyl alcohol. The p-fluoromethyl derivative of fluoro-benzene is obtained in an analogous reaction. Due to the high reactivity of the fluoromethyl derivatives secondary alkylation yields predominantly diphenylmethanes.

$$\bigcirc + HOCH_2F \xrightarrow[\text{30 min. at } 40-50°]{ZnCl_2} \bigcirc^{CH_2F} \qquad (74)$$

$$\bigcirc^{F} + HOCH_2F \xrightarrow[\text{1 hr. at } 40-50°]{ZnCl_2} \bigcirc^{F}_{CH_2F} \qquad (75)$$

Since the product contains reactive halide the reaction is reminiscent of the one described by Bachman and Hellman for the halohydrins (38). Thus, fluorinated hydrocarbons are known to be alkylating agents using BF_3, and a technique is at hand for a combined catalyst sequence leading to novel products.

Many alcohols have been examined as phenol alkylating agents using $ZnCl_2$ and these include n-butyl (97), s-butyl (98), t-pentyl (99), dodecyl (100), cetyl (101), and cyclohexyl alcohols (98). A variety of phenols including cresols (102,103) and guaiacol (104) have been alkylated, and substitution usually occurs in the $para$-position and when this is substituted alkylations take place at the $ortho$-position without $meta$-isomer formation (105). This is similar to BF_3 systems and different from $AlCl_3$ where isomerization can lead to high $meta$-isomer ratios. Comparison of the ring-activating influence of a methyl and phenol group has been made by Degering et al. (105) who found that the hydroxy group directed substitution (equation 76).

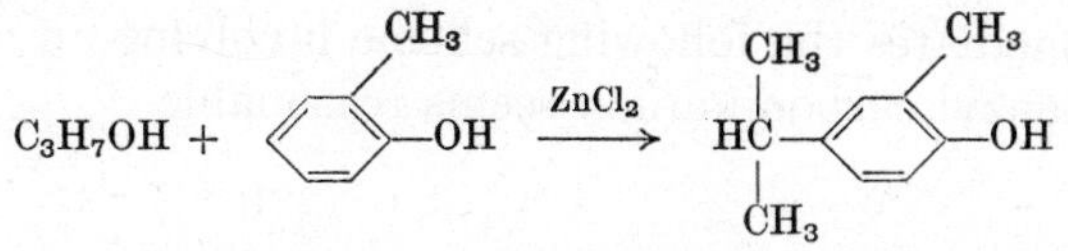

$$C_3H_7OH + \underset{OH}{\overset{CH_3}{\bigcirc}} \xrightarrow{ZnCl_2} HC\underset{CH_3}{\overset{CH_3}{\diagup}}\underset{}{\overset{CH_3}{\bigcirc}}OH \tag{76}$$

When p-cresol is alkylated the corresponding o-alkyl-p-cresol is formed in 70% yields.

When diisobutyl alcohol (2,2,4-trimethylpentan-4-ol) is used to alkylate phenol, a cracking reaction occurs and p-t-butyl phenol is formed.

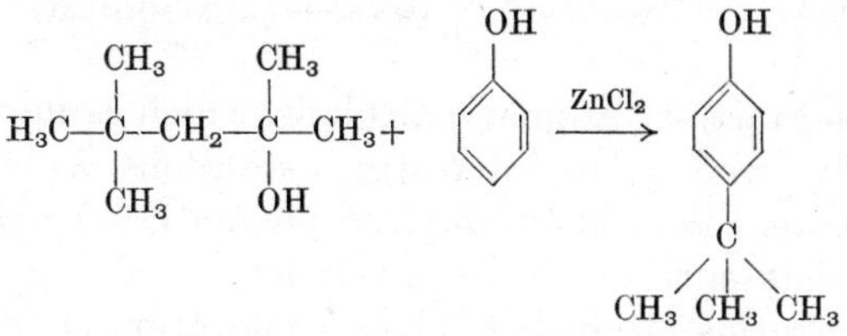

$$H_3C-\underset{CH_3}{\overset{CH_3}{\underset{|}{\overset{|}{C}}}}-CH_2-\underset{OH}{\overset{CH_3}{\underset{|}{\overset{|}{C}}}}-CH_3 + \overset{OH}{\bigcirc} \xrightarrow{ZnCl_2} \overset{OH}{\underset{\underset{CH_3\ CH_3\ CH_3}{C}}{\bigcirc}} \tag{77}$$

This reaction can be almost certainly ascribed to a β-scission of the 2,2,4-trimethylpentyl carbonium ion followed by alkylation.

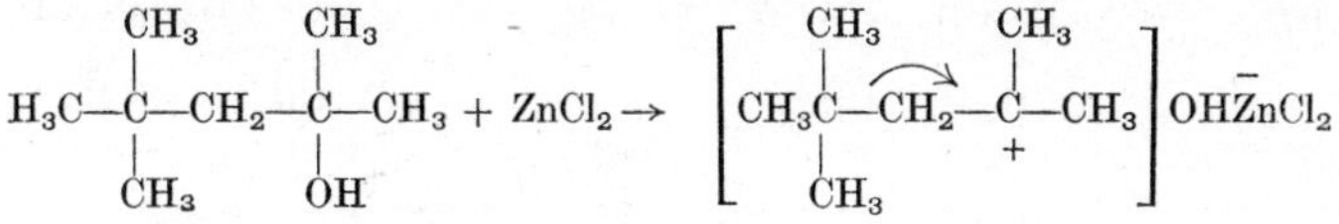

$$H_3C-\underset{CH_3}{\overset{CH_3}{\underset{|}{\overset{|}{C}}}}-CH_2-\underset{OH}{\overset{CH_3}{\underset{|}{\overset{|}{C}}}}-CH_3 + ZnCl_2 \rightarrow \left[CH_3\underset{CH_3}{\overset{CH_3}{\underset{|}{\overset{|}{C}}}}-CH_2\overset{CH_3}{\underset{+}{\overset{|}{C}}}-CH_3 \right] O\overline{H}ZnCl_2 \tag{78}$$

$$H^+ + \overset{OH}{\underset{\underset{CH_3\ CH_3\ CH_3}{C}}{\bigcirc}} \longleftarrow CH_3\overset{CH_3}{\underset{CH_3}{\overset{|}{C^+}}} + CH_2{=}\overset{CH_3}{\underset{CH_3}{\overset{|}{C}}} \tag{79}$$

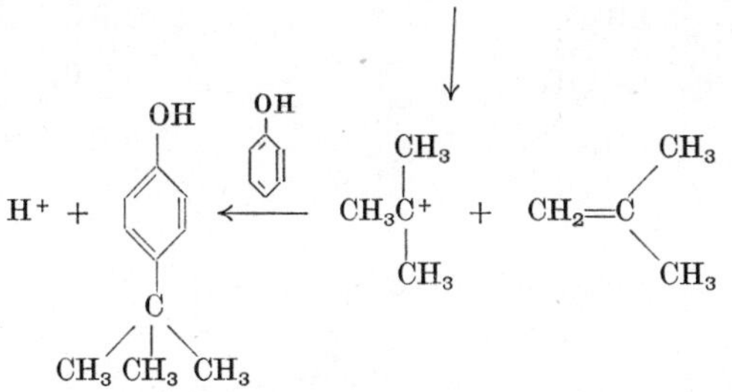

If β-phenylethyl alcohol is used p-(α-phenylethyl)phenol is isolated (106):

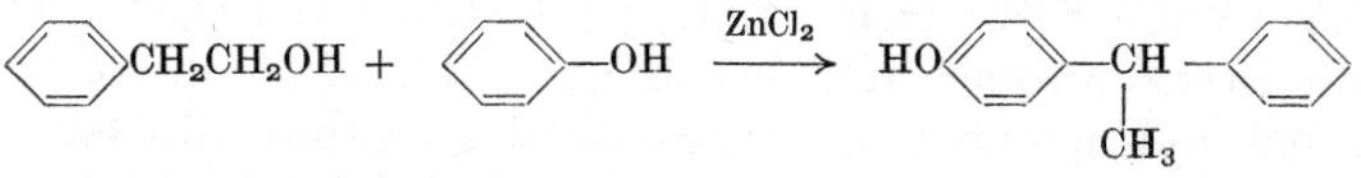

$$\bigcirc CH_2CH_2OH + \overset{}{\bigcirc}{-}OH \xrightarrow{ZnCl_2} HO\bigcirc{-}\underset{CH_3}{\overset{|}{CH}}{-}\bigcirc \tag{80}$$

This reaction has been interpreted in the light of intermediate olefin formation. However, to be consistent with all other data indicating ionic intermediates the following scheme involving an isomerization to give a benzyl carbonium ion seems reasonable.

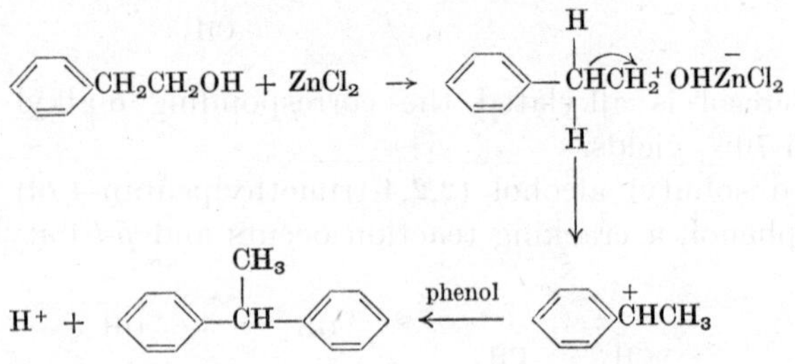

$$\text{C}_6\text{H}_5\text{CH}_2\text{CH}_2\text{OH} + \text{ZnCl}_2 \;\rightarrow\; \text{C}_6\text{H}_5-\overset{\text{H}}{\underset{\text{H}}{\text{C}}}\text{H}\overset{+}{\text{C}}\text{H}_2 \;{}^-\text{OHZnCl}_2 \qquad (81)$$

$$\text{H}^+ + \;\; \text{C}_6\text{H}_5-\overset{\text{CH}_3}{\text{CH}}-\text{C}_6\text{H}_5 \;\xleftarrow{\text{phenol}}\; \text{C}_6\text{H}_5\overset{+}{\text{C}}\text{HCH}_3 \qquad (82)$$

Secondary and tertiary aromatic alcohols, which cannot form olefins, work equally well. An interesting reaction occurs when 4-*t*-octylcyclohexanol is used to alkylate phenol (107). The alkylated product consists entirely of *p-t*-butylphenol. The only reasonable explanation for this product involves a migration of the positive ion followed by a β-scission reaction (equations 83–85).

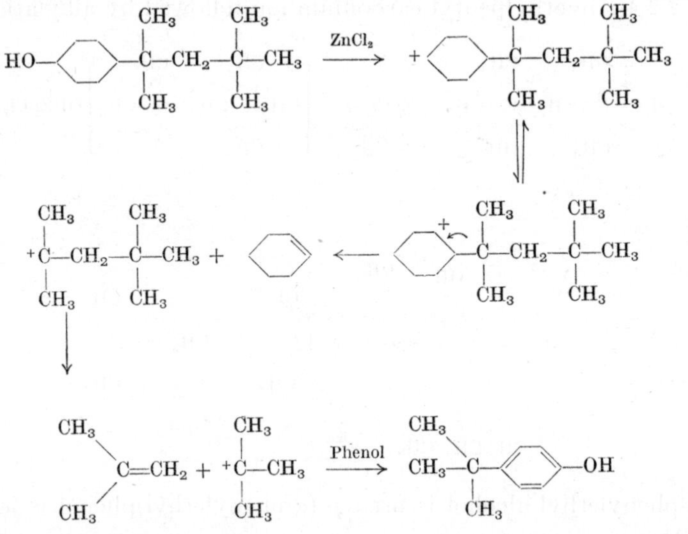

$$\text{HO}-\text{C}_6\text{H}_{10}-\overset{\text{CH}_3}{\underset{\text{CH}_3}{\text{C}}}-\text{CH}_2-\overset{\text{CH}_3}{\underset{\text{CH}_3}{\text{C}}}-\text{CH}_3 \;\xrightarrow{\text{ZnCl}_2}\; + \; \text{C}_6\text{H}_{10}-\overset{\text{CH}_3}{\underset{\text{CH}_3}{\text{C}}}-\text{CH}_2-\overset{\text{CH}_3}{\underset{\text{CH}_3}{\text{C}}}-\text{CH}_3 \qquad (83)$$

$$\overset{+}{\text{C}}\overset{\text{CH}_3}{\underset{\text{CH}_3}{}}-\text{CH}_2-\overset{\text{CH}_3}{\underset{\text{CH}_3}{\text{C}}}-\text{CH}_3 + \; \text{C}_6\text{H}_{10} \;\leftarrow\; \text{C}_6\text{H}_{10}-\overset{+}{\underset{}{}}\overset{\text{CH}_3}{\underset{\text{CH}_3}{\text{C}}}-\text{CH}_2-\overset{\text{CH}_3}{\underset{\text{CH}_3}{\text{C}}}-\text{CH}_3 \qquad (84)$$

$$\overset{\text{CH}_3}{\underset{\text{CH}_3}{}}\text{C}=\text{CH}_2 + \overset{+}{\text{C}}\overset{\text{CH}_3}{\underset{\text{CH}_3}{}}-\text{CH}_3 \;\xrightarrow{\text{Phenol}}\; \text{CH}_3-\overset{\text{CH}_3}{\underset{\text{CH}_3}{\text{C}}}-\text{C}_6\text{H}_4-\text{OH} \qquad (85)$$

Diarylmethylation reactions have been studied in the solvent systems ZnCl_2–$\text{CH}_3\text{CO}_2\text{H}$ and ZnCl_2–HCl–$\text{CH}_3\text{CO}_2\text{H}$. The reactants were anisole and benzhydryl chloride, anisole and diphenylmethyl acetate, and anisole and 4-methoxydiphenylmethyl chloride which are formally similar to alcohols and ethers. It was found that the diarylmethylation reaction is catalyzed by ZnCl_2–$\text{CH}_3\text{CO}_2\text{H}$ and by the ZnCl_2–HCl–$\text{CH}_3\text{CO}_2\text{H}$ mixture in a manner that parallels the effect of these substances on an indicator ionization ratio. The indicator used has a structure similar to the alkylating agent (108).

The conclusion reached is that the main function of the $ZnCl_2$ is the generation of Brønsted acidity by interacting with the co-catalyst HCl and acetic acid. This leads to carbonium-ion formation and the substitution step proper is a bimolecular reaction between diaryl carbonium ions and anisole.

Thus, a rapid and pre-equilibrium step (equation 86) would be set up followed by a rate-determining attack on anisole (equation 87):

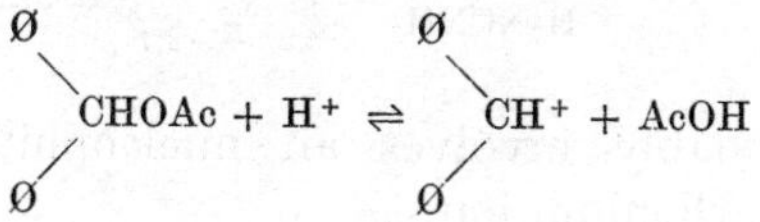

$$\underset{\varnothing}{\overset{\varnothing}{\diagdown}}CHOAc + H^+ \rightleftharpoons \underset{\varnothing}{\overset{\varnothing}{\diagdown}}CH^+ + AcOH \qquad (86)$$

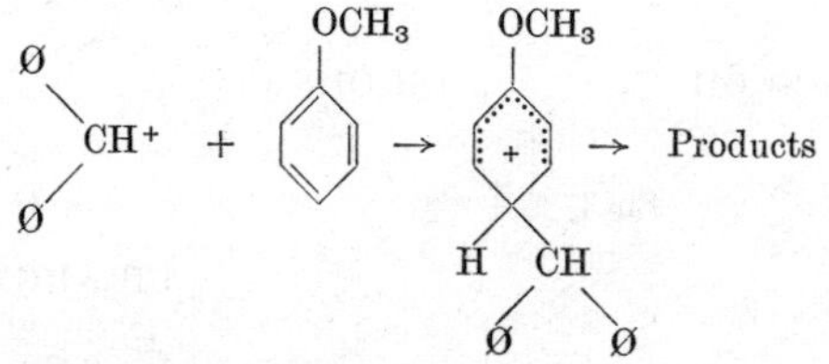

$$\qquad (87)$$

There is no further role for the $ZnCl_2$, such as association with anisole. Phenol has also been alkylated by primary alcohols in the presence of $ZnCl_2$ in HCl at 100–140° (109,110). This reaction is probably mechanistically similar to the preceding reaction and isomerized *para*-derivatives are produced.

b. Ferric chloride

The alkylation of phenol and cresols with tertiary alcohols can be accomplished using $FeCl_3$. The reaction is rapid and requires 0.5–1 g. of $FeCl_3$ (111). Secondary alcohols also react but they require slightly higher temperatures, 50–60°, and increased catalyst amounts. The success of this reaction with primary alcohols depends on the structure of the original alcohol. With iso-alcohols the reaction occurs at higher temperatures (120°) but normal alcohols do not condense with aromatic compounds in the presence of $FeCl_3$ (112).

c. Stannic chloride and titanium tetrachloride

Stannic chloride has also been used as an alkylating agent. An interesting example of its use is in the preparation of substituted acetic acids (113).

$$\left(\!\!\left(\bigcirc\right)\!\!\right)_2 \overset{\displaystyle C-COOH}{\underset{\displaystyle OH}{|}} + C_6H_5OH \xrightarrow[\substack{Temp.\ to \\ melting}]{SnCl_4} \left(\!\!\left(\bigcirc\right)\!\!\right)_2 \overset{\displaystyle C-COOH}{\underset{\displaystyle C_6H_4OH}{|}} \qquad (88)$$

Another example of the use of $SnCl_4$ is the alkylation of urea with benzyl alcohol to give benzylurethane. In this case stronger acids, such as sulfuric, are not useful since they cause dehydration. Again,

$$\underset{\displaystyle \bigcirc}{CH_2OH} + \underset{\displaystyle H_2N\overset{O}{\overset{\|}{C}}NH_2}{} \xrightarrow{SnCl_4} \underset{\displaystyle \bigcirc}{CH_2NH\overset{O}{\overset{\|}{C}}NH_2} \qquad (89)$$

this reaction probably involves an nucleophilic attack on the incipient benzyl carbonium ion.

$$\underset{\displaystyle \bigcirc}{CH_2OH} + SnCl_4 \rightarrow \underset{\displaystyle \bigcirc}{\overset{+\ \ \ \ -}{CH_2OHSnCl_4}}$$

$$\xrightarrow[H_2NCNH_2]{} \underset{\displaystyle \bigcirc}{CH_2NH\overset{O}{\overset{\|}{C}}NH_2} + \begin{matrix} SnCl_4 \\ H_2O \end{matrix} \qquad (90)$$

Recently, titanium tetrachloride has been used as a catalyst for the alkylation of benzene, toluene, and anisole by primary, secondary, and tertiary alcohols (204). At least an equivalent amount of the halide is required for high yields and the temperatures are in the range of 60–100°. It was found that isobutyl alcohol gave tertiary alkyl derivatives and *s*-butyl alcohol gave secondary derivatives. The ease of reaction was in the order tertiary > secondary > primary alcohol. Substitution invariably occurred in the *para*-position indicating a high selectivity and a low degree of polarization of the alcohol–catalyst complex.

2. Proton-donating Acids

Proton-donating acids have long been used for a variety of alkylation studies. Both sulfuric acid and hydrogen fluoride are in use commercially for a variety of olefin–isoparaffin and aromatic–olefin alkylation reactions. A number of investigations have elucidated the fundamentals of a variety of typical acid-catalyzed reactions that may occur in these acids. With respect to alcohol alkylation, two systems have been widely used: sulfuric acid and phosphoric acid. Of these two, phosphoric acid is preferred for phenol alkylation since it gives rise to relatively uncomplicated products.

Other systems have been used such as HF, $HClO_4$, and mixed acids as sulfuric–acetic or acetic acid–HCl. In addition, relatively easy ion formers (such as the triarylcarbinols) have been studied in weak acids as formic.

Various reaction mechanisms have been suggested for the action of these proton-donating species. Such schemes may be realistically reduced to two paths. In the first path, protonation of the alcohol may be envisioned (equation 92). This protonated alcohol may then give rise to a carbonium ion (equation 93) and the resulting ion can undergo an electrophilic attack on a reactive species (equation 94). If the bond is not highly polarized then the intermediate will be similar to the weakly polarized metal halide complexes previously described and similar reaction and selectivity factors will apply. Such weakly polarized species could be present with n-alkyl alcohols or in weakly proton-donating acids. With such systems, the alkylation will probably occur via the protonated alcohol complex as in equation 95.

$$HA \rightleftharpoons H^+ + A^- \tag{91}$$

$$ROH + H^+ \rightleftharpoons ROH_2^+ \tag{92}$$

$$ROH_2^+ \rightleftharpoons R^+ + H_2O \tag{93}$$

$$R^+ + B—H \rightleftharpoons Product + H^+ \tag{94}$$

$$ROH_2^+ + B—H \rightarrow Product + H_2O + H^+ \tag{95}$$

A second mechanism invokes the formation of unsaturated hydrocarbons, presumably by proton loss from R^+, and subsequent transformation of these unsaturated hydrocarbons into alkyl sulfonic acids. These acids then alkylate the reactive species.

Aryl carbonium-ion formation has been amply demonstrated in proton-donating acids as long ago as 1908 by Hantzsch (114). This investigator found that the Van't Hoff i-factors for triphenylmethanol and 4,4',4"-triiodotriphenylmethanol in 100% sulfuric acid were slightly greater than three. Hammett and Deyrup (115) in 1933 demonstrated that an i-factor of exactly four could be obtained for triphenylmethanol in sulfuric acid if water was added to repress the self-ionization of the sulfuric acid. This result showed that these ionic solutions in sulfuric acid exhibit ideal behavior. Recent work by Deno and Taft (116) and Newman and Deno (117) supported this interpretation. In addition, an extensive series of investigations on mono-, di-, and triaryl alcohols

18 + F.C. II

in 100% sulfuric acid shows that these alcohols dissolve to give exactly four particles per molecule of solute and these findings may be summed up in the following equations:

$$\text{Ar}_3\text{COH} + \text{H}_2\text{SO}_4 \rightleftharpoons \text{Ar}_3\text{C}^+ + \text{H}_3\text{O}^+ + 2\text{HSO}_4^- \tag{96}$$

$$\text{Ar}_2\text{CHOH} + \text{H}_2\text{SO}_4 \rightleftharpoons \text{Ar}_2\text{CH}^+ + \text{H}_3\text{O}^+ + 2\text{HSO}_4^- \tag{97}$$

$$\text{ArCH}_2\text{OH} + \text{H}_2\text{SO}_4 \rightleftharpoons \text{ArCH}_2^+ + \text{H}_3\text{O}^+ + 2\text{HSO}_4^- \tag{98}$$

The stability of the monoaryl systems is not high presumably due to competing alkylation and ether formation reactions. In the case of alkyl alcohols no clear-cut physical evidence of this type has been obtained to show that stable carbonium ionic species can be formed, although recent work by Symons has presumably provided spectroscopic evidence for alkyl ions in sulfuric acid. The alkyl cations are many times more reactive than the aryl cations and they undergo reactions such as proton loss to form olefins.

A reasonable test for the validity of such intermediates can utilize the acidity function H_R (118). For example, a reaction of an alcohol that involves an equilibrium ionization to the carbonium ion prior to the rate-determining step should show a dependence of the observed rate constant on the H_R function. This is the result of the following considerations. Consider the ionization equilibria (equation 99) as described by equation 100.

$$\text{R}^+ + \text{H}_2\text{O} \rightleftharpoons \text{ROH} + \text{H}^+ \tag{99}$$

$$K'_{\text{R}^+} = \frac{a_{\text{H}^+}f_{\text{ROH}}C_{\text{ROH}}}{a_{\text{H}_2\text{O}}f_{\text{R}^+}C_{\text{R}^+}} \tag{100}$$

Then equation 101 may be derived by defining H_R so that it equals $-\log H_R$.

$$K_{\text{R}^+}^{\text{Eq}} = \frac{C_{\text{ROH}}}{C_{\text{R}^+}} H_R. \tag{101}$$

A combination of these equations leads to equation 102.

$$H_R = \frac{a_{\text{R}^+}f_{\text{ROH}}}{a_{\text{H}_2\text{O}}f_{\text{R}^+}} \tag{102}$$

Then if the ionization equilibrium is followed by a reaction of the form of equation 103, a new expression, equation 105 may be derived:

$$\text{R}^+ + \text{B—H} \rightleftharpoons [\text{R}^+ \cdot \text{B} \cdot \cdot \text{H}]^{\#} \rightarrow \text{Product} \tag{103}$$

$$\text{Rate} = k C_{\text{R}} \frac{f_{\text{R}^+}}{f_{\text{R}^{\#}}} \tag{104}$$

$$= \frac{k}{K_{\text{R}^+}} C_{\text{ROH}} H r. \frac{f_{\text{R}^+}}{f_{\text{R}^{\#}}} \tag{105}$$

At a specific acid concentration, K_{R^+} and $f_{R^+}/f_{R^{\ddagger}}$ are constant and equation 106 holds.

$$\text{Rate} = k \text{ exp. } C_{ROH} \tag{106}$$

and

$$\log k \text{ exp.} = \log \frac{k}{K_{R^+}} + \log H_R + \log \frac{f_{R^+}}{f_{R^{\ddagger}}} \tag{107}$$

thus

$$\log k \text{ exp.} = \text{Constant} - H_R + \log \frac{f_{R^+}}{f_{R^{\ddagger}}} \tag{108}$$

Providing the last term in equation 108 is constant, a plot of the log of the experimentally determined rate constant versus H_R will give a linear curve with a slope of minus one. At present no data are available on alkylation reactions to test this hypothesis. However, by inference, some data reported in the following sections seem to bear out these speculations.

A. Alkylation by Alcohols using Sulfuric Acid

Alcohols react with benzene in the presence of sulfuric acid to give homologs of benzene. The reaction leads predominantly to *para*-substitution and may give rise to isomerized products involving H and CH_3 shifts. As an example, isobutyl alcohol produces *t*-butylbenzene with benzene and *t*-butyltoluene with toluene.

The primary neopentyl alcohol, alkylates benzene to give a 30% yield of *t*-amylbenzene. This reaction might be compared with $AlCl_3$ catalysis which gave a 9% yield of the unrearranged product, and boron fluoride which also produces *t*-amylbenzene.

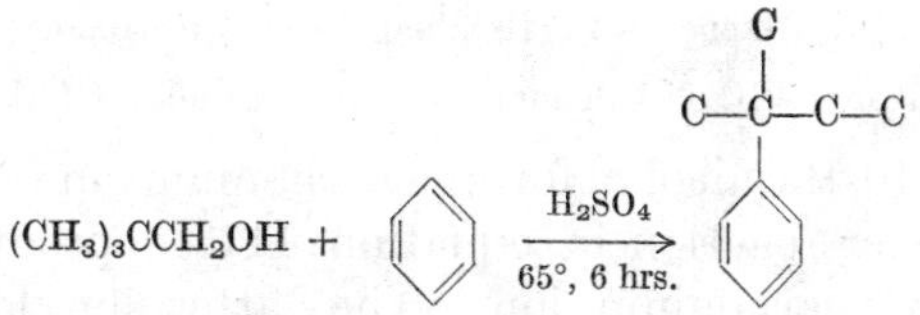

$$(CH_3)_3CCH_2OH + \quad \underset{\text{65°, 6 hrs.}}{\overset{H_2SO_4}{\longrightarrow}} \quad \tag{109}$$

In all cases, primary, secondary, and tertiary ionic intermediates may be involved. Obviously, it is unrealistic to consider the *t*-amyl carbonium ion as a free carbonium ion with each catalyst species. Whether the differences are related to polarity differences of the catalyst–alcohol complexes or differences in the stabilities of the π- or σ-complexes is not known. Certainly, the counter ion is important and cannot be neglected.

Reactions involving alkyl ions in sulfuric acid can become exceedingly complex as shown by recent results obtained during isoparaffin–olefin alkylation. As an example, during isobutylene–isobutane alkylation in sulfuric acid at 25° the isooctyl carbonium ion, which is formed as an intermediate can undergo three reactions. Proton abstraction to yield isooctane, proton elimination to form isooctene or alkylation by another olefin molecule to form a C_{12}^+ species. In addition, isomerization of the isooctyl and C_{12}^+ intermediate can occur involving both hydrogen and methyl shifts (119).

While equivalent studies have not been carried out during alcohol alkylation the intermediates are formally similar. Therefore, it is not surprising to find that sulfuric acid isomerizes the alkylating species (H and CH_3 shift) and causes β-scission reactions. An example of the reactions that can occur with the alkyl alcohols in sulfuric acid is provided by a study carried out by Marschner and Carmody in 1951 (120). These investigators used isobutyl, t-butyl, and isoamyl alcohols to alkylate the isoparaffins, isobutane and isopentane. The active species must be similar to those produced in the isoparaffin–olefin work described previously.

It was found that isoamyl alcohol and isobutane consumed twice as much isobutane as accounted for by simple alkylation. In addition, with isopentane and either isobutyl or t-butyl alcohol almost stoichiometric quantities of isobutane were generated along with isomeric decanes and hexanes.

These reactions may be interpreted on the basis of the following overall equations:

$$C_mOH \rightarrow C_m^+ \tag{110}$$

$$C_n \text{ (isoalkane)} + C_m^+ \rightarrow C_mH + C_n^+ \text{ (isoalkane)} \tag{111}$$

$$C_n^+ \text{ (isoalkane)} \rightleftharpoons C_n \text{ (isoalkene)} + H^+ \tag{112}$$

$$C_n \text{ (isoalkene)} + C_n^+ \text{ (isoalkane)} \rightarrow C_{2n}^+ \text{ (isoalkane)} \tag{113}$$

$$C_{2n}^+ \text{ (isoalkane)} + C_n \text{ (isoalkane)} \rightarrow C_{2n} \text{ (isoalkane)} + C_n^+ \text{ (isoalkane)} \tag{114}$$

In equation 110, the alcohol forms a carbonium ion which undergoes a hydride transfer reaction in equation 111 to produce a paraffin plus an isoalkyl carbonium ion. The latter ion loses a proton in equation 112 to form an olefin which is, in turn, alkylated by another isoalkyl ion in equation 113. This dimer ion then undergoes another hydride transfer reaction to produce the high molecular weight isoalkane plus more isoalkyl ions (equation 114).

The production of decanes and hexanes may be rationalized by a breakdown of the dimer C_{10}^+ ion to hexyl and t-butyl fragments, i.e.,

$$2C_5 \rightleftharpoons C_{10} \rightleftharpoons C_6 + C_4 \tag{115}$$

Cycloalkylation has also been studied in sulfuric acid and, as in the case of phosphoric acid, alkyl shifts are noted. Schrauth (121), for example, studied the alkylation of β-naphthol with the various methylcyclohexanols. In the presence of sulfuric acid only one product is obtained, 4-(1-methylcyclohexyl)phenol. The reaction sequence is surely the same as depicted in Section III-B for H_3PO_4. When a substance capable of forming a tertiary ion directly is present, little alkyl shift occurs and Buu-Hoï found that 1,3-dimethylcyclopentanol yields 6-(1,3-dimethylcyclopentyl)-2-naphthol with β-naphthol (122).

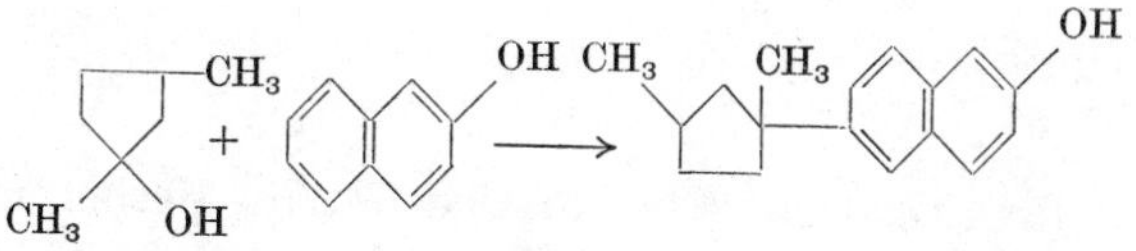

(116)

In the naphthalene series, the naphthalene is first sulfonated by sulfuric acid and the sulfo group then directs the course of the reaction. For instance, in alkylation with isopropyl alcohol an α-sulfonaphthalene leads to a β-isopropyl derivative and a β-sulfo derivative leads to an α-isopropyl derivative (123).

Intramolecular reaction can occur with little or no competing side reactions and an example is the work of Mukherji et al. (124). These investigators studied phenanthrene as follows:

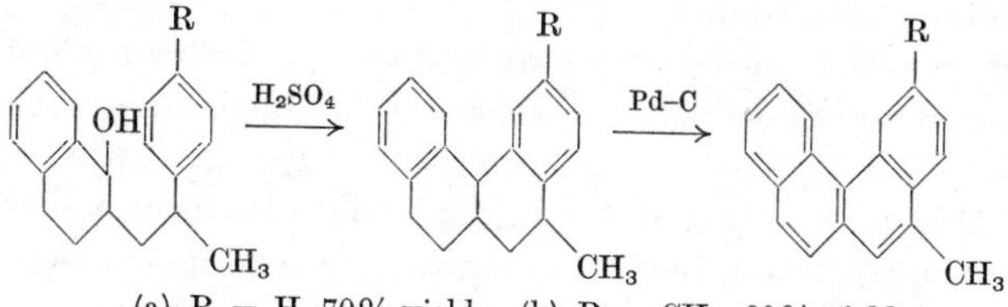

(117)

(a) R = H, 70% yield;   (b) R = CH_3, 60% yield.

Similar cyclodehydration reactions of substituted alcohols (125) have been carried out with the following system:

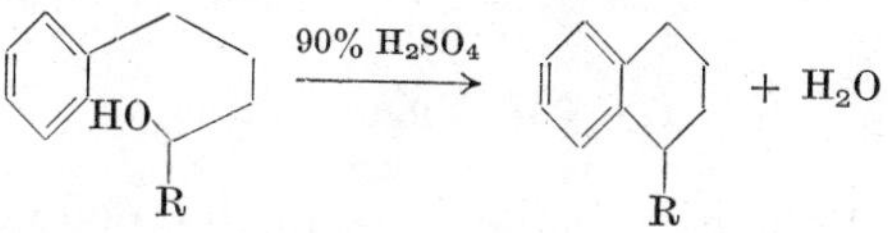

(118)

Considerable variation in the structure of the reacting alcohol is possible. For instance, 1-methyltetralin is formed from 2-, 3-, 4-, or 5-hydroxy-1-phenylpentane as well as from 5-phenylpent-1-ene. Branching on the third carbon from the ring leads partly to indane formation.

Extensive fundamental studies have been carried out with certain aromatic alcohols. An early paper on the mechanism of these reactions suggested that the reaction goes through the intermediate formation of a carbonium ion as follows (126):

$$(C_6H_5)_3COH + H_2SO_4 \rightarrow (C_6H_5)_3COSO_2OH \rightleftharpoons (C_6H_5)_3C^+ + SO_4H^- \qquad (119)$$

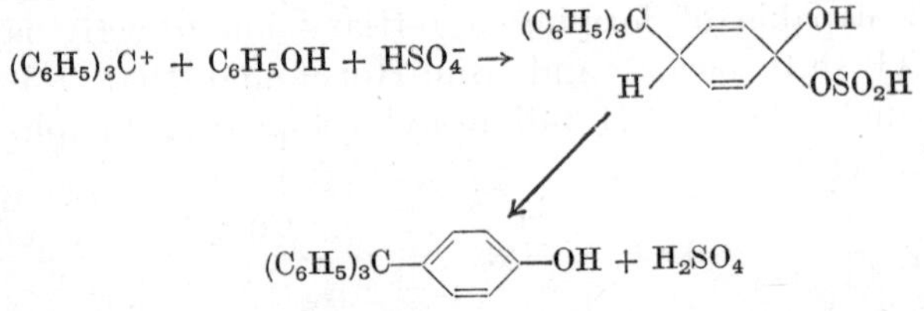

$$(120)$$

More recent investigations were carried out by Bethel and Gold (127) and by Bonner *et al.* (128). Bethell and Gold studied the kinetics of the acid-catalyzed alkylation by diarylmethanols in H_2SO_4–HOAc solutions. Triphenylmethanes were formed and the rates of product formation were investigated at 25° with and without the addition of small amounts of water. In concert, the ionization equilibria of the basic methoxydiphenylmethanol and of 4,4′,4″-tribromotriphenylmethanol were examined in these media. The reactions studied were those between mesitylene and diphenylmethanol, anisole and diphenylmethanol, and mesitylene and 4,4-dichlorodiphenylmethanol.

Kinetic reaction orders and agreement of indicator ionization ratios with reaction velocities indicate a bimolecular attack of the rapidly forming diphenyl carbonium ion on the aromatic. Further proof of this was obtained by finding that deuterium labeling at the seat of substitution had no effect on the reaction velocity.

A summary of the deductions from the kinetic and indicator measurements is as follows:

$$\left. \begin{array}{l} XOH \\ XOAc \end{array} \right\} + H^+ \rightleftharpoons X^+ + \left. \begin{array}{l} H_2O \\ HOAc \end{array} \right\} \text{ Rapid pre-equilibrium} \qquad (121)$$

$$X^+ + ArH \rightarrow ArX + H^+ \quad \text{Rate-controlling} \qquad (122)$$

The reaction is obviously similar both in the mode of generation of the active entity in a pre-equilibrium step, and in the nature of the substitution step proper to aromatic nitration (129).

Bonner *et al.* (128) in a similar investigation have studied the aromatic alkylation reaction. These investigators discuss the triphenylmethylation of *o*-cresol in sulfuric acid–acetic acid mixtures.

The reaction under consideration is the formation of 3-methyl-4-hydroxyphenyltriphenylmethane (equation 123). This reaction

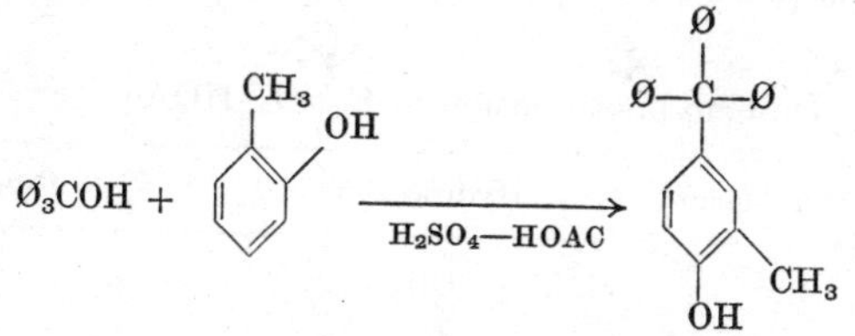

$$\emptyset_3COH + \quad \xrightarrow[\text{H}_2\text{SO}_4\text{--HOAC}]{} \quad \tag{123}$$

was first studied by Baeyer and Villiger (130) who found that phenol formed p-hydroxytriphenylmethane and that anisole formed p-methoxyphenyltriphenylmethane. Later studies by Canoe and Kanna (131) showed that the sulfuric acid is purely a catalyst and could be reduced or replaced by HCl.

Because of the known ability of triphenylmethanol to form the stable triphenylmethyl carbonium ion in sulfuric acid, it would seem reasonable to expect this ion to be the alkylating agent. Bonner *et al.* correlated the rate of alkylation with the degree of ionization of the alcohol. The alkylation rates were linearly related to the ionization ratios over the range of 0–22.5% H_2SO_4. Bimolecular kinetics best fitted the data and a rate expression shown in equation 124 was used as the best fit.

Assuming that

$$\frac{-d[\text{Ph}_3\text{COH}]}{dt} = k_2[\text{Ph}_3\text{COH}][o\text{-cresol}] \tag{124}$$

the reaction is bimolecular between a $\emptyset_3C^+$ ion and o-cresol equation 125 will hold:

$$\text{Rate} = k_0[\text{Ph}_3\text{C}^+][o\text{-cresol}] \tag{125}$$

k_0 is the theoretical rate constant and is medium independent.

$$k_2 = k_0[\text{Ph}_3\text{C}^+]/[\text{Ph}_3\text{COH}] \tag{126}$$

The observed rate, k_2, would therefore be linearly related to the ionization ratio of equation 126. Above 25% H_2SO_4 some difficulties were observed. This was ascribed to the formation of the conjugate acid of o-cresol ($CH_3C_6H_4OH_2^+$) which probably will only enter with difficulty into an electrophilic substitution reaction.

A rather interesting example of steric versus electronic effects in alkylation using bulky alkylating agents concerns data on diphenylmethylation of methylbenzenes. Sulfuric acid–acetic acid mixtures have been used to carry out this reaction and excellent yields of the monoalkylated product are obtained using an excess of hydrocarbon (132). Both o- and p-positions are activated and where such substitution is possible only the p-substituted product is obtained.

TABLE VII. Diphenylmethylation in H_2SO_4–HOAc

Alkylating agent	Hydrocarbon	Product
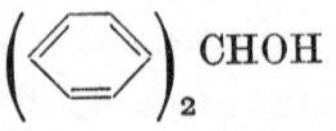 $(C_6H_5)_2CHOH$	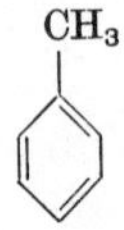 toluene (CH₃-phenyl)	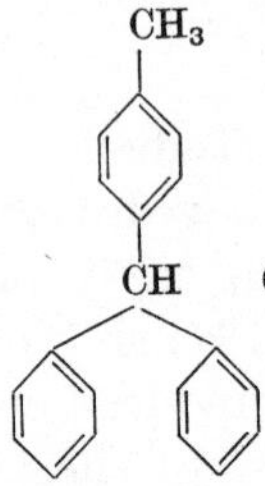 4-methylphenyl–CH(C₆H₅)₂ 61%
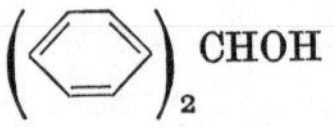 $(C_6H_5)_2CHOH$	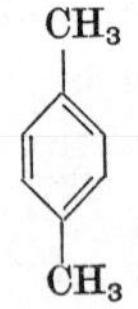 p-xylene (CH₃, CH₃)	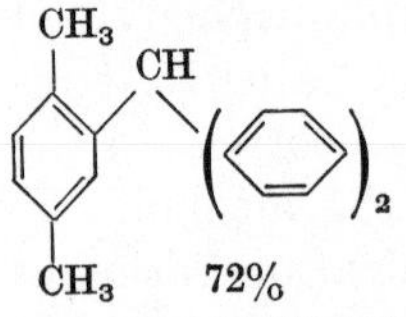 2,5-dimethylphenyl–CH(C₆H₅)₂ 72%

When the *para*-position is blocked, diphenylmethylation occurs in the *ortho*-position in about the same yield.

B. Alkylation by Alcohols using Phosphoric Acid

As previously indicated, phosphoric acid has been extensively utilized in the alkylation reaction involving phenols. This preference for phosphoric acid over other catalysts is due to the fact that equimolar quantities of reacting substances yield monoalkylphenols in yields up to 90%. The quantity of phosphoric acid necessary for the alkylation reaction is usually very large. As an example, 400 g. of phosphoric acid are required per mole of phenol and per mole of alcohol in order to produce alkylphenols (133,134).

Phenolic compounds require raised temperatures with phosphoric acid, and tertiary alcohols react at 70–80°, primary and secondary iso-alcohols react at 80–100°, and normal primary alcohols require a temperature in the region of 100–130° (135). At these conditions the *para*-isomers are reportedly the major product. As expected, benzyl alcohol is the most active primary alcohol studied owing to the ease of formation of the benzyl carbonium ion (133).

Chichibabin has reported, in an extensive investigation, that at

50–65°, phenols condense with secondary and tertiary alcohols to give mainly the alkylphenols with little *para*-derivative (133,134, 136). A later investigation of this selectivity relationship was carried out by Hart who found that *t*-butyl alcohol alkylates *m*-cresol in the position *ortho* to the hydroxyl and *para* to the methyl group (137). Hart also showed that Chichibabin's claim to have formed 2-methyl(*t*-butyl)phenol by alkylation of *o*-cresol with *t*-butyl alcohol was incorrect.

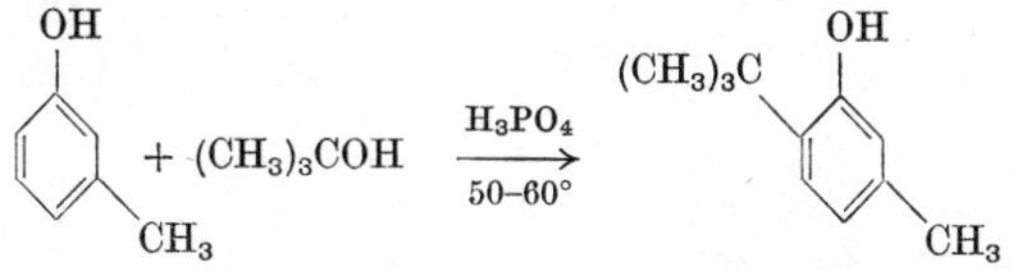

$$\text{(127)}$$

Under the conditions used, the *para*-isomer results and Hart showed that this is probably the result of the isomerization of the initially formed *ortho*-isomer by the influence of catalyst and temperature.

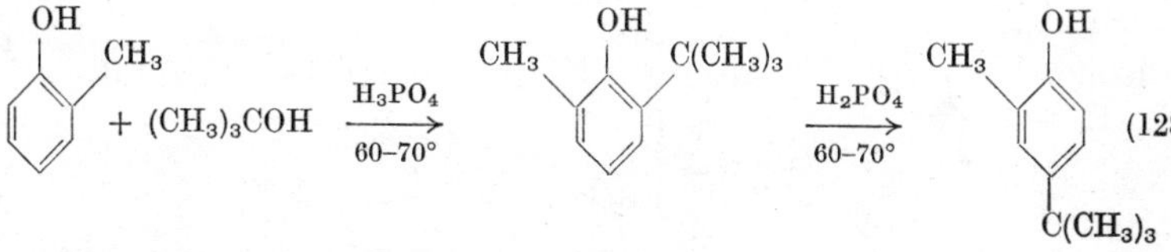

$$\text{(128)}$$

Dubinin has also prepared 4-*t*-butyl-*o*-cresol under these conditions (138). These examples again illustrate the point that product distribution in aromatic alkylation is the result of both alkylation selectivity factors and relative isomerization rates in the presence of the catalyst used.

Phosphoric acid has less tendency to isomerize paraffinic ring systems than $AlCl_3$. Therefore, cyclic alcohols in the cyclo-alkylation reactions tend to give high yields of unisomerized cyclo-alkylphenols. For example, it is possible to prepare *p*-cyclohexyl-phenols in 80.1% yield by the alkylation of phenol with cyclohexanol (139). It is also possible to prepare 4-(1-methylcyclohexyl)phenol in a yield of 79% at 100–120° (140). In the latter case an inter-mediate ether was also formed and this isomerized into the *para*-product.

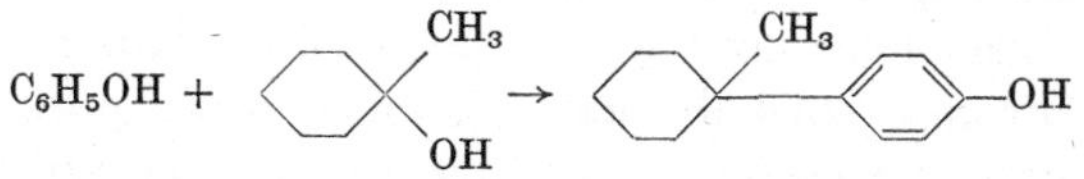

$$C_6H_5OH + \qquad\qquad\qquad \rightarrow \qquad\qquad\qquad -OH \qquad \text{(129)}$$

Naphthols are also alkylated by alcohols over phosphoric acid in varying yields. As an example, cyclohexanol with β-naphthol

18*

gives a small yield of 6-cyclohexyl-2-naphthol (141). The selectivity falls in line with prediction of naphthalene reactivity based on electron-density calculations (142). Methylcyclohexanols were also used in this alkylation reaction and good yields of monosubstituted products were obtained. However, each of the three isomeric methylcyclohexanols generates the same product as shown in equation 130.

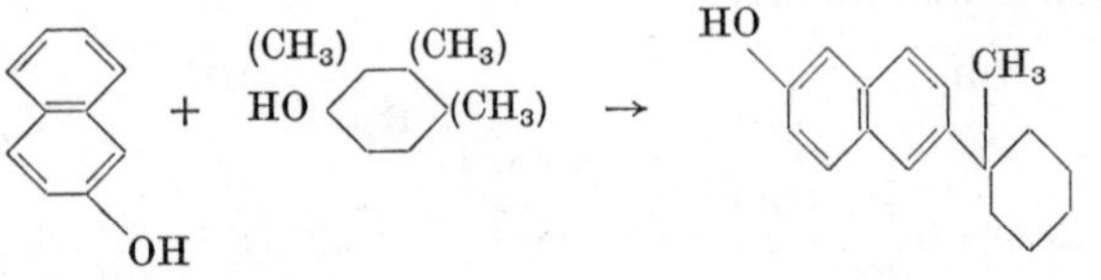

$$+ \quad \text{(CH}_3\text{)} \quad \text{(CH}_3\text{)} \quad \text{HO} \quad \text{(CH}_3\text{)} \quad \rightarrow \quad \text{CH}_3 \tag{130}$$

Evidently an isomerization takes place and this may be depicted as proceeding to give the relatively stable t-methylcyclohexyl carbonium ion.

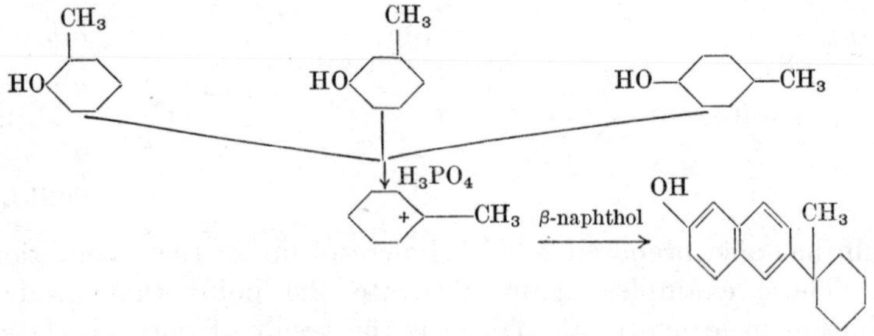

$$\downarrow \text{H}_3\text{PO}_4 \qquad \beta\text{-naphthol} \qquad \text{CH}_3 \tag{131}$$

3. Metal Oxides

While not used as much as proton acids or metal halides, solid oxides have often been employed as catalysts for alkylation reactions involving both alcohols and ethers. These oxides do not have the strong tendency to complex with unsaturated materials, nor do they cause unwanted side reactions such as polymerization as do the other typical alkylation catalysts. Because of these properties they are particularly suited for alkylation reactions involving amines and mercaptans.

The oxides employed are usually mixtures of silica–alumina prepared synthetically or obtained naturally as natural clays or bauxite. They have been long used in the petroleum industry as cracking catalysts. Product distributions obtained with pure compounds over these cracking catalysts are high in iso-structure content and the only reasonable interpretation for these types of products is to postulate positive ionic intermediates (143). Such intermediates can be only produced if the surface has acid properties. A detailed picture of an alumina–silica surface is probably extremely complex and several geometrical configurations have been postulated (143).

Pines has recently reported on an extensive investigation of the chemical properties of aluminas (144). He has concluded that such oxides contain Lewis and Brønsted active centers. How these are generated is still a debatable question. Lewis acidity could arise from the ability of the aluminum atom to accept a pair of electrons. Brønsted acidity might arise from the absorption of a hydroxylic surface group with resulting ionization of a proton–oxygen bond. Yates and Lucchesi have recently reported on an infra-red study of the absorption of acetylene and substituted acetylenes on alumina surfaces. These authors find bonding both to the π-cloud and to the terminal C–H bond. The former bonding can be that of proton donation or absorption on the vacant site of alumina. The latter can be interpreted as being due to proton donation (hydrogen bond formation) to the oxygen atoms present either in the alumina lattice or as bound surface water (145).

A. Alkylation of Benzene and Phenols by Alcohols

Catalytic alkylation of benzene in the vapor phase by alcohols over oxides, such as alumina–silicates, has not been subject to much study. The yields of alkyl-substituted aromatics obtained from methyl and ethyl alcohols or chloride do not exceed 10–15% of the theoretical yield at atmospheric pressure (146–148). Only by operating at superatmospheric pressures was a yield up to 30% of theoretical obtained (149,150). Dolgov and Cherkasov extended this reaction to the higher alcohols at 320° over an alumina–silica catalyst at atmospheric pressure (150). They found that isopropyl alcohol gave a 50–60% yield of the monopropylated derivative. Also, n-propyl alcohol produced 45–58%, isopropyl chloride 58–63%, n-propyl bromide 67%, and isopropyl bromide 70–74% yield of monopropylated compound. Only small yields of alkylbenzenes were found with ethyl, isobutyl, and t-butyl alcohols. Propylene also alkylates benzene at these conditions, but catalyst activity declines.

The alkylated product in all cases is composed of the isomerized derivative. Thus, n-propyl alcohol gives isopropylbenzene and isobutyl bromide gives t-butylbenzene. Propylene also yields the isomerized derivative. Indeed, the reaction is strikingly similar to the low-temperature reactions carried out with so-called "typical" acid catalysts. It only requires the postulate of the formation of polar species as indicated in the opening section to explain product distribution. The formation of isomerized derivatives certainly indicates the presence of relatively free ionic species and strong acid catalysts. Alternative hypotheses of olefin formation do not seem tenable in view of the alkylation reaction carried out by methanol where intermediate olefin formation is not possible.

A similar conclusion may be reached from studies on the alkylation of chlorobenzene by propyl alcohols over alumina–silica catalysts (151).

$$
\begin{array}{c}
\text{Cl} \\
\bigcirc
\end{array}
\xrightarrow[\text{iso-C}_3\text{H}_7\text{OH}\quad 250° \text{ atm. p.}]{\overset{n\text{-C}_3\text{H}_7\text{OH}}{\text{Al}_2\text{O}_3\text{–SiO}_2}}
\begin{array}{c}
\text{Cl} \\
\bigcirc \\
\text{C} \\
\diagup \ \diagdown \\
\text{C} \quad \text{C}
\end{array}
\qquad (132)
$$

Yield of 97% with iso-C$_3$H$_7$OH
Yield of 58% with n-C$_3$H$_7$OH

It was reported that both n- and isopropyl alcohol gave para-isopropylchlorobenzene. The same product is made using sulfuric acid or AlCl$_3$ to alkylate chlorobenzene with isopropyl alcohol. There are other illustrations of the aromatic alcohol reaction described in the patent literature and these are listed in Table VIII.

Many phenolic materials have been alkylated by alcohols over alumina or alumina–silica catalysts. The yields in general are not as high as those employing the more typical "acid" systems and high-temperature flow reaction techniques are usually required. One of the earliest workers in this area was Ipatieff (152–154), who alkylated phenol with methyl alcohol over alumina at 440° and 220 atm. pressure. He obtained both anisole and o-cresol. The high pressures were apparently required since Briner et al. in 1956 reported that phenol and methyl alcohol yield only hexamethyl-benzene at atmospheric pressure (155).

$$
\begin{array}{c}
\text{OH} \\
\bigcirc
\end{array}
\xrightarrow[\text{Al}_2\text{O}_3]{\text{CH}_3\text{OH}}
\begin{array}{c}
\text{CH}_3 \\
\text{CH}_3 \diagup \diagdown \text{CH}_3 \\
\bigcirc \\
\text{CH}_3 \diagdown \diagup \text{CH}_3 \\
\text{CH}_3
\end{array}
\qquad (133)
$$

The mechanism of the latter reaction has not been studied and it represents a rather interesting example of the possible uses of the solid oxides.

Ipatieff also studied ethyl alcohol and n-propyl alcohol alkylation of phenol. Ethyl alcohol is reported to give a lower yield of alkylated material than methanol (156).   Propyl alcohol gives rise to a mixture of products at 400° and 130 atmospheric pressure.   These included o-propylphenol and n-propylphenol.   A later investigation by Cullinane has shown that reaction conditions and catalyst nature are extremely important variables (157).

For example, lowering the temperature to 200° results in the production of anisole from methyl alcohol and phenol over alumina. As the temperature is raised, o-, m-, and p-methyl phenols are formed.   The proportions of these change as the temperature increases.   These results might show that the first product formed is an ether that undergoes subsequent acid-catalyzed rearrangement. However, the data do not justify accurate kinetic analysis and it is not possible to distinguish this path from the alternative postulate of two separate and competing reactions.   These are ether formation and alkylation.   The latter probably has a higher activation energy and, therefore, would only occur at temperatures above those required for ether formation.   The change in ortho-:meta-:para-ratios in the latter path could occur either by a competing iso-merization reaction or via differences in positional attack.   This question has not been studied.   It is also interesting to note that at the same temperature, changes in isomer ratios occur as the catalyst is changed from alumina to alumina–silica (158).   This must reflect a change in the acidity of the catalyst and a consequent change in the nature of polar surface–alcohol complexes.   The entire field has been little studied, however, and it is hardly possible to draw conclusions concerning relative catalyst activities or efficiencies from these data.

B. Alkylation of Naphthalene by Alcohols

Little work has been reported on the alkylation of polycyclics such as naphthalene over oxide catalysts.   It is expected that substitution in the 1-position would be favored rather than sub-stitution in the 2-position (129,158).   Partial rate factors for nitration in the 1- and 2-position of naphthalene are 470 and 50 respectively and atom localization energies also lie in this direction.

Alkylation over alumina–silica type catalysts, however, leads to 2-alkylnaphthalenes exclusively.   Thus, at 450°, methyl alcohol plus naphthalene gives a product that contains 2-methylnaphthalene (52% yield based on naphthalene consumed) plus dimethylnaphtha-lenes and higher alkylated products.   No 1-isomer could be detected (148).

The suggestion was made that this result could be interpreted on the basis of an initial attack on the 1-position followed by iso-merization to the 2-isomer. This possibility was examined by passing 1-methylnaphthalene over an alumina–silica catalyst at 450°. The initial isomer is completely transformed under these conditions and gives the 2-methyl isomer as the main product with smaller amounts of naphthalene and dimethylnaphthalenes (159). These results can be accommodated by a bimolecular reaction in which both groups can either switch to the 2-position or dispropor-tionate thus:

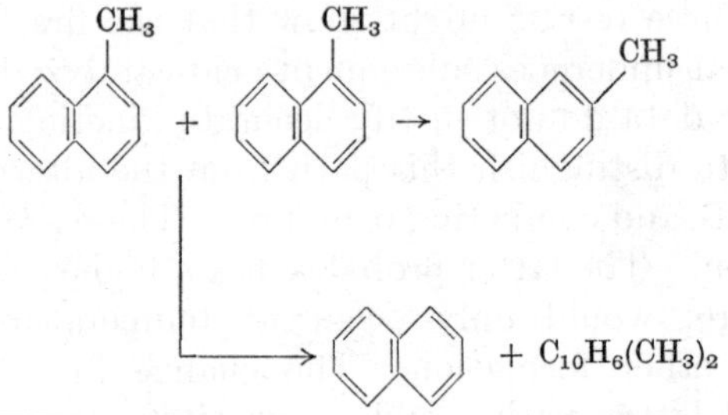

$$+ C_{10}H_6(CH_3)_2 \qquad (135)$$

The question of mode of movement and initial alkylation step is certainly not clear. Operation at low conversions with methanol and with tagged alkylnaphthalenes would seem to be indicated.

With higher alcohols such as dodecyl, tetradecyl, hexadecyl, and octadecyl reaction temperatures may be lowered to 190°. These lead to mono-, di-, and trialkylnaphthalenes in good yield. Struc-tures were not determined, however, and it is not reported whether isomerization of the entering species occurred or whether alkylation occurred at the 1- or 2-position (160).

C. Alkylation of Ammonia by Alcohols

Oxides have been frequently studied for the alkylation of am-monia and primary and secondary amines with alcohols to produce substituted amines. The overall equation is:

$$\overset{H}{\underset{}{H_{(R')}NH_{(R')}}} + R''OH \rightarrow \overset{R'''}{\underset{}{H_{(R')}NH_{(R')}}} + H_2O \qquad (136)$$

where R′, R″ are alkyl or aryl groups
      R‴ is an alkyl group.

Historically, with respect to the ammonolysis reaction, Sabatier and Mailhe (161) in 1909 obtained a mixture of primary, secondary, and tertiary amines by passing vapors of alcohols and ammonia over thoria heated to 360°. In 1923, Smolensky reacted ethyl alcohol with ammonia at 330–350°C to obtain a 53% yield of ethylamines (162).   In 1924, Brown and Reid found that a special silica gel gave fair quantities of amines from ammonia and aliphatic alcohols (163).   Later studies used nickel, copper, and alumina silicates, mixtures of the oxides of iron, chromium, etc., with alumina, etc. (164).

Much of the information regarding this ammonolysis reaction is patented and the details are not clear.   Controversial claims are made and only one recent paper has gone into the reaction in some detail, by studying the reaction of n-butyl alcohol with ammonia to give butylamines and water (164).   This reaction is endothermic to the extent of 5.37 kcal./g.mole and has a free energy of reaction

$$n\text{-}C_4H_9OH_{(g)} + NH_{3(g)} \rightarrow n\text{-}C_4H_9NH_{2(g)} + H_2O_{(g)} \tag{137}$$

ΔF_{25} of $+7.69$ kcal./g.mole.   Equilibrium constant values indicate that at 300°C and 20 atmospheres pressure only about 1% of the amine can be formed.   Heinemann, however, reports a maximum yield over bauxite of 58% (165).

It has been found (164) that temperature, ammonia concentration, reaction time, traces of water, total pressure, and mode of catalyst preparation effect product yield and selectivity.   Other investigators have not studied the reaction as intensively and these variations probably cause the differences in experimental results.

Briefly, the yield of amines increases with temperature up to 325°, after which formation of hydrocarbons starts with a simultaneous diminution in the yield of amines.   When the ammonia to alcohol mole ratio is varied at 300° it was found that at high mole ratios (11.37) primary amine predominates while at low mole ratios primary, secondary, and tertiary amines are made.   No decomposition to hydrocarbons occurs at 300° and only the unisomerized n-butyl derivatives were found.

With respect to reaction time, it was found that about 50% reaction occurred during the first 30 minutes and the next 50% over about a two-hour period at 300°.   Total conversions reached 24% and no decomposition was noted even after five hours indicating that the amines are stable at these conditions.   The effect of water is quite marked and its addition reduces the yield of the amine. Thus, the conversion is decreased from 24 to 15% at a mole ratio of water to alcohol of 2:1 at 300°.   Interestingly enough an increase in total pressure from 300 to 4800 psig reduces the conversion.

Finally, various modes of preparing the catalyst were investigated and an attempt was made to correlate activity with porosity as shown in Table VIII (164).

TABLE VIII.   Activity of various catalysts

Butyl alcohol = 2.5 ml.	Temperature = 300°C
Ammonia = 3.7 liters (N.T.P.)	Time = 2.5 hrs.
Ammonia/alcohol = 6 (mole)	Catalyst volume = 20 ml.

No.	Prep. by Al_2O_3	Porosity expressed as gH_2O/gAl_2O_3	Final psig	% Amines
1	$Al(NO_3)_3$	0.3692	300	24.58
2	$AlCl_3 + H_2O$	0.3521	300	19.98
3	Alum. (potassium)	0.3228	300	11.54
4	$Al_2(SO_4)_3$	0.3151	300	18.94
5	γ-Alumina	0.2736	300	18.12

The decrease in activity is in the same order as the decrease in porosity with the exception of the alumina prepared from potassium alumina.   It is extremely interesting that a postulate of poisoning of active acid sites by the potassium in this case exactly parallels the conclusion of Pines.   The latter finds that alumina containing traces of potassium are relatively inactive for double bond migration and alcohol dehydration.   This is also presumably due to the poisoning of active acid sites.

A detailed picture of the reaction mechanism involving the catalyst, alcohol, and ammonia molecule may be developed from these data.   Using a picture of the catalyst in which the alcohol is polarized to an ionic form:

$$O{=}Al{-}O{-}Al{=}O + R{-}\overset{\displaystyle H}{\underset{\displaystyle H}{C}}{-}OH \rightarrow O{=}Al{-}O{-}Al{=}O + RCH_2^+ \quad (138)$$

$$RCH_2^+ + :\overset{H}{\underset{H}{N}}{-}H \rightarrow \left[R{-}\overset{H}{\underset{H}{\overset{+}{C}}}{-}\overset{H}{\underset{H}{N}}{-}H \right] \rightarrow R{-}\overset{H}{\underset{H}{C}}NH_2 + H^+ \quad (139)$$

$$H^+ + O{-}Al{-}O{-}Al{=}O \rightarrow HOH + O{=}Al{-}O{-}Al{=}O \quad (140)$$

In the first step the alcohol is activated by adsorption on the alumina with a consequent weakening of the carbon–oxygen bond. An entity similar to a carbonium ion is formed which then reacts with ammonia (on the surface) to form the amine and a proton.

The proton reacts with the hydroxyl group to generate water. An alternative scheme involving surface protons may be envisioned; however, until further work is done the above formalism probably explains the facts well enough.

The ion cannot be far from the alumina since only the n-butyl derivatives were observed with no isomerization to the more stable s-butyl ion. An alternative mechanism involving olefin formation as a prerequisite for reaction would seem to be ruled out on two counts. First the authors find few olefins at alkylating conditions when ammonia is not used and secondly the olefin was found to be unreactive under these conditions with ammonia. The small amounts of olefins that are found may be conceived as the results of a secondary reaction involving proton loss from the ionic intermediate.

D. Alkylation of Amines by Alcohols

As early as 1918, Mailhe and deGodon (166) showed that thoria and zirconia are effective for the n-methylation of aniline and that alumina is exceptionally suitable for n-methylating aniline, o-, m-, and p-toluidine. In 1924, Brown and Reid (167) reported that silica gel, which is also used as an alcohol amination catalyst is effective for the n-alkylation of aniline. These investigators studied methyl, ethyl, n-propyl, and n-butyl alcohols at 300–500°. They also found that the alcohols dehydrated to olefins and dehydrogenated to aldehydes in addition to undergoing alkylation. These investigators found both mono- and dialkylation but unfortunately did not state whether isomerization of the alkyl group occurred. Yields averaged about 40% and no correlation of yield (rate) with alkyl groups could be observed.

In 1955 Munroe and Washington (168) reported on a study of the alkylation of ethylaniline by ethyl alcohol over alumina. These investigators found a marked effect of gel water on the yield. An optimum occurring at about 5% water and 300°. They also reported that the same catalyst was effective for ether formation, but no ether formed in the present work. The conclusion was then reached that the reaction took place in two stages, $i.e.$,

$$2C_2H_5OH \xrightarrow{Al_2O_3} C_2H_5OC_2H_5 + H_2O \tag{141}$$

$$C_2H_5OC_2H_5 + PhNHC_2H_5 \xrightarrow{Al_2O_3} PhN(C_2H_5)_2 + C_2H_5OH \tag{142}$$

However, the evidence is not conclusive and formation of a polar intermediate which can undergo two competing reactions is just as likely.

$$C_2H_5OH + Al_2O_3 \rightarrow C_2H_5^+ OH^- \cdot Al_2O_3 \qquad (143)$$

$$Al_2O_3 + H_2O + C_2H_5OC_2H_5 \quad \overset{\displaystyle H}{\underset{C_2H_5OH\ PhNC_2H_5}{\swarrow \qquad \searrow}} \quad PhN(C_2H_5)_2 + H_2O + Al_2O_3 \quad (144)$$

While the above investigators and others obtained only N-alkylation, it is possible to ring alkylate using an alumina at a high temperature, especially in the presence of activators. It is reported that in the alkylation of aniline with methyl and ethyl alcohols, these nuclear products are mainly N-methyl-p-toluidine and N-p-diethylaniline (169).

A study of this nuclear alkylation revealed that alumina produced mainly the n-alkylated derivative. However, certain salts were particularly effective in forming nuclear derivatives.

TABLE IX.   Nuclear derivatives of aniline and methanol

Temp., °C	Catalyst	Salt	% Nuclear alkylation	% Alkylation
250	Al_2O_3	None	3.8	38.0
290	Al_2O_3	None	3.0	19.4
290	Al_2O_3	NaCl	15.0	30.0
290	Al_2O_3	NaBr	58.4	57.8
290	Al_2O_3	NaI	65.1	60.6
290	Al_2O_3	$NiCl_2$	56.0	42.0

The mode of action of the salts at these temperatures is not known. However, it is known that acids will catalyze the rearrangement of N-alkyl aromatics. This subject has been studied intensively over the years and has been recently reviewed by Dewar (170). A mechanism for this reaction therefore might involve initial formation of the N-alkylated derivative over the alumina followed by migration from the nitrogen to the ortho- or para-positions of the ring. This would occur under the influence of acids either formed by reaction of the salts with water at elevated temperatures or with the alumina to form $AlCl_3$. Alternatively, the alcohol could react with the salts to form alkyl halides which could then form aniline derivatives and rearrange. Another conceivable role for the acids formed is to complex with the amino group preventing it from attacking the polarized alcohol molecule.

This theory was attacked by A. G. Hill *et al.* in 1951 (171). These investigators found that at 360°C, a somewhat higher temperature than previously used, aniline is *N*- and *C*-methylated over alumina. They then studied dimethylaniline by itself over alumina at 360° and found that it rearranges to give complex product mixtures including *o*-toluidine, monomethyl-*p*-toluidine, dimethyl-*p*-toluidine, 2,4-xylidine, dimethyl-2,4-xylidine, isoduridine, mesitylene, pentamethylbenzene, and hexamethylbenzene plus a predominant fraction of *p*-toluidine and mesidines. While acid-catalyzed rearrangement almost certainly plays a role, radical reactions at 360–440° cannot be ruled out and some light gases are formed.

The results seem to indicate that alcohol alkylation of anilines over alumina is stepwise. First, the *N*-alkyl derivative is obtained and this subsequently rearranges to the *C*-alkylated compound. More data are needed, however, before definite conclusions on this and on the mechanism of the rearrangement reaction itself are known.

Preliminary experiments also showed that *o*- and *p*-toluidine could be *N*-methylated over alumina at 360° to give about 90% tertiary amine. Higher alcohols were studied and here the yield of tertiary amine was low due to enhanced nuclear alkylation. This is in line with an acid-catalyzed rearrangement of *N*- to *C*-alkylation. Such a rearrangement would be easier as the alkyl groups become larger and more substituted. Various patents have issued on this subject and these are listed in Table 11.

E. Alkylation of Heterocyclics by Alcohols

Heterocyclic compounds are usually susceptible to polymerization at conditions used for alcohol alkylation. There only appears to be one literature reference to such alkylations using alumina type catalysts. This is a study carried out by Kutz and Corson in 1946 using an alumina–silica type catalyst (Filtrol X-143) (172).

They found that thiophene could be alkylated over this catalyst at 200° with isopropyl and *t*-butyl alcohol. A 38–56% yield of the 2-isomer was received. In both cases, further alkylation occurred

$$\text{(thiophene)} + \text{ROH} \xrightarrow[\text{200° C}]{\text{Al}_2\text{O}_3} \text{(alkylthiophene)} + \text{H}_2\text{O} \qquad (145)$$

and this was particularly true with the *t*-butyl derivative. The catalyst appears to be the only usable material for such an alkylation reaction since other systems cause thiophene side reactions.

F. Alkylation of Mercaptans and Hydrogen Sulfide by Alcohols

Alkylation of mercaptans by alcohols has been carried out mainly at elevated temperatures over alumina type systems (173,174). Results are interpretable if the assumption is made that the alcohol is polarized on the alumina surface and reaction then occurs with the mercaptan.

$$ROH + Al_2O_3 \rightarrow [R^+ Al_2O_3^- OH \rightleftharpoons R^+ + Al_2O_3\overline{OH}] \qquad (146)$$

$$R\text{---}S\text{---}R + H_2O + Al_2O_3 \qquad\qquad \begin{array}{c}\text{Cracking}\\ \text{---}H^+, \text{etc.}\end{array}$$

The reaction has been used to generate mercaptans from H_2S (173), thioethers from mercaptans (173), and tetrahydrothiophenes from H_2S and diols (174).

$$H_2S + CH_3OH \xrightarrow{Al_2O_3} CH_3SH + H_2O \qquad (148)$$

$$CH_3SH + CH_3OH \xrightarrow{Al_2O_3} CH_3SCH_3 + H_2O \qquad (149)$$

$$H_2S + HOCH_2CH_2CH_2CH_2OH \xrightarrow[400°]{Al_2O_3} \text{(tetrahydrothiophene)} + H_2O \qquad (150)$$

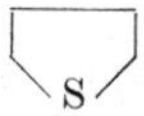

Yields are dependent on conditions, but average about 60–90%. Alcohols higher than butyl give decreased yields probably due to acid-catalyzed cracking side reactions.

IV. Alkylation using Acyclic Ethers as Alkylating Agents

The mechanism of acid-catalyzed alkylations involving ethers as alkylating agents seems to involve positive ionic intermediates. The formation of these entities would, then, be subject to the known laws of carbonium-ion formation and would probably be dependent on the structure of the ether. In order to undergo alkylation an ether must initially cleave, and ether cleavage reactions have been extensively studied and are the subject of a recent review. In summary, primary and most secondary alkyl ethers are cleaved by an S_N2 mechanism, whereas tertiary alkyl, benzhydryl, and trityl ethers probably cleave by S_N1 mechanisms (175,176).

The ether cleavage reaction and subsequent alkylation is certainly a function of the basicity of the ether and the acidity of the catalyst. A more acidic catalyst will complex and cleave more readily than a less acid system. Similarly any structural feature that increases ether basicity will lead to increased reactivity. An example of the former consideration is the finding that solutions of small amounts of ethyl ether in sulfuric acid show freezing-point lowerings corresponding to two particles per molecule of ether. There is little doubt that $(C_2H_5)_2\overset{+}{O}H + HSO_4^-$ are the species involved. In a weak acid, as glacial acetic, ether is not converted to the conjugate acid and the only interaction may be hydrogen bonding (175). No alkylation occurs in the latter acid.

In addition, as mentioned above it would be important to know the dependence of the ether basicity on its structure. Such knowledge would give insight into the factors affecting the rate of nucleophilic displacement versus carbonium-ion reactions. These reactions depend not only on the rate of reaction of the conjugate acid, but also on the equilibrium concentration of the conjugate acid.

It is known that the basicity of the alkoxide ion increases in the series (175):

$$\bar{O}CH_3 < \bar{O}C_2H_5 < \bar{O}C\overset{\displaystyle C}{\underset{\displaystyle C}{<}} OC-C \qquad (151)$$

This correlates well with the known inductive effects. However, with BF_3 as the reference acid basicities decrease in the following sequence and this departure from inductive effect is assigned to F-strain.

$$CH_3OCH_3 > C_2H_5OC_2H_5 > C-\overset{\displaystyle C}{\underset{|}{C}}-O-\overset{\displaystyle C}{\underset{|}{C}}-C \qquad (152)$$

Other acids or solvents might then give altered series and this is found to be the case.

For ethers in sulfuric acid the following increasing basicity (177) series holds:

Anisole $< CH_3OCH_3 < C_2H_5OC_2H_5 <$ Tetrahydrofuran $<$ Tetrahydropyrrole
Tetrahydropyrrole $< 1,4$-Dioxane   (153)

The superior basicity of cyclic ethers is related to their decrease in F-strain owing to the "tying back" of interfering hydrogen atoms. The decrease in basicity of aryl alkyl ethers is considered to be due to contributions to such ether structures of the form (175):

$$
\begin{array}{c}
\text{HC}\!=\!\text{CH} \\
\overset{-}{\text{HC}}\diagup\qquad\diagdown\overset{+}{\text{C}}\!=\!\overset{+}{\text{OR}} \qquad\qquad (154) \\
\diagdown\qquad\diagup \\
\text{HC}\!=\!\text{CH}
\end{array}
$$

It would be desirable to have comparative data on the ether alkylation reaction over the same catalysts at controlled conditions in which the structure of the ether was carefully varied. This would enable a decision to be made covering factors such as the effect of ion stability versus ether basicity on reaction rate. These data, however, are not available.

1. Friedel-Crafts Halides

There have not been extensive studies of the alkylation reactions involving ethers. Therefore, there is not the plenitude of data concerning various catalytic systems as is the case with the alcohols. The only system that has been examined in detail is boron fluoride and boron fluoride complexes with ethers are formed which are similar to those complexes discussed in Section III-1-A (12,178).

A. Alkylation of Benzene and its Homologs by Ethers using Boron Fluoride

The alkylation of benzene with various ethers in the presence of boron fluoride has been the subject of several investigations. Ethers from the simple to complex have been used. In general, the lower molecular weight straight-chain ethers require high temperatures. As branching increases and as the molecular weight goes up it becomes possible to alkylate at milder conditions. Also, as the groups change from alkyl to benzyl the alkylation conditions become less severe. Usually 2 moles of benzene and 0.5–1 mole of boron fluoride for 1 mole of ether are used (12). Isomerization of the alkylating agent invariably occurs and substitution has been reported to be mainly *para*. A rigorous check on this substitution orientation with *s*-butyl methyl ether and toluene revealed the presence of *o*-, *m*-, and *p*-*s*-butyltoluene. The amounts were 37, 21, and 42%, respectively, and this closely checks the ratio reported for toluene alkylation with alkyl halides (179).

These data would seem to leave no doubt that such reactions fit into the basic scheme:

$$RX + \text{Catalyst} \rightleftharpoons R^{\sigma+}X\,\text{Catalyst}^{\sigma-} \tag{155}$$

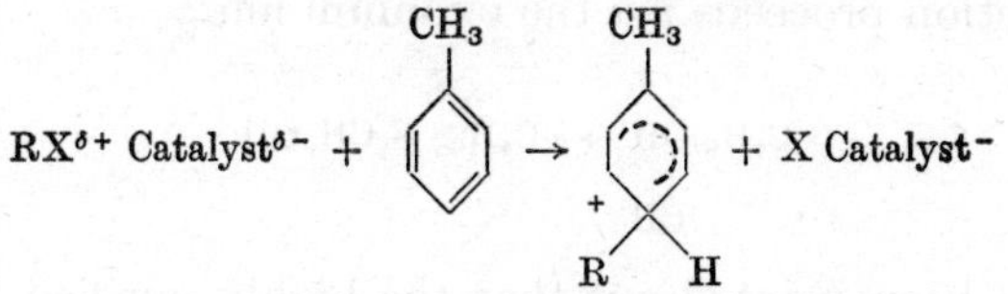

$$RX^{\delta+}\,\text{Catalyst}^{\delta-} + \underset{\substack{}}{\overset{CH_3}{\bigcirc}} \rightarrow \underset{R\quad H}{\overset{CH_3}{\bigcirc}} + X\,\text{Catalyst}^{-} \tag{156}$$

It remains to work out the intimate reaction details with respect to the actual complex nature, structure of transition state, etc.

Originally, it was believed that the ether–boron trifluoride complex decomposed to give a carbonium ion directly, as follows (36):

$$ROR' + BF_3 \rightleftharpoons RR'O\!:\!BF_3 \rightarrow R'OBF_3^- + R^+ \tag{157}$$

It was found, however, that large quantities of strong acids act as "assistants" in alkylation of benzene with boron trifluoride. Burwell *et al.* in a critical study found that absolutely dry catalyst systems were totally ineffective for the reaction of s-butyl methyl ether with benzene even after months of standing at room temperature (180). Direct catalyst decomposition, then, is unlikely, and Brown (181) has reported that isopropyl ether complexes decompose only above 50°. It is likely, therefore, that earlier workers had used systems that contained trace moisture and this was shown to be strongly catalytic, as seen in Table X.

TABLE X.

Promoter	Reaction time, hrs.
None	> 140
H_2SO_4	2.2
H_2O	11–17
CH_3OH	> 360
CF_3COOH	~ 240
$C_2H_5SO_3H$	30–34
BF_3 in excess	24

The results seem to be best interpreted on the basis of the formation of ionic intermediates and the promoter influences their formation:

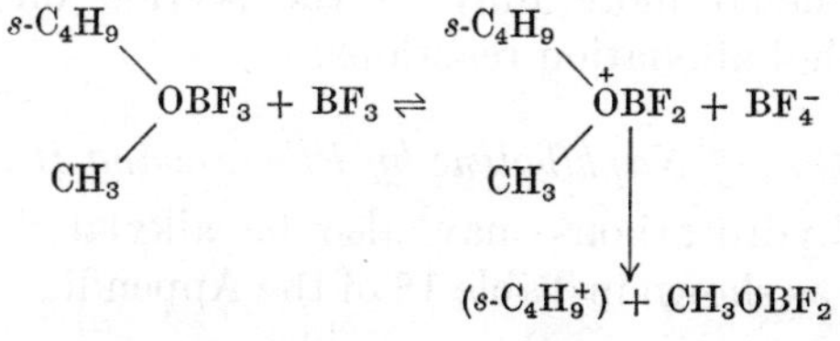

$$\underset{CH_3}{\overset{s\text{-}C_4H_9}{\diagdown}}OBF_3 + BF_3 \rightleftharpoons \underset{CH_3}{\overset{s\text{-}C_4H_9}{\diagdown}}\overset{+}{O}BF_2 + BF_4^- \tag{158}$$

$$\downarrow$$

$$(s\text{-}C_4H_9^+) + CH_3OBF_2$$

In the presence of strong acids, oxygen protonation may occur so that the reaction proceeds *via* the oxonium ion:

$$(s\text{-}C_4H_9)\overset{+}{\underset{\underset{CH_3}{|}}{O}}H \rightarrow s\text{-}C_4H_9^+ + CH_3OH \qquad (159)$$

It has also been pointed out that the highly purified liquid ether complex formed from diethyl ether and BF_3 conducts electrically at room temperature, but does not alkylate benzene except at 160°. To accommodate these facts, the following equilibria could occur:

$$2(C_2H_5)_2OBF_3 \rightleftharpoons (C_2H_5)_2OBF_2^+ + BF_4^- + (C_2H_5)_2O \qquad (160)$$

If the groups are primary elevated temperatures would be required for the ion $R_nOBF_2^+$ to break down to a carbonium-ion species. When one or more groups are secondary decomposition is postulated at room temperature. Further proof of the ionic nature of the reaction arises from studies on alkylation with optically active *s*-butyl methyl ether in the presence of BF_3 (182). Drastic racemization was found and the *s*-butylbenzene recovered was of inverted configuration with an optical purity of little greater than 1%. It was shown that this racemization occurred only during the alkylation step. Therefore the catalyst complex $R^+X\ Cat^-$ is probably composed of relatively "free" carbonium ions. The small rotation observed could well arise from a gegenion shielded transition state.

Alkylation of benzene with 2-methoxypentane yields a mono-alkylate composed of 75% 2-phenylpentane and 25% 3-phenyl-pentane. This is very close to the ratios obtained with 2- and 3-pentanol over $AlCl_3$ or HF and the following isomerization can be postulated:

$$\begin{array}{c} CH_3 \quad CH_2CH_2CH_3 \qquad\qquad CH_3CH \quad CH_2CH_3 \\ \diagdown\,/ \qquad\qquad\qquad\qquad\qquad \diagdown\,/ \\ CH \qquad\qquad\qquad\qquad\qquad\qquad CH \end{array}$$

$$\bigcirc + CH_3CHCH_2CH_2CH_3 \rightarrow \bigcirc \qquad\qquad \bigcirc \qquad (161)$$
$$\underset{OCH_3}{|} \qquad\qquad 75\% \qquad\qquad\qquad 25\%$$

$$CH_3\overset{+}{C}HCH_2CH_2CH_3 \rightleftharpoons CH_3CH_2\overset{+}{C}HCH_2CH_3$$

This was discussed more fully in the section on boron fluoride catalyzed alcohol alkylation reactions.

B. *Alkylation of Naphthalene by Ethers using Boron Fluoride*

Polycyclic hydrocarbons may also be alkylated by ethers and boron fluoride as shown in Table 18 of the Appendix. An interesting facet of this work is that n-propyl benzyl ether forms α-benzyl-naphthalenes and other ethers from β-alkylnaphthalenes (36,39).

As discussed in Section III-3-B, partial rate factors favor α-substitution and such substitution apparently occurs only with the relatively easy ion former, the benzyl group ($\emptyset CH_2^+$). This might represent a situation in which the ion is relatively free and can operate as a free substituting species (similar to NO_2^+). With the other ethers (or alcohols) the entire bulk of the complex is involved ($R^+X\,Cat^-$) and this could be sterically prevented from undergoing a substitution reaction at the α-position.

C. Alkylation of Phenols by Ethers using Boron Fluoride

Phenols are readily alkylated by boron fluoride etherates. For example, when phenol or anisole is heated with boron fluoride–methyl etherate, it is possible to methylate completely to form pentamethylanisole (183).

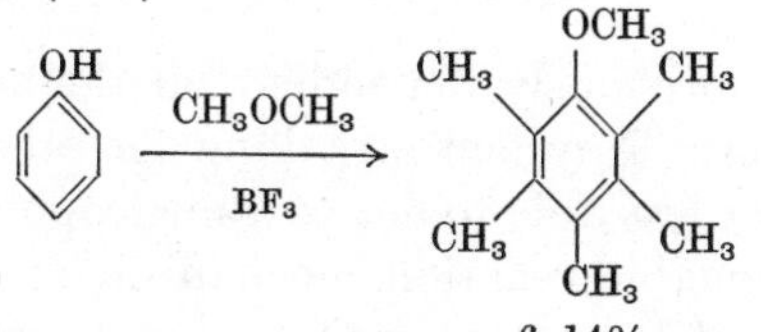

$$\tag{162}$$

6–14%

The ease of alkylation undoubtedly reflects the enhanced activity of phenols. The actual alkylation path is still not elucidated. Questions arise concerning the stepwise nature of the reaction. Kinetic data indicate that anisole is first formed and that the polymethylated anisoles then occur in a stepwise fashion.

D. Alkylation of Active Methylene Groups by Ethers using Boron Fluoride

It was pointed out in the section on alcohols that BF_3 catalyzed a reaction between certain active methylene groups and particular alcohols. This is also true in the ether series and the same products are obtained (42–45) as illustrated in equations 163–167.

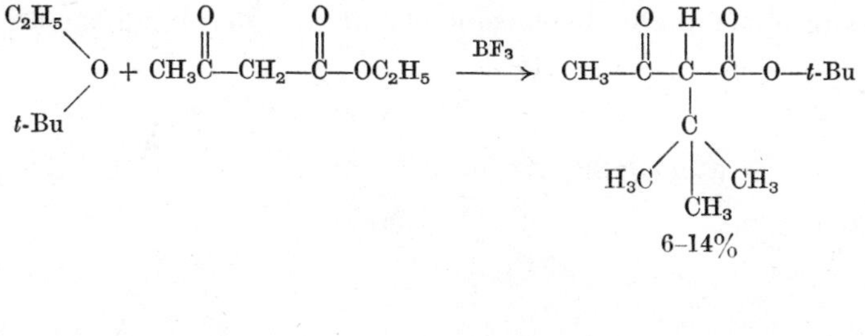

$$\tag{163}$$

6–14%

$$CH_3\overset{O}{\overset{\|}{C}}-CH_2-\overset{O}{\overset{\|}{C}}-OC_2H_5 + (C_6H_5CH_2)_2O \xrightarrow[-10°]{BF_3} CH_3\overset{O}{\overset{\|}{C}}-\underset{\underset{C_6H_5}{\underset{|}{CH_2}}}{\overset{|}{CH}}-\overset{O}{\overset{\|}{C}}-OC_2H_5 \quad (164)$$

$$CH_3\overset{O}{\overset{\|}{C}}-\underset{\underset{CH_3}{|}}{\overset{}{CH}}-\overset{O}{\overset{\|}{C}}-OC_2H_5 + [(CH_3)_2CH]_2O \xrightarrow[14\ hrs.,\ 24°]{BF_3} CH_3\overset{O}{\overset{\|}{C}}-\underset{\underset{CH_3\ \ \ \ CH_3}{\underset{\diagup\ \ \diagdown}{CH}}}{\overset{\underset{CH_3}{|}}{C}}-\overset{O}{\overset{\|}{C}}-OC_2H_5 \quad (165)$$

$$55\%$$

$$CH_3\overset{O}{\overset{\|}{C}}-CH_2-\overset{O}{\overset{\|}{C}}-OC_2H_5 + (n\text{-}C_4H_9)_2O \xrightarrow{BF_3} \text{No Reaction} \quad (166)$$

$$CH_3\overset{O}{\overset{\|}{C}}-CH_2-\overset{O}{\overset{\|}{C}}-OC_2H_5 + (n\text{-}C_3H_7)_2O \xrightarrow{BF_3} \text{No Reaction} \quad (167)$$

The reaction is obviously dependent on the activity of both the ester and the ether. Any factor making the ether less able to form an ion, or the ester less able to act as a nucleophile decreases system activity. A reasonable reaction mechanism involves an attack of the enolate form of the ester on the ether–boron fluoride complex (an alternate mechanism is, however, suggested in Chapter XLVII).

$$CH_3\overset{OH}{\overset{|}{C}}=\overset{H}{\overset{|}{C}}-\overset{O}{\overset{\|}{C}}-OC_2H_5 + RR'O^+ Cat^- \rightarrow (CH_3\overset{OH}{\overset{|}{C}}-\underset{\underset{R'}{|}}{\overset{H}{\overset{|}{C}}}-\overset{O}{\overset{\|}{C}}-OC_2H_5)RO\ Cat.^- \quad (168)$$

$$CH_3\overset{O}{\overset{\|}{C}}-\underset{\underset{R'}{|}}{\overset{H}{\overset{|}{C}}}-\overset{O}{\overset{\|}{C}}-OC_2H_5 + ROH + Cat.$$

An interesting variation of this synthesis is the use of the sodio derivative of the active methylene compound and an oxonium salt (184). Sodiomalonic and sodioacetoacetic esters are alkylated in 35–97% yields *via* the oxonium salt. Such reactions are probably examples of nucleophilic displacement reactions involving the anion of the ester.

$$\overset{+}{Na}\overset{-}{C}\underset{\diagdown COOC_2H_5}{\overset{\diagup COOC_2H_5}{H}} + (C_2H_5O)_3^+ BF_4^- \rightarrow C_2H_5C\underset{\diagdown COOC_2H_5}{\overset{\diagup COOC_2H_5}{H}} + NaF + BF_3 + (C_2H_5)_2O$$

$$(169)$$

2. Metal Oxides

The general aspects of catalysis by acid oxides were developed in the section on alcohols. For ethers it is only necessary that the alcoholic hydrogen be replaced by an alkyl or aryl group.

$$ROR' + Al_2O_3 \rightarrow \overset{\delta+}{R}O\overset{\delta-}{R'}Al_2O_3 \tag{170}$$

$$\overset{\delta+}{R}O\overset{\delta-}{R}Al_2O_3 + SH \rightarrow HOR + S\text{—}R + Al_2O_3 \tag{171}$$

In equation 170 an ether is depicted as absorbing on the alumina surface to produce a polar species. The next step is a typical attack on this species by an agent that can be substituted. It is expected that the ability of the ether to form the polar intermediates will depend on its structure in the usual fashion, and that many of the previously mentioned acceptor molecules may be used.

Unfortunately the plethora of experimental results do not warrant wholesale acceptance of these generalizations. The limited data available, however, fit in well with previous results on other "typical" acid catalysts. Thus, the details of the mechanism of alkylation might change but the above scheme probably describes the phenomena adequately.

A. Alkylation of Benzene and its Homologs by Ethers using Metal Oxides

Benzene, toluene, and the xylenes have been alkylated by various ethers over alumina. As an example, at 400–500° and over, alumina–silica systems (146) dimethyl ether and benzene yield toluene, xylenes, and higher polymethylbenzenes.

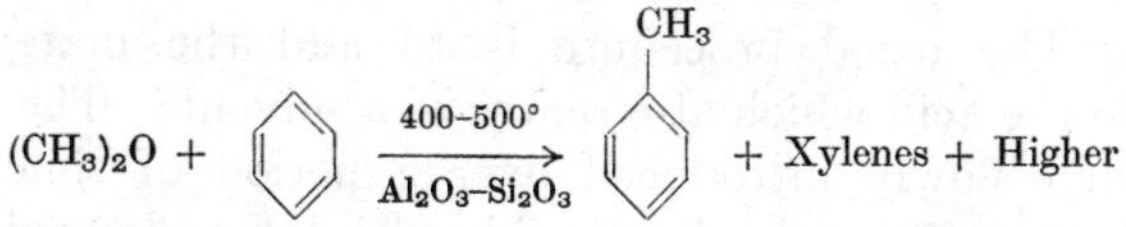

$$(CH_3)_2O + \text{⬡} \xrightarrow[\text{Al}_2\text{O}_3\text{–Si}_2\text{O}_3]{400-500°} \text{⬡–CH}_3 + \text{Xylenes} + \text{Higher} \tag{172}$$

The total methylation at these conditions is 70% based on benzene consumed and 35–50 mole % of the product is toluene. This represents a close approach to calculated equilibrium values. Since methanol is also alkylated, a series of check experiments was conducted using methyl alcohol at the same conditions. Alkylation occurred but the rates are much lower. An alcohol is therefore probably not an intermediate, and the following overall stoichiometry is suggested:

$$C_6H_6 + (CH_3)_2O \rightleftharpoons CH_3C_6H_5 + CH_3OH \tag{173}$$

$$2CH_3OH \rightleftharpoons (CH_3)_2O + H_2O \tag{174}$$

When ethyl- and n-propylbenzene are alkylated with dimethyl ether at 450° over the same catalyst, however, alkyl group scission occurs. This falls in line with the known increase of acid-catalyzed scission as alkyl groups increase in size (185).

B. Alkylation of Naphthalenes by Ethers using Metal Oxides

Naphthalenes have been alkylated by dimethyl ether over a natural acid clay (bauxite). At 450° and 1 atm. pressure, a methylated product is obtained in a 2–3% yield of naphthalene feed. Seventy per cent of this material is a 2:1 mixture of the α/β alkylated product (186). This result gives impetus to suggestions that the initial position on naphthalene attacked over the oxide catalysts is the α-position. This may then be followed by an isomerization to the β-isomer.

C. Alkylation of Phenols by Ethers using Metal Oxides

Various patents refer to alkylation of phenol over acid oxides (187,188). In addition, it is possible to rearrange an alkyl phenyl ether to a nuclear phenol. In this regard the relatively stable ether, anisole, is reported to rearrange.

3. Miscellaneous

Hydrogen fluoride is also an effective catalyst for the alkylation of various ethers. Its scope does not appear to have been widely explored. The first investigators to point out the alkylating ability of HF for aromatic alkylation were Simons and Archer (198). Calcott et al. (199) later reported on an extensive study of various alcohols and ethers as alkylating agents for a variety of aromatic structures. The usual procedure is to add the material to be alkylated to the acid which also serves as a solvent. The alkylating agent is then slowly introduced over a period of time. Certain compounds are not completely miscible with HF and in this situation a heterogeneous system results.

A. Ether Rearrangement

The acid-catalyzed rearrangement of aryl ethers produces nuclear alkylated phenols.

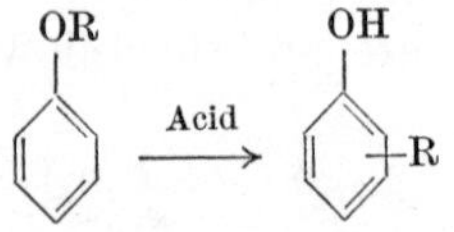

$$\text{OR} \xrightarrow{\text{Acid}} \text{OH} + \text{R} \qquad (175)$$

A new carbon–carbon bond is generated and the overall reaction fits into the alkylation scheme shown in Section I. The Fries reaction, however, has not been reviewed in this chapter since it is the subject of a recent comprehensive article by Dewar (170) and is also discussed in a Chapter XXXIII.

V. Alkylation using Cyclic Ethers as Alkylating Agents

In addition to simple acyclic alkyl or aryl ethers, cyclic ethers (oxides) can also be considered members of the ether class. They undergo an alkylation reaction leading either to disubstituted derivatives or to hydroxylated compounds (82,189,190).

$$\text{Ar} + \text{R}-\underset{\underset{\text{O}}{\diagup}}{\overset{|}{\text{C}}}-\overset{|}{\text{C}}- \xrightarrow{\text{AlCl}_3} \text{Ar}\overset{\text{R}}{\underset{|}{\overset{|}{\text{C}}}}-\overset{|}{\underset{|}{\text{C}}}-\text{OH} \rightarrow \text{Ar}\overset{\text{R}}{\underset{|}{\overset{|}{\text{C}}}}-\overset{|}{\underset{|}{\text{C}}}-\text{Ar} \qquad (176)$$

With such oxides, it is expected that relative reaction rates would correlate with ease of ring opening and ether basicity. These speculations have been presented in Section IV and are borne out to some extent by the work of Searles (191).

Searles finds that the order of reactivity in the AlCl$_3$ catalyzed alkylation of benzene is ethylene oxide > trimethylene oxide > di-n-propyl ether. In addition, the reaction of trimethylene oxide with both benzene and mesitylene produced the unrearranged 3-hydroxypropyl derivative.

$$\text{(177)}$$

$$\text{(178)}$$

These reactions might be compared with the reaction of di-n-propyl ether at the same conditions, which leads to extensive isomerization and formation of isopropylbenzene. A reasonable explanation for this phenomenon is that the cyclic ether, due to its enhanced basicity, coordinates with the AlCl$_3$ in a complex as tight as the alcohol–AlCl$_3$ complex. The cyclic ether alkylation reaction could occur predominantly by a displacement type mechanism, avoiding rearrangement in a fashion similar to that outlined in the general mechanism section.

Limited data indicate that the cyclic oxides alkylate in the *para*-position. For example, Shorygina found that at 5–10° ethylene oxide and toluene gave a 30% yield of *para*-hydroxyethyltoluene using AlCl$_3$. At higher temperature yields decreased, presumably due to polymerization of the oxide (192). Nuclear attack on phenols is also possible although it is not possible to designate those alcohols that will give nuclear attack (193).

The question of the position of substituted oxide ring cleavage is theoretically interesting. Initially it was reported that propylene oxide and benzene yield methylbenzylcarbinol in low yields over an $AlCl_3$ catalyst (194,195). Theimer later reinvestigated this reaction and was able to obtain good yields of the primary alcohol 2-phenyl-propanol-1 (189).

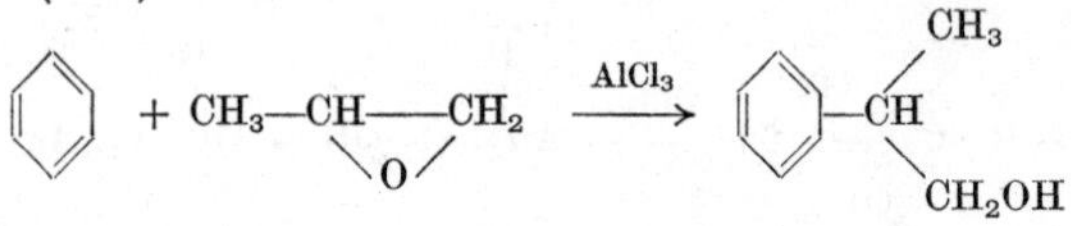

$$\bigcirc + CH_3-CH-\!\!-CH_2 \xrightarrow{AlCl_3} \bigcirc-CH\begin{array}{c}CH_3\\\\CH_2OH\end{array} \qquad (179)$$

While not investigated in detail, the overall reaction can be explained by assuming an initial split to form isopropyl carbonium ions.

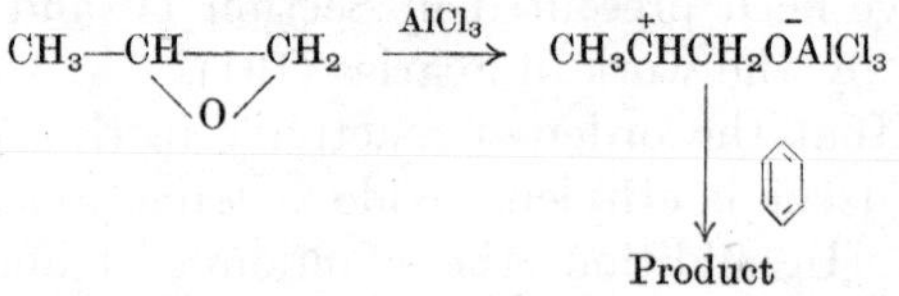

$$CH_3-CH-\!\!-CH_2 \xrightarrow{AlCl_3} CH_3\overset{+}{C}HCH_2\overset{-}{O}AlCl_3 \qquad (180)$$

Product

Alternatively, a concerted mechanism can also be considered involving the reaction of the epoxide–catalyst complex with the aromatic.

A further investigation of the position of ring openings was made by Spoerri who found the following products from the alkylation of benzene with butylene and isobutylene oxide, respectively (196).

Butylene Oxide

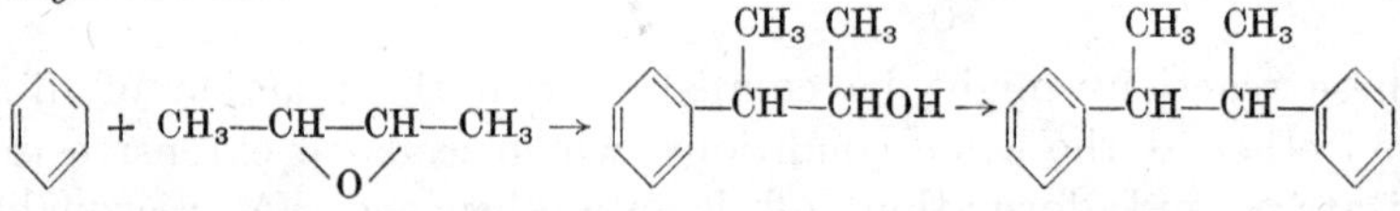

$$\bigcirc + CH_3-CH-CH-CH_3 \rightarrow \bigcirc\!\!-\!\!\overset{CH_3}{CH}-\overset{CH_3}{CHOH} \rightarrow \bigcirc\!\!-\!\!\overset{CH_3}{CH}-\overset{CH_3}{CH}\!\!-\!\!\bigcirc \qquad (181)$$

Isobutylene Oxide

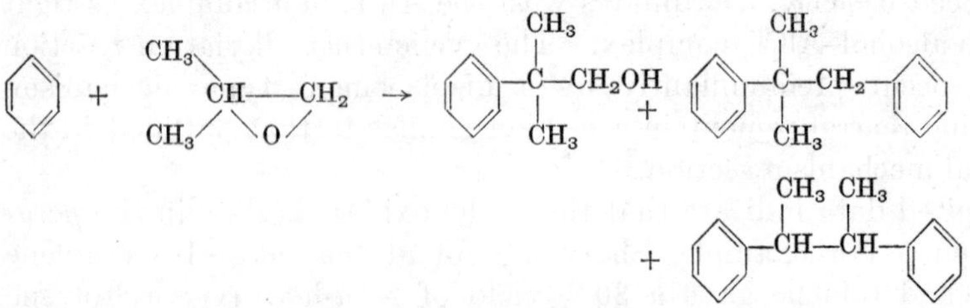

$$\bigcirc + \begin{array}{c}CH_3\\CH-\!\!-CH_2\\CH_3\end{array}\!\!\!\!O \rightarrow \bigcirc\!\!-\!\!\overset{CH_3}{\underset{CH_3}{C}}\!-\!CH_2OH + \bigcirc\!\!-\!\!\overset{CH_3}{\underset{CH_3}{C}}\!-\!CH_2\!\!-\!\!\bigcirc$$

$$+ \bigcirc\!\!-\!\!\overset{CH_3}{CH}-\overset{CH_3}{CH}\!\!-\!\!\bigcirc \qquad (182)$$

In the case of butylene oxide the ring opening is unambiguous and the two products are those of a consecutive reaction sequence as in the case of ethylene oxide. With isobutylene oxide the most reasonable interpretation indicates tertiary ring opening leading to the relatively stable tertiary carbonium ion (equation 183). This would produce 2-methyl-2-phenylpropanol (equation 184), which, in turn, forms α,α-dimethyldibenzyl (equation 185). The latter may undergo a typical acid-catalyzed rearrangement to form *meso*-2,3-diphenylbutane (equation 186).

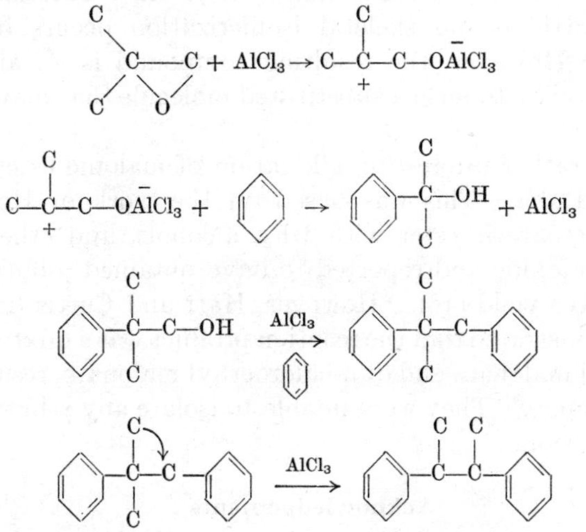

$$\text{(183)}$$

$$\text{(184)}$$

$$\text{(185)}$$

$$\text{(186)}$$

A reaction between 2-methyl-2-phenylpropanol and benzene catalyzed by $AlCl_3$ does produce α,α-dimethyldibenzyl and *meso*-2,3-diphenylbutane.

Further investigation of the oxide reaction was carried out with α-methylstyrene oxide and benzene. In this reaction, 2,2-diphenyl-propan-1-ol together with 1,1,2-triphenylpropane, 1,1-diphenyl-propane, and 1,1-diphenylpropene were formed (197).

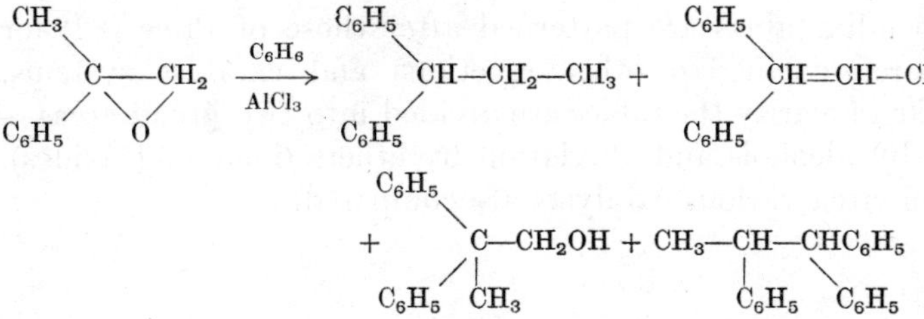

$$\text{(187)}$$

The mechanism of the reaction fits in well with acid-catalyzed rearrangements and a mechanistic scheme involving 1,2-shifts and hydride transfer reactions has been proposed.   As in the isobutylene oxide alkylation, initial scission to a relative stable ion (benzyl) is postulated.

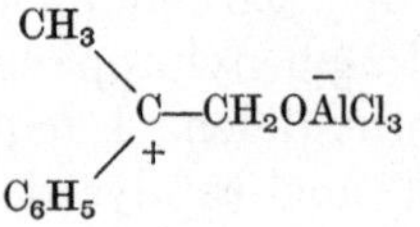

$$\begin{array}{c} CH_3 \\ \diagdown \\ \quad\;\; \overset{-}{C}\!-\!CH_2O\overline{A}lCl_3 \\ \diagup + \\ C_6H_5 \end{array} \qquad (188)$$

The results with the oxides show that their reactions can be complex.   Little or no skeletal isomerization occurs during the initial step.   However, the resulting compound is an alcohol and this can realkylate to form a substituted molecule that may isomerize skeletally.

Finally, a rather interesting alkylation of malonic ester has been claimed by Raha.   This was based on the work of Houser, who alkylated acetoacetic ester with BF_3, alcohols, and ethers.   Raha used ethylene oxide and reported to have obtained γ-butyrolactone in quantitative yield (46).   However, Hart and Curtis (291) subsequently demonstrated that the reaction product was a mixture of ethyl β-chloroethyl malonate and di-β-chloroethyl malonate, resulting from ester interchange.   They were unable to isolate any γ-butyrolactone from the reaction.

Acknowledgements

The author wishes to express his thanks to Mrs. B. Schriesheim for preparing many of the tables; to Miss P. Novak and Miss M. S. Weidner for typing, proofreading, and correcting the manuscript; and to Esso Research & Engineering Co. for providing the facilities and time needed to write this chapter.

VI. Appendix

The appendix tables are patterned after those of Price (82) for easy cross-referencing to other reactions and catalyst systems. For the sake of clarity the tables are divided into two broad areas— alkylation by alcohols and alkylation by ethers (including oxides). Within each area various catalysts are compared.

TABLE 1. Alkylation of benzene with alcohols

Moles of benzene*	Alkylating agent (moles)*	Catalyst (moles)*	Temperature, °C	Time, hrs.*	Products, % yield*	Ref.
6	Methyl alcohol (1)	AlCl$_3$ (2)	90–95	9	Toluene (21)	2
2.7	Ethyl alcohol (0.33)	AlCl$_3$ (0.66)	water bath	2	Alkylbenzenes (85) (ethylbenzene, 25–30)	200
	Ethyl alcohol	Alumina–silica (1:2)	350	6.5	Benzene (25), monoethylbenzene, benzene homologs	147
6 g.	Ethyl alcohol	Alumina–silica (1:4)	(Gives similar results) 300–320		Ethylbenzene (4)	150
	Fluoromethanol	Alumina–silica cat. ZnCl$_2$, anhydrous 1 g. + absolute pyridine	40–50 + mild reflux	45	Benzyl fluoride	96
0.1	Ethyl alcohol (0.1)	ZnCl$_2$ (0.15)	300	—	Ethylbenzene (poor yield)	201
1.6	Ethyl alcohol (0.3)	AlCl$_3$ (0.6)	120–130	10	Ethylbenzene (49), m-diethylbenzene, diethylbiphenyl, and diethylterphenyl	200,2
1.3	Ethyl alcohol (192 g. 3 mol.)	300 g. activated alumina	350	5	Benzene (60 g.) (>15%), ethylbenzene (9 g.) higher boiling homologs (6 g.)	147
0.4	Ethyl alcohol (1.0)	AlCl$_3$ (1.5)	80	3	sym.-Triethylbenzene (65–70)	51
	n-Propyl alcohol	Alumina–silica	300–320	—	Isopropylbenzene (45–58)	150
—	n-Propyl alcohol (—)	H$_2$SO$_4$ (80%) (—)	65	—	Cumene (45), p-diisopropylbenzene, 1,2,4-triisopropylbenzene	59,123
1.6	n-Propyl alcohol (0.5)	AlCl$_3$ (0.7)	110	10	n-Propylbenzene (52), m-di-n-propylbenzene (37)	59,202

Table continued

* Unless otherwise indicated.

19+F.C. II

TABLE 1 (*continued*)

Moles of benzene*	Alkylating agent (moles)*	Catalyst (moles)*	Temperature, °C	Time, hrs.*	Products, % yield*	Ref.
1	n-Propyl alcohol (1)	BF$_3$ (1)	60	9	Cumene (20), p-diisopropylbenzene (20)	21
2	n-Propyl alcohol (0.5)	BF$_3$–P$_2$O$_5$ (0.5)	80	3	Cumene (60), p-diiso-propylbenzene (13)	27
0.7	Isopropyl alcohol (0.7)	H$_2$SO$_4$ (80%) (6)	65	3–4	Cumene (65)	123
	Isopropyl alcohol	Alumina–silica	300–320	—	Isopropylbenzene (50–60)	150
1.69	Isopropyl alcohol (0.50)	AlCl$_3$ (0.32)	75 then r.t.	14	Cumene (37 g.)	200
2–5	Isopropyl alcohol (1.0)	AlCl$_3$ (0.5)	30	24	Cumene (25)	2,49
7.5	Isopropyl alcohol	H$_2$SO$_4$ (80%) (65)	65	5	Cumene (8), p-diisopropylbenzene (22), 1,2,4-triisopropylbenzene (8), 1,2,4,5-tetraisopropylbenzene	123
					propylbenzene	203
1	Isopropyl alcohol (1)	BF$_3$ (0.7)	25	12	Cumene (20), p-diiso-propylbenzene (20)	21
2	Isopropyl alcohol (0.5)	BF$_3$–P$_2$O$_5$ (0.5)	80	—	Cumene (40), p-diiso-propylbenzene (20)	27
7	Isopropyl alcohol (1)	BF$_3$ (—)	—	—	Cumene (22), p-diiso-propylbenzene (14), 1,2,3-triisopropylbenzene (26), 1,2,4,5-tetraisopropylbenzene (28)	205
	Isopropyl alcohol	Benzene (0.55) TiCl$_4$ (0.1–0.2)	b.p.	6	Isopropylbenzene (61)	204
1	Allyl alcohol (1)	BF$_3$ (—)	—	—	Allylbenzene (8)	21
—	Allyl alcohol (—)	HF (—)	—	—	Allylbenzene (11–20), 1,2-diphenylpropane (8–12)	206
—	n-Butyl alcohol (—)	H$_2$SO$_4$ (80%) (—)	70	—	s-Butylbenzene, p-di-s-butylbenzene	123

1	n-Butyl alcohol (1)	BF₃ (1)	60	9	s-Butylbenzene (35), p-di-s-butylbenzene (25)	21
3.38	n-Butyl alcohol (0.33)	AlCl₃ (0.42)	75	3	Butylbenzene (34) (mixture of isomers)	200
2	n-Butyl alcohol (0.5)	BF₃–P₂O₅ (0.5)	80	—	s-Butylbenzene (75), p-di-s-butylbenzene (5–10)	27
—	s-Butyl alcohol (—)	H₂SO₄ (80%) (—)	70	—	s-Butylbenzene, p-di-s-butylbenzene	
2–5	s-Butyl alcohol (1.0)	AlCl₃ (0.5)	30	24	s-Butylbenzene (25, 60)	49,207
1	s-Butyl alcohol (1)	BF₃ (0.7)	25	12	s-Butylbenzene (25, 50), p-di-s-butylbenzene (20, 12)	21,27,207
2	s-Butyl alcohol (0.5)	BF₃–P₂O₅ (0.5)	—	—	s-Butylbenzene (45), p-di-s-butylbenzene (13)	27
2	d-s-Butyl alcohol (0.32)	AlCl₃ (0.3)	0–25	12	dl-s-Butylbenzene (50)	207
1.3	d-s-Butyl alcohol (0.32)	BF₃ (0.2)	25	18	1-s-Butylbenzene (48) (99.5% racemized)	207,208
0.75	1-s-Butyl alcohol (0.16)	H₃PO₄ (0.78)	70	2	d-s-Butylbenzene (12)	208
0.75	1-s-Butyl alcohol (0.16)	H₂SO₄ (0.18)	50	3	d-s-Butylbenzene (37), di-s-butylbenzene (40)	208
0.75	1-s-Butyl alcohol (0.16)	BF₃	20	12	d-s-Butylbenzene (51)	208
0.75	d-s-Butyl alcohol (0.16)	HF (1.62)	16	5	1-s-Butylbenzene (30), di-t-butylbenzene (27)	208
0.08	Isobutyl alcohol (0.1)	ZnCl₂ (0.15)	260–270	48–72	iso- and t-Butylbenzenes	208
13	Isobutyl alcohol (2)	H₂SO₄–SO₃ (30%) (1 kg.)	0	0.7–0.8	t-Butylbenzene (50), p-di-t-butylbenzene (40)	201,92
	Isobutyl alcohol	Alumina–silica	300–320	—	No yield	209
0.2	Isobutyl alcohol (0.2)	H₂SO₄–SO₃ (70–80%) (5)	70	4	t-Butylbenzene (70), p-di-t-butylbenzene (12)	150
1	Isobutyl alcohol (1)	BF₃ (0.7)	—	—	t-Butylbenzene (12), p-di-t-butylbenzene (10)	123
55	s-Butyl alcohol	TiCl₄ (0.1–0.2)	6	b.p.	s-Butylbenzene (61)	21, 204

* Unless otherwise indicated.

Table continued

TABLE 1 (continued)

Moles of benzene*	Alkylating agent (moles)*	Catalyst (moles)*	Temperature, °C	Time, hrs.*	Products, % yield*	Ref.
0.2–0.55	t-Butyl alcohol	TiCl₄ (0.05–0.2)	40–80	1–3	Butylbenzene (20–74), p-di-t-butylbenzene (4–66)	204
—	t-Butyl alcohol	H₂SO₄ (70–80%)	70	—	t-Butylbenzene, p-di-t-butylbenzene	123
2–5	t-Butyl alcohol	Alumina–silica	300–320	—	Trace t-butylbenzene	150
	t-Butyl alcohol (1.0)	AlCl₃ (0.5)	30	24	t-Butylbenzene (67, 84)	2,49
—	t-Butyl alcohol (—)	AlCl₃ (—)	80–95	8	Toluene, ethylbenzene, cumene	2
1	t-Butyl alcohol (1)	BF₃ (0.3)	25	12	t-Butylbenzene (25), di-t-butylbenzene (25)	21
—	t-Butyl alcohol (—)	HF (—)	—	—	t-Butylbenzene (40), p-di-t-butylbenzene (50)	205
5	t-Butyl alcohol (1)	FeCl₃ (1)	25	—	t-Butylbenzene (82)	210
13.5	2-Methyl-2-propanol	Anhydrous AlCl₃ (1.35)	35	overnight	p-Di-t-butylbenzene (1.2), 2-methyl-2-phenyl-propane (55.0), 2-methylpropane (2.2)	211
0.5	n-Amyl alcohol (0.3)	H₂SO₄ (80%) (7)	70	6	2- and 3-Phenylpentanes (60%; ca 3:2)	59
4	n-Amyl alcohol (0.5)	BF₃–P₂O₅ (0.5)	80	—	s-Amylbenzene (85)	27
0.55	t-Amyl alcohol	TiCl₄ (0.1–0.2)	18–80	1–48	t-Amylbenzene (41–74), p-di-t-amylbenzene (11–33)	204
4	t-Amyl alcohol (1)	AlCl₃ (0.5)	25–50	—	No t-amylbenzene	212
2	t-Amyl alcohol (1)	H₂SO₄ (80%) (5)	60–65	3.5	t-Amylbenzene (5)	212
0.8	Isoamyl alcohol (0.8)	H₂SO₄ (80%) (6)	65	5	t-Amylbenzene (36)	59
2.5	2-Pentanol (1.0)	AlCl₃ (0.5)	30	24	2-Phenylpentane (25)	49
13.5	2-Methyl-2-butanol (2.7)	Anhydrous AlCl₃ (1.35)	35	overnight	2-Methyl-2-phenylbutane (40.0), 2-methylbutane (1.8)	

						Ref.*
1	2-Pentanol	AlCl₃	—	—	Monoalkylate (40), 2-phenylpentane (60), 3-phenylpentane (40)	33
1	3-Pentanol (0.114 ml.)	HF (1)	—	—	Monoalkylate (78), (2-phenylpentane, 56; 3-phenylpentane, 44)	33
1	3-Pentanol (0.2)	AlCl₃ (0.2)	below 35° for 1 hr. r.t. over-night		Monoalkylate (80), (2-phenylpentane, 76 3-phenylpentane, 24)	33
2–5	3-Methyl-2-butanol (1.0)	AlCl₃ (0.5)	30	24	3-Methyl-2-phenylbutane (25)	49
7	t-Amyl alcohol (1)	HF (—)	—	—	t-Amylbenzene (40), di-t-amylbenzene (50)	205
0.25	Neopentyl alcohol (0.25)	H₂SO₄ (80%) (3)	65	6	t-Amylbenzene (30)	213
1.0	Neopentyl alcohol (0.25)	AlCl₃ (0.33)	80	8	Neopentylbenzene (9)	213
1.69	1,4-Pentanediol (0.07)	AlCl₃ (0.16)	35–40 then 20–21	24	1-Methyltetrahydro-naphthalene (15), 4-phenylpentan-1-ol (62.5)	
1.13	1,4-Pentanediol (0.1)	AlCl₃ (0.2)	75–85	4	1-Methyltetrahydro-naphthalene (52), 4-phenylpentan-1-ol (16)	214
1.3	Cyclobutylmethanol (0.3)	AlCl₃ (0.2)	25	24	Benzylcyclobutane (29)	215
1.3	Cyclobutylmethanol (0.3)	AlCl₃ (0.2)	75–80	—	Benzylcyclobutane (21)	215
—	2-Methyl-2-pentanol (—)	AlCl₃ (—)	—	—	2-Phenyl-2-methylpentane (50)	99
13.5	2-Methyl-2-pentanol (2.7)	Anhydrous AlCl₃ (1.35)	35	overnight	2-Methyl-2-phenylpentane (32.7), 2-methylpentane (7)	211
—	3-Methyl-2-pentanol (—)	AlCl₃ (—)	—	—	3-Phenyl-3-methylpentane	195
13.5	3-Methyl-3-pentanol (2.7)	Anhydrous AlCl₃ (1.35)	35	overnight	3-Methyl-3-phenylpentane (35.9), 3-methylpentane (10.2)	113

* Unless otherwise indicated.

Table continued

TABLE 1 (continued)

Moles of benzene*	Alkylating agent (moles)*	Catalyst (moles)*	Temperature, °C	Time, hrs.*	Products, % yield*	Ref.
1.1	1-Methylcyclopentanol (0.08)	AlCl₃ (0.05)	boiling	2 hr. addition of AlCl₃ followed by overnight reaction at r.t.	1-Methyl-1-phenylcyclopentane (43)	216
—	2,3-Dimethyl-2-butanol (—)	AlCl₃ (—)	—	—	2,3-Dimethyl-2-phenyl-butane	49
0.7	Cyclohexanol (0.6)	H₂SO₄ (80%) (6)	70	—	Cyclohexylbenzene (50), dicyclohexylbenzene	123
1.0	Cyclohexanol (0.4)	AlCl₃ (0.25)	80	2	Cyclohexylbenzene (62), p- and m-dicyclohexylbenzenes, sym.-tricyclohexylbenzene	217
1	Cyclohexanol (1)	BF₃ (0.7)	—	—	Cyclohexylbenzene (35), p-dicyclohexylbenzene (25)	21
0.4	1-Methylcyclohexanol-1 (0.05)	AlCl₃ (0.025)	water bath	heat until HCl ceased	1-Methyl-1-phenylcyclohexane (50), dialkylated product (15)	140
2.2	1-Phenyl-4-methyl cyclohexanol (0.1)	AlCl₃ (0.12–0.15)	1–15 hr. addition of HCl; overnight standing followed by 2 hrs. of heating	r.t.followed by heating at 50–55° and then to boiling	Methyldiphenylcyclohexanes (30–32) (crude), 1-methyl-1,3-diphenyl-, 1-methyl-1,4-diphenyl-, 1-methyl-3,5-diphenyl-cyclohexanes, methylphenylcyclohexanes, mixture of crude 1-methyl-3-phenyl, 1-methyl-4-phenylcyclohexanes	140

—	Cycloheptanol	AlCl₃	—	—	Cycloheptylbenzene (73)	86
1.7	Cyclopentylmethanol (0.4)	AlCl$_3$ (0.2)	75–80	—	Benzylcyclopentane (45)	215
1.6	Cyclohexylmethanol (0.3)	AlCl$_3$ (0.2)	75–80	—	Benzylcyclohexane (7)	213
9	Benzyl alcohol (—)	HF (—)	cold	—	Diphenylmethane (65–70)	205
—	Benzyl alcohol (—)	H$_2$SO$_4$–HOAC (—)	25	48	Diphenylmethane	218
2	Benzyl alcohol (0.15)	P$_2$O$_5$ (0.2)	25	48	Diphenylmethane (30)	219
2	Benzyl alcohol (0.15)	AlCl$_3$ (0.1)	60	3.5	Diphenylmethane (50)	219
100 cc.	Benzyl alcohol (19.5 g.) in 50 cc. benzene	AlCl$_3$ (56 g.)			Crystalline material (57) yielded pure anthracene (90.3)	83
2.5	Benzyl alcohol (0.5)	AlCl$_3$ (0.3)	30–35	120	Diphenylmethane (55), p- and o-dibenzylbenzenes, anthracene	57
0.3	Benzyl alcohol (0.2)	H$_2$SO$_4$ (70%) (4)	40	3	Diphenylmethane (40–50), p-dibenzylbenzene	123
1	Benzyl alcohol (1)	BF$_3$ (0.7)	—	—	Diphenylmethane (15), p-dibenzylbenzene (20)	21
60.1	Dimethylbenzylcarbinol (3)	Anhydrous AlCl$_3$ (6)	10	2–3/4	meso-2,3-Diphenylbutane (36 g.), α,α-dimethyldibenzyl (108 g.)	147
8	n-Octyl alcohol (1)	BF$_3$–P$_2$O$_5$ (1)	80	—	s-Octylbenzene (79)	27
13.5	2-Methyl-2-hexanol (2.7)	Anhydrous AlCl$_3$ (1.35)	35	overnight	2-Methyl-2-phenylhexane (31.3), 2-methylhexane (2.1)	211
13.5	3-Methyl-3-hexanol (2.7)	Anhydrous AlCl$_3$ (1.35)	35	overnight	3-Methyl-3-phenylhexane (30), 3-methylhexane (1.6)	211
2.5	2-Methyl-2-heptanol (0.5)	AlCl$_3$ (0.25)	25	—	2-Methyl-2-phenylheptane (24)	220

* Unless otherwise indicated.

Table continued

TABLE 1 (continued)

Moles of benzene*	Alkylating agents (moles)*	Catalyst (moles)*	Temperature, °C	Time, hrs.*	Products, % yield*	Ref.
13.5	2-Methyl-2-heptanol (2.7)	Anhydrous AlCl₃ (1.35)	35	overnight	2-Methyl-2-phenylheptane (27.4), 2-methylheptane (8.8)	211
13.5	3-Methyl-3-heptanol (2.7)	Anhydrous AlCl₃ (1.35)	35	overnight	3-Methyl-3-phenylheptane (24.2), 3-methylheptane (9.5)	211
13.5	4-Methyl-4-heptanol (2.7)	Anhydrous AlCl₃ (1.35)	35	overnight	4-Methyl-4-phenylheptane (33.1), 4-methylheptane	211
2.5	2,3-Dimethyl-2-hexanol (0.5)	AlCl₃ (0.25)	10	—	2,3-Dimethyl-2-phenyl-hexane (20)	220
13.5	3-Ethyl-3-hexanol (2.7)	Anhydrous AlCl₃ (1.35)	35	overnight	3-Ethyl-3-phenylhexane (25.1), 3-ethylhexane (14.3)	211
2.5	2,4-Dimethyl-2-hexanol (0.5)	AlCl₃ (0.25)	25	—	2,4-Dimethyl-2-phenyl-hexane (25)	220
13.5	2,4-Dimethyl-2-hexanol (2.7)	Anhydrous AlCl₃ (1.35)	35	overnight	2,4-Dimethyl-2-phenyl-hexane (19.6), 2-methyl-2-phenylpropane (1.30), 2,4-dimethylhexane (3.8), 2-methylpropane (3.1)	211
13.5	2,4-Dimethyl-4-hexanol (2.7)	Anhydrous AlCl₃ (1.35)	35	overnight	2,4-Dimethyl-4-phenyl-hexane (19.2), 2-methyl-2-phenylpropane (2.20), 2,4-dimethylhexane (3.9), 2-methylpropane (4.6)	211
13.5	2,5-Dimethyl-2-hexanol (2.7)	Anhydrous AlCl₃ (1.35)	35	overnight	2,5-Dimethyl-2-phenyl-hexane (21.5), 2,5-dimethylhexane (5.7)	211

2.5	3-Ethyl-2-methyl-2-pentanol (0.5)	AlCl₃ (0.25)	10	—	3-Ethyl-2-methyl-2-phenyl-pentane (18)	220
13.5	3-Ethyl-3-pentanol (2.7)	Anhydrous AlCl₃ (1.35)	35	overnight	3-Ethyl-3-phenylpentane (33.2), 3-ethylpentane (2.3)	211
2.5	2,3,3-Trimethyl-2-pentanol (0.5)	AlCl₃ (0.25)	−15	—	2,3,3-Trimethyl-2-phenyl-pentane (4), t-butyl-benzene (9)	220
13.5	2,4-Dimethyl-2-pentanol	Anhydrous AlCl₃ (1.35)	35	overnight	2,4-Dimethyl-2-phenyl-pentane (22.2), 2-methyl-2-phenylpropane (2.8), 2-methylpropane	211
2.5	2,4,4-Trimethyl-2-pentanol (0.5)	AlCl₃ (0.25)	−15	—	2,4,4-Trimethyl-2-phenyl-pentane (22), t-butyl-benzene (18)	220
13.5	2,4,4-Trimethyl-2-pentanol (2.7)	Anhydrous AlCl₃ (1.35)	35	overnight	2,4,4-Trimethyl-2-phenyl-pentane (14), 2-methyl-2-phenylpropane (20), 2-methylpropane	211
13.5	2,4,4-Trimethyl-2-pentanol (2.7)	Anhydrous AlCl₃ (1.35)	35	overnight	2,4,4-Trimethyl-2-phenyl-pentane (14), 2-methyl-2-phenylpropane (20), 2-methylpropane (4.6)	211
2.5	2,4,4-Trimethyl-2-pentanol (0.5)	AlCl₃ (0.25)	10	—	2,4,4-Trimethyl-2-phenyl-pentane (10), t-butyl-benzene (42)	220
5	α-Phenylethyl alcohol (1)	AlCl₃ (0.5)	10	8 days	1,1-Diphenylethane (65), ethylbenzene (4), di-phenylmethane	221
5	α-Phenylpropanol (1)	AlCl₃ (0.5)	10	12 days	1,1-Diphenylpropane (40), n-propylbenzene (12), diphenylmethane (4)	221

* Unless otherwise indicated.

Table continued

19*

TABLE 1 (*continued*)

Moles of benzene*	Alkylating agent (moles)*	Catalyst (moles)*	Temperature, °C	Time, hrs.*	Products, % yield*	Ref.
0.56	4-Phenylpentanol (0.11)	$AlCl_3$ (0.12)	78–85	4	1-Methyltetrahydro-naphthalene (69)	214
4	n-Dodecyl alcohol (0.5)	BF_3–P_2O_5 (0.5)	80	—	s-Dodecylbenzene (33)	27
2	n-Dodecyl alcohol (0.5)	BF_3–$C_6H_5SO_3H$ (0.5)	80	—	s-Dodecylbenzene (45)	27
0.7	Diphenylmethanol (0.02)	P_2O_5 (0.05)	0	48	Triphenylmethane (70)	219
5	Diphenylmethanol (1)	$AlCl_3$ (1)	10	72	Triphenylmethane (70), diphenylmethane (1)	221
—	p-Methyl diphenylmethanol	P_2O_5 (—)	130–150	2–3	Diphenyl-p-tolylmethane	222

* Unless otherwise indicated.

TABLE 2. Alkylation of halogenated benzene derivatives with alcohols

Aromatic compound (moles)*	Alkylating agent (moles)*	Catalyst (moles)*	Temperature, °C	Time, hrs.*	Products, % yield*	Ref.
Bromobenzene (1.8)	1,1,1-Trichloro-2-methyl-2-propanol (1)	AlCl$_3$ (0.36)	95–100	5	p-(3,3-Dichloro-2-methyl-allyl)bromobenzene (14), α-chloroisobutyric acid (22.6)	88
Chlorobenzene (1)	Ethyl alcohol (0.6)	AlCl$_3$ (1)	80–90	2–3	p-Chloroethylbenzene (40)	223
Chlorobenzene (1)	Isopropyl alcohol (—)	H$_2$SO$_4$ (80%) (—)	70	—	p-Chlorocumene (75)	123
Chlorobenzene (1)	Isopropyl alcohol (1)	AlCl$_3$ (1)	80–90	2–3	p-Chlorocumene (62)	223
Chlorobenzene (337.5 g.)	Isopropyl alcohol (60 g.)	Anhydrous HF (100 g.)–fluoro-sulfonic acid (200 g.)	74	1	4-Chloroisopropylbenzene (113 g.), chlorodiiso-propylbenzene (15 g.)	224
Chlorobenzene (22)	Isopropyl alcohol (1)	Alumina–silica	250	—	Monoisopropylchloro-benzene (97), (mainly para, some ortho)	225
Chlorobenzene (22)	n-Propyl alcohol (1)	Alumina–silica	250	—	Monoisopropylchloro-benzene (55), (mainly para, some ortho)	
Chlorobenzene (1)	s-Butyl alcohol (0.5)	AlCl$_3$ (0.4)	80–90	2–3	p-s-Butylchlorobenzene (50)	151
Chlorobenzene (1.4)	Isobutyl alcohol (1.0)	AlCl$_3$ (1.5)	80–90	2–3	p-t-Butylchlorobenzene (30)	223
Chlorobenzene (1)	t-Butyl alcohol (0.5)	AlCl$_3$ (0.2)	80–90	2–3	p-t-Butylchlorobenzene (65)	223
Chlorobenzene (1)	Isoamyl alcohol (0.5)	AlCl$_3$ (0.6)	80–90	2–3	p-t-Amylchlorobenzene (35)	223
Chlorobenzene (1)	t-Amyl alcohol (0.5)	AlCl$_3$ (0.2)	80–90	2–3	p- and m-t-Amylchloro-benzene (50)	223
Chlorobenzene (20)	1,1,1-Trichloro-2-methyl-2-propanol (10)	AlCl$_3$ (5)	95–100	5	p-(3,3-Dichloro-2-methyl-allyl)chlorobenzene (25), α-chloroisobutyric acid (37.5)	88

* Unless otherwise indicated.

TABLE 3.   Alkylation of toluene with alcohols

Moles of toluene*	Alkylating agent (moles)*	Catalyst (moles)*	Temperature, °C	Time, hrs.*	Products, % yield*	Ref.
2.5	Methyl alcohol (1)	AlCl$_3$ (2)	100	3	Mesitylene (53)	2,225
0.9	Propyl alcohol (0.5)	AlCl$_3$ (0.7)	125	4	m- and p-Propyltoluene (85), dipropyltoluenes (10)	202
0.4	Isopropyl alcohol (0.4)	H$_2$SO$_4$ (80%) (5)	70	—	p-Cymene (35), diisopropyltoluene	123,203
0.47	Isopropyl alcohol	TiCl$_4$ (0.1–0.2)	20–100	0.5–3 days	p-Isopropyltoluene (19–68)	204
0.05	n-Butyl alcohol (0.08)	ZnCl$_2$ (0.15)	300	24	Butyltoluene	201
—	s-Butyl alcohol (—)	H$_2$SO$_4$ (80%) (—)	70	—	p-s-Butyltoluene	123
—	Isobutyl alcohol	TiCl$_4$	b.p.	3–9 days	p-t-Butyltoluene (11–62)	204
11	Isobutyl alcohol (3.3)	H$_2$SO$_4$–SO$_3$ (25%)	25	0.7–0.8	p-t-Butyltoluene (60)	204
0.05	Isobutyl alcohol (0.05)	ZnCl$_2$ (0.15)	300	24	Butyltoluene	201
—	Isobutyl alcohol (—)	H$_2$SO$_4$ (80%) (—)	70	—	p-t-Butyltoluene	123
0.24–47	s-Butyl alcohol	TiCl$_4$ (0.1–0.2)	40–100	3–4.5 days	p-s-Butyltoluene (28–74)	204
—	t-Butyl alcohol	Anhydrous HF + fluorosulfonic acid	10	1.0	p-t-Butyltoluene (90), di-t-butyltoluene	224
294 g.	t-Butyl alcohol (176 g.)	Anhydrous HF (180 g.) + fluorosulfonic acid (300 g.)	10	1	p-t-Butyltoluene (282 g.), di-t-butyltoluene (25 g.) (90% of theoretical based on alcohol)	224
0.47	t-Butyl alcohol	TiCl$_4$ (0.05–0.2)	10–25	3–6	p-t-Butyltoluene (35–74)	204
—	t-Amyl alcohol	TiCl$_4$ (0.1–0.3)	18–40	3–18	p-t-Amyltoluene (57–70)	204
2	Cyclohexanol (0.75)	AlCl$_3$ (0.6)	80	2	m- and p-Cyclohexyltoluene (72), 3-5-dicyclohexyltoluene (18), p-cyclohexyltoluene (45)	226
40 ml.	1-Methylcyclohexanol-1 (0.05)	AlCl$_3$ (0.025)	heat until HCl ceased	water bath	1-Methylcyclohexyl (47), toluene, (mixture of o-p isomers)	140

1	Benzyl alcohol (0.4)	H_2SO_4 (703%) (15)	40	—	p-Benzyltoluene, anthracene	123
—	Benzyl alcohol in toluene	$AlCl_3$	60	3.5	Dimethyl anthracenes from non-volatile sublimate	83
—	2-Octanol (—)	HF (—)	—	—	p-Octyltoluene (42)	226
—	Diphenylmethanol (—)	P_2O_5 (—)	—	—	Diphenyl-p-tolylmethane	222
—	Diphenylmethanol (—)	$SnCl_4$ (—)	—	—	Diphenyl-p-tolylmethane	227
—	Diphenylmethanol	H_2SO_4–HOAC	r.t.	8 days	Diphenyltoluene (61)	132
4	1,1,1-Trichloro-2-methyl-propanol (2)	$AlCl_3$ (0.7)	92	2.7	p-(3,3-Dichloro-2-methylallyl-toluene (19.5)	88

* Unless otherwise indicated.

TABLE 4. Alkylation of various alkylbenzenes with alcohols

Aromatic compound (moles)*	Alkylating agent (moles)*	Catalyst (moles)*	Temperature, °C	Time, hrs.*	Products, % yield*	Ref.
o-Chlorotoluene (0.2)	t-Butyl alcohol (0.25)	AlCl$_3$ (0.1)	80–90	2–3	2-Chloro-x-t-butyltoluene (45)	223
o-Xylene	Benzyl alcohol (—)	H$_2$SO$_4$ (70%) (—)	40	—	3,4-Dimethyldiphenyl-methane, 1-methylanthra-cene	123
o-Xylene (—)	Diphenylmethanol (—)	P$_2$O$_5$ (—)	140	4	3,4-Dimethyltriphenyl-methane	228
m-Xylene (3)	Isopropyl alcohol (0.6)	H$_2$SO$_4$ (80%) (8)	75	16	4-Isopropyl-m-xylene (75)	132
m-Xylene (3)	s-Butyl alcohol (0.6)	H$_2$SO$_4$ (80%) (9)	25	16	4-s-Butyl-m-xylene (50)	229
m-Xylene (1)	Isobutyl alcohol (1)	H$_2$SO$_4$ (5)	45	1	3,5-Dimethyl-t-butylbenzene	230
m-Xylene (1.6)	t-Butyl alcohol (1.2)	HF (25)	0	18	t-Butyl-m-xylene (94)	199
m-Xylene (1.75)	t-Butyl alcohol (0.3)	AlCl$_3$ (0.9)	0	5	5-t-Butyl-m-xylene (89)	2
m-Xylene (3)	t-Butyl alcohol (0.6)	H$_2$SO$_4$ (80%) (9)	25	16	4-t-Butyl-m-xylene (48)	229
m-Xylene (—)	Benzyl alcohol (—)	H$_2$SO$_4$ (70%) (—)	40	—	2,4-Dimethyldiphenyl-methane, 2-methylanthra-cene	123
m-Xylene (—)	Diphenylmethanol (—)	P$_2$O$_5$ (—)	140	4	2,4-Dimethyltriphenyl-methane	228
p-Xylene (1)	Benzyl alcohol (—)	H$_2$SO$_4$ (70%) (—)	40	—	2,5-Dimethyldiphenyl-methane, 2-methylanthra-cene	123
p-Xylene (—)	Diphenylmethanol (—)	P$_2$O$_5$ (—)	140	4	2,5-Dimethyltriphenyl-methane	231
p-Xylene (—)	2,5-Dimethyldiphenyl-methanol (—)	P$_2$O$_5$ (—)	140	4	2,5,2′,5′-Tetramethyltri-phenylmethane (50–60)	232
p-Xylene (0.3)	2-Methyl-5-isopropyl-diphenylmethanol (0.1)	P$_2$O$_5$ (0.1)	140	5	2,2′,5′-Trimethyl-5-isopropyl-triphenylmethane (35)	232

o-Xylene	Diphenylmethanol	H_2SO_4–HOAC	r.t.	8	1-Diphenylmethyl-3,4-dimethylbenzene (75)	132
p-Xylene	Diphenylmethanol	H_2SO_4–HOAC	r.t.	8	1-Diphenylmethyl-2,5-dimethylbenzene (72)	132
m-Xylene	Diphenylmethanol	H_2SO_4–HOAC	r.t.	8	1-Diphenylmethyl-2,4-dimethylbenzene (68)	132
Mesitylene	Diphenylmethanol	H_2SO_4–HOAC	r.t.	8	Diphenylmethylmesitylene (94)	132
Mesitylene	Diphenylmethanol	Sulfuric–acetic acid (1:5 V/V)	r.t.	8 days	2,4,6-Trimethyltriphenylmethane over 90%	127
Mesitylene (12 g.)	4:4'-Dichlorodiphenyl-methanol (2 g.)	Sulfuric–acetic acid (1:5 V/V) (150 ml.)	r.t.	8 days	4,4'-Dichloro-2",4",6"-trimethyltriphenylmethane (98)	127

* Unless otherwise indicated.

TABLE 5.   Alkylation of naphthalene with alcohols

Moles of naphthalene*	Alkylating agent (moles)*	Catalyst (moles)*	Temperature, °C	Time, hrs.*	Products, % yield*	Ref.
100 g.	Cetanol (250 g.)	Acid clay (75 g.)	190–210 heated till more water evolved	—	(260 g. total), monoalkyl-naphthalene (45), dialkyl-naphthalene (35), saturated paraffin hydrocarbon (10), trace of trialkylnaphthalene	160
100 g.	Methanol (77 g.)	Silica–alumina (300 g.)	450	6.5	2-Methylnaphthalene, 52% on naphthalene consumed dimethylnaphthalenes + higher	148
	n-Propyl alcohol	BF_3	165–170	4–6	1,2-Di-n-propylnaphthalenes (88)	41
0.5	Isopropyl alcohol (0.75)	H_2SO_4 (80%) (6)	80	3	α- and β-Isopropyl-1,6- and 2,7-di-, tri-, and tetra-isopropylnaphthalenes	123
—	Isopropyl alcohol (—)	H_2SO_4 (96%) (—)	40–45	—	Diisopropylnaphthalene (m.p. 38°); tetraisopropyl-naphthalene	123
0.5	Isopropyl alcohol (0.5)	$AlCl_3$ (0.35)	90	4	β-Isopropylnaphthalene (33), diisopropylnaphthalenes (15), triisopropylnaphthalenes (11)	233
0.4	Isopropyl alcohol (0.6)	BF_3 (—)	25	—	β-Isopropylnaphthalene (35)	36
0.4	Isopropyl alcohol (1.6)	BF_3 (—)	25	—	Triisopropylnaphthalenes (57)	36
—	Isopropyl alcohol	BF_3	165–170	2.5–3	1,4-Diisopropylnaphthalene, 1- and 2-monoisopropyl-naphthalene oxidatives (naphthalene carboxylic acids)	41
0.25	n-Butyl alcohol (0.25)	$AlCl_3$ (0.33)	—	—	α-Butylnaphthalene (40)	234

	Alcohol	Catalyst	Temp.		Products	Ref.
—	n-Butyl alcohol	BF_3	165–170	2.5–3	1,2-di-n-Butylnaphthalenes (93), 1,4-di-n-butylnaphthalene	41
—	Isobutyl alcohol (—)	H_2SO_4 (80%) (—)	70	—	Di-t-butylnaphthalene (m.p. 142°)	123
0.2	Isobutyl alcohol (0.25)	$AlCl_3$ (0.03)	—	—	$β$- (and $α$)-t-Butylnaphthalenes, di-t-butylnaphthalenes	234
—	Isobutyl alcohol	BF_3	165–170	2.5–3	1- and 2-t-Butylnaphthalenes, 1,4 and 1,2-di-t-butylnaphthalenes, oxidation (naphthalene-1,4-dicarboxylic acid)	127
0.2	s-Butyl alcohol (0.25)	$AlCl_3$ (0.3)	90	5	$α$-s-Butylnaphthalene (20), di-s-butylnaphthalenes (35)	233
0.2	t-Butyl alcohol (0.25)	$AlCl_3$ (0.12)	90	3	$β$- (and $α$)-t-Butylnaphthalene (21), di-t-butylnaphthalene (37) (m.p. 132°)	233
0.4	t-Butyl alcohol (1.0)	BF_3 (—)	25	—	$β$-t-Butylnaphthalene (62), di-t-butylnaphthalenes (5) (m.p. 80° and 145°)	36
1	t-Butyl alcohol (3)	HF (25)	0–5	24	Di-t-butylnaphthalene (m.p. 143°) (76)	194
—	Isoamyl alcohol (—)	$AlCl_3$ (—)	—	—	$β$-t-Amylnaphthalene (62)	234
—	Isoamyl alcohol	BF_3	165–170	2.5–3	1- and 2-t-Amylnaphthalenes (36–40), 1,4-di-t-amylnaphthalene	
0.2	t-Amyl alcohol (0.25)	$AlCl_3$ (0.12)	90	2	$α$- and $β$-t-Amylnaphthalenes (34), di-t-amylnaphthalenes (20)	41
—	n-Amyl alcohol	BF_3	165–170	2.5–3	1- and 2-n-Amylnaphthalenes (98)	233

* Unless otherwise indicated.

Table continued

TABLE 5 (*continued*)

Moles of naphthalene*	Alkylating agent (moles)*	Catalyst (moles)*	Temperature, °C	Time, hrs.*	Products, % yield*	Ref.
—	n-Hexyl alcohol	BF_3	165–170	2.5–3	1 and 2-n-Hexylnaphthalene (98), di-n-hexylnaphthalene (98)	41
0.4	Cyclohexanol (0.45)	BF_3 (—)	25	—	β-Cyclohexylnaphthalene (63), 1,4-dicyclohexylnaphthalene (9)	36,235
0.4	Benzyl alcohol (0.45)	BF_3 (—)	25	—	α-Benzylnaphthalene (28), β-benzylnaphthalene (2), dibenzylnaphthalenes (15), tribenzylnaphthalenes (20)	36
1	Diphenylmethanol (0.5)	P_2O_5 (1)	140–145	4–5	α-Benzhydrylnaphthalene	236
—	Diphenylmethanol (—)	H_2SO_4 (—)			α-Benzhydrylnaphthalene	237

* Unless otherwise indicated.

TABLE 6. Alkylation of miscellaneous polynuclear aromatic compounds with alcohols

Aromatic compound (moles)*	Alkylating agent (moles)*	Catalyst (moles)*	Temperature, °C	Time, hrs.*	Products, % yield*	Ref.
1-Chloronaphthalene (0.5)	Isopropyl alcohol (0.5)	$AlCl_3$ (0.5)	80–90	2–3	1-Chloro-x-isopropyl-naphthalene (45)	223
1-Chloronaphthalene (0.8)	t-Amyl alcohol (0.5)	$AlCl_3$ (0.2)	80–90	2–3	x-t-Amyl-1-chloro-naphthalene (60)	223
β-Naphthalenesulfonic acid (—)	Isopropyl alcohol (—)	H_2SO_4 (80%) (—)	80	—	1- and 2-Isopropyl-1,6-2,6- and 2,7-di-, tri-, and tetraisopropyl-naphthalenes	123
β-Naphthalenesulfonic acid (0.5)	Isopropyl alcohol (3)	H_2SO_4 (96%) (1.3)	120	12	1,6-Diisopropyl-3-naphthalenesulfonic acid	123
β-Naphthalenesulfonic acid (0.5)	Isopropyl alcohol (1.5)	HF (24)	0 → 20	20	Polyisopropyl-2-naphthalenesulfonic acid	199
Acenaphthene (1)	3-Hexanol (1.17)	$ZnCl_2$ (—)	180	—	3-Acenaphthylhexane (32)	238
Phenanthrene (0.75)	t-Butyl alcohol (1.65)	HF (21)	15–20	18	t-Butylphenanthrenes (60)	199

* Unless otherwise indicated.

TABLE 7. Alkylation of phenol with alcohols

Moles of phenol*	Alkylating agent (moles)*	Catalyst (moles)*	Temperature, °C	Time, hrs.*	Products, % yield*	Ref.
—	Methyl alcohol (—)	Al_2O_3	440	—	o-Cresol, anisole	152
ca 0.5	Diphenylmethanol (0.1)	0.5 cc. of 72% perchloric acid, 50 cc. nitromethane	100	4	p-Hydroxytriphenylmethane (crude 63%)	239
ca 0.01	Diphenylmethanol (0.03)	5 drops of 72% perchloric acid + 10 cc. nitromethane	100	4	2, 4, 6-Tridiphenylmethylphenol (crude 86%)	234
0.03	Tri-p-nitrophenylmethanol (0.006)	3 drops of 72% W/W perchloric acid + 3.6 cc. nitromethane	100	3	4-Hydroxy-4'-4"-4"'-tri-nitrotetraphenylmethane (crude 74%)	239
—	Ethyl alcohol (—)	$ZnCl_2$ (—)	180	—	p-Ethylphenol and isomers, and p-ethylphenetole	240,241,242
—	Ethyl alcohol (—	$AlCl_3$ (—)	120–140	6	Diethylphenol (36), o- and p-ethylphenols (24)	50
1	n-Propyl alcohol (2)	Al_2O_3 (0.1)	400	12	o-Propylphenol, n-propylphenyl ether, n-propyl o-propyl-phenyl ether	243
1	n-Propyl alcohol (—)	$AlCl_3$ (—)	120–140	6	o- and p-Propylphenols (73)	50
1	n-Propyl alcohol (1)	BF_3 (0.3)	115–160	1	o-Isopropylphenol (28), p-isopropylphenol (20), 2,4-diisopropylphenyl isopropyl ether (11)	25
1	Isopropyl alcohol (1)	BF_3 (0.3)	115–160	1	o-Isopropylphenol (32), p-isopropylphenol (16), 2,4-diisopropylphenol isopropyl ether (13)	25
—	Isopropyl alcohol (—)	$AlCl_3$ (—)	110–120	6	p- and o-Isopropylphenols (52), p-Isopropylphenol isopropyl ether (23)	50

	Reactant	Catalyst	Temp.	Time (hr.)	Products (% yields)	Ref.
1	p-t-Octylphenol (1)	AlCl₃ (2)	80	10	p-t-Butylphenol (75)	244
0.25	Butyl alcohol (0.50)	100 ml. H₃PO₄	130–150	11	Disubstituted products (70) (mixture of dibutylphenol isomers (28); butyl ether of butylphenol (42); (9) butylphenol + (7) tributylphenol)	
0.25	Butyl alcohol	150 ml. H₃PO₄	140–160	23	Tributylphenol (70)	245
—	n-Butyl alcohol (—)	AlCl₃ (—)	140	6	Butylphenol (72)	245
1	n-Butanol (1)	AlCl₃ (2.5)	120–130	several hours	n-Butylphenol (36.7), o- + p-isomers	50
—	s-Butyl alcohol (—)	H₂SO₄ (—)	—	—	p- and o-s-Butylphenol	246
—	s-Butyl alcohol (—)	AlCl₃ (—)	120–140	6	p- and o-s-Butylphenol (52), s-butylphenyl, s-butyl ether (13)	123
1	t-Butyl alcohol (1–3)	10 cc. of 70% perchloric acid	60	10 min.–20 hrs.	4-t-Butylphenol (5–48), 2,4-di-t-butylphenol (5–44)	50
31–372 **	t-Butyl alcohol (8.5–246 g.)	200–1500 g. of 85%–100% H₃PO₄	—	9–60 min.	Quiaiacol (4–60), 4-t-butyl-quiaiacol (10–46), 5-t-butyl-quiaiacol (8.5–41), 6-t-butylquiaiacol (1–12)	247
1	Isobutyl alcohol (3)	H₃PO₄, 150–200 ml.	110–145	8–22	Butylphenol (10.7–46), dibutyl-phenol (8.7–32), tributyl-phenol (6–7), butyl ether of phenol (9–17), butyl ether of dibutylphenol (7.8–34), tributylphenol (7–37)	248
1.1	Isobutyl alcohol (1.1)	ZnCl₂ (1.0)	180	1	p-t-Butylphenol (70)	245, 90,91,92,249
1.1	Isobutyl alcohol (—)	H₂SO₄ (70%) (—)	80	—	p-t-Butylphenol (ca 80)	123
—	Isobutyl alcohol (—)	AlCl₃ (—)	—	—	p-t-Butylphenol (60–75)	50,250
0.25	t-Butyl alcohol (0.25)	AlCl₃ (0.125)	25–30	3–4	p-t-Butylphenol (45–60)	49,250
—	2-Pentanol (—)	AlCl₃ (—)	100	2	2- and 3-(p-Hydroxyphenyl)-pentane (58)	50

* Unless otherwise indicated.   ** Quiaiacol used.

Table continued

TABLE 7 (*continued*)

Moles of phenol*	Alkylating agent (moles)*	Catalyst (moles)*	Temperature, °C	Time, hrs.*	Products, % yield*	Ref.
—	Isoamyl alcohol (—)	$ZnCl_2$ (—)	180	1	p-t-Amylphenol (40)	90,91,247
1	t-Amyl alcohol (—)	$ZnCl_2$ (2)	180	—	p-t-Amylphenol (65)	251
0.25	t-Amyl alcohol (0.25)	$AlCl_3$ (0.125)	25–30	3–4	p-t-Amylphenol (45–60)	49
0.25	2-Methyl-2-pentanol (0.25)	$AlCl_3$ (0.125)	25–30	3–4	2-(p-Hydroxyphenyl)-2-methylpentane (45–60)	49
0.25	3-Methyl-3-pentanol (0.25)	$AlCl_3$ (0.125)	25–30	3–4	3-(p-Hydroxyphenyl)-2-methylpentane (45–60)	49
0.25	2,3-Dimethyl-2-butanol (0.25)	$AlCl_3$ (0.125)	25–30	3–4	2-(p-Hydroxyphenyl)-2,3-dimethylbutane (45–60)	49
0.1	Cyclohexanol (0.15)	p-Toluenesulfonic acid (0.002)	155	0.5	Cyclohexene (73), p-cyclohexylphenol	252
0.1	Cyclohexanol (—)	H_2SO_4 (0.1)	80	—	p-Cyclohexylphenol (50)	123
0.085	1-Methyl-1-cyclohexanol (0.65)	H_3PO_4 (2.86), 30 ml.	100–120	3	4-(Methylcyclohexyl)phenol (79)	140
0.2	4-Methylcyclohexanol (0.2)	H_2SO_4 (80%) (6)	70	5	p-(Methylcyclohexyl)phenol (55)	123
0.5	Benzyl alcohol (0.5)	$AlCl_3$ (0.25)	20–30	18	p-Benzylphenol (43–55)	75
3	Benzyl alcohol (—)	H_2SO_4 (70%) (—)	40	—	p- and o-Benzylphenols (40)	123
—	Benzyl alcohol (—)	$ZnCl_2$ (—)	—	—	p-Benzylphenol	40,41
—	Benzyl alcohol (—)	H_2SO_4 (—)	—	—	p-Benzylphenol	253
0.5	2-Phenyl-2-propanol (0.16)	$AlCl_3$ (0.08)	90	1	p-Hydroxy-2,2-diphenylpropane (68–72)	254
—	Diphenylmethanol (—)	$SnCl_4$ (—)	—	—	p-Hydroxytriphenylmethane	255
0.04	Diphenylmethanol (0.08)	H_2SO_4 (0.3)	90	4	2,4,6-Triphenylmethylphenol (ca 100)	256
0.75	1,1-Diphenyl-1-ethanol (0.16)	$AlCl_3$ (0.08)	90	1	p-Hydroxy-1,1,1-triphenylethane (80)	254
0.75	1,1-Diphenyl-1-propanol (0.5)	$AlCl_3$ (0.25)	25	80–90	p-Hydroxy-1,1,1-triphenylpropane (98)	81

0.75	1,1-Diphenyl-1-butanol (0.5)	$AlCl_3$ (0.25)	25	80–90	p-Hydroxy-1,1,1-triphenylbutane (46)	81
0.75	1,1-Diphenyl-2-methyl-1-propanol (0.5)	$AlCl_3$ (0.25)	25	80–90	p-Hydroxy-1,1,1-triphenyl-2-methylpropane (73)	81
0.75	1,1-Diphenyl-1-pentanol (0.5)	$AlCl_3$ (0.25)	25	80–90	p-Hydroxy-1,1,1-triphenyl-pentane (30)	81
0.75	1,1-Diphenyl-2-methyl-1-butanol (0.5)	$AlCl_3$ (0.25)	25	80–90	p-Hydroxy-1,1,1-triphenyl-2-methylbutane (13)	81
0.75	1,1-Diphenyl-3-methyl-1-butanol (0.5)	$AlCl_3$ (0.25)	25	80–90	p-Hydroxy-1,1,1-triphenyl-3-methylbutane (40)	81
0.75	1,1-Diphenyl-2,2-dimethyl-1-propanol (0.5)	$AlCl_3$ (0.25)	25	80–90	3-(p-Hydroxyphenyl)-2,2-diphenyl-3-methylbutane (6)	81
0.75	1,1-Diphenyl-1-hexanol (0.5)	$AlCl_3$ (0.25)	25	80–90	p-Hydroxy-1,1,1-triphenyl-hexane (30)	81
0.7	3-Methyl-3-pentanol (0.5)	Phosphoric acid (90 g.)	refluxed	12	Crude, 91 g. of o- and p-(methyldiethyl)methylphenol purification and separation gave 15 g. of o-isomer, 40 g. of p-isomer	81
0.1	Triphenylmethanol (0.01)	H_2SO_4 (0.2)	25	24–48	p-Hydroxytetraphenylmethane	257
—	Triphenylmethanol (—)	H_2SO_4 (trace)	80	0.8	p-Hydroxytetraphenylmethane (80–90)	258
0.05	Triphenylmethanol (0.02)	—	boiling	1	p-Hydroxytetraphenylmethane (97)	131
0.1	p-Methyltriphenylmethanol (0.01)	H_2SO_4 (0.1)	25	24–48	p-Hydroxy-p'-methyltetraphenylmethane	126 227

* Unless otherwise indicated.

TABLE 8.   Alkylation of various phenols and phenolic ethers with alcohols

Aromatic compound (moles)*	Alkylating agent (moles)*	Catalyst (moles)*	Temperature, °C	Time, hrs.*	Products, % yield*	Ref.
Anisole (—)	Isopropyl alcohol (—)	$AlCl_3$ (—)	120	4	p-Isopropylanisole (50), p-isopropylphenol (38)	50
Anisole (—)	Isopropyl alcohol (—)	$AlCl_3$ (—)	140	6	p-Isopropylanisole (30), p-isopropylphenol (64)	50
Anisole (0.2)	Isopropyl alcohol	$TiCl_4$ (0.1–0.2)	100–140	1–3	p-Isopropylanisole (44–53), p-isopropylphenol (14–22)	204
Anisole (0.2)	Isopropyl alcohol	$TiCl_4$ (0.4)	50–160	3	p-t-Butylanisole (0–37.5), p-t-butylphenol (0–37.5)	204
Anisole	Diphenylmethanol	Sulfuric–acetic acid (1:5 V/V)	r.t.	8 days	4-Methoxytriphenylmethane (over 90%)	127
Anisole (—)	s-Butyl alcohol (—)	$AlCl_3$ (—)	100	2	s-Butylanisole (55), di-s-butylanisole (16), s-butylphenol (13)	50
Anisole (0.2)	t-Butyl alcohol	$TiCl_4$ (0.05–0.2)	1–40	10–40	p-t-Butylanisole (53–67)	204
Anisole (0.2)	t-Amyl alcohol	$TiCl_4$ (0.1–0.2) + carbon 25–3 disulfide (30 cc.)	25–3	0–40	p-t-Amylanisole (57–61)	204
Anisole (0.6)	Benzyl alcohol (0.5)	$AlCl_3$ (0.25)	20	48	p-Benzylanisole (46)	75
Anisole (120 cc.)	Diphenylmethanol (0.2)	1 cc. of 72% perchloric acid + 120 cc nitromethane	100	3	p-Methoxytriphenylmethane (crude) (89)	239
Anisole (0.012)	Tri-p-nitrophenyl-methanol (0.002)	2 Drops of 72% perchloric acid + 1.3 g.	100	3	p-Methoxytriphenylmethane (crude) (89)	239
Anisole (4.4)	1,1,1-Trichloro-2-methyl-2-propanol (1.8)	$AlCl_3$ (1)	85–90	2.1	p-(3,3-Dichloro-2-methylallyl), anisole (4), phenol α-chloroisobutyrate (3.7)	88

Aromatic	Alkylating agent	Catalyst	Temperature	Time	Products	Reference
Anisole (0.1)	Triphenylmethanol (0.01)	H_2SO_4 (0.2)	25	120	p-Methoxytetraphenyl-methane	130
o-Nitroanisole (1)	Isopropyl alcohol (1)	HF (12)	10–20	18	2-Nitro-4-isopropylanisole (84)	199
o-Nitroanisole (2.45)	Cyclohexanol (2.25)	HF (18)	15–20	20	2-Nitro-4-cyclohexylanisole (55)	199
Phenetole (0.6)	Benzyl alcohol (0.5)	$AlCl_3$ (0.25)	20	—	p-Benzylphenetole (57)	75
o-Cresol (54 g.)	t-Butyl alcohol (40 g.)	200 g. of 100% H_3PO_4	60–65	8	4-t-Butyl-o-cresol (63.4)	137
o-Cresol (—)	Isobutyl alcohol (—)	$ZnCl_2$ (—)	180	—	4-t-Butyl-2-methylphenol	103
o-Cresol (—)	Isobutyl alcohol (—)	H_2SO_4 (—)	—	—	4-t-Butyl-2-methylphenol	123
o-Cresol (—)	Benzyl alcohol (—)	H_2SO_4 (70%) (—)	—	—	4-Benzyl-2-methylphenol	123
2-Methyl-1,4-dimethoxybenzene (0.079)	1-Methylcyclohexanol (0.096)	25 ml. of 85% H_2SO_4	0–5	6	5-(1'-Methylcyclohexyl)-2-methyl-1,4-dimethoxy-benzene, 62% based on 2-methyl-1,4-dimethoxyben-zene)	258
2-Chloro-1,4-di-methoxybenzene (0.052)	1-Methylcyclohexanol (0.13)	50 ml. of 90% H_2SO_4	0–5	9	Probably a mixture of 5- and 6-(1'-methyl-cyclohexyl)-2-chloro-1,4-dimethoxybenzenes) (50)	258
1,4-Dimethoxy-benzene (3 g.)	2-Methylcyclohexanol (2.5 g.)	15 ml. of 90% H_2SO_4	0–5	20	2,5-Bis-(1'-methylcyclo-hexyl)-1,4-dimethoxy-benzene) (64)	258
1,4-Dimethoxy-benzene (3.0 g.)	1-Methylcyclohexanol (2.5 g.)	5 ml. of 90% H_2SO_4	0–5	30	2,5-Bis-(1'-methylcyclo-hexyl)-1,4-dimethoxy-benzene (9)	258
p-Methoxytri-phenylmethane (0.01)	Diphenylmethanol (0.01)	3 Drops of 72% per-chloric acid + 10 cc. nitromethane	60–70	1	2,4-Bisdiphenylmethyl-anisole (93)	239
o-Cresol (0.9)	Benzyl alcohol (0.9)	$AlCl_3$ (0.5)	30–35	18	4-Benzyl-2-methylphenol (30), 6-benzyl-2-methyl-phenol (2), 4,6-dibenzyl-2-methylphenol (20)	76

Table continued

* Unless otherwise indicated.

TABLE 8 (continued)

Aromatic compound (moles)*	Alkylating agent (moles)*	Catalyst (moles)*	Temperature, °C	Time, hrs.*	Products, % yield*	Ref.
o-Cresol (0.04)	Diphenylmethanol (0.08)	H_2SO_4 (0.3)	90	4	Diphenylmethyl-o-cresol (ca 100%)	259
o-Cresol	Triphenylmethanol	0-40% W/W H_2SO_4 in HAc + 5% H_2O	—	—	4-Hydroxy-3-methylphenyl-triphenylmethane	128
o-Cresol (75 g.)	3-Methyl-3-pentanol (51 g.)	Phosphoric acid (90 g.)	—	12	44 g., Mixture of o- and p-(methyldiethyl) methyl-o-cresol	257
o-Cresol (0.05)	Triphenylmethanol (0.03)	H_2SO_4 (0.1)	25	24	4-Hydroxy-3-methyltetra-phenylmethane (ca 100%)	126
o-Cresol-methyl-ether (0.08)	Triphenylmethanol (0.03)	H_2SO_4 (0.1)	25	48	4-Methoxy-3-methyltetra-phenylmethane (ca 100%)	126
m-Cresol (—)	Isopropyl alcohol (—)	H_2SO_4 (—)	—	—	3-Methyl-4-isopropylphenol	123
m-Cresol (—)	Isobutyl alcohol (—)	H_2SO_4 (—)	—	—	4-5-Butyl-3-methylphenol	123
m-Cresol (1.1)	Benzyl alcohol (0.9)	$AlCl_3$ (0.45)	35	24	4-Benzyl-3-methylphenol (19), 6-benzyl-3-methylphenol (21), 4,6-dibenzyl-3-methylphenol (35)	123
m-Cresol (75 g.)	3-Methyl-3-pentanol (51 g.)	90 g. Phosphoric acid	refluxed	12	30 g., mixture of 2 possible isomers of (methyldi-ethyl)-m-cresol	77
m-Cresol (0.05)	Triphenylmethanol (0.03)	H_2SO_4 (0.1)	48	25	4-Hydroxy-2-methyltetra-phenylmethane (90)	257
p-Cresol (1)	Benzyl alcohol (0.5)	$AlCl_3$ (0.25)	25-30	18	2-Benzyl-4-methylphenol (35), 2,6-dibenzyl-4-methylphenol (36)	126,260
p-Cresol (1.5)	Benzyl alcohol (0.5)	$AlCl_3$ (0.25)	25-30	18	2-Benzyl-4-methylphenol (35), 2,6-dibenzyl-4-methylphenol (36)	78

p-Cresol (0.05)	Diphenylmethanol (0.05)	H_2SO_4 (0.15)	90	5	o,o'-Diphenylmethyl-p-cresol (70)	259
p-Cresol	3-Methyl-3-pentanol	90 g. Phosphoric acid	refluxed	12	35 g. (Methyldiethyl)methyl-p-cresol	257
α-Naphthol (—)	Diphenylmethanol (—)	$SnCl_4$ or $ZnCl_2$ (—)	—	—	4-Diphenylmethyl-1-naphthol	261
β-Naphthol (1.11)	Isopropyl alcohol (4.44)	HF (25)	5	24	Diisopropyl-β-naphthol (94)	199
β-Naphthol (0.74)	3-Methyl-3-pentanol (0.6)	100 g. Phosphoric acid	refluxed	12	46 g. of 6-(Methyldiethyl)-methyl-2-naphthol	257
β-Naphthol (70 g.)	1-Methyl-1-cyclopentanol (48 g.)	100 g. Phosphoric acid	refluxed	16	25 g. 6-(1-Methylcyclopentyl)-2-naphthol	257
β-Naphthol	1-n-Propyl-1-cyclohexanol	Phosphoric acid	refluxed	12–16	6-Cyclohexyl-2-naphthol	257

* Unless otherwise indicated.

TABLE 9. Alkylation of polyhydric phenols with alcohols

Aromatic compound (moles)*	Alkylating agent (moles)*	Catalyst (moles)*	Temperature, °C	Time, hrs.*	Products, % yield*	Ref.
Resorcinol (—)	Isopropyl alcohol (—)	H_2SO_4 (70%) (—)	80	—	4-Isopropylresorcinol, 4,6-diisopropylresorcinol	123
Resorcinol monomethyl ether (—)	Isopropyl alcohol (—)	H_2SO_4 (—)	—	—	Monomethyl ether of diisopropylresorcinol	123
Resorcinol dimethyl ether (—)	Isopropyl alcohol (—)	H_2SO_4 (—)	—	—	Dimethyl ethers of isopropyl and diisopropylresorcinol	123
Hydroquinone (5)	Isopropyl alcohol (6)	HF (42)	5 → 20	24	Isopropylhydroquinone (39)	199
Hydroquinone (1.65)	Isopropyl alcohol (7.6)	HF (—)	—	—	2,4,5-Triisopropylphenol (83)	199
Hydroquinone (3 g.)	1-Methylcyclohexanol (3.1 g.)	15 ml. of 70% H_3PO_4	0–5	1	2,5-Bis-(1-methylcyclohexyl)-1,4-hydroquinone (44)	258
2-Methyl-1,4-naphtholhydroquinone (—)	Cinnamyl alcohol (—)	Oxalic acid (—)	100	24	3-Di-n-amyl-2-methyl-1,4-naphtholhydroquinone (30)	262
2-Methyl-1,4-naphtholhydroquinone (—)	Phytol (—)	Oxalic acid (—)	75	36	2-Methyl-3-phytol-1,4-naphtholhydroquinone (30)	263

* Unless otherwise indicated.

TABLE 10. Alkylation of miscellaneous aldehydes, acids, and quinones with alcohols

Aromatic compound (moles)*	Alkylating agent (moles)*	Catalyst (moles)*	Temperature, °C	Time, hrs.*	Products, % yield*	Ref.
Benzoquinone (0.1)	Diphenylmethanol (0.1)	H_2SO_4 (0.01)	80	12	2,5-Diphenylmethylbenzoquinone	264
β-Naphthoquinone (0.1)	Diphenylmethanol (0.1)	H_2SO_4 (0.01)	80	3	2-Diphenylmethyl-β-naphthoquinone (ca 100%)	264
Salicylic acid (1)	Isopropyl alcohol (2.5)	H_2SO_4 (80%) (60)	75	5	2-Hydroxy-5-isopropylbenzoic acid (50)	123
Salicylic acid (1)	Isobutyl alcohol (2)	$ZnCl_2$ (—)	180	1	p-t-Butylphenol + CO_2	
Salicylic acid (—)	Isobutyl alcohol (—)	H_2SO_4 (80%) (—)	70	—	2-Hydroxy-5-t-butylbenzoic acid (80)	123
Salicylic acid (—)	t-Butyl alcohol (—)	H_2SO_4 (80%) (—)	70	—	2-Hydroxy-5-t-butylbenzoic acid (80)	123
3-Hydroxy-2-naphthoic acid (1)	Isopropyl alcohol (1.2)	HF (33)	15–20	20	Isopropyl-3-hydroxy-2-naphthoic acid	194
Methyl salicylate	Triphenylmethanol (0.02)	— (—)	boiling	1	3-Carboxy-4-hydroxytetraphenylmethane (40)	126

* Unless otherwise indicated.

TABLE 11. Alkylation of aniline with alcohols

Moles of aniline*	Alkylating agent (moles)*	Catalyst (moles)*	Temperature, °C	Time, hrs.*	Products, % yield*	Ref.
1	Methyl alcohol (1.05)	Silica gel	365	4	25.9 PhNHR + 10.9 PhNR$_2$	167
1	Methyl alcohol (2.05)	Silica gel	362–375	4	19–22.7 PhNHR + 10.9–24.9 PhNR$_2$	167
1	Ethyl alcohol (1.05)	Silica gel	385	4	33.4 PhNHR + 6.8 PhNR$_2$	167
1	Ethyl alcohol (2.05)	Silica gel	385	4	46.6 PhNHR + 13.3 PhNR$_2$	167
1	n-Propyl alcohol (1.05)	Silica gel	385	—	28 PhNHR + 6 PhNR$_2$	167
1	n-Propyl alcohol (2.05)	Silica gel	385	—	37.1 PhNHR + 12.0 PhNR$_2$	167
1	n-Propyl alcohol (1)	ZnCl$_2$ (1)	260	8	p-n-Propylaniline	265
1	Isopropyl alcohol (1)	ZnCl$_2$ (1)	260	—	p-Isopropylaniline	265,266
1	n-Butyl alcohol (1.05)	Silica gel	385	—	24.1 PhNHR + 7.9 PhNR$_2$	167
1	n-Butyl alcohol (2.05)	Silica gel	385	—	26.5 PhNHR + 8.5 PhNR$_2$	167
1	Isobutyl alcohol (1)	P$_2$O$_5$ (1)	260	8	p-t-Butylaniline	92,265
1	Isobutyl alcohol (1)	ZnCl$_2$ (1)	260	8	p-t-Butylaniline (40–50)	265,267
—	Isoamyl alcohol (—)	P$_2$O$_5$ (—)	280	—	p-Isoamylaniline (40)	92,268,269
—	Isoamyl alcohol (—)	ZnCl$_2$ (—)	250	—	p-Isoamylaniline (40)	92,268
0.2	t-Amyl alcohol (0.1)	ZnCl$_2$ (—)	270	9	p-t-Amylaniline	270
0.1	n-Octyl alcohol (0.1)	ZnCl$_2$ (0.05)	270–280	8	p-n-Octylaniline	271
0.1	s-Octyl alcohol (0.1)	ZnCl$_2$ (0.05)	280	8	p-s-Octylaniline (15)	271
—	Diphenylmethanol (—)	ZnCl$_2$ (—)	150	—	p-Aminotriphenylmethane	272
—	Di-α-naphthylmethanol (—)	HCl (—)	warm	—	p-Di-α-naphthylmethylaniline	273,274
0.1	Triphenylmethanol (0.02)	HCl (0.1)	115	5	p-Aminotetraphenylmethane	217

* Unless otherwise indicated.

TABLE 12. Alkylation of miscellaneous aromatic amines with alcohols

Aromatic compound (moles)*	Alkylating agent (moles)*	Catalyst (moles)	Temperature, °C	Time, hrs.*	Products, % yield*	Ref.
Dimethylaniline (—)	Benzyl alcohol (—)	$ZnCl_2$ (—)	150	—	p-Dimethylaminodiphenyl-methane	272
Dimethylaniline (—)	Benzhydrol (—)	$ZnCl_2$ (—)	150	—	p-Dimethylaminotriphenyl-methane	272
o-Toluidine (—)	Isobutyl alcohol (—)	$ZnCl_2$ (—)	280	—	2-Amino-3-t-butyltoluene	102
o-Toluidine (—)	Isobutyl alcohol (—)	HCl (—)	280–300	—	2-Amino-5-t-butyltoluene	102
o-Toluidine (—)	n-Octyl alcohol (—)	$ZnCl_2$ (—)	280	—	n-Octyl-o-toluidine (40–50)	102
o-Toluidine (0.15)	Triphenylmethanol (0.1)	HCl (0.15)	115	5	4-Amino-3-methyltetra-phenylmethane	126,276
2,6-Dimethyl-aniline (0.15)	Triphenylmethanol (0.08)	HCl (0.15)	115	0.3	4-Amino-3,5-dimethyltetra-phenylmethane (ca 100%)	276
β-Naphthylamine (0.3)	Methanol (1.0)	HCl (0.3)	240–250	12	1-Methyl-2-naphthol (15), dimethylaminonaphtha-lene, etc.	277
p-Anisidine (0.77)	Cyclohexanol (2)	HF (19)	10–20	18	Cyclohexyl-p-anisidine (23)	199
CH_3OH; C_2H_5OH, C_3H_7OH; C_4H_9OH	Aniline, o- and p-toluidine	Alumina; H_3PO_4 on asbestos and charcoal; other oxides and promoters	300–380	50–225 hrs.	N-mono- and N,N-di-alkylanilines	171
Ethyl alcohol	N-ethylaniline	Alumina containing various percentages of water	300	—	N,N-diethylaniline	168
Methyl alcohol (0.6 g.)	N-methylaniline (2 g.)	Alumina, varying amounts of iodine	250	3.5	N,N-dimethylaniline (32.5–53.5)	169
Methyl alcohol	N-methylaniline	Alumina + chlorides	250	3.5	N,N-dimethylaniline + nuclear alkylation	169

* Unless otherwise indicated.

TABLE 13.   Alkylation of heterocyclic aromatic compounds with alcohols

Aromatic compound (moles)*	Alkylating agent (moles)*	Catalyst (moles)*	Tempera-ture, °C	Time, hrs.*	Products, % yield*	Ref.
Thiophene (1260 g.)	Isopropyl alcohol (180 g.)	Alumina (150 g.)	200 24 atm.	200	Monoalkylthiophene, 56% base on alcohol high boiling, 102 g.	172
Thiophene (1260 g.)	t-Butyl alcohol (222 g.)	Alumina (150 g.)	200 15 atm.	5	Monoalkylthiophene, 38% base on alcohol high boiling, 61 g.	172
Ethyl-5-bromo-2-furoate (—)	t-Amyl alcohol (—)	AlCl$_3$	—	—	4-t-Butyl-5-bromo-2-furoic acid (10)	278
Thiophene (0.7)	Diphenylmethanol (0.6)	P$_2$O$_5$ (—)	—	24	Benzhydrylthiophene	279

* Unless otherwise indicated.

TABLE 14.   Alkylation of benzene with ethers

Moles of benzene*	Alkylating agent (moles)*	Catalyst (moles)*	Temperature, °C	Time, hrs.*	Products, % yield*	Ref.
Benzene (1.8)	Methyl ether (1)	Alumina–silica 1:4**	450	30 sec. contact time	Toluene (13.6)	146
Benzene (0.8–3.4)	Methyl ether (1)	Alumina–silica 1:4	400–500	Varying contact time	Toluene (8.4–17.3), xylene (0–6.0), higher (0–6.0)	146
—	Ethyl ether (—)	$AlCl_3$ (—)	—	—	Hexaethylbenzene (50)	280
3.0	Ethyl ether (0.5)	$AlCl_3$ (1.0)	25–120	48	Ethylbenzene (36)	2
2	Ethyl ether (1)	BF_3 (1)	150	3	Ethylbenzene (25), p-diethylbenzene (20)	281
4	Ethyl ether (1)	$ZnCl_2$ (1)	180	12	Ethylbenzene	281
—	n-Propyl ether (—)	$AlCl_3$ (—)	40	21	Ethylbenzene (0.5), isopropylbenzene (8.1), n-propylbenzene (1.7)	282
2	Isopropyl ether (1)	BF_3 (—)	—	—	Cumene (25), p-diisopropylbenzene (20)	281
7	Isopropyl ether (1)	HF (—)	—	—	Cumene (26), p-diisopropylbenzene (24), 1,2,4-triisopropylbenzene (25), 1,2,4,5-tetraisopropylbenzene (8)	281
2	Isopropyl phenyl ether (1)	BF_3 (—)	—	—	Cumene (25), p-diisopropylbenzene (10)	283
Benzene (6.44)	s-Butyl methyl ether (1)	BF_3 (1) (0–55 ml). Promoters, (H_2SO_4, H_2O, CH_3OH, $CH_3OH + H_2O$, CF_3COOH, $C_2H_5SO_3H$)	25	2–400	s-Butylbenzene	281 31

* Unless otherwise indicated.   ** Best catalyst of several investigated.

Table continued

20+F.C. II

TABLE 14 (continued)

Moles of benzene*	Alkylating agent (moles)*	Catalyst (moles)*	Temperature, °C	Time, hrs.*	Products, % yield*	Ref.
Benzene (7)	s-Butyl methyl ether (1)	BF_3 (1); (H_2O, H_2SO_4, Chlorosulfonic acid, ethanesulfonic acid), added to the extent of 1 mole % of BF_3 present	—	—	Mono- and poly-s-butyl-benzenes	
Benzene	Trimethylene oxide	$AlCl_3$	10	10	3-Phenyl-1-propanol	191
Benzene	Trimethylene oxide and ethylene oxide	$AlCl_3$	6–9	0.92	2-Phenyl-1-ethanol	191
Benzene	Trimethylene oxide	$AlCl_3$	refluxed	1.83	3-Phenyl-1-propanol	191
Benzene (12 ml.)	2,3-Butene oxide (1)	Anhydrous $AlCl_3$ (2)	10–12	2–3/4	3-Phenyl-2-butanol (3), 2,3-diphenylbutane (3.4), 2-methyl-2-phenylpropanol (trace)	196
Benzene (12 ml.)	Isobutene oxide (1)	Anhydrous $AlCl_3$ (2)	10–12	2–3/4	meso-2,3-Diphenylbutane (1), meso-2,3-dimethyldibenzyl (4)	196
2	Isoamyl ether (1)	BF_3 (—)	150	3	t-Amylbenzene (10)	281
2	n-Amyl ether (1)	BF_3 (—)	150	3	s-Amylbenzene (20)	281
—	Benzyl methyl ether (—)	$SnCl_4$ (—)	—	—	Diphenylmethane	285
4	Benzyl methyl ether (0.2)	$TiCl_3$ (0.1)	80	—	Diphenylmethane, p- and m-dibenzylbenzene	286
—	Benzyl ethyl ether (0.15)	P_2O_5 (0.15)	80	—	Diphenylmethane (40)	219,287
2	Benzyl ethyl ether (0.4)	$SnCl_4$ (0.2)	—	—	Diphenylmethane (15)	57,286
4	Benzyl ethyl ether (0.5)	$TiCl_4$ (0.25)	—	—	Diphenylmethane (55), p- and m-dibenzylbenzenes (25)	288
2	Benzyl ethyl ether (1)	BF_3 (—)	—	—	Diphenylmethane (20)	285

4	Benzyl n-propyl ether (1)	BF$_3$ (0.5)	80-90	2	Diphenylmethane (33)	39
3.3	Benzyl n-propyl ether (1)	BF$_3$ (1)	80-90	2	Diphenylmethane (46), cumene (11)	39
—	Benzyl isoamyl ether (—)	SnCl$_4$ (—)	—	—	Diphenylmethane	285
2	Benzyl ether (1)	BF$_3$ (—)	—	—	Diphenylmethane (15), di-benzylbenzenes (20), etc.	281
—	Benzyl ether (—)	HF (—)	0	48	Diphenylmethane (65-70)	283
0.7	Benzhydryl ether (0.01)	P$_2$O$_5$ (0.04)			Triphenylmethane (60)	219
Benzene (20)	α-Methylstyrene oxide (0.74)	Anhydrous AlCl$_3$ (2/1 mole of oxide)	5-10	—	1-1-Diphenyl-1-propene }(348 g.) 1,1-Diphenylpropene } 2,2-diphenyl-1-propanol (102 g.), 1,1,2-triphenyl-propane (357 g.), residue (574 g.)	197

* Unless otherwise indicated.

TABLE 15. Alkylation of toluene with ethers

Moles of toluene	Alkylating agent (moles)	Catalyst (moles)	Temperature	Time	Products, % yield	Ref.
—	Benzyl ethyl ether (—)	P_2O_5	—	—	p-Benzyltoluene	287

TABLE 16. Alkylation of various alkylbenzenes with ethers

Aromatic compound (moles)*	Alkylating agent (moles)*	Catalyst (moles)*	Temperature, °C	Time	Products, % yield*	Ref.
m-Xylene (1)	3-Hexyl ether (0.18)	HF (—)	450	Contact time, 45 sec.	3-(m-Xylyl)hexane (61)	238
Ethylbenzene (30 g.)	Methyl ether (13.3 g.)	Al_2O_3–SiO_2			C_6 12.7 / C_7 11.1 / C_8 39.7 / C_9 8.9 / C_{10} 3.0 } 75.4	185
n-Propylbenzene (42 g.)	Methyl ether (20.2 g.)	Al_2O_3–SiO_2	450	Contact time, 45 sec.	C_6 29.2 / C_7 12.8 / C_8 6.9 / C_9 23.5 / C_{10} Nil } 72.4	185

* Unless otherwise indicated.

TABLE 17   Alkylation of naphthalene with ethers

Moles of naphthalene	Alkylating agent (moles)	Catalyst (moles)	Temperature, °C	Time	Products, % yield	Ref.
Naphthalene (1–2)	Methyl ether (1)	Bauxite	450	15–30 sec.	1-Methylnaphthalene (0.4, 2-methyl-naphthalene (1.6)	186
Naphthalene (1–2)	Methyl ether (1)	Bauxite	250–300	—	Monomethylnaphthalene (7), (1-methyl-2-methylnaphthalene 4:1)	186
—	Benzyl ethyl ether (—)	P_2O_5	—	—	α-Benzylnaphthalene	287
2	Benzyl n-propyl ether (1)	BF_3 (0.5)	—	—	α-Benzylnaphthalene (48)	39

TABLE 18.   Alkylation of miscellaneous polynuclear aromatic compounds with ethers

Aromatic compounds (moles)	Alkylating agent (moles)	Catalyst (moles)	Temperature, °C	Time, hrs.	Products, % yield	Ref.
α-Nitronaphthalene (0.8)	Isopropyl ether (1.2)	HF (23)	0 → 20	20	Isopropyl-1-nitronaphthalene (10), diisopropyl-1-nitronaphthalene (82)	199
nthracene (1.5)	Isopropyl ether (3)	HF (55)	10	3	Diisopropylanthracenes (80)	199

TABLE 19. Alkylation of phenol with ethers

Moles of phenol*	Alkylating agent (moles)*	Catalyst (moles)*	Temperature, °C	Time	Products, % yield*	Ref.
2.7	Benzyl n-propyl ether (1)	BF₃ (0.5)	—	—	p-Benzylphenol (48)	39
0.6	p-Toluenesulfonic acid	Styrene oxide (0.1)	64–72	7 min.	Monoalkylate (0.4 g.), 2-phenoxy-2-phenylethanol (16.1), 1,2-bis-(phenoxy)-1-phenylethane (—)	193

* Unless otherwise indicated.

TABLE 20. Alkylation of various phenols and phenolic ethers with ethers

Aromatic compound (moles)*	Alkylating agent (moles)*	Catalyst (moles)*	Temperature, °C	Time, hrs.	Products, % yield*	Ref.
o-Cresol	Benzyl ether (0.9)	HF (15)	5 → 25	20	Benzyl-o-cresol (54), dibenzyl-o-cresol (10)	199
2-Naphthol (0.15)	p-Toluenesulfonic acid	Styrene oxide (0.5)	140–145	1	Monohydrate (0.1 g.), 1,2,7,8-dibenzo-9-benzylxanthene (21.5), 1-phenyl-1,2-dihydronaphtho-(2,1-b)furan (43)	

* Unless otherwise indicated.

TABLE 21.   Alkylation of miscellaneous aldehydes, acids, and quinones with ethers

Compound (moles)*	Alkylating agent (moles)*	Catalyst (moles)*	Temperature, °C	Time, hrs.*	Products, % yield*	Ref.
Benzoic acid (1.5)	Isopropyl ether (3)	HF (45)	10 → 75	8	m-Isopropylbenzoic acid	199
Ketene	Ethylene oxide	BF$_3$ Etherate (5)	5	1.5	γ-Butyrolactone (5)	289
Ketene	Propylene oxide	BF$_3$ Etherate (5)	9	1.5	γ-Valerolactone (9)	289
Ketene	Propylene oxide	BF$_3$ Etherate (10)	9	1.5	γ-Valerolactone (8)	289
Ketene	Propylene oxide	BF$_3$ Etherate (20)	9	1.5	γ-Valerolactone (11)	289
Ketene	Propylene oxide	BF$_3$ Etherate (5)	12	3.0	γ-Valerolactone (13)	289
Ketene	Propylene oxide	None	9	1.5	γ-Valerolactone (trace)	289
Ketene	Styrene oxide	BF$_3$ Etherate (5)	9	1.5	γ-Phenylbutyrolactone (9)	289

* Unless otherwise indicated.

TABLE 22. Alkylation of miscellaneous aromatic amines with ethers

Aromatic compound (moles)	Alkylating agent (moles)	Catalyst (moles)	Temperature, °C	Time, hrs.	Products, % yield	Ref.
p-Aminophenol (3)	Isopropyl ether (5)	HF (100)	10 → 75	5	Diisopropyl-p-aminophenol (12), 4,4'-dihydroxytetraisopropyldiphenylamine	199
p-Anisidine (2)	Isopropyl ether (3)	HF (60)	10 → 25	20	Diisopropyl-p-anisidine (38), 4,4'-dimethoxytetraisopropyldiphenylamine (50)	199
N,N-Dimethyl-p-aminophenol (2)	Isopropyl ether (2.1)	HF (60)	10 → 25	20	Isopropyl-n-dimethyl-p-aminophenol (42), di-isopropyl-n-dimethyl-p-aminophenol (9)	199
N-Dimethyl-m-phenetidine (0.45)	Isopropyl ether (0.5)	HF (15)	10 → 20	20	Isopropyl-n-diethyl-m-phenetidine (80)	199
2-Methoxy-1-naphthylamine (0.6)	Isopropyl ether (1)	HF (22)	5 → 20	20	Triisopropyl-2-methoxy-1-naphthylamine (46)	199

TABLE 23. Alkylation of heterocyclic aromatic compounds with ethers

Aromatic compound (moles)	Alkylating agent (moles)	Catalyst (moles)	Temperature, °C	Time	Products, % yield	Ref.
Thiophene (0.1)	Benzhydryl ethyl ether (0.1)	$SnCl_4$ (0.1)	cold	—	Dibenzhydrylthiophene (50), benzhydrylthiophene (5)	291

TABLE 24. Alkylation of halogenated compounds with ethers

Aromatic compound (moles)*	Alkylating agent (moles)*	Catalyst (moles)*	Temperature, °C	Time, hrs.*	Products, % yield*	Ref.
Chlorobenzene (450 g.)	Diisopropyl ether (76.5 g.)	Anhydrous HF (150 g.) + fluorosulfonic acid (150 g.)	10	1	4-Chloroisopropylbenzene (128.5 g.), chlorodiisopropylbenzene (31.4 g.)	224

* Unless otherwise indicated.

TABLE 25. Alkylation of esters with ethers

Compound (moles)	Alkylating agent (moles)	Catalyst (moles)	Temperature, °C	Time, hrs.	Products, % yield	Ref.
Ethyl methyl acetoacetate (0.5)	Isopropyl ether (0.5)	Boron trifluoride (—)	24	14	Ethyl-α-methyl-α-isopropylacetoacetate (55)	45
Ethyl acetoacetate (0.5)	Ethyl-t-butyl ether (0.5)	Boron trifluoride (—)	—	—	t-Butyl-α-t-butylacetoacetate (6–14)	45
Ethyl acetoacetate (0.5)	Dibenzyl ether (0.5)	Boron trifluoride (—)	−70 → −10	0.5	Ethyl-α-benzylacetoacetate	45
Malonic ester (0.4)	Ethylene oxide (0.26)	Anhydrous $AlCl_3$— 0.25 + 50 ml. of absolute $CHCl_3$	reflux	—	γ-Butyrolactone—(quantitative)	46

References

1. Burwell, R. L., Jr., *Chem. Rev.*, **54**, 1954.
2. Norris, J. F., and B. M. Sturgis, *J. Am. Chem. Soc.*, **61**, 1413 (1939).
3. Nelson, K. L., and H. C. Brown, *The Chemistry of Petroleum Hydrocarbons*, Vol. 3, Reinhold Publishing Corp., New York, 1955.
4. McCaulay, D. A., and A. P. Lien, *J. Am. Chem. Soc.*, **73**, 2013 (1951).
5. Brown, H. C., and J. D. Brody, *J. Am. Chem. Soc.*, **74**, 3570 (1952).
6. Brown, H. C., and H. L. Young, *J. Org. Chem.*, **22**, 719 (1957); Brown, H. C., and C. R. Smoot, *J. Am. Chem. Soc.*, **78**, 6255 (1956).
7. Brown, H. C., and K. L. Nelson, *J. Am. Chem. Soc.*, **75**, 6292 (1953).
8. Allen, R. H., and L. D. Yats, *J. Am. Chem. Soc.*, **83**, 2799 (1961).
9. Burwell, R. L., and A. D. Shields, *J. Am. Chem. Soc.*, **77**, 2766 (1955).
10. McCaulay, D. A., and A. P. Lien, *J. Am. Chem. Soc.*, **75**, 2411 (1953).
11. Brown, H. C., and C. R. Smoot, *J. Am. Chem. Soc.*, **78**, 2185 (1956).
12. Topchiev, A. V., S. V. Zavgorodnii, and Y. M. Paushkin, *Boron Fluoride and its Compounds as Catalysts in Organic Chemistry*, Chapter V, Pergamon Press, New York, 1959.
13. Bowlus, H., and J. A. Nieuwland, *J. Am. Chem. Soc.*, **53**, 3835 (1931).
14. Topchiev, A. V., S. V. Zavgorodnii, and Y. M. Paushkin, ref. 12, p. 65.
15. Nieuwland, J. A., R. R. Vogt, and W. L. Foohey, *J. Am. Chem. Soc.*, **52**, 1018 (1930).
16. Gamble, E., P. Gilmont, and J. F. Stiff, *J. Am. Chem. Soc.*, **62**, 1257 (1940).
17. Topchiev, A. V., S. V. Zavgorodnii, and Y. M. Paushkin, ref. 12, p. 67.
18. Diehle, P., and R. A. Ogg, Jr., *Nature*, **80** (1957).
19. Gasselin, V., *Bull. Soc. Chim. France*, (3), **9**, 401 (1893).
20. Burwell, R. L., and S. J. Archer, *J. Am. Chem. Soc.*, **64**, 1032 (1942).
21. McKenna, J. F., and F. J. Sowa, *J. Am. Chem. Soc.*, **59**, 470 (1937).
22. Hennion, G. F., and L. A. Auspos, *J. Am. Chem. Soc.*, **65**, 1603 (1943).
23. Welsh, C. E., and G. F. Hennion, *J. Am. Chem. Soc.*, **63**, 2603 (1941).
24. Serijan, K. T., H. F. Hipsher, and L. C. Gibbons, *J. Am. Chem. Soc.*, **71**, 873 (1949).
25. Sowa, F. J., G. F. Hennion, and J. A. Nieuwland, *J. Am. Chem. Soc.*, **57**, 709 (1935).
26. Kolka, A. J., and R. R. Vogt, *J. Am. Chem. Soc.*, **61**, 1463 (1939).
27. Toussaint, N. F., and G. F. Hennion, *J. Am. Chem. Soc.*, **62**, 1145 (1940).
28. U.S. Patent 2,486,417 (1949); *C.A.*, **44**, 2024 (1950).
29. Streitwieser, A., Jr., D. P. Stevenson, and W. D. Schaeffer, *J. Am. Chem. Soc.*, **81**, 1110 (1959).
30. Hennion, G. F., and V. D. Pieronik, *J. Am. Chem. Soc.*, **64**, 2751 (1942).
31. Burwell, R. L., Jr., L. M. Elkin, and A. D. Shields, *J. Am. Chem. Soc.*, **74**, 4570 (1952).
32. Pines, H., W. D. Huntsman, and V. N. Ipatieff, *J. Am. Chem. Soc.*, **73**, 4343 (1951).
33. Pines, H., W. D. Hunstman, and V. N. Ipatieff, *J. Am. Chem. Soc.*, **73**, 4483 (1951).
34. Burwell, R. L., Jr., and A. D. Shields, *J. Am. Chem. Soc.*, **77**, 2766 (1955).
35. Streitwieser, A., Jr., W. D. Schaeffer, and S. Andreades, *J. Am. Chem. Soc.*, **81**, 1113 (1959).

36. Price, C. C., and J. M. Ciskowski, *J. Am. Chem. Soc.*, **60**, 2499 (1938).
37. Topchiev, A. V., G. M. Yegorova, and R. A. Aizinson, *Dokl. Akad. Nauk S.S.S.R.*, **79**, 295 (1950).
38. Bachman, G. B., and H. M. Hellman, *J. Am. Chem. Soc.*, **70**, 1772 (1948).
39. Monacelli, W. J., and G. F. Hennion, *J. Am. Chem. Soc.*, **63**, 1722 (1941).
40. U.S. Pat. 2,390,835 (1945); *C.A.*, **40**, 2849 (1946).
41. Romadin, I. A., *J. Gen. Chem. U.S.S.R.*, **1**, 1898, 2000 (1940).
42. Hauser, C. R., and Breslow, D. S., *J. Am. Chem. Soc.*, **62**, 2389 (1940).
43. Breslow, D. S., and C. R. Hauser, *J. Am. Chem. Soc.*, **62**, 2611 (1940).
44. Hauser, C. R., and J. T. Adams, *J. Am. Chem. Soc.*, **64**, 728 (1942).
45. Adams, J. T., R. Levine, and C. R. Hauser, *J. Am. Chem. Soc.*, **65**, 552 (1943).
46. Raha, C., *J. Am. Chem. Soc.*, **75**, 4098 (1953).
47. U.S. Pat. 2,391,139 (1945); *C.A.*, **40**, 1879 (1946).
48. U.S. Pat. 2,527,794 (1950); *C.A.*, **45**, 2509 (1951).
49. Huston, R. C., and T. J. Hsieh, *J. Am. Chem. Soc.*, **58**, 439 (1936).
50. Tsukervanik, I. P., and Z. N. Nazarova, *Zh. Obshch. Khim.*, **7**, 623 (1937).
51. Norris, J. F., and J. N. Ingraham, *J. Am. Chem. Soc.*, **60**, 1421 (1938).
52. Hortmann, C., and L. Gattermann, *Ber.*, 3531 (1892).
53. Niederl, J. B., and S. Natelson, *J. Am. Chem. Soc.*, **53**, 1928 (1931).
54. Smith, R. A., *J. Am. Chem. Soc.*, **55**, 849, 3718 (1933).
55. Illari, G., *Gazz. Chim. Ital.*, **78**, 904 (1948).
56. Huston, R. C., *J. Am. Chem. Soc.*, **46**, 2775–9 (1924).
57. Huston, R. C., and T. E. Friedemann, *J. Am. Chem. Soc.*, **38**, 2527 (1916).
58. Huston, R. C., and J. Awuapara, *J. Org. Chem.*, **9**, 401 (1944).
59. Ipatieff, V. N., H. Pines, and L. Schmerling, *J. Org. Chem.*, **5**, 253 (1940).
60. Tsukervanik, I. P., and Z. N. Nazarova, *Zh. Obshch. Khim.*, **5**, 768 (1935).
61. Tsukervanik, I. P., *Zh. Obshch. Khim.*, **5**, 117 (1935).
62. Lawson, W., *J. Chem. Soc.*, 4697 (1954).
63. Huston, R. C., and G. W. Hedrick, *J. Am. Chem. Soc.*, **59**, 2001 (1937).
64. U.S. Pat. 2,051,300 (1936); *C.A.*, **30**, 6761 (1936).
65. Huston, R. C., and R. L. Guile, *J. Am. Chem. Soc.*, **61**, 69 (1939).
66. Huston, R. C., and R. C. Meloy, *J. Am. Chem. Soc.*, **64**, 2655 (1942).
67. Huston, R. C., W. R. Langdon, and L. J. Snyder, *J. Am. Chem. Soc.*, **70**, 1474 (1948).
68. Huston, R. C., and W. D. Barrett, *J. Org. Chem.*, **81**, 657 (1946).
69. Huston, R. C., and R. J. Krantz, *J. Org. Chem.*, **13**, 63 (1948).
70. Baddeley, G., *Quart. Rev. (London)*, 355–379 (1954).
71. Baddeley, G., and R. Williamson, *J. Chem. Soc.*, 4647 (1956).
72. Huston, R. C., R. L. Guile, D. L. Bailey, R. S. Curtis, and T. E. Esterdahl, *J. Am. Chem. Soc.*, **67**, 899 (1945).
73. Schriesheim, A., and S. Khoobiar, *J. Am. Chem. Soc.*, **82**, 832 (1960).
74. Schriesheim, A., and S. Khoobiar, *Proceedings Second International Catalysis Congress, Paris, France, 1960*.
75. Huston, R. C., *J. Am. Chem. Soc.*, **46**, 2775 (1924).
76. Huston, R. C., H. A. Swartout, and G. R. Wardwell, *J. Am. Chem. Soc.*, **52**, 4484 (1930).
77. Huston, R. C., and A. L. Houk, *J. Am. Chem. Soc.*, **54**, 1506 (1932).

78. Huston, R. C., and W. C. Lewis, *J. Am. Chem. Soc.*, **53**, 2379 (1931).
79. Huston, R. C., W. C. Lewis, and W. H. Grotemut, *J. Am. Chem. Soc.*, **49**, 1365 (1927).
80. Welsh, L. H., and N. L. Drake, *J. Am. Chem. Soc.*, **60**, 59 (1938).
81. Huston, R. C., and R. I. Jackson, *J. Am. Chem. Soc.*, **63**, 541 (1941).
82. Price, C. C., *Org. Reactions*, VIII, Ch. I, p. 12, John Wiley and Sons, New York, 1946.
83. Ungnade, H. E., E. F. Kline, and E. W. Crandall, *J. Am. Chem. Soc.*, **75**, 3333 (1953).
84. Sidorova, N. G., and I. P. Tsukervanik, *J. Gen. Chem. U.S.S.R.*, **10**, 2073 (1940).
85. Pines, H., A. E. Edeleanu, and V. N. Ipatieff, *J. Am. Chem. Soc.*, **67**, 2193 (1945).
86. Sidorova, N. G., and I. P. Tsukervanik, *J. Gen. Chem. U.S.S.R.*, 1543 (1957).
87. Sidorova, N. G., and I. A. Tushinskaya, *J. Gen. Chem. U.S.S.R.*, **7**, 1830 (1957).
88. Kundiger, D. C., and H. Pledger, *J. Am. Chem. Soc.*, **78**, 6098 (1956).
89. Bruson, H. A., and J. W. Kroeger, *J. Am. Chem. Soc.*, **62**, 36 (1940).
90. Liebmann, A., *Ber.*, **14**, 1842 (1881).
91. Liebmann, A., *Ber.*, **15**, 150 (1882).
92. Senkowski, M., *Ber.*, **24**, 2974 (1891).
93. Anschütz, R., and H. Beckerhoff, *Ber.*, **28**, 407 (1895).
94. Kuchkarov, A. B., *J. Gen. Chem. U.S.S.R.*, 1171 (1952).
95. Kuchkarov, A. B., and N. I. Shuikin, *Bull. Acad. Sci.*, *U.S.S.R.*, 397 (1954).
96. Olah, G., and A. Pavlath, *Acta Chim. Acad. Sci. Hung.*, **3**, 425 (1953).
97. Reilly, J., and W. J. Hickinbottom, *J. Am. Chem. Soc.*, **117**, 122 (1920).
98. Read, R. R., and E. Miller, *J. Am. Chem. Soc.*, **54**, 1195 (1932).
99. Fischer, B., and B. Grutzner, *Ber.*, **26**, 1646 (1893).
100. Brit. Pat. 599,278 (1948); *C.A.*, **42**, 5683 (1948).
101. U.S. Pat. 2,205,591 (1940).
102. Effront, J., *Ber.*, **17**, 2324 (1884).
103. Baur, A., *Ber.*, **27**, 1614 (1894).
104. Tsukervanik, I., and V. Sergeeva, *Zh. Obshch. Khim.*, **17**, 1004 (1947).
105. Degering, E. F., H. J. Gryting, and P. A. Tetrault, *J. Am. Chem. Soc.*, **74**, 3599 (1952).
106. Proell, W. A., C. E. Adams, and B. H. Shoemaker, *Ind. Eng. Chem.*, **40**, 1129 (1948).
107. McGreal, M. E., and J. B. Niederl, *J. Am. Chem. Soc.*, **57**, 2625 (1935).
108. Bethell, D., and V. Gold, *J. Chem. Soc.*, 1930 (1958).
109. U.S. Pat. 2,242,325 (1941); *C.A.*, **35**, 5646 (1941).
110. U.S. Pat. 2,341,798 (1945).
111. Stevens, D. R., *Ind. Eng. Chem.*, **35**, 655 (1943).
112. Parker, E. D., and Z. A. Goldblatt, *Anal. Chem.*, **21**, 807 (1949).
113. Bistrzycki, I., and W. Flattau, *Ber.*, **28**, 989 (1895); *ibid.*, **30**, 124 (1897); Bistrzycki, I., and P. Simons, *ibid.*, **31**, 2812 (1898); Cramer, C., *ibid.*, **31**, 2813 (1848); Simons, P., *ibid.*, **31**, 2821 (1898).
114. Hantzsch, A., *Z. Physik. Chem.*, **61**, 257 (1908); *ibid.*, *Ber.*, **55B**, 953 (1922).

115. Hammett, L. P., and A. Deyrup, J. Am. Chem. Soc., 55, 1900 (1933).
116. Deno, N. C., and R. W. Taft, J. Am. Chem. Soc., 76, 244 (1954).
117. Newman, M. S., and N. C. Deno, J. Am. Chem. Soc., 73, 3644 (1951).
118. Deno, N. C., J. J. Jaruzeeski, and A. Schriesheim, J. Am. Chem. Soc., 77, 3051 (1955).
119. Hofmann, J. E., and A. Schriesheim, Symposium on Recent Advances in Hydrocarbon Catalysis, Chicago 1961 Meeting, American Chemical Society; J. Am. Chem. Soc., 83, 947 (1962).
120. Marschner, R. F., and D. R. Carmody, J. Am. Chem. Soc., 73, 604 (1951).
121. Schrauth, W., and K. Quasebarth, Ber., 57, 854 (1924).
122. Buu-Hoï, N. P., H. Le Bihan, G. Binon, and N. D. Xuong, J. Org. Chem., 16, 988 (1951).
123. Meyer, H., and K. Bernhauer, Monatsh., 53/54, 743 (1929).
124. Mukherji, S. M., V. S. Gaind, and D. N. Rao, J. Org. Chem., 19, 328 (1954).
125. Zook, H. D., and R. B. Wagner, Synthetic Organic Chemistry, John Wiley and Sons, New York, p. 15, 1953.
126. Boyd, D., and Hardy, J. Chem. Soc., 630 (1928).
127. Bethel, D., and V. Gold, J. Chem. Soc., 1905 (1958).
128. Bonner, T. G. B., J. M. Clayton, and G. Williams, J. Chem. Soc., 2867 (1957).
129. DeLaMare, P. B. D., and J. H. Ridd, Aromatic Substitution, Academic Press Inc., New York, pp. 175–180, 1959.
130. Baeyer, A., and V. Villiger, Ber., 35, 3013 (1902).
131. Gomberg, M., and O. Kann, J. Am. Chem. Soc., 39, 2009 (1917).
132. Kundiger, D. G., and E. B. U. Ovist, J. Am. Chem. Soc., 76, 2501 (1954).
133. Chichibabin, A. E., Izv. Akad. Nauk S.S.R., Ser. Khim., 951 (1935).
134. Chichibabin, A. E., Compt. rend., 198, 1239 (1934).
135. Tambovtseva, V., and I. Tsukervanik, Zh. Obshch. Khim., 15, 820 (1945).
136. Chichibabin, A. E., Bull. Soc. Chim. France, (5), 21, 497 (1935).
137. Hart, H., and E. A. Haglund, J. Org. Chem., 15, 396 (1956).
138. Dubinin, B. M., Zh. Obshch. Khim., 18, 2145 (1948).
139. Abdurasuleva, A. S., Zh. Obshch. Khim., 28, 2993 (1958).
140. Sidorova, N. G., Zh. Obshch. Khim., 21, 869 (1951).
141. Buu-Hoï, N. P., H. Le Bihan, and F. Binon, J. Org. Chem., 16, 185 (1951).
142. Daudel, R., N. P. Buu-Hoï, and M. M. Mertin, Bull. Soc. Chim. France, (5), 15, 1202 (1948).
143. Voge, H. H., Catalysis, edited by D. H. Emmett, Vol. 5, Ch. 6, Reinhold Publishing Corp., New York, 1958.
144. Pines, H., and W. D. Haag, J. Am. Chem. Soc., 83, 2847 (1961); see also preceding papers by Pines.
145. Yates, D. J. C., and P. J. Lucchesi, J. Chem. Phys., 35, 243 (1961).
146. Given, D. H., and D. L. Hammick, J. Chem. Soc., 428 (1947).
147. Cullinane, N., S. J. Chard, and R. M. Reattard, J.S.C.I., 67, 232 (1948).
148. Cullinane, N., and S. J. Chard, J. Chem. Soc., 804 (1948).
149. Erichsen, L., Angew. Chem., 61, 322 (1944).
150. Dolgov, B. W., and A. S. Cherkasov, J. Gen. Chem. U.S.S.R., 825 (1954).

151. Turova-Polyak, M. B., N. V. Danilova, and N. V. Kukliva, *J. Gen. Chem. U.S.S.R.*, 2155 (1956).
152. Ipatieff, V. N., N. Orloff, and G. Rasuvaeff, *Bull. Soc. Chim., France*, **37**, 1576 (1925).
153. Ipatieff, V. N., N. Orloff, and A. Petrov, *Ber.*, **60**, 130 (1927).
154. Ipatieff, V. N., N. Orloff, and A. Petrov, *Zhur. Russ. Fiz.-Khim. Obshch.*, **59**, 54 (1927).
155. Briner, E., W. Huss, and H. Paillard, *Helv. Chim. Acta*, **7**, 1046 (1956).
156. Ipatieff, V. N., N. Orlov, and A. Petrov, *Zhur. Russ. Fiz.-Khim. Obshch.*, **29**, 541 (1927).
157. Cullinane, N. M., and S. J. Chard, *J. Chem. Soc.*, 821 (1945).
158. Dewar, M. J. S., T. Mole, and E. W. T. Warford, *J. Chem. Soc.*, 3581 (1956).
159. Cullinane, N. M., and S. J. Chard, *Nature*, **161**, 690 (1958).
160. Kuwatu, T., S. Tomiyama, and M. Takao, *Bull. Chem. Soc. Japan*, **V-22**, No. 2, 66 (1949).
161. Sabatier, P., and A. Mailhe, *Compt. rend.*, **148**, 898 (1909).
162. Smolensky, E., and K. Smolensky, *Roczniki Chem.*, **1**, 232 (1921); *C.A.*, **16**, 3062 (1922).
163. Brown, A. B., and E. E. Reid, *J. Phys. Chem.*, **28**, 1067 (1924).
164. For a good review of the literature in this field see: Krishnamurthy, V. A., and M. R. A. Rao, *J. Indian Inst. Sci.*, **39**, 138–160 (1957).
165. Heinemann, H., R. W. Wert, and W. S. W. McCarter, *Ind. Eng. Chem.*, **41**, 2928 (1949).
166. Mailhe, A., and F. deGodon, *Compt. rend.*, **166**, 467 (1918); *ibid.*, **166**, 564 (1918).
167. Brown, A. B., and E. E. Reid, *J. Am. Chem. Soc.*, **46**, 1836 (1929).
168. Munroe, L. A., and R. A. Washington, *Can. J. Chem.*, **33**, 1502 (1955).
169. Earl, J. C., and N. G. Hills, *J. Am. Chem. Soc.*, 973 (1957).
170. Dewar, M. J. S., Chapter on "Aromatic Rearrangements" in *Theoretical Organic Chemistry*, papers presented to the Kekule Symposium, London, September, 1958, Butterworths Scientific Publications, London, 1959.
171. Hill, A. G., J. H. Shipp, and A. J. Hill, *Ind. Eng. Chem.*, **143**, 1579 (1951); *ibid.*, **143**, 1583 (1951).
172. Kutz, W. M., and B. B. Corson, *J. Am. Chem. Soc.*, **68**, 1477 (1948).
173. Folkins, H. O., and E. L. Miller, general papers presented before the Division of Petroleum Chemistry, American Chemical Society, Chicago Meeting, September 3–8, 1961.
174. Wolf, D. E., and K. Folkers, *Org. Reactions*, John Wiley and Sons, Vol. 6, pp. 464–465, New York, 1944.
175. Burwell, R. L., Jr., *Chem. Rev.*, **54**, 1954.
176. Hart, H., and J. Elia, *J. Am. Chem. Soc.*, **83**, 985 (1961).
177. Arnett, E. M., and L. Y. Wu, *J. Am. Chem. Soc.*, **82**, 4999 (1961).
178. Wirth, H. E., M. S. Sackson, and H. W. Griffith, *J. Phys. Chem.*, **62**, 871 (1958).
179. Burwell, R. L., Jr., L. M. Elkin, and A. D. Shields, *J. Am. Chem. Soc.*, **74**, 450 (1952).
180. Burwell, R. L., Jr., L. M. Elkin, and A. D. Shields, *J. Am. Chem. Soc.*, **74**, 4567 (1952).
181. Brown, H. C., and R. M. Adams, *J. Am. Chem. Soc.*, **64**, 2557 (1942).

182. Burwell, R. L., Jr., L. M. Elkin, and A. D. Shields, *J. Am. Chem. Soc.*, **74**, 4570 (1952).
183. Topchiev, A. V., S. V. Zavgorodnii, and Y. M. Paushkin, ref. 12, p. 160.
184. Meerwein, M., E. Battenberg, H. Gold, E. Pfeil, and G. Willfang, *J. Prakt. Chem.*, **154**, 83 (1939).
185. Given, D. H., and D. L. Hammick, *J. Chem. Soc.*, 1774 (1941).
186. Armstrong, G. P., D. H. Grove, D. L. Hammick, and H. W. Thompson, *J. Chem. Soc.*, 1700 (1948).
187. U.S. Pat. 2,498,492.
188. Brit. Pat. 600,839 (1948); *C.A.*, **42**, 7334 (1948).
189. Theimer, E. T., "Abstracts," Division of Organic Chemistry, 99th Meeting of the American Chemical Society, Cincinnati, Ohio, April, 1940, p. 42.
190. McClellan, P. P., *Ind. Eng. Chem.*, 2402 (1950).
191. Searles, S., *J. Am. Chem. Soc.*, **76**, 2313 (1959).
192. Shorygina, N. V., *Zh. Obshch. Khim.*, **21**, 1273 (1951); *C.A.*, **46**, 2008i (1952).
193. Guss, C. D., H. R. Williams, and L. H. Jules, *J. Am. Chem. Soc.*, **73**, 1257 (1951).
194. Schaarschmidt, A., L. Hermann, and B. Szemzo, *Ber.*, **58B**, 1914 (1925)
195. Smith, R. A., and S. Natelson, *J. Am. Chem. Soc.*, **53**, 3476 (1931).
196. Somerville, W. T., and P. E. Spoerri, *J. Am. Chem. Soc.*, **72**, 2185 (1950).
197. Somerville, W. T., and P. E. Spoerri, *J. Am. Chem. Soc.*, **73**, 697 (1951).
198. Simons, J. H., and S. Archer, *J. Am. Chem. Soc.*, **60**, 986 (1938).
199. Calcott, W. S., S. J. Tinker, and V. Weinmayer, *J. Am. Chem. Soc.*, **61**, 1010 (1939).
200. Tsukervanik, I. P., and Kh. Taveeva, *J. Gen. Chem. U.S.S.R.*, **22**, 1019 (1952).
201. Goldschmidt, H., *Ber.*, **15**, 1067 (1882).
202. Tsukervanik, I. P., and A. Vikhrova, *J. Gen. Chem. U.S.S.R.*, **7**, 632 (1937); *C.A.*, **31**, 5779 (1937).
203. Kirrmann, A., and M. Graves, *Bull. Soc. Chim. France*, (5), **1**, 1494 (1934).
204. Cullinane, N. M., and D. M. Leyshan, *J. Chem. Soc.*, 2952 (1957).
205. Simons, J. H., and S. Archer, *J. Am. Chem. Soc.*, **62**, 1623 (1940).
206. Simons, J. H., and S. Archer, *J. Am. Chem. Soc.*, **61**, 1521 (1939).
207. Price, C. C., and M. Lund, *J. Am. Chem. Soc.*, **62**, 3105 (1940).
208. Burwell, R. L., and S. Archer, *J. Am. Chem. Soc.*, **64**, 1032 (1942).
209. Verley, A., *Bull. Soc. Chim. France*, (3), **19**, 67 (1898).
210. Nightingale, D. V., R. G. Taylor, and H. W. Smelser, *J. Am. Chem. Soc.*, **63**, 258 (1941).
211. Huston, R. C., and R. Smith, *J. Org. Chem.*, **V15**, 1074 (1950).
212. Inatome, M., K. W. Greenlee, J. M. Derfer, and C. E. Boord, *J. Am. Chem. Soc.*, **74**, 292 (1952).
213. Pines, H., L. Schmerling, and V. N. Ipatieff, *J. Am. Chem. Soc.*, **62**, 2901 (1940).
214. Sidorova, N. G., *J. Gen. Chem. U.S.S.R.*, 1015 (1952).
215. Huston, R. L., and K. Goodemoot, *J. Am. Chem. Soc.*, **56**, 2432 (1934).
216. Sidorova, N. G., and E. A. Dubnikova, *J. Gen. Chem. U.S.S.R.*, 1463 (1953).

217. Tsukervanik, I. P., and N. G. Sudorova, *J. Gen. Chem. U.S.S.R.*, **7**, 641 (1937); *C.A.*, **31**, 5780 (1937).
218. Meyer, V., and C. Wurster, *Ber.*, **6**, 963 (1873).
219. Nef, J. U., *Ann.*, **298**, 254 (1897).
220. Huston, R. G., R. L. Guile, I. T. Sculati, and W. N. Wasson, *J. Org. Chem.*, **6**, 252 (1941).
221. Huston, R. C., and T. E. Friedmann, *J. Am. Chem. Soc.*, **40**, 785 (1918).
222. Fischer, E., and O. Fischer, *Ann.*, **194**, 263 (1878).
223. Tsukervanik, I. P., *J. Gen. Chem. U.S.S.R.*, **8**, 1512 (1938); *C.A.*, **33**, 4587 (1937).
224. Brit. Pat. 668,283 (1952); *C.A.*, **47**, 2212 (1953).
225. Norris, J. F., and D. Rubinstein, *J. Am. Chem. Soc.*, **61**, 1163 (1939).
226. Simons, J. H. and G. C. Bassler, *J. Am. Chem. Soc.*, **63**, 880 (1941).
227. Bistrzycki, H., and C. Gyr, *Ber.*, **37**, 659 (1904).
228. Hemilian, W., *Ber.*, **19**, 3061 (1886).
229. Nightingale, D. V., and L. I. Smith, *J. Am. Chem. Soc.*, **61**, 101 (1939).
230. Noelting, E., *Ber.*, **25**, 791 (1892).
231. Hemilian, W., *Ber.*, **16**, 2360 (1883).
232. Elbs, K., *J. Prakt. Chem.*, (2), **35**, 476 (1886).
233. Tsukervanik, I. P., and I. Terenteva, *J. Gen. Chem. U.S.S.R.*, **7**, 637 (1937); *C.A.*, **31**, 5780 (1937).
234. Pavelkina, A. E., *J. Appl. Chem. U.S.S.R.*, **12**, 1422 (1939); *C.A.*, **34**, 3485 (1940).
235. Price, C. C., M. M. Shafer, M. F. Huber, and C. Bernstein, *J. Org. Chem.*, **7**, 517 (1942).
236. Lehne, A., *Ber.*, **13**, 358 (1880).
237. Hemilian, W., *Ber.*, **13**, 678 (1880).
238. Spiegler, L., and J. M. Tinker, *J. Am. Chem. Soc.*, **61**, 1002 (1939).
239. Burton, H., and G. N. H. Cheesman, *J. Chem. Soc.*, 832 (1953).
240. Auer, H., *Ber.*, **17**, 670 (1884).
241. Behal, A., and A. Choay, *Bull. Soc. Chim. France*, **11**, 207 (1894).
242. Evreva, *Gazz. Chim. Ital.*, **14**, 484 (1884).
243. Ipatieff, V. N., N. Orlov, and A. Petrov, *Ber.*, **60**, 1006 (1927).
244. Smith, R. A., and L. J. Rodden, *J. Am. Chem. Soc.*, **59**, 2353 (1937).
245. Sidorova, N. G., *J. Gen. Chem. U.S.S.R.*, 1015 (1952).
246. Shinga, H., and H. Matsushito, *Bull. Inst. Chem. Res., Kyoto Univ.*, **21**, 73 (1950).
247. Sears, C. A., Jr., *J. Org. Chem.*, **13**, 120 (1948).
248. Rosenwald, R. H., *J. Am. Chem. Soc.*, **74**, 4602 (1952).
249. Gurewitsch, A., *Ber.*, **32**, 2424 (1899).
250. Isagulyants, V. I., and P. P. Bagryantsevd, *Neft. Khoz.*, No. 2, 36 1938; *C.A.*, **33**, 8183 (1939).
251. Fischer, B., and B. Grutzner, *Ber.*, **26**, 1646 (1893).
252. Wuyts, H., *Bull. Soc. Chim. Belges*, **26**, 308 (1912).
253. Paterno, E., and M. Fileti, *Gazz. Chim. Ital.*, **5**, 389 (1875).
254. Welsh, L. H., and N. L. Drake, *J. Am. Chem. Soc.*, **60**, 58 (1938).
255. Bistrzycki, H., and C. Herbst, *Ber.*, **35**, 3137 (1902).
256. Shorigin, P., *Ber.*, **61**, 2516 (1928).
257. Buu-Hoï, Ng., H. Le Bihan, F. Binoss, and P. Maleyron, *J. Org. Chem.*, **18**, 4 (1953).

258. Deno, N. C., and H. Chafetz, *J. Org. Chem.*, **19**, 2109 (1954).
259. Shorigin, P., *Ber.*, **61**, 2516 (1928).
260. Shorigin, P., *Ber.*, **60**, 2373 (1927).
261. Vlekke, V., dissertation, Freiburg, 1905.
262. Fieser, L. F., W. P. Campbell, E. R. Fry, and M. D. Gates, Jr., *J. Am. Chem. Soc.*, **61**, 322 (1939).
263. Fieser, L. F., *J. Am. Chem. Soc.*, **61**, 3467 (1939).
264. Mohlau, R., *Ber.*, **31**, 2351 (1898); R. Mohlau and V. Klopfer, *Ber.*, **32**, 2149 (1899).
265. Louis, E., *Ber.*, **16**, 105 (1883).
266. Sachs, F., and W. Weigert, *Ber.*, **40**, 4360 (1907); E. S. Constorn and H. Goldschmidt, *Ber.*, **21**, 1157 (1888).
267. Willgerodt, C., and E. Rampacher, *Ber.*, **34**, 3667 (1901).
268. Merz, V., and W. Weith, *Ber.*, **14**, 2343 (1881).
269. Willgerodt, C., and K. Damann, *Ber.*, **34**, 3678 (1901).
270. R. Anschütz and H. Beckerhoff, *Ann.*, **327**, 218 (1903).
271. Beran, A., *Ber.*, **18**, 132 (1885).
272. Fischer, O., *Ann.*, **206**, 113, 155 (1881).
273. Magidsohn, O., *J. Russ. Phys. Chem. Soc.*, **47**, 1304 (1915); *Chem. Zentr.*, II, 129 (1916).
274. Schmidlin, J., and P. Massini, *Bull. Soc. Chim. France*, (4), **35**, 992 (1924).
275. Van Alphen, J., *Rec. Trav. Chim.*, **46**, 501 (1927).
276. Battegay, M., and M. Kappeler, *Bull. Soc. Chim. France*, (4) **35**, 992 (1924).
277. Hey, D. H., and E. R. B. Jackson, *J. Chem. Soc.*, 1783 (1936).
278. Gilman, H., and J. A. V. Turck, Jr., *J. Am. Chem. Soc.*, **61**, 473 (1939).
279. Levi, L. E., *Ber.*, **19**, 1624 (1886).
280. Jannasch and Bartels, *Ber.*, **31**, 1716 (1898).
281. O'Connor, M. S., and F. J. Sowa, *J. Am. Chem. Soc.*, **60**, 125 (1938).
282. Balsohn, M., *Bull. Soc. Chim. France*, (2), **32**, 618 (1879).
283. Simons, J. H., and S. Archer, *J. Am. Chem. Soc.*, **62**, 1623 (1940).
284. Burwell, R. L., Jr., and L. M. Elkin, *J. Am. Chem. Soc.*, **73**, 502 (1951).
285. Zonew, *J. Russ. Phys. Chem. Soc.*, **48**, 550 (1916); *Chem. Zentr.*, I, 1497 (1923).
286. Khastanov, L. J., *J. Gen. Chem. U.S.S.R.*, **2**, 515 (1932); *C.A.*, **27**, 975 (1933).
287. Meyer, H., *J. Prakt. Chem.*, (2), **82**, 539 (1910).
288. Stadnikov, G. L., and L. I. Kashtanov, *J. Russ. Phys. Chem. Soc.*, **60**, 1117 (1928); *C.A.*, **23**, 2170 (1929).
289. Oda, R., S. Muneimiya, and M. Okano, *J. Org. Chem.*, **26**, No. 5, 1341 (1961).
290. Stadnikov, G. L., and I. Goldfarb, *Ber.*, **61**, 2341 (1928).
291. Hart, H., and O. E. Curtis, Jr., *J. Am. Chem. Soc.*, **77**, 3138 (1955).

CHAPTER XIX

Alkylation of Aromatics with Aldehydes and Ketones

J. E. Hofmann and A. Schriesheim

Esso Research and Engineering Company, Linden, New Jersey

I. Introduction

The use of aldehydes and ketones in acid-catalyzed addition reactions is as old as the original Friedel-Crafts reaction itself. For instance, the condensation of chloral with benzene (Baeyer reaction) in the presence of sulfuric acid was reported as early as 1872 (3). Despite this early research, acid-catalyzed addition reactions of aldehydes and ketones have not been studied to the same extent as the corresponding reactions involving alcohols, alkyl halides, or aryl halides. Perhaps the main reason for such neglect is the generally lower yields and the formation of polymeric by-products when aldehydes and ketones are used. However, aldehydes and ketones still play an important role in acid-catalyzed addition reactions and, in some cases, these additions lead to products that could not be formed simply by other means.

The present review will cover, primarily, addition reactions involving the carbon atom of the carbonyl group and resulting in the formation of a new carbon–carbon bond.

$$\begin{array}{c} R \\ \diagdown \\ C{=}O + HY \xrightarrow[\text{Acid}]{} R{-}\overset{\displaystyle OH}{\underset{\displaystyle R'}{\overset{|}{\underset{|}{C}}}}{-}Y \\ \diagup \\ R' \end{array} \qquad (1)$$

where

R = alkyl or aryl group

R' = alkyl, aryl or hydrogen

Y = any substrate molecule (such as an aromatic)

Aldehydes and ketones may also become involved in addition reactions in other ways. For instance, an aromatic ketone (equation 2)

$$R-X + \text{(aromatic ring)}-\overset{\overset{\displaystyle O}{\|}}{C}-R' \longrightarrow \underset{R}{\text{(aromatic ring)}}-\overset{\overset{\displaystyle O}{\|}}{C}-R' \qquad (2)$$

may be alkylated by a halide or the substrate may contain an aldehyde or keto group (equation 2) or the alkylating agent may be bifunctional and contain both carbonyl and halide groups (equation 3). Neither of these cases involves formation of a carbon–

$$R-\overset{\overset{\displaystyle O}{\|}}{C}-CH_2CH_2X + \text{(aromatic ring)} \longrightarrow R-\overset{\overset{\displaystyle O}{\|}}{C}-CH_2CH_2-\text{(aromatic ring)} \qquad (3)$$

carbon bond at the site of the carbonyl function and, hence, will be only discussed if of interest from the standpoint of competing rates.

The chapter has been divided into five main groups: Addition of Ketene to Aromatics, Addition of Aromatic Aldehydes and Ketones to Aromatics, Addition of Aliphatic Aldehydes and Ketones to Aromatics, Addition of Chloral to Aromatics, and Miscellaneous Reactions of Aldehydes and Ketones. Acid catalysts covered include both the Lewis and Brønsted types. In most cases, similar reactions occur with either type of acid and no definite separation will be made. The two types of catalysts will be distinguished if reactions differ as a result of the acid used.

1. General Mechanism Consideration

The activity of aldehydes and ketones in acid-catalyzed alkylations is generally considered to be the result of a reaction at the carbonyl carbon. This moiety is activated owing to complex formation between the carbonyl oxygen and the acid in question. With Lewis acids, an electron deficiency is generated on the carbonyl carbon by coordination of the oxygen of the carbonyl group with the open sextet of the Lewis acid (equation 4). When protonic

$$\underset{R'}{\overset{R}{\diagdown}}C{=}O + MX_3 \longrightarrow \underset{R'}{\overset{R}{\diagdown}}\overset{\delta+}{C}{-}O{-}\overset{\delta-}{M}X_3 \qquad (4)$$

acids are employed, the electron deficiency is generated by protonation of the carbonyl function (equation 5). The resulting species

$$\underset{R'}{\overset{R}{\diagdown}}C{=}O + HX \longrightarrow \underset{R'}{\overset{R}{\diagdown}}\overset{\delta+}{C}{-}OH \quad \overset{\delta-}{X} \qquad (5)$$

then may be considered to undergo an electrophillic attack on a molecule, such as an aromatic, in the same fashion as other acid-catalyzed addition reactions (equations 6 and 7).   In a case, shown

$$\begin{array}{c}R \\ \diagdown \\ {}^{\delta+}C-O-\overset{\delta-}{M}X_3 + \\ \diagup \\ R'\end{array} + \bigcirc \longrightarrow \left[\begin{array}{c} H \\ R \diagdown \quad \diagup \\ C \\ R' \diagup \quad \diagdown OM\bar{X}_3 \end{array}\right]^{+} \qquad (6)$$

$$\left[\begin{array}{c} H \\ R \diagdown \quad \diagup \\ C \\ R' \diagup \quad \diagdown OM\bar{X}_3 \end{array}\right]^{+} \longrightarrow \begin{array}{c} R \diagdown \\ C-\bigcirc \\ R' \diagup \quad \diagdown OH \end{array} + MX_3 \qquad (7)$$

below, where a hydroxyl compound is formed, it may in turn undergo a subsequent alkylation reaction to form a disubstituted derivative (equation 8).   The bracketed "intermediates" in equations 6 and 7

$$\begin{array}{c} R \\ | \\ R'-C-OH + \bigcirc \\ | \\ \bigcirc \end{array} \xrightarrow{MX_3} \begin{array}{c} R \\ | \\ R'-C-\bigcirc \\ | \\ \bigcirc \end{array} + H_2O \qquad (8)$$

cover a variety of postulated activated complexes including π- and σ-bonded species.   Little work has been reported in this area specifically aimed at elucidating the mechanism of the aldehyde–ketone addition reaction.   Therefore, little attention has been devoted to defining a detailed picture of the addition mechanism. Chapter XVIII on alcohol alkylation has a section on such mechanistic considerations.   This generalized mechanism applies to most of the addition reactions and mono- and disubstituted products have been isolated depending on reaction conditions.   Other competing reactions also occur and these will be treated in more detail in the specific sections.

The ability of Lewis acids to polarize the carbonyl bond of aldehydes and ketones is well documented in the literature and, in some cases, a stable complex between aldehyde or ketone and the metal halide can be isolated.   Complex formation between acetone and boron trifluoride was first reported by Landolph (48) and later by Gaselin (25).   More recently Illari (40) reports a benzaldehyde–AlCl$_3$ complex in ether, and Lombard and Stéphan (49,50) discuss complexes between BF$_3$ and a series of aldehydes and ketones.   In general, these complexes are not particularly stable and decompose to starting materials or polymeric products when heated above room temperature. (For a more detailed discussion of the complexes see Chapter VIII.)

Addition reactions involving such intermediates are notoriously dependent on factors such as the catalyst-complex polarity or the degree of freedom of the ionic intermediates. These variables will not be treated in detail here since little work has been reported in such areas.

II. Addition of Ketene to Aromatics

Ketene is a unique reactant in the aldehyde–ketone series in that it produces a product containing a keto group and thus can be used as an acetylating agent. The general reaction for this addition proceeds according to equation 9. Activation of ketene for

$$RH + CH_2{=}C{=}O \xrightarrow[\text{Acid}]{} R{-}CO{-}CH_3 \tag{9}$$

addition reactions is attributed to polarization of the carbonyl bond in an manner analogous to the activation of other aldehydes and ketones (equation 10). Following addition to some substrate (equation 11), the complex breaks down, presumably through the

$$CH_2{=}C{=}O + MX_3 \rightarrow CH_2{=}\overset{\delta+}{C}{=}\overset{\delta-}{O}{:}MX_3 \tag{10}$$

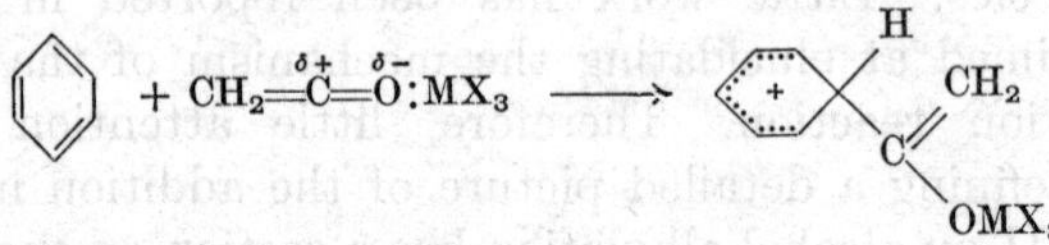

(11)

enol, which immediately rearranges to the more stable keto form (equation 12). The latter reaction accounts for ketone rather than

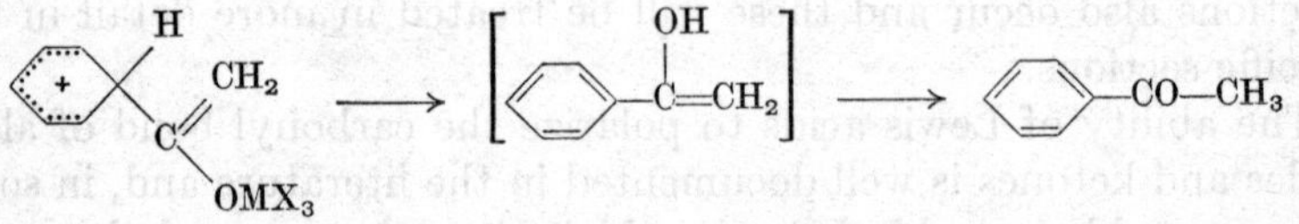

(12)

alcohol formation. Data relating to ketene addition are summarized in Table I (Appendix).

The first recorded research on the acetylation of benzene with ketene was carried out by Van Alphen (78). Van Alphen employed anhydrous HCl as the catalyst, but was unable to obtain any acetylated product. Later, Van Alphen (79) reported the successful acetylation of various hydroxy benzoic acids and esters using HCl (equation 13).

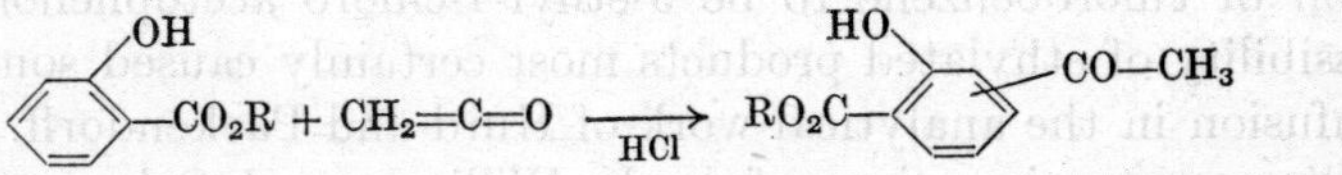

$$\text{(equation 13 structures)}$$

$$\text{OH} \quad \longrightarrow \text{CO}_2\text{R} + \text{CH}_2\text{=}\text{C}\text{=}\text{O} \xrightarrow{\text{HCl}} \text{RO}_2\text{C}\text{—} \text{HO}, \text{CO—CH}_3 \tag{13}$$

Hurd (36) was the first to study ketene addition reactions using AlCl$_3$. With this catalyst, he was able to acetylate a number of different aromatics. The product from the acetylation of anisole, using AlCl$_3$ in CS$_2$, was a mixture of o- and p-methoxyacetophenones along with other higher boiling ketones. When benzene was reacted with ketene over AlCl$_3$, acetophenone was presumed to be the major product although it was not isolated. Naphthalene yielded a mixture of α- and β-naphthylmethyl ketones while acetophenone itself did not react with ketene under the experimental conditions employed. The acetylation of o-dimethoxybenzene was studied by Ploeg (62) and the product was found to be 3,4-dimethoxyphenyl methyl ketone (equation 14)

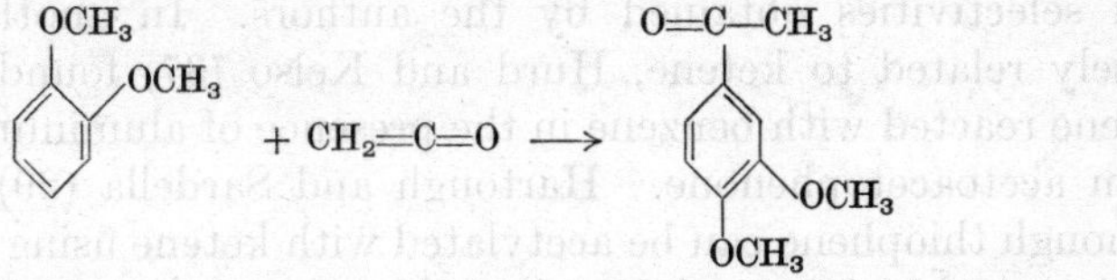

$$\text{OCH}_3 \quad \text{OCH}_3 + \text{CH}_2\text{=}\text{C}\text{=}\text{O} \longrightarrow \text{O=C—CH}_3 \quad \text{OCH}_3 \quad \text{OCH}_3 \tag{14}$$

Packendorff and co-workers (60) also studied the addition of ketone to benzene in the presence of AlCl$_3$, and obtained a 10% yield of acetophenone and also a trace of product identified as benzo-2,3-dihydroquinone (I). In order to determine whether

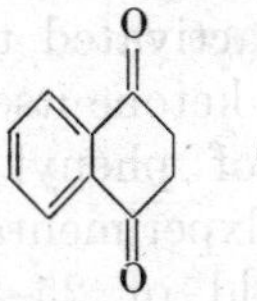

$$\text{(structure I)}$$

(I)

cyclobutanedione was an intermediate in the formation of the latter product, the authors acetylated benzene with the cyclic dione. No product similar to (I) was formed, but a 30% yield of acetophenone was obtained indicating that the cyclic dione was a better acetylating agent than ketene itself. Spring and Vickerstaff (71) were able to isolate acetophenone from the reaction of ketene with benzene using aluminum chloride, and also found p-ethylacetophenone in the reaction product. The latter product undoubtedly arises from ethylene, an impurity produced during formation of ketene by thermal decomposition of acetone. Freri and Maximoff (23) apparently had a similar problem and report the product of acetylation of chlorobenzene to be 3-ethyl-4-chloro acetophenone. The possibility of ethylated products most certainly caused some of the confusion in the analytical work of Hurd and Packendorff.

In an extensive piece of work, Williams and Osborn (85) considerably improved conversion and selectivity by careful control of reaction conditions. Reactions were run at 0°C in a large excess of CS_2, with $AlCl_3$ being added in small portions, until 1.5 moles of $AlCl_3$ had been added per mole of aromatic. Ketene, generated by the pyrolysis of acetone, was kept as pure as possible and used in a 4:1 mole excess over the aromatic substrate. Under these experimental conditions, a 51% yield of acetophenone was obtained from benzene and a 43% yield of α-naphthyl methyl ketone was obtained from naphthalene. When tetralin was used, the β-ketone was the only product formed. With diphenyl, at 30°C, a 23% yield of p-phenylacetophenone was obtained. Undoubtedly, the care taken during this experimental program resulted in the excellent yields and selectivities obtained by the authors. In another reaction, closely related to ketene, Hurd and Kelso (37) found that acetoketene reacted with benzene in the presence of aluminum chloride to form acetoacetophenone. Hartough and Sardella (29) report that although thiophene can be acetylated with ketene using $AlCl_3$, yields are improved when a solid acidic oxide is employed. They attribute this to side reactions that occur between $AlCl_3$ and thiophene.

It is apparent from the foregoing discussions that ketene addition is a fairly simple reaction and results in only mono- addition products even when an excess of ketene is present. This not only means that the acetylated product is deactivated toward further addition by ketene, but also that the new ketone itself does not undergo further reaction. The unreactivity of phenyl ketones will be discussed further in Section III-2. Experimental conditions appear to be fairly important and a yield of 25–50% can be obtained by procedures similar to those outlined by Williams and Osborn (85). The use of a molar excess of $AlCl_3$ was felt to be important by these workers, and reasons for such a molar excess will be discussed in Section III-1.

III. Addition of Aromatic Aldehydes and Ketones to Aromatics

1. Reactions of Benzaldehyde

The acid-catalyzed reaction of benzaldehyde and its derivatives with aromatics leads to fairly complex products and there was considerable discrepancy in the early literature as to the mechanism of formation of these compounds. The initial activation of benzaldehyde is polarization of the carbonyl bond. Illari (40) discusses the formation of a 1:1:1 complex between benzaldehyde, aluminum chloride, and carbon disulfide. This complex can be isolated but decomposes on heating. Illari also mentions a 1:1 complex between benzaldehyde and aluminum chloride in ether solution.

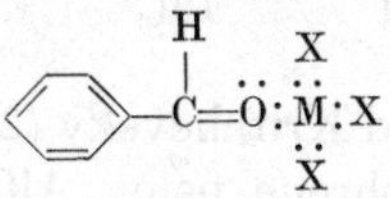

$$\text{C}_6\text{H}_5-\overset{\overset{\text{H}}{|}}{\text{C}}=\overset{..}{\underset{..}{\text{O}}}:\overset{\text{X}}{\underset{\text{X}}{\text{M}}}:\text{X}$$

Lombard and Stéphan (50) discuss the complex between benzaldehyde and boron trifluoride. This complex is crystalline and is formed at $-25°C$. It decomposes slowly in air and completely decomposes when heated to 95–100°C. Clearly these discussions demonstrate the ability of Friedel-Crafts metal halides to coordinate with the carbonyl group of benzaldehyde.

In 1904 Dewar and Jones (15) first reported results of the reaction of benzaldehyde with benzene during some studies on the action of $AlCl_3$ and nickel carbonyl on aromatics. When benzene is treated with aluminum chloride and nickel carbonyl at 0°C benzaldehyde is formed. At 100°C the reaction continues and anthracene is formed as the primary product. The authors concluded that anthracene was formed from condensation of two molecules of benzaldehyde (equation 15). However, when benzaldehyde itself was heated with

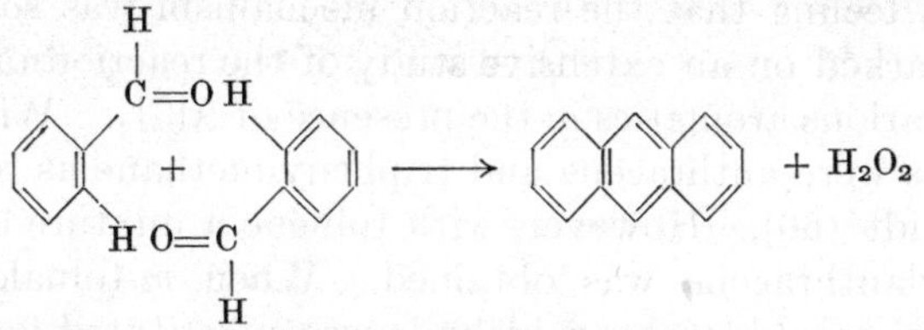

$$\text{(equation 15)} \qquad + H_2O_2 \qquad (15)$$

$AlCl_3$ and benzene the only products formed were benzoic acid and a solid melting at 90°C. Toluene and m-xylene reacted with aluminum chloride and nickel carbonyl in the same fashion as benzene producing dimethyl and tetramethylanthracenes, respectively. According to the mechanism of equation 15, they identified the anthracenes as 2,6-dimethylanthracene from toluene and 2,4,6,8-tetramethylanthracene from m-xylene (equations 16 and 17). In view of more recent work it will be seen that these identifications were erroneous.

CH₃   CHO   CH₃

[structure] + [structure] ⟶ [structure]   (16)

OHC   CH₃   CH₃

CH₃   CHO   CH₃   CH₃

[structure] + [structure] ⟶ [structure]   (17)

CH₃   OCH   CH₃   CH₃

In 1915, Frankforter and Kritchevsky (21) reported the addition of benzaldehyde to phenanthrene using $AlCl_3$ in CS_2. The primary product of this reaction was said to be diphenanthrenephenylmethane along with a resinous product that was tentatively identified as dibenzalmesotriphenanthrene. The former product would correspond to the normal addition product according to equations 7 and 8. The comprehensive work of Hey and others to be discussed subsequently indicates that normal addition very seldom occurs with benzaldehyde. Although Frankforter and Kritchevsky may have obtained the aforementioned products it does not seem likely that they were formed in any significant yields.

Schaarschmidt and co-workers (66) in 1925 reported the formation of triphenylmethane and anthracene from the reaction of benzaldehyde with benzene in the presence of either $AlCl_3$ or $FeCl_3$. (A trace of diphenylmethane is also reported for the reaction with $AlCl_3$.) These authors come to the same conclusions regarding reaction mechanism as Dewar and Jones (15).

Hey (33), feeling that the reaction mechanism was somewhat in doubt, embarked on an extensive study of the reaction of benzaldehyde with various aromatics in the presence of $AlCl_3$. With benzene the products were anthracene and triphenylmethane as reported by Schaarschmidt (66). However, with toluene a mixture of 2,6- and 2,7-dimethylanthracene was obtained. When m-tolualdehyde, p-tolualdehyde, or o-chlorobenzaldehyde was substituted for benzaldehyde and these in turn reacted with benzene, the products in each case were anthracene and triphenylmethane. Clearly the aldehydes served only to provide the meso-carbon atoms in the anthracenoid molecule and the methane carbon atom in triphenylmethane (equations 18, 19, and 20).

CHO   R   R   R

[structure] + 2[structure] →(AlCl₃) [structure] + [structure] + [structure]   (18)

R   R

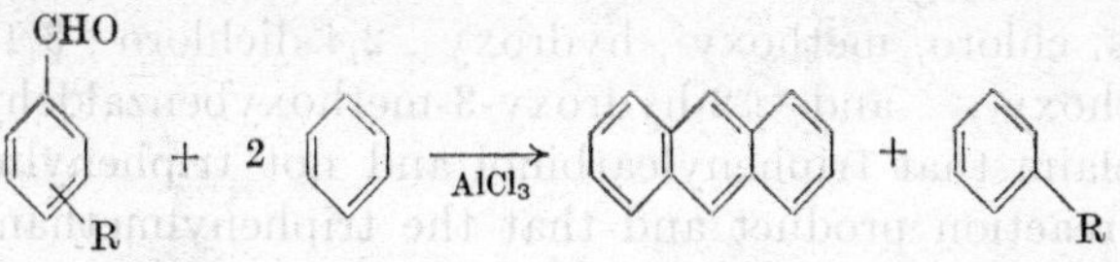

(19)

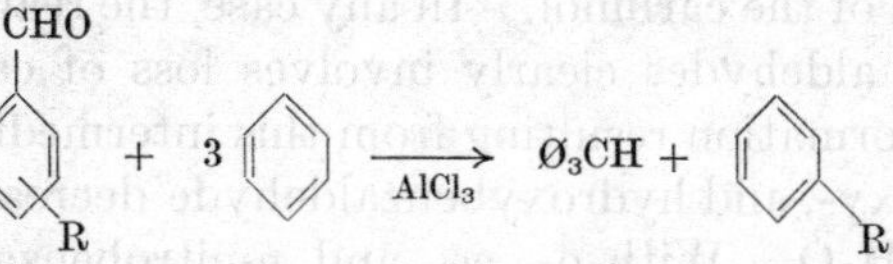

(20)

In order to substantiate these findings furfuraldehyde was reacted with toluene and the product was found to contain dimethylanthracenes (equation 21).

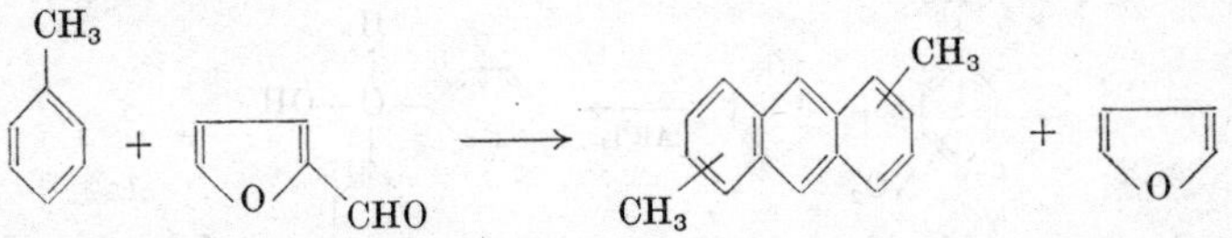

(21)

These results suggested that carbon monoxide was being liberated from the aldehyde and this in turn was reacting with the aromatic to form anthracenes and triphenylmethanes.   Hey (33) demonstrated this hypothesis by showing that carbon monoxide is liberated from the treatment of benzaldehyde with $AlCl_3$ and that anthracene is formed when benzene is treated with carbon monoxide in the presence of hydrogen chloride, aluminum chloride, and cuprous chlorides. In a subsequent paper Hey (17) showed that only a trace of triphenylmethane was formed when carbon monoxide was reacted with benzene in the presence of aluminum chloride alone but upon addition of HCl a significant yield of anthracene was obtained. (HCl is generally evolved when aldehydes are contacted with $AlCl_3$ so that it would have been present during the aldehyde reactions.)   In a later work, Ungnade and Orwoll (77) also find the loss of CO from an aromatic aldehyde in the presence of $AlCl_3$.

In the second paper Hey (17) again confirms that the aldehyde serves to supply only the *meso*-carbon atoms in the anthracene molecule.   All three of the isomeric xylenes were alkylated with benzaldehyde and in each case the expected tetramethylanthracenes were formed.   The reaction of methylene dichloride with each of the three xylenes gave essentially the same product as benzaldehyde.

Ungnade and Crandall (75) continued work along these lines and studied the effect of substituted benzaldehydes during reaction with benzene.   Anthracene and triphenylcarbinol were obtained as products when benzene was reacted with each of the following aldehydes: chloro, methoxy-, hydroxy-, 2,4-dichloro-, 3,4-dichloro-, 2,3-dimethoxy-, and 2-hydroxy-3-methoxybenzaldehyde. The authors claim that triphenylcarbinol and not triphenylmethane is the true reaction product and that the triphenylmethane resulted from reduction of the carbinol. In any case, the reaction mechanism with all these aldehydes clearly involves loss of carbon monoxide with product formation resulting from this intermediate. Yields for chloro-, methoxy-, and hydroxybenzaldehyde decreased in the order $HO > Cl > CH_3O$. With o-, m-, and p-nitrobenzaldehyde carbon monoxide is not lost and normal addition occurs leading to nitrotriphenylmethanes (equations 22 and 23).

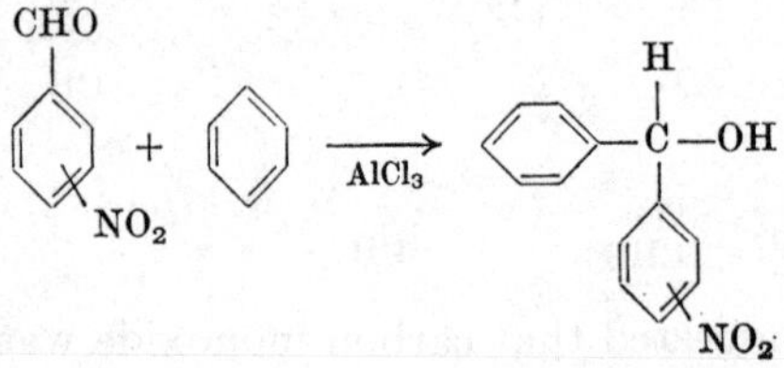

$$\text{(22)}$$

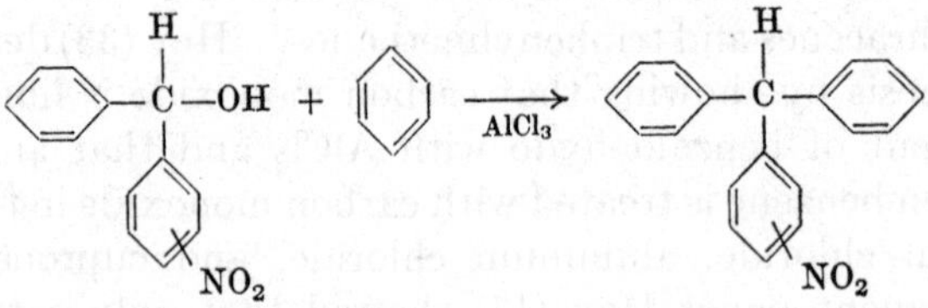

$$\text{(23)}$$

Apparently the powerful electron-withdrawing nature of the nitro group prevents liberation of carbon monoxide and hence the reaction proceeds via direct addition to the carbon of the carbonyl group.

In a continuation of this work, Ungnade and co-workers (76) report the product of reaction of benzaldehyde with diphenyl to be a diphenylanthracene, as expected (equation 24). However, the melt-

$$\text{(24)}$$

ing point of the diphenylanthracene and the diphenylanthraquinone derivative differs considerably from that reported by Ellison and

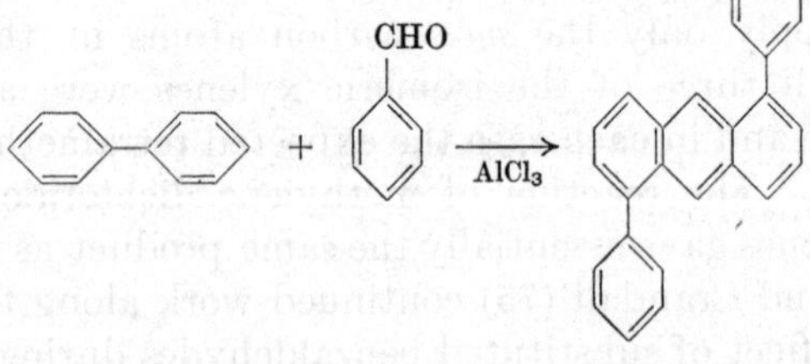

Hey (17).   The reason for this is not exactly clear but it may be due to a different mixture of the 2,6- and 2,7-isomers resulting from the difference in operating conditions.   With mesitylene a disproportionation reaction precedes the addition step and the products include xylenes, tetramethylbenzenes, and tetramethylanthracenes. Aromatic disproportionation catalyzed by $AlCl_3$ is a well-known reaction (57) and apparently is very rapid with mesitylene (equation 25).

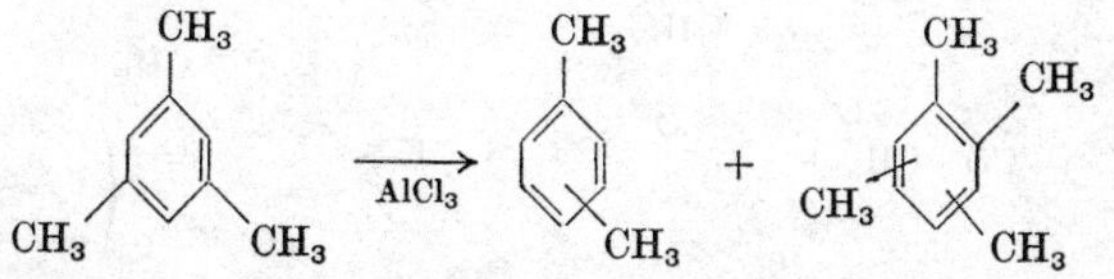

$$(25)$$

The xylenes formed by disproportionation then proceed to react with benzaldehyde to yield the tetramethylanthracenes.   When diphenyl ether is employed as the substrate quite a different and surprising reaction occurs.   The product of reaction with benzaldehyde is found to be 9-phenylxanthydrol (equation 26).   In this case carbon monoxide is not lost and a condensation occurs at the two *ortho*-positions of the diphenyl ether.

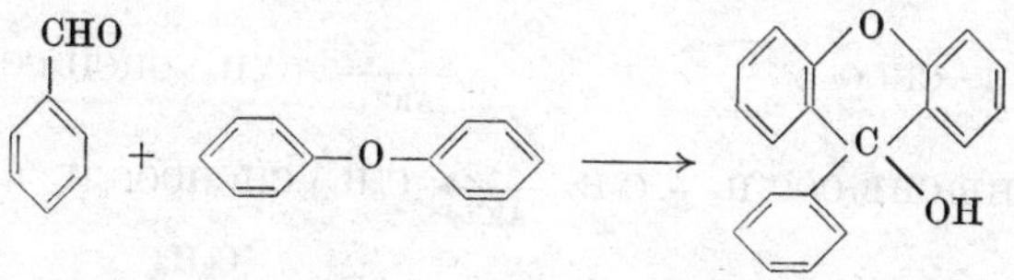

$$(26)$$

Despite all the information that is available on the reaction of benzaldehydes with benzene, the mechanism is somewhat obscure. Yields are not as good when carbon monoxide is substituted for the aldehyde.   This suggests that "free" carbon monoxide is not the active intermediate but that carbon monoxide complexed with $AlCl_3$ in some peculiar active form that can only be derived from an aldehyde may be the active entity.   In summary, the exact steps by which the anthracene forming reaction occurs can still only be subject to conjecture.

2. Reactions of Aromatic Ketones

Although there has not been as much work done on the reactions of aromatic ketones as in some of the other areas, some of the reactions that have been observed are of interest to the chemist.   Reactions involving these ketones generally proceed according to equations 6, 7, and 8. However, if the keto group is adjacent to an aromatic ring, it is rather unreactive and reaction will occur at another active center if available (for instance, if a halogen is available).

McGreal and co-workers (51) studied the addition of acetophenone and p-tolyl methyl ketone to phenol and o-cresol using HCl in glacial acetic acid. In each case, the reaction led to the normal disubstituted product (equation 27) and the authors report yields of

$$R-\!\!\!\langle\ \rangle\!\!\!-CO-CH_3 + \ \underset{OH\ \ R}{\langle\ \rangle} \ \longrightarrow\ R-\!\!\!\langle\ \rangle\!\!\!-\underset{R}{\overset{CH_3}{\underset{|}{\overset{|}{C}}}}\!\!\!\left(\langle\ \rangle\!\!\!-OH\right)_2 \qquad (27)$$

the order of 10–25%. In this case, reaction has occurred at an α-carbonyl, but if other reaction centers are available, reaction occurs preferentially at the other centers. Vorländer and Friedberg (81), using $AlCl_3$ as the catalyst alkylated benzene with benzalacetophenone and $(\alpha, \beta$-dibromo-β-phenyl) ethyl phenyl ketone. Addition at the double bond and substitution for halogen occurred preferentially in each case (equations 27 and 28).

$$\langle\ \rangle\!\!\!-CH\!\!=\!\!CHCO-\!\!\langle\ \rangle \ +\ \langle\ \rangle \ \xrightarrow[AlCl_3]{}\ (C_6H_5)_2CHCH_2COC_6H_5 \qquad (28)$$

$$C_6H_5CHBrCHBrCOC_6H_5 + C_6H_6 \xrightarrow[AlCl_3]{} (C_6H_5)_2CHCHCOC_6H_5 + HBr \qquad (29)$$
$$\underset{C_6H_5}{\overset{|}{}}$$

The former reaction is also reported as a standard organic synthesis (64).

Other comparisons of reactivity are available from the work of Ruggli, Dahn, and Wegmann (65). In this work, α-halogenated acetophenones were reacted with benzene in the presence of $AlCl_3$. With both dichloroacetophenone and trichloroacetophenone halogen substitution occurs and the product is diphenylacetophenone (equation 30). In the later case, reduction must occur in preference

$$C_6H_5-COCHCl_2 + C_6H_6 \xrightarrow[AlCl_3]{} C_6H_5-COCH(C_6H_5)_2 + 2HCl \qquad (30)$$

to substitution of a third phenyl group. Dibromoacetophenone was unreactive under these conditions. However, in a later study, Wegmann and Dahn (83) show that substitution at an α-keto group is favored compared to the β-keto group in a cyclic system. When isatin is reacted with benzene, toluene, or o-xylene, the product is the

3,3-disubstituted oxindole (equation 31).   With thioisatin, a similar reaction occurs (equation 32).

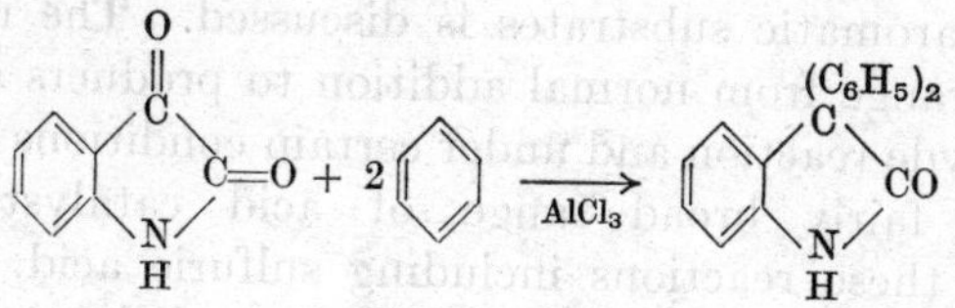

$$\text{(31)}$$

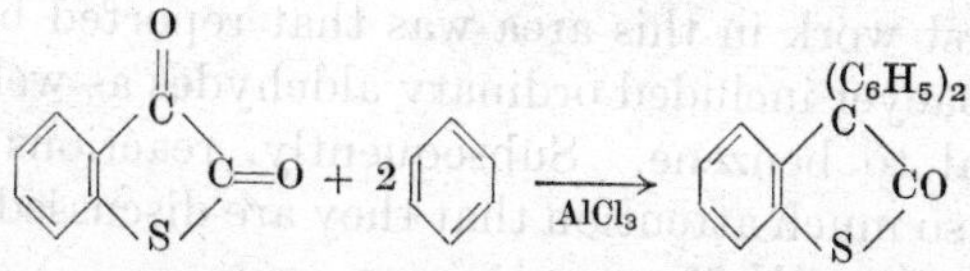

$$\text{(32)}$$

Other non-cyclic diketones have also been studied by Wegmann and Dahn (84). 1-Phenylpropane-1,2-dione does not react with benzene and yields only benzoic acid. However, in a similar reaction, the bromomethyl analog of the dione reacts with benzene to yield (bromomethyl) benzoin (equation 33). In this case, sub-

$$C_6H_5{-}COCOCH_2Br + C_6H_6 \rightarrow C_6H_5{-}COCC_6H_5(OH)CH_2Br \qquad (33)$$

stitution at the carbonyl is preferred over the halogen and reaction occurs at the β-ketone group from the aromatic ring.

It is readily apparent from the preceding data that it would be rather difficult to make accurate predictions concerning molecules with multi-reaction sites. Stability, reactivity, and steric factors must all be considered. No doubt complex formation at a carbonyl *alpha* to the ring will lead to the most stable adduct, through stabilization of the incipient carbonium ion, but by the same token

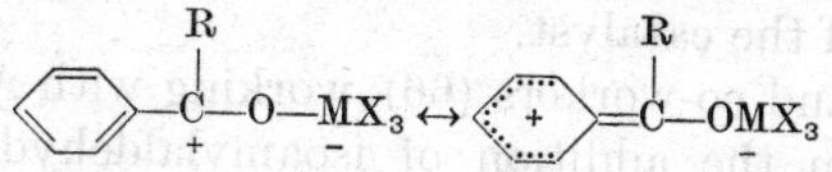

$$\text{(34)}$$

it will also be the least reactive. A balance of stability and reactivity will exist that will determine the ultimate course of the reaction.

From the preceding data it can be seen that it would be rather difficult to formulate general rules as to the reaction of aromatic ketones. However, in most cases, when reactions occur, they proceed through the normal addition steps. It would appear that monosubstituted products could also be isolated if care were taken during addition of reagents. Isolation of these types of products will be discussed in more detail in Section IV-2 dealing with addition of chloral to aromatics.

IV. Condensation of Aldehydes and Ketones with Aromatics

In this section, the condensation of non-aromatic aldehydes and ketones with aromatic substrates is discussed. The reactions are complex and range from normal addition to products analogous to the benzaldehyde reaction and under certain conditions to polymeric materials. A fairly broad range of acid catalysts has been employed for these reactions including sulfuric acid, hydrofluoric acid, hydrochloric acid, aluminum chloride, and aluminum bromide. Among the first work in this area was that reported by Baeyer (3). The work of Baeyer included ordinary aldehydes as well as the addition of chloral to benzene. Subsequently, reactions with chloral have received so much attention that they are discussed as a separate part of this section (IV-2).

1. Reactions of Aldehydes and Ketones

A. Aldehydes

As previously stated, the first work in this area use concentrated sulfuric acid as a catalyst and was reported by Baeyer (3). In addition to chloral, discussed later (Section IV-2), Baeyer also worked with acetaldehyde and the reactions proceeded with relative ease and led to products of disubstitution (equation 35). The driving

$$R—CHO + 2C_6H_6 \xrightarrow{H_2SO_4} RCH(C_6H_5)_2 + H_2O \tag{35}$$

force was considered to be the dehydrating power of the sulfuric acid. Although this may be true to some extent, later work has shown that non-dehydrating acids also catalyze the same reaction and the types of products formed do not correlate directly with the dehydrating power of the catalyst.

Schaarschmidt and co-workers (66), working with AlCl$_3$, observed two products from the addition of isoamylaldehyde to benzene. The first, 1,1-diphenyl-3-methylbutane, is formed *via* the normal addition sequence. The second, 1,1-diphenyl-3-methyl-1-butene, can arise from dehydrogenation of the product of normal addition (equation 36). Such a reaction is a little unusual but it does have

$$(CH_3)_2CHCH_2CH(C_6H_5)_2 \xrightarrow{AlCl_3} (CH_3)_2CHCH=C(C_6H_5)_2 \tag{36}$$

analogies in some of the early products obtained with chloral (see Section IV-2). It is also known that aluminum chloride has the ability to catalyze both hydrogenation (45) and dehydrogenation reactions (for instance in the formation of the characteristic "lower layer" or "red oil," and in the $AlCl_3$ catalyzed hydrogen transfer between olefins and isoparaffins (67)).

When phenol was used as the substrate, similar disubstituted products were reported by the early workers (68). However, von Braun (10) found that pyrolysis of the intermediate polymeric products from condensations involving phenol, using an HCl catalyst, resulted in the formation of saturated monosubstituted products. In a continuation of this work, Niederl and co-workers (56) report excellent yields of saturated monosubstituted addition products for a whole series of aldehydes. The condensation was achieved by bubbling a stream of dry HCl through a solution of aldehyde and phenol (mole per mole) in glacial acetic acid. Following this, the product was pyrolyzed to obtain the mono-addition product that must come about by a disproportionation reaction (equation 36). Niederl used phenol and the three cresols as substrates while the aldehydes ranged from acetaldehyde to heptaldehyde.

$$CH_3-CHO + \underset{HCl}{\overset{OH}{\bigcirc}} \longrightarrow \begin{bmatrix} polymeric \\ products \end{bmatrix} \overset{\Delta}{\longrightarrow} HO-\bigcirc-CH_2CH_3 \quad (37)$$
$$+ \text{ unsaturated residue}$$

Trioxymethylene has also been used fairly extensively as an alkylating agent. Using $ZnCl_2$ and HCl, Blanc (4) obtained addition products between trioxymethylene and several aromatics. Thus, the reaction between benzene and trioxymethylene gave as a major product benzyl chloride and lesser amounts of p-di(chloromethyl)benzene using $ZnCl_2$–HCl. These products arise from mono-addition followed by displacement of hydroxyl by chlorine (equation 38). Similar products were found when toluene and m-xylene were employed as the aromatic substrates. (For a discussion of the chloromethylation reaction see Chapter XXI.)

$$\bigcirc + \tfrac{1}{3}(CH_2O)_3 \longrightarrow \begin{bmatrix} CH_2OH \\ \bigcirc \end{bmatrix} \overset{HCl}{\longrightarrow} \overset{CH_2Cl}{\bigcirc} + H_2O \quad (38)$$

With $AlCl_3$, slightly different products arise from the condensation of trioxymethylene with aromatics. Using benzene, Frankforter and Kokatnur (20) find as the products, approximately equal molar quantities of diphenylmethane and anthracene when $AlCl_3$ is the catalyst. Also, on using $AlCl_3$, toluene and trioxymethylene give rise to ditolylmethane and dimethylanthracene. Similarly, o-xylene yielded dixylylmethane and tetramethylanthracene. In explaining

21—F.C. II

this reaction, Frankforter and Kokatnur place some significance upon the fact that products were formed in equimolar quantities, but this appears to be fortuitous. Additional doubt was cast on the significance of this when Huston and Ewing (39) reported that relative yields of ditolylmethane and dimethylanthracene from toluene and trioxymethylene appeared to depend on reaction conditions. Frankforter and Kokatnur also studied mesitylene and found the products to be dimesitylmethane and tetramethylanthracene. They attributed the latter product to disproportionation of the mesitylene followed by condensation of the resulting xylene. In justification of this, the authors report the presence of benzene, toluene, xylene, and durene in the reaction mixture.

The products described above appear to be somewhat similar to those formed from benzaldehyde (see Section III-1) although the situation does not seem to be quite as clear. No carbon monoxide formation was reported but this does not rule out this possibility. Frankforter and Kokatnur did rule out a secondary intramolecular condensation sequence (equation 39) by showing that diphenyl-

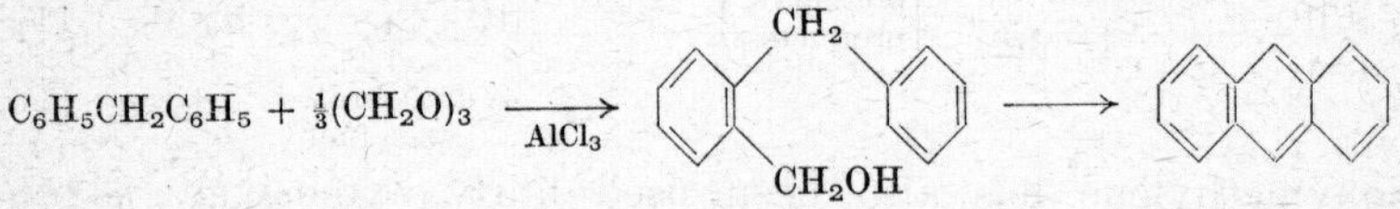

$$C_6H_5CH_2C_6H_5 + \tfrac{1}{3}(CH_2O)_3 \xrightarrow{AlCl_3} \quad \longrightarrow \qquad (39)$$

methane does not react with trioxymethylene to form anthracene. In contrast, Huston and Ewing (38) found that the product from p-xylene and trioxymethylene does undergo secondary intermolecular reactions leading to tri- and tetranuclear aromatics (equations 40 and 41). As this reaction was not studied to the same extent as

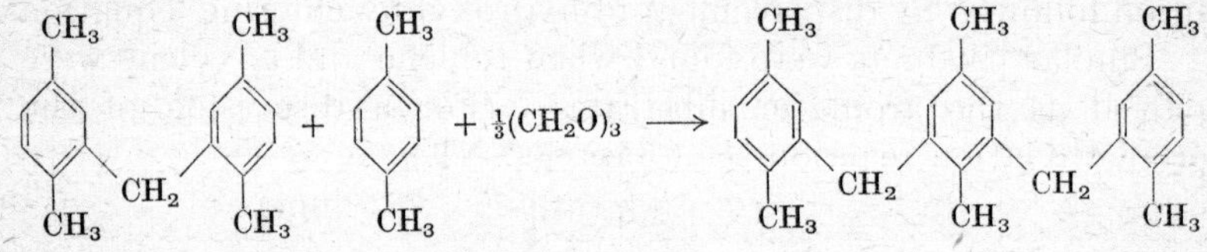

$$(40)$$

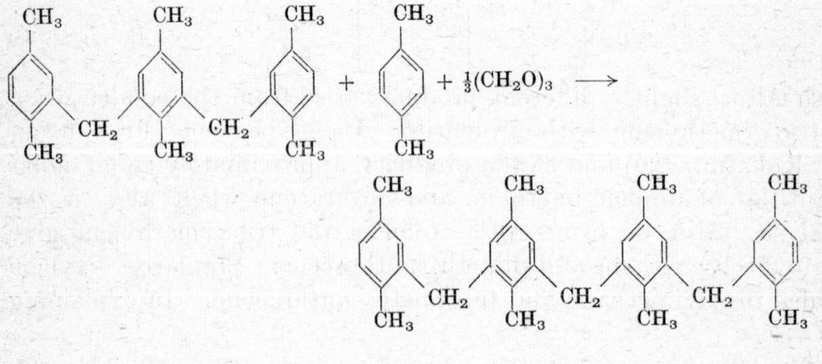

$$(41)$$

the benzaldehyde reaction, the mechanism of anthracene formation cannot be stated unequivocally but something similar to that observed with benzaldehyde appears to be most reasonable.

Trioxymethylene, other forms of formaldehyde, and other aldehydes have also been the subject of a number of patents. In general, the work described has employed liquid hydrogen fluoride as the catalyst (1,2,30,31,43,70). In addition, hydrogen chloride has also been described (46). The products of condensation range from disubstitution similar to compound (III) to polymeric oils most likely

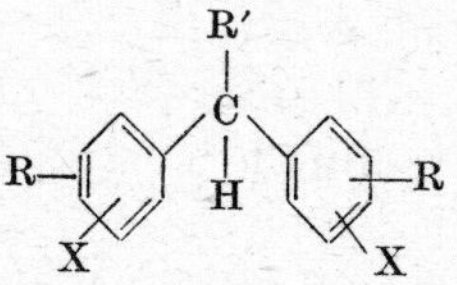

having a formula similar to (III). The predominance of one product or the other appears to depend primarily on the reactant ratio.

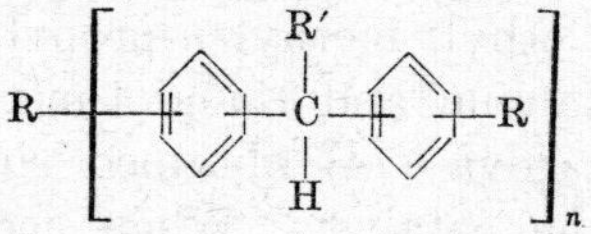

With excess aromatic, disubstitution is favored while excess aldehyde leads to polymer formation. The latter case is very similar to the tri- and tetranuclear aromatics found by Huston and Ewing (38).

B. Ketones

The products from ketone addition to aromatics are similar to those found in the reactions involving aldehydes. Generally, such ketone reactions proceed via disubstitution although there are some exceptions. McGreal, Niederl, and Niederl (51) have condensed a series of ketones with phenol and o-cresol. The conditions employed were about the same as used by Niederl and co-workers during their work with aldehydes (56), i.e., HCl bubbled through glacial acetic acid. As opposed to the aldehydes, however, there is no polymeric intermediate and the disubstituted products were formed directly (equation 42). It was found that the monosubstituted derivatives could be formed by pyrolysis of the initial product (equation 43).

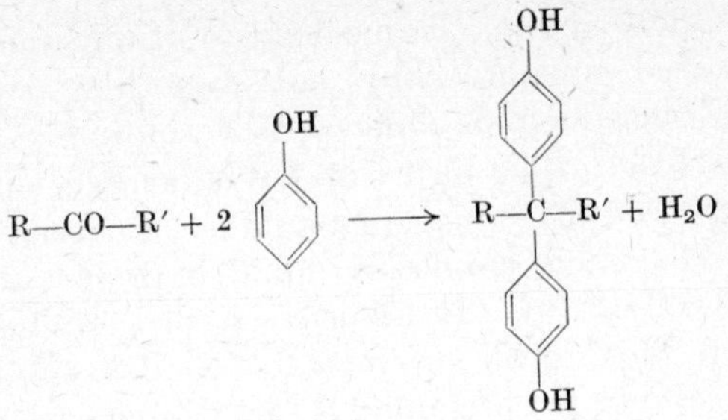

$$R\text{—}CO\text{—}R' + 2\ \overset{OH}{\underset{}{\bigcirc}} \longrightarrow R\text{—}\overset{}{\underset{}{C}}\text{—}R' + H_2O \tag{42}$$

$$R\text{—}\overset{}{\underset{}{C}}\text{—}R' \xrightarrow{\Delta} R\text{—}CH\text{—}R' + \overset{}{\bigcirc}\text{—}OH + \text{resin} \tag{43}$$

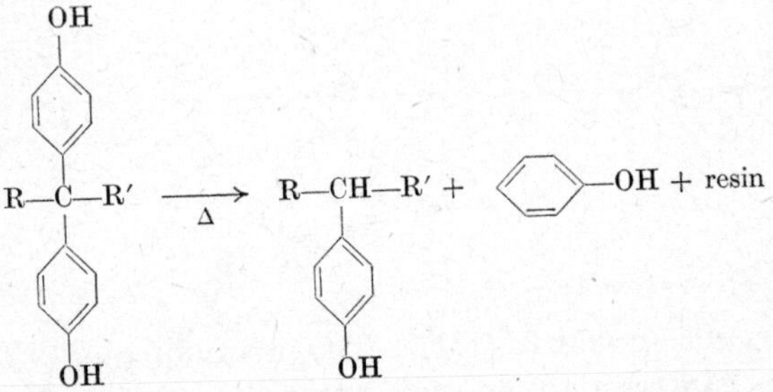

Reaction products appeared to be the same regardless of ketone type, reaction conditions or mole ratios of reagents. Ketones studied included methyl ethyl, methyl n-propyl, methyl isobutyl, cyclopentanone, cyclohexanone, and 3- and 4-methylcyclohexanone.

Tsukervanik and Nazarova (74) obtained similar results with aluminum chloride as the catalyst. When acetone was reacted with phenol the product was found to be di-p-hydroxyphenyl-dimethylmethane which could be decomposed on heating to 2-p-hydroxyphenylpropane. With diethylketone and phenol, decomposition apparently took place at reaction temperature as the primary product was found to be 3-p-hydroxyphenylpentane.

Along a slightly different line Wegmann and Dahn (83) studied the reactions of several α-keto carboxylic acids using both aluminum chloride and sulfuric acid as catalysts. With α-ketopropionic acid and benzene, an 18% yield of α,α-diphenylpropionic acid is obtained at 60°. With bromine-substituted α-ketoacids it is found that the mode of substitution depends both on the reactants and the catalyst. Thus, with α-keto-β-bromopropionic acid and benzene using AlCl$_3$ as the catalyst, bromine-free acid products are obtained. However, when H$_2$SO$_4$ is used a 40% yield of α,α-diphenyl-β-bromopropionic acid is obtained (equation 44). Using the same ketone with toluene

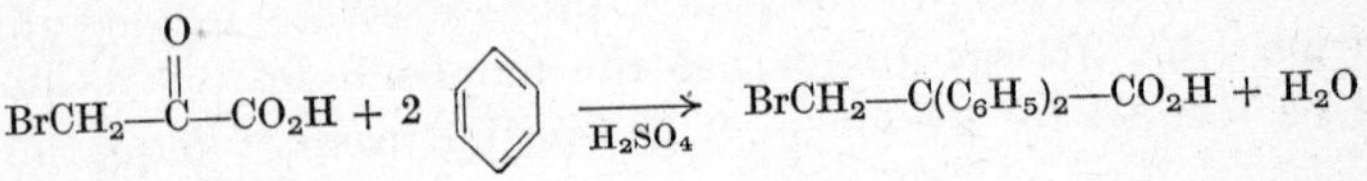

$$BrCH_2\text{—}\overset{O}{\underset{}{C}}\text{—}CO_2H + 2\ \bigcirc \xrightarrow{H_2SO_4} BrCH_2\text{—}C(C_6H_5)_2\text{—}CO_2H + H_2O \tag{44}$$

and $AlCl_3$, α-(p-tolyl)-β-bromolactic acid is obtained (equation 45).

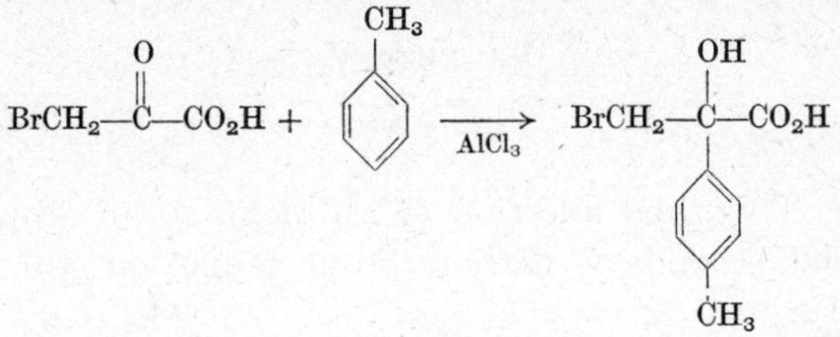

$$BrCH_2-\overset{\overset{O}{\|}}{C}-CO_2H \;+\; \overset{CH_3}{\bigodot} \;\xrightarrow{AlCl_3}\; BrCH_2-\overset{OH}{\underset{\underset{CH_3}{\bigodot}}{\overset{|}{\underset{|}{C}}}}-CO_2H \qquad (45)$$

Likewise, the monosubstituted addition product is also obtained when benzene is reacted with dibromo-α-ketopropionic acid in the presence of $AlCl_3$ (equation 46). As reactant concentrations were

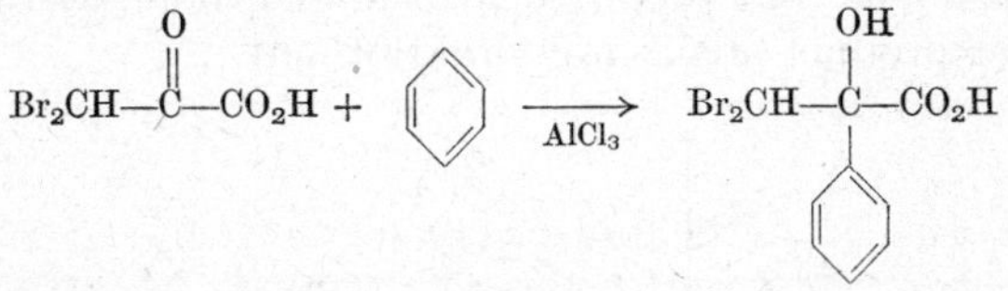

$$Br_2CH-\overset{\overset{O}{\|}}{C}-CO_2H \;+\; \bigodot \;\xrightarrow{AlCl_3}\; Br_2CH-\overset{OH}{\underset{\underset{\bigodot}{}}{\overset{|}{\underset{|}{C}}}}-CO_2H \qquad (46)$$

nearly the same in all the preceding experiments, it is apparent that both the catalyst and the reagents influence the course of reaction.

Several comparisons of reactivity for carbonyls versus carbon–carbon double bonds appear in the literature. Vorländer and Friedberg (81) describe the reaction between benzene and benzalmenthone employing $AlCl_3$ as the catalyst. The product of addition was found to be diphenylmethylmenthone (equation 47). Although at first sight this appears to be normal double bond alkylation, a

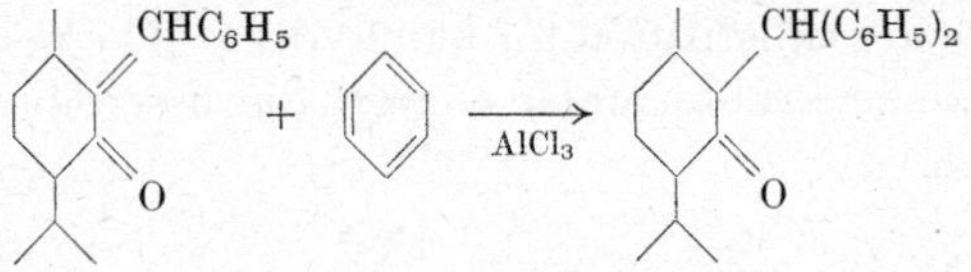

$$\text{(structure with } CHC_6H_5 \text{)} \;+\; \bigodot \;\xrightarrow{AlCl_3}\; \text{(structure with } CH(C_6H_5)_2 \text{)} \qquad (47)$$

reasonable alternative can be proposed where the aluminum halide coordinates through the oxygen and reaction occurs preferentially at only one of the allylic resonant centers (equation 48). This mechanism is supported by a reaction reported in the German patent

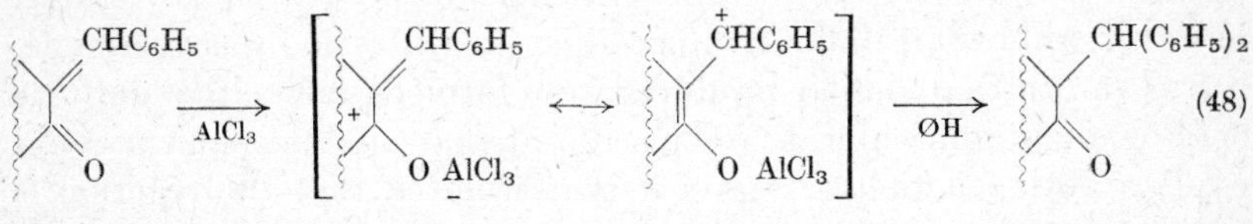

$$\text{(structure } CHC_6H_5 \text{)} \;\xrightarrow{AlCl_3}\; \left[\text{(structure } CHC_6H_5,\; O\;AlCl_3^- \text{)} \;\longleftrightarrow\; \text{(structure } \overset{+}{C}HC_6H_5,\; O\;AlCl_3 \text{)} \right] \;\xrightarrow{\varnothing H}\; \text{(structure } CH(C_6H_5)_2 \text{)} \qquad (48)$$

literature (35). Vinyl methyl ketone was reacted with naphthalene using $AlCl_3$ and the product was reported to be a γ-oxobutylnaph-

$$\text{(naphthalene)}\ CH_2CH_2C{-}CH_3 \quad (IV)$$
$$\underset{\|}{O}$$

thalene (IV). Normal addition of an olefin to an aromatic would occur at the secondary carbon atom (equation 49), whereas a

$$CH_2{=}CH{-}CO{-}CH_3 + \text{(naphthalene)} \xrightarrow{\text{Acid}} \text{(naphthalene)}\underset{|}{\overset{CH_3}{\underset{}{}}}CH{-}CO{-}CH_3 \qquad (49)$$

mechanism such as that proposed for the menthone derivative leads to the proper product structure (equation 50).

$$CH_2{=}CH{-}CO{-}CH_3 \xrightarrow{AlCl_3} \left[H_2C{=}C{-}\overset{O\ \bar{A}lCl_3}{\underset{+}{C}}{-}CH_3 \longleftrightarrow H_2C{-}C{=}\overset{O\ \bar{A}lCl_3}{\underset{\downarrow}{C}}{-}CH_3 \right] \qquad (50)$$
$$\text{Product}$$

This particular reaction provides a technique for synthesizing *n*-alkyl aromatics by alkylation with α,β-unsaturated ketones and then reduction. In contrast to the above work, the addition of mesityl oxide to benzene in the presence of $AlCl_3$ (34) proceeds through normal addition at the double bond.

The patent literature discussed in the case of aldehyde reactions with aromatics in the presence of HF (see Section IV-1-A) also contains references to similar addition and polymer-forming reactions when ketones are substituted for aldehydes. The resulting products have the same general formulae as were discussed in connection with the aldehydes.

2. Reactions of Chloral

The acid-catalyzed condensation of chloral and other simple aldehydes with aromatics was one of the earliest reactions studied involving aldehydes or ketones. At first this reaction, carried out in the presence of sulfuric acid, was regarded as a distinct area of chemistry separate from the Friedel-Crafts reactions. Later, however, after some difficulty in product identification was overcome, it was shown that similar products were formed when either sulfuric acid or aluminum chloride was used and that one mechanism could explain both reactions. Again it is postulated that the reaction is initiated by positive charge formation on the carbon of the carbonyl (reaction 51).

$$CCl_3—CHO + AlCl_3 \rightleftharpoons \left[CCl_3—\overset{+}{\underset{\underset{H}{|}}{C}}—O—\bar{A}lCl_3 \right] \tag{51}$$

It is rather surprising, however, that reactions involving chloral proceed with relative ease since the electron-withdrawing tendency of the trichloromethyl group would decrease the stability of the intermediate and make it more difficult to form.   Despite this, reactions proceed at 0°C and below and with a normal amount of care the mono- or disubstituted products can be isolated in good yield.   With chloral, substitution normally occurs at the carbonyl rather than replacement of one of the halogens.   Some of the products reported in the early literature indicate both carbonyl and halogen substitution but more recent work points to preferential substitution at the carbonyl.   Halogen substitution is undoubtedly limited by the difficulty in removing a halogen from a carbon which has two other halogens attached to it.   Data pertaining to chloral and bromal are summarized in Table IIIB.

As mentioned previously the condensation of chloral with benzene in the presence of concentrated sulfuric acid was reported in 1872 (3).   This reaction came to be known as the Baeyer condensation after the author.   The reaction led to disubstitution with liberation of a molecule of water (equation 52).   Later Fischer (18) working with Baeyer reported a similar reaction with toluene, the product being identified as di-(p-tolyl)trichloroethane.

$$CCl_3CHO + \quad 2 \bigcirc \xrightarrow[H_2SO_4]{} CCl_3—\underset{\underset{\bigcirc}{|}}{\overset{\overset{\bigcirc}{|}}{C}}—H + H_2O \tag{52}$$

Combes (13) reports the first work using $AlCl_3$ for the condensation of chloral with benzene and found four products: diphenylchloral hydrochloride, 1,1-diphenyl-2,2-dichloroethane, 1,1,2,2-tetraphenylethane, and an unknown.   Blitz (5, 6) in a similar work using aluminum chloride in carbon disulfide reported the formation of 1,1-diphenyl-2,2-dichloroethylene, 1,1,2,2-tetraphenylethane, 1,1,2-triphenylvinyl alcohol and an unknown.   This unknown was later identified (7) as 9,10-diphenylanthracene.   Van Lear (80) reports that the initial product is diphenyltrichloroethane and this undergoes subsequent reactions to form triphenyldichloroethane and tetra-phenylchloroethane. Most of the products found by these authors can be explained by a fairly simple stepwise sequence (equation 53).

$$(C_6H_5)_2C=C(C_6H_5)_2$$

$$\uparrow \quad -HCl$$

$$(C_6H_5)_2ClC-CH(C_6H_5)_2$$

$$C_6H_6 \quad \uparrow \quad -HCl$$

$$(C_6H_5)Cl_2C-CH(C_6H_5)_2 \qquad (53)$$

$$C_6H_6 \quad \uparrow \quad -HCl$$

$$Cl_3CCHO + C_6H_6 \longrightarrow \left[\begin{array}{c} OH \\ | \\ Cl_3C-C-C_6H_5 \\ | \\ H \end{array} \right] \xrightarrow{C_6H_6} Cl_3C-CH(C_6H_5)_2 + H_2O$$

$$\downarrow \quad -HCl$$

$$Cl_2C=C(C_6H_5)_2$$

According to this scheme, 1-phenyl-1-hydroxy-2,2,2-trichloro-ethane and diphenyltrichloroethane should be primary products of the reactions. Later work appears to justify this scheme, and indicates that most of the products reported by the early workers were due to subsequent side reactions.

Dienesmann (16) reports the product from condensation of chloral with benzene, at conditions similar to that employed by Combes, to be that expected of mono-addition, hydroxylphenyltrichloro-ethane. Boeseken (8), on the other hand, reports the product of this reaction to be diphenylmethane. Frankforter and Kritchevsky (22) in an attempt to duplicate the earlier work and extend it to other aromatic substrates, found that the reaction with $AlCl_3$ was rather violent and so made every effort to keep the temperature at 0°C or below. They report two products for the reaction of chloral with benzene and toluene. These correspond to substitution at the carbonyl or substitution of one of the halogens (equations 54 and 55).

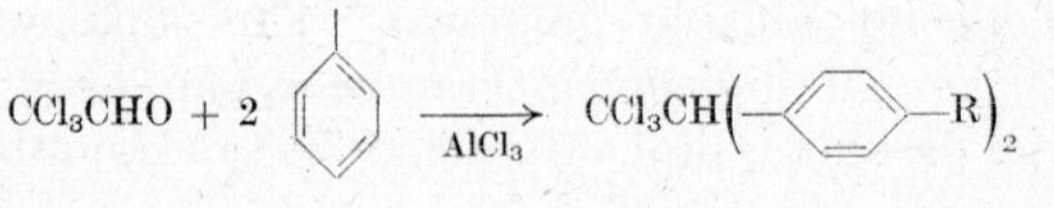

$$CCl_3CHO + 2 \underset{R}{\bigcirc} \xrightarrow{AlCl_3} CCl_3CH\left(-\bigcirc-R\right)_2 \qquad (54)$$

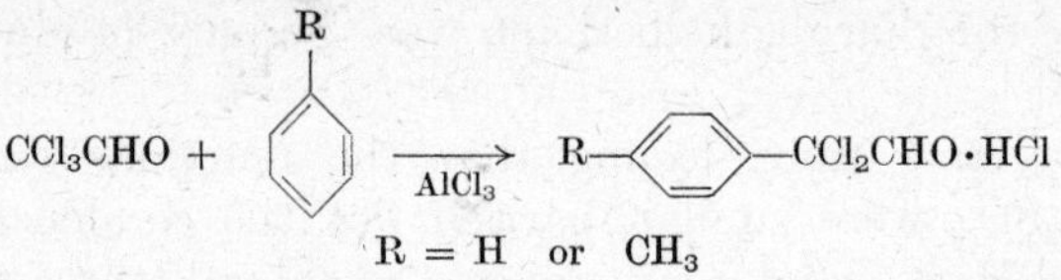

$$\text{CCl}_3\text{CHO} + \underset{\text{R = H   or   CH}_3}{\overset{\overset{\text{R}}{\bigcirc}}{}} \xrightarrow[\text{AlCl}_3]{} \text{R}-\bigcirc-\text{CCl}_2\text{CHO}\cdot\text{HCl} \qquad (55)$$

With xylene, anisole, and phenetol only the diaryltrichloroethanes are reported as products. With benzyl alcohol, benzaldehyde appears to be formed along with unknown products. With phenol, di-p-hydroxyphenyltrichloroethane is formed along with an unknown. Bromal was also condensed with phenetol and the product was found to be diphenetyltrichloroethane.

In a subsequent work Frankforter and Kritchevsky (21) extend the reaction with both chloral and bromal to polynuclear aromatics. With anthracene and AlCl$_3$ in petroleum ether the product was dianthracenetrichloroethane, but with AlCl$_3$ in benzene, 9,10-anthracenedichloroethylene was reported and with AlCl$_3$ in CS$_2$, 9,10-anthracenetrichloroethane was found. In the later case a similar product was found for bromal. These products from reaction in benzene and CS$_2$ arise from intramolecular condensation at the second stage of addition (equation 56). With phenanthrene and AlCl$_3$ in CS$_2$, a similar intramolecular reaction is observed and the product is found to be 9,10-phenanthrenetrihaloethane.

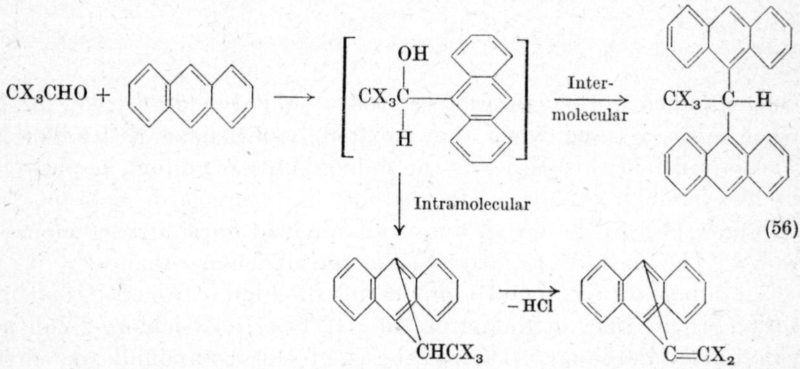

(56)

Harris and Frankforter (28) carried out a whole series of condensations at carefully controlled conditions and obtained yields of the disubstituted products which ranged from 70 to 95%. Aromatic substrates employed during this work included benzene, toluene, anisole, phenetol, p-cresol methyl ether, and p-cresol ethyl ether. Both chloral and bromal were condensed with each of these aromatics.

In each case the diaryltrihaloethane was the only product reported (12).

Chattaway and Muir, feeling that the reactions catalyzed by $AlCl_3$ or H_2SO_4 were similar, carried out the condensation using concentrated H_2SO_4 and a large excess of chloral (three to one mole ratio of aldehyde to aromatic). At these conditions the mono-addition product was isolated with benzene, toluene, and ethylbenzene (equation 57).

$$CCl_3CHO \; + \; \underset{}{\text{(benzene ring with R)}} \; \longrightarrow \; CCl_3\overset{OH}{\underset{H}{C}}\!\!-\!\!\text{(benzene ring)}\!-\!R \qquad (57)$$

$$R = H, \quad CH_3 \quad \text{or} \quad CH_3CH_2$$

However, with iodobenzene, even at a three to one excess of chloral, only the disubstituted product was formed. With iodobenzene, formation of the second intermediate cation is undoubtedly facilitated by conjugation with the iodine atom (equation 58) and this intermediate consumes another molecule of aromatic before chloral has a chance to react.

$$I\!-\!\text{(ring)}\!-\!\overset{OH}{\underset{H}{C}}\!-\!CCl_3 \; \xrightarrow{-OH^-} \; \left[I\!-\!\text{(ring)}\!-\!\overset{+}{\underset{H}{C}}\!-\!CCl_3 \; \longleftrightarrow \; \overset{+}{I}\!=\!\text{(ring)}\!=\!\underset{H}{C}\!-\!CCl_3 \right]$$

$$(58)$$

Quelet and co-workers (63) showed that a similar reaction takes place when $AlCl_3$ is used when they treated naphthalene with chloral. The product in this case was the mono-addition adduct, naphthylhydroxytrichloroethane. The patent literature also contains a reference (44) to the use of fluorosulfonic acid for similar condensations. The products in each case are diaryltrichloroethanes.

An important commercial application of chloral–aromatic condensation is in the manufacture of DDT (1,1,1-trichloro-2,2-di(p-chlorophenyl)ethane). The synthesis of this compound was first reported in 1872 (86) but its superior insecticidal properties were not known until just prior to the Second World War (54). The reaction between chlorobenzene and chloral (or its hydrate) has been studied by numerous investigators since that time and an excellent review has been compiled by Metcalf (52). Haller and co-workers (27) have made an extensive study of the reaction products. The largest impurity is the mono-*ortho* derivative

(1,1,1-trichloro-2-(*p*-chlorophenyl)-2-(*o*-chlorophenyl)ethane) with minor amounts of the di-*ortho*-chloro isomer and the mono-condensation product 1,1,1-trichloro-2-(*p*-chlorophenyl)ethanol. Catalysts employed have included sulfuric acid, oleum and chlorosulfonic acid.

It is clear from the foregoing discussions that the acid-catalyzed reaction of chloral or bromal with aromatics can be a simple synthesis for mono- or diaryltrihaloethanes. The more recent literature points up the fact that the reaction is stepwise and that mono- or disubstitution depends primarily on ratios of reactants. This recent work also indicates that care must be taken to avoid side reactions which can lead to a myriad of different products. Substitution of halogen rather than addition at the carbonyl is a competing reaction but the latter is generally favored.

V. Miscellaneous Additions involving Aldehydes and Ketones

As is apparent from the title, the last section in this review deals with reactions that do not fit in any of the previous sections. Numerous reactions have been carried out and these have covered a whole series of acid catalysts. Of course one obvious large body of work falling in this area is that of acid-catalyzed aldol condensations. As this subject has been summarized elsewhere (24,64), it will not be generally covered in this review. Data pertaining to this section are included in Table IV.

The earliest work reported in this area appeared in 1838 (42) and concerned the action of concentrated sulfuric acid on acetone. This work predated even the Baeyer condensation by some thirty years. The major product from this reaction is mesitylene (reaction 59). Considerable work appeared on this reaction during the nine-

$$3CH_3COCH_3 \xrightarrow{H_2SO_4} \text{mesitylene} + 3H_2O \tag{59}$$

teenth century. An excellent summary of this early work appeared in 1893 (59) by Orndorff and Young. These workers also carried out a careful study to determine the by-products of this reaction. The major by-products were found to be phorone and mesityl oxide. The ability of acetone to form complexes with other Friedel-Crafts catalysts, such as BF_3, has been demonstrated by Landolph (48) and Gasselin (25).

The reaction of aldehydes with olefins catalyzed by dilute sulfuric or phosphoric acids has been reported (53). Diols are formed upon the addition of formaldehyde to either propylene or isobutylene. The mechanism of this reaction is fairly clear based on the preceding discussions (reaction 60). The source of formaldehyde for this

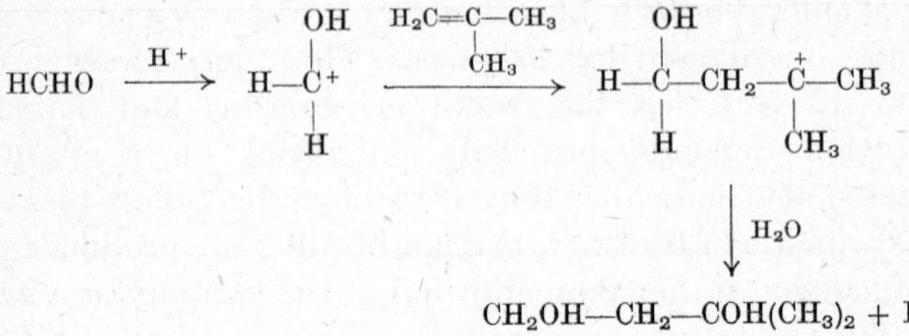

$$HCHO \xrightarrow{H^+} H-\underset{\underset{H}{|}}{\overset{\overset{OH}{|}}{C^+}} \xrightarrow{\overset{H_2C=C-CH_3}{\overset{|}{CH_3}}} H-\underset{\underset{H}{|}}{\overset{\overset{OH}{|}}{C}}-CH_2-\overset{+}{\underset{\underset{CH_3}{|}}{C}}-CH_3 \qquad (60)$$

$$\downarrow H_2O$$

$$CH_2OH-CH_2-COH(CH_3)_2 + H^+$$

reaction was either paraformaldehyde or trioxymethylene. It is also reported (58) that aldehydes and ketones react with alkanes in the presence of concentrated sulfuric acid to produce alcohols and olefins.

Ketene has been used for a number of condensation reactions in addition to those discussed in Section II of this chapter. In general, this work has involved addition to oxygenated compounds to produce lactones. Thus, the patent literature contains several examples (47) (72) of the BF_3–etherate catalyzed reaction of ketene with formaldehyde and acetaldehyde. The products are β-propionolactone and β-butyrolactone, respectively (reactions 61 and 62).

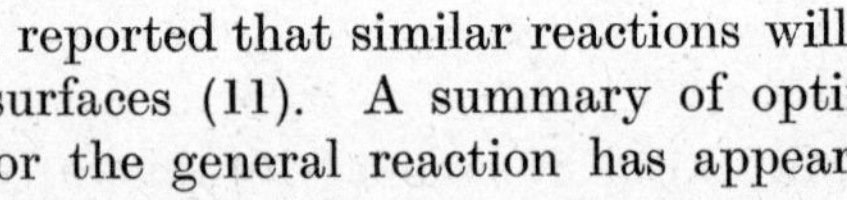

$$CH_2=C=O + HCHO \longrightarrow \underset{\underset{H_2C-O}{|}}{\overset{\overset{H_2C-C=O}{|}}{}} \qquad (61)$$

$$CH_2=C=O + CH_3CHO \longrightarrow \underset{\underset{CH_3HC-O}{|}}{\overset{\overset{H_2C-C=O}{|}}{}} \qquad (62)$$

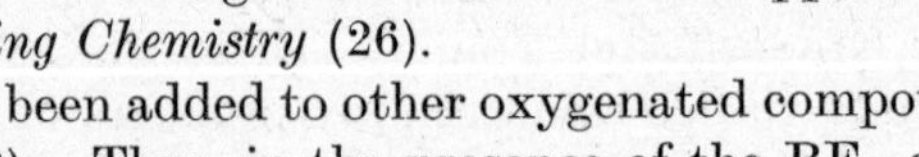

It has also been reported that similar reactions will occur on acidic silica–alumina surfaces (11). A summary of optimum conditions and catalysts for the general reaction has appeared in *Industrial and Engineering Chemistry* (26).

Ketene has been added to other oxygenated compounds to produce γ-lactones (58). Thus, in the presence of the BF_3–etherate, ketene reacts with ethylene or propylene oxide to yield the γ-lactone (reactions 63 and 64). In a like manner the corresponding lactones are also produced from styrene oxide and epichlorohydrin.

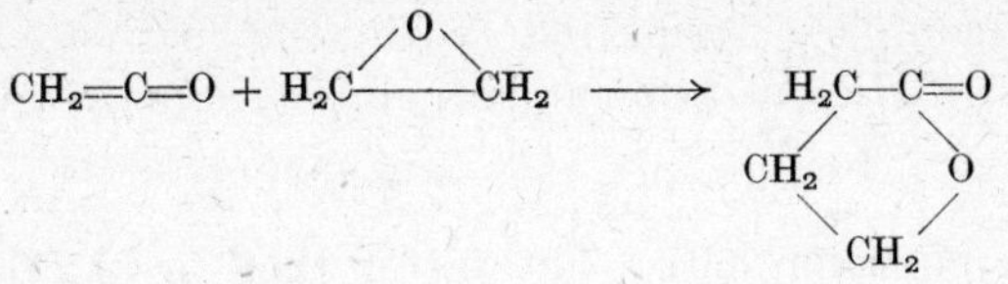

$$CH_2=C=O + H_2C\overset{O}{\diagdown\diagup}CH_2 \longrightarrow \begin{array}{c} H_2C-C=O \\ | \quad\quad | \\ CH_2 \quad O \\ \diagdown\diagup \\ CH_2 \end{array} \qquad (63)$$

$$CH_2=C=O + CH_3CH\overset{O}{\diagdown\diagup}CH_2 \longrightarrow \begin{array}{c} H_2C-C=O \\ | \quad\quad | \\ CH_2 \quad O \\ \diagdown\diagup \\ CH \\ | \\ CH_3 \end{array} \qquad (64)$$

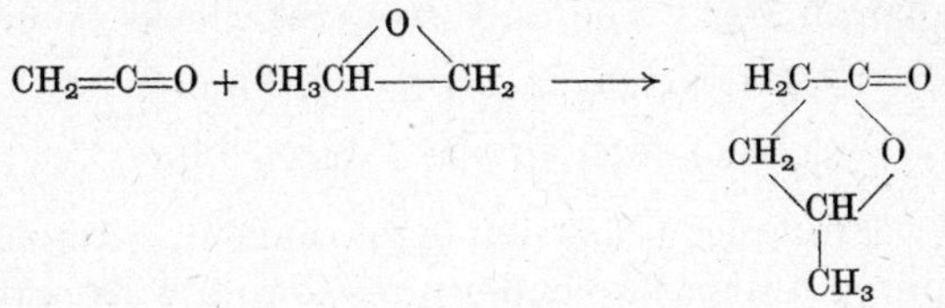

It is possible to visualize the mechanism of the lactone formation in either of two ways. Attack of protonated ketene on the aldehyde (reaction 65) or protonated aldehyde on the ketene (reaction 66).

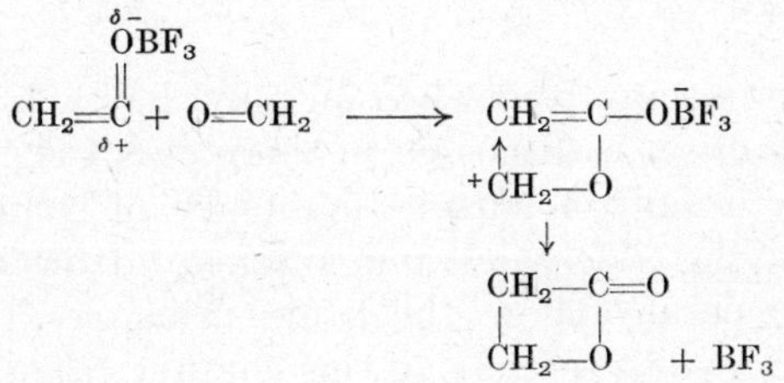

$$CH_2\!\!\underset{\delta+}{=}\!\!\overset{\overset{\delta-}{O}BF_3}{\overset{\|}{C}} + O=CH_2 \longrightarrow \begin{array}{c} CH_2=C-\bar{O}BF_3 \\ \uparrow \quad\quad | \\ {}^+CH_2-O \\ \downarrow \\ CH_2-C=O \\ | \quad\quad | \\ CH_2-O \quad + BF_3 \end{array} \qquad (65)$$

$$H_2\overset{\overset{\bar{O}BF_3}{|}}{C^+} + CH_2=C=O \longrightarrow \begin{array}{c} CH_2-\overset{+}{C}=O \\ | \quad\quad \\ CH_2-\bar{O}BF_3 \\ \downarrow \\ CH_2-C=O \\ | \quad\quad | \\ CH_2-O \quad + BF_3 \end{array} \qquad (66)$$

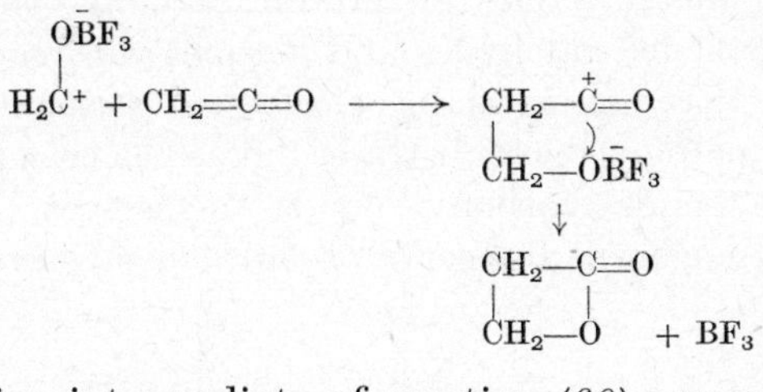

The acylium-ion intermediate of reaction (66) appears to be more favorable than the primary cation of reaction (65) and hence the latter mechanism would seem to be favored. Likewise, reactions with the epoxides would proceed in the same manner.

A final reaction in this area that is rather interesting is the formation of phosgene from aldehydes and carbon tetrachloride (41). Using $AlCl_3$ as the catalyst, the author postulates a mechanism of complex formation with the aldehyde (equation 67), followed by

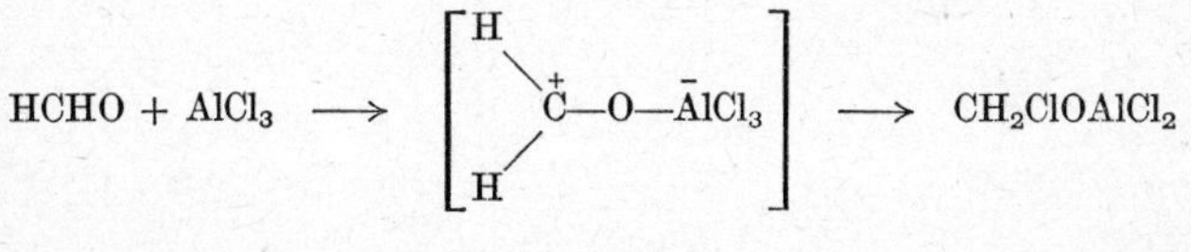

$$HCHO + AlCl_3 \longrightarrow \left[\begin{array}{c} H \\ \diagdown \\ \overset{+}{C}-O-\bar{A}lCl_3 \\ \diagup \\ H \end{array} \right] \longrightarrow CH_2ClOAlCl_2 \qquad (67)$$

subsequent complex formation with the carbon tetrachloride (equation 68). By ionization and recombination, the two end groups

$$CH_2ClOAlCl_2 + CCl_4 \rightarrow CH_2ClOAlCl_3CCl_3 \tag{68}$$

interchange (equation 69). The latter then breaks down to form products (equation 70). The only step that lacks some precedent

$$CH_2ClOAlCl_3CCl_3 \rightleftharpoons CCl_3OAlCl_3CH_2Cl \tag{69}$$

$$CCl_3OAlCl_3CH_2Cl \rightarrow COCl_2 + AlCl_3 + CH_2Cl_2 \tag{70}$$

is the ionization and recombination (equation 69). Actually, though all this is required for the two end groups to rotate around the center (equation 71). Such a mechanism is reasonable when one recognizes

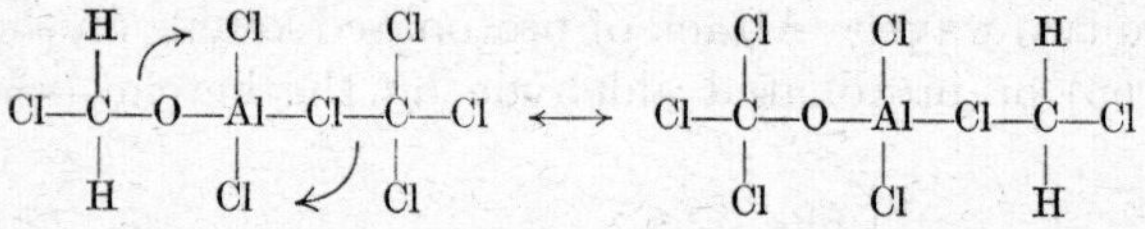

$$\begin{array}{ccc} H & Cl & Cl \\ | & | & | \\ Cl-C-O-Al-Cl-C-Cl & \longleftrightarrow \\ | & | & | \\ H & Cl & Cl \end{array} \quad \begin{array}{ccc} Cl & Cl & H \\ | & | & | \\ Cl-C-O-Al-Cl-C-Cl \\ | & | & | \\ Cl & Cl & H \end{array} \tag{71}$$

that halogens are scrambled when an alkyl halide is contacted with $AlCl_3$. (This subject is discussed in Chapter XVII.)

This section is only a cursory summary of some miscellaneous reactions involving aldehydes and ketones. However, these reactions do, in general, follow the same principles that have been established in previous sections of this chapter. The carbonium-ion nature of the metal halide or proton carbonyl complex is well recognized and hence aldehydes and ketones will react with almost any substrate that has available electrons. Aromatics have been most generally employed as substrates but as has been shown carbon–carbon double bonds, carbonyl bonds themselves, and other unsaturated groupings will also serve as suitable substrates.

VI. Appendix

TABLE I. Friedel-Crafts addition of ketene to aromatics

Reactants		Catalyst reaction conditions	Yield	Product	Ref.
Aldehyde or ketone	Substrate				
Ketene	Benzene	Anhydrous HCl	—	No reaction	78
	Salicylic acid	As above	—	Acetyl-2-hydroxybenzoic acid	79
	p-Hydroxybenzoic acid	As above	—	Acetyl-4-hydroxybenzoic acid	79
	Methylsalicylate	As above	—	Acetyl-2-hydroxybenzoic acid methyl ester	79
	m-Hydroxymethylbenzoate	As above	—	Acetyl-3-hydroxybenzoic acid methyl ester	79
	Anisole	AlCl$_3$ in CS$_2$, 1:1:1 mole ratio of ketene to anisole to AlCl$_3$	~45%	o- and p-Methoxyacetophenone, higher boiling ketone	36
	Benzene	As above	~20%	Acetophenone plus others	36
	Acetophenone	As above		Very little reaction	36
	Naphthalene	As above at 0°C	21–37%	α- and β-Naphthylmethylketone	36
	o-Dimethoxybenzene	AlCl$_3$ added over 1 hour in CS$_2$, bubbled with ketene and HCl		3,4-Dimethoxyacetophenone	62
	Benzene	AlCl$_3$	10%	Acetophenone	60
			trace	1,4-Naphthaquinone	60
	Benzene	AlCl$_3$	30%	Acetophenone	60
	Benzene	AlCl$_3$ at 0°C	~12%	Acetophenone	71
			trace	p-Ethylacetophenone	71
	Phenol	AlCl$_3$ at 80°C	—	Hydroxyacetophenone	71

Table continued

TABLE I (*continued*)

Reactants		Catalyst reaction conditions	Yield	Product	Ref.
Aldehyde or ketone	Substrate				
Ketene	Benzene	CS$_2$ at 0°C. AlCl$_3$ added in smaller amounts	33%	Acetophenone	85
	Naphthalene	As above	35%	1-Acetylnaphthalene	85
	Tetralin	As above	24%	2-Acetyl-5,6,7,8-tetrahydro-naphthalene	85
	Biphenyl	CS$_2$ at 30°C. AlCl$_3$	23%	4-Acetylbiphenyl	85
	Chlorobenzene	AlCl$_3$ in CS$_2$. Ketene added at a rate of 100 cc./15 min. at 18–20°C and solution allowed to stand for 1–2 days at room temperature	~1%	3-Ethyl-4-chloroacetophenone	23
Acetyl ketene	Benzene	AlCl$_3$ added over two hour period	10%	Benzoylacetone	37

TABLE II. Reaction of aromatic aldehydes and ketones with aromatics

| Reactants | | Catalyst reaction conditions | Yield | Product | Ref. |
Aldehyde or ketone	Substrate				
Benzaldehyde	Phenanthrene	$AlCl_3$ in CS_2	—	Diphenanthrenephenylmethane, Dibenzalmesotriphenanthrene	21
	Benzene	$AlCl_3$, 2 hrs. at 40°C, 3 hrs. at 60°C, frequent shaking	21%	Diphenylmethane	66
			30%	Triphenylmethane	66
			30%	Anthracene	66
	Benzene	$FeCl_3$	6%	Triphenylmethane	66
				Anthracene	
	Toluene	$AlCl_3$, 6 hrs. at 60°C	33%	2,6- and 2,7-Dimethylanthracene	33
p-Tolualdehyde	Benzene	As above	30%	Anthracene	33
				Triphenylmethane	
m-Tolualdehyde	Benzene	As above	47%	Anthracene	33
				Triphenylmethane	
o-Chlorobenzaldehyde	Benzene	As above	22%	Anthracene	33
				Triphenylmethane	
Furfuraldehyde	Toluene	As above	70%	Dimethylanthracenes	17
Benzaldehyde	m-Xylene	As above	30%	1,3,5,7- and 1,3,6,8-Tetramethylanthracenes	17
	p-Xylene	As above		1,4,5,8-Tetramethylanthracene	
	o-Xylene	As above	43%	2,3,6,7-Tetramethylanthracene	17
	Biphenyl	$AlCl_3$ in CS_2, 5 hrs. at 35°C, 1 hr. at 40°C	26%	2,6- and 2,7-Diphenylanthracene	17
	Biphenyl	$AlCl_3$, 3.5 hrs. at 60°C	14%	Diphenylanthracene	76
	Mesitylene	As above	—	Xylenes	76
				Tetramethylbenzenes	
				Tetramethylanthracene	

Table continued

TABLE II (continued)

Reactants		Catalyst reaction conditions	Yield	Product	Ref.
Aldehyde or ketone	Substrate				
Benzaldehyde	Diphenyl ether	As above	—	9-Phenylxanthhydrol	76
o-Chlorobenzaldehyde	Benzene	As above	40%	Anthracene	75
			16%	Triphenylcarbinol	75
o-Anisaldehyde	Benzene	As above	—	Anthracene	75
				Triphenylcarbinol	75
Salicylaldehyde	Benzene	As above	—	Anthracene	75
				Triphenylcarbinol	75
Nitrobenzaldehyde	Benzene	As above	65–80%	(Diphenylmethyl)nitrobenzene	75
2,4-Dichlorobenz-aldehyde	Benzene	As above	—	Anthracene	75
				Triphenylcarbinol	75
3,4-Dichlorobenz-aldehyde	Benzene	As above	—	Anthracene	75
				Triphenylcarbinol	75
2,3-Dimethoxy-benzaldehyde	Benzene	As above	—	Anthracene	75
				Triphenylcarbinol	75
Benzaldehyde	Benzene	$AlCl_3$, 6 hrs at 60°C	—	Anthracene	75
				Triphenylcarbinol	75
3,4-Dimethoxy-benzaldehyde	Benzene	As above	—	Guaiacol	75
				Vanillin	75
Benzaldehyde	Toluene	$AlCl_3$	30%	2,6- and 2,7-Dimethylan-thracene	75
Acetophenone	Benzene	$AlCl_3$ in CS_2, Refluxed	—	No reaction	40
	Benzene	$AlCl_3$ in CS_2, Refluxed	—	Anthracene	40
	$C_6H_5N(CH_3)_2$	$AlCl_3$	50%	Triphenylbenzene	14
Chalcone	$C_6H_5N(CH_3)_2$	$AlCl_3$	—	Leuco-Malachite Green	14
ω,ω-Dichloroaceto-phenone	Benzene	$AlCl_3$	20%	Diphenylacetophenone	65

ω,ω,ω-Trichloroaceto-phenone	Benzene	AlCl$_3$	—	Diphenylacetophenone	65
2-Hydroxy-2-phenyl-propionic acid	Benzene	AlCl$_3$, 1 hr. at 65°C	55%	α,α-Diphenylpropionic acid	84
Indole-2,3-dione	Benzene	H$_2$SO$_4$, 0°C	—	α,α-Diphenylpropionic acid	84
	Benzene	AlCl$_3$, 1 hr. at 75°C	69%	3,3-Diphenyl-2-indolinone	84
	Toluene	AlCl$_3$	90%	3,3-Di-(p-tolyl)-2-indolinone	84
	o-Xylene	AlCl$_3$	77%	3,3-Di-(o-xylyl)-2-indolinone	84
1-Benzothiophene-2,3-dione	Benzene	AlCl$_3$, 1 hr. at 70°C	77%	3,3-Diphenyl-1-benzothio-phene-2-one	84
	Toluene	AlCl$_3$	68%	3,3-Di-(p-tolyl)-1-benzothio-phene-2-one	84
Tetrabromo-o-quinone	Benzene	AlCl$_3$	55%	Tetrabromopyrocatechol	84
1-Phenyl-1,2-pro-panedione	Benzene	AlCl$_3$	—	Benzoic acid	83
1-Phenyl-3-bromo-1,2-propanedione		AlCl$_3$	—	2-Phenyl-3-bromomethyl-quinoxaline	83
1,3-Diphenyl-1,2,3-propanetrione	Benzene	AlCl$_3$, 1 hr. at 70°C	—	Bromomethylbenzoin	83
	Benzene	AlCl$_3$, 1 hr. at 60°C	—	Benzophenone	83
Acetophenone	Phenol	HCl bubbled into glacial acetic acid at boiling point	10–25%	α-Phenyl-α,α-bis(4-hydroxy-phenyl)ethane	51
Acetophenone	o-Cresol	As above	10–25%	α-Phenyl-α,α-bis(3-methyl-4-hydroxyphenyl)ethane	51
p-Tolylmethylketone	Phenol	As above	10–25%	α-p-Tolyl-α,α-bis(4-hydroxy-phenyl)ethane	51
Chalcone	Benzene	AlCl$_3$	—	ω,ω-Diphenylpropiophenone	81
Benzalmenthone	Benzene	AlCl$_3$ at room temperature	—	Diphenylmethylmenthone	81
2,3-Dibromo-3-phenylpropiophenone	Benzene	AlCl$_3$ at room temperature	—	α,β,β-Triphenylpropiophenone	81

TABLE IIIA. Reactions of aliphatic aldehydes and ketones with aromatics

Reactants		Catalyst reaction conditions	Yield	Product	Ref.
Aldehyde or ketone	Substrate				
Paraldehyde	Toluene	HF at 0–5°C for 1–3 hrs.	95.5%	Ditolylethane	30
	Xylene (75.5% meta, 24.5% para)	HF at 0–7°C for ½ hr. then temp. raised slowly to 65°C over 1½ hrs.	87.3%	Di-m-xylylethane	30
	p-Xylene (120 parts)	HF, 1½ hrs. at 18–26°C	80.5%	(2,5,2′,5′-Tetramethyl)-diphenylethane	30
	Naphthalene	HF in chlorobenzene at 18–35°C	51.5%	Dinaphthylethane	30
	Biphenyl	HF in chloroform at 10–30°C	65.8%	Biphenylethane	30
Isovaleraldehyde	Benzene	$AlCl_3$	—	2-Methyl-4,4-diphenyl-3-butene 2-Methyl-4,4-diphenylbutane	66
Trioxymethylene	Benzene	$ZnCl_2$ and HCl	80% Small	Benzyl chloride p-bis(Chloromethyl)benzene	4
	Toluene	As above	Major Minor	p-Chloromethyltoluene 2,4- and 3,4-bis(Chloromethyltoluene)	4
	m-Xylene	As above	—	2,4-Dimethylchloromethyltoluene 2,4-Dimethyl-1,5-bis(chloromethyl)benzene	4
	Ethylbenzene	As above	—	p-Chloromethylethylbenzene n-Propylbenzene p-Chloromethyl-n-propylbenzene chlorobenzene p-Chloromethylchlorobenzene cymene, naphthalene $1,2,4\text{-}C_6H_3CH_3(CH_2Cl)(n\text{-}C_3H_7)$ α-Chloromethylnaphthalene	4
Acetaldehyde	Phenol	Dry HCl in acetic acid, 2 hrs. at −5°C	~40%	p-Ethylphenol	56

Reactant	Aromatic	Conditions	Yield	Product	Ref.
Propionaldehyde	o-Cresol	As above	40%	p-Ethyl-o-cresol	56
	m-Cresol	As above	40%	p-Ethyl-m-cresol	56
	p-Cresol	As above	40%	o-Ethyl-p-cresol	56
	Phenol	Dry HCl in glacial acetic acid, 2–3 hrs. at 60–80°C	20–40%	p-n-Propylphenol	56
Butyraldehyde	Phenol	As above	20–40%	p-n-Butylphenol	56
i-Butyraldehyde	Phenol	As above	20–40%	p-Isobutylphenol	56
Valeraldehyde	Phenol	As above	20–40%	p-n-Amylphenol	56
Heptaldehyde	Phenol	As above	20–40%	p-n-Heptylphenol	56
Trioxymethylene	Benzene	AlCl₃ added at 0°C. Temp. varied between 0–20°C	—	Diphenylmethane / Anthracene	20
	Toluene	AlCl₃. Temp. maintained below 65°C and allowed to stand 4 days at room temp.	—	Ditolylmethane / Dimethylanthracene	20
	o-Xylene	AlCl₃. Temp. raised to 65°C then allowed to stand 3 days at room temp.	—	Dixylylmethane / Tetramethylanthracene	20
	Mesitylene	AlCl₃. Temp. raised to 50°C then allowed to stand 2 days at room temp.	—	Dimesitylmethane / Tetramethylanthracene, Benzene, toluene, xylene, durene	20
	p-Xylene	AlCl₃ added over 1 hr. at approx. 45°C. Allowed to stand 5 days at 0°C	3% / 8%	Methylene-bis-(di-p-xylyl-methane) / Di-p-xylylmethane, p-Xylylmethyl-di-p-xylyl-methane	38
Acetone	Phenol	AlCl₃	—	$(p\text{-}HOC_6H_4)_2C(CH_3)_2$ (Decomposes on heating to $p\text{-}HOC_6H_4CH(CH_3)_2$)	74
Diethyl ketone	Phenol	As above	—	$p\text{-}HOC_6H_4CH(CH_2CH_3)_2$	74
Vinylmethyl ketone	Naphthalene	AlCl₃	—	γ-Oxobutylnaphthalene	35
Pyruvic acid	Benzene	AlCl₃, 1 hr. at 60°C	18%	$CH_3C(C_6H_5)_2CO_2H$	84
Bromopyruvic acid	Benzene	H₂SO₄	90%	$CH_2BrC(C_6H_5)_2CO_2H$	84
	Toluene	AlCl₃	—	α-(p-Tolyl)-β-bromolactic acid	84

Table continued

TABLE IIIA (continued)

Reactants		Catalyst reaction conditions	Yield	Product	Ref.
Aldehyde or ketone	Substrate				
Dibromopyruvic acid	Benzene	AlCl$_3$	—	Br$_2$CHC(C$_6$H$_5$)OHCO$_2$H	84
Acetone	m-Cresol	H$_2$SO$_4$, mixed at 0°C and allowed to stand at room temp. for 48 hrs.	—	Phorone di-m-cresyl ether	55
Methyl ethyl ketone	Phenol	HCl bubbled into glacial acetic acid for 3 hrs. and allowed to stand for 1-4 weeks	a	2,2-Di-(p-hydroxyphenyl)butane	48
	o-Cresol	As above	a	2,2-Bis(3-methyl-4-hydroxyphenyl)butane	51
Methyl propyl ketone	Phenol	As above	a	2,2-Di-(p-hydroxyphenyl)pentane	51
Methyl-i-butyl ketone	Phenol	As above	a	2-Methyl-4,4-bis(4-hydroxyphenyl)pentane	51
	o-Cresol	As above	a	2-Methyl-4,4-bis(3-methyl-4-hydroxyphenyl)pentane	51
Cyclohexanone	Phenol	HCl bubbled into glacial acetic acid at boiling point	80%	1,1-Bis-(4'-hydroxyphenyl)cyclohexane	51
	o-Cresol	As above	80%	1,1-Bis(3'-methyl-4'-hydroxyphenyl)cyclohexane	51
4-Methylcyclohexanone	Phenol	As above	70%	1,1-Bis(4'-hydroxyphenyl)-4-methylcyclohexane	51
Cyclopentanone	Phenol	As above	60%	1,1-Bis(4'-hydroxyphenyl)cyclopentane	51
3-Methylcyclohexanone	Phenol	As above	50%	1,1-Bis(4'-hydroxyphenyl)-3-methylcyclohexane	51

a Authors report a general yield of 10-25%.

TABLE IIIB. Condensation of chloral with aromatics

Aldehyde	Reactants		Catalyst reaction conditions	Yield	Product	Ref.
	Substrate					
Chloral	Benzene		conc. H_2SO_4	—	Diphenyltrichloroethane	18
	Toluene		conc. H_2SO_4	—	Di(p-tolyl)trichloroethane	13
	Benzene		$AlCl_3$	—	Diphenylchloralhydrochloride	
					1,1-Diphenyl-2,2-dichloroethane	
					1,1,2,2-Tetraphenylethane	
	Benzene		$AlCl_3$ in CS_2	—	Unknown product	5,7
					1,1,2,2-Tetraphenylethane	
					1,1-Diphenyl-2,2-dichloroethylene	
					1,1,2-Triphenylvinyl alcohol	
					9,10-Diphenylanthracene	
	Benzene		$AlCl_3$	—	1-Hydroxy-1-phenyl-2,2,2-trichloroethane	16
	Benzene		$AlCl_3$	—	Diphenylmethane	14
	Benzene		$AlCl_3$ added over 4 hr. period at <0°C. Mixture allowed to stand in the cold for 48 hrs.	—	2-Phenyl-2,2-dichloroacetaldehyde	22
	Toluene		As above	—	Diphenyltrichloroethane	22
					2-p-Tolyl-2,2-dichloroacetaldehyde	
					Di(p-tolyl)trichloroethane	
	Xylene		As above	—	Dixylyltrichloroethane	22
	Benzyl alcohol		$AlCl_3$ at room temp. for 24 hrs.	—	Benzaldehyde	22
					Unknown products	
	Phenol		$AlCl_3$ for 2 days at 0°C	—	Di(p-hydroxyphenyl)trichloroethane	22
					Unknown products	
	Anisole		$AlCl_3$ for 24 hrs. at 0°C	—	Dianisyltrichloroethane	22
	Phenetol		$AlCl_3$	—	Diphenetyltrichloroethane	22

Table continued

TABLE IIIB (*continued*)

| Reactants | | Catalyst reaction conditions | Yield | Product | Ref. |
Aldehyde	Substrate				
Bromal	Phenetol	AlCl₃ for 24 hrs. at 0°C	—	Diphenetyltribromoethane	22
Chloral	Naphthalene	AlCl₃ at 0°C	—	Di-α-naphthyldichloroethylene	21
Bromal	Naphthalene	AlCl₃ at 0°C for 3 days	—	Dinaphthyldibromoethylene	21
Chloral	Anthracene	AlCl₃ in petroleum ether. Added at 0°C and allowed to warm to room temp. for 24 hrs.	—	Dianthryldichloroethylene	21
	Anthracene	AlCl₃ in benzene at 0°C	—	9,10-bis(Dichloroethylidene)-anthracene	21
Bromal	Anthracene	AlCl₃ in CS₂ at 0°C	—	9,10-bis(Trichloroethyl)anthracene	21
Chloral	Anthracene	AlCl₃ in CS₂ at 0°C	—	9,10-bis(Tribromoethyl)anthracene	21
	Phenanthrene	AlCl₃ in CS₂ at 0°C	—	9,10-bis(Trichloroethyl)-phenanthrene	21
Bromal	Phenanthrene	AlCl₃ in CS₂	—	9,10-bis(Tribromoethyl)-phenanthrene	21
Chloral	Benzene	AlCl₃ in CS₂ added over 3 hr. period at 0°C or below. Stirring continued for an additional ½–1 hr.	80%	Diphenyltrichloroethane	28
	Toluene	As above	80%	Di(*p*-tolyl)trichloroethane	28
	Anisole	As above	94%	Dianisyltrichloroethane	28
	Phenetol	As above	91%	Diphenetyltrichloroethane	28
	p-Cresyl methyl ether	As above	93%	3,3-Dimethyl-6,6-dimethoxy-diphenyltrichloroethane	28
	p-Cresyl ethyl ether	As above	80%	3,3-Dimethyl-6,6-diethoxy-diphenyltrichloroethane	28
Bromal	Benzene	As above	50%	Diphenyltribromoethane	28
	Toluene	As above	85%	Ditolyltribromoethane	28
	Anisole	As above	90%	Dianisyltribromoethane	28

Aldehyde/Ketone	Aromatic	Conditions	Yield	Product	Ref.
Chloral hydrate	Phenetol	As above	85%	Diphenetyltribromoethane	28
	p-Cresyl methyl ether	As above	74%	3,3-Dimethyl-6,6-dimethoxy-diphenyltribromoethane	28
	p-Cresyl ethyl ether	As above	75%	3,3-Dimethyl-6,6-diethoxy-diphenyltribromoethane	28
	Benzene	conc. H_2SO_4	—	1-Hydroxy-1-phenyl-2,2,2-trichloroethane	12
	Toluene	conc. H_2SO_4	—	1-Hydroxy-1-p-tolyl-2,2,2-trichloroethane	12
	Ethylbenzene	conc. H_2SO_4	—	1-Hydroxy-1-(4-ethylphenyl)-2,2,2-trichloroethane	12
	Iodobenzene	conc. H_2SO_4	—	bis(p-Iodophenyl)-2,2,2-trichloroethane	12
Chloral	Naphthalene	$AlCl_3$ in cyclohexane, added in small portions	24%	1-Hydroxy-1-β-naphthyl-2,2,2-trichloroethane	63
Dichloroacetal	Chlorobenzene	H_2SO_4	47%	1,1-Dichloro-2,2-di-p-chlorophenyl)-ethane	19
Chloral	Fluorobenzene	H_2SO_4, 10–30°C	—	p,p′-Difluorodiphenyltrichloro-ethane	9
				o,p′-Difluorodiphenyltrichloro-ethane	
	Chlorobenzene	H_2SO_4 / Oleum, 0–40°C / Chlorosulfonic acid	70–90%	2,2-Bis(p-chlorophenyl)1,1,1-Trichloroethane (DDT)	52
	Toluene	H_2SO_4, 0°	—	4,4′-Dimethyl-DT	73
	Xylene	H_2SO_4, 0°	—	2,4,2′,4′-Tetramethyl-DT	73
	Bromobenzene	H_2SO_4, 90°C, 1 hr.	—	4,4′-Dibromo-DT	73
	Phenol	H_2SO_4:HOAC, 90°C, 1 hr.	—	4,4′-Dihydroxy-DT	73
	Anisole	H_2SO_4:HOAC, 20°C	—	4,4′-Dimethyloxy-DT	73
	α-Chloronaphthalene	H_2SO_4, 30°C, 2 hr.	—	Trichloro-di(4-chloronaphthyl)-ethane	73
	α-Bromonaphthalene	H_2SO_4 at 30°C	31%	1,1,1-Trichloro-2,2-di-(4-bromo-α-naphthyl)ethane	85

Table continued

22*

TABLE IIIB (*continued*)

| Aldehyde | Reactants | | Catalyst reaction conditions | Yield | Product | Ref. |
	Substrate					
Chloral	Ethylbenzene		H_2SO_4 at 0°, 2 hr.	—	4,4'-Diethyl-DT	73
	Phenetole		H_2SO_4:HOAC	42%	4,4'-Diethoxy-DT	73
	Phenyl propyl ether		As above		4,4'-Dipropoxy-DT	73
	Phenyl isopropyl ether		As above		4,4'-Diisopropoxy-DT	73
	Phenyl butyl ether		As above		4,4'-Dibutoxy-DT	73
	Phenyl isobutyl ether		As above		4,4'-Diisobutoxy-DT	73
	Phenyl-*n*-amyl ether		As above		4,4'-Di-*n*-pentoxy-DT	73

DT = -Diphenyltrichloroethane.

TABLE IV. Miscellaneous additions

Reactants					
Aldehyde or ketone	Substrate	Catalyst reaction conditions	Yield	Product	Ref.
Trioxymethylene	CCl_4	$AlCl_3$, refluxed until no further gas evolved	—	Methylene chloride	41
				Phosgene	
Acetaldehyde	CCl_4	$AlCl_3$	—	Phosgene	41
Isobutyraldehyde	CCl_4	$AlCl_3$	—	Phosgene	41
Paraformaldehyde	Acetylene	$ZnCl_2$ in HCl	60%	Benzalchloride plus others	82
	Isobutylene	10% H_2SO_4 at 70°C for 24 hrs.	12%	3-Methyl-1,3-butanediol	53
	Isobutylene	30% H_3PO_4 at 70–100°C	33%	3-Methyl-1,3-butanediol	53
Trioxymethylene	Propylene	3% H_2SO_4 for 17 hrs, at 142°C	51%	1,3-Butanediol	53
	Propylene	3% H_3PO_4 for 22 hrs at 130–140°C	47%	1,3-Butanediol	53
Ketene	Ethylene oxide	BF_3-etherate in ether, 1.5 hrs. at 5°C	5%	γ-Butyrolactone	58
	Propylene oxide	BF_3-etherate in ether, 1.5 hrs. at 90°C	9%	γ-Valerolactone	58
	Epichlorohydrin	BF_3-etherate in ether, 1.5 hrs. at 9°C	10%	γ-Chloromethyl-γ-butyrolactone	58
	Styrene oxide	As above	9%	γ-Phenyl-γ-butyrolactone	58
Acetone	—	H_2SO_4 added dropwise at 0°C. Mixture allowed to stand for 24 hrs. at room temp.	>11.5%	Mesitylene plus others	59
Ketene	Formaldehyde	BF_3-etherate in acetone at −60°C for 1.5 hrs.	64%	β-Propiolactone	47
	Acetaldehyde	BF_3-etherate in ether, 1 hr. at 10–15°C	70%	β-Butyrolactone	47
Formaldehyde	Formaldehyde	Silica–alumina at 10–20°C	70–80%	β-Propiolactone	11
	Acetone	Silica–alumina–zirconia at 20–30°C	—	β-Methyl-β-butyrolactone	11

References

1. Badertscher, D. E., and R. B. Bishop, U.S. Pat. 2,397,398 (1946).
2. Badertscher, D. E., and R. B. Bishop, U.S. Pat. 2,477,538 (1949).
3. Baeyer, A., *Ber.*, **5**, 1094 (1872); **6**, 220 (1873); **7**, 1190 (1874).
4. Blanc, G., *Am. Perfumer*, **17**, 541; through *C.A.*, **17**, 1630 (1923).
5. Blitz, H., *Ber.*, **26**, 1952 (1893); *J. Chem. Soc. Abs.*, **64**, (I), 718 (1893).
6. Blitz, H., *Ann.*, **296**, 219 (1897); *J. Chem. Soc. Abs.*, 533 (1897).
7. Blitz, H., *Ber.*, **38**, 203 (1905); *J. Chem. Soc. Abs.*, 88, (I), 188 (1905).
8. Boeseken, J., *Rec. Trav. Chim.*, **30**, 381 (1911); through *Chem. Zentr.*, I, 897 (1912).
9. Bradlow, H. L., and C. A. Vanderwerf, *J. Am. Chem. Soc.*, **69**, 662 (1947).
10. Braun, J. von, *Ann.*, **507**, 15 (1933).
11. Caldwell, J. R., and H. J. Hagemeyer, U.S. Pat. 2,462,357 (1949).
12. Chattaway, F. D., and R. J. K. Muir, *J. Chem. Soc.*, 701 (1934).
13. Combes, A., *Compt. rend.*, **98**, 678 (1884).
14. Courtot, Ch., and V. Ouperoff, *Compt. rend.*, **191**, 416 (1930).
15. Dewar, J., and H. O. Jones, *J. Chem. Soc.*, **85**, 212 (1904).
16. Dienesmann, A., *Compt. rend.*, **141**, 201 (1905); *Chem. Zentr.*, II, 753 (1905).
17. Ellison, H., and D. H. Hey, *J. Chem. Soc.*, 1847 (1938).
18. Fischer, O., *Ber.*, **7**, 1191 (1874).
19. Forrest, J., O. Stephenson, and W. A. Waters, *J. Chem. Soc.*, 333 (1946).
20. Frankforter, G. B., and V. R. Kokatnur, *J. Am. Chem. Soc.*, **36**, 1529 (1914).
21. Frankforter, G. B., and W. Kritchevsky, *J. Am. Chem. Soc.*, **37**, 385 (1915).
22. Frankforter, G. B., and W. Kritchevsky, *J. Am. Chem. Soc.* **36**, 1511 (1914).
23. Freri, M., and J. Maximoff, *Gazz. Chim. Ital.*, **70**, 836 (1940).
24. Fuson, R. C., *Advanced Organic Chemistry*, John Wiley & Sons, Inc., New York, pp. 437–42, 1951.
25. Gasselin, *Ann. Chim. Phys.*, **3**, 57 (1894).
26. Hagemeyer, H., Jr., *et al.*, *Ind. Eng. Chem.*, **41**, 765 (1949).
27. Haller, H. L., P. D. Bartlett, N. L. Drake, M. S. Newman, S. J. Cristol, C. M. Eaker, R. A. Hayes, G. W. Kilmer, B. Magerlein, G. P. Mueller, A. Schneider, and W. Wheatley, *J. Am. Chem. Soc.*, **67**, 1591 (1945).
28. Harris, E. E., and G. B. Frankforter, *J. Am. Chem. Soc.*, **48**, 3144 (1926).
29. Hartough, H. D., and J. J. Sardella, U.S. Pat. 2,432,991 (1945).
30. Haseltine, Lake & Co., Brit. Pat. 598,068 (1945).
31. Haseltine, Lake & Co., Brit. Pat. 668,283 (1948).
32. Hauser, C. R., and J. T. Adams, *J. Am. Chem. Soc.*, **66**, 345 (1944).
33. Hey, D. H., *J. Chem. Soc.*, 72 (1935).
34. Hofmann, A., *J. Am. Chem. Soc.*, **51**, 2542 (1929).
35. Hopff, H., Germ. Pat. 666,466; *C.A.*, **33**, 2149 (1939).
36. Hurd, C. D., *J. Am. Chem. Soc.*, **47**, 2777 (1925).
37. Hurd, C. D., and C. D. Kelso, *J. Am. Chem. Soc.*, **62**, 1548 (1940).
38. Huston, R. C., and D. T. Ewing, *J. Am. Chem. Soc.*, **37**, 2394 (1915).
39. Huston, R. C., and D. T. Ewing, *J. Am. Chem. Soc.*, **37**, 2401 (1915).
40. Illari, G., *Gazz. Chim. Ital.*, **79**, 892 (1949).
41. Illari, G., *Gazz. Chim. Ital.*, **81**, 439 (1951).

42. Kane, R., "On a Series of Combinations Derived from Pyroacetic Spirit," Graisberry, Dublin, 1838; *J. Prakt. Chem.*, **15**, 129 (1838); *Ann. der. Phys. Pogg.*, **44**, 473.

43. Kemp, W. E., U.S. Pat. 2,548,982 (1949).

44. Kemp, W. E., Can. Pat. 445,094 (1947).

45. Kling, A., and D. Florentin, *Compt. rend.*, **182**, 526 (1926); *C.A.*, **20** 1791 (1926); *ibid.*, **184**, 822–824 (1927); *C.A.*, **21**, 2470 (1927); *ibid.*, **193**, 1198 (1931); *Brit. Chem. Abs.*, A, 152 (1932).

46. Knowles, E. C., J. A. Patterson, and H. D. Kluge, U.S. Pat. 2,734,088 (1950).

47. Küng, F. E., U.S. Pat. 2,356,459; *C. A.*, **39**, 88 (1945).

48. Landolph, *Ber.*, **12**, 1578 (1879).

49. Lombard, R., and J. P. Stéphan, *Compt. rend.*, **237**, 333 (1953).

50. Lombard, R., and J. P. Stéphan, *Compt. rend.*, **239**, 887 (1954).

51. McGreal, M. E., V. Niederl, and J. B. Niederl, *J. Am. Chem. Soc.*, **61**, 345 (1939).

52. Metcalf, Robert L., *Organic Insecticides*, Interscience Publishers, Inc., New York, 1955.

53. Mikeska, L. A., E. Arundale, and H. O. Moffern, Can. Pat. 434,624 (1946).

54. Müller, P., Swiss Pat. 94,122.

55. Niederl, J. B., *J. Am. Chem. Soc.*, **50**, 2230 (1928).

56. Niederl, J. B., *J. Am. Chem. Soc.*, **59**, 1113 (1937).

57. Nightingale, D. V., *Chem. Rev.*, **25**, 329 (1939).

58. Oda, R., S. Muneimiya, and M. Okano, *J. Org. Chem.*, **26**, No. 5 (1961).

59. Orndorff, W. R., and S. W. Young, *J. Amer. Soc.*, **15**, 255 (1893).

60. Packendorff, K., N. D. Zelinskii, and L. Leder-Packendorff, *Ber.*, **66B**, 1069 (1933).

61. Pelc, J. J., U.S. Pat. 2,011,199 (1935).

62. Ploeg, W., *Rec. Trav. Chim.*, **45**, 342 (1926).

63. Quelet, R., C. Borgel, and R. Durand, *Compt. rend.*, **240**, 1900 (1955).

64. Royals, E. E., *Advanced Organic Chemistry*, Prentice-Hall, Inc., New York, pp. 753–54, 1954.

65. Ruggli, P. H. Dahn, and J. Wegmann, *Helv. Chim. Acta*, **29**, 113 (1946).

66. Schaarschmidt, A., L. Herman, and B. Szemzö, *Ber.*, **58B**, 1914 (1925).

67. Schmerling, L., *The Chemistry of Petroleum Hydrocarbons*, Vol. 3, Reinhold Publishing Corp., Inc., New York, pp. 374–377, 1955.

68. Schmidlin, J., and R. Lang, *Ber.*, **43**, 2806 (1910).

69. Shildneck, P. P., *Org. Syn.*, **17**, 51 (1937).

70. Sturrock, M. G., T. Lawe, and W. E. Kemp, U.S. Pat. 2,439,228 (1948).

71. Spring, F. S., and T. Vickerstaff, *J. Chem. Soc.*, 1873 (1935).

72. Steadman, T. R., U.S. Pat. 2,424,589 (1947).

73. Stephenson, O., and W. A. Waters, *J. Chem. Soc.*, 339 (1946).

74. Tsukervanik, I. P., and Z. N. Nazarova, *J. Gen. Chem. U.S.S.R.*, **9**, 33 (1939).

75. Ungnade, H. E., and E. W. Crandall, *J. Am. Chem. Soc.*, **71**, 2209 (1949).

76. Ungnade, H. E., E. F. Kline, and E. W. Crandall, *J. Am. Chem. Soc.*, **75**, 3333 (1953).

77. Ungnade, H. E., and E. F. Orwoll, *J. Am. Chem. Soc.*, **65**, 1736 (1943).

78. Van Alphen, J., *Rec. Trav. Chim.*, **43**, 823 (1924).

79. Van Alphen, J., *Rec. Trav. Chim.*, **44**, 838 (1925).
80. Van Lear, M., *Bull. Soc. Chim. Belges*, **28**, 346 (1919); through *C.A.*, **16**, 2136 (1922).
81. Vorländer, D., and A. Friedberg, *Ber.*, **56**, 144 (1923); *C.A.*, **17**, 3179 (1923).
82. Walker, J. F., U.S. Pat. 2,463,227 (1944).
83. Wegmann, J., and H. Dahn, *Helv. Chim. Acta*, **29**, 415 (1946).
84. Wegmann, J., and H. Dahn, *Helv. Chim. Acta*, **29**, 1247 (1946).
85. Williams, J. W., and J. M. Osborn, *J. Am. Chem. Soc.*, **61**, 3438 (1939).
86. Zeidler, O., *Ber.*, **7**, 1180 (1874).

CHAPTER XX

Alkylation of Aromatics with Esters of Inorganic Acids and Alkyl Arenesulfonates

FRANZ A. DRAHOWZAL

Technical University, Vienna

I. Introduction

The Friedel-Crafts acylation of aromatic compounds with an-
hydrides $(RCO)_2O$ in the presence of Lewis acids is known to result
in the production of the appropriate ketones. It thus follows that
esters $RCOOR_1$ should undergo similar reactions to produce aralkyl
ketones and alkylbenzenes.

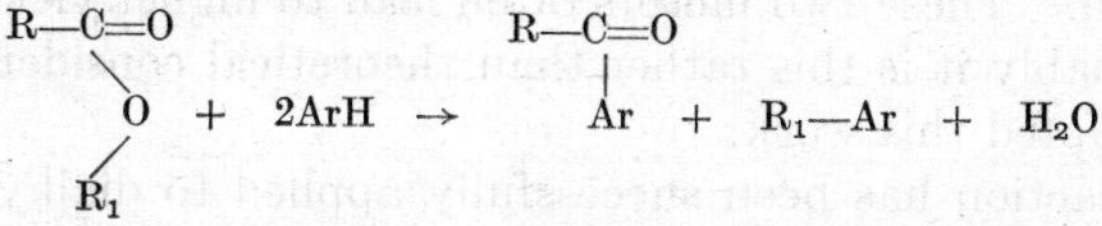

$$R-C=O \diagdown O + 2ArH \rightarrow \begin{array}{c} R-C=O \\ | \\ Ar \end{array} + R_1-Ar + H_2O$$

In fact the latter reaction is well known; the proportions of ketone
and hydrocarbon formed vary with the reaction conditions employed.
If the ester is replaced by an alkyl ester of an inorganic acid then
generally alkylation of the aromatic ring is the sole result and
introduction of the inorganic acid group into the aromatic nucleus
occurs only in exceptional cases. Analogous to the consideration of
alkyl halides as esters of hydrogen halides, the alkylation of aromatic
compounds with esters of inorganic acids may be regarded as an
extension of the widely used Friedel-Crafts alkylation reaction.

The conditions under which the inorganic esters are employed are
vastly different from those pertaining to alkylation with alkyl halides.
One reason for this is that the inorganic acid, inevitably formed as a
by-product, is generally non-volatile and thus cannot escape from the
reaction mixture in the manner of hydrogen halides. The increase
in acid concentration which results as the reaction proceeds may
cause secondary reactions, which thus diminish the yield of the
primary process.

641

The first reaction of this type was reported by Friedel and Crafts in 1877 (13) who observed the ethylation brought about by ethyl chloroformate (EtO_2CCl) which alkylates without the production of any ketones (29).   Since that time a large number of inorganic esters have been used for this purpose and the most suitable reaction conditions determined.

Recent experiments with these esters show that some of the newer and improved analytical techniques could be used to gain an important insight into the mechanism of the Friedel-Crafts alkylation reaction and into a wider field of organic chemistry as a whole.

II. Alkyl Sulfates, Sulfites, Phosphates, Silicates, and Carbonates

Many alkyl esters of inorganic acids are known which react with aromatic substrates in the presence of Lewis acids and yield alkylates as the major product.   The lower alkyl esters of inorganic acids are often used because of their higher boiling points compared to those of the alkyl halides.   Thus there will be smaller losses resulting from the lower volatility, and higher reaction temperatures may be employed.   These two factors often lead to higher yields of alkylate and probably it is this rather than theoretical considerations which has prompted this work.

The reaction has been successfully applied to dialkyl sulfates (1) (R_2SO_4), dialkyl sulfites (4) (R_2SO_3), alkyl phosphates (2) (R_3PO_4), alkyl orthosilicates (16) (($RO)_4Si$), and dialkyl carbonates (16,24) (R_2CO_3).

In almost all of the recorded work on the topic involving aluminum chloride as the Lewis acid the reaction equation quoted does not take into account the necessity of having the Lewis acid present in greater than catalytic amounts.   In such reactions hydrogen chloride is produced and so it may be reasonable to expect that during the course of alkylation the aluminum chloride is converted completely to the acid salt of the ester used, $e.g.$,

$$3(RO)_4Si + 12ArH + 4AlCl_3 \rightarrow 12RAr + Al_4(SiO_4)_3 + 12HCl \qquad (2)$$

$$R_3PO_4 + 3ArH + AlCl_3 \rightarrow 3RAr + AlPO_4 + 3HCl \qquad (3)$$

If dialkyl carbonates are used the reaction takes a slightly different course.   Aluminum carbonate is not formed; instead carbon dioxide and water are produced.

$$R_2CO_3 + 2ArH \xrightarrow{\ AlCl_3\ } 2RAr + CO_2 + H_2O \qquad (4)$$

Kane and Lowy (16) have ascertained that for every mole of ethyl carbonate present, 1.44 moles of aluminum chloride are required. According to equation 4 one mole of water is produced for every mole of carbonate which reacts and this would certainly have a detrimental effect on the efficiency of the aluminum chloride and may account for the excess required in this case. The conversion of the alkyl carbonate to the alkyl chloride, prior to alkylation, by the large excess of aluminum chloride cannot be ruled out, but no data are available on this question and so no valid conclusions may be stated. The same authors alkylated benzene with various amounts of diethyl sulfate (16) and again found that a ratio of 1.44 moles:1 mole aluminum chloride ester gave optimum results, *i.e.*, the highest yield of monoethyl benzene.

Results of alkylations with various esters show that not all the chlorine of aluminum chloride is completely consumed in the course of the reaction. Instead conversion with only partial displacement of the chlorine from the aluminum chloride might well be assumed.

	Mole $AlCl_3$	/	Mole ester	
$3R_2SO_4 + 6ArH + 2AlCl_3 \rightarrow 6RAr + Al_2(SO_4)_3 + 6HCl$	0.66	:	1	(5)
$R_2SO_4 + 2ArH + AlCl_3 \rightarrow 2RAr + AlClSO_4 + 2HCl$	1	:	1	(6)
$R_2SO_4 + 2ArH + 2AlCl_3 \rightarrow 2RAr + (AlCl_2)_2SO_4 + 2HCl$	2	:	1	(7)

The results of Kane and Lowy show that the most preferable amounts of aluminum chloride lie between equations 6 and 7.

Other Lewis acids apparently have not been employed with these esters.

III. Alkyl Borates

Alkyl borates may react according to equation 8 and also require a large amount of Lewis acid.

$$(RO)_3B + 3ArH + AlCl_3 \rightarrow 3RAr + AlBO_3 + 3HCl \qquad (8)$$

Kaufmann (17) has studied the reaction in some detail and has reported the formation, in 90% yield, of *t*-butylxylene from triisobutyl borate and benzene. This is an indication of a carbonium-ion intermediate. He has also reported that with triisobutyl borate in anisole, phenol, or bromobenzene a *p-t*-butyl product is invariably formed. The absence of any *ortho* product is not surprising since the *t*-butyl group has considerable steric requirements and the absence of a *meta*-oriented product suggests an electrophilic substitution mechanism. Further work (20) has resulted in reactions with simple trialkyl borates (ethyl, propyl, butyl, isobutyl, isoamyl, octyl, and 2-ethylhexyl), tribenzyl borate, and borates containing bifunctional groups (allyl, β-chloroethyl, ethylene glycol). Tricyclohexyl borate seems to be the only non-primary borate investigated. These borates have been successfully applied to the alkylation of benzene, toluene, m-xylene, and chlorobenzene in the presence of aluminum chloride. Attempts to replace the aluminum chloride by alkoxides such as the methylate $(Al(OMe)_3)$ or the propylate $(Al(OPr)_3)$ were unsuccessful. In all cases the principal substitution product was $para$-oriented, with a very small amount of the $ortho$-isomer. Ferric chloride (31) was found to be a suitable replacement for aluminum chloride in the reactions of benzene and cumene with triallyl borate. The products were allylbenzene and p-allylcumene respectively.

Mono- and dialkylation products result when triphenyl borate $((C_6H_5O)_3B)$ is allowed to react with alkyl halides in the presence of aluminum chloride. Hydrogen chloride is formed and the products are the free mono- and dialkyl phenols (19). Probably the alkylated triphenyl borates are hydrolyzed during the working-up procedures. On the other hand neither hydrogen chloride nor propyl chloride is produced from tripropyl borate and aluminum chloride in nitrobenzene in the absence of any suitable aromatic substrate (20). Thus alkylation of aromatics with trialkyl borates is effected more readily than the chlorination of the esters by aluminum chloride.

IV. Alkyl Chloroformates, Hypochlorites, Chlorosulfonates, and Chlorosulfites

The first alkylation with esters of inorganic acids was probably carried out quite unintentionally with ethyl chloroformate (13,29). Alkyl chloroformates are esters of chlorocarbonic acid and are thus acyl chlorides. The behavior of acyl chlorides in Friedel-Crafts reactions was previously known, the products having been well characterized as ketones, and so it was expected that alkyl chloroformates would react similarly (see equation 9), but should yield the corresponding carboxylic acid esters.

$$ArH + \underset{RO}{\overset{Cl}{C}}{=}O \xrightarrow[-HCl]{AlCl_3} Ar-CO-OR \tag{9}$$

Phosgene is also closely related to alkyl chloroformates and had been shown to react, under the appropriate conditions, with replacement of one or both of its chlorine atoms.

$$2ArH + COCl_2 \xrightarrow{AlCl_3} Ar-CO-Ar + 2HCl \tag{10}$$

$$ArH + COCl_2 \xrightarrow{AlCl_3} Ar-CO-Cl + HCl \tag{11}$$

However, the reaction with alkyl chloroformates was found to follow an entirely different route, resulting in the formation of the appropriate alkylbenzenes (13,18,29).

$$ArH + ClOOR \xrightarrow{AlCl_3} Ar-R + HCl + CO_2$$

No esters or ketones were found in the products (4) although it is possible that small quantities might have been found using the more sensitive analytical techniques now available.

A further example of the alkylation of aromatic compounds as a consequence of the preferential fission of the oxygen–alkyl bond is to be found in analogous reactions with t-butyl hypochlorite (2). No t-butyl aryl ethers are produced.

$$t\text{-BuOCl} + ArH \xrightarrow{AlCl_3} t\text{-BuAr} + HOCl \tag{12}$$

Similar results are obtained using alkyl chlorosulfonates ($ROSO_2Cl$) and alkyl chlorosulfites ($ROSOCl$).   Benzene and toluene are readily alkylated by chlorosulfonates in the presence of aluminum chloride (1) (2 moles $AlCl_3$ per mole of ester).   Simultaneously benzene is chlorinated in the nucleus and toluene is chlorinated in the side chain.   A substituted benzoic acid is a by-product in the reaction with toluene, indicating complete chlorination of the side chain (1) to a benzotrichloride intermediate.   The corresponding acylation has not been observed except in the case of methyl chlorosulfonates (11,12).   Frèrejacque has reported that the reaction

$$CH_3-O-\overset{\displaystyle O}{\underset{\displaystyle O}{\overset{\displaystyle \|}{\underset{\displaystyle \|}{S}}}}-Cl + ArH \rightarrow CH_3-O-\overset{\displaystyle O}{\underset{\displaystyle O}{\overset{\displaystyle \|}{\underset{\displaystyle \|}{S}}}}-Ar + HCl \tag{13}$$

occurs in the absence of any Lewis acid, but subsequent attempts (1) to repeat this work have not been successful.   Further work evidently is necessary to clarify this point.

With alkyl chlorosulfites alkylation takes place without the simultaneous chlorination peculiar to the chlorosulfonates.   In addition some unidentified products containing sulfur are formed (1). Very little is known about the mechanism of the reactions involving these esters since the experiments recorded were aimed chiefly at the preparation of specific compounds.

V. Alkyl Benzenesulfonates

In any discussion of alkylation with esters of inorganic acids the alkyl esters of arylsulfonic acids occupy a special place since they may be regarded as being midway between inorganic and organic in nature. Nenitzescu (21,22,23) has studied the catalytic effect of free arylsulfonic acids on the reaction, using variously substituted benzyl esters. Historically, Földi (9,10) appears to have been the first to give an account of the reaction of benzyl benzenesulfonate ($C_6H_5SO_3CH_2C_6H_5$) with benzene to give diphenylmethane. The method was developed to include different alkyl esters of arylsulfonic acids and it was noted that the rate of alkylation increases as the reaction proceeds. Hickinbottom and Rogers (15) studied the alkylation reaction with esters of p-toluenesulfonic acid and found that the free arylsulfonic acid was produced simultaneously with the alkylate, according to the equation:

$$Ar-SO_3R + Ar-H \rightarrow ArR + Ar-SO_3H. \tag{14}$$

The autocatalytic effect of the free acid on the reaction was confirmed by the inhibiting effect of carbonate or dioxane (23) and of dimethylformamide (15).

Kinetic measurements (23) have shown that the rate of alkylation is proportional to the square of the free acid concentration. In addition, benzenesulfonates of primary alcohols are less reactive than their secondary or tertiary isomers, requiring a higher temperature and a greater concentration of free acid. The catalytic effect of the free acid has been attributed to the formation of an oxonium salt from the ester and benzenesulfonic acid, a strong proton acid. In view of the large excess of aromatic substrate generally present the alkylations essentially proceed in a non-polar medium, so that no free, independent ions arise. Instead ion pairs are formed and there is presumably association with a second molecule of sulfonic acid. Solvation, or association of two sulfonic acid molecules, would account for the increase in reaction rate proportional to the square of the acid concentration. In the case of benzylation of benzene the rate of reaction is equal to:

$$k[C_6H_5SO_3CH_2C_6H_5] \cdot [C_6H_6] \cdot [C_6H_5SO_3H]^2.$$

The first step in the reaction is the establishment of an equilibrium between the alkyl ester and the associated acid.

$$C_6H_5SO_3CH_2C_6H_5 + 2C_6H_5SO_3H$$

$$\rightleftharpoons \left[C_6H_5SO_3^- \cdot C_6H_5SO_2 - \overset{+}{\underset{H}{O}} - CH_2C_6H_5 \right] + C_6H_5SO_3H \tag{15}$$

The constitution of the aromatic substrate is also a decisive factor in rate determinations. In the case of benzylation toluene is more reactive than benzene by a factor of 2.6 and m-xylene reacts more rapidly than toluene by a similar factor. However, the aromatic reactant does not enter the alkylation process until the second step, for which two mechanisms can be considered:

(a) Alkylation through a carbonium-ion intermediate, $i.e.$, electrophilic substitution of the aromatic ring.

$$\left[C_6H_5SO_3^- \, C_6H_5SO_2 \!-\! \overset{+}{\underset{\underset{H}{|}}{O}} \!-\! CH_2C_6H_5 \right] \rightarrow C_6H_5\overset{+}{C}H_2 + C_6H_5SO_3^- + C_6H_5SO_3H \qquad (16)$$

$$C_6H_5\overset{+}{C}H_2 + Ar\!-\!H \rightarrow \left[\underset{\underset{H}{|}}{Ar} \overset{CH_2C_6H_5}{\overbrace{}} + \right] \rightarrow ArCH_2C_6H_5 + H^+ \qquad (17)$$

According to Nenitzescu this is a first-order reaction, the rate-determining step being mainly the formation of the carbonium ion.

(b) A reaction of second-order character involving a direct nucleophilic displacement by the aromatic substrate with no discrete carbonium-ion intermediate.

$$\left[C_6H_5SO_3^- \, C_6H_5SO_2 \!-\! \overset{+}{\underset{\underset{H}{|}}{O}} \!-\! CH_2C_6H_5 \right] + \bigcirc \longrightarrow$$

$$\underset{C_6H_5SO_3^-}{C_6H_5SO_2\!-\!\overset{\delta^+}{\underset{\underset{H}{|}}{O}}\cdots\cdots \overset{C_6H_5}{\underset{\underset{\delta^+}{\bigcirc}}{CH_2}}} \quad H \rightarrow C_6H_5SO_3H + \overset{CH_2-C_6H_5}{\bigcirc}\qquad (18)$$

$$+ \, C_6H_5SO_3^- + H^+$$

The effect of substituents in the ring of the benzyl group should vary according to whether the reaction proceeds via a first- or second-order mechanism. An investigation has shown the reaction rate is affected in the following order (23) p-CH$_3$ > H > p-Cl > m-NO$_2$. Comparing these results with those of exchange reactions of various benzyl halides and benzyl p-toluenesulfonates it is found that they are indicative of a first-order process. In a second-order process the $meta$-nitro substituent causes an increase in the reaction rate compared with a $para$-methyl group. The retarding effect of the $meta$-nitro and $para$-chloro groups is regarded by Nenitzescu (23) as evidence for the carbonium-ion first-order route.

Brown (4a) has expressed the contrary opinion that a gradual nucleophilic displacement of the acid group by the aromatic substrate occurs, according to mechanism (b) involving σ-complex type intermediates.   Such complexes were formerly thought to be unstable but Olah and co-workers have succeeded in isolating and characterizing several of these (25,26,27).   The isolated complexes may be subsequently decomposed to alkylbenzenes by proton elimination. This latter step is inevitably unimolecular and in the case of the more stable complexes can be the rate-determining factor for the alkylbenzene formation.   The isolation of the relatively stable σ-complexes has proved that in these cases they are real intermediates.

Further proof of carbonium-ion formation has been demonstrated (15,23) by the rearrangement of certain alkyl groups entering the aromatic ring.   Propyl benzenesulfonate and benzene yield a propylbenzene which contains 95% isopropylbenzene and racemic s-butylbenzene is obtained from optically active s-butyl benzenesulfonate and benzene.

So far the reaction has not been successfully applied to the methylation of aromatics.   The effect of the methyl group in methyl benzenesulfonate is thought to be responsible for this failure.

VI. Alkyl p-Toluenesulfonates

The most widely used alkylating agents of the sulfonic acid ester type are the alkyl esters of p-toluenesulfonic acid.

$$\text{Ar—H} + p\text{-CH}_3\text{C}_6\text{H}_4\text{SO}_3\text{R} \rightarrow \text{Ar—R} + p\text{-CH}_3\text{C}_6\text{H}_4\text{SO}_3\text{H} \tag{19}$$

Clemo and Walton (7) were the first to report reactions of this nature. They observed that β-chloroethyl p-toluenesulfonate alkylates benzene, in the presence of aluminum chloride, yielding β-chloroethyl benzene.

$$\text{C}_6\text{H}_6 + p\text{-CH}_3\text{C}_6\text{H}_4\text{SO}_3\text{CH}_2\text{CH}_2\text{Cl} \xrightarrow{\text{AlCl}_3} \text{C}_6\text{H}_5\text{CH}_2\text{CH}_2\text{Cl} + p\text{-CH}_3\text{C}_6\text{H}_4\text{SO}_3\text{H} \tag{20}$$

No β-phenylethyl p-toluenesulfonate or β-phenylethyl alcohol is produced.   Thus the p-toluenesulfonate moiety effects the alkylation of the aromatic substrate more rapidly than does the β-chloroethyl halide.   All Friedel-Crafts alkylations with alkyl toluenesulfonates require a large excess of aluminum chloride.   The free sulfonic acid formed during the reaction reacts with some of the aluminum chloride to form hydrogen chloride.   Consequently the β-chloroethylbenzene previously mentioned could also have been formed from a primary reaction yielding β-phenylethyl p-toluenesulfonate followed by a further reaction with hydrogen chloride or aluminum chloride.

$$p\text{-}CH_3C_6H_4SO_3CH_2CH_2Cl + C_6H_6 \xrightarrow[-HCl]{AlCl_3} p\text{-}CH_3C_6H_4SO_3CH_2CH_2C_6H_5 \xrightarrow[AlCl_3]{HCl\ or}$$
$$p\text{-}CH_3C_6H_4SO_3H + ClCH_2CH_2C_6H_5 \quad (21)$$

In fact in the alkylation of benzene with ethylene glycol di-p-toluenesulfonate in the presence of excess aluminum chloride one of the by-products was β-chloroethylbenzene (8). However, reactions of aromatics with simple alkyl p-toluenesulfonates do not generally yield appreciable amounts of alkyl halides, even in the presence of substantial quantities of hydrogen chloride. Obviously there is a special mode of reaction in the case of the disubstituted compounds analogous to that observed with di- and polyhalogenated alkanes.

Some attempt has been made to gain an insight into the mechanism of the aluminum chloride catalyzed alkylations. However the experimental and analytical techniques employed leave much to be desired in terms of present-day knowledge and future work could usefully be concentrated in this area.

A striking feature of the reaction is the rapid formation of dialkyl-benzenes at the start. This then decreases regularly indicating an equilibrium state:

$$2C_6H_5R \rightleftharpoons C_6H_4R_2 + C_6H_6 \quad (22)$$

In the presence of various quantities of benzene the equilibrium constants, calculated from the yields, lie between 0.23 and 0.75, with most of them falling between the values 0.34 and 0.57. The addition of butylbenzene, dibutylbenzene, nitrobenzene, or petroleum ether does not shift the equilibrium in any definite direction but the presence of diethyl ether causes a large scatter in the values obtained from alkylations with butyl p-toluenesulfonate. In order to obtain reproducible equilibrium constants it seems to be necessary to have present the catalyst formed from aluminum chloride and the alkyl p-toluenesulfonate. The free acid content of the catalyst is particularly important. Aluminum chloride alone, with various mixtures of benzene, butylbenzene, and dibutylbenzene, does not yield any significant results. Such investigations, however, are still in a preliminary stage (8) and much work remains to be done on this aspect of the subject.

The possibility of converting p-toluenesulfonates into the corresponding alcohols has been discussed many times. In fact, in the presence of aluminum chloride, such a transformation has been observed if the reaction involves long-chain alkyl p-toluenesulfonates. In fact with increasing chain length of the alkyl moiety the alkylating effect decreases when alcoholic solutions of aluminum chloride hydrate are employed, and alcohol formation increases. The careful exclusion of moisture and rigorous pre-drying of all reactants is therefore essential to inhibit alcohol formation. Under these conditions long-chain alkyl p-toluenesulfonates frequently give higher yields of alkylates than the corresponding alkyl chlorides (8).

Shirley and Zeitz (30) have described alkylations with n-octadecyl p-toluenesulfonate. No rearrangement of the aliphatic chain was observed as a consequence of the reaction, in agreement with results obtained (14) using the corresponding alkyl halides.

If n-butyl p-toluenesulfonate is treated with aluminum chloride in carbon disulfide solution in the absence of other aromatic compounds two reactions occur. Butylation products of the aromatic ring of the toluenesulfonate may be isolated and substitution of the sulfonic acid group by hydrogen takes place. Thus the course of the reaction seems to be lacking in uniformity.

If the alkyl group is replaced by a function capable of forming an anion containing the bridged oxygen of the sulfonate then formation of a sulfone with fission of the ester occurs. This is an intramolecular sulfoacylation. For example 2,4-dinitrophenyl p-toluenesulfonate and benzene, in the presence of aluminum chloride, yield p-tolylphenyl sulfone and 2,4-dinitrophenol (8).

$$p\text{-}CH_3C_6H_4SO_2\text{---}O\text{---}\langle\text{ring}\rangle\text{---}NO_2 + C_6H_6 \xrightarrow{AlCl_3}$$

$$p\text{-}CH_3C_6H_4SO_2C_6H_5 + \underset{HO}{\langle\text{ring}\rangle}\overset{NO_2}{\underset{NO_2}{}} \quad (23)$$

Detailed experimental conditions have been published by Bowden (4). Esters of acids which decompose readily should be added slowly to the reaction mixture, so that at any one time there is only a low concentration of the ester present. In the case of more inert esters the rate of reaction may be controlled by careful heating. At one time it was thought that the ester first decomposed to the corresponding alkene and that this alkene was the true alkylating agent, but present-day knowledge indicates that this is somewhat doubtful, especially in the case of the highly reactive benzyl esters, which have no corresponding alkene to form. It is, however, still possible that aluminum chloride or strong proton acids may give rise to an equilibrium between ester and alkene as well as catalyzing the alkylation. With the high volatility of the lower alkenes this can lead to appreciable losses. The actual course of the alkylation reaction is far more likely to consist of one of the two possibilities already mentioned—electrophilic substitution of the intermediate carbonium ion or a reaction through the σ-complex without formation of a discrete carbonium ion (25,26). In neither of these cases is preliminary alkene formation necessary and the failure of methyl benzenesulfonate to methylate aromatics cannot be attributed to the lack of alkene formation since the benzyl ester is a powerful benzylating agent under similar reaction conditions. It has been shown, however, that with esters of higher secondary alcohols, the corresponding alkenes of which are not too volatile, an enrichment of these alkenes in the reaction medium does, in fact, precede the actual alkylation. In the presence of aromatic hydrocarbons these alkenes react to form alkylbenzenes after prolonged reflux with benzenesulfonic acid. In spite of this the alkene is not generally regarded as the real intermediate in the alkylation reaction since in addition to the benzylating effect of the benzyl arylsulfonic esters the equilibrium between the ester and the alkene has been demonstrated.

$$C_6H_5SO_3CH \begin{matrix} CH_2-CH_2 \\ \diagup \qquad \diagdown \\ \qquad\qquad CH_2 \\ \diagdown \qquad \diagup \\ CH_2-CH_2 \end{matrix} \rightleftharpoons C_6H_5SO_3H \; + \; \bigcirc \qquad (24)$$

The formation of this equilibrium is also promoted by free benzenesulfonic acid. As the alkylation takes place the equilibrium is continuously shifted in favor of the ester and free benzenesulfonic acid is produced. The presence of the free acid also favors the ester side of the equilibrium.

$$C_6H_5SO_3C_6H_{11} + ArH \rightarrow C_6H_{11}Ar + C_6H_5SO_3H \qquad (25)$$

At the start of the reaction the equilibrium may be in favor of a high alkene concentration since the alkene formation is more rapid than alkylation and is catalyzed by free sulfonic acid. If the alkene so formed is volatile it may be lost from the reaction mixture and the equilibrium reaction will then proceed in an undesirable direction.

Equilibrium is also established from the alkene and benzenesulfonic acid (21). In an inert solvent such as ethylene dichloride, cyclohexene and benzenesulfonic acid attain equilibrium after 14 hours at 20°. This mixture can be utilized for the preparation of cyclohexyl benzenesulfonate and yields about 80% of the ester. Free benzenesulfonic acid appears to be important for the establishment of equilibrium since with the pure ester equilibrium is achieved only in the absence of basic reagents. Even dioxane will prevent the alkene formation, indicating that a thermal decomposition is not involved; instead a proton-catalyzed reaction takes place (21).

Unfortunately many of the alkylation reactions have been carried out in the presence of aluminum chloride. Here one cannot expect a clear picture of simultaneous alkene formation and alkylation since the aluminum chloride reacts with the free sulfonic acid produced, with the liberation of hydrogen chloride. Consequently the catalytic effect of the Lewis acid is constantly changing.

An attempt has been made (8) to determine the maximum number of alkyl groups which may be transferred by one mole of anhydrous aluminum chloride in alkylation reactions with p-toluenesulfonates. Three stoichiometric equations must be considered:

$$3Ts—R + 3ArH + AlCl_3 \rightarrow 3RAr + Ts_3Al + 3HCl \qquad (26)$$

$$2Ts—R + 2ArH + AlCl_3 \rightarrow 2RAr + Ts_2AlCl + 2HCl \qquad (27)$$

$$Ts—R + ArH + AlCl_3 \rightarrow RAr + TsAlCl_2 + HCl \qquad (28)$$

$$Ts \equiv p\text{-}CH_3C_6H_4SO_3$$

Experiments show that aluminum chloride consumption lies mainly between equations 27 and 28, indicating that between one and two alkyl groups react for every mole aluminum chloride present. However, reaction 27 may be construed as being the second stage of 28:

$$Ts—R + ArH + TsAlCl_2 \rightarrow RAr + Ts_2AlCl + HCl. \qquad (29)$$

In fact, after the interaction of molar amounts of alkyl p-toluenesulfonate and aluminum chloride with an excess of benzene, the latter may still be alkylated further with other alkyl p-toluenesulfonates without the further addition of aluminum chloride. If an alkyl chloride is used in the latter stage in place of a p-toluenesulfonate, then as many as seven moles of alkyl chloride can be smoothly converted to alkylbenzenes. Treatment of the reaction mixture with anhydrous hydrogen chloride before the second stage invariably leads to an improved yield of alkylates (8). It may thus be conjectured that the following equilibria would be important, since excess hydrogen chloride should displace these in favor of the free sulfonic acid. The effectiveness of these acids in catalyzing the reaction has already been demonstrated.

$$p\text{-}TsAlCl_2 + HCl \rightleftharpoons p\text{-}TsH + AlCl_3 \qquad (30)$$

$$p\text{-}Ts_2AlCl + HCl \rightleftharpoons p\text{-}TsH + p\text{-}TsAlCl_2 \qquad (31)$$

Such equilibria would be influenced by many factors, both direct and indirect (temperature, concentration, solvent, etc.) and the actual experimental conditions would have a considerable effect on the course of the reaction. This has been found to be the case (8), since the mixed aluminum chloride toluenesulfonates remaining after the alkylation are always of varying composition. Thus no conclusions can be drawn from the analytical composition of these residues. Precise measurement of the hydrogen chloride evolved, which is liberated as the alkylation proceeds, might afford a better insight into the reaction mechanism.

In alkylation reactions with chloroformate esters and esters of hypochlorous acid the requirement of aluminum chloride has been repeatedly demonstrated. This indicates a tendency for the aluminum to complete its bonding valence shell by inclusion of the oxygen atom.

$$
\begin{array}{cc}
R & Cl \\
\diagdown & \diagup \\
& O \\
& \downarrow \\
Cl\!-\!Al\!-\!Cl \\
| \\
Cl
\end{array}
$$

The formation of $AlCl_4^-$ does not seem to be favored in this case, otherwise alkoxylation and ketone formation would be expected. With aluminum chloride, in the absence of other aromatic compounds, p-toluenesulfonates react to give the corresponding alkyl chlorides.

$$p\text{-Ts}\!-\!R + AlCl_3 \rightarrow RCl + p\text{-TsAlCl}_2 \tag{32}$$

Nevertheless prior formation of alkyl chlorides in alkylation reactions cannot be assumed, since if the reaction is prematurely quenched no alkyl chloride or unchanged ester can be found in the reaction mass.

Other catalysts, such as boron trifluoride, sulfuric acid, and arylsulfonic acids have been used, with success, in place of aluminum chloride.

VII. Alkyl Perchlorates

An investigation of the metathetic conversions of alkyl halides and silver perchlorate has been reported by Burton et al. (5), who have shown that in the presence of an aromatic substrate ring alkylation may occur. Experiments indicate that primary alkyl halides give very low yields of alkylate compared with the amount of product obtained when *t*-butyl chloride is used and alkylations with perchlorate (6) have demonstrated that *n*-butyl perchlorate has practically no value as an alkylating agent, whereas *t*-butyl perchlorate gives high yields of *t*-butyl derivatives.

This suggests that the alkylation is preceded by the formation of a covalent alkyl perchlorate resulting from the metathetic exchange reaction between the alkyl halide and silver perchlorate.

$$R—X + AgClO_4 \rightarrow ROClO_3 + AgX \qquad (33)$$

The investigations of Burton *et al.* covered a range of alkyl halides and various aromatic compounds. With reactive aromatic substrates even relatively inert alkyl halides will function as alkylating agents although the general order of reactivity has been shown to be: *t*-Bu > *s*-Bu > *n*-Bu > *n*-Pr > Et > Me. From kinetic investigations with secondary and tertiary butyl halides the yield of alkylbenzenes is proportional to the reaction time, but this is not the case with *n*-butyl and methyl halides. Excess of aromatic compound does not improve the yield in the latter case, so an equilibrium between the *n*-alkyl perchlorate and the alkylbenzene can be eliminated.

$$BuClO_4 + Ar—H \rightleftharpoons\!\!\!/\!\!\!\rightleftharpoons BuAr + HClO_4 \qquad (34)$$

The reaction is thus independent of time and a mechanism analogous to that of silver salts with alkyl halides in hydroxylated solvents has been suggested.

$$RX + AgY + R'OH \rightarrow ROR' + AgX + HY \qquad (35)$$

$$AgY + RX \rightarrow AgX + RY \qquad (36)$$

The two reactions proceed simultaneously. If the hydroxylated solvent is replaced by an aromatic compound and silver perchlorate is used the equations may be written:

$$RX + AgClO_4 + ArH \rightarrow RAr + AgX + HClO_4 \qquad (37)$$

$$AgClO_4 + RX \rightarrow AgX + RClO_4 \qquad (38)$$

In the case of *s*- or *t*-butyl groups the perchlorates formed according to equation 38 are stable and the silver salt present catalyzes the electrophilic substitution so that the aromatic is converted to an alkylbenzene during the course of the reaction. The aromatic substrate forms a polar complex with silver perchlorate, displaying a measure of nucleophilic activity, and is thus made accessible to electrophilic substitution by the alkyl group. Four equations are required to describe the scheme.

$$C_6H_5R + AgClO_4 \rightleftharpoons C_6H_5R\cdots\overset{\delta+}{Ag}\cdots\overset{\delta-}{ClO_4} \tag{39}$$

$$R'X + C_6H_5R\cdots\overset{\delta+}{Ag}\cdots\overset{\delta-}{ClO_4}
\begin{cases} \nearrow\ C_6H_5R + R'ClO_4 + AgX \tag{40}\\ \\ \searrow\ C_6H_4RR' + HClO_4 + AgX \tag{41} \end{cases}$$

$$R'ClO_4 + C_6H_5R\cdots\overset{\delta+}{Ag}\cdots\overset{\delta-}{ClO_4} \rightarrow C_6H_4RR' + HClO_4 + AgClO_4 \tag{42}$$

The last reaction, which has not been observed with n-alkyl perchlorates, is assumed to involve a carbonium-ion intermediate analogous to that generally accepted for Friedel-Crafts alkylations. Evidence for this is that isobutyl perchlorate yields t-butyl derivatives and optically active 2-bromopentane leads to a completely racemized product.

If methyl nitrate is used as solvent some nitrogenous products result in addition to unsaturated material of high molecular weight.

The explosive nature of perchlorates in general demands special care in carrying out all experimental procedures. The mild reaction conditions thus necessary and the special methods of working up the ensuing reaction mixtures may be the cause of many peculiarities associated with the reaction.

For equation 41 Burton has assumed a mechanism analogous to the alkylation route proposed by Brown (4a). In this connection later work by Olah and co-workers (25,26,27) has resulted in the low-temperature isolation of complexes between aromatics, boron trifluoride, and hydrogen fluoride and between aromatics, boron trifluoride, and alkyl fluorides, always in the ratio 1:1:1. Complexes of the former type dissociate on heating into their respective starting materials whereas those of the latter type yield hydrogen fluoride, boron trifluoride, and the corresponding alkylated aromatic compound. The homogeneous state of the complex formed from mutually immiscible components, as well as its deep color, increased conductivity and spectroscopic properties (ultraviolet and n.m.r.) suggest that it is the σ-complex, postulated by H. C. Brown, but previously considered to be unstable.

$$\text{C}_6\text{H}_6 + RF + BF_3 \longrightarrow \left[\overset{+}{\underset{H\ \ R}{\bigcirc}} \right] BF_4^- \longrightarrow \underset{R}{\bigcirc} + HF + BF_3 \tag{43}$$

The complex must thus be regarded as the stable intermediate in Friedel-Crafts alkylations.

If the fluoride, RF, is not readily available the complex may be prepared from the corresponding chloride, silver tetrafluoroborate, and aromatic substrate (27).

$$
\bigcirc + RCl + AgBF_4 \longrightarrow AgCl + \left[\begin{array}{c} + \\ H \quad R \end{array} \right] BF_4^- \longrightarrow
$$

$$
\bigcirc_R + BF_3 + HF \qquad (44)
$$

Although there is an obvious resemblance between the above alkylations and those with alkyl perchlorates, the corresponding σ-complexes have not been isolated in the case of perchlorates. It is possible, however, that they are considerably less stable than the fluoroborate complexes and that the overall reaction proceeds rapidly.

$$
\bigcirc + RCl + AgClO_4 \longrightarrow AgCl + \left[\begin{array}{c} + \\ H \quad R \end{array} \right] ClO_4^- \longrightarrow \bigcirc_R + HClO_4 \quad (45)
$$

The formation of a covalent alkyl perchlorate would be avoided by direct formation of a σ-complex. If the σ-complex is the intermediate in this reaction then alkyl perchlorate formation assumes the nature of a competitive reaction. Ester formation is not possible in the metathetic exchange between silver tetrafluoroborate and alkyl halide and the incipient carbonium ion is necessarily formed.

Despite their unpleasant explosive properties, the preparation of several alkyl perchlorates has been achieved (28) and the alkylating effect of secondary and tertiary members has been verified (30). Thus ester formation preceding alkylation with n-alkyl halides and silver perchlorate must be considered as an alternative to direct metathesis and formation of ionic σ-complexes.

The readiness of the aromatic substrate to enter into such complexes is, of course, strongly influenced by the inductive and mesomeric effects of ring substituents. It is thus conceivable that suitably substituted aromatics could be alkylated by n-alkyl perchlorates.

VIII. Alkyl Nitrates

Alkyl nitrates represent a different class of compound from the esters so far discussed. No alkylations of aromatics in the presence of Lewis acids have been reported, but these esters are useful when it is desired to nitrate the aromatic nucleus.   Ethyl nitrate has been used for such reactions (3).

$$Et—O—NO_2 + ArH \rightarrow ArNO_2 + EtOH \tag{46}$$

The Lewis acids present obviously promote the formations of nitronium ions necessary for nuclear nitration through an electrophilic substitution mechanism.

$$Et—O—NO_2 + AlCl_3 \rightarrow NO_2^+ \; [Et—OAlCl_3]^- \tag{47}$$

Although no alkylation of any aromatic substrate present in excess has been reported, it is conceivable that appropriate reaction conditions could be found in order to bring about this transformation.

References

1. Barkenbus, C., R. L. Hopkins, and J. F. Allen, *J. Am. Chem. Soc.*, **61**, 2452 (1939).
2. Berman, N., and A. Lowy, *J. Am. Chem. Soc.*, **60**, 2596 (1938).
3. Boedtker, E., *Bull. Soc. Chim. France*, (4), **3**, 726 (1908); through *Chem. Zentr.*, II, 404 (1908).
4. Bowden, E., *J. Am. Chem. Soc.*, **60**, 645 (1938).
4a. Brown, H. C., and M. Grayson, *J. Am. Chem. Soc.*, **75**, 6285 (1953).
5. Burton, H., D. A. Munday, and P. E. G. Praill, *J. Chem. Soc.*, 3933 (1956).
6. Cauquil, G., H. Barrera, and R. Barrera, *Bull. Soc. Chim. France*, 1111 (1953).
7. Clemo, G. R., and E. Walton, *J. Chem. Soc.*, 723 (1928).
8. Drahowzal, F., D. Klamann, and F. Haas, *Ann.*, **580**, 210 (1953).
9. Földi, Z., *Ber.*, **61**, 1609 (1928).
10. Földi, Z., U.S. Pat. 1,897,795 (Feb. 14, 1933); *C.A.*, **27**, 2693 (1933); *Chem. Zentr.*, II, 136 (1933).
11. Frèrejacque, M., *Compt. rend.*, **183**, 607 (1926).
12. Frèrejacque, M., *Ann. Chim. Phys.*, (10), **14**, 156, 159 (1930); through *Chem. Zentr.*, I, 264 (1931).
13. Friedel, C., and J. M. Crafts, *Compt. rend.*, **34**, 1450 (1877); *Ann. Chim. Phys.*, (6), **1**, 527 (1884).
14. Gilman, H., and J. A. V. Turck, *J. Am. Chem. Soc.*, **61**, 478 (1939).
15. Hickinbottom, W. J., and N. W. Rogers, *J. Chem. Soc.*, 4124 (1957).
16. Kane, H. L., and A. Lowy, *J. Am. Chem. Soc.*, **58**, 2605 (1936).
17. Kaufmann, A., Germ. Pat. 555,403 (July 23, 1930); French Pat. 720,034 (Feb. 15, 1932); Brit. Pat. 367,292 (March 10, 1932); *C.A.*, **26**, 5101 (1932).
18. Kunckell, F., and G. Ulex, *J. Prakt. Chem.*, (2), **86**, 518 (1912).
19. Kuskov, V. K., and T. A. Burtseva, *Dokl. Akad. Nauk S.S.S.R.*, **125**, 811 (1959); through *C.A.*, **53**, 19940e (1959).
20. Kuskov, V. K., D. M. Sheiman, and Z. I. Maksimova, *J. Gen. Chem. U.S.S.R.*, **27**, 1454 (1957); through *C.A.*, **52**, 2741h (1958).
21. Nenitzescu, C. D., V. Ioan, and L. Teodorescu, *Ber.*, **90**, 585 (1957).
22. Nenitzescu, C. D., S. Titeica, and V. Ioan, *Bull. Soc. Chim. France*, 1272, 1279 (1955); *C.A.*, **50**, 2259 (1956).

23. Nenitzescu, C. D., S. Titeica, and V. Ioan, *Acta Chim. Acad. Sci. Hung.*, **12**, 195 (1957); *C.A.*, **52**, 9983a (1958).
24. Norris, J. F., and B. M. Sturgis, *J. Am. Chem. Soc.*, **61**, 1413 (1939).
25. Olah, G. A., and S. J. Kuhn, *J. Am. Chem. Soc.*, **80**, 6535 (1958).
26. Olah, G. A., A. E. Pavlath, and J. A. Olah, *J. Am. Chem. Soc.*, **80**, 6540 (1958).
27. Olah, G. A., and S. J. Kuhn, *J. Am. Chem. Soc.*, **80**, 6541 (1958).
28. Radell, J., J. W. Connolly, and A. J. Raymond, *J. Am. Chem. Soc.*, **83**, 3958 (1961).
29. Rennie, E. H. J., *J. Chem. Soc.*, **41**, 33 (1882).
30. Shirley, D. A., and J. R. Zeitz, Jr., *J. Am. Chem. Soc.*, **75**, 6333 (1953).
31. Société des usines chimiques Rhone-Poulenc. Brit. Pat. 787,615 (Dec. 11, 1957); *C.A.*, **52**, 10171h (1958); French Pat. 1,124,561 (Oct. 15, 1956); *C.A.*, **53**, 15006i (1959).